M

CARNEGIE INSTITUTION OF WASHINGTON

PUBLICATION No. 376

1927

INTRODUCTION
TO THE
HISTORY OF SCIENCE

VOLUME I

FROM HOMER TO OMAR KHAYYAM

BY
GEORGE SARTON
Associate in the History of Science
Carnegie Institution of Washington

PUBLISHED FOR THE
CARNEGIE INSTITUTION OF WASHINGTON
BY
THE WILLIAMS & WILKINS COMPANY
BALTIMORE

Reprinted 1945, 1950, 1953

CONTENTS

PAGE

Introductory Chapter 3–51

I. Purpose of this work, 3. II. Ancient science, 8. III. Mediaeval science, 14. IV. Scholasticism, its cause and its cure, 21. V. Three aspects of the fundamental unity of life, 29. VI. A survey of human civilization, 32. VII. Some remarks on the history of science in India, Central and Eastern Asia, 35. VIII. Chronological basis, 37. IX. Bibliographic basis, 39. X. Principles of selection, 41. XI. Errors of this work and their correction, 43. XII. The author expresses his gratitude, 44.

Appendix: Notes on the transcription of Greek, Hebrew, Syriac, Arabic, Persian, Sanskrit, Chinese, and Japanese words, 46.

Chapter I

The Dawn of Greek and Hebrew Knowledge (ninth and eighth centuries B. C.) 52–59

I. Summary, 52. II. Earliest monuments of European literature, 53. III. The first Hebrew prophets and a great king, 57. IV. Egyptian law, 59.

Chapter II

The Dawn of Iranian Knowledge (seventh century B. C.) 60–64

I. Summary, 60. II. Dawn of Iranian knowledge, 60. III. Greek music, 61. IV. Greek law, 62. V. Assyrian learning, 62. VI. Hebrew law and history, 62. VII. More Hebrew prophets, 63.

Chapter III

The Time of Thales and Pythagoras (sixth century B. C.) 65–80

I. Summary, 65. II. Chinese, Hindu, and Hebrew prophets, 66. III. Babylonian astronomy, 71. IV. Birth of natural philosophy, 71. V. Greek technicians, 75. VI. Hindu and Greek medicine, 76. VII. Egyptian and Greek geography, 78. VIII. Chinese, Hebrew, and Greek historians, 79. IX. Greek, Roman, and Chinese law, 79.

Chapter IV

The Time of the Two Hippocrates (fifth century B. C.) 81–110

I. Brief survey of science in the fifth century B. C., 81. II. Greek, Hebrew, and Chinese philosophy, 84. III. Greek mathematics, 91. IV. Greek astronomy, 93. V. Chinese, Persian, and Greek technicians, 94. VI. Greek and Chinese medicine, 96. VII. Carthaginian and Greek explorers, 103. VIII. Greek and Hebrew mining, 104. IX. Greek and Hebrew historiography, 105. X. Hebrew, Greek, and Roman law, 109. XI. Greek, Sanskrit, and Chinese philology, 110.

Chapter V

The Time of Plato (first half of fourth century B. C.) 111–123

I. Survey of science in first half of fourth century B. C., 111. II. Plato and the Academy, 113. III. Greek mathematics, 116. IV. Greek astronomy, 118. V.

Greek physics and technology, 171. VI. Progress of the medical arts in Greece and China, 119. VII. Greek historiography and sociology, 122. VIII. Sanskrit philology, 123.

CHAPTER VI

The Time of Aristotle (second half of fourth century B. C.)............ 124–148

I. Survey of science in second half of fourth century B. C., 124. II. Alexander the Great, 127. III. Aristotle and the Lyceum, 127. IV. Other philosophers, Greek and Chinese, 136. V. Greek mathematics, 139. VI. Greek astronomy, 141. VII. Greek physics, 142. VIII. Greek and Roman technology, 142. IX. Greek botany, 143. X. Greek geography, geology, and meteorology, 144. XI. Greek anatomy, physiology, and medicine, 146. XII. Greek historiography, 146. XIII. Hindu and Roman sociology and law, 147. XIV. Greek study of the history of science, 148.

CHAPTER VII

The Time of Euclid (first half of third century B. C.).................. 149–164

I. Survey of science in first half of third century B. C., 149. II. Development of the Jewish Scriptures, 151. III. Greek and Chinese philosophy, 152. IV. Hellenistic mathematics, astronomy, and physics, 153. V. Hellenistic anatomy, physiology, biology, and medicine, 158. VI. Hellenistic technology, 161. VII. Hellenistic, Hebrew, and Chinese historiography, 161. VIII. Greek philology, 164.

CHAPTER VIII

The Time of Archimedes (second half of third century B. C.)........... 165–176

I. Survey of science in second half of third century B. C., 165. II. Development of Buddhism in India, 167. III. Unification of China, 168. IV. Chinese and Greek philosophy, 168. V. Greek mathematics, astronomy, and physics, 169. VI. Introduction of Greek medicine in Rome, 175. VII. Chinese and Hellenistic technology, 175. VIII. Greek and Roman historiography, 176. IX. Chinese writing, 176.

CHAPTER IX

The Time of Cato the Censor (first half of second century B. C.)........ 177–190

I. Survey of science in first half of second century B. C., 177. II. Development of the Jewish Scriptures, 180. III. Greek, Roman, and Chinese philosophy, 181. IV. Hellenistic and Chinese mathematics, 181. V. Hellenistic astronomy, 183. VI. Hellenistic physics and technology, 184. VII. Hellenistic geography 185. VIII. Roman husbandry, 185. IX. Hellenistic, Roman, and Chinese medicine, 186. X. Roman and Hellenistic historiography, 187. XI. Roman law, 188. XII. Greek philology, 189.

CHAPTER X

The Time of Hipparchos (second half of second century B. C.).......... 191–200

I. Survey of science in second half of second century B. C., 191. II. Chinese and Hellenistic philosophy, 193. III. Hellenistic and Chinese mathematics and astronomy, 193. IV. Hellenistic and Chinese physics and technology, 195. V. Hellenistic and Chinese geography, 196. VI. Chinese, Carthaginian, Roman, and Hellenistic botany, 197. VII. Hellenistic medicine, 198. VIII. Hellenistic and Chinese historiography, 198. IX. Sanskrit and Greek philology, 199.

CHAPTER XI

The Time of Lucretius (first half of first century B. C.) 201–218

I. Survey of science in first half of first century B. C., 201. II. Philosophical background in the West, 203. III. Hellenistic and Chinese mathematics, 208. IV. Hellenistic astronomy, 211. V. Hellenistic physics and technology, 213. VI. Hellenistic botany, 213. VII. Hellenistic medicine, 214. VIII. Hellenistic and Roman historiography, 216. IX. Roman writing, 217.

CHAPTER XII

The Time of Virgil (second half of first century B. C.) 219–234

I. Survey of science in second half of first century B. C., 219. II. Cultural background in the West, 221. III. Roman, Hellenistic, and Chinese mathematics and astronomy, 222. IV. Roman physics and technology, 223. V. Roman and Hellenistic husbandry and botany, 225. VI. Roman, Hellenistic, and Chinese geography and geology, 227. VII. Hellenistic and Roman medicine, 230. VIII. Roman, Hellenistic, and Chinese historiography, 231. IX. Latin and Greek philology, 233.

CHAPTER XIII

The Time of Celsus (first half of first century) 235–242

I. Survey of science in first half of first century, 235. II. Religious background, 236. III. Roman and Hellenistic astronomy, 237. IV. Hellenistic alchemy, 238. V. Roman geography, 239. VI. Roman and Hellenistic medicine, 239. VII. Roman historiography, 241.

CHAPTER XIV

The Time of Pliny (second half of first century) 243–266

I. Survey of science in second half of first century, 243. II. Religious background, 246. III. Philosophical and cultural background, 247. IV. Hellenistic mathematics, 253. V. Hellenistic and Chinese astronomy, 254. VI. Roman and Hellenistic physics and technology, 255. VII. Roman and Hellenistic botany, 256. VIII. Roman, Hellenistic, and Chinese geography, 257. IX. Hellenistic medicine, 258. X. Jewish, Roman, and Chinese historiography, 262. XI. Greek and Latin philology, 264.

CHAPTER XV

The Time of Ptolemy (first half of second century) 267–287

I. Survey of science in first half of second century, 267. II. Religious background, 269. III. Hellenistic philosophy, 270. IV. Roman and Hellenistic mathematics, 271. V. Hellenistic and Chinese astronomy, 272. VI. Roman, Hellenistic, and Chinese physics and technology, 278. VII. Hellenistic geography, 279. VIII. Hellenistic, Roman, and Hindu medicine, 280. IX. Roman and Hellenistic historiography, 284. X. Roman law, 285. XI. Chinese and Greek philology, 285.

CHAPTER XVI

The Time of Galen (second half of second century) 288–313

I. Survey of science in second half of second century, 288. II. Religious background, 290. III. Hellenistic, Roman, and Chinese philosophy, 295. IV. Roman and Chinese mathematics, 299. V. Syrian and Chinese astronomy, 299. VI. Hellenistic natural history, 300. VII. Hellenistic and Roman geography, 300. VIII. Hellenistic and Chinese medicine, 301. IX. Hellenistic, Roman, and Chinese historiography, 310. X. Roman law, 311. XI. Greek philology, 312.

Chapter XVII

The Time of Alexander of Aphrodisias (first half of third century)...... 314–329

I. Survey of scientific research in first half of third century, 314. II. Religious background, 316. III. Hellenistic and Chinese philosophy, 318. IV. Chinese and Hellenistic mathematics, 321. V. Hellenistic, Roman, Chinese, and Jewish astronomy, 322. VI. Hellenistic and Roman natural history, 322. VII. Roman and Chinese geography, 323. VIII. Hellenistic, Roman, Hindu, Chinese, and Jewish medicine, 324. IX. Hellenistic historiography, 326. X. Roman and Jewish law, 328.

Chapter XVIII

The Time of Diophantos (second half of third century)................ 330–343

I. Survey of science in second half of third century, 330. II. Religious background, 332. III. Hellenistic and Chinese philosophy, 334. IV. Hellenistic and Chinese mathematics, 336. V. Hellenistic and Chinese chemistry and physics, 339. VI. Roman, Hellenistic, and Chinese natural history, 340. VII. Roman, Hellenistic, and Chinese geography, 341. VIII. Chinese medicine, 342. IX. Chinese historiography, 342. X. Roman law, 343. XI. Chinese and Greek philology, 343.

Chapter XIX

The Time of Iamblichos (first half of fourth century)................ 344–358

I. Survey of science in first half of fourth century, 344. II. Religious background, 346. III. Hindu, Hellenistic, Latin, and Chinese philosophy, 351. IV. Hellenistic and Roman mathematics and astronomy, 353. V. Hellenistic and Chinese physics and chemistry, 354. VI. Roman husbandry, 355. VII. Hellenistic and Chinese medicine, 356. VIII. Hellenistic historiography, 357. IX. Roman law, 357. X. Chinese, Gothic, Latin, and Egyptian philology, 358.

Chapter XX

The Time of Oribasios (second half of fourth century)................ 359–376

I. Survey of science in second half of fourth century, 359. II. Religious background, 361. III. Hellenistic and Hindu philosophy, 365. IV. Hellenistic, Roman, Jewish, and Chinese mathematics and astronomy, 367. V. Roman and Chinese technology, 368. VI. Roman and Hellenistic natural history and husbandry, 369. VII. Roman and Hellenistic geography, 371. VIII. Hellenistic and Roman medicine, 372. IX. Roman historiography, 375. X. Roman law, 376.

Chapter XXI

The Time of Fa-hsien (first half of fifth century).................... 377–398

I. Survey of science in first half of fifth century, 377. II. Religious background, 380. III. Hellenistic and Roman philosophy, 385. IV. Hellenistic, Hindu, and Chinese mathematics and astronomy, 386. V. Hellenistic and Chinese alchemy, physics and technology, 388. VI. Chinese and Armenian geography, 390. VII. Roman, Hellenistic, Hindu, and Korean medicine (including botany and biology), 391. VIII. Hellenistic, Roman, Armenian, and Chinese historiography, 393. IX. Roman and Barbarian law, 396. X. Armenian and Greek philology, 397.

Chapter XXII

The Time of Proclos (second half of fifth century).................. 399–413

I. Survey of science in second half of fifth century, 399. II. Religious background, 401. III. Hellenistic, Syriac, and Latin philosophy, 402. IV. Latin,

Hellenistic, and Hindu mathematics, 408. V. Latin, Hellenistic, Chinese, and Hindu astronomy, 409. VI. Chinese geography, 410. VII. Latin and Singhalese historiography, 411. VIII. Roman and Barbarian law, 412. IX. Chinese philology, 413.

CHAPTER XXIII

The Time of Philoponos (first half of sixth century)................... 414–442

I. Survey of science in first half of sixth century, 414. II. Religious background, 419. III. Byzantine, Syriac, and Latin philosophy, 421. IV. Byzantine, Latin, and Hindu mathematics, 427. V. Hindu, Chinese, Byzantine, and Latin astronomy, 425. VI. Byzantine physics and technology, 430. VII. Byzantine and Latin botany; Chinese husbandry, 431. VIII. Chinese and Byzantine geography, 431. IX. Latin, Byzantine, Syriac, Persian, and Chinese medicine, 433. X. Byzantine, Latin, Syriac, and Chinese historiography, 436. XI. Roman and Barbarian law, 438. XII. Byzantine, Latin, and Chinese philology and pedagogy, 440.

CHAPTER XXIV

The Time of Alexander of Tralles (second half of sixth century)......... 443–459

I. Survey of science in second half of sixth century, 443. II. Religious background, 445. III. Persian philosophy, 448. IV. Byzantine and Chinese mathematics, 449. V. Chinese technology; its diffusion west and east, 451. VI. Byzantine husbandry, 452. VII. Byzantine geography, 453. VIII. Byzantine, Korean, and Japanese medicine, 453. IX. Byzantine, Latin, Syriac, Persian, and Chinese historiography, 454. X. Sanskrit and Chinese lexicography; Chinese education, 458.

CHAPTER XXV

The Time of Hsüan Tsang (first half of seventh century).............. 460–487

I. Survey of science in first half of seventh century, 460. II. Religious background, 464. III. Philosophers and patrons of learning in the Latin and Byzantine worlds, in India, Japan, and China, 471. IV. Chinese and Hindu mathematics, 474. V. Byzantine, Muslim, Chinese, and Japanese astronomy, 475. VI. Chinese geography, 476. VII. Byzantine, Hindu, Chinese, and Japanese medicine, 478. VIII. Byzantine, Persian, Chinese, and Japanese historiography, 481. IX. Barbarian and Japanese law, 484. X. Arabic, Tibetan, and Chinese philology, 485.

CHAPTER XXVI

The Time of I-ching (second half of seventh century).................. 488–502

I. Survey of science in second half of seventh century, 488. II. Religious background, 490. III. Latin, Syriac, and Muslim philosophy, 492. IV. Syriac and Chinese mathematics and astronomy, 494. V. Byzantine and Muslim alchemy, 494. VI. Byzantine, Latin, Syriac, and Chinese geography, 495. VII. Byzantine, Latin, and Chinese medicine, 497. VIII. Latin and Syriac historiography, 499. IX. Barbarian, Muslim, and Japanese law, 499. X. Latin, Syriac, Arabic, and Japanese philology, 500.

CHAPTER XXVII

The Time of Bede (first half of eighth century)....................... 503–519

I. Survey of science in first half of eighth century, 503. II. Religious background, 506. III. Philosophical background and general advance of civilization, 510. IV. Latin and Chinese mathematics and astronomy, 513. V. Byzantine and Muslim alchemy; Japanese technology, 514. VI. Japanese, Chinese, and Latin geography, 515. VII. Japanese and Latin historiography, 516. VIII. Barbarian, Byzantine, Muslim, Chinese, and Japanese law, 517. IX. Arabic and Japanese philology, 518.

CHAPTER XXVIII

The Time of Jābir ibn Ḥaiyān (second half of eighth century).......... 520–542

I. Survey of science in second half of eighth century, 520. II. Religious background, 524. III. Cultural background, east and west, 527. IV. Muslim and Latin mathematics and astronomy, 530. V. Muslim and Latin alchemy; Japanese technology, 532. VI. Muslim, Chinese, and Japanese natural history, 534. VII. Latin and Chinese geography, 535. VIII. Latin, Syriac, Muslim, Hindu, Tibetan, Chinese, and Japanese medicine, 536. IX. Latin, Muslim, and Japanese historiography, 539. X. Muslim philology, 541.

CHAPTER XXIX

The Time of al-Khwārizmī (first half of ninth century)................ 543–582

I. Survey of science in first half of ninth century, 543. II. Religious background, 550. III. Cultural background—Byzantine, Latin, Muslim, and Hindu philosophy, 554. IV. Muslim, Latin, Byzantine, and Hindu mathematics and astronomy, 562. V. Muslim and Latin natural history, 570. VI. Latin, Muslim, and Chinese geography and geology, 571. VII. Byzantine, Arabic, and Japanese medicine, 573. VIII. Latin, Byzantine, Syrian, Muslim, and Japanese historiography, 576. IX. Barbarian, Chinese, and Japanese law, 580. X. Latin, Semitic, and Japanese philology and education, 581.

CHAPTER XXX

The Time of al-Rāzī (second half of ninth century)................... 583–618

I. Survey of science in second half of ninth century, 583. II. Religious background, 590. III. Philosophical background; Greek, Latin, English, Syriac, and Arabic writings, 594. IV. Arabic and Latin mathematics and astronomy, 597. V. Muslim alchemy and physics; Chinese technology, 604. VI. French and Scandinavian travel and exploration; English and Muslim geography, 605. VII. Latin, Byzantine, Muslim (or Arabic), Jewish, and Coptic medicine, 607. VIII. Latin, English, Byzantine, Syrian, Muslim, and Japanese historiography, 614. IX. Byzantine and Japanese law, 617. X. Latin, English, Byzantine, Slavonic, Syriac, and Arabic philology, 618.

CHAPTER XXXI

The Time of al-Mas'ūdī (first half of tenth century).................. 619–645

I. Survey of science in first half of tenth century, 619. II. Religious background, 624. III. Cultural background in Israel and Islam, 626. IV. Muslim, Byzantine, and Chinese mathematics and astronomy, 630. V. Byzantine, Muslim, and Chinese physics, alchemy, and technology, 632. VI. English and Muslim botany, 633. VII. Muslim and Japanese geography, 635. VIII. English, Byzantine, and Arabic medicine, 639 IX. Latin, Arabic, and Chinese historiography, 641. X. Latin, Barbarian, and Japanese law. Muslim sociology, 643. XI. Hebrew and Arabic philology, 644.

CHAPTER XXXII

The Time of Abū-l-Wafā' (second half of tenth century).............. 646–692

I. Survey of science in second half of tenth century, 646. II. Religious background, 655. III. Cultural background—Byzantine, Latin, Muslim, Jewish, and Chinese philosophers, 656. IV. Muslim, Latin, Chinese, and Japanese mathematics and astronomy, 663. V. Latin and Muslim alchemy and technology, 673. VI. Byzantine, Muslim, and Chinese natural history, 673. VII. Muslim, Jewish, Scandinavian, and Chinese geography, 674. VIII. Muslim, Persian, Jewish, Byzantine, and Japanese medicine, 677. IX. Latin, Byzantine, Jewish, Muslim, and Chinese historiography, 684. X. Arabic, Syriac, Hebrew, Byzantine, Latin, English, and Sino-Japanese philology, 688.

CHAPTER XXXIII

The Time of al-Bīrūnī (first half of eleventh century) 693–737

I. Survey of science in first half of eleventh century, 693. II. Philosophical and theological background, 703. III. Latin, English, Muslim, and Hindu mathematics and astronomy, 714. IV. Latin, English, Syrian, Muslim, and Chinese physics, chemistry, and technology, 720. V. Muslim natural history, 724. VI. Icelandic discovery of America; Latin geography; Muslim geography, mineralogy, and geology, 724. VII. Latin, Byzantine, Muslim (or Arabic), and Chinese medicine, 725. VIII. Latin, Muslim, Armenian, and Syrian historiography, 732. IX. German, Hebrew, Syriac, and Chinese philology, 736.

CHAPTER XXXIV

The Time of Omar Khayyam (second half of eleventh century) 738–783

I. Survey of science in second half of eleventh century, 738. II. Philosophical and theological background, 748. III. Latin, Byzantine, Muslim, and Chinese mathematics and astronomy, 756. IV. Latin, Persian, and Chinese physics and technology, 762. V. Latin, Byzantine, Muslim, and Chinese natural history, 764. VI. Latin and Muslim geography, 767. VII. Latin, Byzantine, Muslim, and Chinese medicine, 769. VIII. French, Latin, Byzantine, Jewish, Muslim, Chinese, and Japanese historiography, 773. IX. Lombard, English, Byzantine, Muslim, Hindu, and Chinese law and sociology, 778. X. French, Latin, Greek, Hebrew, Arabic, Persian, Chinese, and Japanese philology, 781.

Brief Index 785–839

INTRODUCTION TO THE HISTORY OF SCIENCE

Volume I

From Homer to Omar Khayyam

BY GEORGE SARTON

Homo sum, humani nihil a me alienum puto.

—*Terence.*

INTRODUCTORY CHAPTER

I. Purpose of this Work. II. Ancient Science. III. Mediaeval Science. IV. Scholasticism, its Cause and its Cure. V. Three Aspects of the Fundamental Unity of Life. VI. A Survey of Human Civilization. VII. Remarks on the History of Science in India, Central and Eastern Asia. VIII. Chronological Basis. IX. Bibliographical Basis. X. Principles of Selection. XI. Errors of this Work and their Correction. XII. The Author expresses his Gratitude.

Appendix: Notes on the transcription of Greek, Hebrew, Syriac, Arabic, Persian, Sanskrit, Chinese, and Japanese words.

Before explaining the purpose and methods of this work, it is expedient to call attention to a material feature of immediate concern. Each chapter is devoted to a single period; the first to a period of indeterminate length, the three following to centuries, and all of the remaining ones, thirty in number, to periods of half a century each. Each begins with a summary of the main facts, a simplified account of the development of science during that period. The first section of each chapter and this introductory chapter are the only parts of my work which are intended for continuous reading. The remainder of the material is incorporated for purposes of study and reference. Statements contained in these summaries are sometimes a little too dogmatic, because many qualifications had to be omitted for the sake of brevity, but these qualifications will be found in their proper places in one of the following sections.

Thus, the best way of using this work is to read the introductory chapter and the first section of succeeding chapters, and to consult the other sections only as far as may be necessary to satisfy one's curiosity or to find an answer to a definite question. This arrangement is rather unconventional, but I believe it will prove convenient, as it will enable the reader to obtain easily a general view of the main substance of the book and to obtain as much additional information on any subject as he may wish for.

I. PURPOSE OF THIS WORK

The purpose of this work is to explain briefly, yet as completely as possible, the development of one essential phase of human civilization which has not yet received sufficient attention—the development of science, that is of *systematized positive knowledge*. I am not prepared to say that this development is more important than any other aspect of intellectual progress, for example, than the development of religion, of art, or of social justice. But it is equally important; and no history of civilization can be tolerably complete which does not give considerable space to the explanation of scientific progress. If we had any doubts about this, it would suffice to ask ourselves what constitutes the essential difference between our and earlier civilizations. Throughout the course of history, in every period, and in almost every country, we find a small number of saints, of great artists, of men of science. The saints of to-day are not necessarily more saintly than those of a thousand years ago; our artists are not necessarily greater than those of early Greece; they are more likely to be inferior; and of course, our men of science are not necessarily more intelligent than those of old; yet one thing is certain, their knowledge is at once more extensive and more accurate. *The acquisition and systematization of positive knowledge is the only human activity which is truly cumulative and progressive.* Our civilization is essentially different from earlier ones, because our knowledge of the world and of ourselves is deeper, more precise, and more certain, because we have gradually learned to disentangle the forces of nature, and because we have contrived, by strict obedience to their laws, to capture them and to divert them to the gratification of our own needs.

My work contains but very few references to political or to economic history. This does not mean that I underestimate political and economic factors. On the contrary, I clearly realize that these factors are very often not only important, but decisive. If we had to write the biography of a great man, we would not lay too much stress upon the diseases from which he suffered in the course of his life; yet we would be mindful of the fact that those diseases which interrupted and may be thwarted his activity might have stopped it altogether, in which case there would have been, perhaps, no biography to write. We are not interested in the pathological history of mankind (at any rate, not for its own sake); we believe that men were born not to fight, but to love and help one another; yet we must remember that wars and other calamities do happen, and that they often interfere with the accomplishment of mankind's essential task. I do not refer to political and economic events, which form the material background of human history, because there are a number of excellent books wherein the reader may easily find such information, should he need it.

Nor do I deal with the history of art, for a similar reason. That history is extremely significant, but a number of good textbooks are devoted to it, and it is not expedient to load my own account with information which can be obtained elsewhere with very little trouble. Scholars who have followed me since 1912 know well enough that I attach much importance to the development of art, under which term I would include every human activity, the purpose of which is aesthetic or playful (fine arts, music, decorative arts, pure literature, sports, and games). For one thing, the transmission of artistic ideas—say, architectural ideas—can often be traced with remarkable precision, and these ideas did not travel alone; many others, including scientific ideas, traveled in their wake. Thus the historian of art can help the historian of science in many ways. But works of art are precious to us, above all, because they enable us to understand at once, as we could in no other manner, the people who produced them. Each gives us an intuitive, synthetic, and immediate knowledge of their deepest aspirations.

On the other hand, I have felt obliged to devote much space to the history of religion. To be sure, we have some excellent treatises on the subject, but I am not aware of a single one which contains an account of the religious experience of mankind in strict chronological order. The average scholar (who is not an expert in that field) is thus in danger of overlooking some part of our spiritual background. He is not made to realize with sufficient concreteness the bewildering complexity of religious life. If we would understand the intellectual development of a people, we must take into account its religious problems and feelings, and this implies some knowledge not only of its own religion, but of various other religions.

But even if the historians of religion had given us a chronological account of religious experience, I should have been obliged to deal with it to some extent in my own work. Political history and the history of art, however important, do not really belong to our subject; they throw light upon it but, so to say, from the outside. On the contrary, until relatively modern times, theology was an intrinsic part of science, and not only that, but, in the opinion of most men, all other sciences were subordinated to it. The whole history of mediaeval thought, in almost every part of the world, is dominated by a continual and desperate endeavor to reconcile the facts of rational experience with some system of knowledge considered a priori as perfect and unimpeachable. Nothing could be more pathetic than the spectacle of such efforts which were doomed to remain sterile. It is easy enough to see this now, but we must not be too proud of our wisdom, for it is of relatively recent date, and we should not have it at all but for the century-long disputes and perplexities of our ancestors. Their delusion, once its source is known, is natural and excusable enough. By some strange concatenation of circumstances they were brought to believe that a number of theological statements were absolutely certain. In those days the art of observation was so undeveloped (let alone the art of experimentation) that the facts which it revealed seemed very changeable and shaky; whatever positive knowledge they had was not very reliable; any one of their scientific statements could easily be challenged. Compared with that, the theological constructions seemed unshakable; they were not based upon observation, hence no amount of observation could destroy them; they were not based upon deduction, hence no amount of logic could impugn them. They stood apart and above the world of experience.

Let me illustrate this with a couple of examples. From the point of view of Mīmāṃsā philosophy, the Veda is uncreated and existent from all eternity. Thus the main problem of a Mīmāṃsist is not to try to understand a moving and delusive reality, but to conform himself as strictly as possible to the eternal standards contained in the Veda. How could we possibly appreciate his thoughts and actions if we did not take that central fact into account?

Muslim faith was anchored upon a similar certitude. Most Mohammedans believed that the Qur'ān was uncreated. It is true some theologians of a more liberal type ventured to discuss that doctrine, thus starting a religious quarrel which caused considerable rancor. Many Muslim doctors lost their heads, figuratively—and not a few of them, literally—in that controversy. But even those who considered the Qur'ān as having been created were agreed that it represented the very word of God. Thus (could they say) while the knowledge which we obtain by means of our erring senses and of our infirm minds is essentially fragile and precarious, that enounced in the Qur'ān is absolutely true and sure. I ask once more, how could we reach a correct understanding of Muslim science if we did not fully grasp its gravitation around the Qur'ān?

Such a mental attitude was universal throughout the Middle Ages. Theology was at once the core of science and the prop of religion. Hence, science and religion were inseparable, and we can not hope to understand one without the other. Our inquiry is restricted to the study of positive knowledge, but it can not be fair unless we base it not upon *our* definition of positiveness, but upon *theirs*. Now, as I have indicated, theology from their point of view was not only positive knowledge, but—if I may coin the phrase—superpositive knowledge. The center of gravity of their thought was radically different from ours.

However, it would not be wise to look down upon them from the point of view of our superior knowledge—a knowledge which we owe at least partly to their efforts—because there are still more points of contact between them and us than we would be pleased to imagine. The greatest conquest of science, philosophically speaking, is the notion of the relativity of knowledge; that is, our trust in science, though steadily increasing, is always qualified and limited. But the vast majority of modern scientists have not yet understood that notion, or else they have understood it only with their minds; it has not yet sunk into their hearts, it has not yet become a part of their substance. Many scientists have a conceited view of their knowledge (not necessarily their personal knowledge, but the general knowledge of their time); this is perhaps natural enough, inasmuch as it is relatively easy to measure one's knowledge and to wonder at it, while it is impossible to fathom one's ignorance. Such conceit is obvious enough in the fragments of Lucretius which will be quoted in the following section, but equally good examples could be found at any time, and particularly in our own. Thus it would not behoove us to judge the self-satisfaction of ancient and mediaeval scientists with too much severity.

Our main object is not simply to record isolated discoveries, but rather to explain the progress of scientific thought, the gradual development of human consciousness, that deliberate tendency to understand and to increase our part in the cosmic evolution. But it is clear that we can not properly explain that progress without giving at least a brief account of the intellectual delusions which often delayed our advance or threatened to sidetrack it. If we failed to do that, our survey would be incomplete, untrue and deceiving. Moreover, as I have already pointed out, to appreciate correctly the scientific ideas of any people, we must consider them not only from our point of view, but also from their own, however wrong the latter may seem. Thus it will be necessary to outline the development of some pseudo-sciences, such as astrology, alchemy, physiognomy, and oneirology. It should be noted that it is not always easy to distinguish a pseudo-science from one which is sound but imperfect; in some cases it is almost impossible; we can do it now with reference to the past, but it is not certain that we can always do it with regard to the present. We might say that a pseudo-science is one which is based upon wrong principles or whose aims are unsound, but the principles and even the aims of science are not immovable. At any rate, the reader will find in my work a condensed history of astrology and other delusions; I have made no attempt to tell that history with any completeness, for the history of error is, of its very nature, infinite. Besides, as I am bent upon explaining the progressive—not the regressive—tendencies of human civilization, I have kept these fallacies in the background, where they belong. Indeed, they never represented the main current of human endeavor, but were rather like undertows. It would be equally wrong to ignore them altogether or to attach too much importance to them.

I may seem to be inconsistent in speaking so much of religion and so little of magic and superstition, but in this there is no real inconsistency. Though they used different methods, theologians were trying to reach the same goal as the men of science; they generalized prematurely; they were walking along the same road, but much too fast. Magicians did not follow that road at all; they were sidetracked or turned in hopeless circles; their purpose was but too often of a sordid nature. The theologians' aim was a noble and disinterested one; they inculcated the habit of considering things *sub specie aeternitatis*. Now this religious attitude is also a scientific attitude. It is no wonder that a relatively large number of scientists were the sons of ministers. Are not the ultimate teachings of pure religion and those of pure science identical?

It was my original purpose to deal only with the history of pure science, but it is often difficult, if not impossible, to draw the line between pure science and its applications. Sometimes the applications were discovered first and the principles deduced from them; sometimes it was the contrary; but in any case the pure and applied sciences grew together. Yet a line must be drawn somewhere, for while the number of pure scientists is relatively small, that of physicians, teachers, engineers, and other practitioners has always been considerable. My rule is to speak of a physician, an engineer, or a teacher only if he added something definite to our knowledge, or if he wrote treatises which were sufficiently original and valuable, or if he did his task in such a masterly way that he introduced new professional standards.

My work contains also some of the materials of a history of music. Indeed, the theory of music was considered a part of mathematics almost until modern times. It was one of the main divisions of the quadrivium which dominated mediaeval education.

I have attached much importance to the early history of philology. The discovery of the logical structure of language was as much a scientific discovery as, for example, the discovery of the anatomical structure of the body. The systematic organization of language, its transformation from an instinctive and unconscious tool into one of increasing precision, was one of the most important preliminary tasks which were required for the development and transmission of knowledge. The scientific study of language was considerably stimulated in mediaeval times by the religious necessity to interpret sacred writings which were supposed to be infallible (that is, it was worth while to consider their every letter or accent) and also because of the practical necessity, which occurred more than once, of translating a number of scientific treatises and of creating rapidly an adequate terminology for that purpose. Moreover, as I shall explain more fully below, mediaeval thinkers were led to attach excessive significance to words and to their origins, irrespective of the objects represented. It is only after centuries of apparently sterile but necessary quarrels and after the final establishment of the experimental method and attitude, that we have slowly learned to consider words as symbols, which, as far as scientific purposes are concerned, would be usefully replaced by arbitrary signs having no signification but the one explicitly defined. The distinction between names and things is now so deeply rooted in the minds of scientifically trained men that they would find it difficult to understand how they could ever be confused, if they did not detect examples of such confusion almost every day in their own environment. The emancipation of science from verbalism was as slow and painful a process as its emancipation from theology; it is not yet completed in either case.

Nowhere did the verbal incubus weigh more heavily than in the field of historical research. It might be said of historiography—as of medicine—that it is one of the oldest arts, but one of the youngest sciences. The scientific organization of that great discipline is so recent that there are still many men of science who do not realize that historical research is (or at any rate can be) as much a scientific undertaking as, say, physical or geological research. However crude the early methods of historians, we owe to them a large amount of our positive knowledge with regard to the past, especially with regard to those periods which were nearest to their own present. I have thus tried to mention the main historical works which were produced in each period. This account of ancient and mediaeval historiography is of necessity very incomplete. Many annals, which may be of considerable value for the historical study of a certain locality, are omitted, either because I do not know of them or because I have no means of measuring their importance. It should be noted that the historical value of any writing depends not only upon its intrinsic worth but also upon a number of other factors. For example, if all historical books were destroyed except Mr. Wells's "Outline of History," that Outline would become at once a source of primary importance. Many mediaeval chronicles have no other title to our consideration than their uniqueness. It is as yet impossible to write a history of mediaeval historiography, but my work includes the rudiments of such history.

Similar remarks might be made with regard to juridical and sociological works, a few of which will be quoted in the following pages. However, there is an essential difference in that many of these works were the juridical realities of their age, not interpretations of realities, but real monuments, as objective as natural phenomena. It is true the same can be said to some extent of historical works or any works; whatever their intrinsic value, we may always consider them as products and symbols of their age; whatever their lack of objectivity, we may always consider them as representative objects.

I have said enough to indicate the general scope of my investigations. The reading of the introductory sections of a few chapters will give a more concrete idea of them than I could impart otherwise. It will suffice to add that the reader ought to keep in mind the primary purpose—to outline the history of science—and to distinguish carefully between the facts which actually belong to that story and those which are introduced only for the sake of evoking the intellectual milieu.

II. ANCIENT SCIENCE

Considering the class of readers who will approach this book, it seems hardly necessary to emphasize the significance of ancient, and, especially, of Greek science. One has often spoken of the "Greek miracle" with reference to the sudden bloom of a wonderful literature and to the unequaled creations of their sculptors and architects, but the development of Greek science was not a bit less marvelous. Of course we realize now that it was not entirely spontaneous, but rather the fructification of a long evolution of which we find many impressive vestiges in Mesopotamia, in Egypt, and in the Aegean world. Yet what a distance between those crude empirical efforts and the clear-cut, pregnant dicta of the early Greek philosophers and mathematicians! If science is more than an accumulation of facts; if it is not simply positive knowledge, but systematized positive knowledge; if it is not simply unguided analysis and haphazard empiricism, but synthesis; if it is not simply a passive recording, but a constructive activity; then, undoubtedly, Hellas was its cradle. The progress of our own studies makes us see more and more clearly how much they borrowed from earlier peoples, but by way of contrast this enhances our opinion of their originality and fortifies our admiration of their scientific genius. It becomes increasingly easy to tell where they found their rough material, but this hardly helps us to understand what enabled them to assume a scientific attitude and to give the earliest conspicuous examples of scientific investigations which were at once deliberate and disinterested. How did it come to pass that some of those early Greek philosophers managed to distinguish scientific issues and to discuss them with a clarity, directness, and freedom from prejudice which remained almost unequaled until modern times? Where did they get that genius for striking the nail on the head? We try to explain this by referring to racial qualities, to geographic and meteorological considerations, to politics and religion, but in reality our explanations do not explain, and it is that very failure which we express when we speak of the Greek miracle. The most philosophically minded of our contemporary men of science would not hesitate to repeat Lucretius's invocation to Epicuros, though they would not think of Epicuros only, but of the Greek scientific spirit which he symbolizes—a beacon which suddenly appeared in the darkness:

"E tenebris tantis tam clarum extollere lumen
qui primus potuisti inlustrans commoda vitae,
te sequor, o Graiae gentis decus, inque tuis nunc
ficta pedum pono pressis vestigia signis,
. . . .
Tu, pater, es rerum inventor, tu patria nobis
suppeditas praecepta, tuisque ex, inclute, chartis,
floriferis ut apes in saltibus omnia libant,
omnia nos itidem depascimur aurea dicta,
aurea, perpetua semper dignissima vita.
. . . .
His ibi me rebus quaedam divina voluptas
percipit atque horror, quod sic natura tua vi
tam manifesta patens ex omni parte retecta est."[a]

These lines are Englished by H. A. J. Munro as follows:

"Thee, who first wast able amid such thick darkness to raise on high so bright a beacon and shed a light on the true interests of life, thee I follow, glory of the Greek race, and plant now my footsteps firmly fixed in thy imprinted marks. . . . . Thou, father, art discoverer of things, thou furnishest us with fatherly precepts, and like as bees sip of all things in the flowery lawns, we, O glorious being, in like manner feed from out thy pages upon all the golden maxims, golden I say, most worthy ever of endless life. . . . . At all this a kind of godlike delight mixed with shuddering awe comes over me to think that nature by thy power is laid thus visibly open, is thus unveiled on every side."

The last lines would perhaps bring smiles to their faces, for educated scientists do not believe any more that nature has yet been unveiled on every side, but they would easily forgive Lucretius his conceit, itself a tribute to the Greek masters who had taught him everything he knew. Indeed, Greek science had been a true revelation—mind you, a lay revelation, the earliest one, and for a very long time, the only one, of its kind.

We might be tempted to conclude that if mankind had walked humbly and constantly in their footsteps, the progress of civilization would have been con-

[a] De rerum natura, beginning of Book III.

siderably accelerated. But if we did this, we should have shown that we did not entirely understand the nature of progress. It is undoubtedly a function of the increase of positive knowledge, but not only of that. However necessary, knowledge is never sufficient. If there is one lesson which history has taught us, it is the fundamental importance of will power, as much for nations as for individuals, and in every circumstance of life, great or small. Greek civilization ended in failure, not because of the lack of intelligence, but because of the lack of character, of morality.[b]

After that dismal failure it seemed as if everything had to be started all over again, and, to begin with, it was necessary to build a sound body politic. The maxim "mens sana in corpore sano" applies as strongly to nations as to individuals. Progress implies stability: there can be no durable progress unless there is an organized resistance to it, a social inertia, aggressive to-day, protective to-morrow. Roman culture was an instinctive reaction along these lines. Their insistence upon the material conditions of stability was so strong that the Greek tradition of disinterested research was stifled. Thus, even in her days of greatest prosperity, Rome gave but little encouragement to science. Lucretius was preaching in the desert. No investigations were countenanced except those which were immediately profitable. The pendulum had swung to another extreme, and mankind was taught a second fundamental lesson: When people determine to care for nothing but what is directly and obviously useful, the days of their own usefulness are already numbered.

But before going any further, I must say a few words on an important type of civilization, which was neither Greek nor Roman, but a combination of both and of various other elements besides, the so-called Hellenistic civilization which flourished after the time of the great Alexandrian adventure. It would seem that for a few centuries the conditions for the progress of science were as favorable in Alexandria and in a few other Mediterranean cities as they have ever been anywhere in the world. The result was a magnificent efflorescence, not only of scientific talent, but also of scientific genius of the highest order. One has sometimes the impression that there was less real genius in those days than before, because the tendencies of the age were of a more analytic nature. Men like Euclid and Herophilos, Archimedes and Apollonios, had already realized the futility of premature synthesis, or at least they felt that enough had been done in the line of philosophical coordination and that the time had come for a new attack on the individual problems of science by the combined efforts of a number of specialists; they initiated a series of deeper investigations, which would make possible later, much later, a new synthesis.

That wonderful civilization lacked the qualities which had given the golden age of Greece its subtlest charm—that exquisite blending of spontaneity with reticence, of soberness with pregnancy; yet it combined some of the noblest features of Greek genius with new aspirations derived from Egyptian and Eastern sources. In our final appreciation of Greco-Roman culture we must not forget that it was subjected to a terrible ordeal. Indeed, it was during that period that

[b] Of course I mean not only personal but public morality, not only the repression of self-indulgence, but also a sufficient subordination of individual ambitions to the common weal—the essence of fair play and team work. The noblest ethical movement of antiquity, Stoicism, failed for a similar reason; it was individual, not social.

there occurred one of the greatest intellectual conflicts of history, the clash between Greek ideals and various oriental religions, chiefly Judaism and Christianity. Every notion was put into the crucible; new scales of values were slowly adjusted. That gigantic struggle between lay and religious ideals lasted many centuries. It was not by any means as simple as my brief statement of it may suggest; it was complicated by various heterogeneous factors, and chiefly by the existence of a popular system of philosophy, Neoplatonism, which attempted a sort of compromise.

The reader knows that this protracted struggle ended with the triumph of Christianity. It was a distinct gain from the point of view of morality, but a loss from the point of view of scientific research. This might be considered a third tempering of mankind. The Greeks had taught the nobility of scientific study and that the pursuit of disinterested knowledge is the greatest purification; the Romans had urged the necessity of applying knowledge to immediate needs; the Christians were now insisting that if we have not charity it profits us nothing. The Greeks laid stress upon truth and beauty; the Romans upon strength and usefulness; the Christians, upon love. The value of the last message in a barbarous and cruel world can hardly be overestimated. Unfortunately, most men are incapable of grasping an idea, unless they exaggerate it to the exclusion of all others. Thus, in this case, most of the people who finally understood that charity was essential did not stop there, but jumped to the conclusion that it was all-sufficient. This led them to consider scientific research not only useless, but pernicious. Thus the ruin of science, begun by Roman utilitarianism, was in danger of being completed by Christian piety. It has taken about one millennium and a half to make people generally understand that knowledge without charity and charity without knowledge are equally worthless and dangerous; a great many people do not understand it yet.

Even as the geographical atlas of our childhood, wherein Switzerland occupied one page and Russia covered another, gave us a false sense of proportion, a rapid sketch like this may leave the reader an impression of swiftness in human evolution which is decidedly misleading. Therefore it is worth while to insist that each of the periods of which I have spoken was considerably longer than we often imagine. For example, the development of Hellenic science, leaving out of account the period of anonymous preparation, which must have been very long, but can not be measured, lasted at least four and a half centuries; the development of Hellenistic and Greco-Roman science extended over seven and a half centuries or more (the upper limit can not be determined); the triumph of Christianity was not complete until the sixth century after the advent of the Messiah.[c]

There are such a number of excellent reference books dealing with classical antiquity that it is generally easy to obtain information on almost any subject, even a strictly scientific one. But my investigations were not restricted to classical antiquity; they included all the contemporary events within our field, wherever they happened. I would be ready to admit that, all considered, the

[c] If we consider the modern period as beginning with the American or with the French Revolution, it has lasted now about one century and a half. Thus the Hellenic period lasted at least three times longer; the conflict between Pagan and Christian ideals four times longer; the Hellenistic and Greco-Roman period five times longer.

civilization which developed around the Mediterranean basin was the most nearly complete and perfect, but it was not the only one. Great cultural events happened at the same time in many other parts of the world: in Judea—so near and yet so far (many centuries had to elapse before the Greek people realized the existence of that neighboring civilization)—in Mesopotamia, in Iran, in India, in China. Some of these events influenced directly the development of science and their repercussion was bound to be felt sooner or later all over the world. It could not be felt at once, because the relations between the distant parts of the world were neither so direct nor so swift as they are now. As the repercussion reached different countries at different times, it is clear that the only logical procedure is to describe these events, not when they were understood here or there, but when they actually happened. This is what I have tried to do, and the result may be at first a little bewildering; but the reader will soon satisfy himself that if one wishes to tell the history, not of a single province, but of the whole of mankind, there is no other way out.

Our conception of ancient culture has been strangely adulterated by the very scholars who had assumed the task of explaining it. The horizon of most classical scholars, instead of being as largely human as their humanistic claims would warrant, was clouded and limited in two essential respects.

In the first place, they chose and even affected to ignore the development of science, and thus one of the most admirable aspects of the Greek miracle remained largely unknown to them. I would have much to say on that kind of obscurantism, but it is more politic to quote the words of one of them, the late Viscount Milner, in his splendid address to the Classical Association in January 1922. Said Lord Milner:

"I wonder what Plato and Aristotle, if they could appear amongst us today, would say to an education that was purely linguistic, even if the literature with which it occupied itself was the best ever known? Looking with wondering eyes upon the achievements of science, which have so transformed the world since their day and given to mankind a control over physical forces such as they never dreamed of, would they not be seized with an intense desire to probe these marvels to the bottom, to know all about their causes, the methods and steps by which such great results have been attained?

"And what would they think of a man who, living in the midst of these achievements, took no interest in them except in so far as they affected his personal convenience and well-being, enabling him to satisfy his wants cheaply, to travel with rapidity and comfort, to communicate in a few minutes with the uttermost ends of the globe, to escape suffering, avert disease, and even postpone the advent of death, and who never felt impelled to go more deeply into the matter and to learn something of the inner nature of the mysterious forces the discovery of which is so rapidly transforming the life of man upon this earth?

"Certainly no Greek philosopher, revisiting the world today, would rest content with a superficial knowledge of the results of modern science, or admit that a man wholly unacquainted with its foundations had had a really liberal education. He would surely condemn him as a misfit, a creature unsuited to its environment.

"We should be false to the teaching of the greatest classics, if we did not recognize to the full the claims of science, of which, if they could come to life again today, they would themselves be the most fervent votaries. In truth the idea that the classical spirit is in any sense opposed to the scientific spirit is a complete mistake. . . . . "[d]

In the second place, they seemed to profess that classical antiquity was the whole of antiquity, and that the achievements of races other than those of the Near East and the Mediterranean basin were not worth considering. Of course they had some knowledge and appreciation of Hebrew antiquities, but even that was not properly integrated with their classical learning; it remained outside of it, for among Western people religion is but too often shockingly dissociated from life. Thus their vision of the past remained provincial; the fact that their province was magnificent does not alter the case. What the Iranians, the Hindus, and the Chinese had done they did not know, and did not care to know, as if those people were beyond the pale of humanity. This provincialism was carried so far that, though most of them were Christians, they were not well acquainted even with the ancient Christian philosophers. It is true they might have read, for theological reasons, some of the "Fathers of the Church," but that gave them an incomplete view of Christian philosophy, for the Fathers contributed on the whole very little to the transmission of ancient knowledge. But while the Fathers were engaged in their mission—a purely religious one, the defense of their faith against internal and external dangers—other Christians were continuing the traditions of Greek philosophy.[e] By the middle of the sixth century, if not a little earlier, the school of Alexandria was entirely Christianized. This is significant, because it is partly through these Christian commentators that ancient science was handed over to other Eastern Christians—Syrians and Armenians—and finally to the Muslims. Yet the majority of humanists were so deeply engrossed by Neoplatonism that they failed to pay attention to those Christian philosophers who were far more important from the point of view of cultural continuity than the contemporary Neoplatonists and theologians. It would be difficult to find a better example of shortsightedness; it proves conclusively that their humanism is not by any means as open-hearted as they represent it, but dominated by prejudice.

This Introduction begins with Homer. Of course, I am well aware that Homer did not jump suddenly out of chaos. The Iliad is not a beginning, but a climax. If I have not dealt with the dawn of science as it developed in Egypt, in Mesopotamia, in the Aegean world, and maybe in other places, it is partly because that account does not lend itself as yet to a strict chronological arrangement, and partly because I do not feel that I have a sufficient philological and archaeological equipment to undertake such a task. Moreover, so much research is being done in that direction to-day by a legion of specialists, our knowledge of pre-Hellenic science is increasing so fast, that it is perhaps wiser to postpone the necessary synthesis until a little later. The same remark applies to Chinese antiquity. What we know to-day definitely of early China[f] is comparatively little, but our knowledge may become more substantial within the course of this generation. However, it is not likely that our knowledge of ancient China will ever be comparable to our knowledge of Egypt and Babylonia.

My account of ancient science begins, then, with Homer. Where does it end?

---

[d] A large part of that address will be found in Isis, V, 137–140.

[e] The most conspicuous example is Philoponos, q.v., first half of sixth century.

[f] Meaning China in pre-Homeric days, and even in pre-Confucian days.

It is difficult to say. Even from a purely Mediterranean point of view, it is almost impossible to decide when ancient thought ended and mediaeval thought began. In some respects, the Fathers of the Church opened the mediaeval period, yet the Pagan civilization continued for many centuries. Even the closing of the school of Athens in 529 is not a sufficient landmark. The end of the last Pagan school of philosophy was not unimportant, but its main significance lay in another fact—it created a new contact between Greek and Persian thought. By the middle of the sixth century Athens had become a small provincial school, far less influential than the schools of Alexandria, Beirut, and Constantinople, which were already Christian and thus survived. From a world point of view, the difficulty of fixing a line of demarcation is even greater, in fact, insuperable. But this need not worry us. There is no reason for drawing such a line. To find out the limits of the Middle Ages is as futile as asking where the rainbow ends. We must conceive antiquity, the Middle Ages, and other conventional periods, not as exclusive, but as overlapping. There never was a sharp discontinuity; neither will there be any discontinuity in my account. The reader will thus be able to witness the ancient times fading away imperceptibly into the Middle Ages.

III. MEDIAEVAL SCIENCE

This work contains the first tolerably complete account of mediaeval science. And this is true not only as for ancient science, in the sense that it is the first attempt to integrate Western and Eastern science into a single synthesis; it is true also if we consider Western developments alone; this is the first tolerably complete account of mediaeval science in Christian Europe. This may seem a bold statement, especially if one recall the relatively large number of scholars who devote all of their time to the study of mediaeval questions, and it will seem bolder still, almost impudent, when one realizes that he who makes it is not himself a professional mediaevalist.

I do not claim to be a mediaevalist. I am simply a historian of science, and the period which interests me most is the modern (meaning the eighteenth and nineteenth centuries), of which it is my privilege to teach the history at Harvard University. The progress of science has been so tremendous during the last century that we have the exhilarating feeling of being able to look at the universe from a much higher point of view than had ever been possible before; it is almost as if we were contemplating a new universe, infinitely greater, infinitely more complex and yet amenable to unifying conceptions, infinitely more harmonious, more beautiful and yet infinitely more mysterious. We know too much to believe, as did Lucretius, that all the veils have been unfolded, but there is no doubt that many have been lifted during the last decades and that we are coming nearer and nearer to nature's sacred bosom. To behold these marvelous achievements is an inexhaustible source of joy and, on the other hand, to witness the crises through which science is passing in our days gives one a keener sense of its vitality, of its unflinching courage, of its depth, than if it were perfect, or if we believed it to be so. When the very progress of science created new riddles, stirred up new contradictions, which seemed more difficult than ever to explain, when one revolutionary discovery after another seemed to put everything into question, how often have I not repeated to myself:

"Bliss was it in that dawn to be alive
But to be young was very heaven!"

Next to the modern period, I love most the Greek, which was in many ways nearest to it. For a long time, indeed, like most men of science, I took no interest in the doings of mediaeval scholars. I thought of the Middle Ages only as "dark ages," a time of regression, of intellectual perversity, which it were better to dismiss from one's mind altogether. It seemed such a waste of energy to look for a few pearls in that overwhelming heap of rubbish. Later, as my own historical sense developed, I became necessarily more inquisitive. To illustrate, when one tries to reconstruct the history of astronomy, the first task is of course to determine the amount of knowledge attained by the great astronomers. For instance, we may wish to find out exactly how much Ptolemy knew; we may even read the text of his work. However, even if we did all that, we should have carried out only a part of our historical study. The other part is introduced by the following question: "How did Ptolemy's knowledge come down to us?" It is hardly necessary to show that this second question is just as important as the first. From the point of view of the history of science, transmission is as essential as discovery. If the results of Ptolemy's investigations had been hidden instead of published, or if they had been lost in transit, they would be almost as if they had never been.

Now, this second question opens up the study of mediaeval science and justifies it. If there were no other reason to study mediaeval science than to find out how ancient knowledge was handed down to us, that reason would be sufficient. The average man of science, perhaps lacking in historical training, can not imagine the complexity of the problems involved. The transmission of modern science is almost automatic; a discovery published in any scientific journal is, within a relatively short time, quoted and discussed in a number of other papers which circulate all over the world. Any scientist, working along the same line, is bound to hear of it, either directly or indirectly, and in the latter case he will have no great difficulty in obtaining a copy of the original text. A hundred agencies have solved the problem of transmission so completely that the individual scientist does not think of it any more. In the Middle Ages these agencies did not exist, publication in manuscript form was necessarily very limited, and it could never be standardized. Moreover, political vicissitudes caused innumerable difficulties. Some discoveries had to cross in slow stages the whole of Asia and of Europe before reaching the West and being finally integrated into the main scientific current which has come down to us. Some writings had to be translated many times before reaching their final assimilation; thus many Greek texts became a part of our intellectual patrimony only after having been translated from Greek into Syriac, from Syriac into Arabic, then into Latin, and finally into our own language. These transmissions were imperfect, and in the case of important works, seldom unique; thus occurred conflicting traditions which raised new difficulties.

It does not matter whether we like mediaeval science or not; the fact is that we can not arbitrarily neglect it, if we would understand the continuity of human progress. Even if mediaeval scientists had not made any original contributions, we should still be obliged to study their activity, else it would be impossible to explain the origin of our present knowledge. Whatever we learned from the ancients could not be taught us directly; it could only reach us by some continuous traditions which it is our duty to ferret out.

But it would be very misleading to consider the Middle Ages only as a period of transmission. In the first place, it did not transmit everything; it was, for good or evil, selective, and whatever finally filtered through was transmitted irregularly. It was an organic transmission, original and capricious, which left out many things and added others. In the second place, there was perhaps as much real originality in mediaeval times as there is now, or, more exactly, as there would be if we were trammelled by the same political, economic, and religious restrictions. The reader will find abundant examples in this volume. The spiritual life of the Middle Ages was very rich, even exuberant, but, not unlike that of antiquity, it was limited to a relatively small group of men, because the large mass was still inarticulate. But we might ask ourselves, even in our days of public and compulsory education, of omniscient and ubiquitous newspapers, is the task of advancing civilization much more popular? The bulk of our people are better educated, but the vanguard is, and in all probability will ever be, very small.

How is it, then, that mediaeval thought has not been better studied? To be sure, we have already a pretty good knowledge of its most forbidding aspect, theology, and of its loveliest visage, that exquisite art so full of naïveté and tenderness. We know much also about mediaeval religion, and recently an American scholar has given us an elaborate account of mediaeval magic and superstition. An enormous amount of study has been devoted to scholasticism, but this very abundance has distorted our conception of mediaeval thought. It is a case of wrong emphasis. The advocates of mediaeval philosophy, who would make us believe that that philosophy was the great mediaeval triumph, might be compared to people who would presume to judge a symphony after having attended a rehearsal of a few odd instruments. I shall come back to that philosophy in the next chapter; for the present it will suffice to say that, in my opinion, mediaeval progress—a progress which was never entirely checked everywhere—occurred not because, but in spite of, that philosophy, and that it was due largely to activities which the great majority of mediaevalists have chosen to ignore.

Even as classical scholars, with regard to antiquity, mediaevalists have failed to give us a true picture of the Middle Ages, because (with very few exceptions) they have disregarded the progress of science. They have even done worse, for, being obnubilated by scholastic philosophy, they have been unable to perceive the most original developments, they have misunderstood the main scientific issues. Classical scholars have no interest in science; mediaevalists have an erroneous conception of it, which is undoubtedly worse.

A second essential cause of failure was the ignorance or neglect of oriental evolution. We had to make the same reproach in the case of the classical scholars, but with them the lacuna was far less serious. The greatest achievements of antiquity were due to the Greek, Western, genius; the greatest achievements of the Middle Ages (especially during the period covered in this volume) were due to the Muslim, Eastern, genius. Of course I do not forget that a number of scholars have devoted themselves to the study of Eastern, and especially of Muslim, thought, and that a few of them have investigated its scientific contributions, but the fact remains that the majority of the teachers and historians speaking of mediaeval thought have dealt with Western, and especially with Latin, writings. Now, it is true that a number of important works were composed in Latin, but many others, just as worthy of consideration, were written in Greek, in Syriac, in Persian, in Sanskrit, in Chinese, even in Japanese. The most valuable of all, the most original and the most pregnant, were written in Arabic. From the second half of the eighth to the end of the eleventh century, Arabic was the scientific, the progressive language of mankind. During that period, anyone wishing to be well informed, up-to-date, had to study Arabic (a large number of non-Arabic speaking people did so), even as now anyone who wants to follow the intellectual advance must begin by mastering one of the great Western languages. It is not necessary to substantiate these statements, for my whole work is a proof of them. It will suffice here to evoke a few glorious names without contemporary equivalents in the West: Jābir ibn Ḥaiyān, al-Kindī, al-Khwārizmī, al-Farghānī, al-Rāzī, Thābit ibn Qurra, al-Battānī, Ḥunain ibn Isḥāq, al-Fārābī, Ibrāhīm ibn Sinān, al-Mas'ūdī, al-Ṭabarī, Abū-l-Wafā', 'Alī ibn 'Abbās, Abū-l-Qāsim, Ibn al-Jazzār, al-Bīrūnī, Ibn Sīnā, Ibn Yūnus, al-Karkhī, Ibn al-Haitham, 'Alī ibn 'Īsā, al-Ghazzālī, al-Zarqālī, Omar Khayyam! A magnificent array of names which it would not be difficult to extend. If anyone tells you that the Middle Ages were scientifically sterile, just quote these men to him, all of whom flourished within a relatively short period, between 750 and 1100.

To sum up, mediaevalists have given us an entirely false idea of the scientific thought of the Middle Ages, because of their insistence upon the least progressive elements and of their almost exclusive devotion to Western thought, when the greatest achievements were accomplished by Easterners. Thus did they succeed, not in destroying the popular conception of the Middle Ages as "Dark Ages," but, on the contrary, in reënforcing it. The Middle Ages were dark indeed when most historians showed us only (with the exception of art) their darkest side; in fact, those ages were never so dark as our ignorance of them.

I can not abandon this topic without trying to answer a question which must necessarily arise in the reader's mind. How did it come to pass that Muslims were so far ahead of the Christians from the eighth to the eleventh century?

I showed in the previous section that the Greek tradition of disinterested research was stifled in the West by the extreme Roman utilitarianism. It was not so much the migrations of the Barbarians as the stolid indifference of the Romans which caused the fall of ancient science and silenced the scientific spirit for centuries. Roman utilitarianism was followed by theological expediency, which was hardly better, and later still by a theological domination which seemed for a long while to destroy every hope of a genuine scientific revival. Moreover, the Latin world had gradually drifted away from the Eastern Empire and its contact with Greek civilization had become more and more remote, in some cases almost intangible. On the contrary, as soon as the Persianized Muslims had discovered the Greek and Hindu sources of knowledge, they were fired with such an enthusiastic curiosity that they spared no pains to study them as completely as possible. Obviously, they were endowed with a fair amount of scientific genius, and under the stimulus of the Greek models and of their own abundant competition (for Muslim culture radiated from a number of centers which were distributed all the way from Spain and the Maghrib to Central Asia), they had time to accomplish numerous and remarkable investigations in mathematics, astronomy, chemistry, physics, technology, geography, and medicine, before being thwarted by an obscurantism even more tyrannical than that of the West. The final halt did not occur until a much later time than the period considered in this volume, for they continued to produce some great scientists in the thirteenth, the fourteenth, and even the fifteenth century. But, in the meanwhile, conditions had improved in the Christian West, and by the twelfth century the intellectual supremacy of the Muslims had already come to an end.

The superiority of the East over the West during these four centuries was considerably increased by the following circumstance: Hellenistic science was not all equally pure; it contained a good deal of dross, which is not surprising if one recalls the highly heterogeneous character of that civilization. In particular it allowed the development of a pseudo-science, astrology, which caused the more harm in that its scientific aspect and its technicality gave it considerable prestige. I am wrong in calling it a pseudo-science; it is that of course from the point of view of our time, and from the point of view of any time it became gradually a pseudo-science, as it was contaminated by all sorts of magical fancies. But at the beginning it was a sound body of knowledge, based upon a premise, which proved to be erroneous, but which was not unreasonable, namely, that planets and stars can and do influence human events. Thus a scientific study of planetary motions would enable one to interpret and to foretell these events.

It is easy enough to understand the growth of that fallacy if one realizes the appeal which periodical phenomena have never ceased to make upon people of all kinds, whether educated or not. One of the geysers of Yellowstone Park, the Old Faithful, spouts with perfect regularity every sixty-five minutes. The performance of a geyser is itself very striking, but nothing impresses people more than that uncanny regularity. Numbers derive their fascination from the same instinct, one which is sound enough, but can be very easily perverted. It would take a large volume to tell the history of number mysticism, for some form or other of it may be found in every period and in every country. Symmetry and periodicity form the very substance of science and also of art,[g] and the more intricate, the subtler they are, the more impressive once they have been discovered and truly felt; it is in this respect that we can say that the pleasure derived from an elegant mathematical theory and from a symphony are of the same order. We may assume that even at the very dawn of civilization, the more thoughtful men had been awed by the extraordinary periodicities in the motions of the stars, of the moon, and of the sun. And, by and by, as they discovered the more complicated periodicities involved in the apparently erratic displacements of the planets, their appreciation of cosmic harmony, their awe and trust increased in proportion.

Thus were the astrological assumptions naturally introduced. They received an extraordinary confirmation from two terrestrial phenomena which exhibited similar periodicities and were immensely impressive because of their universality, of their complexity, and of their mathematical rigor: the tides of the sea and the menstruation of women. Both phenomena were explained by planetary influences; the explanation was essentially right in the first case and wrong in the second.[h] That error was a very pardonable one. And if some of the planets

---

[g] For a development of these views, see my essay on "The Principle of Symmetry" in Isis, IV, 32–38, 1921; VII, 367.

[h] That is, as far as we know. If we understand universal gravitation, we understand the tides; the additional difficulties are purely mathematical. But we can not say in the same sense that we understand menstruation.

It is interesting to note that Galileo was so afraid of astrological explanations that he rejected Kepler's lunisolar theory of the tides and suggested one which involved only the earth's own movements.

could thus affect the bodies of women, nay, their very souls, was it unreasonable to assume that they might influence as well the destinies of men?

Now, astrology spread East and West and was very popular everywhere. But in Islam it was balanced to a certain extent by a vigorous development of astronomy and the persistence of a few sound scientific traditions, while in the West, where the contact with such traditions was almost completely lost, it was entirely unmitigated. If astrology had remained relatively pure, it would not have mattered so much, but these theories, being erroneous, were naturally sterile and unprogressive; as they could not progress, they deteriorated, and as they blocked the stream of thought, they gathered around them all the superstitions which it carried. Moreover, the higher form of astrology did not penetrate into the Latin West before the twelfth century, and if it had penetrated, the Christians would have been unable to understand it; thus their astrology was largely of the baser kind. To sum up, the scientific progress of the Latin West had been stunted, and for that very reason the spurious explanations of the astrologers were more readily accepted; it was a sort of vicious circle. Having no personal experience of science, they were more completely ensnared than the Muslim elite could possibly be. Of course, after the eleventh and the twelfth centuries, the situation was gradually reversed; the light which had come from the East began to shine in the West and its flame has been growing there ever since, while it has been slowly dying out in its former home.

The historian of science can not devote much attention to the study of superstition and magic, that is, of unreason, because this does not help him very much to understand human progress. Magic is essentially unprogressive and conservative; science is essentially progressive; the former goes backward; the latter, forward. We can not possibly deal with both movements at once except to indicate their constant strife, and even that is not very instructive, because that strife has hardly varied throughout the ages. Human folly being at once unprogressive, unchangeable, and unlimited, its study is a hopeless undertaking. There can not be much incentive to encompass that which is indefinite and to investigate the history of something which did not develop.

On the contrary, it appears clearly from what I have said that the history of astrology must be carefully considered and that a large part of it is so intimately connected with the history of science that it can not be dissociated from it. This remark applies with even greater force to alchemy, for in this case there was considerably more scope for the continual integration of new experimental facts, which were valuable in spite of wrong interpretations. Indeed, good experimental facts have a permanent value: they might be compared to the indestructible stones of a building; the building, that is, the scientific system, is bound to become obsolete and to be wrecked sooner or later, but the good stones will be used again for the new building. Thus did the alchemical facts outlast the alchemical structure; many of them are now integral parts of our chemical knowledge.

We should make a great mistake indeed if we criticized too severely some of the astrological and alchemical theories (leaving out of account the crass superstitions which were occasionally added to them). To judge fairly the scientific achievements of any period, we must compare them not with our own, but with those which had been attained just a little earlier. We must ask ourselves whether the new achievements marked a progress upon the previous ones, whether they were made in the right direction. To take a step forward in the right direction is always a great thing, and the first steps are always the most difficult and the most creditable. We forget it but too often, and our histories are full of injustice, because we are almost always too generous toward those who made the last steps and reaped the result of all antecedent efforts, and too little generous to those who made the first and least profitable steps. One might say that the whole mediaeval period has been the victim of that injustice. It can not be denied that much of their scientific endeavor was nullified by superstitious tendencies or sidetracked by the consideration of pseudo-problems. Yet it is none the less the historian's duty to investigate mediaeval knowledge as carefully and completely as possible; there can be no excuse for condemning it wholesale without examination; the amount of valuable knowledge which we owe them can be determined only when all the evidence has been sifted (which, by the way, is far from being done); whether that amount be large or small, the investigation is equally necessary; it would be justified in the most unfavorable case, even as the biological study of a desert is justified to determine how sterile it is. The historian of science who is not tolerably familiar with mediaeval developments might be compared to an anatomist who does not know any embryology. In order to explain our present civilization, it is necessary to take into account the whole of its previous evolution, with as little discontinuity as possible.

There is still this to be said: There were perhaps as many men of genius in the Middle Ages as now; at least, my survey gives that impression, which would be confirmed, I am sure, by statistical inquiry. If these mediaeval scientists did not always make a good showing, we may ask ourselves what men like Gauss, Faraday, or Claude Bernard would have done if they had been born in the eighth or ninth century instead of being able to take advantage of another millennium of human effort? A large part of our knowledge and of our technique was attained, not at all in a logical way, but by the method of trial and error, which works well, but is exceedingly slow. The whole history of thought points to the conclusion that some errors at least were unavoidable, that is, mankind could learn how to avoid them only by making them. From that point of view, the history of error is useful; it is a catalogue of the things which we ought not to do, and, by studying it, we may hope to save much time and trouble. Thus we were spared some errors only because our ancestors had made them before us. Indeed, these mediaeval scientists are our direct ancestors; if they had been such idiots, how could we be so clever? It is extremely probable that if we had been living under the same circumstances as they, we should not have proceeded much faster. The progress of science is, on the whole, an accelerated one; thus, in any retrospective survey, we must expect the progress to become slower and slower as we penetrate more deeply into the past.

And above all we must remember that science could not progress along certain lines without traversing vested interests and prejudices and without hurting the feelings of the community. To proceed in the face of such opposition has always required a great deal of intellectual courage. There were many more such sensitive lines in the Middle Ages than now, and thus there was a far greater need for that particular kind of heroism. In the whole sweep of history there is nothing more impressive than the spectacle of noble men who had the spirit to fight unreason and ignorance and who did not hesitate, not only to renounce material advantages, but even to jeopardize life and happiness in order to increase the amount of beauty, of justice, and of truth which is the essential part of our patrimony. There were a few such men in mediaeval times, East and West, even as now, and, in the last analysis, it is because of their presence that the study of their times is as inspiring and exhilarating as it is, in spite of many shadows, in spite of scholastic and obscurantist tendencies which repel the modern mind.

IV. SCHOLASTICISM, ITS CAUSE AND ITS CURE

There is one aspect of mediaeval thought which is so important that I have reserved it for separate discussion. The Latin philosophers, having inherited on the one hand a large body of Christian doctrine, together with commentaries by the Fathers of the Church, and on the other hand a number of writings representing more or less faithfully the views of Greek philosophy, chiefly Aristotelian and Neoplatonic, took great pains to reconcile these divergent traditions. This was of course impossible, for the premises and the methods of the two traditions were essentially different. Christian doctrine was based primarily upon faith, Greek philosophy was an attempt to interpret experience rationally; the fact that that experience was often erroneous and the deductions faulty does not alter the case. The Christian schoolmen made desperate efforts to combine the loyalty of their intelligence with that of their hearts; this could be done only by the reconciliation of faith and reason; obviously a pseudo-problem, very much like the attempt to square the circle or to create a perpetual motion; but this they did, or would not see. Considering their purpose, their methods could not be entirely rational; they relied largely upon deduction, which they handled with considerable skill, but their arguments depended also to an inordinate extent upon authorities. The formalism or the stiffness of their methods was impressive (if not repellent) and gave a feeling of structural elegance and solidity and of rigor, which apparently satisfied them. We must take into account the fact that they could not realize as vividly as we do that a plausible and authoritative argument which would carry the day in a court of justice is not necessarily valid in the field of science: it has taken more than two thousand years to prove that, and even to-day only a small minority of people has understood it thoroughly. Starting from a priori premises which they considered absolutely certain, and assuming that all the rest of their knowledge must be consistent with these premises, they proceeded to evidence the logical relations. Having no doubts whatever with regard to the existence of these relations, their task consisted solely in disentangling them. In the course of their discussions they used some experimental data which had come down to them from antiquity, and maybe they added some others which they had discovered themselves at rare intervals; but that experimental knowledge was exceedingly small and uncertain, and they did not attach much importance to it. An experimental fact might be produced in an argument, but it could never be placed on the same level as a dogmatic fact. The latter was basal, transcendent, immovable; the former was secondary and precarious. In their arguments, experience was subordinated to reason, and reason to faith.

There were various modalities of that philosophy and a great part of the schoolmen's time and energy was spent in quarreling about technical matters or about the forms of arguments, or sometimes in deeper discussions, such as those raised by the problem of universals, but the spirit and the method of all these philosophies—as opposed to the experimental method—were essentially the same. It is not too much to say that mediaeval thought was dominated by that philosophy which they looked upon as the very crown of knowledge.

Modern scientists who associate the Middle Ages with scholasticism are thus not entirely wrong. Scholasticism was a characteristic and supreme feature of mediaeval life (not only, as I shall show presently, of Christian life). But they go too far when they disdain mediaeval thought on that account, or dismiss it altogether from their minds. To begin with, in spite of its predominance, scholasticism was not the whole of intellectual life—there were many other little streams which finally led to modern science, as the readers of this work will find out; and in the second place, it is unwise to see only the evil side of it. That it checked the progress of science, instead of hastening it, is certain. Scholasticism was sterile, as far as its essential purpose was concerned, but it does not follow that it was entirely sterile. Men are often better than the system in which they happen to be imprisoned. In spite of their intellectual perversion, which was even more scandalous than that of the astrologers and the alchemists, because it went so much deeper, some of the schoolmen were the leading thinkers of their time; we owe them some gratitude, if not for their heroic efforts to accomplish the impossible, at least for many humble but positive additions to our knowledge. I have taken considerable pains to explain in detail all that we owe them, and to give them full credit for whatever they did in the line of scientific progress.

After all, their error was natural enough; granted an implicit faith in certain dogmas and a great confidence in some of the conclusions attained by the ancient philosophers, inasmuch as truth must be single, it must be possible a priori to reconcile these statements, however divergent. The cause of their delusion was ever present and the cure as yet unknown. The fact remains that modern insistence on scholastic philosophy has contributed to a large extent to discrediting mediaeval thought. And whenever the study of scholasticism has been undertaken (as it generally is) with an afterthought of religious propaganda, it has necessarily awakened the antagonism of all those who resented, or suspected, such propaganda.

The schoolmen enjoyed so much prestige that they gradually transformed the whole intellectual atmosphere and even influenced the writings of men who kept aloof from them and had a genuine scientific bent. That influence can easily be traced in a large number of scientific writings down to the seventeenth century and it survived considerably longer in a few others. It reveals itself in a very formal manner of statement, in the extreme love of classification—we might say, in over-classification—and in the importance attached to technical terms and to names generally. Thus, a student of botany would quote the names of plants, often in many languages, and not take sufficient pains to identify the names with definite plants or to make his identifications clear to the reader.

It is of course expedient to name things, especially if one is careful to give the same names to the same things and other names to others. To name a thing is a distinct step forward, for it implies that one has recognized its separate existence, but instead of being the last step, as mediaeval scholars seemed but too often to believe, it is only the first. Even to this day a number of people imagine that to know a thing it suffices to know its names; it apparently never occurs to them that it would be worth while to consider the thing itself, to walk around it, to touch it, maybe to go inside it and experiment with it—for them the name is the thing. That attitude was usual in the Middle Ages and the scholastic way of looking at things was certainly one of its causes. Under the influence, not of scholasticism this time, but of magic, many people believed also that by giving a certain name to a thing special properties were conferred upon it. Though such belief is seldom expressed nowadays, people's conduct is still influenced by it.

A good example of the verbalist tendencies of the Middle Ages is the famous work of Saint Isidore of Seville, properly called Etymologies. The significant fact is not so much that this work was composed, but that it wielded considerable authority for many centuries. The importance generally attached to names and words, whether it be under the influence of philosophy or religion or magic, increased enormously the interest in philological studies. This is one of the reasons why I am obliged to include a brief account of the progress of those studies in my survey.

To be sure, we still attach considerable value to names and to classifications—we can not do without them—but unless we are belated schoolmen (there are still a good many among us) we are no longer hypnotized by them; we do not consider them as aims, but only as means of knowledge.

True scholasticism lasts just as long as one assumes that the knowledge of real things must be subordinated to that of sacred ones, and science to theology. As soon as one has perceived that such subordination is impossible or meaningless, because science and theology belong to different spheres, scholasticism is bound to fall under its own weight. It does not matter how well the edifice was constructed, the superstructure is too heavy for the foundations; it can not stand without props and buttresses.

The revival of interest in scholastic philosophy, in so far as it is not purely historical, is largely due to religious reasons. This is strange indeed, and I fail to understand why it should be so, but it is so. A heart as yet untouched by the grace of faith might be opened by the vision of beautiful and mysterious things, by the warm rays of charity; scholastic arguments would be more likely to close it. But men are strange creatures, anyhow.

It would not be right to mistake the strong antagonism to scholastic tendencies which every man of science can not help feeling, for an antagonism to religion, or even to any dogmatic religion. For example, a number of Roman Catholic scientists, who are faithful sons of their church, have no patience whatever with scholastic arguments. Their faith occupies, so to say, one part of their brain and their scientific knowledge another, absolutely separated from the first. This was forcibly expressed by Pasteur, who was himself very pious: "Only a misguided mind" said he, "tries to introduce religion into science. More misguided still, he who attempts to introduce science into religion, because he entertains greater respect for the scientific method."[i] The domains of science and of religion are essentially different. Science is reason organized and systematically applied. Religion is a reasoned and not unreasonable abdication of reason with regard to problems which *are not* amenable to scientific treatment. There can be no conflict between science and religion, except when they trespass on each other, as, for example, when theologians would extend the mental surrender to questions which *are* amenable to scientific treatment.

The amount of positive knowledge available in the Middle Ages was exceedingly small both in quantity and in quality. There was little opportunity for induc-

---

[i] As quoted in Pasteur and his work by L. Descour, translated by A. F. and B. H. Wedd (p. 206, New York). Pasteur expressed similar ideas somewhat differently in other circumstances.

tion, and knowledge, under scholastic influence, took almost exclusively a deductive form. There was not much choice; granted the arbitrary premises of the theologians and the scarcity of positive knowledge, scholasticism was almost an unavoidable consequence. Now, of these two conditions, the first could hardly be changed, for we have to accept people's beliefs, but the second was bound, however slowly, to disappear. In spite of political crises and of obscurantist tendencies, positive knowledge must increase and accumulate; every progress in that direction, be it ever so small, was final and irrevocable. Thus we may say that the cure of scholasticism was simply the progress of positive knowledge, and this means the progress of the experimental method. Inversely, as long as that method was not understood and the educated people received no experimental training, scholasticism continued to enjoy considerable prestige.

During the Middle Ages the applications of science were limited, and not only that, but whatever was done in the line of application was done more often by illiterate technicians than by scientists proper. In the popular opinion the leading scientists were the schoolmen and these did not lower themselves to the consideration of applications; they preferred to discuss science in the abstract. Thus, the worst that could happen to them was to be defeated in an argument; they never received the severe but invaluable penalties which Nature distributes impartially to those who experiment. Their methods were excellent to detect logical errors, but the fundamental errors of their premises remained unchecked. The experimental philosopher can never be wrong indefinitely; should he persist in his evil ways, he is bound sooner or later to burn his fingers. Reputable schoolmen never burned their fingers; provided they respected the rules of logic, they could argue their heads off, so to speak, and never feel the worse for it.

With the partial exception of mathematics, science can not progress unless more and better observations and experiments are made all the time. The deductive exploitation of a limited amount of experimental data is limited. Any attempt to overexploit it must necessarily imply a reversion to scholasticism. If, after having made their first electrical experiments, the eighteenth century physicists had insisted on discussing the nature of electricity, *more scholastico*, they would have condemned themselves to ignore it and to turn indefinitely in a circle. But it is of course perfectly proper to reopen such discussion each time that new experimental data enable us to consider the subject from a new angle.

And this is the very spirit of science—the continual alternation of experimental research, of mathematical elaboration (if possible), of theoretical deduction and discussion suggesting new experiments. Or, in other words, the continual alternation of analysis and synthesis—analytic investigations without synthetic attempts must necessarily degenerate into crude empiricism and into superstition; synthetic constructions without periodic experimental contact must necessarily degenerate into a sterile dogmatism. This is exactly what happened in the Middle Ages, though in the case of scholasticism, that dogmatism was aggravated by the fact that it was not even based upon experimental data, but upon arbitrary beliefs; whatever experimental data were used by the schoolmen were inserted by them, not in the foundation, but somewhere in the superstructure of their theories.

The progress of science implies not only the accumulation of knowledge, but its organization, its unification, and this involves the periodical invention of new syntheses, coordinating existing knowledge, and of new hypotheses, which give us methods of approaching the unknown. Science is essentially a system, but instead of being, as it was for the schoolmen, a closed system, it is never closed, but always subject to revision or even to complete discard. The true scientist considers his theories not as perfect and permanent, but as essentially incomplete and precarious; he is ever ready to abandon any part or the whole of them, should new experimental facts make it necessary. There are scientific methods; there are no scientific dogmas; there is no scientific orthodoxy. Of course this does not mean that there are no scientific doctrines; there are at any time many of them which are binding as long as they have not been shown to be erroneous, but not a moment longer; an orthodoxy as mobile as that is not a real orthodoxy as theologians understand it. Nor does it mean that men of science are never dogmatic, for, being men, they are necessarily frail. In this sense, we might say that men of science are essentially heterodox. Their heterodoxy is not restricted to this or that doctrine; it extends potentially to every doctrine. We would never think of saying that a genuine man of science is loyal to this or that theory as he would be loyal to his church or country; he knows no such scientific loyalty; his only loyalty is to truth, a loyalty which causes him to abandon his most cherished opinions as soon as they are invalidated. This has been proved repeatedly during the last thirty years, for a number of revolutionary discoveries have put his scientific conscience into the crucible. For example, the discovery of radioactivity, the introduction of quanta, and the theories of relativity have obliged every physicist and chemist to change radically his ways of thinking about essential things; they have done it as soon as their conviction was completed, if not without reluctance (it is not easy, especially for older men, to change the intellectual habits of a lifetime), at least without struggle and without rancor. As for the younger men, the more revolutionary the theories, the more exhilarating; it gave them the impression of being the witnesses of a new revelation, of a new beginning. Science is not a being, but a becoming. Thus the love of science is not the love of this or that system, which is bound sooner or later to be superseded by a better one, but simply the love of truth.

This gives us another reason to be interested in mediaeval science. The history of science may always be considered under two aspects, either positively as the gradual unfolding of truth, the increase of light, or negatively as the progressive triumph over error and superstition, the decrease of darkness. The modern scientist studying mediaeval science gets a little impatient, because he is accustomed to a much faster pace; he would like to be able to watch the progress of science, and for many centuries the pace was often so slow, with so many stops and regressions, that one has the feeling that there was no progress at all. It is well, then, to turn one's attention not so much to the advance as to the struggle which made it possible. The cure of scholasticism was experimental science, and every experimental discovery, however humble, was a step forward, a definite one. We may conceive the progress of science as a continual fight between empiricism and dogmatism, between the creative interpretation of new facts and the attempt to squeeze them within an accepted frame, between discovery and classification, between the experimental and the scholastic spirit; the gradual reclamation of one little intellectual field after another by experimental methods. However great the scholastic inertia, it must needs be overcome sooner or later. The process was slow, sometimes beyond endurance, but we receive an impression of necessity, of unavoidableness, which is comforting. After all, speed is not the object, but going steadily forward in the right direction, getting nearer and nearer to the goal, even if we feel that we can never actually reach it. From that point of view, the history of mediaeval science is as fascinating as that of any other period. The odds against science were enormous, but the struggle became the more exciting. At some times when scholasticism or superstition were overwhelmingly strong, the advance was slower than usual or altogether halted, or mankind was driven backward, but that did not affect the general advance. There is no reason to be impatient when time does not count and we know the outcome anyhow. But this explains why the progress of mediaeval science was by no means uniform; it was rather spasmodic; it did not occur unless a more independent man made an experimental discovery and the scholastic control was momentarily loosened.

When we speak of "scholasticism," we generally think of Christian scholasticism, because it is the one which has been most elaborately studied[i] and the one with which we are most familiar. But the mental attitude which we designate by that term was not by any means specifically Christian. If we define scholasticism in a general way as the attempt to reconcile lay knowledge with theology, and if we recognize as its characteristics the habit of premature generalization, excessive deduction from arbitrary beliefs and from a small and limited body of experimental data, also excessive reverence for canonical writings and other authorities, then scholasticism was almost universal during the Middle Ages.

The Muslims were very prone to such a type of philosophizing, and if one takes into account their absolute reverence for the Qur'ān and their great intellectual curiosity, it is clear that they were bound to fall into scholastic ways of thinking. It was unavoidable. The reader will find some of the elements of a history of Muslim scholasticism in my Introduction; it will suffice to say now that by the second half of the eleventh century that special form of scholasticism had already reached in the works of al-Ghazzālī a perfection which it did not attain in Christendom until the time of St. Thomas Aquinas, two centuries later.

Jewish scholasticism was in a way older than Muslim scholasticism, though it did not develop until much later. The pure Talmudists were not schoolmen according to our definition; they were concerned only with the Torah and the Talmud and had no interest in positive knowledge; they did not attempt to syncretize the lay and sacred sciences. True Jewish scholasticism was largely an echo of Muslim scholasticism, and in its turn it deeply influenced the Christian doctrines. Think, for instance, of Ibn Gabirol, who flourished in the first half of the eleventh century; however, their greatest doctor, Maimonides, did not appear until the second half of the twelfth century, that is, just halfway between al-Ghazzālī and Aquinas.

The earliest type of scholasticism was the Buddhist, and this is just what we should expect, considering that Buddhism was at once a very early religion, antedating Christianity by some five centuries, and that it manifested from the beginning a scientific attitude. In fact, pure Buddhism was the most scientific of all religions and Buddhist scholasticism developed rapidly and reached its climax, that is, its first climax, the Hindu climax, under Buddhaghosa, in the first half of the fifth century, eight centuries before St. Thomas!

---

[i] See, for example, the admirable work recently published by Louis Rougier. La scolastique et le thomisme. 856 p. Paris, 1925 (Isis, VIII, 219–221).

Another form of scholasticism developed in India, probably partly under Buddhist stimulation, though its religious inspiration was Brahmanical, i. e., anti-Buddhist, and was carried to its highest pitch in the first half of the ninth century by Śaṅkara, the greatest exponent of Vedantic philosophy.

Strange to say, Chinese scholasticism, the so-called Neo-Confucian philosophy, Hsing-li, was extremely slow in developing. We have to wait until the second half of the eleventh century for its true beginning with Chou Tun-i and it did not reach its climax until a century later. It would be interesting to find out why Chinese scholasticism was delayed so long, but this would take us too far out of our subject. I will simply suggest as an explanation that the Chinese were neither very religious nor very scientifically minded. They were practical, business-like, artistic, pragmatistic, superstitious, rather than idealistic and intellectually adventurous, the very opposite of the Hindus, whose strong scholastic tendencies appeared, as we have seen, quite early.[k]

This universal occurrence of scholasticism is the more impressive in that it was certainly not due to the spreading and branching out of a single influence; there are at least three independent streams, the Near Eastern, the Hindu, and the Chinese, and there is good reason to believe that in spite of many interrelations, the Jewish, Muslim, and Christian forms, as also the Buddhist and Vedantic forms, were largely autonomous. The contemplation of so many independent, yet convergent, streams of thought seems to leave us no alternative but to conclude that scholasticism was a necessary stage in human progress. Religion and science can be traced back to the very dawn of civilization; for a time the various intellectual needs remained confused; later, as humanity became more self-conscious and more critical, religious and scientific systems developed and became more and more elaborate. Thus was reached, at different times by different peoples, a stage when the instinctive wish for unification led their most prominent thinkers to attempt the logical subordination of experimental facts and rational concepts to their religious dogmas, which were naturally given the supremacy. It is highly instructive to see that this same problem (or pseudo-problem), the amalgamation of rationalism and faith, had to be solved over the entire civilized world. The faiths involved were different, but the problem remained essentially the same. The most impressive comparison is that relative to the three great Mediterranean religions, because in those three cases the intellectual experience was to a large extent identical. Thus we can witness the desperate efforts of a large number of Muslim, Jewish, and Christian schoolmen to reconcile Hellenic rationalism with three different sets of religious dogmas. What is most extraordinary is that they all succeeded in doing this to their satisfaction.

However, the satisfaction was not complete, or at least it could not endure; rival schoolmen discovered faults in the systems of their predecessors and tried to do better; long quarrels ensued, which were easily embittered, because nobody was right anyhow. In the meanwhile, scientific experience increased, more and more facts were discovered, and the difficulty of reconciling positive knowledge with faith increased in proportion. The experimental pressure grew slowly but steadily, and, sooner or later, became unendurable. This marked the beginning of the scholastic decadence and fall. The process of decadence was itself slow

---

[k] However, Buddhist scholasticism developed in China, as also in Japan. I explain that in my work.

(that is, much slower than the experimental advance), because considerable religious inertia resisted it, and because a great many schoolmen refused to consider the evidence of their senses and preferred to abide in their intellectual perversion rather than to acknowledge their errors.[l] In fact, scholasticism is still alive today, even as magic and superstition, and not only in backward, but also in the most enlightened countries.

After that dismal experience of a thousand years, during which it seemed as if the human spirit would remain forever sidetracked, and after the magnificent triumphs of science which have followed its emancipation from scholasticism, it is impossible to resist the conclusion that science and religion must be left separate. To be sure, their ideals and distant purposes are the same; there is not and there can not be any opposition between science and religion when both are at their best. Yet they satisfy absolutely different needs of our nature and their intellectual methods are absolutely different. Any attempt to subordinate one to the other is a menace to both. The history of scholasticism proves this conclusively and the whole history of science also proves that whenever theologians have tried to inject religious issues into scientific controversies they have finally been beaten, much to the detriment of their own ideals.[m]

This question has been obscured, especially in Anglo-Saxon countries, by the great delicacy of the leading thinkers in their discussion of religious matters. Whatever their own conclusions, they would not say anything which might possibly hurt the religious feelings of other people. That is right conduct, but some have gone farther and have used equivocal language which might countenance a scholastic revival. From the point of view of science, to equivocate is a heinous crime, one which one can never be justified in committing. I wish thus to emphasize that the progress of science is absolutely dependent upon its emancipation from non-scientific issues, whatever they be, and in particular, upon its laicization.

This is sufficiently proved, as my book will show in considerable detail, by the relative sterility of scholasticism and by the immense, almost unconceivable, fertility of modern, i. e., of lay science. But another striking proof is afforded by the comparison of Eastern and Western evolution.

In the Middle Ages, the difference between East and West was not very great. The leading philosophers of all countries were engaged in the same sort of activity. Before the twelfth century, one of the Eastern groups, the Muslim, was considerably ahead of all the others, East and West. Muslims were then in the van of mankind. From the twelfth century on, the supremacy passed gradually to the Latin world, but this process was not completed until the end of the Renaissance, when the laicization of Western science was well under way. Until the sixteenth century (included), there is good reason to consider both Eastern and Western developments, but after that time Western science began to grow at an

---

[l] One of the best examples of such attitude was given as late as 1610 by the men who refused to look through Galileo's telescope, lest they should see what he had seen! See Opere di Galileo Galilei, edited by A. Favaro (vol. 10, letters 379 and 436, 1900); J. J. Fahie, Galileo (101 sq., 1903).

[m] Abundant examples of this were collected by the late Andrew Dickson White, the first president of Cornell University, in his "History of the Warfare of Science and Theology in Christendom" (2 vols., New York, 1896).

accelerated pace, while Eastern civilization remained at a standstill, or even deteriorated. The difference in pace of the two types of civilization, the Eastern and the Western, became then so great, and increasingly so, that a comparison between them is no longer useful. There is no point in comparing things which are too disparate. Thus if it be granted me to continue my history beyond the sixteenth century, I shall no longer consider Eastern developments, but restrict my account to the West.

Now, how did that divergence begin, and having begun, go on? How did it come to pass that after having traveled together until the Renaissance, Eastern and Western peoples separated at that point, the former standing still or unlearning what they had learned, the latter proceeding faster and faster along the road of discovery? The explanation of this is very simple. Western and Eastern peoples were subjected to the great scholastic trial, but the Western people weathered it, while the Eastern failed. The Western people found the cure, the only cure, the experimental method; the Eastern people did not find it, or did not fully understand it, or neglected to apply it. The inquisitive reader may ask further: Why did the Eastern people not find the cure? To this it is impossible to answer. The historian can analyze to some extent the actions of people; he can not explain them. He can show that the Western people applied the experimental method gradually, and with an immense success, to a great variety of problems; he can show also that the Eastern people failed to do that and, instead of progressing, marked time. Would the explanation be, perhaps, that Eastern people, say the Muslims, had reached the limit of their development, that they were like those gifted children who startle the world by their precocious achievements and then suddenly stop and become less and less interesting, while others, at first less brilliant, pass far ahead of them?

Whatever the real explanation may be, the essential difference between East and West is that the latter overcame scholasticism, while the former did not. "Oh! East is East and West is West and never the twain shall meet," said Kipling. I have just indicated the true significance of this. It is not so much a matter of temperament, for there are men of Eastern temperament (for instance, the belated schoolmen) in the West, and vice versa. It is a matter of fundamental method. People can not possibly meet as long as they walk along diverging roads; but it would suffice to change their method, that is, follow the same road, and they would meet quite often. For example, Japan is becoming more and more a part of the West, as far as the intellectual mission of mankind is concerned. On the contrary, some European nations, which prefer argument to experiment, are orientalized, I mean immobilized, to that extent. The great intellectual division of mankind is not along geographical or racial lines, but between those who understand and practice the experimental method and those who do not understand and who do not practice it.

V. THREE ASPECTS OF THE FUNDAMENTAL UNITY OF LIFE

In spite of the widespread delusions which paralyzed and obnubilated mediaeval thought, such as scholasticism, astrological and magical fancies, my work will show that there never was a complete interruption of scientific progress. Of course, if we chose to restrict our horizon to a single branch of science or to the activities of a single nation, interruptions would soon occur. In the same way, no part of the world is entirely sterile from the zoological or botanical point of view, but if we were looking only for a single species or even for a single genus of animals or plants there would be many discontinuities; or if we were studying only the flora or fauna of a single country, our views on natural history would be incomplete. There are no real discontinuities in the intellectual life of the world if we take into account the achievements of all peoples in every direction. Our survey must be comprehensive in two ways: it must be encyclopaedic and ecumenical. It is worth while to consider these two points separately.

In the first place, we must consider not the history of one or of many sciences, but the history of every branch of positive science, the history of all sciences, or more correctly, the history of science. That history is considerably more than the arithmetical sum of the histories of all sciences, for it explains not only the progress of each science, but its relations to all the others. Of course, histories of separate branches of science, or even of special departments or subdepartments, are exceedingly useful from the technical point of view (we have some excellent ones, especially for mathematics, chemistry, and medicine), but they are utterly insufficient to explain the progress of civilization. It should be noted that they are often insufficient even for their own special purposes, and the historian of physics, for example, is obliged to make frequent allusions to the development of mathematics and of other sciences if he would completely explain his own subject. This is due to the fact that our division of science into many branches is largely artificial; we must consider them all as if they were the branches of a living tree, which have no separate existence, but grow all together. Thus the progress of each science is dependent upon the progress of all the others. Moreover, it happened frequently, even more in the past than in our age of extreme specialization, that the same man carried on investigations in many departments of science. Those who study his activity from the point of view of a single discipline can not fully appreciate its complexity and unity, its real greatness.

It is precisely because of the centrifugal tendencies of modern science that the study of the history of science is so useful. It helps the scientist, whom circumstances have obliged to restrict his attention to a relatively small subject, to eschew lopsidedness and other intellectual deformations and to keep alive within him a unitary view of knowledge. The scientist who has become unable to understand or appreciate other scientific activities than his own is but too prone to imagine that his own studies are the very center of knowledge; in that respect he is on the same intellectual level as those ancients who believed that Delphi or Jerusalem was the navel of the world.

In the second place, it is not sufficient to consider the evolution of a single nation, because that evolution may have been handicapped, interrupted, or altogether halted by wars and other calamities, or even it would seem by sheer intellectual exhaustion. It is as if certain peoples, after having made a great intellectual effort, were obliged to lie fallow for a while and thus recruit enough strength to go further ahead. But whenever a nation dropped out of the race, another was ready to take up the torch and to continue mankind's eternal quest. Almost every chapter of my work will contain some illustration of this; the most impressive of all is that afforded by the intellectual supremacy of the Muslims from the eighth to the eleventh century and its gradual decline after that. Mediaeval historians, who have neglected to consider Arabic literature, have thus given us not only an incomplete, but an entirely false view of their subject.

The main postulate of science is the unity of nature, a unity indirectly confirmed by the whole development of knowledge. It is clear enough that if there were no unity in nature, if the universe were not a cosmos, but a chaos, if there were no regularities, no laws, but only an erratic succession of miracles, there would be no occasion for scientific research, no possibility of scientific progress. The discovery of every new law is a new confirmation of that postulate, and each time that one has succeeded in determining a constant of nature—e.g., the electric charge of an electron[n]—by various independent methods, one has given a quantitative proof of it. *Nature is one.*

The history of science establishes the unity of science in at least two different ways. First, the progress of each science is dependent upon the progress of the others; this implies of course that the sciences are not independent, but interrelated in a number of ways, and that the interrelations are not accidental, but organic. Second, the simultaneity of scientific discoveries made in different places and sometimes by means of different methods implies also an internal congruency. We may liken any science to a chain of facts which are linked together in an invariable order. Now, it has happened over and over again that various portions of such logical chains had been completed, but that the links connecting them were still missing. These links were eventually discovered, often by the help of scientific considerations of a radically new order, that is, borrowed from another science, and it was then possible to complete the whole chain in a rigorous and unexceptionable manner. If such an event had happened but once, we might ascribe it to chance, but it has happened so often that the probability of these occurrences being due to hazard is infinitely small, and we can draw no conclusion but this: *Science is one.*

Finally, the very fact that these simultaneous discoveries have been made by different nations, and that the chains begun by one people were harmoniously completed by another, proves that however different men may seem, they are all following the same purpose, they are all accomplishing the same task, the human task *par excellence*—a task so great that only a few men are able to conceive it in its integrity, and that in most cases their collaboration is as blind as that of the bees of a hive. This confirms the view that in spite of many disparities and animosities, *mankind is one.*

It is hardly necessary to enlarge on this, or to show that these three unities—the unity of nature, the unity of science, and the unity of mankind—are but three different visages of the same unity. In all probability there are still other aspects, though less obvious and less certain, for example, the unity of art and the unity of religion.

Because of its very comprehensiveness, my work will be a continual illustration of that fundamental unity, and especially of the unity of knowledge and the unity of mankind. And this helps us to understand the real significance of human progress; it is the gradual transformation of that potential or hidden unity into an actual unity, one that all can see and no one deny.

This sublime conception of mankind's purpose—a conception that is probably dormant in the heart of every man of science—is not simply exhilarating in itself, but it gives also a new meaning to our lives. We feel more conscious of an immense collaboration, which extends throughout space and time; we feel more conscious also of the relative futility of our personal contributions, that is, if

---

[n] See Isis, II, 195.

these contributions were not parts of a whole, but isolated. What each man, even the greatest, can do is but little as compared with the achievements of united mankind. This helps to destroy the conceit which may be in us and to give us a proper sense of proportion. Moreover, we may be proud, as men, when we contemplate the immense task already accomplished by our ancestors and our contemporaries, but our historical experience makes it easier to realize that, however immense, it is small in comparison with what remains to be done. We have begun the ascent of a formidable mountain, but we are as yet hardly above the plains. We are surrounded by infinities and mysteries everywhere; the possibilities of the cosmos of which we form such an infinitesimal part are hardly explored. It is difficult to know which is more admirable, our knowledge or our ignorance. Newton expressed a similar feeling in an exquisite way when he remarked, shortly before his death:

"I do not know what I may appear to the world, but to myself I seem to have been only like a boy playing on the seashore, and diverting myself in now and then finding a smoother pebble or a prettier shell than ordinary, whilst the great ocean of truth lay all undiscovered before me."[o]

Thus the humility of the true man of science is not restricted to himself, it extends to the whole of mankind. When we feel sorry for the mistakes and crimes committed by members of our own race, we may comfort ourselves by thinking that in spite of the glorious achievements of science, the higher phase of human civilization has but just begun.

One of the main reasons for studying and teaching the history of science is to illustrate these views and to give to educated men in general, and to professional scientists in particular, a better sense of proportion. Even as one might say that no man can be a good citizen who does not know the history of his country, even so no man of science is doing all his duty in his particular sphere if he does not make an effort to understand the genesis and development of his own subject at least and, if possible, of the whole of science. Even as we would be ungracious, if we did not think with reverence and gratitude of the men to whom we owe our political liberties and the blessings of our environment, even so the scientist is uneducated and crude who does not pay homage within himself to the great men to whom he owes almost everything that he knows, and but for whose efforts and devotion he would be but an ignorant child, groping his way in the dark.

The history of science is the history of mankind's unity, of its sublime purpose, of its gradual redemption.

VI. A SURVEY OF HUMAN CIVILIZATION

The previous sections were intended to explain the purpose and spirit of my work. In this and the following sections I shall deal with matters of method.

Perhaps the briefest way of intimating the general method is to compare my activity with that of a mapmaker. Though I have taken considerable pains to insure the accuracy of every detail, however small, my main interest is not in any of them, however important, but in the whole structure. Even as the cartographer's purpose is to evidence the relations of the geographical facts, my main

---

[o] Sir David Brewster: Memoirs of . . . . Sir Isaac Newton (vol. 2, 407, 1855).

purpose has been to show the relations of the historical facts. This has never been done on the same scale, for no one has ever attempted to consider at one and the same time the progress of every branch of knowledge and the achievements of every nation. In this sense it would not be incorrect to say that my Introduction, modest as it is, is the first survey of human civilization (the reader being trusted to add the political, economic, and artistic background). I have tried to draw a map of that civilization which would be as complete and accurate as possible, and yet simple enough, sufficiently free from unessential details, sufficiently condensed, not to obstruct the general view.

The main practical value of such a survey is to give in a relatively small compass an account of the knowledge already attained, and, what is even more important, to give some idea of all the work which remains to be done. This is the more necessary in that the History of Science, being a new discipline, is not yet well organized or well circumscribed, and attracts the attention, not only of experienced scholars, but of amateurs, dilettanti, and cranks. If the publication of my work had no other result than to discourage futile investigations and to encourage the necessary ones, it would still be justified. Many paragraphs will seem bare; in some cases this is due to our general ignorance, in others to my own ignorance. Sometimes the gaps and insufficiencies of our knowledge are explicitly indicated; in most cases they are not specifically mentioned, but the implication is clear enough. The amount of work which remains to be done is immense; some parts of our subject have hardly been scratched. There is perhaps not a single page of this Introduction the complete elaboration of which would not require at least as much time and energy as I have been able to devote to the whole work. And, by the way, it would not be amiss to observe that the drawing of such a map is the best, if not the only, way of measuring our knowledge (or ignorance). Even so, a geographer may often have the impression that a country is already well known, because a number of monographs have been devoted to it. It is only when he begins to plot his map that he realizes how much of his knowledge is incomplete or uncertain. Happily, the *terrae incognitae* are not the least interesting parts of a map; they are certainly the most stimulating.

Some readers may wonder why, after having taken so much pains to reach this point, I did not make an additional effort and write the history more fully myself, instead of publishing only a sketch of it. I was anxious to complete my work as fast as was consistent with accuracy and comprehensiveness. I thought that I would serve the Republic of Letters better by publishing this sketch now than by postponing publication for a number of years in order to give a fuller account, which even then would have been restricted to a much shorter period. I had to choose between giving the skeleton of a relatively long period—the present volume covers two thousand years—or a more elaborate study of a much shorter period. The skeleton is undoubtedly more useful, as it may from now on guide the activity of a large number of scholars. It will allow them to undertake the special investigations which are needed to complete our knowledge of almost every topic, without losing their sense of proportion and perspective.

My special contribution to the History of Science is the creation of this map, or architectural plan—the first of its kind—and the rough preparation of the many stones which will eventually be required to construct the building. A full-fledged history, realizing completely the promise of my sketch, will be the work of another generation.

The reader will observe that within each chapter devoted to a definite period (generally half a century) my material has been subdivided as much as possible along topical lines. For example, one section deals with mathematics, another with astronomy (these two are often combined), others still with geography, natural history, medicine, etc. This will be rather awkward for the student of, say, Chinese or Muslim science, but I could not meet the needs of all scholars at the same time. I chose this system of classification because I intended to show the continuity of international collaboration in the gradual building up of science. Moreover, I will eventually publish separate volumes dealing, say, with Chinese or with Muslim science, wherein all the pertinent data contained in the present volume will be coordinated from that special angle and enriched with a number of additional details, which would not interest the average historian of science, but are full of significance for the Arabist or the Sinologue.

It may be permitted here to recall that the general scope of my undertaking involves the creation of three series of books:[p]

First Series—A purely chronological survey in the form of cross-sections of civilization for each half century. The present volume is the first of that series, which will require seven or eight more volumes of the same size to be complete.

Second Series—Surveys of different types of civilization, e.g., Jewish, Muslim, Chinese. This series ought to include also an account of pre-Hellenic civilizations, and another dealing with prehistoric and popular science, that is, with the knowledge attained by prehistoric and primitive people and by the uneducated people in our own midst. This would require seven or eight volumes, e.g., as follows: (I) Pre-Hellenic; (II) Classical antiquity and Iranian civilization (to the Hegira); (III) Semitic; (IV) Mediaeval (Latin and Greek); (V) Hindu and Central Asiatic; (VI) Far Eastern; (VII) Prehistoric and ethnologic; (VIII) Index.

Third Series—Survey of the evolution of special sciences. Of course this is less necessary, for such sciences at least as mathematics and medicine, for which excellent accounts are already available. Yet it would be worth while to recoordinate the material arranged in other ways in the first two series, adding all the technical details which would have been out of place in the earlier volumes. This would again require some eight or nine volumes, e.g., as follows: (I) Logic and mathematics (knowledge of forms); (II) Physical sciences (knowledge of inorganic nature); (III) Biological sciences (knowledge of organic nature); (IV) Sciences of the earth (implying a knowledge of both inorganic and organic nature); (V) Anthropological and historical sciences (knowledge of man, past and present); (VI) Medical sciences; (VII) Educational sciences (the methods of imparting and diffusing knowledge); (VIII) Philosophy (main concepts of science; its unification and classification); (IX) Index.

It would also be desirable to add to each series special volumes or atlases containing maps, synoptic charts to exhibit the genealogy of ideas, and facsimiles of title-pages, etc., to establish beyond doubt the most important dates.

Heaven knows how many of these volumes I shall be able to write or edit myself. Even if I found enough collaborators, I would not expect to complete the three series, but I hope to work out a sufficiently large share to show exactly what I am driving at. I should deem myself very fortunate if it were granted me to

---

[p] See also Isis, IV, 23–31, 1921. The general classification is illustrated in the Critical Bibliographies which have appeared in Isis since its inception (1913).

finish the first series down through the eighteenth century (i.e., a total of five or six volumes like this one), parts of Volumes III and VI of the second series, and Volume II of the third series. Each volume has its own unity and may be considered independently of the others, yet its value would be increased by every one of these.

It is clear that when these three series are completed, supposing the work to have been done as well as contemporary knowledge permitted, we shall have a fairly good notion of the progress of human civilization. Each of these surveys is necessary and none is sufficient. The Chinese, who have a knack at expressing things in a pithy way, love to say that the four essentials of true education are the comparative, the historical, the universal, and the special.[q] That is, everything must be considered from these four points of view, and it is only when we have learned to make these points of view converge upon any topic that we may claim to understand it.

I trust that this first volume will be a sufficient illustration of my method. It has the advantage of dealing with a period considerably longer than that of any other volume. It is a sort of fresco of intellectual progress during the course of two millenniums. The reader will find in it a history of mathematics from Thales and Pythagoras to Omar Khayyam, a history of theoretical music from Terpander to Guido of Arezzo, a history of astronomy from Philolaos to al-Zarqālī, a history of geography from Hecataeos to al-Bīrūnī, a history of exploration from the time of the Phoenician navigators to that of the Scandinavian, a history of medicine from Alcmaeon to Ibn Sīnā—in brief, a vast intellectual panorama extending from the Iliad to the Chanson de Roland. He will realize, as he could not before, the fullness and the complexity of human civilization, its progressive character in spite of many vicissitudes. He will understand that the continuity of human progress implies a continuity of effort, but not necessarily a continuity of success.

VII. SOME REMARKS ON THE HISTORY OF SCIENCE IN INDIA, CENTRAL AND EASTERN ASIA

I have already indicated the enormous importance of Muslim efforts in mediaeval times. The study of these efforts can be undertaken in the same way as the study of Latin and Greek contributions; it does not involve special difficulties beyond those of a philological nature. Of course the student of Muslim science must have some understanding of Muslim culture, but this will be acquired together with his philological equipment. The vast majority of Muslim contributions were published in Arabic (some in Persian; a few in Turkish) and thus the study of Arabic is as essential as that of Latin and Greek; in fact, for the period to which the end of this volume is devoted (eighth to eleventh centuries), it is by far the most important language. An enormous amount of work remains to be done in that direction, but the way is clear enough.

The study of science in India, Central and Eastern Asia involves additional difficulties which we shall presently consider. I shall not speak any more of linguistic

[q] Hêng² shu⁴ p'u³ chuan¹ (3915, 10079, 9513, 2702). The words hêng and shu suggest crosswise (horizontal) and vertical comparisons, which is just what I mean. Hêng is the point of view of my first series; shu, of the third. Chuan is illustrated by the pains taken to insure the accuracy of every detail; p'u, by the general frame, the order, my synthetic conception of history. One must learn that every detail deserves to be carefully studied even if it has no individual importance.

difficulties, which we take for granted, and which have to be solved each in its own slow and painful way.

The study of Hindu science is made exceptionally difficult because of the lack of definite chronology. For this reason, my account of it is necessarily incomplete; I have been obliged to omit a number of works which it was impossible to place anywhere because of chronological doubts. (Of course, these works will eventually be considered in the general study of Hindu science which is to be a part of the second series.) And even among those which I have included, many were placed in one period rather than another without sufficient conviction. In the same way a cartographer is sometimes obliged to draw the course of a river or the relief of a mountain without adequate knowledge. This is regrettable, but can not be entirely avoided. Needless to say, whenever there was occasion for such doubts, they were exactly stated. In a general way, Hindu dates are sufficiently sure only when they are confirmed by foreign—i. e., Greek, Arabic, or Chinese—accounts. The uncertainty of Hindu chronology is vexing, because it makes it almost impossible to solve questions of priority: For example, were the Greeks influenced by the Hindus or vice versa? Some of these questions are discussed in my Introduction.

The study of Tibetan culture raises chronological difficulties of a different kind. Practically the whole of Tibetan knowledge is incorporated in two enormous canonical collections, the Kanjur and the Tanjur.[r] The works contained in those collections were translated from the Sanskrit, the Chinese, and the Uighur, but they contain Tibetan accretions. It is as yet impossible to date the translations and in many cases the original writings are lost.

When we turn to China we are less troubled by chronological difficulties, at any rate for the mediaeval period. The Chinese kept excellent records of all their activities and their chronologies are reliable, except for the earlier (pre-Hellenic) period. In general I have had no trouble in fixing the dates of their men of science, though in many cases we know only that they flourished under such or such a dynasty. However, this chronological accuracy is but a meager consolation as compared with our general ignorance of the scientific writings involved. It is not too much to say that almost everything remains to be done in that direction. Though I may claim to have given in my book the earliest tolerably complete account of Chinese science, I have no illusions with regard to the value of that account. Most of it is but a catalogue of names. In some cases I do not even know whether the works quoted have a genuine scientific value or not. This applies chiefly to the immense Taoïst literature, which includes treatises on the elements, on cosmology, alchemy, astrology, geography, hygiene, and other scientific or pseudo-scientific subjects. Very few of these treatises are available to Western scholars, and none have been analyzed from our special point of view. It may be added that many parts of the Taoïst canon are imperfectly dated.[s]

It would have been easy for me to increase considerably my enumeration of Chinese scholars and writings, for the Chinese have always been fond of literary

---

[r] See my note on Tibetan Buddhism in the first half of the seventh century.

[s] We owe a study of this canon and of Taoïsm in general to Father L. Wieger: Le canon taoïste (1911); Les pères du système taoïste (1913). This is valuable, but hardly more than an introduction.

catalogues (shu^{1}-mu^{4*}, 10024, 8080) and have published a number of them, even as early as the Han dynasty.[t] But I have generally avoided naming men unless I had something specific to say about them. There was no point in duplicating the Chinese catalogues or the lists included in the dynastic histories, for these works are available to Sinologues and would be of no interest to other scholars. On the contrary, I took considerable pains (with slight success, I must admit) to give some information on the purpose and contents of the writings mentioned.

The main merit of the Chinese part of my survey is that it is the first attempt of its kind. However, if it had no other consequences but to stimulate investigations, and in particular to encourage the critical edition and the translation of some of the scientific treatises quoted (or of some others which I failed to quote) I should feel amply rewarded.

Similar remarks might be made with regard to Japanese science. Whatever study has been made hitherto of Japanese scientific literature has been far too superficial. Lists of titles do not satisfy us; we would like critical editions of the main texts, together with translations and commentaries.

In brief, the indications which I have been able to give on Oriental (except Muslim) science are insufficient, suggestive rather than explicative, but it would be difficult to do much better at the present time. These are by far the largest *terrae incognitae* of my map. I hope that, imperfect as it is, my account will awaken the curiosity of orientalists and initiate research in that virgin field. As it is, it is well to keep in mind that my account is a *minimum* account. I said that the Hindu and the Chinese did this and that; it is probable that they did considerably more, but that remains to be shown. If Sanskrit, Tibetan, Chinese, and Japanese investigations were accelerated to the extent of making this little account appear ridiculous within twenty-five or thirty years, no one would be more delighted than the author.

VIII. CHRONOLOGICAL BASIS

An essential point of my method is the insistence upon strict chronology. History is full of incertitudes; even when we have managed to arrange our facts in chronological order, we are not sure that the antecedents have influenced the consequents. But at any rate, we are sure that the consequents have not influenced the antecedents, and historical certainty is so rare that, when we find it, we must stick to it as closely as possible.

Of course, all historians are agreed that chronology furnishes the very basis of their investigations; it is for that reason, for instance, that so much importance is attached to numismatics. Yet scholars dealing with the mediaeval period are often lax in this respect. Even good scholars do not seem to realize that the Middle Ages lasted about a thousand years, and that their development, far from being monotonous, was exceedingly varied. The centuries lasted just as long in those times as they do now and each generation brought in sundry changes of its own. Moreover, political vicissitudes were even more brutal than they are now and introduced frightful discontinuities in many countries. Many scholars believe that they are sufficiently accurate when they say of two men that they flourished in the tenth century. They do not seem to realize that it makes a

[t] A few of them will be mentioned in the course of my work. For the earliest, see my note on Liu Hsin (second half of first century B. C.).

great difference whether they flourished at the beginning, in the middle, or at the end of the century, whether they belonged to the same generation or not. If one flourished at the beginning and the other toward the end of the century, it is probable that they were not contemporaries and it is even possible that their generations were separated by a third one. If in the course of an argument we heard somebody mention Poincaré, Newton, Gauss, Einstein, and d'Alembert and discuss their activities in that order, we should be irritated. The habit of speaking of mediaeval scholars without sufficient discrimination, putting together people of different ages, is just as annoying. If we would understand the evolution of mediaeval thought, we must first of all focus our investigations upon specific parts of that immense field, then, taking a broader view of the whole, we must do it in such a way that we keep full account of the passing of time.

In order to accomplish this purpose I have divided my account into periods of half a century each, a length which approximates that of man's intellectual life. It may be objected that such a classification is highly artificial. It surely is, but no natural classification would be applicable to all sciences and all nations. And if our classification can not help being artificial in some respects, it is wiser to choose deliberately one which is absolutely conventional and which has the advantage of dividing the past into periods of sufficient brevity and equal length. Comparisons between one period and another, many examples of which will be found in my work, become then very convenient.

Every classification has the disadvantage of introducing artificial discontinuities in the continuity of life. It must necessarily happen that contemporaries are dealt with in two successive chapters, because one was active at the end of one century and the other at the beginning of the following century; they were flourishing almost at the same time, but at different sides of the cut. This drawback is unavoidable, but is not really objectionable, unless the reader is unaware of it. In a general way I must warn scholars using my book that if they are interested in any one period, say the time of Proclos (second half of the fifth century) they must read not only the chapter relative to that period, but the two adjacent ones, dealing respectively with the first halves of the fifth and the sixth centuries. I may add that it is part of my program to publish from time to time (e. g., in Volume III) a chronological summary, which will reestablish the continuity artificially deranged, by replacing in their due succession a number of dates borrowed from different chapters.

I have taken pains to distribute my material as well as possible. When men have left dated works, it is these dates which have determined my choice. But often the works can not be dated exactly and some other method must be resorted to. It is easy to see that a method which is frequently used, the arraying of men in the chronological order of their death dates, is misleading. After many experiments I have satisfied myself that the best method is that used by the ancients—that is, in the absence of any contradictory information, to consider as man's floruit the date at which he was about forty years of age. It is probable that the greatest scientific discoveries were made, and the most pregnant resolutions taken by men younger than forty, but the accomplishment of their work took considerable time and the maturing of their thought extended over many years. It would be interesting to investigate this subject statistically. In the meanwhile, I have the feeling that the fortieth year would be on the average the nearest to the intellectual climax of most men. This holds chiefly with regard to the truly creative activity; if we took into account the mere accumulation of erudition and experience, the age would probably be higher, that is, if life permitted. The classification of our own contemporaries is often confused by the fact that the age of greatest prestige is generally different from that of greatest activity. Indeed, it takes a considerable time before the activity of a truly original mind is properly appreciated; it happens often that a man does not reach the intellectual prestige to which his creations entitled him until his time of activity, if not his very life, is over.

Each chapter of my Introduction is called after the most representative man of the period considered. It would not be wise to attach too much importance to these titles, the purpose of which is purely mnemonic. We should find it difficult to remember that such or such a man flourished in the first half of the ninth century, and such or such another in the second half of the same century, but we can more easily recall that the former flourished at about the same time as al-Khwārizmī, while the other will naturally cling in our memory to the personality of al-Rāzī.

All of the men whose names have thus been chosen to symbolize a period are representative and important men, but they are not necessarily the most important. To illustrate, it is clear that a list of forty-eight cities, each the main city of one of the United States, would be quite different from a list of the forty-eight main cities of the United States.

IX. BIBLIOGRAPHIC BASIS

Bibliography is another essential basis of historical or scientific investigations of any kind. My account is brief, often of Linnaean brevity, but I have attempted to complete each item with a list of the main sources and of many other publications. Thus the reader will have abundant means of controlling every word of my statements and of continuing the study of any topic to any extent.

I have tried to give a sufficient bibliography; I have not tried to make it complete; in fact, I have deliberately avoided doing so. For example, I have omitted to mention a number of publications which I knew to be futile. It does not follow that every publication I have named is important, because I have preferred to leave the benefit of my doubts to the author. With the help of a number of bibliographic tools which are well known to any scholar, and with all the resources of a well-equipped library, it is now relatively easy to publish enormous bibliographies on almost any subject. But such bibliographies, which have become numerous, are of little use. At the rate at which publications accumulate in our days, these bibliographical lists will increase faster and faster and will become more and more bewildering and less and less useful. What we need is not complete lists, wherein the valuable publications are lost in a mass of rubbish, but selected critical lists, the items of which have been examined *internally* by competent scholars, and which are properly analyzed, appreciated, and classified.[u]

The enormous bibliographical lists, such as are often issued by libraries, are of little value, not only because the best publications are actually lost in them, but also because they are bound to omit some of the most important. Indeed, every scholar knows that some of the most valuable information on any subject is

[u] I have developed these views in Synthetic bibliography, Isis, III, 159–170, 1920; see also Isis, VI, 567, 1925.

likely to be found in books or papers which deal specifically with other subjects. In my bibliography, which is essentially an internal and critical one, I have been anxious to quote the unsuspected sources of evidence.

Moreover, I have often added critical notes. The significance of these notes should not be unduly extended. It is not my habit to make implicative statements; I am generally outspoken. Thus if I say of a publication "important," this does not mean that other publications quoted in the same paragraph are unimportant; it means what it says and nothing more. If I say nothing of a publication, this may be due to my ignorance or to a suspension of judgment or to an unwillingness to commit myself.

The amount of bibliographic information contained in my work is considerably larger than it appears, because I have added a great many references to Isis. The additional information, which is thus given indirectly, varies considerably; it may be restricted to a more nearly complete description of the item, or it may be a brief criticism, a longer discussion, or even a full-fledged review throwing new light on the subject. Sometimes two references to Isis are quoted for the same work; indeed, it has happened that a work has been criticized twice, and even if one such criticism suffices, some readers may have access to one volume of Isis and not to the other.

In most cases I have indicated the number of pages of the books or articles quoted, because it is of interest to the reader to have some idea of the size of the publications to which he is referred. But I have done this only *grosso modo*, discarding the niceties of bibliographic description and writing, for example, 400 p. instead of xv + 384 p.

Some obvious sources of reference, such as August Potthast and Ulysse Chevalier, have never been quoted, because I take it for granted that the mediaeval scholar has them at his elbow. On the contrary, others, such as Pauly-Wissowa, for classical antiquity, have been quoted often, because the number of volumes and supplements increases the difficulty of referring to them, and even discourages the attempt. I have sometimes referred to the Encyclopaedia Britannica or other encyclopaedias when particularly good articles seemed to deserve separate mention.

A few references will be found to be more up to date than my own text, because I have not hesitated to introduce them at the eleventh hour, when I was no longer able to avail myself of them. My guiding principle in all these matters has been to serve the reader as well as possible.

In spite of every effort, this bibliography is bound to be erroneous by commission and by omission, and I count upon the collaboration of my readers to complete it gradually. If a new edition of this volume is ever called for, I shall be able to improve the bibliography by the addition of a number of new titles, but even more by the suppression of many others. The point is this: while the number of publications relative to any subject is likely to be great and to increase continually, the number of truly important publications is generally small. An ideal bibliography is one which is large enough to include all that is good, yet too small to include anything which is mediocre.

It is obvious that such a bibliography can be produced only by a scholar intimately acquainted with the subject. Bibliographical work is unpleasant, and thus every scholar ought to do his share of it. The task is aggravated by the fact that the number of publications which are obviously and absolutely worthless is almost as small as that of the excellent publications. The great majority are mediocre, yet contain some items worth considering. The scientific bibliographer is thus obliged to examine them carefully to determine whether these items justify inclusion or not. My policy has been a broad one, but because of that, I am afraid I have included many publications which did not really deserve it.

I still have to make a few remarks with regard to incunabula and other early printed books. I have often quoted early editions and have mentioned the princeps, whenever I could, but I have done so simply to give the reader some idea of the time at which such or such a text became available in print. I have not tried at all to give complete lists of incunabula. The readers needing such information will have to look for it in other books, especially in the "Gesamtkatalog der Wiegendrucke," which is now in the course of publication. Incunabula have received considerable attention on the part of collectors and bibliographers, and their importance has been unduly exaggerated. In many cases the manuscript tradition of a text was better than that of the early printed editions. Scholars interested in ideas rather than in books prefer to use scientific editions which are based not only upon the printed, but also upon the manuscript tradition. In fact, as soon as the text of the incunabula has been duly collated with that of the manuscripts and edited by an able scholar, the incunabula themselves have no other value than that of an archaeological witness and are no longer read by anybody, least of all by those who describe them so minutely, or who pay a king's ransom to obtain possession of them.

X. PRINCIPLES OF SELECTION

One of the most delicate problems to be solved in the preparation of a general survey like this is to know exactly where to draw the line between the personalities which are to be included and the others. It is relatively easy to determine the most important personalities; it is somewhat more difficult to agree upon personalities of the second order, and the difficulty increases considerably as we try to cast a larger net. Very often the inclusion of one scientist entails the admittance of a number of others whose merit was of the same kind, and so on indefinitely, unless one decides more or less arbitrarily to stop here or there. Thus, while it is improbable that I have overlooked any really important personality, it is probable that I have included a few whom it would have been better to omit; it is clear that no selection would please everybody.

It would have been easy to increase my list considerably, e. g., to name more physicians or more Muslim mathematicians. But my first rule has been not to mention a man unless I had something specific to say about his activity; that he had discovered this or that, or written such or such a book. In the second place, bearing in mind the great importance of origins, I have tried to name the people who were the first to do this or that; to take the first step in the right direction is always significant, however simple it may seem.

In determining the value of a man, I have also taken into account the opinion of contemporaries and of later scholars, even if it were wrong. This may seem the perpetuation of an injustice. No, because I have tried to indicate also his intrinsic value and have given the supremacy to the man whose activity was the most remarkable even from the point of view of modern science. Moreover, when a man has exerted a great deal of influence he is important, whether he deserved that prestige or not. If a great many people believe that John Doe is a "big man," he is big, at least to that extent. There are, even in our days, many men who have no more greatness than the moon has light. Yet the moonlight is none the less real for being borrowed.

The fact to keep in mind is that men may be influential for intrinsic and also for extrinsic reasons. The first case is by far the most interesting, but we have no right to disdain the second, if we would understand the progress of thought. There is far more moonlight than sunlight in the intellectual world; we must speak of both, if we would show how much light there was at any time. For a similar reason, a mediaeval author becomes at once more worthy of attention if his works have been carefully edited and are easily accessible, or if, for any reason, special studies have been devoted to him. Again, it has occasionally been necessary to pay some attention to an unimportant man who was deemed important at any time, because he was confused with another.

My account of each personality has been as brief as possible. But it is sometimes much easier to indicate a great achievement than a much smaller one, and thus some of the notes devoted to second-rate personalities are much longer than one would expect. This does not matter in itself, but the reader is warned not to try to measure the importance of a man by the length of the note devoted to him; there is no relation between the two.

I may have made accidental errors in my choice, by omission or commission, but I do not believe that I have made systematic errors. The only cause of such errors I can think of would be a racial, national, religious, or scientific bias. For example, if I had been primarily an historian of geography, with only an indirect interest in other branches of science, my account would very likely contain an exaggerated number of geographers and travelers. Or if I had read only German publications, it would probably give too much importance to German contributions. But, as a matter of fact, I am almost equally interested in every department of science; I am not conscious of despising any, and I am reading regularly publications in English, French, German, Dutch, and Italian. Moreover, I am a Belgian by birth, of mixed French and Flemish (i. e., Latin and Germanic) ancestry, my wife is English-born, and we have become American by adoption. I have friends in many countries and I am not conscious of prejudice against any. With regard to religion, I am equally neutral. My only prejudice perhaps, is against people who are irreligious, who lack gravity and reverence, or who are unable to understand religious feelings which they do not share. I have little patience with such people, but I did not come across many of their kind in mediaeval times.

I have tried to be as concrete as possible, that is to say, to indicate the specific achievements or contributions in the clearest and briefest way. That was never easy, often difficult, sometimes impossible. Even as in our own days, there were a number of people in the Middle Ages who obtained considerable prestige and rendered undeniable services, yet of whom it can not be said positively he did this or that. In such cases, where the influence was of an indefinite nature, I have been obliged to be vague. In a few other cases I have been reduced to a similar vagueness by my ignorance.

The correct naming of the men mentioned in my survey involved some special difficulties. Of course, permanent surnames are of relatively modern origin; they did not exist at all in the Middle Ages. There were many ways of naming a person, and much ambiguity is thus caused. I have taken pains to quote all the names of each person dealt with, and to select one of these as the best. When mentioning that person I have always used that same name, resisting the temptation to use another for the sake of style or variety.

In my selection of the principal name I have been guided primarily by usage; in cases of doubt, or sometimes to avoid duplication, I have chosen the most specific name. For example, I prefer to say Charlemagne, rather than Charles the Great: there is only one Charlemagne, there may be many Charleses who were called Great.

The Muslim names are especially difficult. I have given, whenever I could, a large part of their names, not necessarily the whole of them, because this would involve a genealogy of indefinite length. No consistent method was available for the selection of the chief names, for Muslim usage has been inconsistent on the subject. For example, they say al-Khwārizmī, Ibn Khaldūn, Abū-l-Wafā', al-Jāḥiẓ, representing four different methods: the first name means "he of Khwārizm" (south of the Aral Sea); the second, "son of Khaldūn (cfr. Johnson, Peterson); the third, "father of Wafā'; the fourth, "the goggle-eyed." Whenever there was a well-established usage I have respected it; in other cases I have tried to select a name which would be as convenient and as characteristic as possible. I have particularly avoided names which were too common, e. g., those referring to well-known places, such as al-Baghdādī, al-Majrīṭī (he of Bagdad, he of Madrid). I have also avoided the Latin names which have been handed down to us by Mediaeval translators (such as Avicenna, Alhazen, etc.). As I am not writing in Latin, there is no more sense in giving a Latin name to a Muslim than in giving a German name to an Italian; it is obviously wiser to give each man a name which reveals his origin, and not one which hides it.

The case of Chinese and Japanese names is even more difficult, because, according to their customs, names are not only changed during life, but even after death, and many men are best known under a posthumous name. Thus the young Chinese receives at birth a "milk name"; later, when he goes to school, he is given a "book name"; when he marries, he receives two new names, the *hao* and the *tzŭ* or great name (style); in the course of time he may assume a literary name, a religious name, one or more official names. Each of these names may have to be modified because of various taboos. After his death he may be granted a posthumous name, and that name, too, may have to be changed. In the midst of such confusion my first rule has been to conform to usage and my second to use the name which would be least equivocal.

Needless to say, many (if not all) of these alternative names are quoted in the index, being followed by cross-references to the chief names.

XI. ERRORS OF THIS WORK AND THEIR CORRECTION

It may be shown that the probability of error, which is never null, increases considerably, all other things being equal, with the widening field of one's studies. It is even probable that it increases much faster than that field, e. g., with its square. As the field of my own studies is immense, the total probability of error must needs be great, even if the relative probability is small. Thus, in spite of every precaution, this book contains, probably, many errors. After having done his duty, the scholar must humbly accept that contingency.

"Errare humanum est sed perseverare diabolicum." If we can not help failing in many ways, at least we can do our best to atone for our errors and to correct them. This I will gladly do by means of Isis. Every error pointed out to me (barring of course those which are obvious or futile) will be published in the Critical Bibliography of Isis, together with the announcements of the newer publications on the subject. Thus, a scholar especially interested in the eleventh century will find in the sections devoted to that century at once the new publications and the necessary corrections to the corresponding chapters of my Introduction. The last Critical Bibliography of which I was able to avail myself in the preparation of this volume was the eighteenth (Isis, VIII, 526-667, 1926). Thus students using my book will find periodical supplements to it in the Critical Bibliographies of Isis, beginning with the nineteenth (end of Vol. VIII). It will thus be relatively easy to keep one's information up to date on any subject.

I trust that this method will appeal to the more scholarly readers, and that on account of it they will be more ready to forgive the author his many sins.

XII. THE AUTHOR EXPRESSES HIS GRATITUDE

There is no part of his work which the author writes with greater pleasure than this one; but his indebtedness is so great and so varied, he has availed himself of the labor of so many scholars, and has been helped by so many friends, that to express his gratitude with sufficient fullness would require a large amount of space.

My first debt is to the scholars who have written histories of special sciences, mathematics, medicine, chemistry—without which it would have been impossible to attempt the present work. Works on the history of science in general proved less useful. The most elaborate one work of that kind, Dannemann's,[v] is elementary and altogether insufficient; I have not used it at all. After having collected the greatest part of my material, I hoped to complete it by reference to the work compiled by Ludwig Darmstaedter[w] with the collaboration of a number of German scholars. I made a careful scrutiny of it down to the year 1500, and while this enabled me to fill a few gaps, I could not help noticing an inordinate number of errors. I like to assume that that work is more valuable for later periods; for the period just named it is not reliable.

My own work, begun in Wondelgem (near Ghent), Belgium, was interrupted by the war. Before abandoning my home, I buried my notes in the garden and did not recover them until 1919; they did not become truly available until the middle of 1920. Though I was able to accumulate considerable material during these years of suspense, I could not resume actual writing until January 12, 1921.

In 1915, being stranded in London, my friend Aldo Mieli, champion of the history of science movement in Italy, offered me the hospitality of his house in Chianciano, near Siena, for myself and family. It so happened that instead of going to Siena, I finally sailed to New York, but I will never forget that generous offer. During those years of distress, when I never knew whether I should not be obliged to abandon my dream and turn to a more prosaic and profitable employment, I received assistance from a number of friends. Thanks to David Eugene

[v] Friedrich Dannemann: Die Naturwissenschaften in ihrer Entwicklung und in ihrem Zusammenhange (4 vols., Leipzig, 1910–1913; 2d ed., 4 vols., 1920–1923. Isis, II, 218; IV, 110, 563; V, 198; VI, 115).

[w] Handbuch zur Geschichte der Naturwissenschaften und der Technik (Zweite Auflage, Berlin, 1908).

Smith, Nevil Monroe Hopkins, and the late Admiral Stockton, I received my first opportunity in Washington, D. C.; thanks to Leo H. Baekeland, L. J. Henderson, Theodore W. Richards, Charles Homer Haskins, Edward C. Streeter, and others, a second opportunity was extended to me in Harvard University, Cambridge, Massachusetts; finally (in 1918), thanks to the late R. S. Woodward, a new appointment was created for me by the Carnegie Institution. Then, for the first time since 1914, I had a feeling of relative security and could devote all of my energy, without undue anxiety, to my self-imposed task.

During the course of a short vacation in Pemaquid, Maine, in September 1920, I became happily acquainted with Dr. Duncan B. Macdonald, professor in Hartford Theological Seminary, who has been ever since my faithful and indefatigable mentor for all matters pertaining to Islām. As the amount of Muslim material to be considered increased enormously, I have been obliged since then to study Arabic under the guidance of Professor James Richard Jewett, but Dr. Macdonald has remained my main guide, and my debt to him is one which can not be requited. My Harvard colleague, H. M. Sheffer, has kindly read this introductory chapter and suggested many corrections.

I am deeply grateful to the Harvard Library. I have enjoyed for years the invaluable privilege of a private study within that library, where my own books and notes could be safely arranged and preserved. This privilege was the more precious to me because for a long time I have been practically homeless; even now I have no fixed home of my own. As far as my books and apparatus are concerned, the Harvard Library is my real home. I wish to express my deep appreciation to every officer of the library.

It is not possible to thank adequately the Carnegie Institution of Washington. It will suffice to say that without its patronage my book could not have been written, and being written it is probable that it could not have been published. I often think with gratitude of my benefactor, Robert Simpson Woodward, the second president of the Institution, to whom I owe my appointment. I wish to thank also Dr. John C. Merriam, the third president, who has shown me much kindness and patience during the slow elaboration of my work.

I can not begin to thank the American and foreign friends and scholars who have helped me in many ways, not simply with their learning but also with their sympathy. Some specific acknowledgments will be found passim in this book where they belong, and it should not be forgotten that every quotation of a source, especially one followed by a critical note, is an implicit acknowledgment of indebtedness. It is not possible to name these friends; they are too many; nor is it necessary, for every reader of Isis is familiar with their names. Indeed, it is well to bear in mind that the editing of Isis and the preparation of this Introduction were two closely related activities, different in appearance, but having the same ultimate purposes, namely, to defend the ideal of the New Humanism, to organize the History of Science as an independent and reputable discipline, having its own tools and methods, and placed on the same level as, say, the history of art or the history of religion.

I must thank also the authors who sent their publications regularly to the Editor of Isis. They have thus enabled me to obtain immediate knowledge of a number of facts which it would have cost me much effort to obtain otherwise, and which might have escaped my attention altogether. I trust they will continue to help me (and indirectly all other students of the history of science) in the same way; their publications will be faithfully recorded and maybe analyzed and discussed in Isis and in subsequent volumes of this Introduction.

To all of these friends, named and unnamed, I wish to say once more how much their collaboration and sympathy have meant to me. I hope they will also help me to remove the faults which may occur in my work. The scholar's best friends are those who do not hesitate to show him the error of his ways. To these last friends, as yet unknown to me, I express also my deepest thanks.

George Sarton.

Harvard Library, Room 185,
Cambridge 38, Massachusetts, *June 10, 1926.*

APPENDIX

Notes on the Transcription of Greek, Hebrew, Syriac, Arabic, Persian, Sanskrit, Chinese, and Japanese Words

I wish to explain briefly the methods which I have followed in transliterating or transcribing consistently the words which were not originally written by means of our own alphabet.

The supreme desiderata of any system of transliteration are consistency and simplicity. I have been guided always by the written language, which is relatively fixed, rather than by the spoken, which may vary considerably. That is, I have tried to write foreign words in such manner that the original written form might be easily reconstructed or found in a dictionary.

It is not possible to deal with every oriental language represented in this volume; I must limit myself to the consideration of the most important ones, those mentioned in the title. For the reader's convenience, I shall deal with them in alphabetic order.

1. ARABIC

I have used the following letters or symbols to represent the letters of the Arabic alphabet in its natural order:

', b, t, th, j, ḥ, kh, d, dh, r, z, s, sh, ṣ, ḍ, ṭ, ẓ, ʿ, gh, f, q, k, l, m, n, h, w, y.

As to vowels, the fatḥa is always represented by a; the kasra by i, and the damma by u. Long vowels are indicated as follows: ā, ī, ū.

To avoid disturbing readers who are not conversant with Arabic, I have not indicated the assimilation of the final l of the article with certain consonants (dentals, sibilants, r, l, n); thus I have written ʿAbd al-Rahmān, though the correct pronunciation is ʿAbd ar-Raḥmān; that is, I have followed the written usage rather than the spoken.

The three vowels are pronounced in the Italian manner (or as in the English word *ruminant*). The following examples may help to distinguish between the short and the long vowels: *cat, father; pin, pique; push, rule.* The diphthongs ai and au are pronounced respectively as those in *buy, thou.*

The hamza ('), spiritus lenis, is pronounced like the French h aspirée; *les héros, la haine.*

th hard th as in *thing*
j as in *jewel, James*
ḥ strong h with friction
kh like German hard ch, Spanish j
dh soft th as in *this*
r always trilled, as in Romance languages
z as in *zeal, maze*
s as in *kiss*
sh as in *shore, wash*
ṣ emphatic s
ḍ upper palatal d
ṭ emphatic t
ẓ th said far back
(These four letters are pronounced with broad of tongue, the tip being held against the lower teeth.)
ʿ (ain) "This sound arises by squeezing the violently compressed glottis." Must be heard.
gh sound of gargling. Must be heard.
q deep emphatic k. Must be heard.
n as in English, but slightly nasalized before k as in *sank;* nb sounds rather like mb.
h as in English, but always distinct.

For additional remarks on the transliteration of Arabic, see my note in Isis, VI, 410–412, 1924.

After the Arabic title of a treatise I have sometimes added the Latin and Hebrew translations, because some titles are better known in the translated than in the original form. The same remark applies to proper names.

2. CHINESE

It is impossible to represent Chinese characters adequately, simply, and without ambiguity. Thus, from the point of view of accuracy, nothing can replace a Chinese character except a reference to that character in a dictionary.

I have adopted the second edition of Herbert A. Giles's Chinese English Dictionary (London, 1912), which is widely used in the English-speaking world. For each Chinese character I have indicated the standard romanization selected by the author, together with the tone number suggesting the intonation and the number which distinguishes that character from all others.

There are four tones represented by the numbers 1, 2, 3, and 4; but each of these may be slightly modified, the modification ("entering tone") being indicated by an asterisk. It is useless to try to explain the different tones in writing; they can only be learned experimentally. They are indicated here for the sake of readers who are somewhat familiar with Chinese, and need not bother the others. Giles's dictionary gives also the romanization of each character in a number of Chinese dialects, as well as in Korean, Japanese, and Annamese.

Thus when I write hsiang^4 (4287)—meaning elephant, chess, etc.—the reader wishing to know the Chinese character will find it easily in that dictionary; it is character No. 4287.[a] Of course, Chinese scholars would prefer to have the char-

[a] It is important to note that the numbers were the same in the first edition of Giles's dictionary (1892). The new edition, though considerably larger, contains only 67 new characters out of a total of 10,926. Giles's dictionary is often used as a Chinese telegraphic code.

acter itself without further ado, but it did not seem wise to increase considerably the cost of this book for the sake of an exceedingly small number of readers.

The aspirates are generally represented by an inverted apostrophe, as in ch'êng[2] (763) meaning city wall. I have replaced that inverted apostrophe by an ordinary one in order to simplify the printer's task; thus I have written ch'êng. There can be no ambiguity in this, inasmuch as only one kind of apostrophe is used in Chinese romanizations, but the reader must remember that the apostrophe is here the symbol of a true aspiration.

For the transcription of Chinese words, I was helped first by Dr. Yuen Ren Chao, of Tsing Hua College, Peking, and later by F. K. Huang, a student in philosophy at Harvard University. I renew my thanks to both.

In some cases I have given the Japanese equivalent of Chinese characters, as Western scholars are likely to come across the Japanese forms as well as the Chinese, and the former may be widely different from the latter. Thus the Buddhist patriarch Bodhidharma[y] is called by the Chinese Ta-mo, but the selfsame characters are pronounced by the Japanese Daruma. We might write the equation

$$\text{Ta}^{2*}\text{-mo}^{2} = (10473), (7974) = \text{Daruma}$$

wherein the central part stands for the Chinese characters. The new form of Buddhism founded by Ta-mo was called Ch'an[2] (348), a word which the Japanese pronounce Zen. It is typical that most people know that sect only under its Japanese name.

3. GREEK

The transliteration of Greek would offer no difficulties, if we were not the prisoners of tradition.[z] I prefer to be inconsistent rather than pedantic, but only to a certain point. Thus I have transliterated the letter κ and the diphthongs αι and ου according to English usage (c, ae, u) in order not to give too strange an aspect to familiar words, but I have done so regretfully. On the other hand, I see no sufficient reason for replacing the final ος and ον by us and um. This would be justified if we were writing in Latin, but not otherwise. The termination in os, instead of us, has the distinct advantage of distinguishing Greek from Latin writers: Epicuros, Epictetos—Lucretius. Moreover, according to English usage, the vowel u represents the diphthong ου, and it would thus be ambiguous to use it also to represent o.

To show the extent of English inconsistency in this matter, it will suffice to mention the two following facts. The Hellenic Society recommends a system according to which Greek proper names are transliterated in one way (the Augustan one with various restrictions) and the common names in another! Many English scholars transliterate Greek names in one way and Byzantine names in another. Thus they will write Aristarchus (of Samos!) and Eudoxus (of Cnidos!), but Psellos and Moschopulos.

To minimize the insufficiency of my transliteration, and also to indicate the accent, I have given all Greek names in the original script.

To the original titles of some Greek works I have added the Latin titles, because the latter are quoted as often as the former.

---

[y] For whom see first half of sixth century.

[z] See a note of Aldo Mieli in Isis, I, 707.

4. HEBREW

The transliteration of Hebrew words has been greatly simplified because of the existence of an authoritative work, the Jewish Encyclopedia (New York, 12 vol., 1901–1906), which may be found in most reference libraries. I have consistently followed the Jewish Encyclopedia, except in my using the letter q instead of dotted k. This implied retaining a number of proper names which occur in the Bible—such as Moses, Isaac, Saul, Solomon—in the form given to them in the Authorized Version (1611). In cases of doubt I have referred to my Harvard colleague, Professor Harry Austryn Wolfson, whom I wish to thank.

I have occasionally added to the Hebrew names their Arabic equivalent. The titles of Hebrew writings have been quoted in Arabic or Latin translation whenever this seemed expedient.

5. JAPANESE

Japanese words may be represented by Chinese characters, which the Japanese pronounce in their own way, or by means of a syllabary, called kana. The kana contains 47 syllables and exists in various forms, of which the main ones are the katakana and the hiragana. For a brief history of the kana see my notes on Kibi Makibi (first half of the eighth century) and on Kōbō daishi (first half of ninth century).

I might have represented all the Japanese names quoted in my Introduction in exactly the same way as the Chinese names, by reference to Giles's Chinese dictionary, but this would have been an unnecessary complication. Thanks to the efforts of the Romanization Society (Rōmaji Kwai), a system of transliterating Japanese by means of 22 letters of our alphabet is becoming more and more popular. I have transliterated Japanese words according to that system, being guided by the excellent Unabridged Japanese-English Dictionary published by the late Captain Frank Brinkley (1841–1912), with the collaboration of Japanese scholars (Tōkyō, 1896). The reader will have no trouble in finding in that dictionary the Chinese characters and the Japanese kana corresponding to each name. For proper names I have followed E. Papinot's Historical and Geographical Dictionary (Tōkyō, 1910), wherein the Chinese characters may also be found. Thus even if there is a little inconsistency in my transliterations it does not matter so much, because the original form of the words quoted can so easily be obtained.

I must add a word concerning the pronunciation of Rōmaji Japanese words. Roughly speaking, we may say that the vowels are pronounced as in Italian and the consonants as in English. (The most notable exception is the letter f, which is distinctly aspirated). However, the sound of letters varies considerably according to their combination with other letters. It is not possible to go into this here. I must refer the reader for such details to a Japanese grammar or to the introduction of Brinkley's dictionary.

For the Japanese forms of Chinese names, see the end of my note on Chinese, above.

6. PERSIAN

After the Islamization of their country, the Persians adopted the Arabic alphabet, but were obliged to add four letters to represent sounds of their own old language, Pahlawī, which did not exist in Arabic. Thus the problem of transliterating Persian is essentially the same as that concerning Arabic, except that we have four more letters to consider, to wit:

p, ch (as in *church*), zh (as in *azure* or French *bijou*), and g (as in *go*, *get*). The last letter is different from the Arabic (and Persian) one which we represented by gh, but the strongly guttural sound of which it is almost impossible to suggest.

The Persian pronunciation of Arabic consonants is sometimes different from the Arabic, but for these differences I must refer the reader to Persian grammars. I will only observe that the sound of ain (ʿ) strongly guttural in Arabic, almost disappears in Persian. Letters are more readily interchanged in Persian than in Arabic because of strong dialectical influences.

7. SANSKRIT

For the transliteration of Sanskrit words, I have followed the "Sanskrit-English Dictionary" of Sir Monier Monier-Williams, in the new edition which appeared shortly after his death (Oxford, 1899). My transliteration differs from his in one minor respect only: I designate the first of the three sibilants by ś (instead of ṡ). For the proper names I have been guided mainly by Moriz Winternitz's "Geschichte der indischen Litteratur," (3 vols., Leipzig, 1907–1922; vol. 1 being the second edition), but my transliteration is somewhat different from his.

The simplest way to indicate the system I have followed is to write the transliterated letters in the natural order of the Nāgarī (or Devanāgarī) alphabet. The English words placed between parentheses after each letter suggest the approximate pronunciation.

a (mic*a*), ā (f*a*ther), i (f*i*ll), ī (pol*i*ce), u (f*u*ll), ū (r*u*de), ṛi (me*rri*ly), ṛī (ma*ri*ne), lṛi (reve*lry*), lṛī (same longer), e (pr*ey*), ai (*ai*sle), o (g*o*), au (German H*au*s).
k (*k*ill), kh (in*kh*orn), g (*g*un, do*g*), gh (fo*gh*orn), ṅ (ki*ng*)
c (*ch*urch), ch (chur*chh*ill), j (*j*oin), jh (he*dgeh*og), ñ (si*nge*).
ṭ (*t*rue), ṭh (an*th*ill), ḍ (*d*rum), ḍh (roa*dh*ouse), ṇ (*n*one).
t (wa*t*er as the Irish say it), th (nu*th*ook), d (*d*ice), dh (a*dh*ere), n (*n*ot).
p (*p*ot), ph (u*ph*ill), b (*b*ee), bh (a*bh*or), m (*m*an).
y (*y*et), r (*r*oad), l (*l*ane), ḷ, ḷh, v (*e*v*e*; like w after a consonant).
ś (*s*ure), sh (*sh*are), s (*s*on), h (*h*eap).

The anusvāra ("after-sound"), a pure nasal sound (as in French *bon*), is indicated by means of a dot or line under the letter, ṉ, ṃ. The visarga, a final hard breathing, is represented by ḥ. For the complicated rules of sandhi, that is, the euphonic combination and assimilation of letters, see a Sanskrit grammar. The tendency of that language is to treat every sentence as if it were an unbroken chain of syllables; hence the occurrence of words which are apparently endless.

Pāli, a language closely akin to Sanskrit, is of considerable importance, because it was the vehicle of primitive Buddhism. In a few cases I have given the Pāli equivalent of Sanskrit words. The rules of transliteration and pronunciation are essentially the same as for Sanskrit.

For some works (especially Buddhist works) I have given not only the Sanskrit or the Pāli title, but also its translation in Chinese and eventually in Japanese, whenever I have thought it expedient to do so for the reader's convenience.

In cases of doubt, I have been helped by my Harvard colleague, Professor James Haughton Woods, to whom I renew my thanks.

8. SYRIAC

I have transliterated the Syriac alphabet as follows:

', b, g, d, h, w, z, ḥ, ṭ, y, k, l, m, n, s, ', p, ṣ, q, r, sh, t.

It will be noticed that the order of the letters is similar to that of the Hebrew alphabet. (The Arabic alphabet was originally arranged in the same way; witness the numerical value of the letters.)

Long and evanescent vowels have been represented respectively as follows: ā, ū; ĕ. The consonants b, g, d, k, p, and t may be followed by an h to indicate a softening; this can cause no ambiguity, because if the real letter h was meant, it would be separated from the previous consonant at least by an evanescent vowel.

When in doubt I have referred to my Harvard colleague, Dr. William Thomson, whose kindness is hereby acknowledged.

CHAPTER I

THE DAWN OF GREEK AND HEBREW KNOWLEDGE

(Ninth and Eighth Centuries B. C.)

I. Summary. II. Earliest Monuments of European Literature. III. The First Hebrew Prophets and a Great King. IV. Egyptian Law.

I. SUMMARY

1. It is not yet possible to give a continuous account of early Babylonian, Egyptian, and Chinese knowledge, and therefore it has seemed more expedient to begin our own survey with Homer. For example, the golden age of Egyptian science seems to have occurred about the twentieth to the fifteenth century B. C., and though we know that the Greeks were influenced by the Egyptians in many ways, it is impossible to tell with any completeness or precision how Egyptian lore was transmitted to Greece. The same can be said of early Babylonian lore; the transition is not clear. We are sure of the existence of a chain connecting Babylonia and Greece, but too many links are still missing. As to pre-Confucian China, our knowledge of it is extremely uncertain. For all of these reasons I prefer to give accounts of our debts to those early civilizations in separate chapters devoted to them, outside of this chronological series. I will not write these special chapters until the first part of this Introduction (down to the sixteenth century) is completed. I hope that by that time our knowledge of these very difficult subjects will be materially improved, for it is developing faster than ever before.

2. *Earliest Monuments of European Literature*—Our survey begins thus with "Homer," the earliest phase and not the least astounding of the "Greek miracle." When reading the Iliad and the Odyssey, it is hard to believe that these magnificent poems are the earliest monuments of European literature. They contain implicitly the earliest account of European knowledge and craftsmanship. It is impossible to date them with any precision; but we may say, roughly, that they were composed some time in the ninth century and had developed into something like their present shape by the middle of the eighth century, if not before. Soon after this, before the end of the eighth century, appeared another Greek poem, the Works and Days of Hesiod, which gives us a better knowledge of Greek husbandry and navigation and of their early thoughts on many subjects.

3. *First Hebrew Prophets and a Great King*—In the meanwhile, an entirely different development had taken place in another country, not far distant from the Greek world, in Judah. The difference is well expressed by St. Paul in his First Epistle to the Corinthians (1, 22): "For the Jews require a sign and the Greeks seek after wisdom." The earliest Greek works are didactic poems; the earliest Hebrew utterances are prophecies. The Greeks are interested chiefly in positive knowledge, the Hebrews in morality and apocalypses. The latter introduced the notion of monotheism, which may be considered a scientific hypothesis. The earliest Hebrew prophet, Amos (flourished c. 765 to 750), may be called the founder

of monotheism. He was followed by Hosea (c. 750 to 734), Micah (c. 745 to 700) and Isaiah (c. 740 to 700). The activity of these seers was strengthened by the efforts of a more practical man, Hezekiah, King of Judah (c. 719 to 690), who sanctioned their ideals and caused great public works to be undertaken. The Siloam tunnel constructed under him was a triumph of engineering.

4. *Egyptian Law*—Toward the end of the same period an Egyptian king, Bocchoris the Wise, reformed the laws of his country; we know this through Greek tradition. It would seem that his reforms influenced Greek jurisprudence, and they constitute a valuable link in the history of Greek origins.

II. EARLIEST MONUMENTS OF EUROPEAN LITERATURE

HOMER

Ὅμηρος. The greatest epic poet, the "educator of Greece" (Plato says they called him so; quite correctly). It is impossible to state exactly where and when he lived. It is likely that he was a European Greek rather than an Ionian, for he lived probably in the ninth century, that is, before the colonization of Asia Minor. The fact that the Iliad and the Odyssey are the very first monuments of Greek literature and yet are so perfect has been a cause of perpetual wonder. Before attempting to appreciate the significance of these works from our special point of view, it is essential to discuss briefly their origin.

In 1795, Friedrich August Wolf (1759 to 1824) published a book entitled "Prolegomena ad Homerum,"* in which he tried to explain the composition of these wonderful poems by restricting Homer's authorship. This was the beginning of the so-called "Homeric question." Wolf's revolutionary theories were carried considerably further by his followers. However, since the end of the last century, under the leadership of Andrew Lang (1893, etc.), Walter Leaf, and others, a reaction has set in and the general trend of opinion is now (with one restriction, to be indicated presently) the old orthodox one: Homer is the main author of the Iliad and the Odyssey; the interpolations and rearrangements of later times are relatively of small importance.

The restriction is relative to the dual authorship of the Iliad and the Odyssey. These two poems have very much in common, notably the style, "rapid, plain in thought, plain in diction, and noble" (Matthew Arnold), yet they differ widely. The Iliad is much more historical in tone and character, more rational, too—it is an epic of warfare; the Odyssey is full of magic and romance, it contains more descriptions of social life, it is at once more superstitious and more moral, it represents a more advanced stage of culture and the beginning of urban life. The style of both poems may be the same, but the mood is very different. One can easily imagine an interval of at least half a century between the composition of the poems. May it not be possible that there were two Homers: The Elder who composed the Iliad, and the Younger, a son or grandson or faithful disciple, who composed the Odyssey?

I spoke of the great event of 1795, the publication of Wolf's "Prolegomena." Another outstanding date in the history of Homeric study was the discovery of the Mycenaean walls by Wilhelm Dörpfeld (born in 1853) at Hissarlik in 1893. Even as Wolf's pen had revolutionized the philological study a century before,

* More fully: Sive de operum Homericorum prisca et genuina forma variisque mutationibus et probabili ratione emendandi. Vol. I, Halle, 1795 (this was the only volume published).

Dörpfeld's spade revolutionized the archaeological outlook. It made one realize more deeply that the Homeric poems were not in any sense primitive productions, but the fruits of a civilization already very old. It would be misleading to call these poems Mycenaean, though it may be claimed that they reflect the Mycenaean civilization, at least indirectly and from a considerable distance, and even that they contain some Mycenaean fragments.[a] They were certainly composed after the Dorian invasion which broke the Mycenaean power about 1000 B. C. This invasion spread over a considerable time; it was essentially a victory of iron over bronze weapons. The Iliad and the Odyssey were probably composed in the ninth century (the Odyssey possibly only in the eighth); both poems had probably grown into something like their present form by the middle of the eighth century. Hence we may say that they give us a view of Hellenic culture toward the end of the prehistoric period.

It is not the place here to give the history of the Homeric question, for this does not concern so much "Homer"—that is, the poems which we may take as they are without further ado—as the development of classical scholarship in the nineteenth century. I shall simply remark that while many scholars tried to prove that Wolf's ideas were wrong, Victor Bérard wrote a "war"-book to prove that they were not original: "Un mensonge de la science allemande: Les prolégomènes à Homère de F. A. Wolf" (290 pages, Paris, 1917). It is quite true that Wolf did not invent any of the arguments which he used to throw doubt upon Homer's authorship. He had many forerunners, the earliest being François Hédelin, abbé d'Aubignac (1604 to 1676) whose "Conjectures académiques" appeared in 1715 (reprinted in Paris, 1925, see Isis, VIII, 528), and the others Ch. Perrault, L. Küster (1696), R. Bentley (1713), S. Clarke (1729, etc.), P. H. Mallet (1755 to 1756), R. Wood (1769, etc.). The fact remains that it was Wolf's "Prolegomena" which really opened the Homeric question. He clinched the argument and obliged the whole republic of letters to take notice. The date 1795 is thus a very important one in the history of Homeric scholarship.

The Iliad and the Odyssey may be considered in the first place as *history*. Epics are the primitive form of history; one might even say that as soon as they cease to be considered true histories by the very people who produce them, they cease to be true epics. It is noteworthy that classical historians like Herodotos and Thucydides speak of Homer as an historian. The historical value of the Iliad and the Odyssey is becoming better appreciated as archaeological investigations increase our knowledge of Homeric times and of ancient Troy and other Homeric localities. The poems contain valuable information about the early peoples of Greece. Our appreciation of them as historical documents has also been improved by the study of mediaeval epics, chiefly the "Chanson de Roland,"[b] the sources of which could be more easily traced.

The Homeric poems reveal the existence of an already developed practice of medicine and wound surgery, of professional physicians, and of women having some knowledge of drugs (Iliad, XI, 740). Accurate descriptions are given of wounds, their after effects and treatment; painkillers, healing draughts (*φάρμακον*

[a] The Catalogue of Achaeans and Trojans at the end of Iliad II (494–877) is possibly an old geographical document of, say, the thirteenth or twelfth century B. C., representing the political geography of that time.

[b] See my note under History in the second half of the eleventh century.

νηπενθές, Odyssey, IV, 221, opium?); medical use of iron rust, hellebore, etc.; sulphur burned to purify a house (Odyssey, XXII, 481). The extent of anatomical knowledge is implied from some 150 special words. The life spirit (θυμός, ψυχή) is seated in the diaphragm (φρένες).[c]

We are also apprised of the existence of the following specialized craftsmen: the smith (χαλκεύς) using the simple tools which we know; the potter (κεραμεύς) using the potter's wheel; the carpenter (τέκτων); the worker in leather (σκυτοτόμος). Women spin and weave and use the loom harness and oil in weaving. Agricultural use of animal manure is mentioned (Odyssey, XVII, 297). Knowledge of gold, silver, bronze, tin, lead, iron, steel (steel tempered by plunging into cold water, Odyssey, IX, 391). Decorative use of amber (ἤλεκτρον).

There is no explicit mention of *writing* in the Homeric poems. It is highly probable that their transmission remained purely oral for a considerable time. This fact must be taken into account when their authorship is discussed.

Text—The editio princeps was published in Florence in 1488 by Demetrios Chalcondylas. Among the innumerable modern editions I will quote, only those of J. van Leeuwen: Iliad (Leiden, 1912–13), Odyssey (Leiden, 1917), with introductions and notes in Latin. Because of its exceptional beauty, the Odyssey was printed in Robert Proctor's type, Oxford University Press, 1909. Because of their convenience, the Odyssey and the Iliad with English translation by A. T. Murray (4 vols. of the Loeb Library, London, 1919, 1925), and the Odyssey with French translation and commentary by Victor Bérard (3 vols., 1924).

Indexes and Concordances—Heinrich Ebeling (editor): Lexicon homericum (2 vols. Leipzig, 1871–85). August Gehring: Index homericus (878 p., Leipzig, 1891; Appendix, 1895). Very readable lexicological notes at the end of Michel Bréal: Pour mieux connaître Homère (Paris, 1906, p. 133–309). Richard John Cunliffe: A Lexicon of the Homeric dialect (London, 1924).

Guy Lushington Prendergast: Concordance to the Iliad (416 p., London, 1875). Henry Dunbar: Concordance to the Odyssey and Hymns (424 p., Oxford, 1880).

General Studies—Victor Terret: Homère (650 p., Paris, 1898; p. 531–624, bibliography). Engelbert Drerup: Die Anfänge der hellenischen Kultur (146 p., 105 illust. München, 1903; new enlarged ed. 1915). Michel Bréal: Pour mieux connaître Homère (312 p., Paris, 1906). Thomas Day Seymour: Life in the Homeric age (720 p., London, 1907). Andrew Lang: The World of Homer (324 p., London, 1910). Carl Rothe: Die augenblickliche Stand der homerischen Frage (94 p., Berlin, 1912). Walter Leaf: Homer and History (391 p., London, 1915). Ulrich von Wilamowitz-Moellendorff: Die Ilias (530 p., Berlin, 1916). Thomas William Allen: Homer, The Origins and the Transmission (357 p., Oxford, 1924).

Iconography—Hugo Magnus: Die antiken Büsten des Homers, eine augenärztliche-aesthetische Studie (70 p., Breslau, 1896).

Archaeology—Wolfgang Helbig: L'épopée homérique expliquée par les monuments (616 p., many illust., Paris, 1894; first German edition, Leipzig, 1884; second, 1887). A good summary of the results of later discoveries is given by F. H. Marshall: Discovery in Greek Lands (Cambridge, 1920; Isis, IV, 59).

Homeric Science in General—I do not know of any general survey of the positive knowledge revealed in the Homeric poems, as the historian of science would like to have it.

Medicine, Anatomy, and Physiology—Galen wrote a book on the practice of

[c] Hence our words phrenesis, phrenetic, phrenology, etc.

medicine in Homer, which is lost. Joseph François Malgaigne: L'anatomie et la physiologie d'Homère (30 p., Paris, 1842). Ch. Daremberg: La médecine dans Homère (96 p., Paris, 1865). Herman Fröhlich: Die Militärmedizin Homers (65 p., Stuttgart, 1879). Otto Körner: Wesen und Werth der homerischen Heilkunde (Wiesbaden, 1904). André Floquet: Homère médecin (90 p., Paris, 1912—based on Malgaigne and Daremberg, but contains also a chapter on psychology). Oswald Schmiedeberg: Über die Pharmaka in der Ilias und der Odyssee (Schriften der wiss. Ges. in Strassburg, 36; 29 p., 1918). Benvenuto Coglievina: Die homerische Medizin (49 p., Graz, 1921). Léon Moulé: L'hygiène dans les poèmes homériques (Bull. soc. franç. hist. med., t. 17, 350–77, 1923).

Botany, Husbandry—Friedrich Günther: Die Ackerbau bei Homer, Die Viehzucht bei Homer (2 Progr., 34 p., 40 p., Bernburg, 1866–67). Stephan Fellner: Die homerische Flora (84 p., Wien, 1897). Heinrich Meier: Die Bauern in Homer (142 p., Luzern, 1903).

Astronomy—Anton Krichenbauer: Beiträge zur homerischen Uranologie (93 p., Wien, 1874).

Technology—Franz Bader: Die Baukunst in der Odyssee (Progr., 29 p., Eutin, 1880). Wolfgang Reichel: Homerische Waffen (2te umgearb. Aufl., 172 p., 92 ill., Wien, 1901; first ed. 1894). E. Assman: Das Floss der Odyssee, sein Bau und sein phönikischer Ursprung (Berlin, 1904).

Psychology—Martin P. Nilsson: Götter und Psychologie bei Homer (Arch. für Religionwiss., vol. 22, 363–90, 1924).

Geography—There is an abundant literature dealing with Homeric geography, but by far the largest part of it is concerned with the identification of specific places, for example, Ithaca. The geographical value of the Odyssey was already discovered by the ancients: Eratosthenes (q. v., second half of third century B. C.) minimized it, but later, toward the end of the first century B. C., Strabon magnified it. There have been many other fluctuations, the present attitude being one of reaction against extreme and sterile scepticism.

However, we are chiefly interested, not in the identification of specific places, but rather in determining the extent of Homer's geographical knowledge. On this subject see K. H. W. Völcker: Über homerische Geographie und Weltkunde (159 S., Hanover, 1830). Hermann Hahn: Die geographischen Kenntnisse der ältern griechischen Epiker (19 and 16 S., Progr., Beuthen O. S., 1878–1881). Thomas W. Allen: The Homeric Catalogue of Ships, edited with a commentary (202 p., 2 maps, Oxford, 1921. Expansion of an article published in the Journal of Hellenic Studies in 1910; Allen endeavors to show that this Catalogue —Iliad, II, 494–877—is a true picture of the geography and political situation of the Homeric Age).

The Odyssey, and more particularly the Nostos, lends itself admirably to geographical investigations. Victor Bérard has written a great work on the wanderings of Odysseus: Les Phéniciens et l'Odyssée (2 vols., 600 and 636 p., 98 and 144 fig., and maps, Paris, 1902–3); also Introduction à l'Odyssée (3 vols., Paris, 1924, 1925). See also Philippe Champault: Phéniciens et Grecs en Italie d'après l'Odyssée (602 p., Paris, 1906). Both Bérard and Champault have tried themselves to repeat the wanderings of Odysseus; they have often reached different conclusions, which is but natural, considering the highly controversial nature of their subject. Champault is much bolder than Bérard, but less convincing (Revue de synthèse histor., t. XIV, p. 98–100). Gustav Lang: Untersuchungen zur Geographie der Odyssee (Karlsruhe, 1905). Hans Hugold von Schwerin: Odysseus' irrfärder (151 p., Lunds univ. årsskrift, vol. 6, No. 3, Lund, 1909, with German summary). Walter Leaf: Troy, a study of Homeric geography (422 p., London, 1912).

HESIOD

Ἡσίοδος. Born in Ascra, near Mount Helicon in Boeotia, in the eighth century, probably in the first half. The father of Greek didactic poetry. Of the works ascribed to him only one, the most important, is certainly genuine, namely, the "Works and Days" (Ἔργα καὶ ἡμέραι). The "Theogony" (Θεογονία), second in importance, is probably also a work of Hesiod's, but with later interpolations. The "Works and Days" is of special interest to us because it contains precepts of husbandry and navigation, a calendar of lucky and unlucky days, etc. The nucleus of this work is certainly anterior to the seventh century. Hesiod's conception of the Five World Ages, four of which are distinguished by metals—gold, silver, bronze, iron—is also of considerable interest. There is nothing astral in it, but it may be based partly on Babylonian experience (see L. W. King, History of Babylon, 1915, p. 302, New York). The first part of the "Theogony" deals with cosmogony.

Text—The princeps edition of the "Works and Days" was published by Demetrios Chalcondylas, Milano, 1493. The first complete edition is an Aldine of 1495. Of the many modern editions I will quote only two: (1) because of its convenience—Hugh Gerard Evelyn-White's edition of Hesiod, the Homeric Hymns and Homerica in the Loeb classical library, London, 1914; (2) because of its extraordinary beauty—Paul Maron: Les Travaux et les Jours d'Hésiode, texte grec et traduction nouvelle, suivis de La Terre et l'Homme d'Anatole France, decorés de 114 bois originaux de Paul Emile Colin, Paris, Pelletan, 1912.

Criticism—Albert Rehm: Mythographische Untersuchungen über griechische Sternsagen (48 S., München, 1896; 2. Teil, Zur sog. hesiodischen Astronomie). Milan R. Dimitrijević: Studia Hesiodea (234 p., Leipzig, 1899). Pierre Waltz: Hésiode et son poème moral (230 p., Bordeaux, 1906). Heber Michel Hays: Notes on the Works and Days of Hesiod (226 p., Chicago, 1918). Walter Schiller: Das Hungerödem bei Hesiod (Janus., t. 25, 37–44, 1921). A. Le Marchant: Greek Religion in the Time of Hesiod (185 p., Manchester, 1924).

III. THE FIRST HEBREW PROPHETS AND A GREAT KING

AMOS

'Āmōṣ. Native of Tekoa, south of Bethlehem; he preached at Bethel and flourished some time between 765 and 750. The earliest Hebrew prophet of whom we have any definite knowledge; he may thus be called the founder of monotheism. At any rate, the ethical theory of the world and the conception of a God, unique, conscientious, and just, which are published under his name, are the earliest of their kind extant.[d] The Book of Amos (in 9 chapters) is a part of the Old Testament, both in the Jewish and in the Christian canon. Amos VIII, 9, is possibly an allusion to the Nineveh solar eclipse of 763, an eclipse of great importance to fix the chronology of Babylonia and Egypt.[e] The text of Amos is one of the best preserved among the prophetic books.

William Rainey Harper: Critical and exegetical Commentary on Amos and Hosea (424 p., Internat. critical comm., New York, 1905). Louis I. Newman: Parallelism in Amos (Berkeley, 1918).

---

[d] That is, if the Gāthās are younger than the Book of Amos, which is not certain (see my note on Zoroaster, seventh century B. C.); at any rate, the Hebrews and Iranians discovered monotheism independently.

[e] The date, 787, often written in the margin of Bibles for this eclipse, is incorrect.

Note on Egyptian Monotheism—It has been claimed by some Egyptologists that the real founder of monotheism was Amenhotep IV, a king of the eighteenth dynasty, who reigned from c. 1375 to c. 1358. Such a statement is correct or not, according to one's definition of monotheism. In a sense the idea of the Oneness of God is much older than that,[f] but this was a shallow and inconsistent monotheism which did not preclude the worship of many other gods or subgods. Moreover, Egyptian monotheism did not insist so much on morality and justice. Hebrew monotheism is of such great interest to the historian of science, because it is the earliest assumption of moral unity, as contrasted with the physical unity postulated a little later by the Ionian philosophers. Both assumptions were necessary steps toward the recognition of the unity of knowledge and the unity of mankind.

To come back to Amenhotep IV, he did not invent the One God, but he introduced (or rather, tried to introduce, for he failed) the exclusive worship of that ancient god, Aten, the Solar Disc. It is then that he assumed a new name Akhunaten (or Ikhnaton).

H. R. Hall: Egypt and the External World in the Time of Akhenaten (Journal of Egyptian Archaeology, t. 7, 39–53, 1921; Isis, V, 269). Arthur Weigall: The Life and Times of Akhnaton (Rev. ed., London, 1923). Sir Ernest A. Wallis Budge: Tutânkhamen (London, 1923; Isis, VIII, 580).

HOSEA

Hōshēa'.[g] Flourished in the Northern Kingdom[h]—Israel—some time about 750 to 734. One of the greatest Hebrew prophets. The text of the Book of Hosea (14 chapters)[i] is very corrupt; it contains probably many interpolations. Hosea reënforced considerably the ethical side of Hebrew monotheism, insisting on the idea of mercy (love).

MICAH

Micaiah. Flourished at Moresheth-Gath in Judah, between 745 and 700. Hebrew prophet. Chapters 1 to 3 of the Book of Micah[j] are certainly his work; the other chapters (4 to 7) are the results of later revisions or additions.

J. M. P. Smith, W. H. Ward, J. A. Bewer: Commentary on Micah, Zephaniah, Nahum, Habakkuk, Obadiah, and Joel (New York, 1911).

ISAIAH[k]

Flourished at Jerusalem from c. 740 to the beginning of the seventh century. One of the earliest and greatest Hebrew prophets. The book of the Old Testament[l] bearing his name is a collection of prophecies of different ages extending from Isaiah's own time to the third century B. C. or even later (66 chapters). Isaiah lays stress on justice, goodness, on the essential morality of God.

---

[f] It can even be traced back to the Ancient Empire.

[g] Also Osee.

[h] The three other prophets of the eighth century belonged to the Southern Kingdom, Judah.

[i] A part of the Old Testament canon, both Jewish and Christian.

[j] A part of the Old Testament canon, both Jewish and Christian.

[k] In Hebrew Y^{e}sha'yāhū, meaning "Jehovah is salvation" or "the source of salvation."

[l] In both the Jewish and the Christian canons.

The eclipse referred to in Isaiah, XXXVIII, 8, is probably a large partial eclipse of the sun, visible in Jerusalem on January 11, 689. I have already remarked in my note on Amos that the date of Amos's eclipse is 763, not 787. Taking this correction of 24 years into account, Biblical chronology tallies with Babylonian and Assyrian chronology (S. A. Mitchell, Eclipses of the Sun, 1913, 29).

Robert H. Kennett: Composition of Isaiah in the Light of History and Archaeology (100 p., London, 1910). George Buchanan Gray and Arthur S. Peake: Commentary on Isaiah (New York, 1912). William Popper: Parallelism in Isaiah (Berkeley, 1918). Thomas Fletcher Royds, Virgil and Isaiah, a study of the Pollio with translation and notes (Oxford, 1918).

HEZEKIAH

King of Judah, c. 719 to 690 B. C.[m] He fought local superstitions and endeavored to purify the national worship and to strengthen his people. He was a patron of learning.[n] He fortified Jerusalem and improved its water-supply. To this effect, the Siloam tunnel was constructed, the rock being pierced simultaneously at both ends and the workmen finally meeting in the middle. It is an underground aqueduct, more than 500 meters long and semicircular in shape. The so-called Siloam inscription[o] recording this great event is the oldest Hebrew inscription of of any length (II Chronicles, XXXII, 30).

IV. EGYPTIAN LAW

Bekneranef,[p] Bocchoris the Wise, Egyptian king of the twenty-fourth dynasty; he flourished at Sais, in the Delta, about the end of the eighth century B. C. Egyptian legislator. According to a tradition of Greek times, which is probably correct, he reformed the laws of his country, and Greek (and Roman) laws were probably influenced by this legislation.

G. C. Lee: Historical Jurisprudence (1900, 60). Alex. Moret: De Bocchori rege (97 p., Paris, 1903). J. H. Breasted: History of Egypt (1905, 547). Eugène Révillout: Précis de droit égyptien (2 vols., Paris, 1903); Les origines égyptiennes du droit civil romain (170 p., Paris, 1912).

---

[m] These dates are disputed, but it is certain that Hezekiah was ruling toward the end of the eighth and the beginning of the seventh century, a very critical period in the history of Western Asia.

[n] The Song of Solomon and Ecclesiastes were attributed to him and his school. These attributions, though incorrect, are significant.

[o] Now in the Museum at Constantinople. The script is similar to that of Moabite and various Phoenician inscriptions. The Siloam inscription is unfortunately undated, but it is not of a later time than that of Hezekiah. See articles by Philippe Berger in Jewish Encyclopaedia, t. XI, 1905, 339–341 (with facsimile), and by Stanley Arthur Cook in Encyclopaedia Britannica, 1911, vol. 13, 440.

[p] This is the Egyptian name, far less known than the Greek name; less certain, too.

CHAPTER II

THE DAWN OF IRANIAN KNOWLEDGE

(Seventh Century B. C.)

I. Summary. II. Dawn of Iranian Knowledge. III. Greek Music. IV. Greek Law. V. Assyrian Learning. VI. Hebrew Law and History. VII. More Hebrew Prophets.

I. SUMMARY

1. The seventh century is everywhere, except perhaps in Iran and in Assyria, a period of preparation and transition, rather than one of growth and original activity.

2. *Dawn of Iranian Knowledge*—If the Iranian prophet Zoroaster appeared in the seventh century (and that dating is very plausible but not certain), that century saw the beginning of a new civilization of a very high type, a civilization which is still a living force in the world of to-day.

3. *Greek Music*—During the first quarter of the century, Terpander of Lesbos developed Greek music and established at Sparta the earliest musical school of Europe.

4. *Greek Law*—The codification of Greek law began in the seventh century. The earliest written code (outside of Babylonia and Egypt) was that of the city of Locri Epizephyrii, a Greek colony in South Italy. This code dates from 663; the earliest code of Athenian law was promulgated in 621.

5. *Assyrian Learning*—The time of Ashurbanipal (king of Assyria from 667 to 626) was the golden age of Assyrian art and learning, but as this learning was rather a reflection of more ancient knowledge than an original development, I prefer to deal with it more fully in a later chapter devoted to Babylonia and Assyria.

6. *Hebrew Law and History*—The last book of the Pentateuch was probably completed about 640. This is also a code of law, but in a much broader sense, as the Semitic peoples have always understood it. It is not simply a penal code; it is a code of morality, a standard of orthodoxy, a rule of conduct.

The main part of the Books of Samuel, explaining the history of the early kings of Judah, dates probably from the same time or a little later.

7. *More Hebrew Prophets*—In the meanwhile, Hebrew prophecy went on: Zephaniah (c. 639 to c. 609); Jeremiah, who began to prophesy in 626; Nahum (bef. 606); Habakkuk (end of the century).

II. DAWN OF IRANIAN KNOWLEDGE

ZOROASTER[a]

Ζωροάστρης. Flourished in the seventh century B. C. or before, mainly at Balkh, in Bactria. Iranian philosopher and prophet. Founder of what was the religion of Iran from the time of the Achaemenian kings to the end of the

[a] The old Iranian name was Zarathushtra (Zaratūsht in Pahlavi and Zardusht in Persian).

Sassanian period. (It is called Zoroastrianism or Mazdaism.) He was most probably the author of the Gāthās, religious hymns, which form the oldest part of the Avesta.[b] The Gāthās preach an ethical monotheism not inferior to the Hebrew one.[c] Zoroastrianism was a civilizing force of the highest type (cfr. its insistence on moral values, especially truth, justice, purity, and also on agricultural labor).

There is much incertitude as to Zoroaster's time and birthplace. A. V. W. Jackson (1899) would place him in the second half of the seventh century (born c. 660, died c. 583), but that can be accepted only as a minimum date. Other scholars would place him much earlier, even as early as c. 1000 B. C. The strongest argument for an earlier date is furnished by the many linguistic and other affinities between the Gāthās and the Rig-Veda; yet such an argument is not convincing. As to Zoroaster's birthplace, according to some it was in the vicinity of Lake Urmīyah in Adharbāyjān (Atropatene); according to others, in al-Ray (Rhages) in the province of al-Jibāl (Media); according to others still, in Bactria.

Zoroastrianism is still represented by very small remnants in the Persian province of Fārs (Yazd and Kirmān) and by a large and very prosperous community in the Bombay presidency.

Text—Christian Bartholomae: Die Gatha's des Awesta, Zarathushtra's Verspredigten (Strassburg, 1905). For other texts of the Avesta, see my chapter on Iran.

Criticism—A. V. Williams Jackson: Zoroaster (338 p., New York, 1899 (1898)); Die iranische Religion, in Grund, Iran. Phil. (t. 2, 1904). L. H. Mills: Zarathushtra, Philo, the Achaemenids and Israel (Chicago, 1906). James Hope Moulton: Early Zoroastrianism (Hibbert lectures, 1912; 488 p., London, 1913). M. N. Dhalla: Zoroastrian Theology from the Earliest Times to the Present Day (New York, 1914). G. F. Moore: History of Religion (Rev. ed., 1920, 357–405, good summary). Carl Clemen: Die griechischen und lateinischen Nachrichten über die persiche Religion (Giessen, 1920). J. Carnoy: Zoroastrianism in Dictionary of Religion and Ethics (vol. 12, 862 to 868, 1922). Jarl Charpentier: The Date of Zoroaster (Bull. School Oriental Studies, vol. 3, 747 to 755, London, 1925; flourished tenth century B. C.; Isis, VIII, 529).

For the books ascribed to Zoroaster in mediaeval times, see Lynn Thorndike: History of Magic (1923, t. 1, 296).

III. GREEK MUSIC

TERPANDER

Terpander of Lesbos (Τέρπανδρος, flourished c. 710 to 670, at Sparta), father of Greek music. He founded at Sparta the earliest musical school of Europe. He improved the cithara, which was already heptachord,[d] by adding a note at the top of the scale and leaving out the third from the top, so as to obtain an octave with one note of the scale omitted. He developed the art of singing to the cithara (κιθαρῳδική) and wrote hymns for it. Two-part compositions may date back to his time.

L. Whibley: Companion to Greek Studies (3d edition, Cambridge, 1916, 131, 373).

---

[b] Chapters 28 to 54 of the Yasna, the liturgical portion of the Avesta.

[c] Rather superior in that salvation and retribution, according to Zoroaster, are individual, not national. Zoroastrian dualism is a later development.

[d] It is not true that it had only four chords and that he added three.

IV. GREEK LAW

The earliest Greek body of law is the one promulgated by Lycurgos at Sparta and traditionally dated 884 B. C. But these laws of Sparta were unwritten, Lycurgos having expressly forbidden them to be written down—and thus they could not constitute a true code. The earliest written law dates from the seventh century. The earliest was that given by Zaleucos in 663 at Locri Epizephyrii in Southern Italy, and it was still in force in some parts of Southern Italy in the fifth century B. C. The earliest written legislation of Crete may date from about the same time (see under fifth century B. C., Laws of Gortyn). Finally, the earliest written code of Athenian law was published by Dracon in 621.

Our main source for the history of Greek law is Aristotle's Constitution of Athens ('Αθηναίων πολιτεία), of which the first edition, by F. G. Kenyon, appeared in London in 1891. It has been frequently re-edited. I will mention only the edition by G. Kaibel and U. von Wilamowitz-Moellendorff, Berlin, 1891, and that by J. E. Sandys, London, 1893. English translation by F. G. Kenyon. The importance of this source is such that every history of Greek law anterior to its publication in 1891 is necessarily obsolete. J. H. Lipsius: Von der Bedeutung des griechischen Rechtes (Leipzig, 1893). G. Gilbert: Zur Entwicklungsgeschichte des griechischen Rechtes (Jahrbuch für Klass. Philol., Leipzig, 1896). H. J. Hitzig: Die Bedeutung des altgriechischen Rechtes für die vergleichende Rechtswissenschaft (Stuttgart, 1906). R. Hirzel: Themis, Dike und Verwandtes (Leipzig, 1907).

V. ASSYRIAN LEARNING

Ashurbanipal, King of Assyria from 667 (and of Babylonia from 647) to his death in 626, was a great patron of learning. He caused the oldest Babylonian and Assyrian records to be transcribed in the Assyrian style and provided with annotations. A large part of his royal library is still extant. It contains not only books on grammar, dictionaries, and historical archives, but also a number of medical, botanical and chemical texts. However, as these scientific texts are really of an older age, it seems better to study their contents in a future section of this Introduction devoted to Babylonia and Assyria. For the present I will simply refer to the recent publications, among others, of Reginald Campbell Thompson, Assyrian Medical Texts (Oxford, 1923; Isis, VII, 256); the Assyrian Herbal (London, 1925; Isis, VIII, 506), the Chemistry of Ancient Assyrians (London, 1925; Isis, IX). For a proper understanding of the cultural background of this golden age of Assyrian learning and art see for example, Robert William Rogers: History of Babylonia and Assyria (vol. 2, Cincinnati, 1900); A. T. Olmstead; History of Assyria (New York, 1923). Bruno Meissner: Babylonien und Assyrien (2 vols., Heidelberg, 1920, 1924; Isis, VIII, 195; contains much information of scientific interest).

VI. HEBREW LAW AND HISTORY

HEBREW LAW

The only part of the Pentateuch which can be dated with any precision is the fifth and last part called Deuteronomy[a] (in 34 chapters). This book, or at least

[a] From the Greek word δευτερονόμιον, found in chapters 17, 18, where it means a duplicate copy of the law there referred to.

the kernel of it,[b] was discovered in the Temple in 621 B. C. It inspired Josiah's revolutionary decision to centralize all formal worship in one place, Jerusalem. There is good reason to believe that Deuteronomy was composed not long before the date of its discovery, possibly about the end of Manasseh's reign.[c] It was based on the older parts of the Pentateuch (the Jahvistic and Elohist narratives), the traditional law (especially, of course, that of Jerusalem), and the messages of the early prophets (eighth century). It attempted to combine and harmonize these elements: traditions, ideals, and realities. Its importance in the history of institutions and of law can not be overestimated. Our present text of Deuteronomy contains additions dating from the following century.

S. R. Driver: Commentary on Deuteronomy (Intern. crit. comm.; 554 p., New York, 1895; again 1902).

HEBREW HISTORY

The Books of Samuel[d] were probably composed for the first time about the end of the seventh century or perhaps the beginning of the sixth. They deal with the history of the early kings, Samuel and Saul (1050–1010) and David (1010, etc.), and were based upon early manuscripts of considerable value. To this the "Deuteronomic" editors[e] added a commentary. New additions and revisions were made later, possibly even after the Exile (586). It seems probable, at any rate, that the present text was not established until that time. The literary value of the Books of Samuel is supreme and their historical value considerable. They compare favorably with Herodotos's narrative.

Henry Preserved Smith: Commentary on Samuel (460 p., New York, 1899).

VII. MORE HEBREW PROPHETS

ZEPHANIAH

Flourished in Judah about 639 to c. 609. The book of Zephaniah (3 chapters) is the ninth in the collection of the minor prophets. It is included in both the Jewish and the Christian canons.

See Micah (eighth century B. C.). Sidney Zandstra: The Witness of the Vulgate, Peshitta, and Septuagint to the Text of Zephaniah (56 p., New York, 1909).

JEREMIAH

Born near Jerusalem; began to prophesy in 626; deported to Babylonia after the fall of Jerusalem in 586. The Book of Jeremiah (52 chapters) contains prophecies and narratives of contemporary events.[f]

---

[b] Chapters 5 to 26 and 28, which are a development of the earlier Hebrew code contained in Exodus, chapters 20 to 23 and 34, 12 to 26.

[c] Manasseh was king of Judah from 695 to 641; Josiah from 638 until his death at the battle of Megiddo in 609.

[d] These two books (in 55 chapters) of the Christian Bible formed only one in the original Hebrew canon. The division into two was made by the LXX.

[e] By which is meant those belonging to the time and school of thought characterized by Deuteronomy.

[f] It is part of the Old Testament canon, both Jewish and Christian. But there are great differences between the Hebrew and the Greek texts; the oldest Greek version is much shorter than the Hebrew. The so-called Lamentations of Jeremiah (5 poems included in both canons) are not all by the same poet, and there is no reason to believe that Jeremiah composed any of them. They date probably from the sixth century B. C.

Walter Baumgartner: Die Klagegedichte des Jeremia (100 p., Giessen, 1917). Sigmund Mowinckel: Zur Komposition des Buches Jeremia (68 p., Norwegian Academy, Hist. cl., 1913, 5; 1914). George Adam Smith: Jeremiah (The Baird Lecture, 1922; 404 p., London, 1923).

NAHUM

Flourished in Judah about the middle of the seventh century or in the latter half, certainly before 606. The Book of Nahum (3 chapters) is the seventh in the collection of the minor prophets.[g]

See Micah, eighth century B. C.

HABAKKUK

Flourished in Judah, probably at Jerusalem, toward the end of the seventh century. The Book of Habakkuk (3 chapters) is the eighth in the collection of the minor prophets.[h]

See Micah, eighth century B. C.

---

[g] It is included in both the Jewish and the Christian canons. The text is very corrupt.

[h] It is included in both Jewish and Christian canons.

CHAPTER III

THE TIME OF THALES AND PYTHAGORAS

(Sixth Century B. C.)

I. Summary. II. Chinese, Hindu, and Hebrew Prophets. III. Babylonian Astronomy. IV. Birth of Natural Philosophy: Thales, Anaximander, Cleostratos, Anaximenes, Xenophanes, Pythagoras. V. Greek Technicians. VI. Hindu and Greek Medicine. VII. Egyptian and Greek Geography. VIII. Chinese, Hebrew, and Greek Historians. IX. Greek, Roman, and Chinese Law.

I. SUMMARY

1. As compared with the three previous centuries, the sixth century is a period of far greater activity—one has the feeling of witnessing a real explosion of intellectual energy, and not only in one place but all over the world—in Greece, in Judah, in Babylonia, in India, in China. How is it that the human mind seems to reach its maturity, a relative maturity, at about the same time in so many countries, each so distant from the others?

2. *Chinese, Hindu, and Hebrew Prophets*—To begin with, there appears a series of wise men, prophets, founders of religion, men who persuade their fellowmen to adopt a new conception of the universe and of themselves, and who transform radically the intellectual atmosphere of their time: Lao Tzŭ (604 to c. 510), the founder of Taoism; Confucius (551 to 479), the founder of Confucianism; the Buddha (c. 560 to c. 483-477), the founder of Buddhism; Mahāvīra, the founder of Jainism. Note the simultaneity: about the year 520, Lao Tzŭ was a very old man, Confucius was 31, and the Buddha, 40. And there were still a few Hebrew prophets: Ezekiel, Haggai, Zechariah. Seven prophets in one century, and four of them founders of new philosophies or religions—that is something immense.

3. *Babylonian Astronomy*—During the second half of the century, the Babylonians began to make astronomical observations of a more scientific nature.

4. *Birth of Natural Philosophy*—It is impossible to say when Babylonian and Egyptian observations reached Greece. It is probable that they percolated gradually for a long time. At any rate, it is in this period that Greek philosophy, "natural philosophy," was born, first in Ionia: Thales, Anaximander, Cleostratos, the astronomer, Anaximenes, Xenophanes; and a little later in southernmost Italy, Pythagoras. These philosophers are at once poets, seers, and men of science. They try to give complete explanations of the Cosmos; and the striking fact is that these explanations, however immature, are not irrational. They are not idle fancies, but hasty inductions, premature hypotheses. The fragments of their writings and ancient testimonies concerning them that have come down to us contain some of the earliest discoveries in mathematics, astronomy, geography, physics, palaeontology, and medicine.

5. *Greek Technicians*—We have records also of many Greek inventors and engineers: the Scythian Anacharsis, who flourished in Athens c. 592; Glaucos of Chios, Chersiphron of Cnossos and his son Metagenes, Theodoros of Samos, Eupalinos of Megara, Mandrocles.

6. *Hindu and Greek Medicine*—According to Hindu tradition, the earliest medical schools of Ātreya and Suśruta date from the age of the Buddha. The work of Suśruta is of very great importance, especially as it relates to surgery. However, its historical value is considerably impaired, for example, with regard to the discussion of the relations between Greek and Hindu medicine, by the great uncertainty of its date. Toward the end of the sixth (or the beginning of the fifth) century we note the appearance of the two earliest Greek physicians of importance, both of the school of Pythagoras: Alcmaeon, the father of Greek medicine, to whom many anatomical discoveries are ascribed, and Democedes, physician to the king of Persia.

7. *Egyptian and Greek Geography*—Necho, king of Egypt from 609 to 593, attempted toward the end of his reign to build a canal connecting the Nile Delta and the Red Sea. He ordered a circumnavigation of Africa, which was accomplished in three years.

To the Ionian philosophers already named might have been added Hecataeos of Miletos (c. 550 to c. 475), but I separated him from the others because he devoted himself almost exclusively to the study of geography; indeed, he is the Father of Geography.

8. *Chinese, Hebrew, and Greek Historians*—Much work was done in the field of history. Our oldest source for the history of early China is the "Shu ching," by Confucius, and we owe to him also annals of the State of Lu from 722 to 481 (Ch'un ch'iu). "The Book of Judges" and "The Books of Kings," which form parts of the Jewish and Christian Scriptures, date probably from the sixth century, and the oldest Greek historian, Cadmos of Miletos (still another Ionian!), flourished about the middle of the same century.

9. *Greek, Roman, and Chinese Law*—Many steps forward in social organization were due to the Athenian Solon in the first half of the sixth century. During the second half of the same century we meet the earliest Roman jurist, Sextus Papirius and the statesman Kung-sun Ch'iao, to whom the foundation of Chinese criminal law is ascribed.

II. THE PROPHETS

LAO TZŬ[a]

Lao^{3} Tzŭ^{3} (6783, 12317). Born in Honan, 604; flourished at Lo^{4*}-yang^{2} (7328, 12883) capital of the Chou dynasty; he died in an unknown place, about the end of the sixth century. Chinese philosopher. Presumed author, at the end of his life, of the Tao^{4} tê^{2*} ching^{1} (10780, 10845, 2122), the "Canon or Classic on Reason[b] and Virtue." This work inculcated the doctrine of wu^{2}-wei^{2} (12753, 12521) (inaction, non-assertion, the being without desire, submission to the universal tao). The noblest part of the philosophy (or religion) called Taoism originated with it. It is the fountain-head of Chinese mysticism in its purest and highest form. Chapter 80 (the last but one) contains an allusion to writing by means of knotted cords, chieh^{2*} shêng^{2} (1470, 9886).

---

[a] The "Old Philosopher." He was also called Lao^{3} Chün^{1} (3269) and Lao^{3} Tan^{1} (10620). His surname was Li^{3} (6884) and his name Erh^{3} (ears) (3336).

[b] The word tao can not be exactly translated; it means way (cfr. odos, N. T.), reason, logos. It is perhaps better to leave it untranslated, even as we often do for the word logos. According to Wieger in "Les pères du système Taoïste" (1913, 3) the words tao and tê should be translated by "principle" and "action" (Traité du principe et de son action). The Tao tê ching was consecrated as a classic in 666.

Text—Chinese-English edition with transliteration, translation word by word, and notes, by Paul Carus (380 p., Chicago, 1898; containing also the text of Ssŭ¹-ma³ Ch'ien¹ (10250, 7576, 1711)'s biography with translations). English translation by James Legge in the Sacred Books of the East (vol. 39, 1891; see also vol. 40 of same collection, p. 311–19). German translation, Das Buch des Alten vom Sinn und Leben, by Richard Wilhelm (Jena, 150 p., 1911; Isis, I, 118). Chinese-French edition by Father Léon Wieger in volume 2 of his Taoïsme: Les pères du système taoïste, Lao-tzeu, Lie-tzeu, Tchoang-tzeu, Texte revu sur les anciennes éditions taoïstes, traduit d'après les commentaires et la tradition taoïste (Ho-kien-fou, 1913).

Criticism—Thomas Watters: Lao-tzŭ (Hong Kong, 1870). H. A. Giles: Biographical Dictionary (1898, 416–18). For Giles, the Tao-tê-ching is a forgery dating probably from the beginning of the Han dynasty, but most European and Chinese scholars consider it genuine. Henri Borel: Wu Wei, translated from the Dutch (77 p., London, 1903, re-edited under the title "The rhythm of life" in the Wisdom of the East series, London, 1921). Moses Chiu: Lau-Tsze und sein Lehre (Diss., Berlin, 83 p., 1911). Léon Wieger: Taoïsme (Ho-chien-fu, 1911–13). The second volume has been mentioned above; the first, 338 p., contains an elaborate bibliography of Taoïsm (Bibliographie générale, I: Le Canon, Patrologie; II: Les Index officiels et privés).

CONFUCIUS[c]

K'ung³ Fu¹ Tzŭ³ (6605, 3612, 12317),[c] born in 551 at Tsou¹ (11811) in the state of Lu³ (7388), Shantung. He served the Duke of Lu until c. 494, when he began his long wanderings in the neighboring states. He returned to Lu, c. 482, and died there in 479. Chinese philosopher, statesman and educator. The Confucian philosophy, than which none has influenced the Chinese people more deeply,[d] originated with him, but was materially modified and elaborated by later commentators (chiefly in the twelfth century). His name is connected with four of the Five Classics and one of Four Books. He himself wrote one of the Classics, Spring and Autumn (Ch'un¹ Ch'iu¹, 2854, 2302), very meager annals of the state of Lu from 722 to 481;[e] and appendixes to the Book of Changes (I⁴ Ching¹, 5497, 2122). Two other Classics were possibly edited by him: the Book of History (Shu¹ Ching¹ or Shang⁴ Shu¹, 10024, 2122 or 9733, 10024), covering a period of seventeen centuries (our oldest source for pre-Confucian history[f]); and the Book of Poetry (Shih¹ Ching¹, 9918, 2122) a collection of more than 300 ancient odes.

The first of the Four Books is an account of his conversations with his disciples, the so-called Confucian Analects (Lun² yü,³ 7475, 13626, discourses and dialogues).[g]

---

[c] The philosopher K'ung; K'ung Ch'iu¹ (2310). The personal name Ch'iu should not be written (entirely) nor uttered. Confucius is called in Japanese Kōshi (also Bunsen-Ō); Confucianism is called Judō (or Jukyō).

[d] Whether Confucianism is a philosophy or a religion is largely a matter of definition. Confucius's concern was primarily ethical.

[e] They have been elaborated by his disciple Tso³ Ch'iu¹ Ming² (11753, 2310, 7946) in the Tso³ Chuan⁴ (11753, 2703) and by later commentators. The Ch'un Ch'iu were the earliest Chinese annals (pien¹ nien², 9178, 8301) as distinguished from dynastic and other histories, and were the model followed by later annalists (e. g., Ssŭ¹-ma³ Kuang¹, 10250, 7576, 6389, second half of eleventh century).

[f] According to Chavannes and Pelliot, however, about half of the Shu Ching would be a forgery of the third century or of the beginning of the fourth century.

[g] Called Rongo in Japanese. According to Japanese traditions, the Rongo were brought to Japan from Kudara, Korea, in 284 (or 404?) by the Korean Ajiki (or Aji Kishi), this being the introduction of Chinese literature into Japan (?).

Texts—All of the books mentioned, except the I Ching, have been edited, Englished, and copiously annotated by James Legge in his Chinese Classics, Hongkong, 1861 to 1872. He has given an English translation of the I Ching in the Sacred Books of the East (vol. 16, 1882).

I must also mention, among many others, two editions of the Analects: F. S. Couvreur (S. J.): Les Quatre Livres (Ho Kien Fou (Ho[2] Chien[4] Fu[3]) (3936, 1601, 3682), 2d ed., 1910), containing the Chinese text with transliteration and translations into Latin and French; William Edward Soothill: The Analects (1036 p., Yokohama, 1910), containing the Chinese text with commentary and English translation. The translation refers continuously to the previous ones by Legge, Father Zottoli (1879), Ku[1] Hung[2] Ming[2h] (6200, 5269, 7945), and Father Couvreur.

Criticism (*Confucius and Confucianism*)—Long study by James Legge in volume 1 of his Chinese Classics (p. 56–113, 1861); also in his Religions of China (New York, 1881). Thomas Watters: A Guide to the Tablets in a Temple of Confucius (279 p., Shanghai, 1879). Tozaburo Kudo: The Ethics of Confucius (Tokyo, 1904). Ed. Chavannes: Les Mémoires historiques (t. 5, 283–445, 1905; translation of Ssŭ[1]-ma[3] Ch'ien[1]'s (10250, 7576, 1711) bibliography of Confucius in the Shih[3]-chi[4] (9893, 923), with abundant commentary). Ssŭ-ma Ch'ien was the first to establish a well-ordered account of the life of Confucius, and this record is of fundamental importance. Albert Tschepe: Heiligertümer des Konfuzianismus in K'ü-fu und Tschou-hien (Jentschou, 1906). Ch'en Huan-Chang: Economic Principles of Confucius (2 vols., New York, 1911). James Legge: Article "Confucius" in Encycl. Brit. (1911, 11 cols.). Wang Ching-Dao: Confucius and New China (Shanghai, 1912). Robert Cornell Armstrong: Light from the East; Studies in Japanese Confucianism (341 p., Toronto, 1914). Herbert Allen Giles: Confucianism and its Rivals (Hibbert lectures; 280 p., New York, 1915). L. Wieger: La Chine (1920, especially p. 104–107, giving a brief account of the fixation of the Confucian Canon under the later Han). Otto Franke: Studien zur Geschichte des konfuzianischen Dogmas und der chinesischen Staatsreligion (329 p., XI pl., Hamburg, 1920; Isis, VI, 137).

Eclipses Recorded in the Confucian Writings—The Shih Ching, possibly edited by Confucius, mentions an eclipse of the moon followed by an eclipse of the sun. The former took place on August 21, 722 B. C., the latter on September 6 of the same year. This fixes absolutely the first certain dates in the history of China.

The Ch'un Ch'iu records no less than 36 eclipses of the sun, of which it has been possible to identify 32. The earliest occurred on February 22, 720 B. C., the latest on July 22, 495. (S. A. Mitchell: Eclipses of the Sun, 1923, 7 to 9.)

THE BUDDHA

Buddha[i] (Gautama,[j] prince of the Śākya clan, born c. 560 in the Lumbini grove, near Kapilavastu in Southern Nepal, died c. 483–477 at Kuśanagara, in the country of the Mallas). Hindu philosopher. Founder of an entirely new system of philosophy,[k] which later developed into a religion.

Early Buddhism was based essentially not on any faith, but on knowledge and

---

[h] R. F. Johnston speaks very highly of Ku Hung Ming's translation (from Peking to Mandalay, p. 381, 1908).

[i] The Buddha means the Enlightened; prince Gautama became "the Buddha" only after his enlightenment under the Bodhi-tree; before, he was simply a Bodhisattva, a potential Buddha. He is also called: Śākyamuni, the sage of the Śākyas; Siddhārta, he who has accomplished his purpose; Tathāgata, he who has arrived at the truth, the Perfect One.

[j] Or Gotama in Pāli.

[k] Though it may be partly based on the Sāṃkhya system.

love—on knowledge first. The agnosticism, rigorous logic, hatred of superstition and self-delusion, respect for reason and truth which characterized it would have provided ideal conditions for the development of scientific thought, had they not been accompanied—and, so to say, neutralized—by an almost complete lack of scientific curiosity. The Buddha's purpose was primarily philosophical, ethical, but his thought was distinctly of a scientific nature, and the historian of science should give him a place of honor.

Hermann Oldenberg: Buddha, sein Leben, seine Lehre and seine Gemeinde (6th ed., Stuttgart, 1914; 1st ed., 1881); Die Lehre der Upanischaden und die Anfänge des Buddhismus (374 p., Göttingen, 1915). Th. Wm. Rhys Davids: Buddhism (London, 1877, very often reprinted and revised); Buddhism (New York, 1896); Early Buddhism (London, 1908). Mrs. C. A. F. Rhys Davids, Buddhism (London, 1912). Hendrik Kern: Histoire du bouddhisme dans l'Inde (2 vols., Annales du Musée Guimet, Paris, 1901–1903). Julius Dutoit: Das Leben des Buddha; Eine Zusammenstellung älter Berichte aus den kanonischen Schriften der südlichen Buddhisten. Aus dem Pali übersetzt und erläutert (Leipzig, 1906). Alfred S. Geden: Article in Dictionary of Religion and Ethics (t. 2, 1910, 881–5). Edmund Hardy: Der Buddhismus nach älteren Pali-Werken dargestellt (Neue Ausgabe besorgt von Richard Schmidt, Münster i. W., 1919). K. J. Saunders: Gotama Buddha, a biography based on the canonical books of the Theravādin (125 p., New York, 1920).

For Chinese, Tibetan, and Burmese lives of the Buddha, see the histories of Buddhism.

Richard Fick: The Social Organization in Northeast India in Buddha's time, translated by Shishirkumar Maitra (384 p., Calcutta, 1921; German text, Kiel, 1897). A. B. Keith: Buddhist philosophy in India and Ceylon (339 p., Oxford, 1923).

MAHĀVĪRA

Also called Vardhamāna, born in Kollāga, died at Pāvā within the Buddha's lifetime.[l] The last prophet of Jainism, and probably its real founder. Familiar discourses ascribed to him are preserved in the Jain canon.[m] Jainism is, like Buddhism, a heretic separation from Brāhmanism. This fact, their monastic tendencies, and some similarities of teaching give both religions some outward resemblance. For example, Buddhists and Jains agree in accepting the Brāhmanic doctrine of karma (act-and-result, causality) and saṃsāra (continual round of rebirth; Ocean of Life and Death). Their ultimate goal is the same: nirvāṇa, liberation from the saṃsāra. Yet Jainism, like the Sāṃkhya and the Yoga (but unlike Buddhism), admits a fundamental dualism of matter and soul. Jaina physics postulates the existence of dissimilar atoms, endowed with various qualities.[n]

The fortunes of Buddhism and Jainism have been almost opposite. Buddhism has become a world religion, but has disappeared from its native country; Jainism

---

[l] He is identical with the Nigganṭha Nātaputta referred to in Buddhist sources (nigganṭha means free from bonds).

[m] The Jains are divided into two sections: the Śvetāmbaras (white-robed) and the Digambaras (sky-clad). The canon of which I speak is that of the Śvetāmbaras; it was constituted in A. D. 454 or possibly in 514; its language is Jain Prākrit. The Jain scriptures were composed probably in Western India.

[n] Compare with the Vaiśeshika physics. This qualitative atomism is very different from the purely quantitative atomism of Democritos (fifth century B. C.).

has remained a purely Hindu religion; it has not spread, but is still flourishing at home.[o]

Texts—Hermann Jacobi: Gaina sūtras, translated from Prākrit, Sacred Books of the East (vol. 22, 45, 1884–95).

Criticism—Manak Chand Jaini: Life of Mahāvīra (Allahabad, 1908). Georg Bühler: Über die Indische Secte der Jainas (Wien, 1887, Englished by Jas. Burgess, 83 p., London, 1903). Armand Guérinot: Essai de bibliographie jaina (605 p., Ann. Musée Guimet, t. 22, Paris, 1906); Répertoire d'épigraphie jaina, précédé d'une esquisse de l'histoire du Jainisme d'après les inscriptions (318 p., Publ. de l'Ecole française d'Extrême Orient, t. 10, Paris, 1908). Hirachand Liladhar Jhaveri: First Principles of Jain Philosophy (60 p., London, 1910). Margaret Stevenson: Notes on Modern Jainism (Oxford, 1910); The Heart of Jainism (360 p., Religious Quest of India, Oxford, 1915). Herbert Warren: Jainism in Western Garb as a Solution to Life's Great Problems (Madras, 1912). Jagmanderlal Jaini: Outline of Jainism (edited with preliminary note by F. W. Thomas, Cambridge, 1916).

Ājīvikas *in* Dictionary of Religion and Ethics by A. F. R. Hoernlé (t. 1, 1908, 259–68); Jainism by Hermann Jacobi (t. 7, 1915, 465–74).

EZEKIEL

Born probably at Jerusalem, of a priestly family, he was included in the first deportation to Babylonia in 597. He flourished at Tel-Abib (near Babylon), where he began to prophesy in 592; his latest prophecy dates from 570. His messages are distinctly apocalyptic. He has been called the "father of Judaism." The Book of Ezekiel (in 48 chapters) is part of both the Jewish and Christian canons; it has hardly been revised and seems to have come down to us in the form which Ezekiel himself gave to it. The Hebrew text is very corrupt, perhaps because of this very lack of intermediate revisions.

Wilhelm Neuss: Das Buch Ezechiel in Theologie und Kunst bis zur Ende des XII. Jahrh. (350 p., Münster i. W., 1912).

HAGGAI

Flourished at Jerusalem, in his old age, c. 520 to 516. In 520 he urged the necessity of rebuilding the Temple, and he took part in its dedication in 516 (under the reign of Darius I). The Book of Haggai (in 2 chapters) is part of both the Jewish and the Christian canons.

Hinckley G. Mitchell, J. M. P. Smith, and J. A. Bewer: Commentary on Haggai, Zechariah, Malachi, and Jonah (New York, 1912; Int. crit. comm.).

ZECHARIAH

The son of Berechiah, son of Iddo, flourished at Jerusalem c. 520. He prophesied in 520. His tone is strongly ethical and Messianic. The Book of Zechariah (in 14 chapters) is a part of both the Jewish and the Christian canons; the end of it (chapters 9 to 14) is certainly the result of later additions (some possibly as late as the beginning of the second century B. C.).

---

[o] According to the census of 1901, there were 1,334,140 Jains in India; that is, less than 0.5 per cent of the whole population, but it is largely a religion of the educated classes. Jains are scattered all over India; most of them are merchants or money-lenders.

III. BABYLONIAN ASTRONOMY

Babylonian astronomy (or more properly astrology) is extremely old and it is highly probable that it was the fountain-head of European astronomy. The frequent references to "Chaldean" knowledge in the astrological literature of Europe, even to this day, are witnesses of the Babylonian origin. The seven days of our week, the twelve double hours of our days, the sexagesimal division of our angles, are other witnesses, equally eloquent. As early as the close of the third millennium, Babylonian astronomers recorded heliacal risings and settings of the planet Venus.[p] There is also a fragment of another early text showing that they attempted to determine the position of stars. However, these observations were very simple and crudely made. Thus the early Babylonian astronomy was very primitive; there is no trace of a more scientific study until the sixth century B. C. and even that neo-Babylonian astronomy was still very empirical and entirely dominated by theological or magical purposes. The Babylonians bequeathed a large number of valuable observations to the Greeks, but the astronomical science was essentially and almost entirely a Greek creation.

"The earliest scientific document in the strict sense of the word dates from the second half of the sixth century, when we find for the first time that the relative positions of the sun and moon were calculated in advance, as well as the conjunction of the moon with the planets and of the planets with each other, their positions being noted in the signs of the zodiac. But the tablets afford no evidence that the Babylonian astronomers possessed any knowledge of the precession of the equinoxes before the close of the second century B. C., and the traditional ascription of the discovery to Hipparchos of Nicaea, working between the years 161 and 126 B. C. on the observations of his Babylonian predecessors, may be accepted as accurate." Leonard W. King, A History of Babylon (London, 1915, 312; see also p. 106.)

A more elaborate discussion of this topic will be included in the chapter on Babylonia and Assyria; the present note has been inserted merely to introduce the earliest scientific observations of Babylonian astrologers in their chronological sequence.

Literature—Books of Kugler and Schiaparelli quoted above. Paul V. Neugebauer und Ernst F. Weidner: Ein astronomischer Beobachtungstext aus dem 37. Jahre Nebukadnezars II (—567/6) (Ber. der sächs. Ges. der Wiss., t. 67. 89 p. Leipzig, 1915).

IV. BIRTH OF NATURAL PHILOSOPHY

On the early Greek philosophers in general, see Hermann Diels: Doxographi Graeci (864 p., Berolini, 1879). H. Diels: Fragmente der Vorsokratiker Griechisch und Deutsch (3te Aufl. 2 vols., Berlin, 1912). Paul Tannery: Pour l'histoire de la science hellène; De Thalès à Empédocle (404 p., Paris, 1887). Theodor Gomperz (1832 to 1912): Griechische Denker (Bd. 1, Leipzig, 1896; English translation, vol. 1, London, 1901). Arthur Fairbanks: The First Philosophers of Greece. An edition and translation of the remaining fragments of the pre-Socratic philosophers, together with a translation of the more important accounts of their opinions (310 p., London, 1898). William Arthur Heidel: A Study of the Conception of Nature among the Pre-Socratics (Proc. American Academy of

---

[p] F. X. Kugler used these observations in his "Sternkunde und Sterndienst in Babel," 1907-1913, for chronological purposes. See also G. V. Schiaparelli: "Venusbeobachtungen und Berechnungen der Babylonier" (1906; Isis, VIII, 505).

Arts and Sciences, vol. 45, 79–133, 1910). Aldo Mieli: I prearistotelici (Vol. I, Le scuole ionica, pythagorica ed eleata, 520 p., Firenze, 1916; Isis, IV, 347). John Burnet: Early Greek Philosophers (3d ed., 385 p., London, 1920; 1st ed., 1892; 2d ed., 1908). Burnet's account is very sound, very clear, and very suggestive; Mieli's is of special interest to us because it is a part of a general history of science and the scientific point of view is given due prominency.

R. Ganszyniec: Die biologische Grundlage der ionischen Philosophie (Archiv für die Geschichte der Naturwissenschaften, t. 9, 1–19, 1920).

THALES

Thales of Miletos. Θαλῆς, born c. 624, still living in 548. Thales was an Ionian, but possibly had some Phoenician blood in his veins. One of the Seven Wise Men (σοφοί). The founder of Greek science and philosophy. Traveled many years in Egypt, where he became familiar with Egyptian mathematics and astronomy. Predicted the solar eclipse of May 28, 585. (Tannery says it was the eclipse of September 30, 610; this would not be inconsistent with the birth year which is generally quoted, 640.) On the basis of Egyptian empirical knowledge he founded abstract geometry. Various geometrical propositions and applications are explicitly ascribed to him. Knowledge of the loadstone; first notion of natural law; founder of the Ionian school of philosophy; the first to give a general explanation of the universe: water is the principle of all things, or all things are water. No writings of Thales have remained.

Fr. Decker: De Thalete Milesio (77 p., Halae, 1865). Paul Tannery: La tradition touchant Pythagore, Oenopide et Thalès (Bull. d. sciences mathémat., t. 10, p. 115–128, Paris, 1886). L. Hugo: Sur quelques passages anciens relatifs à Thalès et à la géométrie des Egyptiens (Comptes Rendus, t. 108, p. 767–8, Paris, 1889). August Döring: Thales (Zeits. für Philosophie und philosophische Kritik, Bd. 109, S. 179–95, 1896). Ludwig Schlachter: Altes und Neues über die Sonnenfinsternis der Thales (28. Progr. des Freien Gymnasiums, 27 p., Bern, 1898; concludes that Thales could not have predicted the eclipse of 610).

ANAXIMANDER

Anaximander of Miletos (Ἀναξίμανδρος) born in or about 610; died about 545. A pupil of Thales. No writings of his have remained. He is said to have introduced the use of the gnomon, to have discovered the obliquity of the ecliptic, in the 58th Olympiad (548 to 544), and to have been the first to construct a map. He wrote a book of natural philosophy (περὶ φύσεως)—the first Greek book of philosophy—in which he considered as principle (ἀρχή) of all things the indefinite (ἄπειρον). A geometrical summary (ὑποτύπωσις) is also ascribed to him. First theory of organic evolution.

Karl Schwartz: Über das ἄπειρον Anaximanders (Progr., 25 p., Wiesbaden, 1867). Jos. Neuhäuser: Anaximander Milesius sive vetustissima quaedam rerum universitatis conceptio restituta (444 p., Bonnae, 1883). Ludwig Otten: Anaximander. Ein prinzipieller Beitrag zur Geschichte der antiken Philosophie (Diss.) (45 p., Münster, 1911). P. Tannery: Mémoires scientifiques (vol. 7, 187–194, 309–314; Isis, IX).

CLEOSTRATOS

Κλεόστρατος, from Tenedos, flourished in the latter half of the sixth century B. C. There is a tradition according to which Thales died at Tenedos. Ionian astronomer, possibly successor to Thales. The introduction of the signs of the zodiac and of the eight years' cycle of intercalations (ὀκταετηρίς) may be ascribed to him.

He wrote an astronomical poem (ἀστρολογία) which, like many others, was eclipsed by Aratos's φαινόμενα (first half of third century B. C.).

H. Diels: Fragmente der Vorsokratiker (3. Aufl., 2. Bd., 197, 1912, containing the texts relative to Cleostratos). J. K. Fotheringham: Cleostratus (Journal of Hellenic studies, vol. 39, 164–184, 1919; very elaborate study with more complete collection of texts. See Isis, V, 203). E. J. Webb: Cleostratus redivivus (*ibid.*, vol. 41, 70–85, 1921; sharp criticism of Fotheringham's paper. See Isis, V, 490).

ANAXIMENES

Anaximenes of Miletos, 'Αναξιμένης, flourished about 546, died about 528. A pupil of Anaximander. No writings of his have remained. Air (πνεῦμα) is the principle of all things. Development takes place by thickening (πύκνωσις) or thinning (μάνωσις). That is, Anaximenes had thought out not simply a first principle but also a process of evolution. The planets are supported upon the air. The moon receives its light from the sun.

P. Tannery: Un fragment d'Anaximène dans Olympiodore le chimiste (Archiv für Gesch. d. Philos, 1, 314–321, 1888; Mémoires, 7, 121–129; Isis, IX).

XENOPHANES

Xenophanes of Colophon (Ξενοφάνης), born in Colophon, Ionia, flourished about 540. Poet and philosopher. Crude cosmological ideas, but correct interpretation of fossils. He considered them as witnesses of periodical submergences of the dry land. Monistic philosophy (monotheism or pantheism?). Reputed founder of the Eleatic school in Elea, Southern Italy.

Nektarios Mavrokordatos: Der Monotheismus des Xenophanes (Diss., 44 p., Leipzig, 1910; with bibliography). Sir Archibald Geikie: Founders of geology (33, 1905).

PYTHAGORAS

Pythagoras of Samos (Πυθαγόρας), flourished about 532, died in Metapontum in 497/6. Founded in Croton, southern Italy, a sort of religious brotherhood, which became a very important scientific school. No writings of his have remained and it is almost impossible to distinguish between his own theories and those of his school. The early Pythagoreans attached great importance to mathematics and raised it to the rank of a science. Many geometrical discoveries are ascribed to them. They founded the theory of numbers and the mathematical study of acoustics and music. First notion of incommensurable quantities. The earth is a globe. Harmony of the spheres. The beginnings of medical theory may be ascribed to this school, perhaps also the notion of crisis and of critical days. Pursuit of disinterested knowledge is the greatest purification. Numbers are the very essence of things; this philosophy led on the one hand to number mysticism, on the other to a quantitative study of nature. The older Pythagorean school died off in the second half of the fourth century B. C. Its history and that of its founder were soon obscured by uncritical hagiographers.

Antelme Edouard Chaignet: Pythagore et la philosophie pythagoricienne (2d ed., 2 vols., Paris, 1874). P. Tannery: Sur le secret dans l'école de Pythagore (Archiv für Gesch. d. Philos., vol. 1, 28–36, 1887; Mémoires, 7, 109–119); Une opinion faussement attribuée à Pythagore. (*ibidem*, vol. 4, 1–11, 1890; Mémoires 7, 155–167; Isis, IX, apropos of the harmony of the spheres and the distances of the planets). Wilhelm Bauer: Der ältere Pythagoreismus (240 p., Bern, 1897) Friedrich Boehm: De symbolis Pythagoreis (60 p., Diss., Berlin, 1905). Wolfgang Schütz: Pythagoras und Heraklit (118 p., Leipzig, 1905). Augusto Rostagni: La vita e l'opera di Pitagora secondo Timeo (Atti d. R. Accad. delle scienze di Torino, vol. 49, p. 373–395, 1914); Le vicende della scuola pitagorica secondo Timeo (*ibidem*, p. 554–574). R. O. Moon: The Influence of Pythagoras on Greek Medicine (XVIIth Congress of Medicine, hist. sect., p. 55–62, 1914). Armand Delatte: Etudes sur la littérature pythagoricienne (Biblioth. de l'école des hautes études) (314 p., Paris, 1915). This is a collection of papers some of which are of special interest to the historian of mathematics: (V) Anecdota arithmologica; (VI) Deux traités d'arithmologie pythagoriciens; (VII) Un fragment d'arithmologie dans Clément d'Alexandrie; (VIII) La tétractys pythagoricienne. The last chapter (IX) Le catéchisme des acousmatiques, is also of great interest. Augusto Rostagni: Il verbo di Pitagora. Torino, 1924 (Journal des Savants 1924, 129).

Max Offner: Die pythagoreische Lehre vom Leeren (Abh. aus dem Gebiet der klass. Altertums-Wiss. Wilh. von Christ dargebracht., S. 386–396, München, 1891.

There is an abundant literature on Pythagorean mathematics and chiefly on the so-called Theorem of Pythagoras (about the square of the hypotenuse) and on the Oriental sources of Pythagoras's knowledge. There is no doubt that Thales and Pythagoras were the main importers of Egyptian and Babylonian lore into Greece. Yet it is hardly possible to measure the reciprocal influences of Greece and the East, and such questions will always remain highly controversial. The discussion of Hindu influences is even more difficult on account of the great uncertainty with regard to the dates of the Hindu works. Some of the writers quoted below (for ex., G. Milhaud, 1910) claim that Pythagorean geometry may have been partly inspired by Hindu models. Their argument is based upon the assumption that the high antiquity of Āpastamba's work is proved. It is not. The dates of the Śulvasūtras (rules of the cord) are so uncertain that I can not deal with them in this part of the Introduction, but will discuss them in a chapter on Hindu mathematics. It is highly probable that the Śulvasūtras date from a period posterior to 500 B. C. and pre-Christian. They are most probably post-Pythagorean. (See G. R. Kaye's paper in Isis, II, 328, 1919.) On Baudhāyana, Āpastamba, and Kātyāyana (who seem to have followed one another in the order indicated) see also M. Cantor: Geschichte der Mathematik (t. 1^3, 1907, 636, and by index).

Paul Tannery: Sur l'arithmétique pythagoricienne (Bull. des sciences mathématiques, t. IX, p. 69–88, 1885; also Mémoires scientifiques, t. II, p. 179–201) G. Eneström: Note historique sur une proposition analogue au Théorême de Pythagoras (Bibliotheca Mathematica, 1898, p. 113–114). Friedrich Hultsch: Die Pythagoreischen Reihen und Diagonalen von Quadraten und ihre Umbildung zu einer Doppelreihe ganzer Zahlen (Bibliotheca Mathematica, I, p. 8–12, 1900). K. Löschhorn: Über das Alter des Pythagoräischen Lehrsatzes (Z. f. math Unterricht, t. 33, 1902, p. 183, referring to the Indian knowledge of it). F. J. Obenrauch: Die erste Raumkurve der Pythagoräischen Schule, ihre orthogonale. und imaginäre Projektion (Monatsch f. Math., t. 14, p. 185–205, 1903). H. G. Zeuthen: Théorême de Pythagore, Origine de la géométrie scientifique (Rapports et comptes rendus du 2e congrès internat. de philosophie, p. 833–854, Genève, 1905). Max C. Schmidt: Altphilologische Beiträge, 2. Heft. Terminologische Studien (Leipzig, 1915, about the word ὑποτείνουσα introduced by Pythagoras?).

One will find a complete discussion of the Theorem of Pythagoras (Greece, Egypt, India, China) in Heath's translation of Euclid, vol. 1, Cambridge, 1908, p. 350–368. Heath's conclusion on the theory of Indian discovery is that the Hindoos had discovered this theorem independently of the Greeks, but that their discovery was purely empirical. H. Vogt: Die Geometrie des Pythagoras (Bibliotheca Mathematics, t. IX, p. 15–54, 1908). H. A. Naber: Das Theorem des

Pythagoras, wiederhergestellt in seiner ursprünglichen Form und betrachtet als Grundlage der ganzen Pythagoreischen Philosophie (252 p., Haarlem, 1908. Learned but uncritical and erratic). Gaston Milhaud: La géométrie d'Āpastamba. Revue générale des sciences (t. 21, p. 512–520, Paris, 1910). H. Wipper: 46 Beweise des Pythagoreischen Lehrsatzes nebst kurzen biographischen Mitteilungen über Pythagoras (aus dem Rüssischen übersetzt. 2. Aufl., 51 p., Berlin, 1911. 1st ed., Leipzig, 1888). Ernst Müller: Weiteres über Begründung und Grundlagen des Pythagoräischen Lehrsatzes (Ann. d. Natur u. Kulturphilosophie, t. 12, p. 170–186, 1913). Erich Frank: Plato und die sogenannten Pythogareer (318 p., Halle, 1923; Isis, VI, 48–52).

V. GREEK TECHNICIANS

ANACHARSIS

Ἀνάχαρσις, Scythian prince who came to Athens c. 592, in search of knowledge. Friend of Solon. He was renowned for his wisdom and various inventions were ascribed to him by Ephoros of Cyme (q. v., second half of fourth century B. C.) who counted him among the Seven Wise Men: Anchor (with two arms), bellows, potter's wheel.

W. Schmid, in Pauly-Wissowa, t. 2, 1894, 2017–8.

GLAUCOS

Glaucos of Chios (Γλαῦκος) flourished probably about the time of Alyattes, King of Lydia, ruling from 617 to 560. (According to Herodotos; according to the Parian chronicle, Alyattes's reign began in 605; according to Eusebios, in 609). Greek technician. Inventor of the art of soldering iron (σιδήρου κόλλησις).

Pauly-Wissowa, vol. 13, 1910, 1421–1422.

CHERSIPHRON AND METAGENES

Chersiphron of Cnossos in Crete (Χερσίφρων), died probably before 546 B. C. Greek architect. He began the construction of the great Temple of Artemis at Ephesus. He invented a new method to transport the huge columns. His son Metagenes (Μεταγένης) continued the construction of the Temple and improved the method of transportation of columns and architraves and of putting them into place. They wrote a treatise on the subject (quoted by Vitruvius and Pliny).

Fabricius in Pauly-Wissowa, t. 6, 1899, 2241.

THEODOROS

Theodoros of Samos (Θεόδωρος) flourished at Ephesus at an uncertain date, possibly c. 532 B. C. Greek architect and engineer, to whom many inventions are ascribed: level, square rule, lathe, key. He is said to have introduced bronze casting from Egypt into Greece. He polished the natural surfaces of precious stones.[q] When the foundations of the Temple of Ephesus were being laid[r] he used various means to solidify the marshy ground.

[q] For the next step in the polishing of precious stones we have to wait until 1476. See my note on Berken (fifteenth century).

[r] This must be the second temple, or else Theodoros lived in the second half of the seventh century. It is possible also that the many inventions ascribed to one Theodoros were made by many men bearing the same name and possibly of the same family.

What little we know of him is derived from late sources: Pliny and Diogenes Laërtios (q. v., first half of the third century) and is very uncertain. The various inventions mentioned above may have been ascribed to him from a natural desire to account for their origin.

EUPALINOS

'Eupalinos of Megara (Εὐπαλῖνος) flourished in Samos, probably under Polycrates, who died in 522. Greek engineer, who built the extraordinary water-conduits of Samos, the remains of which were found in 1882. This water system included a tunnel about 1,000 meters long and 1.75 meters high and wide; at the bottom of the tunnel there was a trench, about 0.60 meter wide and reaching at the south end a depth of 8.30 meters, wherein the clay pipes were embedded. The construction of the tunnel was started from both ends.

The tunnel is described by Herodotos, III, 60. See Fabricius, in Pauly-Wissowa, t. 11, 1159, 1907. For the technical problems involved in the construction see Wilhelm Schmidt, Nivellierinstrument und Tunnelbau im Altertume, Bibliotheca Mathematica, t. 4, 7–12, 1903.

MANDROCLES

Mandrocles of Samos (Μανδροκλῆς) flourished c. 513 B. C. Greek engineer. When Darius I made his expedition against the Scythians in 513, Mandrocles built a bridge of boats across the Bosphorus for the passage of the Persian army (Herodotos, IV, 87–89). This is the earliest bridge of the kind on record.

VI. HINDU AND GREEK MEDICINE

HINDU MEDICINE

Hindu tradition places the earliest Hindu medical schools of Ātreya and Suśruta at some time in the sixth century, a date supported by the Vedas. I quote this statement from A. F. Rudolf Hoernlé (Studies in the Medicine of Ancient India, Oxford, 1907), who seems inclined to accept it. This opens the question whether Greek anatomy and medicine were influenced by Hindu anatomy and medicine, or were the Hindus influenced by the Greeks—a question which it will never be possible to solve entirely. As in the case of mathematics (see above, under Pythagoras) both developments may have been independent, or the influences exchanged may have been of a very general and vague nature.

It is impossible to date the activity of Ātreya and Suśruta with any precision. The date tentatively accepted by Hoernlé may be considered a terminus a quo; on the other hand, Suśruta is quoted in the Bower manuscript (c. 450) which gives us a terminus ad quem. Unfortunately these two limits are extremely distant. Keeping that in mind, we may recite the following Hindu tradition (preserved in the Buddhist Jātakas). In the age of the Buddha there existed two great universities in India, Kāśī (or Benares) in the East and Takṣaśilā (or Taxila on the Jhelam river) in the West. Ātreya, the physician, taught in the latter university, and his younger contemporary, Suśruta, the surgeon, in the former.

The work of Suśruta is one of the greatest of its kind in Sanskrit literature. It is especially important from the surgical point of view; it describes a number of operations (including extraction of cataract, removal of hernia, caesarean section, lithotomy, etc.) and contains the earliest accounts of plastic surgery and of surgical use of the magnet; it explains the particularities of a great many special instruments; it lays stress on the elaborate training which is needed to produce skillful surgeons. Other parts deal with anatomy, physiology, pathology, obstetrics, pediatrics. The work is marred by excessive scholasticism, the inordinate love of classifications. Stress is laid on careful diagnosis and a few diseases can be readily identified (e. g., diabetes mellitus). Some 760 medicinal plants are noted, many of them antidotes and aphrodisiacs; also soporifics such as henbane (*Hyosciamus niger*) and Indian hemp (*Cannabis indica;* hashish). Full attention is paid to diet and bathing.

For the tradition of the school of Ātreya, see my note on Caraka (first half of second century).

Text—The Suśruta or system of medicine taught by Dhanwantari and composed by his disciple Suśruta, edited by Sri Madhuṣūdana Gupta, 2 vols. Calcutta 1835–1836; Englished by Udoy Chānd Dutt and A. Chattopadhya, Calcutta, 1883–1891 (not completed); also by A. F. R. Hoernlé: The Suçruta-saṃhitā part 1, 98 p. (Calcutta, 1897). English translation of the Sushruta Saṃhita edited and published by Kaviraj Kunja Lal Bhishagratna (3 vols., Calcutta, 1907–1916; Isis, VII, 270).

Criticism—E. H. F. Meyer: Geschichte der Botanik (t. 3, 3–18, 1856). Iwan Bloch in Puschmann's Handbuch (t. 1, 1902, 131–133). A. F. R. Hoernlé: Studies in the Medicine of Ancient India (Oxford, 1907).

ALCMAEON

Alcmaeon of Crotona (Ἀλκμαίων), a younger contemporary of Pythagoras and perhaps his disciple. The most famous of the Greek physicians preceding Hippocrates; the Father of Greek medicine. His book (περὶ φύσεως) is lost and only a few fragments of his writings have remained. He was the first to make sections, discovered the optic nerve, distinguished in the cadaver empty veins (φλέβες) and veins carrying blood (αἱμόρροοι φλέβες), knew the trachea (ἀρτηρίη). He gave explanations of sleep, of the origin of sperm, of sense impressions, and made physiological experiments. He was first to recognize that the brain is the central organ of intellectual activity. Health and disease are respectively an equilibrium and a rupture of equilibrium of the organism (ἰσονομία vs. μοναρχία). Dualistic philosophy: everything in nature is a conflict between opposites (cf. Chinese and Iranian dualism).

Charles Daremberg: Etat de la médicine entre Homère et Hippocrate (Paris 1869). Max Wellmann: Fragmentsammlung der griechischen Aerzte (Berlin, 1901). Alessandro Olivieri: Alcmeone di Crotone (Memorie d. R. Accademia di Archeologia, vol. IV, 29 p., Napoli, 1917). G. M. Stratton: Theophrastus and the Greek Physiological Psychology before Aristotle (London, 1917). M. Wellmann: Über Träume (Archiv für Geschichte der Medizin, t. 16, 70–72, 1924).

DEMOCEDES

Democedes (Δημοκήδης), born at Crotona, flourished at Aegina, Athens, Samos, then at the court of Darius, King of Persia from 521 to 485, at Susa, finally at

Crotona. Greek physician; the most famous physician of his time. He cured Darius and the queen Atossa. Pythagorean.

Ludwig Weniger: Erlebnisse eines griechischen Arztes (32 p., Hamburg, 1890). E. Wellmann, in Pauly-Wissowa (t. 5, 132, 1903, the main source is Herodotos, III, 125, 129–138). P. Menetrier and R. Houdry: La guérison du cancer de la reine Atossa (Bull. soc. franc. hist. méd., t. 15, 285–289, 1921—it was not a real cancer; Isis, V, 204). Robert Houdry: La vie d'un mèdecin du vi[e] siecle. Démocédès (Thèse) (48 p., Paris, 1921).

VII. EGYPTIAN AND GREEK GEOGRAPHY

NECHO

Second king of the twenty-sixth Egyptian dynasty, ruled from 609 to 593. Toward the end of his reign he attempted to reëxcavate the ancient canal connecting the eastern arm of the Nile in the Delta with the Red Sea. This undertaking was interrupted, probably for fear of flooding Egypt, the engineers believing that the level of the Red Sea was higher than that of the Delta. He ordered a crew of Phoenician sailors to circumnavigate Libya (Africa) and this they accomplished within three years.

J. H. Breasted: History of Egypt (584, 1905).

HECATAEOS

Hecataeos of Miletos (Ἑκαταῖος), born about 550, died about 475. The author of a book called "Circuit of the Earth" (Γῆς περίοδος), which, if it is genuine—and it probably is—entitles him to be named the Father of Geography. Only fragments of it have remained. It embodied the Ionian knowledge of the earth and was divided into two parts: one on Europe, the other on Asia including Libya. Hecataeos is also supposed to have improved Anaximander's map. Herodotos drew extensively from him.

Text—Rud. Heinrich Klausen: Hecataei Milesii fragmenta et Scylacis Caryandensis periplus (324 p., map, Berlin, 1831). Müller: Fragmenta historicorum graecorum (I, p. IX–XVI, 1–31, Paris, 1841, with Latin translation, Didot collection).

Criticism—Giacomo Tropea: Ecateo ed i fragmenti della περιήγησις (70 + 55 p., Messina, 1896–1897). J. V. Prášek: Hekataios als Herodots Quelle zur Geschichte Vorderasiens (Klio, t. IV, p. 193–208, Leipzig, 1904). J. Wells: The Genuineness of the περίοδος of Hecataeus (Journal of Hellenic Studies, vol. 29, p. 41–52, London, 1909). Wells admits that Hecataeos has probably written his περίοδος, but holds that this work was lost at once, as was that of his famous contemporary, Scylax of Caryanda. The fragments that profess to come from it are the work of some forger of the third century, probably an Alexandrian. Bern. Schulze: De Hecataei fragnentis quae ad Italiam meridionalem spectant. (Diss., 117 p., Leipzig, 1912, with bibliogr.). Joseph Grossstephan: Beiträge zur Periegese des Hekatäus (Diss., 45 p., Strassburg, 1915).

VIII. CHINESE, HEBREW, AND GREEK HISTORIANS

For Chinese history, refer to my note on Confucius in section II.

Hebrew History

The Book of Judges[s] is unmistakably a product of the Deuteronomic school of the sixth century, though our present text has been revised by later editors. It deals with the period immediately following the conquest of Canaan by the Israelites led by Joshua (first half of the twelfth century?). In spite of too many handlings and interpolations, the historical value of Judges is great.

The Books of Kings[t] relate the history of the kings of Judah and Israel from the time of Solomon to the beginning of the post-exilic period (c. 971 to c. 561). The point of view is religious and didactic rather than political. The first draft of that history was certainly made before the fall of Jerusalem (586), possibly even before the beginning of the sixth century, though very close to it. This first version was permeated with the spirit of Deuteronomy, and it is safe to assume that the influence of that book was not felt at once after its discovery (621). A second version was made during the exile or soon after. The following tentative dates have been suggested: some time between 597 and 586 for the first, and between 561 and 536 for the second version. At any rate, it is clear that the editors were able to use historical material of great value; they were not unbiased, however, and they probably published only such materials as answered their religious purpose.

G. F. Moore: Commentary on Judges (Intern. crit. comm., New York, 1895). C. F. Burney: Notes on the Hebrew text of Kings (432 p., Oxford, 1903). Johann Döller: Geographische und ethnographische Studien zum 2. und 4. Buche der Könige (395 p., Wien, 1904).

Greek History—Cadmos

Cadmos of Miletos (Κάδμος Μιλήσιος) flourished about the middle of the sixth century B. C. The oldest historian about whom we have definite information. A history of the foundation of Miletos and of the whole of Ionia, in four books, is ascribed to him (Κτίσις Μιλήτου καὶ τῆς ὅλης Ἰωνίας). He wondered what caused the periodical floods of the Nile (Diodoros, I, 37, 3).

Text—C. Müller: Fragmenta historicorum graecorum (t. 2, 2–4).
Criticism—F. Jacoby, in Pauly-Wissowa (t. 10, 1473–6, 1919).

IX. GREEK, ROMAN, AND CHINESE LAW

Greek Law—Solon

Solon (Σόλων), Athenian, died c. 558, at the age of eighty. Legislator, statesman, poet, philosopher, one of the Seven Wise Men of Greece. He replaced, in 594, Dracon's drastic code (621) by one more humane. Reforms of the calendar, of weights and measures, and coinage are also ascribed to him.

Bruno Keil: Die Solonische Verfassung nach Aristoteles (Berlin, 1892). A full account of Solon's life and works has been given by Ivan M. Linforth: Solon the Athenian (325 p., Berkeley, 1919). It contains a critical biography, the text

---

[s] The eighth in the Christian Old Testament (in 21 chapters). It is also a part of the Jewish canon. The "Judges" (shōphēṭ) were leaders or rulers in Israel.

[t] Two books of the Christian Bible (in 47 chapters), but only one in the Hebrew canon. The division is purely arbitrary. There are some considerable differences between the Hebrew and the Greek texts.

and translation of Solon's poems and various appendixes, of which one offers an elaborate bibliography, and another a study of the changes in weights, measures, currency, and calendar ascribed to Solon (p. 287–297). Linforth's conclusion is that none of these changes can be proved to be really due to him. (See Journal of Hellenic studies, t. 40, 126).

Roman Law—Papirius

Sextus Papirius (flourished under the reign of Tarquinius Superbus, seventh and last king of Rome, from 534 to 510). Roman jurist who collected the leges regiae, thus forming what is called the Jus (Civile) Papirianum (lost). However, according to Mommsen, this Jus Papirianum is an apocryphal compilation made from pontifical records about the middle of the first century B. C.(?)

Chinese Law—Kung-sun Ch'iao

Kung¹-sun¹ Ch'iao² (6568, 10431, 1395). Also called Tzŭ³ Ch'an³ (12317, 360). His tablet was placed in the Confucian temple in 1857. Born in the State of Chêng⁴ (724), a part of modern Honan, a grandson of Duke Mu⁴* (8082); died in 521. Chinese statesman and jurist. He compiled, c. 535, a penal code which is said to be the foundation of Chinese criminal law.

H. A. Giles: Biographical Dictionary (1898, 394). Article "Law," by E. T. C. Werner, in Encyclopaedia Sinica, 291, 1917.

CHAPTER IV

THE TIME OF THE TWO HIPPOCRATES

(Fifth Century B. C.)

I. Brief survey of science in the fifth century B. C. II. Greek, Hebrew and Chinese philosophy. III. Greek mathematics. IV. Greek astronomy. V. Chinese, Persian, and Greek technicians. VI. Greek and Chinese medicine. VII. Carthaginian and Greek explorers. VIII. Greek and Hebrew mining. IX. Greek and Hebrew historiography. X. Hebrew, Greek, and Roman Law. XI. Greek, Sanskrit, and Chinese philology.

I. BRIEF SURVEY OF SCIENCE IN THE FIFTH CENTURY B. C.

1. The enormous intellectual activity of the sixth century was still to a very large extent unspecialized. There were of course physicians, engineers, lawgivers, and a few other "specialists," but the greatest intellectual effort was made by prophets and by natural philosophers, men who took as their province the whole of nature and the whole of humanity, past, present, and—future. It was a period of synthesis; we would be tempted to say, of premature synthesis, but every synthesis is in a way premature, however necessary it may be. The natural philosophers of the sixth and fifth centuries accomplished the first systematic exploration of nature; this daring feat stimulated the activities of the early men of science and caused their investigations to be easier and more fruitful.

The necessity of a provisional synthesis was still so great in the fifth century, at least in its first half, and some of the Greek philosophers of that time exerted such a powerful influence upon the progress, not simply of philosophy, but of scientific research in many directions, that I must begin my survey of the fifth century with a brief account of their work.

2. *Greek, Hebrew, and Chinese Philosophy*—Pythagorean philosophy was represented by Epicharmos, but chiefly by Philolaos (fl. c. 450), who was the first to publish the teachings of that school. Philolaos did much research in mathematics and physiology, but his outstanding contributions were in the field of astronomy, and therefore I deal with him below in section 4. About the beginning of the century, Heraclitos opened a stream of thought which is still flowing today: he may be called the father of relativism. Another powerful stream originates with the school of Parmenides: Zeno's paradoxes (c. 462) have exercised mathematical minds down to our days; Hippon tried to reconcile the teachings of Parmenides with those of Thales. Anaxagoras (c. 459), the last Ionian philosopher, stimulated scientific work in every direction, as well by his own investigations as by his encyclopaedic understanding. The same can be said of his Sicilian contemporary, Empedocles (c. 450), who originated the theory of four elements and proved the material nature of air. Archelaos, disciple of Anaxagoras, tried to explain heat and cold. Protagoras (c. 445), the first sophist and the first Greek grammarian, amplified the relativism of Heraclitos. The atomistic philosophy was founded about the middle of the century by Leucippos of Miletos and elaborated by his successor Democritos of Abdera (c. 420), the most synthetic mind of the period. To indicate the importance of this new philosophy, it will be enough to remark

that a history of atomism would provide one of the best cross-sections of the whole history of science. So much philosophizing had already taken place in Athens by the beginning of the second half of the century, scepticism and sophistry had been carried so far, that a reaction was bound to occur. The leader of that reaction was the genial Socrates, and his heroic death, in 399, was a splendid termination of that period, one of the greatest in the history of philosophy.

Hebrew philosophy of the same time was represented by the Book of Job; Chinese philosophy by Confucius's grandson, K'ung Chi, author of the Doctrine of the Mean, and by Mo Ti, the exponent of extreme altruism, said to be the founder of Chinese logic.

3. *Greek mathematics*—Students who are interested only in the history of a special branch of science ought to refer to the sections dealing with the other branches and chiefly to the more general sections. Thus, the historian of mathematics ought to read the paragraphs devoted to the philosophers Zeno, Philolaos, who studied the regular solids, and Democritos, who determined the volume of the pyramid and cone.

But the fifth century, as I said above, saw the beginning of scientific specialization, and, for instance, we meet already a number of fully differentiated mathematicians. In the first place, Hippocrates of Chios (c. 450–430), one of the greatest mathematicians of all times, the first to reduce geometrical knowledge to a system. Oenopides of Chios solved various geometrical problems; Hippias of Elis (of Platonic fame) discovered the quadratrix (c. 420); Theodoros of Cyrene developed the theory of irrational numbers; Antiphon and Bryson, following Anaxagoras, prepared the way for the discovery of the method of exhaustion.

4. *Greek astronomy*—The Pythagorean philosopher Philolaos (c. 450) published the astronomical views of his school, and his account is probably the earliest attempt to give a complete and scientific explanation of the movements of the celestial bodies. The Pythagoreans knew that the earth is a sphere, and so did the philosopher Parmenides, but the other Greek philosophers do not seem to have shared that conviction. A disciple of Philolaos, Hicetas of Syracuse, went so far as to suggest the diurnal rotation of the earth around its axis. The mathematician Oenopides of Chios (c. 439) discovered (or rediscovered) the obliquity of the ecliptic and introduced into Greece the astronomical period of 59 years. Meton of Athens discovered a shorter period, the "Metonic cycle" of 19 years. In 432 Meton and Euctemon improved the accuracy of solstitial observations.

5. *Chinese, Persian, and Greek Technicians*—Sun Wu wrote, probably c. 500, a treatise on the art of war, which was very influential in the Far East. The Persian Artachaees built a canal across the Athos peninsula in 480. Agatharchos of Samos (c. 439) developed the art of perspective with special regard to theatrical needs. Hippodamos of Miletos (c. 450) may be called the founder of scientific town-planning.

6. *Greek and Chinese Medicine*—Many of the philosophers dealt with in section 2 were deeply interested in anatomy, physiology, and medicine: Anaxagoras, Archelaos, Empedocles, Democritos, Philolaos (see section 4). Still another philosopher, Diogenes of Apollonia, paid so much attention to anatomy and medicine that I preferred to deal with him in this section; he made a special study of the vascular system.

There were already in this period three famous schools of medicine: the schools of Cos and of Cnidos in Ionia and the school of Sicily. The school of Cos is of course the most famous of all, because it was there that the Father of Medicine, Hippocrates, flourished toward the end of the century. The very long note devoted to Hippocrates and the Hippocratic Corpus is preceded by a briefer one devoted to Hippocrates's teacher, Herodicos, the earliest expounder of the medical value of gymnastics and physical exercise. It is not necessary to insist upon the supreme importance of the Hippocratic doctrines, whatever their origin. The school of Cnidos gave us two great physicians: Euryphon, editor of the "Cnidian sentences," and Ctesias, better known (see below) as one of the earliest historians of Persia and India. Finally, the school of Sicily, founded by Empedocles, produced at least one other great physician, Acron (c. 430).

The only Chinese physician with whom I could deal is Pien Ch'iao, who flourished in the State of Chêng, possibly in the first half of the century. He was probably the author of the Nan ching, one of the most popular treatises on medicine. He is said to have discovered the Chinese theory of the pulse. It is noteworthy that Diogenes, who flourished in the second half of the century, had also some knowledge of the pulse.

7. *Carthaginian and Greek Explorers*—A Carthaginian fleet, led by Hanno, explored the western coast of Africa, reaching the latitude of c. 7° 30′ North. Another Carthaginian expedition, led by Himilco, explored the western coast of Europe and reached the "Tin Islands."

Scylax of Caryanda, who flourished under Darius I, made a coasting survey of the Mediterranean Basin.

The philosopher Anaxagoras gave the first correct explanation of the rising of the Nile.

8. *Greek and Hebrew Mining*—The exploitation of the Laurium silver mines was especially intense during the fifth and fourth centuries, and this helps to explain the political and artistic history of Athens. Brief references to the mining of gold and silver and to precious stones are found in the Book of Job, chapter 28.

9. *Greek and Hebrew Historiography*—This century witnessed the activity of two of the greatest historians of all times: Herodotos of Halicarnassos (c. 444), whose work contains a large amount of ethnographic information, and the Athenian Thucydides (c. 420). Ctesias of Cnidos, who flourished in Persia from 417 to 398, wrote valuable accounts of Persia and India.

The Hexateuch (that is, the Pentateuch, the Hebrew Torah, plus Joshua) was essentially constituted about the middle of the century. It is not simply an account of early Jewish history; it contains almost all that we know of Hebrew cosmogony and Hebrew law. Ezra flourished about the middle of the century, and Nehemiah a little later (c. 438). The books of the Old Testament bearing their names are later (third century B. C.) productions based upon their own memoirs.

10. *Hebrew, Greek, and Roman Law*—The source for the study of Hebrew law is the Pentateuch, dealt with in the previous section.

The inscriptions found at Gortyn in Crete give us specific instances of early Greek law (fifth and fourth centuries).

The "Twelve Tables," the new code prepared by order of the Roman Republic upon Greek models, was completed in 450.

11. *Greek, Sanscrit, and Chinese Philology*—The earliest European grammarian was the sophist Protagoras (c. 445), dealt with in the second section.

The earliest Sanscrit grammarian was Yāska, who flourished about the beginning of the sūtra period. He wrote the Nirukta, a philological commentary on the Vedas. The Brāhmi alphabet, so perfect, existed already in the fifth century.

The earliest Chinese dictionary, the Êrh Ya, was probably compiled by Tzŭ Hsia, a disciple of Confucius, born in 507.

12. *Final Remarks*—I entitled this chapter "the Time of the Two Hippocrates," because from the point of view of positive science, Hippocrates of Chios and Hippocrates of Cos were by far the two greatest personalities of that period. But the title is a little misleading, because, strictly speaking, the time when these two great men flourished was the second half of the century; the mathematician flourished in the third quarter, and the physician in the last quarter.

In a more general way, we may observe that the most important scientific work of the century was done during its second half. The first half of the century was still very much, like the preceding century, an age of brilliant generalizations and reckless hypotheses: Heraclitos, Parmenides, Zeno, Anaxagoras, and Empedocles belong to it. This kind of activity was not entirely suspended during the latter half of the century, witness the birth of atomic philosophy; but the healthy reaction initiated by Socrates might be considered a scientific reaction against premature and excessive philosophizing. Then, if we place the "floruit" of each man in his fortieth year according to ancient usage, we find that practically all of the Greek mathematical, astronomical, and medical work was done about the middle and during the second half of the century. The great historians too, Herodotos (c. 444), Thucydides, and Ctesias, as well as Ezra and Nehemiah, belong to that second half.

This century (even more the second half of it) was essentially a Greek century. A few achievements are due to men of other races, but they are comparatively so small that they do not affect the general atmosphere of the picture, which is Greek. This again justifies my Greek title.

II. GREEK, HEBREW, AND CHINESE PHILOSOPHY

Greek Philosophy

It is hardly necessary to refer to the "Greek Thinkers" of Theodor Gomperz and to other standard works quoted in section 4 of chapter iii, but the following studies specially devoted to the fifth century are less known and deserve to be mentioned:

A. E. Taylor: Parmenides, Zeno and Socrates (Proc. of the Aristotelian Society, vol. 16, p. 234–289, London, 1916; Isis, III, 317). John Walter Beardslee: The Use of φύσις in fifth century Greek Literature (Thesis, 126 p., Chicago, 1918).

EPICHARMOS

Ἐπίχαρμος. Born in the island of Cos in the second half of the sixth century, of an Asclepiades family; flourished in Megara, Sicily, and from c. 484 in Syracuse; died at the age of ninety. Greek poet and playwright. The founder of Greek comedy. Pythagorean philosopher and physician (?). Ennius devoted to him one of his philosophical poems.

Text—H. Polman Kruseman: Epicharmi fragmenta (144 p., Haarlem, 1834). F. W. A. Mullach: Fragmenta philosophorum graecorum (Paris, Didot, 1860). Aug. O. Fr. Lorenz: Leben und Schriften des Koers Epicharmos nebst einer Fragmentensammlung (Berlin, 1864).

Criticism—M. Croiset. Littérature grecque (t. 3, 2d ed., p. 440–456, 1899.)

For Philolaos, the greatest representative of Pythagorean doctrine in those days, see section 4.

HERACLITOS

Heraclitos of Ephesos (Ἡράκλειτος) flourished in Ephesos, Ionia, about the beginning of the fifth century. A poet and philosopher rather than a scientist, yet he deeply influenced scientific thought. He was younger than Pythagoras and Xenophanes, but older than Parmenides. Three main ideas: (1) Fire is the principle of all things; (2) everything flows (πάντα ῥεῖ), that is, the principle of relativity of all things; (3) the apparent disharmony of the world hides a profound harmony—for every change happens in concordance with a law universal (λόγος); the apparent strifes of opposites are the opposite tensions which hold the world together.

Text—Hermann Diels: Herakleitos von Ephesos (Griechisch und deutsch, 2te Aufl., 100 p., Berlin, 1909, 1st ed., 1901). Emilio Bodrero: Eraclito. Testimonianze e frammenti (246 p., Torino, 1910, with elaborate bibliography).

Criticism—Oswald Spengler: Der metaphysische Grundgedanke der heraklitischen Philosophie (Diss., 52 p., Halle, a. S., 1904). A. Brieger: Die Grundzüge der heraklitischen Physik (Hermes, t. 39, 182–223, 1904). Wolfgang Schultz: Pythagoras und Heraklit (118 p., Leipzig, 1905). Emanuel Loew: Das heraklitische Wirklichkeitsproblem und seine Umdeutung bei Sextus (Gymn. Progr., 34 p., Wien, 1914). Pierre Bise: La politique d'Héraclite (284 p., Paris, 1925; Isis, VIII, 529). P. Tannery: Mémoires, 7, 103–107, 141–145, 1925 (Isis, IX).

PARMENIDES

Parmenides of Elea, southern Italy (Παρμενίδης), lived in the first half of the fifth century. He came to Athens at the age of fifty-six, about the middle of the century. What is (τὸ ἐόν) is a finite, spherical, motionless, continuous plenum, and there is nothing beyond it. There is neither coming into being nor ceasing to be. This radicalism encouraged both scientific research and scepticism. The sole philosopher of his time, outside of the Pythagoreans (perhaps he had been one himself?) to recognize the spherical form of the earth. Divides the earth into five zones. The universe is made up of concentric layers, of which the earth is the nucleus.

Text—Hermann Diels: Parmenides Lehrgedicht griechisch und deutsch. Mit einem Anhang über griechische Thüren und Schlösser (164 p., Berlin, 1897).

Criticism—Ernst Friedrich Apelt: Parmenidis et Empedoclis doctrina de mundi structura (14 p., 1 pl., Jena, 1857). Karl Reinhardt: Parmenides und die Geschichte der griechischen Philosophie (Bonn, 1916).

ZENO OF ELEA*

Ζήνων, flourished about 462. Pupil of Parmenides, he fortified his master's doctrine by showing that the admission of plurality and change leads to contradiction. Attacked especially the reality of motion and analyzed geometrical continuity. Zeno's paradoxes on time, space, and number contributed to increase logical and mathematical rigor. They have acted as a ferment even until our days. Only a few short fragments of his remain.

---

* Or Velia in Lucania, Italy.

Charles Dunan: Les arguments de Zénon contre le mouvement (45 p., Paris, 1884). Bertrand Russell: Principles of mathematics (Cambridge, 1903). Florian Cajori: The History of Zeno's Arguments on Motion. Phases in the Development of the Theory of Limits (American Mathematical Monthly, vol. 22, passim, 1915). Ph. E. B. Jourdain: The Flying Arrow, an Anachronism (Mind, vol. 25, p. 42–55, Aberdeen, 1916; Isis, III, 277). Fl. Cajori: The Purpose of Zeno's Arguments on Motion (Isis, III, 7–20, 1920, wherein many other references will be found).

HIPPON

Ἵππων (short for Ἱππῶναξ), from Lower Italy or from Samos, flourished in Athens in the second third of the fifth century B. C. Greek philosopher who tried to reconcile the teachings of Parmenides with those of Thales. According to him, the moist (τὸ ὑγρόν) was the first principle. Various physiological and pathological facts were explained by him as processes of desiccation or humidification.

Robert Fuchs in Puschmann's Geschichte der Medizin (t. 1, 171, 1902). Theodor Gomperz: Greek Thinkers (vol. 1, 377, 573, 1906). E. Wellmann, in Pauly-Wissowa (t. 16, p. 1889, 1913).

ANAXAGORAS

Anaxagoras of Clazomenae (Ἀναξαγόρας), born about 499, died about 428 at Lampsacos. The last philosopher of the Ionian school. Introduced the scientific spirit into Athens. Founded a school in Lampsacos, Troad. Many fragments from his book on nature (περὶ φύσεως) remain. There is neither coming into being nor ceasing to be, but only commixtures (συμμίσγεσθαι) and decompositions (διακρίνεσθαι). The universe was originally a chaos of innumerable seeds (σπέρματα) to which Mind (νοῦς) gave order and form by a movement of rotation (περιχώρησις). Deeply interested in anatomy and medicine. Made experiments and practiced dissection of animals. Dissected the brain and recognized its lateral ventricles. Acute diseases are caused by black or yellow bile which permeates the blood and the organs. Attempt to square the circle. Beginning of the theory of perspective (for theatrical purposes). The great meteoric stone which fell in 468–67 at Aegos Potamoi was said by him to have fallen from the sun. The world began by a vortex set up by Mind; complete cosmogony based upon this vortex theory, which is to some extent a very crude anticipation of Kant and Laplace. The sun is a red-hot stone on fire, larger than the Peloponnese; the moon receives its light from the sun; it is of the same nature as the earth and has in it plains and ravines. The earth and other planets are flat. Explanation of sun and moon eclipses by the interposition of moon, earth, or other bodies. Various other astronomical theories, remarkable but incorrect, and sometimes contradictory. Correct explanation of the annual rising of the Nile: melting of snow in Aethiopia.

Max Heinze: Über den νοῦς des Anaxagoras (45 p., Ber. d. Kgl. Sächs. Gesell. d. Wissensch., 1890). H. Diels: Alte und neue Kämpfe um die Freiheit der Wissenschaft (Internationale Wochenschrift f. Wissenschaft u. Technik p. 2–10, 1908). Aldo Mieli: La teoria di Anaxagora e la chimica moderna (Isis, I, p. 370–376, 1913; Le teorie delle sostanze nei presokratici greci—Parte 2 da. Anaxagora e gli atomisti (Scientia, t. 14, p. 329–344, 1913). Felix Löwy-Cleve: Die Philosophie des Anaxagoras, Versuch einer Rekonstruction, 111 p., Wien, 1917).

ARCHELAOS

Archelaos of Athens (Ἀρχέλαος), disciple of Anaxagoras. Philosopher who contributed to the elaboration of medical theory. Combined the ideas of his master with those of earlier philosophers. He explained heat and cold by the condensation and rarefaction of the original substance, air (cfr. Anaximenes). (The notions of heat and cold recur continually in ancient physiology and pathology.) The air was not simply the origin of matter but also of mind (νοῦς); he thus avoided Anaxagoras's dualism (cfr. Diogenes of Apollonia).

EMPEDOCLES

Empedocles of Acragas (Agrigentum, Sicily) (Ἐμπεδοκλῆς), born about 490, died in the Peloponnese about 435. There is an uncertain tradition according to which he died by approaching too close to the crater of Etna. Poet, philosopher, physicist, physician, social reformer. He soon became a legendary hero. Postulated the existence of four elements or roots (ῥιζώματα), fire, air, water, earth, and of two moving forces, love (φιλία) and strife (νεῖκος). Phases of synthesis and disintegration follow in the world's evolution as the former or the latter force dominates. Proved experimentally the corporeality of air. Discovered the labyrinth of the ear. First to formulate a theory of the flux and reflux of blood from and to the heart. These tides constitute the respiratory rhythm. Respiration takes place not simply through the lungs but through the whole skin. Importance of blood-vessels, blood being the carrier of innate heat. Sense impressions are caused by effluxes from the objects, but are not merely passive. Vague notion of organic evolution and adaptation. Founder of the medical school of Sicily. Health is conditional upon the equilibrium of the four elements in the body. First Greek mention of the use of water-clocks (clepsydra). Empedocles conceived the heavens as an egg-shaped surface made of crystal; the fixed stars are attached to it, but the planets are free. Various original but incorrect views on astronomy are ascribed to him. He believed that light moves in space with a finite velocity.

Aug. Gladisch: Empedokles und die Aegypter (160 p., Leipzig, 1858). J. Bidez: La biographie d'Empédocle (188 p., Gand, 1894, apparently exhaustive). Emilio Bodrero: Il principio fondamentale del sistema di Empedocle. Preceduto da un saggio bibliografico e dalla traduzione dei frammenti empedoclei (175 p., Roma, 1904). Clara Elizabeth Millerd: On the interpretation of Empedocles (Diss., 94 p., Chicago, 1908). W. Kranz: Empedokles und die Atomistik (Hermes, t. 47, 18–42, 1912). Ettore Bignone: Empedocle—Studio critico, traduzione e commenti delle testimonianze e dei frammenti. (700 p., Torino, 1916). Walter Veazie: Empedocles' psychological doctrine (Archives of Philosophy, No. 14, 27 p., New York, 1922; Isis, V, 491).

D. N. Mallik: Optical Theories, Cambridge, 1917; first chapter contains a statement of Empedocles's theory of vision and an interesting comparison with Nyāya speculations. The Nyāya sūtra was written, according to Mallik, between 500 and 200 B. C. It is well-nigh impossible to find which of the theories, Greek or Indian, preceded the other, and whether they influenced one another. Similar theories may have developed independently in both countries or the influence may have been very vague.

PROTAGORAS

Πρωταγόρας, born at Abdera in Thrace, c. 485; traveled extensively in the Greek world; died in 411. The first of the sophists.[a] He carried the relativism of Heraclitos one step further. His works are lost. One of them was probably entitled Truth (Ἀλήθεια), another, Art (Τέχνη), the former possibly more theoretical, the latter more practical. He taught that man is the measure of all things. He seems to have been the first to attempt a logical analysis of language, that is, the first grammarian: he distinguished genders of nouns and certain tenses and modes. Pericles intrusted to him the writing of a constitution for the new colony of Thurii (c. 445). The Hippocratic work on The Art (of medicine), περὶ τέχνης, has been ascribed to him (by Gomperz); but this ascription is doubtful.

Text—Handy edition of the περὶ τέχνης by W. H. S. Jones, in the Hippocrates of the Loeb Library, vol. 2, 1923, 186–217 (Isis, VII, 175).
Criticism—Theodor Gomperz: Griechische Denker: Bd. 1^2, 352–380, 1903. Philipp Illmann: Die Philosophie des Protagoras nach der Darstellung Platos (Progr., Friedland i. Meckl., 1908). Emilio Bodrero: Protagora (2 vols., Bari, 1914). Benedict Lachmann: Protagoras, Nietzsche, Stirner (71 p., Berlin, 1914).

LEUCIPPOS

Leucippos of Miletos (?) (Λεύκιππος). Philosopher, contemporary of Anaxagoras and Empedocles. Founder with his successor Democritos of the atomic theory. Aristotle considered him the real author of this theory.

On the controversy as to the existence of Leucippos started by E. Rohde in 1880, see P. Bokownew: Die Leukippfrage (19 p., Dorpat, 1911).

DEMOCRITOS

Democritos of Abdera (Δημόκριτος) flourished about 420, born about 460 in Abdera, Thrace, died about 370. Disciple and successor of Leucippos, from whose views his own are difficult to distinguish. One must speak of the atomistic philosophy as a joint creation of both. Only a few lines of Leucippos but considerable fragments of Democritos have remained. Democritos might be called the Aristotle of the fifth century; his practical and constructive point of view as contrasted with the increasing scepticism of his age also suggests a comparison with Socrates. Greek atomism was not inspired by Indian atomism, as the Vaiśeshika and Nyāya systems are certainly of a much later date[b] (see R. Garbe: Das Sāṃkhya-Philosophie, Leipzig, 1894, p. 87). The atomists distinguish between the full (πλῆρες, στερεόν) and the empty, the vacuum (κενόν, μανόν). They were the first to affirm the existence of empty space. The full consists of an infinity of indestructible atoms (ἄτομα), differing from one another in shape, order, and inclination, that is, only geometrically. Mechanical explanation of the universe. Vague anticipation of the notions of conservation of matter and energy. Democritos studied mathematical continuity and discovered that the volumes of a pyramid and a cone are the third of the volumes of a prism and a cylinder, respectively, which have the same base and height. Investigated the anatomy of the chameleon, the physiology of the senses and of reproduction, the pulse (φλεβοπαλία), explained inflammation (by an accumulation of phlegm), hydro-

[a] The first to teach for payment.
[b] However, see my remark on Jaina atomism in my note on Mahāvīra (sixth century B. C.).

phobia, epidemic contagion. Books on psychotherapy and musical therapeutics are ascribed to him.

Democritos explained dreams as due to the influence of simulacra of other beings or objects upon the soul of the sleeper. This is the earliest explicit theory of dreams, but the interpretation of dreams goes back of course to a remote antiquity both in Mesopotamia and Egypt; it was certainly practiced in the healing temples of the Greek world (at least from the sixth century on). After Democritos almost every encyclopaedic philosopher or physician dealt with dreams; —the science of dreams (oneirology, oneirocriticism) or the art of interpreting the future by their means (oneiromancy), a pseudoscience, which was gradually involved in astrology, obtained great importance until the end of the Middle Ages, and is still lingering. As my aim is to describe the progress of science, rather than the undercurrents and aberrations which accompanied it, I will not attempt to give a full account of oneirology, but will mention as I come to them some of the most important works dealing with it.

For a general statement of the subject see Paul Diepgen: Traum und Traumdeutung als medizinisch-naturwissenschaftliches Problem im Mittelalter (43 p. Berlin, 1912). Lynn Thorndike: History of Magic (vol. 2, 290–302, 1923). M. Wellmann: Über Träume: Archiv für Geschichte der Medizin (t. 16, 70–72, 1924).

Paul Tannery: Démocrite et Archytas (Bull. des sciences math., t. X, p. 295–303, 1886). Paul Natorp: Die Ethika des Demokritos. Text und Untersuchungen (206 p., Marburg, 1893). Albert Goedemeyer: Epikurs Verhältnis zu Demokrit in der Naturphilosophie (158 p., Strassburg, 1897). Adolf Dyroff: Demokritstudien (188 p., Leipzig, 1899, with bibliography). A. Brieger: Demokrits angebliche Leugnung der Sinneswahrheit (Hermes, vol. 37, p. 56–83, 1902.) A. Dyroff: Über die Abhängigkeit des Aristoteles von Demokritos (Philologus, Bd. 63, p. 41–53, 1904). Adolf Brieger: Die Urbewegung der demokritischen Atome (Philologus, Bd. 63, p. 584–596, Leipzig, 1904). L. Löwenheim: Die Wissenschaft Demokrits und ihr Einfluss auf die moderne Naturwissenschaft (256 p., Berlin, 1914). Heinrich Laue: De Democriti fragmentis ethicis (Diss., 134 p., Göttingen, 1921). Michel Stephanides: Περὶ τοῦ χυμευτοῦ Δημοκρίτου. (Δελτίον ἑταιρ, vol. 2, 122–125; Isis, VII, 176).

The Georgica ascribed to Democritos by Diogenes Laërtios (IX, 48) and quoted by Columella (Res rustica, XI, 3, 2) is probably a work of Bolos Democritos who flourished c. 200 B.C.[c] See M. Wellmann: Die Georgica des Demokritos (Abhd. der preuss. Ak. der Wiss., phil. Kl., 58 p., 1921, including the text of all extant fragments; Isis, V, 205).

Hermann Diels: Über die auf den Namen des Demokritos gefälschten Schriften (Berlin Ak., Sitzungsber., 1902). M. Wellmann: Pseudodemocritea Vaticana (Berlin Ak., Sitzungsber., t. 31, 625–30, 1908). I. Heeg: Pseudodemokritische Studien (Abhdl. d. preuss. Ak., phil. Kl., 59 p., 1913; text of the first century?).

SOCRATES

Σωκράτης, born in Athens c. 470, died there in 399. Philosopher; teacher of Plato. He embodied the revolt of Greek common sense against the intellectual extravagances of the early philosophers. Although he distrusted science—brought into disrepute by the sophists—few men have contributed more to its development. His method of investigation prepared the elaboration of the

[c] On this Bolos (Βόλος) of Mendes, Egypt, see also E. H. F. Meyer: Geschichte der Botanik (t. 1, 277–84, 1854); and Wellmann's article in Pauly-Wissowa (t. 5, 1897, 676).

method of inductive science; it was characterized by: insistence upon clear definition; use of induction; incessant war against vagueness of thought; deep sense of duty; reasoned skepticism (the very skepticism of the scientist who refuses to believe a thing until it has been proved to him). Socrates's moderation, his wisdom, make one think of the masterpieces of the sculptors of his time.

A large part of the immense literature devoted to Socrates deals with the discussion of the conflicting traditions concerning him. Do we have to believe Plato rather than Xenophon, and why? It is impossible to separate the books dealing with this unsolvable problem from the others, for any author writing on Socrates has been obliged to consider it, however briefly, and to make a stand.

Alfred Fouillée: La philosophie de Socrate (2 vol., Paris, 1874). George Grote: Plato and the Other Companions of Socrates (New ed., 4 vol., London, 1888). August Döring: Die Lehre des Sokrates als sociales Reformsystem (625 p., München, 1895; based exclusively upon Xenophon's "Memorabilia"). Edmund Pfleiderer: Sokrates und Plato (937 p., Tübingen, 1896). Karl Joël: Der echte und der Xenophontische Sokrates (2. t. in 3 vols., Berlin, 1893–1901). Hubert Röck: Der unverfälschte Sokrates—Der Atheist und Sophist und das Wesen aller Philosophie und Religion (546 p., Innsbruck, 1903). Léon Robin: Les Mémorables de Xénophon et notre connaissance de la philosophie de Socrate (L'année philosophique, vol. 21, p. 1–47, Paris, 1911). A. E. Taylor: Varia Socratica (Oxford, 1911). G. C. Field: Socrates and Plato—A Criticism of Taylor's Socratica (40 p., Oxford, 1913). Heinrich Maier: Sokrates. Sein Werk und seine geschichtliche Stellung (650 p., Tübingen, 1913). John Burnet: The Socratic Doctrine of the Soul (Proc. British Academy, Vol. VII, 27 p., London, 1916). Ch. P. Parker: The Historical Socrates in the Light of Burnet's Hypothesis (Harvard Studies in Classical Philology, vol. 27, p. 67–75, Cambridge, Mass., 1916). A. E. Taylor: Plato's Biography of Socrates (Proc. British Academy, vol. 8, 40 p., London, 1917). Taylor, like Burnet, believes that the Platonic Socrates is the real one; the last-mentioned paper is an interesting attempt to reconstruct Socrates's biography on the basis of Plato's dialogues exclusively. An implication of this theory is that the Platonic dialogues represent to a larger extent Socrates's thought. That is, one can not find the real Socrates in that way, without losing what one used to regard as the real Plato. G. Lefèvre: Sur l'historicité de Socrate (Congrès internat. d'histoire de Bruxelles, 1923). Eugène Dupréel: La légende socratique et les sources de Platon (Bruxelles, 1922). Miles Menander Dawson: The Ethics of Socrates (382 p., New York, 1924; anthology with commentary, Isis, VIII, 529).

Hebrew Philosophy

One of the greatest books of the world's literature, the Book of Job, was written in Palestine during the Persian domination, or possibly at the beginning of the Greek period. The most plausible date is the fifth century. Its burden is to show that suffering is not necessarily retributive and that the justice of God is impenetrable.

The Book of Job is a part of the Old Testament canon. It contains 42 chapters. It is of very great importance to us because of the scientific spirit which permeates it. Interesting allusions to ancient mining are found in chapter 28.

John Owen: The Five Great Skeptical Dramas of History (405 p., London, 1896. Prometheus vinctus; Job; Faust; Hamlet; El magico prodigioso). Carl Fries: Das philosophische Gespräch von Hiob bis Platon (Tübingen, 1904). Joseph H.

Wicksteed: Blake's Vision of the Book of Job (168 p., pl., London, 1910). S. R. Driver and G. B. Gray: Commentary on Job, together with a new translation (2 vols., New York, 1921).

Chinese Philosophy

K'UNG CHI[d]

K'ung[3] Chi[2]* (6605, 842). Born c. 500, flourished in the state of Lu[3] (7388). Chinese philosopher. Grandson and disciple of Confucius. Author of the Chung[1] yung[1] (2875, 13462) Doctrine of the Mean,[e] one of the Four Books. The Great Learning,[f] Ta[4] hsüeh[2]* (10470, 4839), another of the Four Books, is also ascribed to him.

Text—Legge: Chinese Classics (vol. 1, Hongkong, 1861, Chinese and English). Séraphin Couvreur: Les Quatre Livres (2 ed., Ho Kien Fou, 1–67, 1910, Chinese, Latin, and French). Both texts have been included in the Li[3] chi[4] (6949, 923) (Record of Rites[g]) one of the Five Classics, which was completely translated into English by Legge in 1885 (Sacred Books of the East, vol. 27, 28) and into French by Father Couvreur.
Criticism—H. A. Giles: Biographical Dictionary (397, 1898).

MO TI[h]

Mo[4]* Ti[2]* (8022, 10932). Flourished in the state of Sung some time after Confucius and before Mencius. Chinese philosopher. He combined utilitarian views with extreme altruism. Founder of Chinese logic.

Text—Only 53 books or chapters of his works are extant. Ernst Faber published an analysis, chapter by chapter—Die Grundgedanken des alten chinesischen Sozialismus (102 p., Elberfeld, 1877). English translation of Faber's summary by Kupfer, Shanghai, 1897. First complete translation (in German) with elaborate introduction by Alfred Forke (652 p., Berlin, 1923; Isis, VI, 138).
Criticism—James Legge: Chinese Classics (t. 2, 103–125). Salv. Cognetti de Martiis: Un socialista cinese del v. sec. av. C. Atti della r. acc. d. Lincei (Mem. vol. 3, 248–281, 1887). Alexandra David: Le philosophe Meh-ti et l'idée de solidarité (185 p., London, 1907).

III. GREEK MATHEMATICS

The historian of mathematics ought to read the notes devoted to Zeno and Democritos in Section II and the one devoted to Philolaos in Section IV.

HIPPOCRATES OF CHIOS

Ἱπποκράτης. Flourished in Athens about 450 to 430. One of the greatest Greek mathematicians. Made a deep study of the quadrature and duplication problems. The former problem led him to the quadrature of the lunes (the first curvilinear figures to be squared, and by the way, the only ones which can be squared in an elementary manner). He reduced the latter problem to finding two mean proportionals between one straight line and another twice as long. Wrote the first

[d] Or Tzŭ[3] Ssŭ[1] (12317, 10271). His tablet was placed in the Confucian temple in 1108.
[e] This title is translated also: The middle way; the universal order; l'invariable milieu; etc.
[f] Or Learning for adults; la grande étude.
[g] This compilation reached its present form probably in the second century of our era.
[h] Or Mo[4]* Tzŭ[3] (8022, 12317); also written Mih, Meh, Mu. Latin form Micius.

text-book of geometry; may have been the first to use letters in geometrical figures, which implied a great progress in scientific symbolism (possibly inspired by the Pythagorean pentagon); invented the method of geometrical reduction (ἀπαγωγή), even perhaps the reductio ad absurdum (ἡ εἰς τὸ ἀδύνατον ἀπαγωγή), and may have used it to prove Euclid XII, 2 (circles are to one another as the squares of their diameters).

Ferdinand Rudio: Der Bericht des Simplicius über die Quadraturen des Antiphon und des Hippokrates. Griechisch und Deutsch. Mit einem historischen Erläuterungsberichte als Einleitung, im Anhange ergänzende Urkunden, verbunden durch eine Übersicht über die Geschichte des Problems von der Kreisquadratur vor Euclid (194 p., Leipzig, 1907). This publication supersedes all previous ones excepting the account included in Cantor's "Vorlesungen," Stillcke: Der Lehrsatz des Hippokrates und die Geometrie krummliniger Figuren des Leonardo da Vinci (Zeitschrift f. math. Unterricht, t. 41, p. 203–207, 1910).

OENOPIDES

Oenopides of Chios (Οἰνοπίδης), a younger contemporary of Anaxagoras. Mathematician, astronomer. Gave new constructions to the two following problems: to draw a perpendicular to a given line from an outside point (Euclid I, 12); to construct on a given line an angle equal to another (Euclid I, 23). He (or Pythagoras) discovered the obliquity of the ecliptic. He introduced into Greece the "great year" (μέγας ἐνιαύτος) of 59 years, or he rediscovered it himself. (Assuming the lengths of the year and the month to be 365 and $29\frac{1}{2}$ days, 59 is the least integral number of years which contains an exact number (730) of lunations. 730 lunations equal 21,557 days. Thus each year of the Great Year would count $365\frac{22}{59}$ days, that is, a little less than 365 days, 9 hours.)

Paul Tannery: La tradition touchant Pythagore, Oenopides et Thalès (Bull. des sciences mathémat., t. x, p. 115–128, Paris, 1886). J. L. E. Dreyer: History of the Planetary Systems (p. 38, Cambridge, 1906). Pierre Duhem: Le système du monde (I, p. 72, Paris, 1913). Sir Thomas Heath: Aristarchus (130–133, 1913).

HIPPIAS

Hippias of Elis (Ἱππίας). Flourished c. 420. Sophist, mathematician. Chiefly known through the two Platonic dialogues bearing his name. Discovered about 420 a curve by means of which an angle might be trisected. The curve was used later by Dinostratos to square the circle and called by him quadratrix.

See Cantor's "Vorlesungen" (Vol. I, 3d ed., 1906) and Gino Loria: Le scienze esatte nell' antica Grecia (2d ed., 1914). W. Zilles: Hippias aus Elis (Hermes, t. 53, 45–56, Berlin, 1918. Supplementing the information given by Gomperz; no reference to his mathematical work).

THEODOROS

Theodoros of Cyrene (Θεόδωρος). Flourished in Athens at the end of the fifth century. Mathematician, Pythagorean, teacher of Plato in mathematics. Showed that the square roots of 3 and other non-square numbers up to 17 are irrational. Some would ascribe the first notion of irrationality to him, and not to Pythagoras. But the fact that he is not quoted as having proved the irrationality of $\sqrt{2}$, implies that this was known before, probably by Pythagoras (diagonal of a square).

Heinrich Vogt: Die Geometrie des Pythagoras (Bibliotheca Mathematica, t. IX, p. 14–54, Leipzig, 1908), denying Pythagoras's authorship of this discovery. T. L. Heath: The Thirteen Books of Euclid's Elements (vol. III, p. 1–2, 522, 524–525, Cambridge, 1908; concludes against Vogt, as summarized above).

ANTIPHON

Ἀντιφῶν, a contemporary of Socrates. Mathematician. Attempted to square the circle by inscribing into it a polygon, then another with twice as many sides, etc.

Ferdinand Rudio: Der Bericht des Simplicius über die Quadraturen des Antiphon und des Hippokrates (Urkunden zur Gesch. d. Math. im Altertume, 1. Heft., 194 p., Leipzig, 1907). Contains Greek text and German translation of all the relevant texts, with copious notes and glossary; apparently exhaustive.

BRYSON

Bryson of Heraclea (Βρύσων), a contemporary of Antiphon. Mathematician. Pythagorean. Went a step further than Antiphon toward the quadrature of the circle by considering not simply inscribed polygons of an increasing number of sides, but also circumscribed polygons. Believed erroneously that the area of the circle was the arithmetical mean between the areas of inscribed and circumscribed polygons. Antiphon and Bryson prepared the elaboration of the method of exhaustion.

IV. GREEK ASTRONOMY

The notes of this section ought to be completed by reference to the note on Parmenides in section II and to the one on Oenopides in Section III.

See also J. K. Fotheringham: A Neglected Eclipse (The Observatory, vol. 43, 189–191, 1920). The total eclipse of c. –462, April 30, alluded to by Pindar.

PHILOLAOS

Φιλόλαος, born in Southern Italy, flourished about the middle of the fifth century. Mathematician, astronomer; Pythagorean, hence it is difficult to state exactly which were his personal discoveries. Pythagoras did not leave any writings, and Philolaos is supposed to be the author of the first publication of the school. Fragments of it remain. He explains the daily rotation of the stars and motion of the sun by assuming that the earth describes a circle in twenty-four hours around a central fire, the hearth of the universe (ἑστία τοῦ παντός). This fire is hidden from the earth by the counterearth (ἀντίχθων). Hence there are ten orbits or spheres around the central fire, to wit: Counterearth, Earth, Moon, Sun, Venus, Mercury, Mars, Jupiter, Saturn—the sphere of the fixed stars. (Various Pythagoreans may have differed as to the order of these orbits.) The moon is a body like the earth, with plants and animals. Philolaos called the cube a geometrical harmony because the numbers of edges (12), angles (8) and sides (6) form a harmonic progression. He knew four or five regular solids and associated them with the four or five elements (the fifth element, aether, was possibly introduced for the sake of symmetry, when the last regular solid, the dodecahedron, was discovered; the early history of the five solids is, of course, very obscure). He distinguished between sensory, animal, and vegetative functions, which he localized respectively in the brain, the heart, and the navel. Heat builds up the body, breathing cools it. Diseases are caused by bile, blood, and phlegm.

On the authenticity of the fragments of Philolaos, which has been suspected, see Ueberweg. Gesch. der Philos. des Altertums (11te Aufl., p. 53*, Berlin, 1920). August Boeckh: Philolaos des Pythagoreers Lehren nebst den Bruchstücken seines Werkes (200 p., Berlin, 1819). Thomas Henri Martin: Hypothèse astronomique de Philolaüs (Bullett. di bibliografia e di storia d. sci. matemat., t. 5, p. 127–157, Roma, 1872). A. E. Chaignet: Pythagore et la philosophie pythagoricienne contenant les fragments de Philolaüs et d'Archytas (2 vols., Paris, 1874). P. Tannery: Sur un fragment de Philolaos (Archiv für Gesch. der Philos., Bd. 2, 379–386, 1889; Mémoires, 7, 131–139). G. Gundermann: Philolaos über das fünfte Element (Rheinisches Museum f. Philologie, t. 59, p. 145–148, 1904). Paul Tannery: A propos des fragments philolaïques sur la musique (Revue de philologie t. 28, p. 233–249, Paris, 1904; Mémoires, t. 3, 233–49; Isis, IV, 338). R. Newbold: Philolaus (Archiv f. Gesch. d. Philos., t. 19, p. 176–217, 1905). Erich Frank: Plato und die sogenannten Pythagoreer (Halle, 1923; Isis, VI, 48–52) contains a long critical study of Philolaos's fragments (p. 263–335). Frank concludes that they are not genuine, but must date from about the middle of the fourth century B. C.; they must be the work of a disciple of Plato, probably Speusippos ?).

HICETAS

Hicetas of Syracuse (Ἱκέτας), younger than Philolaos. Pythagorean philosopher, astronomer. Would have gone a step further than Philolaos and taught that the earth rotated on its own axis in twenty-four hours.

J. L. E. Dreyer: History of the Planetary Systems (p. 49–50, Cambridge, 1906).

METON

Μέτων. Flourished in Athens about 432. Discovered the so-called Metonic cycle, a period of 19 solar years almost equivalent to 235 lunar months.[i] (This period has nothing in common with the Babylonian saros, the length and purpose of which were different; it is still used to fix the date of Easter.) Meton and Euctemon made in Athens in 432 the first accurate solstitial observations; thus they established with more precision the length of the seasons. Meton tried to connect medicine with astronomy.

Meton's and Euctemon's observations are known through the so-called "Papyrus of Eudoxos" of the Musée du Louvre. For relevant bibliography see P. Duhem: Le système du monde (I, p. 108, Paris, 1914). See also G. Bigourdan: Le calendrier babylonien (20 p. Annuaire du Bureau des Longitudes, Paris, 1917). Max Neuburger: Geschichte der Medizin (1. Bd., p. 173, Stuttgart, 1906).

V. CHINESE, PERSIAN, AND GREEK TECHNICIANS

SUN WU

Sun[1] Wu[3] or Sun[1] Tzŭ[3] or Sun[1] Wu[3] Tzŭ[3] (10431, 12744, 12317), native of the Ch'i[2] (1074) State, flourished c. 500 B. C. Author of a treatise on the Art of War,

---

[i] The difference is about half an hour. The average year counted then $365\frac{5}{19}$ days, i. e., about 30′9″ too much. It is doubtful whether his reform was ever adopted by the Athenian state.

probably written some time between 505 and 496, which has long remained a classic in the Far East and has been the subject of many Chinese and Japanese commentaries.

Text—Art militaire des Chinois ou Recueil d'anciens traités sur la guerre composé avant l'ère chrétienne par différents généraux chinois. Traduit en français par le P. Amiot, revu et publié par M. Deguignes (412 p., 4to, Paris, 1772; very bad translation). Sonshi—The Chinese military classic translated by E. F. Calthrop (83 p., Tokyo, 1905, Chinese and English, poor translation.) The Book of War translated from the Chinese by E. F. Calthrop (132 p., London, 1908; imperfect translation). Sun Tzu: Art of War (translated by Lionel Giles, 285 p., London, 1910. First scientific edition; Chinese text, with English translation, notes and glossary; the notes summing up Chinese commentaries).
Criticism—A. Wylie: Chinese Literature (90, 1902). Distinguishes Sun and Wu, placing the former in the sixth century and the latter in the fourth century B. C. H. A. Giles: Biographical Dictionary (697, 1898). Lionel Giles: Introduction to his Edition (53 p., 1910).

ARTACHAEES

'Αρταχαίης; died c. 481. Persian engineer who directed the construction of a canal across the Athos peninsula, near Acanthos, to allow the passage of Xerxes's fleet in 480.

See Herodotos, VII, 22, 117. Rawlinson's translation contains references on the subject and a plan of the canal, the building and use of which can no longer be doubted. F. Cauer in Pauly-Wissowa (t. 3, 1302, 1895); also article on Mount Athos by Oberhummer (ibidem, t. 4, 2066–2069).

AGATHARCHOS

'Αγάθαρχος came originally from Samos, flourished in Athens c. 460 to 417.[k] Greek painter who is said to have invented scenography, which involves a knowledge of perspective.[l] He produced scene-paintings for Aeschylos (525–456) and wrote a technical memoir (ὑπομνήματα) on the subject.

O. Rossbach in Pauly-Wissowa (t. 1, 741, 1894). J. Six: Agatharchos (Journal of Hellenic Studies, t. 40, 180–189, 1920; Isis V, 204).

HIPPODAMOS

'Ιππόδαμος, native of Miletos, flourished in Athens about the middle of the fifth century B. C. Greek scientist and architect. The founder of scientific "town-planning." He planned the construction of the town of Piraeos (before 446) and of the Athenian colony of Thurii (445); but he did not build Rhodes (408).

K. F. Hermann: De Hippodamo Milesio ab Aristotelis Politic., II, 5. (58 p., Marburg, 1841). M. Erdmann: Hippodamos von Milet und die symmetrische Städtebaukunst der Griechen (Philologus, t. 42, 193–227, 1883). Fabricius in Pauly-Wissowa (t. 16, 1731–1734, 1913). Pierre Bise: Hippodamos (Arch. für Gesch. der Philos., t. 28, 13–42, 1923; Isis, VII, 175).

---

[k] Olympiads 80 to 90.
[l] See my note on Anaxagoras.

VI. GREEK AND CHINESE MEDICINE

Greek Medicine

See the notes devoted to Anaxagoras, Archelaos, Empedocles, Democritos, in Section II, to Philolaos in Section IV, and to Ctesias in Section IX.

DIOGENES

Diogenes of Apollonia in Crete (Διογένης), a younger contemporary of Anaxagoras. Wrote a book on nature (περὶ φύσεως), of which fragments remain. Ascribed to the air of Anaximenes also intellectual qualities (cfr. Archelaos). Pneumatic theory of medicine. Diogenes knew the pulse and attached special attention to the study of the vessels by means of which air is distributed into the body. The oldest Greek descriptions of the vascular system are due first to Syennesis the Cypriote and second to Diogenes. The influence of Diogenes (or the influence of his school) can be traced in the little book on the heart (περὶ καρδίης; de corde) of c. 400 B. C., which is the best anatomical work of the Hippocratic corpus.

Jules Soury: Diogène d'Apollonie (Revue scientifique, 7 mai, 1898; reprint, 29 p.). Ernst Krause: Diogenes von Apollonia (16 p., Progr., Posen, 1909, with a plate showing the blood-vessels according to Diogenes; Janus, 228–241, 570–584, 1909; 380–384, 1914; 314–326, 505, 1915.

School of Cos

HERODICOS

Ἡρόδικος, of Selymbria, in Thrace, on the Propontis; the form Prodicos (Πρόδικος) seems erroneous. Flourished about the middle of the fifth century B. C. Greek physician. Teacher of Hippocrates. He attached great importance to gymnastics, claiming that physical activity and diet must complete and balance one another; and to the treatment of diseases by means of frictions and unctions (ἰατραλειπτική).

The Hippocratic treatise on diet (περὶ διαίτης)[m] is probably derived from Herodicos's teaching.

Pauly-Wissowa (t. 15, 978, 1912).

HIPPOCRATES

Hippocrates of Cos, Ἱπποκράτης, born c. 460, died at a very old age in Larissa, Thessaly. The Father of Medicine; one of the greatest clinical physicians of all times. He dissociated medicine from superstition, systematized the empirical knowledge which had accumulated in Egypt and in the schools of Cnidos and Cos, and founded inductive and positive medicine. He did for medicine what Socrates did for philosophy. He established the medical deontology which is still valid to-day. First principles of public health. Principle of vis medicatrix naturae, expectant therapy tempered by common sense. Theory of critical days (cfr. Pythagoras); theory of four humours. Admirable descriptions of disease (e. g., phthisis, puerperal convulsions, epilepsy, various fevers; facies Hippocratica). Clinical cases faithfully reported (42; 25 of them with a fatal conclusion). His

---

[m] For which see my note on Hippocrates.

surgery remained in some respects unsurpassed until the nineteenth century (e. g., dislocation of the hip, shoulder, and jaw).

The Hippocratic corpus is very large, but the greater part of it is certainly not genuine; yet very much is the direct or indirect fruit of Hippocrates's teaching, and it is better to study it as a whole (expecting the most spurious writings), for it has been transmitted and has influenced medical practice and doctrine as such. The number of Hippocratic writings varies greatly according to the selection made in the complete corpus by each author. Neuburger (Gesch. d. Med., I, 1906, pp. 177–182) gives a catalogue of 59 works which deserve to be called Hippocratic because they reproduce more or less faithfully the knowledge and spirit of the master. The enumeration of these writings would take too much space, but they are subdivided as follows: (I) Generalities, 8; (II) Anatomy and physiology, 10; (III) Dietetics, 2; (IV) General pathology, 10; (V) Special pathology, 8; (VI) Therapeutics, 2; (VII) Surgery, 8; (VIII) Ophthalmology, 1; (IX) Gynecology, obstetrics, pediatrics, 10.

The Pythagorean Treatise on Seven (περὶ ἑβδομάδων, de hebdomadibus) is probably pre-Hippocratic. It dates possibly from the beginning of the fifth century, and some parts of it may be earlier still. W. H. Roscher claims that the first eleven paragraphs are an Ionian text of the sixth century, anterior even to Pythagoras. On the other hand, Franz Boll does not think that this treatise is of an earlier date than the middle of the fifth century. If this treatise is pre-Hippocratic, this helps us to understand the apparition a little later of the doctrine of critical days (ascribed to Hippocrates by Galen); but on the other hand, upon the same assumption, the humoral theory of disease can no longer be credited to Hippocrates, inasmuch as it is already implied in the περὶ ἑβδομάδων.

Wilhelm Heinrich Roscher: Über Alter, Ursprung u. Bedeutung der hippokratischen Schrift von der Siebenzahl. Ein Beitrag zur Geschichte der ältesten griechischen Philosophie und Prosaliteratur (Abh. d. philol.-hist. Klasse der Kgl. sächs. Ges. d. Wissensch., 154 p., Leipzig, 1911); Das Alter der Weltkarte in Hippokrates περὶ ἑβδομάδων und die Reichskarte des Darius Hystaspis (Philologus, t. 70, p. 529 sq., 1911). Franz Boll: Die Lebensalter, Ein Beitrag zur antiken Ethnologie u. zur Gesch. d. Zahlen (N. Jahrb. f. d. Klass. Altertum, Bd. 31, 89 sq., Leipzig, 1913). W. H. Roscher: Die hippokratische Schrift von der Siebenzahl in ihrer vierfachen Überlieferung (Studien zur Gesch. u. Kultur des Altertums, 6. Bd., Heft 3–4, 187 p., Paderborn, 1913). Die hippokr. Schrift von der Siebenzahl u. ihr Verhältniss zum Altpythagoreismus. Ein Beitrag zur Geschichte der ältesten Philosophie und Geographie (114 p., Leipzig, 1919).

The following treatises are possibly also pre-Hippocratic: Prorrhetic I (Προῤῥητικὸν α'; Praedicta lib. I); Coan prenotions (Κωανακαὶ προγνώσεις; Praenotiones Coacae) and the Oath (Ὅρκος; Jusjurandum)—that is, the substance of the Oath may be anterior to Hippocrates and even to the fifth century. W. H. S. Jones does not think that these works are pre-Hippocratic; he would place all the aphoristic writings of the Hippocratic corpus in the following order (tentative dates): Prorrhetic I, c. 440; Prognostic and Aphorisms, c. 415; Coan prenotions, c. 410; Nutriment, c. 400; Dentition, later still (Loeb Hippocrates, vol. 2, XXIX).

For the Oath see below the paragraph dealing with medical deontology.

The following works are probably genuine. At any rate, they date from the time of Hippocrates, but no importance should be attached to the order in which they are quoted.

(1) The Sacred Disease (περὶ ἱερῆς νόσου; de morbo sacro), dealing in a rational way with epilepsy, which was supposed to be of divine origin. Epilepsy is a disease of the brain, not of the heart or diaphragm. This treatise contains much anatomical information.

Ulrich von Wilamowitz-Moellendorff: Die hippokratische Schrift περὶ ἱρῆς νούσου (Sitzungsber. d. Kgl. Preuss. Akad. d. Wissensch., I, 2–23, Berlin, 1901). Jules Soury: Nature et localisation des fonctions psychiques chez l'auteur du traité de la maladie sacrée (Annuaire de l'Ecole pratique des hautes études, sc. hist. et. phil., p. 1–35, 1907).

(2) Airs, waters, and places (περὶ ἀέρων ὑδάτων τόπων; de aere, aquis et locis) showing the importance of meteorology, climatology, and astronomy from the medical point of view. It explains climatic and geographical influences upon organisms and upon the causation and spread of diseases. It might be considered the first treatise on medical geography; also one of the first geographical introductions to history. The second part is ethnographical rather than medical. It contains the earliest attempt to classify races of men according to their physical features.[n]

G. Gundermann: Hippocratis de aere, aquis, locis mit der alten lateinischen Übersetzung (Kleine Texte f. Vorlesungen, 77; 50 p., Bonn, 1911). Felix Jacoby: Zu Hippokrates περὶ ἀέρων, etc. (Hermes, t. 26, p. 518–567, 1911). Gustav Hellmann: Bibliographie der gedruckten Aufgaben, Übersetzungen und Auslegungen der Schrift περὶ ἀέρων (Beitr. zur Gesch. der Meteorologie, Bd. 3, 6–8, 1922, first edition recorded 1529; last, 1911).

(3) On diet (περὶ διαίτης; de diaeta), dating probably from the end of the fifth century, deals with diet and exercise. It contains the first scientific treatment of animals, and also general views on evolution and biology. Some of these views, it is true, are more speculative than those found in the more genuine Hippocratic writings.

(4) On wounds of the head (περὶ τῶν ἐν κεφαλῇ τρωμάτων; de capitis vulneribus), dating also from c. 400. A very scientific treatise containing descriptions of various kinds of skulls (e. g., variations in the sutures). Theory of fracture by contrecoup.

(5) Prognostic (προγνωστικόν; prognosticum). Dealing with the prognosis of acute diseases.

(6) Regimen in acute diseases[o] (περὶ διαίτης ὀξέων; de diaeta in acutis). Sort of supplement to Prognostic. It deals with diseases characterized by high fever, chiefly chest complaints.

(7) Epidemics I and III (Ἐπιδημιῶν α', γ'; epidemiorum libri I, III). These two books form a single work and that "the most remarkable product of Greek science."[p]

Der Volkskrankheiten erstes und drittes Buch (c. 434–430 B. C.). Übersetzt und erläutert von G. Sticker (135 p., Klassiker der Medizin, 28, Leipzig, 1923).

---

[n] (1) and (2) were probably composed by the same author, whoever he was—probably a younger contemporary of Socrates.

[o] Also called On the ptisan; Against the Cnidian sentences.

[p] Thus, W. H. S. Jones, its latest editor. According to him the authenticity of (5), (6), and (7) is more certain than that of any other treatise; so much that he uses them to define **Hippocrates**: Hippocrates is the author of these three treatises.

Greek-English edition by W. H. S. Jones in Loeb Library, 1923. Gualt. Braeutigam: De Hippocratis epidemiorum libri sexti commentatoribus (Diss., 92 p., Regimonti, 1908).

(8) Ancient medicine (περὶ ἀρχαίης ἰητρικῆς; de prisca medicina). According to W. H. S. Jones, probably composed c. 430 to 420. It contains a defense of the empirical study of medicine against the a priori method (i. e., against the use of ὑποθέσεις, preliminary axioms).

See Modestino del Gaizo: Il libro de antiqua medicina (Atti dell' Acc. Pontaniana, t. 48, 15 p., Napoli, 1918; Isis, VI, 138). M. Pohlenz: Das zwanzigste Kapitel von Hippokrates de prisca medicina (Hermes, vol. 53, 396–421, 1918).

The three following treatises, which also belong to the Hippocratic corpus, date from about the same time as the preceding, but are certainly the works of another school:

(1) Nutriment (περὶ τροφῆς; de alimento), dating probably from the end of the fifth century. It is very distinctly Heraclitean in style and spirit. Complicated theory of digestion; comparisons with phenomena in plants and animals and with physical facts. Chapter 48 contains what is probably the earliest mention of pulse in Greek literature, but the great importance of pulse is not yet realized. It was not realized before about 340 B. C. The almost complete disregard of pulse in Hippocratic literature is the more surprising in that allusions to it are found already in the Ebers papyrus.

(2) The Art (περὶ τέχνης; de arte). Sophistic treatise written by a non-medical man about the end of the fifth century, to justify the existence of the medical art.[a]

Julius Hirschberg: Ärztliche Bemerkungen über die in der hippokratischen Sammlung überlieferte Schrift περὶ τέχνης (Archiv f. Gesch. d. Naturw., VI, p. 163–173, 1913).

(3) Breaths (περὶ φυσῶν, de flatibus). Also a sophistic treatise, probably of the same time as the preceding, to prove that air is the prime cause of disease. The author was probably a layman.

Axel Nelson: Die hippokratische Schrift περὶ φυσῶν. Text und Studien (Diss., 118 p., Upsala, 1909).

For the treatise on the Nature of Man, see my note on Polybos (first half of fourth century B. C.). See also my note on Hippocratic treatises of the fourth century B. C. (first half).

Collected Works, Text, and Translations—Earliest Greek edition, prepared by Fr. Asulanus, Venice, 1526; a Latin translation by Fabius Calvus had appeared the year before in Rome; each in one volume folio. The second Greek edition, prepared by Janus Cornarius and published by Froben, folio, Bale, 1538, was already much more complete and accurate. Of other early works the most important by far are the Oeconomia Hippocratis alphabeti serie distincta by Anutius Foesius (Frankfurt, 1588), which is a "perfect mine of medical lore" (W. H. S. Jones), and Foes's edition of "Hippocrates" (1 vol. fol., Frankfurt, 1595, reprinted 1621, 1624, 1645; Geneva, 1657). Emile Littré: Oeuvres complètes d'Hippocrate (10 vol., Paris, 1839–1861). Monumental edition of a new Greek text with French

[a] Ascribed by Gomperz to Protagoras (q. v.).

translation, the first 554 pages of Volume I are an introduction (Vol. X contains additional remarks, tables and indexes; for detailed contents of each volume, see Isis, VIII, 87). Francis Adams: The Genuine Works of Hippocrates (2 vols., printed for the Sydenham Society, London, 1849, contain 17 Hippocratic writings in English). Fr. Zacch. Ermerins: Hippocratis et aliorum medicorum veterum reliquiae (Greek and Latin. 3 large vols., Utrecht, 1859–1864). This is the best complete edition thus far available. Joseph Petrequin: Chirurgie d'Hippocrate (Textes grec et francais, 2 vols., Paris, 1877–1878. General introd. of 180 p. to Vol. I; Vol. II was edited posthumously by Emile Jullien). Joh. Ilberg and Hugo Kuehlewein: Hippocratis Opera quae feruntur omnia rec. Hugo Kuehlewein—Prolegomena conscripserunt Ioan. Ilberg et H. Kuehlewein (2 vols., Leipzig, 1894–1902). These two volumes represent only a part of this complete edition in progress. Sämmtliche Werke ins deutsche übersetzt und ausführlich commentiert von Robert Fuchs (3 vols., München, 1895–1900). There is no English edition of the Hippocratic collection and no complete English translation! However, a very convenient collection of select works is now being edited by W. H. S. Jones for the Loeb Classical Library (vols. 1 and 2, 1923; Isis, VI, 47; VII, 175).

For criticism of the manuscripts, see Hermann Diels: Die Handschriften der antiken Ärzte, 1 Teil: Hippokrates und Galenos. (Abhandl. d. Kgl. Preuss. Akad. d. Wissensch., 158 p., Berlin, 1905). This is the basis of the edition to be included in the Corpus medicorum graecorum. The Hippocratic writings are considered in the order given by Littré.

Anthologies—C. Pruys van der Hoeven: Chrestomathia Hippocratica (The Hague, 1824, Greek and Latin). Ch. V. Daremberg: Oeuvres choisies (2d ed., Paris, 1855). Theodor Beck: Hippokrates Erkenntnisse. Im griechischen Text ausgewählt, übersetzt und auf die moderne Heilkunde vielfach bezogen (392 p., Jena, 1907).

Apocrypha—K. Sudhoff: Die pseudohippokratische Krankheitsprognostik nach dem Auftreten von Hautausschlägen "Secreta Hippocratis" oder "Capsula eburnea" genannt (Archiv für Geschichte der Medizin, t. 9, 79–116, 1915, critical edition and commentary).

Ancient commentaries—Fr. R. Dietz: Apollonii Citiensis, Stephani, Palladii, Theophili, Meletii, Damascii, Ioannis, aliorum scholia in Hippocratem et Galenum primum graece (2 vols., Königsberg, 1834). Other commentaries will be quoted under the names of the commentators (e. g., Galen). A list of Arabic editions and commentaries was published by Flügel in Ersch and Gruber's "Allgemeine Encyklopädie der Wissenschaften und Künste" (2. Section, 8. Theil, p. 344–347, Leipzig, 1831). Anutius Foesius: Oeconomia Hippocratis alphabeti serie distincta (folio, Frankfurt, 1588. See above).

General criticism and authenticity—See the introductions to the editions quoted above. Carl Fredrich: Hippokratische Untersuchungen (244 p., Berlin, 1899). Joh. Jurk: Ramenta Hippocratea (Diss., 60 p., Berlin, 1900). Wilh. Schonack: Curae Hippocraticae (Diss., 110 p., Berlin, 1908); Zur Hippokrates Philologie (Janus, t. 14, p. 661–683, Haarlem, 1909). J. Mewaldt: Galenos über echte und unechte Hippocratica (Hermes, t. 44, p. 111–134, Berlin, 1909; important). Julius Hornyánsky: A görög felvilágosodás tudománya. Hippokrates (published by the Hungarian acad. of sciences, 521 p., Budapest, 1910). This book, written in Magyar, has been analyzed at great length by v. Györy in the Mitteil. zur Gesch. d. Medizin, t. 10, p. 480–489, 1911. Hermann Schöne: Echte Hippokratesschriften (Deutsche medizin. Wochenschrift, n. 9 u. 10, 1910, see Mitt. zur Gesch. d. Medizin, IX, p. 425–428, Theod. Beck). Theodor Gomperz: Einige Bemerkungen zum Corpus Hippocrateum (Anzeiger d. kaiserl. Akad. d. Wiss. in Wien, phil. hist. Kl., IV, p. 20–25, 1910). Herm. Diels: Über einen neuen Versuch die Echtheit einiger Hippokratischen Schriften nachzuweisen (Sitzber. d. k. Preuss. Akad. d. Wiss., phil. hist. Kl., t. 53, p. 1140–1145, 1910). Wilh. Schonack: Coniectanea in Hippocratem (Leipzig, 1910). S. Hornstein: Untersuchungen zum hippokratischen Korpus (Primitiae Czernovicienses, p. 54–82, 1911; the humoral theory is the author's criterion of authenticity). Theodor Gomperz: Die hippokratische Frage und der Ausgangspunkt ihrer Lösung (Philologus, t. 70, p. 213–241, 1911). William Arthur Heidel: Hippocratea I (Harvard studies in Classical Philology, t. 25, p. 139–203, Cambridge, Mass., 1914). H. Diels: Hippokratische Forschungen (I–V, Hermes, t. 45, 126–150, 320, 1910; t. 46, 260–285; t. 48, 378–407; t. 53, 57–87, 1918). Max Pohlenz: Zu den hippokratischen Briefen (Hermes, t. 52, 348–353, 1917; Isis, IV, 127). Jonathan Wright: Modern Commentaries on Hippocrates (Annals of Medical History, II, p. 34–43, 126–135, New York, 1919; Scientific Monthly, IX, p. 62–72, New York, 1919). Otto Regenbogen: Hippokrates und die hippokratische Sammlung (Neue Jahrbücher für das klassische Altertum, t. 47, 185–197, 1921). W. Capelle: Zur hippocratischen Frage (Hermes, t. 57, 247–265, 1922). Julius Hirschberg: Vorlesungen über hippokratische Heilkunde (103 p., Leipzig, 1922). Robert Oswald Moon: Hippocrates and his Successors (Fitzpatrick lectures, 180 p., London, 1923).

Hippocratic Tradition—See above, ancient commentaries. For the Jewish tradition see the article by Max Schloessinger in the Jewish Encyclopaedia, t. 6, 403, 1904. For the Muslim tradition see the article Buqrāt by Carra de Vaux in Encyclopaedia of Islam, t. 1, 784, 1912.

Karl Sudhoff: Eine mittelalterliche Hippokrates vita (Archiv für Geschichte der Medizin, t. 8, 404–413, 1915). E. Wallach: Eine Hippokrateslegende (*ibidem*, t. 16, 220–221, 1925).

Medical Deontology—Georg Weiss: Die ethischen Anschauungen im Corpus Hippocraticum (Arch. f. Gesch. d. Medizin, t. 4, p. 235–262, 1910). Theod. Meyer-Steineg und Wilhelm Schonack: Hippokrates über Aufgaben und Pflichten des Arztes in einer Anzahl auserlesener Stellen aus dem Corpus Hippocraticum (27 p., Kleine Texte f. Vorlesungen, Bonn, 1913). Very convenient edition of the Hippocratic writings on medical duty, to wit: Ὅρκος, νόμος, περὶ τέχνης, περὶ ἀρχαίης ἰητρικῆς, περὶ ἰητροῦ, περὶ εὐσχημοσύνης, παραγγελίαι. J. F. Bensel: De medico libellus ad codicum fidem recensitus (Philologus, t. 78, 88–130, 1922). W. H. S. Jones: The Doctor's Oath (62 p., Cambridge, 1924). Contains the text of the Hippocratic oath and of Christian and Arabic versions, together with a full discussion; see also Jones's short notice in the Loeb Hippocrates (vol. 1, 1923, 291–301).

Criticism of Special Subjects—A Courtade: La rhinologie dans Hippocrate (Archives internationales de laryngologie, 18 p., 1903; *id.*, L'otologie. *Ibidem*, 32 p., 1904). Rud. Burckhardt: Das koische Tiersystem, eine Vorstufe der zoologischen Systematik des Aristoteles (Verhdl. d. Naturf. Gesells., Bd. XV, Basel, 1904). Natvig: Kenntniss des menschlichen Uterus bei den Hippokratikern (Z. f. Geburtsh. u. Gynäkol., LVII, Heft 1, 1906). Theodor Beck: Das wissenschaftliche Experiment in der hippokr. Büchersammlung. (Verhandlungsber. d. 49. Philologenkongr., p. 197–201, 1908); Haben die Hippokratiker das Secale cornutum therapeutisch verwendet? (Archiv f. Gesch. d. Med., t. 2, 279–284, 384, 1908). Robert Fuchs: Die Einrichtung der Fingerknocken mit der Eidechse (Archiv für Geschichte der Medizin, t. 5, 129–132, 1911). H. Schricker: Die hippokr. Geräte zur Einrichtung von Frakturen und Luxationen (Diss., 43 p., Jena, 1911). C. M. Gillespie: The use of εἶδος and ἰδέα in Hippocrates (Classical Quarterly, t. 6, 179–203, 1912). Theod. Meyer-Steineg: Die Bedeutung der Prognose in den hippokrat. Schriften. (Archiv. f. Gesch. d. Naturw., VI, p. 258–262, 1913). W. Johannsen: Die Vererbungslehre bei Aristoteles und Hippokrates im lichte heutiger Forschung (Die Naturwissenschaften, Jahrg. 5, p. 389–397, 1917). Willy Rech: Zahnärztliches aus dem hippokratischen Schriften-Korpus (Diss., 62 p., Leipzig, 1920). Jonathan

Wright: The Psychiatry of the Greek Tragic Poets in its Relation to that of Hippocrates (Journal of Nervous and Mental Diseases, vol. 54, 481–492, 1921).

Archaeology—For the archaeological research conducted in Cos see the Archaeologischer Anzeiger, 1901, 1903, 1905. See also: R. Herzog: Bericht über eine epigraphisch-archäolog. Expedition auf der Insel Kos in Sommer 1900 (Jahrb. d. K. D. Arch. Inst., XVI, 3, 1901). Theod. Meyer-Steineg: Hippokrates Erzählungen (Arch. f. Gesch. d. Medizin, VI, p. 1–11, 1921. Popular traditions collected by the author in the island). W. Allan Jamieson and John D. Comrie: A Visit to the so-called Fountains of Hippocrates in Cos, with Remarks on the Statements of Hippocrates on Mineral Springs (Edinburgh Medical Journal, p. 118–123, 1912). Richard Caton: The Temples, Hospital, and Medical School of Cos (XVIIth Congress of Med., 1913, histor. section, 19–23, London, 1914). For a summary of archaeological research in Cos—F. H. Marshall: Discovery in Greek Lands (p. 82–84, 1 illustr., Cambridge, 1920). "The impression gained from the remains at Kos is that the treatment there was a rational rather than a wonder-working one, such as we find at Epidauros." (Isis, IV, 59.)

School of Cnidos—Euryphon

Εὐρυφῶν, contemporary of Hippocrates. One of the greatest physicians of the school of Cnidos in Caria. It is highly probable that he is one of the authors or editors of the "Cnidian Sentences" (Κνίδιαι γνῶμαι) and that he is responsible for many of the Cnidian writings of the Hippocratic collection. Made anatomical studies, wrote a book on "livid fever" (πελιὴ νόσος), explained pleurisy as a lung affection, treated consumption with milk and a red-hot iron. The insufficient evacuation of the faeces is a cause of disease. Hemorrhage can occur from the arteries as well as from the veins. Obstetrical and gynecological treatments also ascribed to him.

The school of Cnidos is represented also by Ctesias with whom I deal in Section IX.

Max Neuburger: Geschichte der Medizin (I, p. 167–168, Stuttgart, 1906).

School of Sicily—Acron

Ἄκρων, disciple of Empedocles, flourished at Agrigentum, still living in 430. One of the most important members of the Sicilian medical school. He distinguished between different currents of air, and from their mixtures drew conclusions concerning man's state of health. He ordered fires to be lighted to purify the air during the plague of Athens.

Max Wellmann: Die Fragmente der sikelischen Ärzte, Akron, Philistion und des Diokles von Karystos. Berlin, 1901. Short note, by same, in Pauly-Wissowa (vol. 1, 1199, 1894).

Chinese Medicine—Pien Ch'iao

Pien[3] Ch'iao[3]* (9172, 1388), nickname under which the physician Ch'in[2] Yüeh[4]* Jên[2] (2093, 13781, 5624) is best known. Born at Po[4]*-hai[3] (9425, 3767), i. e., Ho[2]-chien[4]-fu[3] (3936, 1601, 3682), Chihli, flourished in the Chêng[4] (724) State in the first half of the fifth century. Semimythical Chinese physician. The Nan[2] ching[1] (8135, 2122), a medical treatise in 81 chapters, is ascribed to him. At any rate, the Nan ching is one of the earliest Chinese medical treatises and also one of the most popular, not less than eleven commentaries being devoted to it before the Ming dynasty.[r] The Chinese theory of the pulse is ascribed to him.[s]

Text—The text of the Nan ching may be found in the Ku[3]-chin[1] t'u[2] shu[1] chi[2*] ch'êng[2] (6188, 2027, 12125, 10024, 906, 762), vol. 842. Many separate editions, for example, one published in 1693 by Shên[3] Wei[1]-yüan[2] (9849, 12586, 13762). F. Huebotter has made a German translation of it, hitherto (Nov., 1924) unpublished.

Criticism—A. Wylie: Chinese Literature (1876 (1902) 97; with information on later commentaries). H. A. Giles: Biographical Dictionary (155, 1898). F. Huebotter: Berühmte Chinesische Aerzte (Archiv für Geschichte der Medizin, t. 7, 115–128, 1913). Contains an annotated translation of chapter 105 of the Shih-chi, Pien Ch'iao's biography. L. Wieger: La Chine (41, 57, 449, 1920). F. Huebotter: Guide (10–15, Kumamoto, 1924; includes brief analysis of the Nan ching; Isis, VII, 259).

VII. CARTHAGINIAN AND GREEK EXPLORERS.

HANNO'S PERIPLUS

A Carthaginian suffete, named Hanno[t] (Ἄννων), led a fleet of 60 ships beyond the Pillars of Hercules (the Strait of Gibraltar) and navigated along the western coast of Africa, reaching the latitude of c. 7° 30′ N. (that is, if, as generally admitted, the remotest point reached was an island in Sherbôro Sound, British Sierra Leone[u]). Hanno's navigation along the Western African coast extended to a total of 29 degrees of latitude, or about 2,600 miles from Gibraltar. In the island above mentioned, Hanno observed hairy women, whom the interpreters called gorillas (ἃς οἱ ἑρμηνέες ἐκάλουν γορίλλας); these women were probably negritos.

The account of Hanno's expedition was originally written in Phoenician and inscribed on a tablet hung up in the temple of Melkarth in Carthage. It was later translated into Greek and a short Greek text beginning thus: Ἄννωνος Καρχηδονίων βασιλέως περίπλους τῶν ὑπὲρ τὰς Ἡρακλέους Στήλας Λιβυκῶν τῆς γῆς μερῶν. . . . has come down to us. The authenticity of this text and of the journey itself is now generally accepted, but it is impossible to date it with any precision. Hanno's voyage took place probably in the fifth century (or at the end of the sixth?) and probably in the first half of that century.

Text—Editio princeps, Basle, Frobenius, 1533. Numerous other editions. I quote only a few. Thomas Falconer: The Voyage of Hanno, translated and accompanied with the Greek text, explained from the accounts of modern travelers, defended against the objections of Dodwell, etc., London, 1797. Fr. Wilhelm Kluge: Hannonis navigatio (55 p., Leipzig, 1829). C. W. Müller in Geographi Graeci minores (Paris, 1853, with valuable commentary). Wilfred H. Schoff: The Periplus of Hanno (32 p., Philadelphia, 1913).

Criticism—G. B. Ramusio's commentary accompanying a translation of the text in his Navigazioni e Viaggi (vol. 1, 121–124, 1550), is interesting as partly based upon Portuguese exploration. There are many other early commentaries. August Mer: Le périple d'Hannon (Paris, 1885). Curt Theodor Fischer: De

---

[r] Only one is extant, the Nan[2]ching[1]pên[3]i[4] (8135, 2122, 8846, 5454) by Hua[2*] Shou[4] (5022, 10019) who flourished about the end of the Yüan dynasty (1368).

[s] By Ssŭ-ma Ch'ien (q. v., second half of second century B.C.) in the Shih-chi, cap. 105.

[t] This is a common Carthaginian name. Not less than 27 Hannos are dealt with in Pauly-Wissowa, t. 7, 2353–2363, 1912.

[u] According to the Greek text an island in a bay, called Horn of the South.

Hannonis periplo (134 p., Leipzig, 1893). Karl Emil Illing: Der Periplus des Hanno (Progr., Wettiner Gymn., 46 p., Dresden, 1899). Article by Daebritz in Pauly-Wissowa (t. 9, 2360–2363, 1912).

HIMILCO'S VOYAGE

Another Carthaginian expedition, mentioned by Pliny as having occurred at about the same time as Hanno's, was led by Himilco (Ἱμίλκων). The aim was to explore the outer coasts of Europe. Himilco reached the Oestrymnides (Cassiterides Insulae, Tin Islands). What little we know of that expedition is derived from a fourth century poem by R. F. Avienus (q. v., second half of fourth century).

E. H. Bunbury: History of Ancient Geography (1879).

SCYLAX

Scylax of Caryanda.[v] (Σκύλαξ, flourished in the reign of Darius I, king of Persia from 521 to 485.) Traveler, geographer. Made a coasting survey (περίπλους) all around the Mediterranean, the Euxine, and the other seas connected with them. The relation of this Periplus, still extant, seems to have been written between 360 and 347. If it be genuine, it is of considerable importance.

Text—Anonymi vulgo Scylacis Caryandensis periplum Maris Interni cum appendice iterum recensuit B. Fabricius (Heinrich Theodor Dittrich), 41 p., Leipzig, 1878.

Commentary—Reinhold Issberner: Inter Scylacem et Herodotum quae sit ratio (Diss., 42 p., Berlin, 1888). Curt. Theod. Fischer: Quaestionum Scylacearum specimen. Griechische Studien Hermann Lipsius dargebracht (p. 141–152, Leipzig, 1894).

For Anaxagoras's views on the rising of the Nile see section II.

VIII. GREEK AND HEBREW MINING

The silver mines of Laurium (Λαύριον), in the southern part of Attica, had been exploited before the fifth century (perhaps already in prehistoric times?), and they were exploited for some time afterward, but this century witnessed their greatest period of activity. Some of the ancient shafts and galleries can still be seen in situ, also some of the devices used to extract the metal. These mines are thus very important for the study of ancient mining. Their importance is equally great in other respects, for we can not understand the glory of Athens without taking them into account. Indeed, in the fifth century these mines provided a substantial part of the revenue of the Athenian State. They were State property, farmed out to capitalists, all the work being done by slaves. Some time after the Battle of Marathon (490) Themistocles persuaded the Athenian citizens to use the revenue derived from the mines to build a fleet (instead of dividing it among themselves): Thus was prepared the naval supremacy of Athens and the victory of Salamis (480). It is probable that part of the same revenue was used also for the enormous expenditures made by Pericles to embellish Athens. By the end of the century the amount of silver extracted began to decrease; by the time of Strabon (q. v., second half of first century B. C.) the Athenians were already reduced to working over the tailings; by the time of Pausanias (q. v., second half of second century after Christ) the mines were no longer exploited. The ex-

[v] In Caria; on a little island near Halicarnassos.

ploitation has been started again, not for the sake of the silver, but to obtain lead, cadmium, and manganese.

Very elaborate account by Edouard Ardaillon: Les mines du Laurion dans l'antiquité (218 p., illustr., Bibliothèque des écoles françaises d'Athènes et de Rome, fasc. 77, Paris, 1897). Alfred Eckhard Zimmern: The Greek Commonwealth—Politics and Economics in Fifth Century Athens (Third ed., revised, 462 p., Oxford, 1922, chapter 16, 397–419; 1st ed. 1914; 2d, 1915; 4th, 1924).

Brief references to Hebrew mining will be found in the Book of Job, chapter 28.

IX. GREEK AND HEBREW HISTORIOGRAPHY

HERODOTOS

Herodotos of Halicarnassos (in Caria, almost opposite the island of Cos). Ἡρόδοτος, born c. 484, died at Thurii in Lucania, Southern Italy, c. 425. The first great historian, the first to combine properly art and science in his work. His history in nine books is an elaborate account of the struggles between the Greeks and the Persians. Herodotos had traveled extensively in Europe, Asia, and Africa and in his descriptions of the many peoples and countries involved in his history he often gives the result of his own observations, remarkably truthful and accurate. He is not critical in the modern sense, but perfectly fair. His history is of considerable importance because of the large amount of geographic and ethnographic information which it contains. For example, we find in it (V, 16) probably the only first-hand description of a prehistoric lake-village (in Macedonia).[w]

Herodotos ascribed the formation of the defile of Tempe (in northern Thessaly) to an earthquake. His detailed and truly admirable description of Egypt contains a long discussion of the Nile. He had noticed the yearly deposits of silt over the land and concluded that Egypt was a gift of the Nile. From the presence of petrified sea-shells in the hills he deduced that the sea had once spread over Lower Egypt.

He describes (VII, 37) an eclipse which occurred in the spring preceding the Battles of Thermopylae and Salamis (480). But no eclipse occurred in that year!

Text—Editio princeps. Aldo Manuzio, Venice, 1502. Critical edition by Heinrich Stein (2 vols., Berlin, 1869–1871), by H. R. Dietsch (Leipzig, 1872, etc.), by Charles Hude (2 vols., Oxford, 1908). Greek-English edition by A. D. Godley in the Loeb classical library (4 vols., 1921–1924).

Criticism (*Generalities and Unclassified Material*)—W. W. How and J. Wells: Commentary on Herodotus (2 vols., Oxford, 1912). Victor Ehrenberg: Zu Herodot. (Klio. t. 16, 318–331, 1921; Isis, IV, 573). J. T. Shotwell: An Introduction to the History of History (144–61, 1922). Jonathan Wright: The Science of Herodotus (Scientific Monthly, t. 16, 638–648, 1923). Joseph Wells: Studies in Herodotus (238 p., Oxford, 1923). Terrot Reaveley Glover: Herodotus (316 p., Univ. California, 1924).

Herodotos on Egypt—Archibald Henry Sayce: The Egypt of the Hebrews and Herodotus (2d ed., 358 p., London, 1896; first ed., 1895). Camille Sourdille: La durée et l'étendue du voyage d'Hérodote en Egypte (260 p., Paris, 1910, important); Hérodote et la religion de l'Egypte (436 p., Paris, 1910). Ernst Obst: Die Beschreibung des Nilpferdes bei Herodot, II, 71 (Klio, t. 14, 390–391, 1914).

[w] There is a brief allusion to lake dwellings in the Hippocratic treatise on Airs, Waters, Places, ch. 15, dwellers on the Phasis, east of the Black Sea.

Geography—J. Talboys Wheeler: The Geography of Herodotus Explained and Illustrated from Modern Researches and Discoveries (683 p., London, 1854). Richard Neumann: Nordafrika (mit Ausschluss des Nilgebietes) nach Herodot. (174 p., Leipzig, 1892). Fr. Westberg: Zur Topographie des Herodot., III, 7, Herodots Stadion (Klio, t. 14, 338–344, Leipzig, 1914). Herodotos's stadium = 148.55 meters.

Geology—Sir Archibald Geikie: The Founders of Geology (2d ed., 1905). P. Duhem: Etudes sur Léonard de Vinci (t. 2, 291–299, 1909).

Ethnology—Anton Grassl: Herodot als Ethnologe (Diss., 78 p., Sulzbach i. O., 1904). W. R. Halliday: The First Description of a Lake Village (Discovery, vol. 1, 235–238, London, 1920; Isis, IV, 127).

Botany—Fried. Kanngiesser: Die Flora des Herodot. (Archiv für Gesch. der Naturw., t. 3, 81–102, 1910).

Medicine—Carl Moeller: Die Medizin im Herodot. (36 p., Berlin, 1903). Jonathan Wright: The Medical Fakirs of Athens and the Sexual Problems in Babylon in the Days of Herodotus (New York Medical Journal, 118, 257–262, 1923).

Chemistry—E. O. von Lippmann: Technologisches und Kulturgeschichtliches aus Herodot. (Chemiker Z., 1924, p. 1, 29–31, 38; Isis, VII, 175).

THUCYDIDES

Θουκυδίδης, Athenian, born not long before 460, died c. 400–395. One of the very greatest historians of all times. He may be called the founder of philosophic or scientific historiology. His history of the Peloponnesian War, of which he had been a witness[1] is one of the greatest literary—and I would say, scientific—classics of the world. He explains his method at the beginning of his work and gives a brief account of the evolution of Greek society from the earliest times to his own day. His description of the "plague" of Athens (430 to 425) is classical. His description of the solar eclipse of Athens on August 3, 431, is the earliest detailed description of an eclipse (solar crescent, visibility of certain stars).

Text—First edition, Venice, 1502. I can quote but a few of the main editions. I. Bekker (Berlin, 1821); J. Classen (8 vols., Berlin, 1862–78); Alfred Croiset (Bks. I–II, Paris, 1886); H. S. Jones (2 vols., Oxford, 1899–1901); Karl Hude (2 vols., Leipzig, 1898–1901).

English translation by B. Jowett (2 vols., Oxford, 1881). Greek text with English translation by C. Forster Smith (Loeb Library, 4 vols., London, 1919–1923).

German translations by Gottfried Boehme (2 vols., Leipzig, 1852–1854). Greek text with French translation by Ambroise Firmin Didot (4 vols., Paris, 1833); Ch. Zévort, Paris, 1852; Bétant.

Lexicons—E. A. Bétant: Lexicon Thucydideum (2 vols., Genève, 1843–1847; incomplete). M. H. N. von Essen: Index Thucydideus (460 p., Berlin, 1887).

Criticism—Alfred Croiset: Littérature grecque (t. 4^2, 87–172, 1900). Jane Ellen Harrison: Primitive Athens as Described by Thucydides (180 p., Cambridge, 1906). Francis Macdonald Cornford: Thucydides Mythistoricus (268 p., London, 1907). Friedrich Fischer: Thucydidis reliquiae in papyris et membranis aegyptiacis servatae (Diss., Giessen, 34 p., Leipzig, 1913). Eduard Meyer: Thukydides und die Entstehung der wissenschaftlichen Geschichtsschreibung (25 p., Wien, 1913). Alfred Eckhard Zimmern: The Greek Commonwealth—Politics and Economics in Fifth Century Athens (3d ed., 462 p., Oxford, 1922). J. T. Shotwell: History of History (162–78, 1922).

---

[1] The war lasted from 431 to 404, but Thucydides's History stops short in 411.

The Plague of Athens—The plague which desolated Athens in 430–425 was described by Thucydides in Book II of his History. The true nature of this epidemic[v] has been the subject of long discussions. According to Sprengel, it was bubonic plague; to Krause, Daremberg, Kobert—smallpox; to Häser, Kanngiesser—typhus fever; to Seitz—typhoid fever; to Krauss, Hecker—an extinct plague, etc.

See Wilhelm Ebstein: Die Pest des Thukydides (48 p., Stuttgart, 1899; also Janus, t. 7). Fr. Kanngiesser has written many papers on the subject since 1912. The latest I know of, through G. Sticker's review in the Mitt. zur Gesch. der Med., t. 16, 401, is Die Seuche des Thukydides (Typhus exanthematicus). Z. f. Hygiene, 82. Bd., 1917. Raymond Crawfurd: The Typhus Character of the Plague of Athens (XVIIth International Congress of Medicine, historical section, 457–465, 1914).

Eclipses—Three eclipses are correctly recorded by Thucydides: (1) Solar eclipse seen in Athens on August 3, 431; it was seven-eighths total and thus some stars (or planets) could be seen (II, 28); (2) annular solar eclipse of March 21, 424 (IV, 52); (3) lunar eclipse of August 27, 413 (VII, 50). See S. A. Mitchell: Eclipses of the Sun (32–34, 1923).

CTESIAS

Κτησίας flourished in Persia at the end of the century. Eminent physician of the school of Cnidos; was taken prisoner by the Persians about 417 and became a physician to the Persian court; he returned to his country about 398. Chiefly known as the author of two books, the *Περσικά* and the *'Ινδικά*, the former a history of Persia, the second an account of the natural phenomena of the portions of India known to the Persians and the manners and customs of its inhabitants. He mentions the occurrence of natural gas in Carmania. He also wrote on the medical use of hellebore and improved its dosage.

Editio princeps, H. Stephanus, 1557. J. C. F. Baehr: Ctesiae Cnidii Operum reliquiae (477 p., Francofurti ad Moenum, 1824). Later edition of the Fragments by Karl Müller in the Greek-Latin Herodotos of the coll. Didot, Paris, 1844. J. W. McCrindle: Ancient India as described by Ktesias the Knidian (transl. of the fragments of his Indica and of Photios's abridgment of it; 112 p., Calcutta, 1882. Reprinted with additions from the Indian Antiquary, 1881). The fragments of the Persika, of less interest to us, have been edited by John Gilmore (220 p., London, 1888).

HEBREW HISTORY AND LAW

The Hexateuch is the collection of the first six books of the Old Testament, that is, Genesis, Exodus, Leviticus, Numbers, Deuteronomy—these five forming the Pentateuch,[z] plus Joshua. It is better to consider the collection of the first six books than that of the first five, as it has been proved that Joshua is closely connected with them, or in other words, because a critical study of these writings has shown that some strands pass through all of them. More exactly, of the four main strands which constitute the Hexateuch, three may be recognized in all six parts except Deuteronomy, while the fourth can be found in Deuteronomy and

---

[v] There were two outbreaks of it, the first lasting two years, being followed by an intermission of about eighteen months.

[z] Or, in Hebrew, the Tōrāh, meaning the Law.

Joshua only. It follows from this that it is not possible to separate Joshua from the rest without breaking the unity and jeopardizing our understanding of the whole. It may be advantageous, however, to subdivide the Hexateuch into four parts, remembering always that they are not entirely independent: (1) Genesis; (2) Exodus, Leviticus, Numbers; (3) Deuteronomy; (4) Joshua.

The Hexateuch contains almost all that we know of the earliest history of Israel from the creation to the time of Joshua included (c. 1200?), of Hebrew cosmogony, and of Hebrew law. It is thus a combination of historical narrative and of codification which it is difficult to disentangle.

The composition of that great body is extremely complex. The results of modern research may be summarized as follows: The earliest parts of the Hexateuch are the so-called Jahvistic and Elohist narratives. Their unknown authors are called respectively J and E; they flourished before the middle of the sixth century, possibly a long time before; they may have been contemporaries of the early prophets. It is possible that J wrote in Judah and E in the Northern Kingdom. To this double narrative was added after 621 a new strand (D) reflecting the Deuteronomic point of view. In the meanwhile another collection had been growing, itself a combination of narrative and law, called the Priestly document. It is represented by P (or PC when only its legal part, the Priests' Code, is meant). Some time in the fifth century, probably toward the middle of it, in Ezra's time,[a] these four strands were woven together and the Hexateuch was thus essentially constituted.

To complete this story, I may add that the Pentateuch and the Historical Books (Joshua–Kings)[b] were probably edited in the present order some time before or about 300 B. C., though a standard Hebrew text was not finally established until the second century after Christ.

J. Estlin Carpenter: The Hexateuch According to the Revised Version (2 vols., 1900; vol. 1 contains a full analysis of the Hexateuch; vol. 2 has the text printed in such a manner as to show clearly the different strands). C. F. Kent: The Student's Old Testament (1904, etc).

Alfred Loisy: Les mythes babyloniens et les premiers chapitres de la Genèse (226 p., Paris, 1901). Heinrich Zimmern: Biblische und babylonische Urgeschichte (40 p., 2. unver. Aufl., Leipzig, 1901). John Skinner: Commentary on Genesis (551 p., New York, 1910). Walther Eichrodt: Die Quellen der Genesis (Giessen, 1916).

Olaf A. Toffteen: The Historic Exodus (361 p., Chicago, 1909). Maurice Fluegel: Exodus, Moses, and the Decalogue legislation (308 p., Baltimore, 1910).

George Buchanan Gray: Commentary on Numbers (541 p., Edinburgh, 1903).

For Deuteronomy see seventh century B. C.

EZRA

Or Esdras, flourished c. 458–444. Hebrew priest and historian who came from Babylon to Jerusalem in 458 (the seventh year of Artaxerxes). He wrote a book of history c. 443. Some of his memoirs are included in the so-called Book

[a] See my note on Ezra.

[b] For Judges and Kings see my note on Hebrew History in the sixth century B. C.; for Samuel, see my note on Hebrew History in the seventh century B. C. The exquisite story of Ruth (sandwiched in the Christian Bible between Judges and First Samuel) is a much later composition.

of Ezra (Old Testament),[c] written probably about 300 B.C. It was probably Ezra who introduced from Babylonia a new code of law, the so-called Priests' Code or the whole Pentateuch (that is, as much of it as was already available).

Loring W. Batten: A Critical and Exegetical Commentary on the Books of Ezra and Nehemiah (International Critical Commentary, 400 p., New York, 1913). Arthur Ernest Cowley: Jewish Documents of the Time of Ezra, translated from the Aramaic (100 p., London, 1919); Aramaic papyri of the fifth century B.C. Edited with translation and notes (352 p., Oxford, 1923). James T. Shotwell: Introduction to the History of History (chapter 9, 102–104, New York, 1922).

NEHEMIAH

Flourished c. 445 to 433. Governor of Palestine in the 20th year of Artaxerxes (445). He carried through the building of the walls of Jerusalem. He came to that city a second time in 432. His memoirs are included in the so-called "Book of Nehemiah" (Old Testament), written probably after 300 B.C. by the same hand which wrote the "Book of Ezra."

X. HEBREW, GREEK AND ROMAN LAW

For Hebrew law, see my note on the Hexateuch in the previous section.

Greek Law

The Laws of Gortyn (fifth and fourth centuries). An early code of Greek Law is preserved in a very long inscription on a wall, 27 feet long and 5 feet high, discovered in 1884 at Gortyn in Crete. This discovery was of great importance for the study both of Greek law and of comparative jurisprudence. In fact, that discovery, together with the publication of the Constitution of Athens seven years later, may be said to have placed Greek Law in an entirely different perspective and to have originated an entirely new study of it. There is a cast of the inscription in the Cambridge Museum of Classical Archaeology.

Text—First edition by E. Fabricius in Ath. Mitth., t. 9, 1885, 362–384. Franz Bücheler und Ernst Zittelmann: Das Recht von Gortyn (190 p., Frankfurt, 1885).
Criticism—See the references in my note on Greek Law in the seventh century B.C. Domenico Comparetti: Le leggi di Gortyna, Milano, 1893. Hermann Lipsius: Zum Recht von Gortyn, Leipzig, 1909. William Wyse, in Companion to Greek studies, 3d ed., 1916, 465–470.

Roman Law

The Twelve Tables. The establishment of the Roman Republic in 510 involved necessarily a new investigation and codification of the law. This was decided in 462 and a mission was sent to Athens to study the laws of Solon. The new Roman code was prepared in 452 to 450 by a body of ten patricians (decemviri legibus scribundis) and was called Lex XII Tabularum.[d]

Text—Rudolf Schoell. Legis duodecim tabularum reliquiae (185 p., Leipzig,

---

[c] It is convenient to consider the Book of Ezra together with the Book of Nehemiah. They form but one book (called Ezra) in the Hebrew Old Testament and occupy in it the last place of that portion which records the history of Israel. They deal with the period extending from the return to Palestine at the end of the Babylonian captivity (536) to Nehemiah's second visit to Palestine (432). A few chapters of Ezra (IV, 8 to VI, 18; VII, 12–26) were originally written in Aramaic, which gradually replaced Hebrew in Palestine from the fifth century on.

[d] Because these laws were published on twelve tables. Ten tables had been published before the end of 451; two more tables containing additional matter were published in 450.

1866). Also in Rudolf Gneist: Institutionum et regularum iuris romani syntagma (Leipzig, 1858, 2d ed., 1880).

Criticism—Moritz Voigt: Die XII Tafeln. Geschichte und System des Civil- und Criminalrechtes, wie-| Prozesses der XII Tafeln nebst deren Fragmenten (2 vols., Leipzig, 1883). Edouard Lambert: Le problème de l'origine des XII tables (60 p., Paris, 1902). Eugène Révillout: Les rapports historiques et légaux des Quirites et des Egyptiens depuis la fondation de Rome jusqu'aux emprunts faits par les auteurs de la loi des XII tables au code d'Amasis (172 p., Paris, 1902). David Heinrich Müller: Die Gesetze Hammurabis und ihr Verhältnis zur mosaischen Gesetzgebung sowie zu den XII Tafeln (285 p., Wien, 1903).

XI. GREEK, SANSKRIT, AND CHINESE PHILOLOGY

For Greek philology, see my note on Protagoras in Section II.

Sanskrit Philology—Yāska

Flourished in India about the fifth century B. C.[e] Hindu grammarian and commentator of the Vedas. Of the many grammarians who preceded Pāṇini, he alone survives. His main work is the Nirukta,[f] a commentary on the Vedas wherein etymological considerations predominate. His grammatical terminology is substantially the same as Pāṇini's.[g]

Text—Rudolph Roth: Nirukta, sammt den Nighantavas, Göttingen, 1848–1852. The Nirukta with commentaries, edited by Satyavrata Sāmaśramī, 4 vols., Bibl. Indica, Calcutta (1882–1891). The Nighaṇṭu and the Nirukta, the oldest Indian treatise on etymology, philology, and semantics. Edited with English translation, notes and indexes by Lakshman Sarup, London, 1920.

Criticism—A. A. Macdonell: Sanskrit literature (London, 1900).

Chinese Lexicography

According to Chinese tradition, their earliest dictionary is the so-called Ěrh[3] Ya[3] (3354, 12807) (Nearing the Standard), which some would ascribe to the Duke of Chou[1] (2450) (twelfth century B. C.). It is more generally accepted as the work of Tzŭ[3] Hsia[4] (12317, 4227), a disciple of Confucius, born in 507. Chu[1] Hsi' (2544, 4081) said it was compiled even later. It was first edited by Kuo[1*] P'o[4*] (6617, 9443) (q.v., first half of fourth century), with a commentary and *illustrations*. An additional commentary was provided by Hsing[2] Ping[3] (4618, 9297) (932–1010), author of a book on weather-lore. The illustrations (256 in number) of modern editions go back to the Sung dynasty (maybe to the time of Hsing Ping?). The words registered in the Ěrh Ya are classified in nineteen categories, as follows: Explanations; terms; instructions; relationships; buildings; utensils; music; heaven; earth; hills; mountains; waters; plants; trees; insects; fishes; birds; animals; domestic animals.

E. Bretschneider: Botanicon sinicum (part I. Journal N. China branch R. A. S., t. 16, 34–37, 1881; part II. *ibidem*, t. 25, 1893, 20–130, extensive study of the botanical part). L. Giles: Index to the T'u[2]shu[1] (12128, 10024) (p. v, 1911).

---

[e] That is, about the beginning of the sūtra period.

[f] Meaning etymology. One of the six classes of Vedāṅgas (limbs of the Vedas) or Vedic commentaries. The text of the Rigveda upon which the Nirukta was based was already essentially identical with our text.

[g] The Brāhmi alphabet of the Sanskrit language existed already in the fifth century. It has remained unmodified ever since. It is based on the Semitic alphabet, but contains 46 letters instead of 22. That is, all the sounds of the language are represented in it. The letters are classified according to a scientific method. This alphabet is far superior to our own from the phonetic point of view.

CHAPTER V

THE TIME OF PLATO

(First Half of Fourth Century B. C.)

I. Survey of science in the first half of the fourth century B. C. II. Plato and the Academy. III. Greek mathematics. IV. Greek astronomy. V. Greek physics and technology. VI. Progress of the medical arts in Greece and China. VII. Greek historiology and sociology. VIII. Sanskrit philology.

I. SURVEY OF SCIENCE IN THE FIRST HALF OF THE FOURTH CENTURY B. C.

1. We have seen that the most important scientific work of the fifth century was done during its latter half. In fact, the middle of that century must be considered a very important landmark in the history of civilization. If I were asked to say at what time a more specifically scientific activity began to assert itself and to be at once more intense and more common, I should answer, about the year 450 B. C.

This scientific activity increased in almost every direction during the fourth century, being again distinctly greater during the second half. So much work was accomplished during that century, that I have found it expedient to divide my account into two parts. The circumstances favored such division, because each half of the century was dominated by an immense personality, the first half by Plato, the second half, by Aristotle.

2. *Plato (428 to 348) and the Academy (c. 388 B. C. to 529 A. D.)*—The genius of Socrates revived in Plato, but enriched by considerable learning and mellowed by all the sweetness and fascination of literature. Plato's scientific training was chiefly mathematical, and his philosophy was thus, naturally, a mathematical philosophy, rather than an experimental one. It exerted an immense influence upon people of all times, and its charm can hardly be resisted even to this day.

Plato founded the earliest great school of philosophy in a garden called Academia, near Athens. The school was thus named "Academy." After Plato's death it was headed by Speusippos and later still by Xenocrates, two mathematicians with whom I shall deal in the next chapter. In spite of many vicissitudes the school lasted until 529 A. D., that is, more than nine centuries. (I shall have to refer to it from time to time in the following chapters.) However, the progress of Platonism was largely independent of the school and its influence was felt most powerfully many centuries after the suppression of the Academy.

3. *Greek Mathematics*—The magnificent development initiated by Hippocrates of Chios about the middle of the previous century was bound to progress under the stimulating influence of the Academy. Theaetetos (c. 380) improved the theory of surds and wrote on the five regular solids; Leon (c. 377) corrected Hippocrates's treatise; Archytas made many arithmetical and geometrical investigations and began the study of pure mechanics; Thymaridas of Paros invented a remarkable method of solving a system of linear equations; the astronomer Philip of Opus studied polygonal numbers.

The last of these in point of time, Eudoxos of Cnidos (c. 367), was also and by far the greatest; in fact, one of the greatest mathematicians and astronomers of all times. He completed the theory of surds and that (of such great importance in Greek art) of the Golden Section; he discovered the method of exhaustion and used it to prove various theorems.

4. *Greek Astronomy*—I have already dealt with the greatest astronomer of that time, Eudoxos. He expounded the theory of homocentric spheres which was the foundation of scientific astronomy. Two other astronomers, both Pythagoreans, deserve to be mentioned: Ecphantos of Syracuse, at the beginning of the century, postulated the rotation of the earth; Philip of Opus, a contemporary of Eudoxos, gave an account of Pythagorean astronomy.

5. *Greek Physics and Technology*—The mathematician Archytas, who made a special study of mechanics, is said to have constructed an automaton; the astronomer Philip of Opus studied refraction and tried to explain the rainbow (?); the great Eudoxos carried on various investigations in acoustics and mechanics.

Aeneas Tacticos, the earliest Greek writer on military science and poliorcetics, flourished about 360 B. C.; he devised systems of telegraphy and cryptography.

6. *Progress of the Medical Arts in Greece and China*—Various "Hippocratic" treatises date from the beginning or the middle of the fourth century: On fractures and dislocations, of great interest for the study of early Greek anatomy; various works on generation, possibly of Cnidian origin, containing an account of a doctrine of pangenesis and valuable remarks on human and comparative embryology; the earliest independent treatise on anatomy; on the heart, an elaborate description, probably of Sicilian origin, the heart being conceived as the seat of intellect and innate heat.

The three great medical schools are represented during this period: the school of Cos, by the embryologist Polybos, son-in-law of Hippocrates (a treatise ascribed to him is our main source for the theory of the four humors); the school of Sicily, by Philistion of Locroi, who did much research in anatomy and physiology; the school of Cnidos by Chrysippos. A new school, the Dogmatic school, professing to continue Hippocratic traditions, but with syncretic tendencies, was represented by Diocles of Carystos, "the second Hippocrates," who was much interested in anatomy, embryology, and physiology.

The student of botany ought to refer to the fragments of Chrysippos and Diocles; the latter wrote the earliest book on medical botany.

The student of zoology should study some of the works of the historian Xenophon.

Our knowledge of early Chinese medicine is very unprecise with regard to chronology, but it is probable that the treatises traditionally ascribed by the Chinese to the legendary emperors Shên Nung and Huang Ti are (in their present form at least) not earlier than the fourth century B. C.

7. *Greek Historiology and Sociology*—The only historian of the period is Xenophon, who led the famous retreat of the Ten Thousand across Mesopotamia and Asia Minor (401–400) and told it admirably in his "Anabasis." Xenophon wrote many other books which are of considerable historical, sociological, and philosophical interest.

8. *Sanskrit Philology*—It is probable that Pāṇini, the greatest Hindu grammarian, who fixed the Sanskrit language, flourished at this time. He attached much importance to phonetics.

9. *Final Remarks*—This is almost exclusively a Greek period, especially if one

consider that my references to Chinese medicine and Hindu philology are, of necessity, very uncertain with regard to dates. The age which produced a Plato, an Eudoxos, and a Xenophon was a golden age indeed.

II. PLATO AND THE ACADEMY

Plato (Πλάτων) Born c. 428 at Aegina (or Athens), died at Athens 348–347. Disciple of Socrates. Philosopher, mathematician. Founded the philosophic school called Academy which lasted under various forms until 529 A. D. Theory of ideas. Idealistic cosmology. Influenced by Pythagorean number mysticism; strong belief in the educational value of mathematics. Invented or perfected mathematical analysis and introduced rigorous definitions (straight line; plane surface (?); solid (?)); began the study of the golden section. New rule to find square numbers which are the sum of two squares:[a] Between two square numbers there is one mean proportional number and between two cube numbers there are two mean proportional numbers (Euclid, VIII, 11, 12). The five regular solids are called "Platonic figures." Plato's astronomical ideas seem less advanced than those of contemporary Pythagoreans. The earth is a sphere around which the heavens move in twenty-four hours. The lunar light is reflected from the sun. Explanation of lunar phases. Myth of the vanished island Atlantis. Geometric number (Republic, VIII) The Laws of Plato, a codification of Athenian law, was the basis of Hellenistic, and through that, of Roman law. Plato may be called, because of it, the founder of jurisprudence.[b]

One of the most important works of Plato is the Timaeos, not, however, because of its intrinsic value, but because of its immense influence upon mediaeval thought.[c] This influence was largely an evil one. The Timaeos contains the theory of the macrocosm and the microcosm (an extreme form of hylozoism, highly systematized), which became one of the fundamental doctrines of the Middle Ages. Until the translation of the Meno and the Phaedo, c. 1156, Timaeos was the only work of Plato directly known to the Latin West.[d]

Text—Editio princeps by Aldus and Musurus (Venice, 1513). Latin translation by Marsilio Ficino completed in 1477 and printed in 1482. Later Greek edition by Henri Estienne with Latin translation by Serranus (3 vols., folio., Paris, 1578. The pagination of this edition is reproduced in the margins of most subsequent editions.) Best critical edition by John Burnet (5 vols., Oxford, 1899–1906). English translation by Benj. Jowett (5 vols., Oxford, 1871, sq.). Henri Alline: Histoire du texte de Platon (Biblioth. de l'Ecole des Hautes Etudes, sci. hist., Paris, 1915. See M. Croiset in Journal des Savants, t. 15, p. 145–146, Paris, 1917). Ernst Howald: Die Platons Briefe (204 p., Zürich, 1923).

General criticism—George Grote: Plato and the Other Companions of Socrates (3 vols., London, 1865; 3d ed., 1875; new ed. in 4 vols., 1888). Alfred Fouillée: La philosophie de Platon (2 vols., Paris, 1869; 2d ed., 4 vols., 1888–89; 3d ed. of vols. 1–2, 1904–6). Walter Pater (1839–1904): Plato and Platonism (263 p., London, 1893). Wilh. Windelband: Platon (Stuttgart, 1900; 5te Aufl., 1910). Lothar Brieger-Wasservogel: Plato and Aristoteles (192 p., Klassiker der Natur-

---

[a] $(2n)^2 + (n^2 - 1)^2 = (n^2 + 1)^2$.

[b] J. Burnet: Legacy of Greece (p. 84, 1921).

[c] Through Posidonios (q. v., first half of first century B. C.) and Chalcidius (q. v., first half of fourth century).

[d] And the translation by Chalcidius, through which it was known, was restricted to the first fifty-three chapters.

wiss., V, Leipzig, 1906). Alfred Edw. Taylor: Plato (157 p., London, 1908). Carra de Vaux: Article Aflāṭūn, in Encyclopedia of Islam (t. 1, 173–175, 1913. On the influence of Plato on Muslim thought). Max Wundt: Platons Leben und Werk (174 p., Jena, 1914; Isis, III, 452). Paul Elmer More: Platonism (318 p., Princeton, 1917). Ulrich von Wilamowitz-Moellendorff: Platon (2 Bde., Berlin, 1919; 1920. I: Leben und Werke; II: Beilagen und Textkritik). Constantin Ritter: Platons Stellung zu den Aufgaben der Naturwissenschaft (Sgbr. der Heidelberger Ak., phil. Kl., 119 p., 1919 (Isis, V, 205). Erich Frank: Plato und die sogenannten Pythagoreer (Halle, 1923; Isis, VI, 48–52). Ernst Howald: Platons Leben (110 p., Zurich, 1923).

P. Tannery: La stylométrie (Revue philosophique, t. 47, 159–69; Mémoires, VII, 277–92; Isis, IX); Article Platon in Grande Encyclopédie (Mémoires, VII, 320–370).

Criticism of Special Works—Meno—A. J. H. Vincent: Essai d'explication d'un passage géométrique du Ménon (Revue archéologique, XIIIme année, 1856). Adolf Benecke: Über die geometrische Hypothesis in Platons Menon (34 p., Elbing, 1867). C. Demme: Die Hypothesis in Platons Menon (Gymn. Progr., 22 p., Dresden, 1888). See also below under mathematics.

Critias—Gregor Demm: Ist die Atlantis in Platons Kritias eine poetische Fiktion? (Gymn. Progr., 43 p., Straubing, 1905). Friedr. Kluge: De Platonis Critia (51 p., Halle, 1909). See also below under Atlantis.

Timaeos—The Commentaries of Proclus of the Timaeus in 5 books Containing a Treasury of Pythagoric and Platonic Physiology (Transl. by Thomas Taylor, 2 vols., London, 1820). J. Simon: Du commentaire de Proclus sur le Timée (Paris, 1839). Th. H. Martin: Etudes sur le Timée (2 vols., Paris, 1841). Br. Wl. Switalski: Der Chalcidius Kommentar zu Platons Timaeus (121 p., Beitr. zur Gesch. d. Philos. d. Mittelalters, vol. III, 6, Münster, 1902). Hans Krause: Studia neoplatonica (Leipzig, 1904; last chapter: de antiquis Timaei interpretibus). Giuseppe Fraccaroli (1849–1918): Timeo (442 p., Torino, 1906. Italian translation with copious commentary). Timaios und Kritias übersetzt und erläutet v. Otto Apelt (224 p., Leipzig, 1919). See also below under astronomy.

Logic and Theory of Knowledge—Wincenty Lutoslawski: The Origin and Growth of Plato's Logic (565 p., London, 1897; reissue 1905). Martin Altenburg: Die Methode der Hypothesis bei Platon, Aristoteles und Proklus (Diss., 242 p., Marburg, 1905). Marie V. Williams: Six Essays on the Platonic Theory of Knowledge as Expressed in the Later Dialogues and Reviewed by Aristotle (140 p., Cambridge, 1908). A. E. Taylor: Parmenides, Zeno and Socrates (Proc. of the Aristotelian Soc., XVI, p. 234–289, London, 1916. Discusses the use made in Parmenides of the appeal to an infinite regress). Max Hiestand: Das Sokratische Nichtwissen in Platons ersten Dialogen—Eine Untersuchung über die Anfänge Platons (110 p., Zürich, 1923).

Mathematics (See also above under Meno)—P. Tannery: L'hypothèse géométrique du Ménon (Revue philosophique, 1876, t. II, p. 285–289; Mémoires, I, 39–45). Hermann Cohen: Platons Ideenlehre und die Mathematik (31 p., Marburg, 1878). P. Tannery: L'éducation platonicienne (Revue philosophique, t. 10 to 12, 1880–1; Mémoires, VII, 1–102; Isis, IX); La langue mathématique de Platon (Ann. de la Faculté des Lettres de Bordeaux, 1884, t. I, p. 95–105; Mémoires, II, 91–104). P. Tannery: L'hypothèse géométrique du Ménon (Archiv f. Gesch. der Philosophie, II, 509–514, 1889; Mémoires, II, 400–406). Théon de Smyrne: Exposition des connaissances mathématiques utiles pour la lecture de Platon (Texte grec et trad. franc. par J. Dupuis, 432 p., Paris, 1892). D. Kitao: Eine Methode mittelst zweier rechtwinkligen Lineale Cubikwurzeln zu finden (Sugaku butsurigaku Kwai, Kiji 5, p. 175–176, Tokyo, 1894. About a method used by Japanese carpenters essentially similar to Plato's). G. Milhaud: Platon, le géomètre et le métaphysicien (Leçon d'ouverture, 1898, publiée dans les Etudes sur la pensée scientifique des Grecs, p. 77–100, Paris, 1906). Gaston Milhaud: Les philosophes géomètres de la Grèce. Platon et ses prédécesseurs (387 p., Paris, 1900). A. Crespi: Intorno all' interpretazione di un luogo matematico di Platone (Rivista di filosofia, V, 343, Bologna, 1903). G. Vailati: A proposito d'un passo del Teeteto e di una dimostrazione di Euclide (Riv. di filisofia, VI, 11 p., Bologna, 1904). Irving Elgar Miller: The Significance of the Mathematical Element in the Philosophy of Plato (Diss., 96 p., Chicago, 1904, with bibliography). Rudolf Ebeling: Mathematik und Philosophie bei Plato (Gymn. Progr., 18 p., München, 1909). Heinrich Vogt: Die Entdeckungsgeschichte der Irrationalen nach Plato und anderen Quellen des 4. Jahrhunderts (Bibliotheca Mathematica, X, p. 97–155, Leipzig, 1910; important). Eva Sachs: Die fünf platonischen Körper (Philologische Untersuchungen, H. 24, 252 p., Berlin, 1917). Julius Stenzel: Zahl und Gestalt bei Platon und Aristoteles (152 p., Leipzig, 1924; Isis, VII, 177).

Astronomy—August Böckh: Untersuchungen über das kosmische System des Platon (158 p., Berlin, 1852). George Grote: Plato's Doctrine Respecting the Rotation of the Earth and Aristotle's Comment upon that Doctrine (35 p.; London, 1860. Reprinted in Grote's Minor Works, 1873, p. 237–275). Th. Häbler: Über zwei Stellen in Platons Timäus und im Hauptwerke von Coppernicus. (Grimma 1898). Karl Kerényi: Astrologia platonica. Archiv für Religionwiss., vol. 22, 245–256, 1924 (Isis, VIII, 530).

Geometrical or Nuptial Number—Paul Tannery: Le nombre nuptial dans Platon (Revue philosophique 1876, t. 1, p. 170–188; Mémoires, I, 12–38). C. Demme: Die platonische Zahl (Zeits. f. Mathematik, t. 32, 1887, hist. Abt. 81–99, 121–132). James Adam: The Nuptial Number of Plato: Its Solution and Significance (79 p., London, 1891). J. Dupuis: Le nombre géométrique de Platon (appendix to his edit. and French transl. of Theon of Smyrna, p. 365–400, Paris, 1892. The same author had published previously four other memoirs on the same subject; the number is 760,000). G. Albert: Die platonische Zahl und einige Conjecturen zu Platon sowie zu Lukrez (Wien, 1896). P. Tannery: Ya-t-il un nombre géométrique de Platon? (Revue des études grecques, 1903, t. 16, 173–179; Memoires, III, 188). G. Albert: Die platonische Zahl als Präcessionszahl und ihre konstruktion (Wien, 1907); Der Sinn der platonischen Zahl (Philologus, t. 66, p. 153–156, 1907). Arthur Ungnad: Die platonische Zahl (Zeitsch. f. Assyriologie, t. 41, p. 156–158, 1917).

Atlantis (see above under Critias)—This subject lends itself to the elaboration of fantastic theories and many papers dealing with it should be quoted in a history of human folly, but they would be out of place in my bibliography. I will quote, however, for the sake of curiosity, Jean Sylvain Bailly: Lettres sur l'Atlantide de Platon et sur l'ancienne histoire de l'Asie. Pour servir de suite aux lettres sur l'origine des sciences adressées à. M. de Voltaire par M. Bailly (Paris, 1st ed. 1779; new ed. 1804, 444 p.). John Francis, 12th Baron Arundell of Wardour: The Secret of Plato's Atlantis (108 p., London, 1885). Study provoked by Ignatius Donnelly's Atlantis: The Antediluvian World (7th ed., London, 1883; Donnelly's theory being that the Biblical tradition of a deluge originated with the subsidence of the island called Atlantis by Plato!). Sir Daniel Wilson: The Lost Atlantis and other Ethnographic Studies (p. 1–36, New York, 1892). Pierre Termier· L'Atlantide (Bull. de l'Institut Océanographique, No. 256, Paris, 1913) (transl. in the Smithsonian Report for 1915, p. 219–234). Geologically speaking, says Termier, the Platonic history of Atlantis is highly probable. C. Schuchert: Atlantis and the Permanency of the North Atlantic Ocean (Proc. National Acad. Sci., III, 65–72, Washington, 1917). William Diller Matthew: Plato's Atlantis in paleogeography (*ibidem*, t. 6, 17–18, 1920. It is a mere fable). Lewis Spence: The Problem of Atlantis (243 p., 16 pl., London, 1924). One might also refer to Ed. Suess: La Face de la Terre (Vol. II, p. 416, 491).

Physics and Chemistry—B. Rothlauf: Die Physik Platons, eine Studie auf Grund seiner Werke (2 Progr., 51 + 90 p., München, 1887–1888). Edm. O. von Lippmann: Chemisches und Physikalisches aus Platon (Abhandl. u. Vortr., II, p. 28–63, 1913; first published in Journ. f. prakt. Chemie, t. 76, p. 513 sq., 1907). Fr. Strunz: Chemisches bei Platon (Chemiker Zeitung, p. 1047, 1907; also in Beiträge und Skizzen zur Gesch. d. Naturw., p. 27–38, Hamburg, 1909). H. Diels: Über Platons Nachtuhr (Sitzungsber. d. Kgl. preuss. Akad. d. Wiss., 824–830, 1915. According to Athenaeos, Plato constructed the first alarm-clock! Isis, IV, 395). L. Robin: Étude sur la signification et la place de la physique dans la philosophie de Platon (96 p., Extrait de la Revue philosophique, 1918, Paris, 1919).

Other Sciences—Jegel. Platons Stellung zur Erziehungsfragen (Archiv f. Gesch. d. Philos., t. 26, p. 402–430, 1913). J. W. Courtney: The Views of Plato and Freud on the Etiology and Treatment of Hysteria (Boston Medical and Surgical Journal, p. 649–652, 1913). (See above under Timaeos).

III. GREEK MATHEMATICS

THEAETETOS

Theaetetos of Athens (Θεαίτητος, flourished c. 380). Mathematician; pupil of Socrates and Theodoros. Friend of Plato, who called one of his dialogues after him. Essential contributions to the theory of surds. Euclid X, 9 ascribed to him. Discovered the octahedron and the icosahedron, and was first to write on the *five* regular solids.

Eva Sachs: De Theaeteto Atheniensi mathematico (Diss., 70 p., Berlin, 1914); *Idem'* Die fünf platonischen Körper (Philologische Untersuchungen, H. 24, 252 p., Berlin, 1917).

LEON

Λέων, younger than Plato, older than Eudoxos. Mathematician. Wrote "Elements of Geometry" superior to those of Hippocrates by the number and usefulness of the proved propositions. Introduced or improved diorismi (διορισμός = determinatio; definition, specification).

ARCHYTAS

Archytas of Tarentum (Ἀρχύτας, flourished in the first half of the fourth century). Mathematician, mechanician, statesman, Pythagorean philosopher. A friend of Plato. The founder of theoretical mechanics. Distinction between arithmetic, geometric, and harmonic proportions. Very ingenious duplication of the cube by means of two intersecting surfaces (first example of a curve of double curvature). Proof that there is no numerical geometric mean between n and n + 1. Contributions to harmonics. Construction of automaton.

O. F. Gruppe: Über die Fragmente des Archytas und der alten Pythagoreer (173 p., Berlin, 1840). A. E. Chaignet: Pythagore et la philosophie pythagoricienne (2e ed., 2 vols., Paris, 1874). Paul Tannery: Sur les solutions du problème de Délos par Archytas et par Eudoxe (Mémoires de la soc. des sci. phys. et natur. de Bordeaux, t. II, 277–283, 1878; also: Tannery's Mémoires, I, 53–61, 1912). Fried. Blass: De Archytae Tarentini fragmentis mathematicis (Mélanges Graux, p. 573–584, Paris, 1884). P. Tannery: Démocrite et Archytas (Bull. d. sci. mathém., t. 10, p. 295–303, Paris, 1886). G. Fazzari: Metodo di Archita per la soluzione del problema delle due medie proporzionali (Il Pitagora, t. 6, 16–17, Palermo, 1900). P. Tannery: A propos des fragments philolaïques sur la musique (Revue de philologie, t. 28, p. 233–249, 1904; Mémoires, III, 220–243; Isis, IV, 338); Un traité grec d'arithmétique antérieur à Euclide (Bibliotheca Mathematica, VI, 225–229, Leipzig, 1905, important; Mémoires, III, 244–250; Isis, IV, 339). C. Thaer: Über die Würfelverdoppelung des Archytas (Bericht, Math. Sem., Jena, p. 13–15, 1908).

THYMARIDAS

Thymaridas of Paros (Θυμαρίδας, flourished in the fourth century, probably in the first half). Mathematician. Called prime numbers linear numbers (ἀριϑμοὶ εὐϑυγραμμικοί). Invented a method (ἔφοδος) to solve a system of linear equations of this type:

$$x_1 + x_i = a_{i-1}$$
$$x_1 + \Sigma x_i = s \qquad (i = 2 \text{ to } n)$$

the a_{i-1} and s being known quantities (ὡρισμένα), the x_i the unknown (ἀόριστα) The solution was given by

$$x_1 = \frac{\Sigma\, a_{i-1} - s}{n - 2}$$

This remarkable method was called the flower (ἐπάνϑημά) of Thymaridas.

Paul Tannery: Sur l'age du pythagoricien Thymaridas (Annales de la faculté des lettres de Bordeaux, t. III, p. 101–104, 1881; also Tannery's Mémoires, I, 106–110, 1912).

For Philip of Opus (c. 368) see the following section dealing with astronomy.

EUDOXOS

Eudoxos of Cnidos (Εὔδοξος, flourished c. 367, born c. 408, died c. 355). Studied geometry under Archytas, medicine under Philistion and Theomedon, philosophy under Plato. The greatest mathematician and astronomer of his time; one of the greatest of all times. He extended the theory of proportions to incommensurable quantities as explained in Books V and VI of Euclid. Developed the theory of the golden section. Discovered the method of exhaustion. Was first able to prove the theorems concerning the volumes of pyramid and cone, and the one stating that the areas of circles are to one another as the squares of their diameters. His astronomical work led him to the study of a spherical lemniscate, called hippopede (ἵππου πέδη).

His theory of homocentric spheres was the foundation of scientific astronomy; it was the first serious attempt to account quantitatively for the irregular motions of the sun, moon, and planets among the stars (27 spheres, all concentric to the earth, were needed to account for these motions). Eudoxos wrote two books entitled "The Mirror" (ἔνοπτρον) and "The Phaenomena" (Aratos's poem, v. 19–732, drawn from it), a third on "Speeds" (containing his astronomical theory; lost), and possibly a fourth one on "Sphaerics," dealing also with astronomy. He may be the inventor of Aristarchos's method of measuring the sizes and distances of the sun and moon. He introduced or modified the eight-year period, octaëteris. Research in acoustics and applied mechanics also ascribed to him.

Text—Ernest Maas: Eudoxi Cnidii fragmenta ex Hipparcho conlecta (*In* Aratea, Berlin, 1892, c. VII, p. 279–304).

Criticism—A. J. Letronne: Sur les écrits et les travaux d'Eudoxe d'après Ludwig Ideler (35 p., extr. du Journal des Savants, Paris, 1840–1841). Giov. Virg.

Schiaparelli: Die homocentrischen Sphären des Eudoxus, des Kalippus und des Aristoteles, übersetzt v. W. Horn (Suppl. zur hist. literar. Abt. d. Z. f. Math. u. Physik., XXII, p. 101–198, Leipzig, 1877. Fundamental; appeared first in the Pubblic. del R. Osservatorio di Brera, No. IX, Milano, 1875). Paul Tannery: Note sur le système astronomique d'Eudoxe (Mém. de la soc. des sciences physiques de Bordeaux, t. I, p. 441–449, 1876; Mémoires, I, 1–11); *id.*, Sur les solutions du problème de Délos par Archytas et par Eudoxe (*ibidem*, t. II, p. 227–283, 1878; Mémoires, I, p. 53–61); Seconde note sur le système astronomique d'Eudoxe (*ibidem*, t. V, 129–147, 1883; Mémoires I, p. 317–338); *id.*, L'art d'Eudoxe (Revue de philologie, t. XIII, p. 143–150, 1889; Mémoires, II, 407–417). H. Künssberg: Der Astronom, Mathematiker und Geograph Eudoxus (120 p. and 2 pl., in two parts, Progr., Dinkelsbühl, 1888–1890). P. Tannery: Article in the Grande Encyclopedie, c. 1893 (Mémoires, III, 366–369). Max. Thiel: Eudoxeum (Griechische Studien Hermann Lipsius dargebracht, p. 179–182, Leipzig, 1894). Julius Höpken: Über die Entstehung der Phaenomena des Eudoxos—Aratos (37 p., 3 pl., Gymn. Progr., Emden, 1905). Paul Mansion: Le système des sphères homocentriques comme origine du système des épicycles (Archiv für Geschichte d. Naturwiss., I, p. 376–379, Leipzig, 1909). Enrico Rufini: Gli studi geometrici di Eudosso da Cnido (Archivio di storia della scienza, vol. 2, 222–239, Roma, 1921; Isis, IV, 396). Friedrich Gisinger: Die Erdbeschreibung des Eudoxos von Knidos (148 p., Leipzig, 1921).

For the so-called "Papyrus of Eudoxus" or Ars Eudoxi, see my note on Astronomy in the first half of the second century B. C.

IV. GREEK ASTRONOMY

The greatest astronomer of the period was Eudoxos (c. 367) with whom I have just dealt. Two others, both Pythagoreans, one older than Eudoxos and the other a contemporary, will now be considered.

ECPHANTOS

Ecphantos of Syracuse (Ἔκφαντος, flourished in the beginning of the century). A late Pythagorean, possibly a disciple of Hicetas (q. v., fifth century). He believed "that the earth, being in the center of the universe, moves about its own center in an eastward direction." Combined Pythagorean and atomistic doctrines.

The very few references to Ecphantos are collected by Diels in the Fragmente der Vorsokratiker, cap. 38.

P. Tannery: Ecphante. Archiv für Gesch. der Philos., Vol. XI, 263–269, 1898 (Mémoires, VII, 249–57). E. Wellmann, in Pauly-Wissowa (t. 5, 2215, 1905).

PHILIP OF OPUS[a]

Φίλιππος ὁ Ὀπούντιος, a disciple of Plato. Mathematician, astronomer. Published after his master's death the Epinomis (ἐπινομίς), the most Pythagorean of all Platonic treatises, a sequel to the Laws (important for the study of Platonic astronomy and physics). Wrote on polygonal numbers and on many astronomical subjects, but no writings of his remain. Explained the rainbow as a phenomenon of refraction (?, Cantor I, 248, 1907).

V. GREEK PHYSICS AND TECHNOLOGY

For Archytas and Eudoxos, see Section III; for Philip of Opus, see Section IV.

---

[a] **Most probably identical with Philip of Medma (or Mende).**

AENEAS TACTICOS

Aeneas Tacticos (Αἰνείας, Arcadian, or at any rate, Peloponnesian, who had seen service in the Aegean and in Asia Minor, flourished c. 360). Earliest Greek writer on military science (περὶ τῶν στρατηγηματικῶν ὑπομνήματα).

In the fragment that has come down to us he explained how to conduct defensive warfare and how to resist a siege (πολιορκητικά; Commentarius poliorceticus). This book was very probably composed in 357–6. It was abridged by Cineas, Pyrrhos's adviser. The hydraulic telegraph invented by Aeneas was described by Polybios.[f] Aeneas explains a system of cryptography.

Text—Τακτικὸν ὑπόμνημα περὶ τοῦ πῶς χρὴ πολιορκουμένους ἀντέχειν. Commentarius poliorceticus, edited by Arnold Hug, (Leipzig, 1874). French translation with commentary by the comte de Beausobre (Amsterdam, 1757). Aeneas Tacitus, Asclepiodotus, Onasander (Greek text with an English translation by members of the Illinois Greek Club, Loeb Classical Library, London, 1923).

Criticism—Schwartz, in Pauly-Wissowa (t. 1, 1019–1021, 1894). A Croiset: Littérature grecque (t. 4, 2me ed., 198–199, 1900). W. A. Oldfather's introduction to the Loeb edition, 1923.

VI. PROGRESS OF THE MEDICAL ARTS IN GREECE AND CHINA

Hippocratic Treatises

On Fractures and Dislocations (generally quoted as two separate works, περὶ ἀγμῶν, de fractis, περὶ ἄρθρων ἐμβολῆs, de articulorum repositione)—The original work was written early in the fourth century (or earlier) for it was known to Diocles. It may have been a genuine Hippocratic treatise, but the work which has come down to us contains many interpolations of a later date, say of the end of the fourth century, or even later. It represents the high-water mark of Athenian anatomy or the beginning of Alexandrian endeavors. It is a splendid surgical treatise. One passage of it implies human dissection. For the περὶ ἄρθρων, see my note on Apollonios of Citium (first half of first century B. C.).

Text—Littré (vol. 3, 339–563, vol. 4, 1–328); Francis Adams (vol. 2, 507, 1849); Joseph Petrequin: Chirurgie d'Hippocrate (2 vols., Paris, 1877–1878, Greek and French; best edition).

Criticism—E. Gurlt: Geschichte der Chirurgie (Bd. 1, 1898).

On Generation (περὶ γονῆs).—One may give this collective name to a group of Hippocratic treatises (of Cnidian origin?) respectively entitled: περὶ γονῆs, on semen; περὶ φύσιος παιδίου, on the nature of the child; περὶ νούσων δ', four books on diseases, because they really form one treatise on generation. It dates probably from the first quarter of the fourth century B. C. and is the earliest important treatise on the subject. It contains a very elaborate account of a doctrine of pangenesis, "not wholly unlike that of Darwin,"[g] in order to explain inheritance (inheritance of acquired characteristics is admitted); also a very detailed description of a specimen of exfoliated membrana mucosa uteri (mistaken for an embryo). The author suggests an embryological study, day by day, of the chick and compares the human embryo with that of the chick (he assimilates wrongly the umbilical cord to the chalazae of the incubated egg). The generation of man and animals is compared to that of plants; he also compares the generation of plants from cuttings with that from seeds.

---

[f] Karras: Geschichte der Telegraphie (t. 1, 16, Braunschweig, 1909).
[g] C. Singer, op. cit., 14.

Text—Littré, vols. 6 and 7.
Criticism—C. Singer: Greek Biology and Medicine (p. 14–16, Oxford, 1922).

Anatomy (*περὶ ἀνατομῆς*), dating probably from the middle of the fourth century. It is the earliest separate treatise on the subject extant.[h] It is a brief popular account of the anatomical knowledge attained in those days.

Text—Littré, vol. 8, 536–42.

On the Heart (*περὶ καρδίης*).—Another anatomical treatise of the same time (middle of the fourth century B. C.), representing clearly Sicilian influences. It is probably a little later than the Anatomy, but is far more elaborate. The heart is conceived as the seat of intellect and innate heat. Description of auricles, auriculo-ventricular and semi-lunar valves, columnae carneae, chordae tendinae. Experiments to test the valves.

Text—Littré (vol. 9, 76–93). Friedrich Karl Unger: Liber de corde editus cum prolegomenis et commentario (101 p., Utrecht thesis, Leiden, 1923).

School of Cos

Polybos (Πόλυβος, son-in-law of Hippocrates, flourished about the beginning of the fourth century B. C.). Greek physician. Apparently the greatest of Hippocrates's immediate successors, and probably the head of his school after his death. The Hippocratic treatise on the nature of man (*περὶ φύσιος ἀνθρώπου*) is ascribed to him. It is the main source for the theory of four humors (blood, yellow bile, black bile, phlegm) combined with the four qualities (wet, hot, dry, cold) and the four seasons. Chapter 12 contains a confused description of the vascular system.[i] He carried on embryological investigations.

Text—Littré (vol. 6, 32–69). Oskar Villaret: De natura hominis ad codicum fidem recensitus (Diss., 88 p., Berlin, 1911).
Criticism—E. Gurlt: Geschichte der Chirurgie (t. 1, 1898, 304). Hermann Aubert and Friedrich Wimmer: Edition and German translation of Aristotle's zoology (Leipzig, 1868, figure of Polybos's vascular system).

School of Sicily

Philistion of Locroi (Φιλίστιον, flourished at the beginning of the century). The most prominent representative of the medical school of Sicily. Adherent of Empedocles. Plato came into touch with him in Syracuse. It is not always easy to dissociate his own ideas from those of his school, to which much anatomical and physiological progress is due. They did a great deal of animal dissection, especially with regard to the vessels. They considered the heart as the main regulator of life, the central organ of the pneuma and the seat of the soul. The Hippocratic writings *περὶ καρδίης* and *περὶ διαίτης* were possibly influenced by them. Philistion holds that disease is caused by irregularities in the movement of the pneuma or by a disharmony of the four elements, or the four qualities. The four fevers (continued, quotidian, tertian, quartan) correspond to the four elements. His therapeutics was chiefly dietetical. He did much to diffuse the medical knowledge of Sicily and insure its synthesis with the knowledge of Cos and Cnidos.

---

[h] Diocles's treatise (q. v.) was probably earlier, but only fragments of it remain.
[i] Aristotle ascribes that chapter to Polybos.

Max Wellmann: Die Fragmente der sykelischen Ärzte Akron, Philistion und des Diokles von Karystos (Berlin, 1901).

School of Cnidos and Sicily

Chrysippos of Cnidos (Χρύσιππος, flourished c. 365). Physician, anatomist. Pupil of Eudoxos and of Philistion. Wrote a book on the various kinds of vegetables (chiefly on cabbage) and their medical uses (περὶ λαχάνων). Poultices are also ascribed to him.

He objected to venesection and to the use of purgatives, but recommended the bandaging of limbs to reduce hemorrhages. Treatment of dropsy ascribed to him.

It is not certain that the second paragraph refers to the same man as the first. At least, Max Wellmann would have it that what I have said in the second paragraph does not apply to the elder Chrysippos mentioned in the first, but to a grandson of his, living at the end of the century. (See Pauly-Wissowa: Real-Encyclopädie (3. Bd., under Chrysippos, §15 and §16, 1899.)

Dogmatic School (School of Cos and Sicily)

Diocles of Carystos, Euboea (Διοκλῆς, flourished in the first third of the century). The most important representative of the Dogmatic School in the fourth century, called by the Athenians a second Hippocrates. He syncretized the theories of Sicily and of Cos. Many writings are ascribed to him. He was the first physician to write in the Attic dialect and to use a Hippocratic collection (possibly made by himself?). His physiology was very similar to that of Philistion, his pathology a compromise between Coan and Sicilian theories. He considered fever as a symptom of other disorders. He made embryological, gynaecological, and obstetrical studies, and carried on animal dissections (e. g., he dissected the womb of mules). He held that both sexes contribute "seed" towards the formation of the embryo. He described human embryos (of 27 and 40 days). He dissected animals and described cotyledonous placenta. He was the first to write a book entitled "anatomy" (περὶ ἀνατομῆς), and he improved our knowledge of the vessels. His ῥιζοτομικόν, a book of medical botany, is the oldest botanical textbook; Theophrastos drew much upon it.

Max Wellmann: Die Fragmente der sykelischen Ärzte Akron, Philistion und des Diokles von Karytos (Fragmentsammlung der griechischen Ärzte, Bd. I, Berlin, 1901). This book deals chiefly with Diocles.

Max Wellmann: Die pneumatische Schule (Berlin, 1895); Das älteste Kräuterbuch der Griechen (Festgabe für Franz Susemihl, 1898). J. Heeg: Über ein angebliches Diokleszitat (Sitzungber. d. Kgl. Preuss. Akad. d. Wissensch., p. 991–1007, Berlin, 1911; fragment dealing with the influence of the moon upon disease). M. Wellmann: Zu Diokles (Hermes, t. 47, p. 160, 1912). W. Haberling: Die Entdeckung einer kriegschirurgischen Instrumentes des Altertums. Deut. militärärztl. Z., p. 658–660, 1912; on the so-called spoon of Diocles to extract an arrow from a wound).

Botany

See my notes on Chrysippos and Diocles, above.

Zoology

See my note on Xenophon in Section VII.

Chinese Medicine

The oldest Chinese views on physiology and pathology are explained in a work traditionally ascribed to the legendary Yellow Emperor Huang^{2} Ti^{4} (5124, 10942) B. C. 2698–2598) and entitled "The Simple Questions of Huang Ti, Huang Ti Nei^{4}-ching^{1} Su^{4}-wên^{4}" (8177, 2122, 10348, 12650). This work is probably not earlier than the fourth century B. C. It is written in the form of a dialogue between Huang Ti and the scientists of his court.

The core of the Shên^{2}-nung^{3} Pên^{3}-ts'ao^{3} (9819, 8408, 8846, 11634) may be even older than that of the Nei ching; it is impossible to say. The fact that Shên-nung (B. C. 2838–2698) reigned before Huang Ti proves nothing, of course.

F. Huebotter: Guide (Kumamoto, 3–9, 1924; Isis, VII, 259; with references, unfortunately too brief, to Japanese investigations on the subject).

VII. GREEK HISTORIOLOGY AND SOCIOLOGY

XENOPHON

Ξενοφῶν, born at Athens c. 430, died after 355, probably at Corinth. Greek historian. Disciple of Socrates. Leader of the ten thousand Greek mercenaries in their five months' retreat (401–400) from Cunaxa on the Euphrates through Kurdistan and the highlands of Armenia and Georgia to Trapezos (Trebizond) on the Black Sea. Xenophon's recital of this up-country march (Ἀνάβασις) is one of the masterpieces of historical literature (written in Scillos near Olympia between 379 and 371). He wrote also the Hellenica (Ἑλληνικά) in 7 books continuing Thucydides down to the Battle of Mantinea (411–362; written at Corinth); the Cyropaedia (Κυροπαιδεία), a political romance; a treatise on horsemanship (Ἱππική, de re equestri); a treatise on hunting (Κυνηγετικός, Cynegeticus), including notes on the breeding of dogs (both treatises based on first-hand knowledge); on the Revenues of Athens (Πόροι ἢ περὶ προσόδων, de vectigalibus; written in 355); the Memorabilia of Socrates in 4 books (Ἀπομνημονεύματα Σωκράτους) one of our two fundamental sources for the study of Socrates; the Banquet (Συμπόσιον); and the Oeconomics (Οἰκονομικός) dealing with the management of home and farm. The Banquet and the Oeconomics are complements to the Memorabilia.

Texts—Complete editions. Princeps, Florence, 1516. Complete Latin edition, Bale, 1534; Greek and Latin, Bale, 1545. Greek, Latin, and French edition by J. B. Gail (7 vols., Paris, 1797–1808). Greek and Latin edition by Friedrich Dübner (Paris, Didot, 1838). Greek edition by Gustav Sauppe (5 vols., Leipzig, 1865–1866). Greek edition by E. C. Marchant (5 vols., Oxford, 1900–1910).

Anabasis. Edited by Wilhelm Gemoll (Leipzig, 1899); by Paul Couvreur (4th ed., 640 p., Paris, 1908).

Hellenica. (Venice, 1503). Greek and English ed. by Carleton L. Brownson (Loeb Library, London, 1918).

Cyropaedia. Latin edition, Rome, 1474. Edited by Wilhelm Gemoll (475 p., Leipzig, 1912). Greek and English ed. by Walter Miller (Loeb Library, 2 vols., London, 1914).

Memorabilia. Edited by Raphael Kühner (6. Aufl., Leipzig, 1902); by Walter Gilbert (Leipzig, 1911).

Scripta minora. Post Lud. Dindorf ediderunt Th. Thalheim et F. Ruehl (2 vols., Leipzig, 1910–1912).

Lexicons—Gustav Sauppe: Lexicologus Xenophonteus (150 p., Leipzig, 1869).

Criticism—A. Croiset: Littérature grecque (t. 4, 2e ed., 337–411, 1900). John Pentland Mahaffy: The Progress of Hellenism in Alexander's Empire (160 p., Chicago, 1905).

Erwin Scharr: Xenophons Staats- und Gesellschaftsideal und seine Zeit (321 p., Halle, 1920; Max Pohlenz, in Gött. gel. Anz., 118–24, 1921).

Anabasis—Eduard von Hoffmeister: Durch Armenien, eine Wanderung und der Zug Xenophons bis zum Schwarzen Meere (260 p., ill., Leipzig, 1911). Arthur Boucher: L'Anabase avec un commentaire historique et militaire (Paris, 1913).

Hellenica—Herwart Lohse: Quaestiones chronologicae ad Xenophontis Hellenica pertinentes (108 p., Leipzig, 1905).

Memorabilia—Albert Chavanon: Etude sur les sources des Mémorables (106 p., Paris, 1903). Léon Robin: Les Mémorables et notre connaissance de la philosophie de Socrate (L'année philosophique, t. 21, 1–47, 1911).

Scientific Topics—Th. Beck: Medizinisches und Naturwissenschaftliches aus Xenophons Anabasis (Schweiz. Corr. Bl., t. 35, 24, 1905). A. Borchard: Beitrag zur Geschichte der Frostgangrän (Zentralblatt für Chirurgie, 1916, 142; Anabasis, IV, 5).

VIII. SANSKRIT PHILOLOGY

Pāṇini. Flourished in the extreme northwest of India, about the middle of the fourth century B. C.[j] The greatest Hindu grammarian. His grammar, called Ashṭādhyāyī,[k] is not simply the earliest grammar extant of any language, but one of the greatest grammatical works ever produced. He fixed the Sanskrit language. He recognized the Brāhmi alphabet.[l] It is clear that his remarks referred principally to a *spoken* language; hence the great importance given by him (and other Sanskrit grammarians) to phonetics.[m]

Text—Edited by Otto Böhtlingk (Bonn, 1839–40). Again with German translation, Leipzig (1886–1887).

To Pāṇini's grammar were appended two glossaries: a list of some 2,000 verbal roots (Dhātupāṭha) and a list of word-groups (Gaṇapāṭha) to which certain rules apply. Many commentaries were devoted to Pāṇini's grammar, the most important ancient commentary being Patañjali's (see second half of second century B. C.).

Criticism—Theodor Goldstuecker: Pāṇini, his place in Sanskrit literature (283 p., London, 1861). A. A. Macdonell: Sanskrit Literature (London, 1900).

---

[j] That is, about the middle of the sūtra period. I am giving the date which is accepted by most scholars, but it is uncertain.

[k] Because it consisted of eight lectures (adhyāya).

[l] For which see my note on Yāska (fifth century B. C.).

[m] In this, the Hindu grammarians were considerably ahead of the European.

CHAPTER VI

THE TIME OF ARISTOTLE

(Second Half of the Fourth Century B. C.)

I. Survey of Science in the Second Half of the Fourth Century B. C. II. Alexander the Great. III. Aristotle and the Lyceum. IV. Other Philosophers, Greek and Chinese. V. Greek Mathematics. VI. Greek Astronomy. VII. Greek Physics. VIII. Greek and Roman Technology. IX. Greek Botany. X. Greek Geography, Geology, and Meteorology. XI. Greek Anatomy, Physiology, and Medicine. XII. Greek Historiography. XIII. Hindu and Roman Sociology and Law. XIV. Greek Study of the History of Science.

I. SURVEY OF SCIENCE IN SECOND HALF OF FOURTH CENTURY B. C.

1. Thus far we have paid no attention to political events, but during the period under consideration, the natural development of civilization was suddenly interrupted and then stimulated by the conquests of Alexander (334 to 323). These events were of such magnitude, and their consequences so deep and widespread, that we must take them into account.

2. *Alexander the Great*—By the second half of the fourth century, Greek civilization, as represented by its artistic and scientific achievements, had already reached its climax. When all circumstances are considered, this climax was so high that the human race has hardly surpassed it or even reached it at any other time. This unique civilization was carried by Alexander as far as the Indus and the Jaxartes (Syr Darya), that is, into the very heart of Asia. This was the first contact on a large scale between East and West. In 332, Alexander founded the city of Alexandria, which was to become one of the greatest centers of cultural exchange and diffusion, and this again brought forth far-reaching consequences in the intellectual development of both sides of the world, the East and the West.

Under the influence of his teacher Aristotle, Alexander had acquired a modicum of scientific curiosity, and his expeditions were, to some little extent, scientific expeditions. Alexander was probably the first conqueror who organized, however crudely, scientific research, and this was typical of the civilization of which he had become, in such wretched way, the herald.

3. *Aristotle (384 to 323) and the Lyceum (335 B. C. to the third century after Christ)*—The prodigious activity of Aristotle marks the climax of the golden age of Greece. The very existence of his works proves not simply that he had an encyclopaedic mind of the highest order, but also that a large amount of scientific research had already been accomplished by his time. Unlike his teacher Plato, Aristotle was not essentially a mathematician. He had a deep mathematical knowledge, but that knowledge was happily balanced by a very extensive acquaintance with every branch of natural history. Thus his philosophy was naturally more experimental, more inductive than that of Plato. And yet, such was the capacity and vigor of his mind, that he was also the founder of logic. His mind embraced everything.

In 335, Aristotle founded a new school in the Lyceum, near Athens. It would seem that the teaching was imparted in the gardens while master and pupils were walking together, hence the name, Peripatetic school.[a] After Aristotle's death, the school was led by Theophrastos, and later still by Straton. It lasted only until the third century after Christ; but Aristotle's philosophy has remained a motive power until to-day. The history of Peripateticism is to a large extent a history of scientific thought. Reciprocally, it is impossible to outline the history of science without explaining the fortunes of Peripateticism, its conflicts with various theologies and with Platonism. The reader will have many glimpses of all this in my Introduction.

4. *Other Philosophers, Greek and Chinese*—Of Aristotle's successor, Theophrastos, I shall speak below in the section dealing with botany. The philosophical vitality of that period is attested by the creation of many new schools of thought: Pyrrhon, who went with Alexander to India, was the leader of the Sceptics; Euhemeros (c. 316) attempted to rationalize religion; Epicuros, who is best known for his ethical views (Epicureanism, hedonism), continued the atomistic tradition; Zeno of Citium founded the Stoic philosophy, which for many centuries (at least five) exerted a deep influence upon the morality of people and molded, or at least colored, their world-conception. Stoicism was already to some extent a fruit of the new political situation created by Alexander; it was, from the beginning, cosmopolitan, and later, under Roman rule, it became the earliest philosophy of international importance.

Mencius, the greatest Confucian philosopher after the master himself, flourished about 332. Two Taoist philosophers, Yang Chu, the Epicurean, and Lieh Tzŭ, the metaphysician, may have lived at about the same time.

5. *Greek Mathematics*—Aristotle contributed to the systematization of mathematics, improving the definitions and discussing the fundamental concepts. In the meanwhile the Academy remained deeply interested in the subject. Speusippos, who was its director from 348 to 339, wrote on the theory of numbers; Xenocrates, its director from 339 to 314, solved a problem of combinatorial analysis and wrote a history of geometry. Menaechmos discovered the conic sections, and both he and his brother Dinostratos contributed to the geometrical textbook of the Academy edited by Theudios of Magnesia. The Peripatetic Eudemos of Rhodes wrote histories of mathematics and astronomy. The greatest mathematician of the period was Aristaeos the elder, who flourished toward the end of the century, and made a deeper study of geometrical methods and loci, of the regular solids, and of the conics.

6. *Greek Astronomy*—The greatest and most original astronomer of that time was Heraclides of Pontos (c. 348), who anticipated the geoheliocentrical system of Tycho Brahe. Callippos improved the theory of Eudoxos, using 34 homocentric spheres (instead of 27); Aristotle added more spheres still, in the attempt to account for all the facts (σώζειν τὰ φαινόμενα). He tried to estimate the size of the earth; he postulated the existence of a fifth element, aether, the natural movement of which is circular; the celestial bodies are made of aether and are incorruptible. Autolycos (c. 310) wrote treatises on spherical (astronomical) geometry and pointed out some difficulties in the theory of homocentric spheres.

7. *Greek Physics*—If Aristotle is the author of the treatise on mechanics ascribed

---

[a] Περιπατέω, to walk around, about.

to him, he is the real founder of theoretical mechanics. He made investigations in acoustics, meteorology, even chemistry. However, the most important work of the time is that of Aristoxenos, the greatest theorician of music in antiquity. The most systematic account of physical phenomena was that given by the Stoa (for which see my note on Zeno among the philosophers); it was also for many centuries the most influential, but it is impossible to determine to what extent it was already constituted by the end of the fourth century.

8. *Greek and Roman Technology*—Lysistratos (c. 328) was the first to take plaster casts from the human face.

Appius Claudius Caecus built the Aqua Appia and the Via Appia during his censorship (312 to 308).

9. *Greek Botany*—Outside of the ubiquitous name of Aristotle, there is but one important name to mention in this section: Theophrastos of Eresos (372 to 288), successor of his master at the head of the Lyceum in 322, and second only to him. If there had been no Aristotle, this period would have been called the time of Theophrastos. His encyclopaedic activity was eclipsed by that of his master. While Aristotle's botany is lost, the admirable treatises of Theophrastos have survived. Their comprehensiveness, while implying that much botanical knowledge had already been accumulated before him, places him in the front rank of botanists of all times. A friend of Theophrastos named Phanias wrote a treatise on plants.

10. *Greek Geography, Geology, and Meteorology*—The Periplus of Scylax was probably written between 360 and 347. The historian Ephoros of Cyme (with whom I shall deal presently) attached great importance to the geographical basis of history.

Pytheas of Massilia (c. 330) sailed to Britain and possibly reached the Arctic circle. He noted the influence of the moon upon the tides. In 327 to 325, Alexander's admiral, Nearchos, descended the Hydaspes and the Indus and returned to Susa by sea. Dicaearchos of Messina made geodesical measurements, estimated the height of mountains, and wrote geographical treatises; he noticed the influence of the sun upon the tides.

Theophrastos wrote a treatise on stones.

Both Aristotle and Theophrastos wrote on meteorology, Aristotle's treatise being the earliest systematic account of the subject.

11. *Greek Anatomy, Physiology, and Medicine*—Praxagoras of Cos, who succeeded Diocles at the head of the Dogmatic school (c. 330), distinguished clearly between veins and arteries and studied the pulse. Two of his disciples must be mentioned: Philotimos, who insisted on gymnastics and diet, and Mnesitheos, who wrote a medical compendium and dissected animals. Theophrastos is credited with having replaced the seat of intelligence in the brain (against Aristotle, who placed it in the heart). A pupil of Aristotle, Menon, wrote a history of medical doctrines.

12. *Greek Historiography*—About the middle of the century, Ephoros of Cyme wrote a universal history; he attached much importance to geography. Theopompos of Chios, who wrote two treatises on Greek history down to 336, laid special stress on psychological analysis. Euhemeros, already mentioned among the philosophers, may be counted the first historian of religion. The early Stoa also encouraged the scientific study of religion.

13. *Hindu and Roman Sociology and Law*—Kauṭilya, minister of Candragupta, the first Emperor of India (322–298), himself a Hindu Machiavelli, wrote a trea-

tise on law and administration, the Arthaśāstra, which is of inestimable value for the study of Maurya civilization.

Claudius Caecus (c. 312), mentioned in section 8, is the earliest Roman jurist about whom we have definite information.

14. *Greek Study of the History of Science*—The fact that already in this time a few Greek scientists found it necessary to write the history of various branches of science speaks volumes for the amount of scientific work which had been accomplished. Especially during the last century (450 to 350 or to 325) the mass of investigations had increased so much that it had become confusing and historical accounts were already needed to find one's bearings. Thus, toward the middle of the century, Xenocrates wrote a history of geometry; a little later Theophrastos compiled a history of natural philosophy; the physician Menon wrote a history of medicine; finally (c. 320), Eudemos wrote historical accounts of arithmetic, astronomy, and geometry.

15. *Final Remarks*—In spite of two brilliant exceptions, the Chinese Mencius and the Hindu Kauṭilya, this period was again one of Greek achievement. But the ancient world has been deeply stirred by the Macedonian explosion, East and West have been brought into close contact, and the consequences of this will appear in the next centuries. The whole fourth century was a Greek century, almost exclusively.

II. ALEXANDER THE GREAT

'Αλέξανδρος, born in Macedonia in 356, died in Babylon c. June 13, 323. Pupil of Aristotle. His campaigns, from 334 to his death, increased considerably the knowledge of geography and natural history and carried Greek civilization into the very heart of Asia. Alexander's scientific curiosity was apparently great, and to his and Aristotle's initiative are probably due the first scientific expeditions and the first attempts at organization of science on a larger scale. Founded the city of Alexandria in Egypt in 332–331.

Robert Geier: Alexander und Aristoteles in ihren gegenseitigen Beziehungen (245 p., Halle, 1856). Hugo Bretzl: Botanische Forschungen des Alexanderzuges (424 p., Leipzig, 1903; important). Wilhelm Reese: Die griechischen Nachrichten über Indien bis zum Feldzuge Alexanders des Grossen (106 p., Leipzig, 1914).

For the itineraries of Alexander's and Nearchos's expeditions see also the histories of ancient geography.

For the Muslim traditions see in the Encyclopedia of Islam (t. 2, 533–535, 1921), the anonymous articles al-Iskandar and Iskandar-nāma (the romance of Alexander). For the Christian medieval traditions see Lynn Thorndike: History of Magic (vol. 1, pp. 551–565, 1923), the story of Nectanebus, or the Alexander legend. See also Oswald Feis: Die Geburt Alexanders des Grossen—Die Wandlung einer Geburtsgeschichte (Archiv für Geschichte der Medizin, t. XI, 260–277, 1919).

III. ARISTOTLE AND THE LYCEUM

'Αριστοτέλης, born in 384 at Stagira in Chalcidice, died in 322–321 in Euboea. His father was physician to the King of Macedonia. Disciple of Plato. Teacher of Alexander. In 335–334 he founded in the Lyceum of Athens a new philosophic school, the so-called Peripatetic school. One of the greatest philosophers and scientists of all times. His was such an encyclopaedic genius and his works were so comprehensive that it is hardly possible to give an adequate summary of them within a brief compass, and I must restrict myself to a few orientating remarks.

Of the large number of Aristotelian writings, some are genuine, that is, his own writings or lecture notes from his pupils, others are productions of his school, others are entirely apocryphal. Hence the Aristotelian corpus raises innumerable problems of authenticity, which will never be finally solved.

Aristotle is one of the founders of the inductive method. He was first to conceive the idea of organized research and himself contributed considerably to the organization of science by his systematic survey and classification[b] of the knowledge of his time. He took pains to evidence the fundamental principles of each science in particular and of science in general. He may be called the founder of logic, and his systematization of it in the Organon was so masterful that it still dominates the teaching of to-day.

He prepared the systematization of geometry by his investigations of its more fundamental and philosophical aspect, in particular by his introduction of new or better definitions and his discussion of the concepts of continuity and infinity.

He completed the system of homocentric spheres of Eudoxos and Callippos, using a total of 55 spheres to account for all the celestial motions. His is the oldest attempt to estimate the size of the earth. To the four elements he added the quintessence called aether, the natural movement of which was circular. The celestial bodies are made of aether and are perfect and incorruptible. This theory stood until 1610 (Galileo's discovery of sun-spots, etc.).

If the mechanical writings be genuine, Aristotle had done much profound thinking on the subject, but whether he was fundamentally right (Duhem) or fundamentally wrong (Mach) depends entirely upon one's interpretation of his thought. He discovered the law of the lever. Sound is transmitted by vibrations of the air. First systematic study and first text-book of meteorology. First treatise on chemistry.

Aristotle carried on immense botanical, zoological, and anatomical investigations. He clearly recognized the fundamental problems of biology: sex, heredity, nutrition, growth, adaptation. He outlined the theory of evolution (scala naturae) and a scientific classification of animals. He proposed theories of generation and heredity. He may be called the founder of comparative anatomy (e. g., comparative study of the womb). Many of his anatomical descriptions are admirable (e. g. reproduction of selachians, especially placental development of the dog-fish;[c] embryonic development of the chick; stomach of ruminants, etc.).

In this introduction, I insist more upon the anticipations of truth than upon the errors. Some of Aristotle's errors are extremely important, however, because of their far-reaching influence. Thus his denial of the sexuality of plants (he assimilated their reproduction to nutrition and growth) was the main cause of the enormous delay in its discovery (Camerarius, 1694). In spite of earlier Hippocratic views, he considered the heart as the seat of intelligence, the function of the brain being then simply to cool the heart by the secretion of phlegm and to prevent its overheating. He realized that the arterial system duplicates the venous system, but failed to understand the real difference between arteries

---

[b] Aristotle divided the sciences into three main classes: theoretical (θεωρητική); practical (πρακτική), and productive or mechanical (ποιητική). The first class was subdivided into physics, mathematics, and metaphysics; the third, into politics, economics, and ethics.

[c] An amazing account which was not confirmed until 1842, by Johannes Müller. See bibliography below.

and veins; he believed that arteries contain air as well as blood. Here again Aristotle's views were the main cause of the extraordinary tardiness of the discovery of the circulation of the blood (Harvey, 1628).

He attempted an inductive study of politics, and wrote a history and critical account of Greek constitutional law. The modern definition of psychology as "the positive science of the behavior of living things" is a return to the standpoint of Aristotle.[d] His theory of dreams was far more rational than that of Democritos (q. v., fifth century B. C.); he tried to explain them by the persistence of sense impressions; he had observed the exaggerated excitement caused by slight stimuli if they interrupt a dream.[e]

Aristotle's influence, for good or evil, in every department of knowledge, was so tremendous that a good history of Aristotelianism would include a large part of the history of science and of thought down to the eighteenth century.

Aristotelian literature is very large, and its mass is the more bewildering in that there are no comprehensive publications of such importance and depth as to make it unnecessary to consider previous ones. My bibliography has been divided into twenty-five paragraphs as follows:

(1) Text and commentaries; (2) Translations; (3) Lexicon; (4) Bibliography; (5) Life of Aristotle and general survey of his thought; (6) Aristotelian tradition; (7) Aristotelian science in general; (8) Logic and theory of knowledge; (9) Mathematics; (10) Astronomy; (11) Mechanics; (12) Physics; (13) Harmonics and music; (14) Meteorology; (15) Chemistry; (16) Biology in general; (17) Botany; (18) Zoology; (19) Geography; (20) Geology; (21) Psychology; (22) Medicine; (23) Politics; (24) Sociology; (25) Apocryphal writings.

(This classification is of necessity only approximate and its various parts overlap more or less.)

(1) *Text and Commentaries*—Editio princeps, Aldine, 1495–98. I quote only the latest complete editions; critical editions of special works are quoted in the following paragraphs whenever I find it expedient.

Aristotelis opera edidit Academia regia borussica (5 vol., Berlin, 1831–1870; this text, due to Immanuel Bekker, is the one most frequently quoted). Opera ex recensione Im. Bekkeri (11 vols., Oxford, 1837). Didot edition, by Fred Dübner, Em. Heitz, and U. C. Bussemaker (5 vols., Paris, 1848–1874). A new critical edition, being a part of the Teubner collection, Leipzig, is in progress; the volumes of this edition of special interest to us are quoted below.

The Berlin Academy has edited a monumental collection of Greek commentaries; Commentaria in Aristotelem graeca (23 vols., containing 47 parts, 1882–1909). Since 1885, the Academy is also editing a Supplementum Aristotelicum. The latest part of it which I have seen is Vol. III, 1, 1903, containing a new edition of the Res publica Atheniensium by F. G. Kenyon.

Ernst Howald: Die Schriftenverzeichnisse des Aristoteles und des Theophrasts (Hermes, t. 55, 204–221, 1920).

(2) *Translations*—German translation with Greek text by various authors, Engelmann, Leipzig (1854, etc.) (incomplete). French translation by Barthélemy Saint-Hilaire (Paris, 1837, etc.); a great undertaking unfortunately based upon

---

[d] William McDougall: Psychology (Chapter I, London, 1912).

[e] His treatises on the subject: *περὶ ὕπνου καὶ ἐγρηγόρσεως* (on sleeping and waking), *περὶ ἐνυπνίων* (on dreams), *περὶ μαντικῆς τῆς ἐν τοῖς ὕπνοις* (on oneiromancy), were, directly or indirectly, one of the main sources of the extensive mediaeval literature. See my note on Democritos (fifth century).

an insufficient study of the text. An excellent English translation by various authors is in progress since 1908 (Oxford University Press). See, for example, Isis, VI, 138; VII, 532 (giving contents of the eleven volumes).

(3) *Lexicon*—Herm. Bonitz: Index Aristotelicus (896 p., 4to, Berlin, 1870; forming the last volume of Bekker's edition).

(4) *Bibliography*—Some idea of the extent of Aristotelian literature is given by the fact that by 1884 the printed catalogue of the British Museum devoted 110 columns to Aristotle! Moïse Schwab: Bibliographie d'Aristote (380 p., autographié, Paris, 1896). Catalogue des imprimés de la Bibliothèque Nationale, extrait du tome 4 (Paris, 1900).

(5) *Life of Aristotle and General Survey of His Philosophy*—George Grote: Aristotle (ed. by Alexander Bain and G. Croom Robertson, 2 vols., London, 1872). Thomas Davidson (1840–1900): Aristotle and Ancient Educational Ideals (269 p., New York, 1892. Many later editions). Clodius Piat. Aristote (Paris, 1903. From the Roman Catholic point of view with frequent references to St. Thomas Aquinas). Lothar Brieger-Wasservogel: Plato und Aristoteles (Klassiker der Naturwissenschaften, V, 196 p., Leipzig, 1906). Edwin Wallace: Outlines of the Philosophy of Aristotle (3d ed., 142 p., Cambridge, 1908; 1st ed., 1875; preface to 3d ed. dated 1883. It is an anthology with brief commentary; see Chapter V. Philosophy of Nature, p. 75–85). A. E. Taylor: Aristotle (2d ed., 126 p., Edinburgh, 1919; 1st ed. 1912). Octave Hamelin (1856–1907): Le système d'Aristote, publié par L. Robin (Paris, 1920). Werner Jaeger: Aristoteles (442 p., Berlin, 1923). W. D. Ross: Aristotle (308 p., London, 1923). John Burnet: Aristotle, 18 p., London, 1924).

(6) *Aristotelian tradition*—In the Christian World: Amable Jourdain (1788–1818): Recherches critiques sur l'âge et l'origine des traductions latines d'Aristote et sur des commentaires grecs ou arabes employés par les docteurs scholastiques (Nouv. éd. revue par Charles Jourdain, 487 p., Paris, 1843). Richard Schute (1849–1886): On the History of the Process by which the Aristotelian Writings arrived at their Present Form (203 p., Oxford, 1888). Clemens Baeumker: Zur Rezeption des Aristoteles im lateinischen Mittelalter (Philosophisches Jahrbuch, 27. Bd., p. 478–487, Fulda, 1914). Martin Grabmann: Forschungen über die lateinischen Aristoteles Übersetzungen des XIII. Jahrhunderts (Beiträge zur Gesch. d. Philos. des Mittelalters, XVII, 256 p. Münster i. W. 1916. Lynn Thorndike: History of Magic (1923, chiefly chapter 48, 246–278, on the Pseudo-Aristotle).

Among the Arabs, the Syrians, and the Jews: Ernest Renan: De philosophia peripatetica apud Syros (74 p., Paris, 1852). Julius Lippert: Studien auf dem Gebiete der griechisch-arabischen Übersetzungs-Litteratur. I. Quellenforschungen zu den arabischen Aristoteles Biographien (Braunschweig, 1894, with text and translation of the life by Abū-l-Wafā' al-Mubashshir). Anton Baumstark: Syrischarabische Biographien des Aristoteles. Syrische Commentar zur Εἰσαγωγή des Porphyrios—Aristoteles bei den Syrien vom V–VIII Jahrh. (I, Leipzig, 1900). S. Horovitz: Die Stellung des Aristoteles bei den Juden des Mittelalters (18 p., Leipzig, 1911). Articles in Jewish Encyclopedia, vol. 2, 1902, 98–102: Aristotle in Jewish legend by Louis Ginsberg; Aristotle in Jewish literature by A. Löwenthal. Article Arisṭāṭālīs in the Encyclopedia of Islam (t. 1, 432–434, 1913) by T. J. De Boer.

(7) *Aristotelian Science in General*—The Aristotelian literature is immense, yet there does not yet exist a comprehensive and up-to-date survey of Aristotle's scientific knowledge and of his influence upon scientific progress. The two most comprehensive works I know of are: George Henry Lewes: Aristotle—A Chapter from the History of Science, including Analyses of Aristotle's Scientific Writings (416 p., London, 1864; of mere historical interest, for it is full of errors); Thomas East Lones: Aristotle's Researches in Natural Science (282 p., London, 1912; see

Isis, I, 505–509). The greatest part of this book is devoted to the biological sciences; of course mathematics are not even considered.

Leonh. Spengel: Über die Reihenfolge der naturwissenschaftlichen Schriften des Aristoteles (27 p., München, 1849). Ignatz Tokstein: Der Begriff der Wissenschaft mit besonderer Beziehung auf den aristotelischen Lehrbegriff. (Diss., 51 p., Rostock, 1870). Giuseppe Sottini: Aristotile e il metodo scientifico nell' antichità greca (311 p., Pisa, 1873). Joh. Schmitz: De φύσεως apud Aristotelem notione (Diss., 42 p., Bonn, 1884). Fr. Pochenrieder: Die naturwissenschaftlichen Schriften des Aristoteles in ihrem Verhältnis zu den Büchern der hippokratischen Sammlung (Bamberg, 1887. Aristotle has used the Hippocratic writings, but with masterly independence.) John Daniel Logan: The Aristotelian Concept of φύσις (Philos. Review, p. 18–42, 386–400, 1897). P. Tannery: Des principes de la science de la nature chez Aristote (Congrès de philosophie, 1900, Histoire, p. 211–221, 1902; also Mémoires, VII, 299–307). A. Dyroff: Über die Abhängigkeit des Aristoteles von Demokritos (Philologus, t. 63, p. 41–53, 1904). G. Milhaud: Le hasard chez Aristote et Cournot (Revue de métaphysique et de morale 1902; reprinted in Etudes sur la pensée scientifique chez les Grecs et les modernes, p. 137–158, Paris, 1906). Paul Mansion: Sur le caractère réaliste de la doctrine des cinq éléments d'Aristote (Annales de la soc. scientif. de Bruxelles, t. 30, I, p. 114–117, 1906. Very short, but pregnant). Hermann Kalchreuter: Die μεσότης bei und vor Aristoteles (Diss., 67 p., Tübingen, 1911. The author considers Aristotle's moderation as a central point of his thought, and shows its relation inter alia, to medical experience). A. Mansion: La notion de nature dans la philosophie aristotélicienne (Annales de l'institut supérieur de philosophie, t. I, p. 459–567, Louvain, 1912). Eugen Rolfes: Die Philosophie des Aristoteles als Naturerklärung und Weltanschauung (395 p., Leipzig, 1923).

(8) *Logic and Theory of Knowledge*—P. Tannery: Sur un point de la méthode d'Aristote. (Archiv für Gesch. der Philos., Bd. 6, 468–474, 1893; Mémoires, VII, 171–178); Notes sur Aristote (Revue de philosophie, 1900, 426–429; Mémoires, VII, 293–297; Isis, IX). W. Freytag: Die Entwicklung der griechischen Erkenntnistheorie bei Aristoteles (Halle, 1905). Martin Altenburg: Die Methode der Hypothesis bei Plato, Aristoteles und Proclus (Diss., 240 p., Marburg in Hessen, 1905). Marie V. Williams: Six Essays on the Platonic Theory of Knowledge as Expounded in the Later Dialogues and Reviewed by Aristotle (140 p., Cambridge, 1908).

(9) *Mathematics*—Gust. Schilling: Aristotelis de continuo doctrina (31 p., Gissae, 1840). R. Stölze: Die Lehre vom Unendlichen bei Aristoteles (80 p., Würzburg, 1882). Albert Görland: Aristoteles und die Mathematik (218 p., Marburg, 1899). T. L. Heath: On an Allusion in Aristotle to a Construction for Parallels (Abh. zur Gesch. d. Math., 9. H., p. 153–160, Leipzig, 1899). Dutordoir: Sur la différence de la philosophie naturelle et des mathématiques d'après Aristote (Annales de la Societé scientif. de Bruxelles, t. 24, p. 52–54, 1900). M. E. Gans: Psychologische Untersuchung zu der von Aristoteles als platonisch überlieferten Lehre von den Idealzahlen aus dem Gesichtspunkte der platonischen Dialektik und Ästhetik. (Progr., 45 p., Wien, 1901). Paul Mansion: Aristote et les mathématiques (Revue de philosophie, t. III, p. 832–834, Paris, 1903. Important). Gaston Milhaud: Aristote et les mathématiques (Archiv für Gesch. d. Phil., t. 16, p. 367–392, 1903; also in Etudes sur la pensée scientifique, p. 101–135, Paris, 1906). J. L. Heiberg: Mathematisches zu Aristoteles (Abh. z. Gesch. d. math. Wissensch., 18. H., p. 1–49. Leipzig, 1904. Important). F. Rudio: Notiz zur griechischen Terminologie (Vierteljahrschrift d. Naturf. Gesellschaft, t. 53, p. 481–484, Zürich, 1908; about the word τμῆμα). Léon Robin: La théorie platonicienne des idées et des nombres d'après Aristote (720 p., Paris, 1908). P. Duhem: Sur l'infiniment petit et l'infiniment grand (Etudes sur Léonard de Vinci, t. 2, 4–7, 1909). Leo

Reiche: Das Problem des Unendlichen bei Aristoteles (Diss., 94 p., Breslau, 1911). Annibale M. Pastore: Le definizioni matematiche secondo Aristotele e la logica matematica (Atti d. R. Accad. d. sci., t. 47, p. 478–494, Torino, 1912). Florian Cajori: A Greek Tract on Indivisible Lines (Science, t. 48, p. 577–578, New York, 1918; about the de lineis insecabilibus). Enrico Rufini: I principii della geometria greca secondo Aristotele (Archivio della storia della scienza, t. 4, 78–92, 1923). Julius Stenzel: Zahl und Gestalt bei Platon und Aristoteles (152 p., Leipzig, 1924; Isis, VII, 177).

(10) *Astronomy*—George Grote: Plato's Doctrine Respecting the Rotation of the Earth and Aristotle's Comment upon that Doctrine (35 p., London, 1860; reprinted in his Minor Works, 1873, p. 237–275). Pluzanski: Aristotolea de natura astrorum opinio ejusque vices apud philosophos tum antiquos, tum medii aevi (145 p., Paris, 1887). P. Duhem: La pluralité des mondes (Etudes sur Léonard de Vinci, t. 2, 59–63, 1909). Ernst Goldbeck: Die geozentrische Lehre des Aristoteles und ihre Auflösung (Progr., 27 p., Berlin, 1911). (See under Physics, and also the papers quoted apropos of Eudoxos.)

(11) *Mechanics*—The μηχανικά ascribed to Aristotle is possibly of Straton's time or even of a later date, yet a part of it may be Aristotelian. The best text is that edited by Otto Apelt, Leipzig, 1888; English translation by E. S. Forster, Oxford, 1913.

Mathias Kappes: Die aristotelische Lehre über Begriff und Ursache der κίνησις (Diss., 46 p., Bonn, 1887). Karl Sperling: Aristoteles' Ansicht von der psychologischen Bedeutung der Zeit untersucht an seiner Definition derselben als "Zahl der Bewegung" (Diss., 73 p., Marburg, 1888). Maurice Gallian: Sur les problèmes mécaniques attribués à Aristote (Annales internationales d'histoire, Congrès de Paris 1900, 5e section, p. 101–107, Paris, 1901). See also P. Tannery (Mémoires, III, 32–36). P. Duhem: Sur l'axiome d'Aristote (Origines de la statique, t. 2, 291–301, 1906); Sur l'équilibre des mers (Etudes sur Léonard de Vinci, t. 1, 58, 1906); Sur la résistance des matériaux (Ibidem, 289). Florian Cajori: Aristotle and Galileo on Falling Bodies (Science, t. 51, 615–616, 1920). T. East Lones: Mechanics and Engineering from the Time of Aristotle to that of Archimedes (Trans. Newcomen Society, vol. 2, 61–69, 1923).

(12) *Physics: Texts*—Physica, rec. Carolus Prantl (Leipzig, 1879. Largely metaphysical). De coloribus, de audibilibus, physiognomonica, rec. C. Prantl (Leipzig, 1881). Über die Farben, erläutert durch eine Übersicht der Farbenlehre der Alten v. C. Prantl (München, 1849). De coelo et de generatione et corruptione, rec. C. Prantl (Leipzig, 1881). Problemata physica ed. C. Ae. Ruelle, recog. Herm. Knoellinger, editionem post utriusque mortem curavit, praefatione ornavit Jos. Klek (333 p., Leipzig, 1922).

P. Tannery: Sur la composition de la physique d'Aristote (Archiv für Gesch. der Philos., 7, 224–229, 1893; 9, 115–118, 1895; Mémoires, VII, 179–185, 195–199; Isis, IX).

Commentaries—Ernst Friedrich Eberhard: Das Licht nach Aristoteles (21 p., Coburg, 1836). Ernst Richter: De Aristotelis Problematis (Diss. philologica, 47 p., Bonn, 1885). J. Ziaja: Zur Aristoteles Lehre vom Lichte (Progr., Schrimm, 1901). E. Hoffmann: De Aristotelis physicorum libri septimi origine et auctoritate (Diss., 33 p., Berlin, 1905. This VIIth book is certainly apocryphal). P. Duhem: Du temps où la scolastique latine a connu la physique d'Aristote (Revue de philosophie, 15 p., Paris, 1909). Salomon Reinach: Une allusion à Zagreus dans un problème d'Aristote (Revue archéologique, t. 9, 162–172, 1919; Isis, V, 205). Henri Carteron: Physique, IV, 1–5. Traduction et commentaire (70 p., Montpellier, 1923; Isis, VII, 176); La notion de force dans le système d'Aristote (294 p., Paris, 1924; Isis, VII, 176).

(13) *Harmonics and Music*—Franc. Aug. Gevaert et J. C. Vollgraff: Les

problèmes musicaux d'Aristote—Texte grec avec trad. franç., notes philologiques, commentaire musical et appendice (447 p., Gand 1903. The musical problems are the 19th section of the Problems of Aristotle, about which see Physics; the Problems are a product of the Aristotelian school). Paul Tannery: Note rédigée à la demande de MM. Eugène d'Eichtal et Théodore Reinach et faisant suite à leur étude sur les Problèmes musicaux dits d'Aristote (Revue des études grecques, V, p. 51–52, 263, 1892; also in Tannery's Mémoires, II, p. 440–441). Maurice Emmanuel: Le corps de l'harmonie d'après Aristote (Revue des études grecques, t. 32, 179–189, 1919). R. C. Archibald: Aristotle's Knowledge of Acoustics (Q. 1, Isis, VI, 533, 1924).

(14) *Meteorology*—The μετεωρολογικά contains four books, but the fourth is really independent of the others and is considered below, under Chemistry. The best edition of the text is due to F. H. Fobes (Cambridge, Mass., 1919; see Isis, III, 278); but the edition by J. L. Ideler must still be quoted: Meteorologicorum libri IV. Graeca verba denuo post Bekkerum recensuit, novam interpretationem latinam confecit, excerpta ex commentariis Alexandri, Olympiodori et Ioannis Philoponi, suos commentarios adjecit, de auctoritate, integritate et fide librorum, deque criticis subsidiis praefatus est J. L. Ideler (2 vols., Leipzig, 1834–1836). English translation by E. W. Webster (New York, 1923; Isis, VI, 138).

Berthold Suhle: Zur Meteorologie des Aristoteles (Progr., 30 p., Bernburg, 1864). G. Hellman: Bibliographie der gedruckten Ausgaben, Übersetzungen und Auslegungen der Meteorologie des Aristoteles (Beiträge zur Geschichte der Meteorologie, II. Bd., 3–45, Berlin, 1917. A capital study in which 147 works are quoted, dating from 1474 to 1901. It is interesting to note that of these 147 editions, 37 are incunabula and 135 were printed before 1601).

(15) *Chemistry*—Jacob Lorscheid: Aristoteles Einfluss auf die Entwicklung der Chemie (58 p., Münster 1872). Edmund O. von Lippmann: Chemisches und Alchemisches aus Aristoteles (Archiv f. Gesch. d. Naturw., 1910, t. II, 233; also Abh. u. Vortr., II, p. 64–156). E. O. von Lippmann: Die Entsalzung des Meerwassers bei Aristoteles (Chemiker Zeitung, Nr. 70, 1911, Nachtrag ibidem nr. 127; also Abh. u. Vortr., II, 157–167). Ingeborg Hammer-Jensen: Das sogenannte IV. Buch der Meteorologie des Aristoteles (Hermes, t. 50, p. 113–136, Berlin, 1915; see Isis III, 279). Walter Brieger: Zur Entsalzung des Meerwassers bei Aristoteles (Chemiker Zeitung, p. 302, Cöthen, 1918). Michel Stéphanidès: Une théorie chimique d'Aristote, contact et affinité (Rev. scientif., 1924, 626–627; Isis, VII, 178).

(16) *Biology in General*—Of the texts I can quote only Wilhelm Biehl's critical edition of the Parva Naturalia (Leipzig, 1896).

The most comprehensive study of Aristotelian biology is Thomas East Lones: Aristotle's Researches in Natural Science (282 p., London, 1912; Isis, I, 505). Hans Meyer: Die Entwicklungsgedanke bei Aristoteles (154 p., Bonn, 1909). W. W. Jaeger: Das Pneuma im Lykeion (Hermes, t. 48, p. 29–74, Berlin, 1912). W. D'Arcy Thompson: On Aristotle as a Biologist (Herbert Spencer lecture, 1912, 31 p., Oxford, 1913. Very suggestive). C. W. Schmidt: Der Entwicklungsbegriff in der aristotelischen Naturphilosophie (Arch. f. Gesch. d. Naturw., VIII, p. 49–65, Leipzig, 1917). M. A. Herzog: Aristoteles' Anschauungen über die Lehre von Winterschlaf im Vergleich zu unsern heutigen Kenntnissen (Festschrift für Zschokke, No. 41, 28 p., Basel, 1920; Isis, IV, 128). C. Singer: Greek Biology in Singer's Studies (vol. 2, 1921; Isis, IV, 380); also Greek Biology and Medicine (Oxford, 1922, p. 18–54; Isis, V, 532).

(17) *Botany*—F. Wimmer: Phytologiae Aristotelicae fragmenta (Breslau, 1838). Const. Kontopulos: De physiologia plantarum secundum Aristotelem et Theophrastum (Diss., 37 p., Berlin, 1848). C. Jessen: Über des Aristoteles Pflanzenwerke (Rheinisches Museum für Philologie, XIV, p. 88–101, Frankfurt a. M., 1859).

(18) *Zoology: Texts*—Histoire des animaux, avec la traduction française par Armand Gaston Camus (1740–1804) (2 vols., Paris, 1783. The second volume is entirely devoted to notes, some of which are very valuable and would still repay study to-day). De animalibus historia, ed. by Leon Dittmeyer (Leipzig, 1907). De animalium motione et de animalium incessu, Pseudo-Aristotelis de spiritu libellus, ed. W. W. Jaeger (Leipzig, 1913). Gunnar Rudberg: Textstudien zur Tiergeschichte des Aristoteles (Uppsala Universitets Årsskrift., 133 p., Upsala, 1908. Contains Will. of Moerbeke's Latin translation of Hist. anim., bk. I, with textual criticism of this translation, a study of its Greek sources and of the textual tradition of Hist. anim.). Guilelmi Moerbekensis translatio commentationis Aristotelicae de generatione animalium edidit Leonardus Dittmeyer. (Progr., 53 p., Dillingen a. D., 1915).

Commentaries—Arend Fried. Aug. Wiegmann: Observationes zoologicae criticae in Aristotelis Historiam animalium (42 p., Leipzig, 1826). Const. Lambert Gloger: De avibus ab Aristotele commemoratis (64 p., Breslau, 1830). Joh. Müller: Ueber den glatten Hai des Aristoteles (Berlin, 1842). P. W. Forchammer: De ratione quam Aristoteles in disponendis libris de animalibus secutus sit (Kiel, 1846). Heinrich Thiel: De zoologicorum Aristotelis librorum ordine ac distributione imprimis de librorum περὶ ζῴων μορίων primo (Progr., 50 p., Breslau, 1855). Ludwig Sonnenburg: Zoologisch-kritische Bemerkungen zu Aristoteles Thiergeschichte (Progr., 27 p., Bonn, 1857). Hermann Aubert: Die Cephalopoden des Aristoteles in zoologischer, anatomischer und naturgeschichtlicher Beziehung (Z. f. wissensch. Zoologie, 12. Bd., Leipzig, 1862). Carl J. Sundewall: Die Thierarten des Aristoteles von den Klassen der Säugethiere, Vögel, Reptilien und Insekten (Übers. aus dem Schwedischen, 242 p., Stockholm, 1863). Bernh. Langkavel: Scholien und naturhistorische Bemerkungen zu Aristoteles über die Theile der Thiere (Progr., 35 p., Berlin, 1863). T. H. Huxley: Certain Errors Respecting the Structure of the Heart, Attributed to Aristotle (Nature, Nov. 6, 1879; reprinted in Science and Culture, p. 180). Ludwig Heck: Die Hauptgruppen des Thiersystems bei Aristoteles und seinen Nachfolgern (Diss., 74 p., Leipzig, 1885). Franz Susemihl: Kritische Studien zu den zoologischen Schriften des Aristoteles (Rheinisches Museum für Philologie, t. 40, p. 563–598, Frankfurt a. M. 1885). Leonh. Dittmeyer: Textkritisches zur aristotelischen Tiergeschichte (Abh. aus dem Gebiete der klass. Altertumwiss., 1891). Will. W. Fowler: Aristotle on Birds, *in his* Summer Studies of Birds and Books (London, 1895). Karl Hammerschmidt: Die Ornithologie des Aristoteles (Progr., 80 p., Speier, 1897). Rud. Burckhardt: Das erste Buch der aristotelischen Tiergeschichte (Zool. Ann., t. I, Würzburg, 1904). N. Polek: Die Fischkunde des Aristoteles und ihre Nachwirkung in der Literatur (Primitiae Czernovicienses hrg. von I. Hilberg und J. Jüthner, p. 31–45, Czernowitz, 1909). Karl E. Bitterauf: Der Schlussteil der Aristotelischen Biologie (Progr., 48 p., Kempten im Allgäu, 1913. History and criticism of the text of de gener. anim.; second part published, ibidem, in 1914, 33 p.). August Steier: Aristoteles und Plinius—Studien zur Geschichte der Zoologie (310 p., Würzburg, 1913. Three studies reprinted from Zoolog. Ann., t. IV, V, and of which the third only deals with Aristotle; see Isis, II, 202). E. W. Gudger: Aristotle's Echeneis not a suckling-fish (Science, vol. 44, 316–318, 1916). Joseph Kleck: Die Bienenkunde des Aristoteles und seiner Zeit (Archiv f. Bienenkunde, t. 1, 1919). C. Ferckel: Zu Cor ultimum moriens (Mit. zur Gesch. der Medizin, t. 19, 305, 1920). Arthur Platt: Aristotle on the Heart (Studies in the History of Science, vol. 2, 521–532, Oxford, 1921). Heinrich Balss: Studien über Aristotle als vergleichende Anatom (Arch. di storia d. scienza, t. 5, 5–11, 1924; Isis, VII, 176).

(19) *Geography*—Charles Jourdain: De l'influence d'Aristote et de ses interprètes sur la découverte du nouveau monde (Journal général de l'instruction pub-

lique, 30 p., Paris, 1861). Paul Bolchert: Aristoteles Erdkunde von Asien und Libyen (112 p., Quellen u. Forsch. zur alten Gesch. u. Geogr., 15 Heft, Berlin, 1908). Joseph Partsch: Des Aristoteles Buch über das Steigen des Nil (Kgl. Sächs. Ges. d. Wiss., phil. hist. Kl., t. 27, p. 551–600, Leipzig, 1909. The *περὶ τῆς τοῦ* Νείλου *ἀναβάσεως* is certainly apocryphal and probably post-Eratosthenian; Partsch believes, however, that it was written by a contemporary of Aristotle if not by the master himself). H. Habenicht: Das Aristotelische Phänomen (Weltall, Dez., 1913. Deals with the progressive drying up of continents. Of special interest to South African peripateticians!). A. Endrös: Die Gezeiten, Seiches und Strömungen des Meeres bei Aristoteles (Sitzungsber. d. bayer. Ges. d. Wiss., math. phys. Kl., 355–385, München, 1915. Important paper showing that Aristotle understood the phenomenon called "seiche" and was in a way a predecessor of F. A. Forel, Isis, IV, 395).

(20) *Geology*—I do not know of any special study of Aristotelian geology, but some of the papers quoted under Chemistry may interest the geologist. For Aristotle's views on earthquakes, volcanoes, changes of the earth's surface, flood, origin of metals, see Sir Archibald Geikie; "The Founders of Geology," or Th. E. Lones, op. cit.; Chapter III. See also P. Duhem: Etudes sur Léonard de Vinci (t. 2, 284–285, 1909). Max Wellmann: Aristoteles de lapidibus (Sitzungsber. der Preuss. Ak. der Wissensch., Phil. Kl., 79–82, 1924). See in my section on apocryphal writings, the paragraph devoted to the liber de elementis.

(21) *Psychology*—The apocryphal *φυσιογνωμονικά* may be placed under this heading (or under anthropology?). Critical text ed. by C. Prantl (Leipzig, 1881), later by Richard Foerster in Scriptores Physiognomonici (2 vols., Leipzig, 1893). See also Rich. Foerster: De translatione latina Physiognomonicorum quae feruntur Aristotelis (Progr., 27 p., Kiel, 1884); Die Physiognomik der Griechen (23 p., Kiel, 1884). See paragraph below devoted to apocryphal writings.

(22) *Medicine*—(See the section on zoology, above, for anatomical and physiological studies). H. Diels: Medizin in der Schule des Aristoteles (Preuss. Jahrbücher, 74, 412–429, 1893). Gerhard Grundmann: Zahnärztliches aus den Werken des Aristoteles und seiner Schüler Theophrast und Menon (Diss., 32 p., Leipzig, 1922).

(23) *Politics*—It is legitimate to include this topic, for Aristotle had applied the methods of inductive science to its study. *Texts*—The Politics of Aristotle, Greek text with introduction and notes by W. L. Newman (4 vols., Oxford, 1887–1902). Politica recog. Otto Immisch (Leipzig, 1909). The Constitution of Athens (ed. F. G. Kenyon, London, 1891; many later editions; latest, Oxford 1920). *Commentary*—Ernest Baker: The Political Thought of Plato and Aristotle (581 p., New York, 1906). Georges Mathieu: Constitution d'Athènes. Essai sur la méthode suivie par Aristote dans la discussion des textes (144 p., Biblioth. de l'Ecole des hautes Etudes, sci. hist., Paris, 1915).

(24) *Sociology*—Maurice Defourny: Aristote. L'évolution sociale (Ann. de l'Institut supérieur de philosophie, t. 5, 529–696, 1924; Isis, VII, 177). Henry Lowenfeld: Justice in Dealings on Aristotle's Plan (147 p., London, 1924).

(25) *Apocryphal Writings*—I quote a few of the pseudo-Aristotelian works which are of special interest to us. For others, which may be incidentally mentioned in the text, see index.

Liber de causis: See under Proclos (second half of fifth century).

Theologia (the "Theology of Aristotle"): A late Neoplatonic work which it is difficult to date exactly (fourth to sixth century). I have devoted a special paragraph to it in the chapter dealing with the second half of the fifth century.

Liber de elementis (also called de proprietatibus elementorum, de naturis rerum): This treatise is most certainly a Muslim work. The Muslims considered it a work of Aristotle. It is important because of the geological and astromomical ideas it contains, e. g., that mountains have not been formed merely by Neptunian action, but primarily by a Plutonian cause. There is a long argument against the physicists who claim that the oceans move periodically on the surface of the earth. Assuming that if such movement existed, it would necessarily be controlled by the celestial motions, the author of de elementis shows that it can not possibly take place; this includes a discussion of the tides and of the precession of the equinoxes. A deeper analysis of the Arabic text, if still extant, and at any rate of the Latin text, should enable one to date this treatise approximately. Such a study is highly desirable. *Text*—Aristotelis Opera (fol. 464–469, Venice, Gregoriis, 1496). *Criticism*—P. Duhem: Etudes sur Léonard de Vinci (t. 2, 1909, 299–302; geology); Système du monde (t. 2, 1914, 226–229, 386–390; other topics).

Secreta secretorum, vel liber de regimine principum (in Arabic, sirr al-asrār): see the chapter on the first half of ninth century.

Physiognomonica Pseudo-Aristotelis (Ἀριστοτέλους φυσιογνωμονικά): Text published by Richard Foerster in his Scriptores physiognomonici graeci et latini (t. 1, 5–91, Leipzig, 1893, with the Latin translation of Bartholomaeus de Messina, thirteenth century; see indexes at the end of t. 2, chiefly 485–489). Aristotle's Physiognomonica, whether genuine or not, would seem to be the earliest treatise on the subject and one of the sources of an abundant branch of medieval literature, one of the most popular pseudo-sciences, even to this day. The History of Animals contains also a few physiognomic observations.

On the Rising of the Nile (περὶ τῆς τοῦ Νείλου ἀναβάσεως): See above, (19) Geography.

περὶ θαυμασίων ἀκουσμάτων: Hermann Schrader: Über die Quellen der pseudoaristotelischen Schrift περὶ θαυμασίων ἀκουσμάτων (Jahrbuch für classische Philologie, 219–232, 1868).

De mundo: William Laughton Lorimer: The Text Tradition of the Pseudo-Aristotle De mundo, together with an appendix containing the text of the medieval Latin versions (106 p., St. Andrews University, 1924).

IV. OTHER PHILOSOPHERS, GREEK AND CHINESE

For Theophrastos see Section IX, dealing with botany.

PYRRHON

Πύρρων, from Elis in Peloponnesos, born c. 360, flourished in Elis, died c. 270. Greek philosopher. Founder of the Sceptical (or Pyrrhonian) school. Together with his master Anaxarchos (of the school of Democritos) he joined Alexander's expedition into India (329–326).[f] Happiness (ἀταραξία) is based on a suspension of judgment (ἐποχή, ἀφασία, ἀκαταληψία) for certain knowledge on any subject is unattainable.

Criticism—A Croiset: Littérature grecque (t. 5, 71–75, 1899).

EUHEMEROS

Εὐήμερος, born in Messina, Sicily; flourished at the court of Cassander in Macedonia c. 316 or after. Greek philosopher. He traveled down the Red Sea and around the coast of Asia, and reached in the Indian Ocean the islands called Panchaea (?), where he found inscriptions. These he explained in his book "The Sacred Inscription or Chronicle" (Ἱερὰ ἀναγραφή), the aim of which was to ration-

---

[f] J. Burnet remarks (Legacy of Greece, 58, 1921), that this is "the earliest authenticated instance of a Greek thinker coming under Indian influence and what he brought back from the East was rather the ideal of quietism than any definite philosophical doctrine."

alize religion (Euhemerism), to replace superstition by knowledge. Ennius popularized these ideas in verse.

Text—Némethy: Euhemeri reliquiae (Buda-Pesth, 1889).

Criticism—Raymond de Block: Evhémère, son livre et sa doctrine (Mons, 1876). Franz Susemihl: Griechische Litteratur in der Alexandrinerzeit (t. 1, 316–322, 1891).

EPICUROS

Ἐπίκουρος, born in Samos in the beginning of 341, died in Athens in 270. Philosopher, founder of a new philosophic school in Athens. Adopted and transmitted the atomic theories. Although he held that ignorance and superstition are the chief obstacles to happiness, his teaching marked on the whole a reaction against science.

Text—Epicurea edidit Herm. Usener (525 p., Leipzig, 1887). Ettore Bignone: Epicurea (Atti. d. R. Accad. d. scienze, vol. 47, p. 670–690, Torino, 1912; Pap. Herc. ined. 168 col., 1; Schol. in Epic. ep. ad Her., §42 sq.). Ett. Bignone: Epicuro—Opere, frammenti, testimonianze sulla sua vita. Tradotti con introd. e. comm. (Bari, 1919). Epistulae tres et ratae sententiae a Laertio Diogene servatae; ed. Peter von der Mühll. Accedit Gnomologium Epicureum vaticanum (79 p., Leipzig, 1922).

General Studies—E. Joyau: Epicure (Les grands philosophes, 223 p., Paris, 1910). Alfr. Edw. Taylor: Epicurus (128 p., London, 1911).

Special Studies—Albert Goedemeyer: Epikurs Verhältnis zu Demokrit in der Naturphilosophie (Diss., 157 p., Strassburg, 1897). Carl Krücke: Unklarheiten im Begriff Natur bei Epicur (Diss., 63 p., Goettingen, 1906). Franz Sandgathe, Die Wahrheit der Kriterien Epikurs (83 p., Berlin, 1908; also in the form of a Diss., Berlin, 1909). Fried. Merbach: De Epicuri canonica (Diss., 54 p., Weidae Thuringorum, 1909). Peter von der Mühll: Epikurs Κύριαι δόξαι und Demokrit. Festgabe Adolf Kaegi (Frauenfeld, 1919, p. 172–178). Michel Stéphanidès: On a Magnetic Theory of Epicuros (in Greek, Ἀνθρωπότης, vol. 3, 1–5; Isis, VII, 178).

ZENO OF CITIUM[g]

Ζήνων, flourished about the end of the century, born c. 336, died c. 264. Philosopher. Founder of the Stoic school of philosophy in Athens.[h] The complete elaboration of Stoic philosophy took about a century, but it is probable that the fundamental principles were already established by Zeno. (His works being lost, no final judgment is possible.) The new school was deeply influenced by the views of Heraclitos and Socrates. Its teaching was a combination of materialism and pantheism. The three main parts of philosophy (or knowledge) are physics, logic, and ethics; physics being the foundation, logic the instrument, ethics the end. The Stoics conceive the existence everywhere of forces or tensions, coextensive with matter (for everything, even the soul, is corporeal); these tensions cause the flux and reflux of the universe. The Socratic idea that virtue is knowledge is developed; true goodness consists in living according to reason or to nature, the reason of the world, but this implies sufficient knowledge of nature. This obliged them also to elaborate the (Platonic) parallel between macrocosm and microcosm and to attach much importance to divination. Finally Stoicism was cosmopolitan; it was the earliest philosophical school which developed an international conception of morality. Its influence upon the progress of morality

---

[g] In Cyprus.

[h] The teaching took place in the "painted porch" (στοὰ ποικίλη) in the market-place of Athens. Hence the name of the school.

can not be overestimated. It stimulated scientific research, especially in the field of grammar (because of their interest in logical analysis), history, archaeology, and geography.

Text—Alfred Chilton Pearson: The Fragments of Zeno and Cleanthes, with Introduction and Notes (344 p., London, 1891). Johann von Arnim: Stoicorum veterum fragmenta (vol. 1, Zeno et Zenonis discipuli, Leipzig, 1905).
Commentary—Karl Troost: Zenonis Citensis de rebus physicis doctrinae (87 p., Berliner Studien für classische Philologie und Archaeologie, XII, 3, Berlin, 1891).

Chinese Philosophy

MENCIUS

Born in the State of Tsou[1] (11811), modern Shantung, in 372; he died in 289 and is buried at Tsou[1] hsien[4] (11811, 4545) in Yen[3]-chou[1] fu[3] (13115, 2444, 3682), Shantung. Chinese philosopher. Pupil of K'ung Chi (q. v., fifth century). The greatest representative of Confucianism after Confucius. The collection of his conversations with his disciples (edited by them or by himself) forms one of the Four Books.[j]

Text—James Legge: Chinese Classics (vol. 2, Hongkong, 1862; Oxford, 1895, Chinese and English). F. S. Couvreur: Les Quatre Livres (2e ed., 297–654, 1910, Chinese, Latin, and French).
Criticism—H. A. Giles: Biographical Dictionary (582–583, 1898). Albert Tschepe: Heiligtümer des Konfuzianismus in K'ü-fu und Tschou-hein (Jentschoufu, 1906).

YANG CHU[k]

Yang[2] Chu[1] (12878, 2544). Flourished in the fourth century B. C. at the court of Liang[2] (7021), in the State of Wei[4] (12542). Chinese philosopher whose thought is known chiefly through the seventh book of Lieh Tzŭ. He was a Taoist professing a sort of Epicureanism and advocating extreme selfishness.[l]

Text—See my note on Lieh Tzŭ. Anton Forke's study in the Journal of the Peking Oriental Society (vol. 3, 203–258, 1893) contains a translation of book 7 of Lieh Tzŭ and of all the passages referring to Yang Chu scattered in the other books. See also Anton Forke: Yang Chu's Garden of Pleasure. English translation with an introduction by Hugh Cranmer-Byng (Wisdom of the East) (64 p., London, 1912; Isis, I, 516).
Criticism—H. A. Giles: Chinese Biographical Dictionary (899, 1898).

LIEH TZŬ[m]

Lieh[4]* Tzŭ[3] (7081, 12317). Flourished probably in the fourth century B. C.[n] Chinese philosopher whose work contains (in Bk. I) a clear account of Taoist cosmology. Discussion of infinity, of time, and of space.

---

[i] Latinized form of Mêng[4] Tzŭ[3] (7795, 12317), the philosopher Mĕng. Mĕng was his surname and K'o[1] (6085) his name. This name should not be written or uttered. His tablet was admitted in the Confucian temple in 1088; he is one of the "Four Associates of the Master." He is often called the Second Prophet, Ya[4] Shêng[4] (12810, 9892). The Japanese call him Mōshi.

[j] It is longer than the three other books together.

[k] Or Yang[2] Tzŭ[3] (12878, 12317), the philosopher Yang.

[l] Condemned by Mencius even as Mo Ti's altruism (q. v., fifth century B. C.).

[m] The philosopher Lieh. His full name was Lieh[4]* Yü[4]-k'ou[4] (7081, 13646, 6180). Latinized form, Licius.

[n] His very existence is far from certain. It is possibly a literary fiction created by Chuang Tzŭ (q. v). F. H. Balfour in his Chinese Scrapbook calls Lieh "the philosopher who never lived" . . . . China owed it to herself to have at least one such philosopher. . . .

Text—Lieh's work was first edited in the fourth century by Chang[1] Chan[4] (416, 313) with commentary. French translation by Ch. de Harlez: Textes Taoïstes (Annales du Musée Guimet, 1891). Léon Wieger: Patrologie Taoïste (1913). Partial English translations by Frederic Henry Balfour, in Leaves from my Chinese Scrapbook (London, 1887), and Lionel Giles, in Taoist Teachings (Wisdom of the East) (121 p., London, 1912; Isis, I, 516). German translation by Richard Wilhelm: Das wahre Buch vom quellenden Urgrund (204 p., Jena, 1911; Isis, I, 119).

Criticism—Anton Forke: Yang-Chu the Epicurean in his Relation to Lieh-Tse the Pantheist (Jour. Peking Oriental Soc., vol. 3, 203–258, 1893; containing a translation of book 7, which deals with Yang-Chu). H. A. Giles: Biographical Dictionary (482, 1898). Encyclopaedia Sinica (307, 1917). A. Forke: The World conception of the Chinese (London, 1925; Isis, VIII, 373).

V. GREEK MATHEMATICS

SPEUSIPPOS

Σπεύσιππος. Born in Athens; flourished about 348 to 339. Philosopher, mathematician. Nephew of Plato, succeeded him in 348–347 as head of the Academy. Wrote on prime, linear, and polygonal numbers, triangles, and pyramids.

Fragments of his book remain and were edited by F. Ast in Theologumena arithmetica (Leipzig, 1817). Paul Tannery: Un fragment de Speusippe (Ann. de la Faculté des Lettres de Bordeaux, t. V, p. 375–382, 1883; Mémoires, I, 281–289). This contains a French translation of the fragment with commentary. The same translation may also be found in Tannery's Pour l'histoire de la science hellène (Paris, 1887, p. 386–390).

J. G. Felix Ravaisson: Speusippi de primis rerum principiis placita qualia fuisse videantur ex Aristotele (Diss., 45 p., Paris, 1838). Paul Lang: De Speusippi academici scriptis. Accedunt fragmenta (Diss., 89 p., Bonn, 1911). Erich Frank: Plato und die sogenannten Pythagoreer (Halle, 1923; Isis, VI, 48–52). Frank would ascribe to Speusippos the fragments generally ascribed to Philolaos. If Frank's hypothesis is correct, Speusippos becomes a greater personality. (See my note on Philolaos, fifth century B. C.).

XENOCRATES

Xenocrates of Chalcedon[a] (Ξενοκράτης, born c. 397, died c. 314). Philosopher, mathematician. He succeeded Speusippos as head of the Academy, from 339–8 to 315–4. A history of geometry in five books is ascribed to him (that is, if we understand the title right, for nothing has remained of it). Solved a problem of combinatorial analysis (the number of syllables which can possibly be written with all the letters of the alphabet is 1,002,000,000,000). Theory of indivisible lines (ἄτομοι γραμμαί).

Richard Heinze: Xenokrates—Darstellung der Lehre und Sammlung der Fragmente (216 p., Leipzig, 1892. Erkenntnislehre, Metaphysik, Physik. Dämonenlehre. Psychologie und Ethik, Fragmente).

MENAECHMOS

Μέναιχμος, flourished about the middle of the century. Pupil of Eudoxos. Mathematician. He discovered the conic sections and used them as a means of solving the problem of the doubling of the cube. This may be considered the

[a] In Bithynia, at the entrance of the Bosphorus, nearly opposite to Byzantium.

earliest solution of a cubic equation. Contributed to the geometrical text-book of the Academy written by Theudios of Magnesia. Defined the meaning of the term "elements" (in geometry) and discussed with Speusippos the relative extension of the terms "theorem" and "problem."

Thomas L. Heath: Apollonius of Perga (chapter I, Cambridge, 1896).

DINOSTRATOS

Δινόστρατος, flourished in the second half of the century. Mathematician. Menaechmos's brother. Applied Hippias's quadratrix to the squaring of the circle (hence its name, τετραγωνίζουσα). Collaborated on Theudios's text-book of geometry.

See Cantor. No article is devoted to him in Pauly-Wissowa's Real-Encyclopädie (1903). Sir Thomas Heath: History of Greek Mathematics (Oxford, 1921).

THEUDIOS

Theudios of Magnesia (Θευδιος). Flourished in the second half of the century. Editor of the geometrical text-book of the Academy; he "put together the elements admirably, making many partial propositions more general." (Proclos.)

EUDEMOS

Eudemos of Rhodes (Εὔδημος ὁ Ῥόδιος, flourished c. 320). Mathematician, historian of science. Pupil of Aristotle, friend of Theophrastos. Wrote on the angle (περὶ γωνίας) and discussed its nature. He wrote also a history of arithmetic (ἀριθμητικὴ ἱστορία), a history of astronomy (ἀστρολογικὴ ἱστορία) and a history of geometry (γεωμητρικὴ ἱστορία). The last history is especially important; ancient writers frequently refer to it, and the fragments remaining are a fundamental source for the history of pre-Euclidian geometry. Various peripatetic text-books were composed by him.

Text—Eudemi Rhodii peripatetici fragmenta quae supersunt collegit Leonardus Spengel (188 p., Berlin, 1866. Not really a critical edition). Many fragments have been admirably edited by H. Diels in his edition of Simplicios's Commentary on Aristotle's Physics (Berlin, 1882–1895).

Commentary—Paul Tannery: Sur les fragments d'Eudème de Rhodes relatifs à l'histoire des mathématiques (Ann. de la Faculté des lettres, t. IV, p. 70–76, Bordeaux, 1882; Mémoires, I, 168–177); Le fragment d'Eudème sur la quadrature des lunules (Mém. de la société des sci. phys. et natur., t. V, p. 217–237, Bordeaux, 1883; Mémoires, I, 339–370). Cfr. also Heath's Euclid (Vol. I, p. 35–38, Cambridge, 1908).

ARISTAEOS

Aristaeos the Elder, Ἀρισταῖος, flourished about the end of the century. Mathematician. Collaborated with Euclid and Apollonios in the composition of the "treasury of analysis" (τόπος ἀναλυόμενος), a geometrical method for advanced students. Wrote on the "comparison of the five figures" (i. e., the five regular solids) and proved that "the same circle circumscribes both the pentagon of the dodecahedron and the triangle of the icosahedron when both solids are inscribed in the same sphere" (Euclid, so-called Bk. XIV, prop. 2). Wrote five books of solid loci (στερεοὶ τόποι) connected with the conics (that is, a treatise on conics regarded as loci). This treatise was more important and more original than the one written later by Euclid on the same subject and its object and point of view were different. Aristaeos called the conics respectively sections of right-angled, acute-angled, and obtuse-angled cones. He discussed the three-line and four-line locus.

See Thomas Heath: Euclid; Apollonius (chapter II, Cambridge, 1896); History of Greek Mathematics (Oxford, 1921).

VI. GREEK ASTRONOMY

HERACLIDES

Heraclides of Pontos (Ἡρακλείδης ὁ Ποντικός). Born in Heracleia on the Black Sea c. 388 (not earlier), died c. 315 to 310. Astronomer. Pupil of Plato and Aristotle. A writer original to the point of eccentricity, very prolific and very gifted. A probable association with the Pythagorizing members of the Academy may have acquainted him with the theories of Hicetas and Ecphantos (q. v.). The universe is infinite. Originator of the geoheliocentrical system (later developed by Tycho Brahe), that is: (1), the sun, the moon and the superior planets revolve around the earth; (2) Venus and Mercury revolve around the sun; (3) a daily rotation of the earth around its own axis replaces the daily rotation of the whole system around the earth supposed at rest.

Giov. Virg. Schiaparelli: I precursori di Copernico nell' antichità (Pubbl. del R. Osservatorio di Brera, 51 p., Milano, 1873). Otto Voss: De Heraclidis Pontici vita et scriptis (Diss., 95 p., Rostock, 1896. Contains an elaborate collection of fragments, p. 35–93). G. V. Schiaparelli: Origine del sistema planetario eliocentrico presso i Greci (Mem. del R. Instituto Lombardo di sci. e lett., vol. 18, p. 61 sq., Milano, 1898; Isis, VIII, 506). In this his second memoir Schiaparelli claims that Heraclides has finally regarded all the five planets as revolving around the sun—thus anticipating Tycho's system; he even went so far as to claim that Heraclides had anticipated Copernicus! Both assertions seem equally unfounded. H. Staigmüller: Herakleides Pontikos und das heliocentrische System (Archiv f. Gesch. d. Philosophie, t. XV, p. 141–165, 1902). Sir Thomas Heath: Aristarchus (249–283, Oxford, 1913).

CALLIPPOS

Callippos of Cyzicos[p] (Κάλλιππος). Born c. 370, flourished in Athens c. 330. Improved the astronomical system of Eudoxos by introducing 7 more spheres, that is, using in all 34 spheres. Better determination of the length of the seasons (beginning with the spring; 94, 92, 89 and 90 days; the errors ranging from 0.08 to 0.44 day). Improved also the 19-year cycle of Meton, dropping one day out of every period of (19 × 4 =) 76 years. The epoch of this new era was possibly June 29, 330. Whether the Callippos cycle had only a theoretical interest (Schmidt) or was actually applied (Aug. Mommsen) is a moot question.

Same references as for Eudoxos. For the Callippos period see F. K. Ginzel: Handbuch der mathematischen und technischen Chronologie (Bd. 2, 409–419, 1911).

AUTOLYCOS

Autolycos of Pitane, Aeolis (Αὐτόλυκος, flourished c. 310). Astronomer, mathematician. A contemporary of Euclid, but a little older. He wrote two treatises

[p] On the island of the same name in the Sea of Marmora.

on mathematical astronomy: on the moving sphere (περὶ κινουμένης σφαίρας) and on risings and settings (περὶ ἐπιτολῶν καὶ δύσεων), both collected later in the "Little Astronomy." The moving sphere is the sphere of the stars; the book deals with mathematics (e. g., sections of the sphere by planes) rather than with astronomy. Euclid used Autolycos's results in his Phaenomena, but the latter's knowledge was derived from an older treatise on sphaerics, possibly due to Eudoxos or even older. Autolycos was the first to try to explain certain difficulties involved by the theory of homocentric spheres, notably the fact that the apparent differences in the relative sizes of sun and moon and the differences in the brightness of the planets suggest variations in their distances from the earth.

Text—Fr. Hultsch: Autolyci de sphaera quae movetur liber, de ortibus et occasibus libri duo (Leipzig, 1885).

Commentary—Paul Tannery: Autolycos de Pitane (Mém. de la soc. des sci. phys. et natur., t. II, p. 173–199. Bordeaux, 1886; also Mémoires, II, 225–255). F. Hultsch: Autolycus und Euklid (Ber. Sächs. Ges. d. Wiss., Phil. Cl. 128–155, Leipzig, 1886).

VII. GREEK PHYSICS

ARISTOXENOS

Aristoxenos of Tarentum (Ἀριστόξενος). Flourished in the second half of the century. Pupil of Aristotle. Philosopher, mathematician. The greatest theorician of music in ancient times. 435 books attributed to him, many of them dealing with philosophical and ethical matters.

Paul Marquard: Die harmonischen Fragmente des Aristoxenus. Griechisch und Deutsch mit kritischen und exegetischen Commentar und einem Anhang die rhythmischen Fragmente des Aristoxenus enthaltend (452 p., Berlin, 1868). Bernhard Brill: Aristoxenus rhythmische und metrische Messungen im Gegensatz gegen neuere Auslegungen namenlich Westphal's und zur Rechtfertigung der von K. Lehrs befolgten Messungen (88 p., Leipzig, 1870). Charles Emile Ruelle: Eléments harmoniques d'Aristoxène (148 p., Paris, 1871). Rudolf Westphal: Aristoxenus. Melik und Rhythmik des classischen Hellenenthums (2 vols., Leipzig, 1883. Greek and German text with abundant commentary). Henry S. Macran: The Harmonics of Aristoxenus (edited with translation, notes, introduction, 303 p., Oxford, 1902). Louis Laloy: Aristoxène et la musique de l'antiquité (418 p., Paris, 1904. Very elaborate; includes also a lexicon; new edition 1924; see Isis, VIII, 530).

P. Tannery: Sur un point d'histoire de la musique grecque (Revue archéologique, t. 39, 49–54, 1902; Mémoires, III, 90; Isis, IV, 339); Sur le spondiasme dans l'ancienne musique grecque (Ibidem, t. 1, 1911, 41–50; Mémoires, III, 299). C. F. Abdy Williams: The Aristoxenian Theory of Musical Rhythm (208 p., Cambridge, 1911). Léon Boutroux: Sur l'harmonie aristoxénienne (Revue générale des sciences, t. 30, p. 265–274, Paris, 1919. Short and clear comparison of Pythagorean and Aristoxenian musical theories; Isis, III, 317).

VIII. GREEK AND ROMAN TECHNOLOGY

LYSISTRATOS

Lysistratos[a] (Λυσίστρατος). Of Sicyon, Northeast Peloponnesos, flourished c. 328. Greek sculptor who was the first, for the sake of accuracy, to take plaster casts from the faces of his sitters. (Mentioned by Pliny, Bk. 34, chap. 19).

---

[a] Brother of Lysippos, the great sculptor, Alexander's favorite.

CLAUDIUS CAECUS

Appius Claudius Caecus. Censor in 312; he became blind (hence his name); died very old, after 280. Roman statesman and civil servant. During his censorship, which lasted four years (312 to 308), he built the famous aqueduct and road named after him (Aqua Appia, Via Appia). He is the earliest Roman writer of whom we know anything, also the earliest Roman jurisconsult (his book "de usurpationibus" is lost).

Karl Sieke: Appius Claudius Caecus, Censor i. J. 444 U. C. (80 p., Marburg 1890). F. P. Bremer: Iurisprud. antehadrianae quae supersunt (Leipzig, 1896–98). Münzer, in Pauly-Wissowa (t. 3, 2681–2685, 1899).

IX. GREEK BOTANY

THEOPHRASTOS

Theophrastos of Eresos, Lesbos (Θεόφραστος, born c. 372, died c. 288). Pupil of Plato and Aristotle and successor of the latter as head of the Lyceum (from 323 to c. 288). Philosopher, scientist. The founder of botanical science and one of the greatest botanists of all times. Many of his observations were probably made in the garden of the Lyceum, but his knowledge was not limited to the flora of Greece and Asia Minor; it included many plants brought from inner Asia by Alexander's followers. Wrote a number of books on many different subjects. Only two complete works preserved, both on botany, one descriptive (περὶ φυτῶν ἱστορίαι), the other more philosophical (περὶ φυτῶν αἰτιῶν). Among his other writings, the following are particularly noteworthy: On stones (περὶ λίθων), describing various rocks and minerals and indicating their sources and uses; on odors, on winds, on weather signs, on the senses, on poisonous animals, on weariness, on dizziness, on sweat. Theophrastos apparently replaced the seat of intellect in the brain (against Aristotle). His φυσικῶν δόξαι have been often drawn upon by ancient writers and are thus indirectly the root of almost all we know on early Greek natural philosophy. He wrote also a history of geometry, astronomy, and arithmetic, unfortunately lost. By far the most popular of his works was the Characters (Ἠθικοὶ χαρακτῆρες)—of uncertain genuineness—a series of thirty sketches of various types of human weakness.

Text—Princeps edition, Aldine, 1495–1498. Latin translation by Theodore Gaza (Treviso, 1483. Important especially because it was made upon a different manuscript from any now known). Greek edition by Joannes Bodaeus à Stapel (Amsterdam, 1644. With very important botanical commentary). Friedrich Wimmer: Theophrasti Eresii quae supersunt omnia (Leipzig, 1854–1862: vol. I, Historia plantarum, 1854; vol. II, de causis plantarum, 1854; vol. III, fragmenta, de sensu et sensibilibus, de lapidibus, de igne, de odoribus, de ventis, de signis tempestatum, de lassitudine, de vertigine, de sudore, de animi defectu, de membrorum solutione, metaphysica; accessit Prisciani Lydi metaphrasis in Theophrasti libros de sensu et de phantasia, 1862). The same text has been reprinted with Latin translation in the Didot series (Paris, 1866). On Winds and on Weather Signs, translation with introduction, notes, and an appendix on the direction, number, and nomenclature of the winds in classical and later times by James George Wood (97 p., London, 1894). Enquiry into Plants and Minor Works on Odours and Weather Signs, Greek text with English translation by Sir Arthur Hort (2 vols., Loeb Classical Library, London, 1916). Theophrastus and the Greek Physiological Psychology before Aristotle. Greek text of the fragment on the senses, English translation, introduction and notes by George Malcolm Stratton (227 p., New York, 1917). Gotthelf Bergsträsser: Neue meteorologische Fragmente des Theophrast arabisch und deutsch. Mit Zusätzen von Franz Boll (Sgbr. der Heidelberger Ak., phil. Kl., 30 p., 1918; ex Constantinople MS., Ashir Efendi, I, 1164).

Ernst Howald: Die Schriftenverzeichnisse des Aristoteles und des Theophrasts (Hermes, t. 55, 204–221, 1920).

Commentary—(*A*) *Botany:* Const. Kontopulos: De physiologia plantarum secundum Aristotelem et Theophrastum. (Diss., 34 p., Berlin, 1848). Hermann Stadler: Theophrast und Dioscorides (Abhdl. aus dem Gebiet der klass. Altertumswiss. Wilh. von Christ dargebracht, p. 176–187, München, 1891. A study of the plant names used by both authors; 236 names are common to both; 249 and 152 are special respectively to Dioscorides and Theophrastos). Hugo Bretzl: Botanische Forschungen des Alexanderzuges (424 S., 11 Abb., 4 Kart. Leipzig, 1903). Paul Wirtz: De Theophrasti Eresii libris phytologicis (Diss., 62 p., Strasbourg, 1898). Edw. Lee Greene: Landmarks of Botanical History (Part I, p. 52–142, Washington, 1909. This is a very elaborate study of Theophrastian botany. The reader will find on p. 140–142 a list of 17 specific botanical facts the discovery of which may be ascribed to Theophrastos). Ludwig Hindenlang: Sprachliche Untersuchungen zu Theophrasts botanischen Schriften (Diss., 200 p., Strassburg, 1910). G. Senn: Die Pflanzensystematik bei Theophrast (Verhdl. der Schweiz. Naturf. Gesellschaft, II, Teil, 302, Bern, 1922; Isis, VI, 139).

(*B*) *Other Subjects*—Joh. Boehme: De Theophrasteis quae feruntur περὶ σημείων excerptis (Diss., 85 p., Hamburg, 1884). Maxim. Robert Heeger: De Theophrasti qui fertur περὶ σημείων libro (Diss., 72 p., Leipzig, 1889).

Herm. Joachim: De Theophrasti libris περὶ ζῴων (68 p., Bonn, 1892).

K. B. Hofmann: Notiz zur Geschichte des Wasserbades und Reagenzpapiers (Archiv f. Gesch. d. Naturw., III, p. 307–308, Leipzig, 1911).

P. Duhem: Etudes sur Léonard de Vinci (t. 2, p. 473, 1909, geology).

Lynn Thorndike: Disputed Dates, Civilization and Climate, and Traces of Magic in the Scientific Treatises ascribed to Theophrastus (Essays dedicated to K. Sudhoff, 14 p., Zurich, 1924; Isis, VII, 178).

PHANIAS

Or Phaenias (Φανίας, Φαινίας) of Eresos in Lesbos. Disciple of Aristotle, friend of Theophrastos. He wrote many works on various subjects, but all are lost. One of them dealt with plants. A few fragments of it have been preserved in the Banquet of Athenaeos (q. v., first half of third century). He seems to have paid special attention to the shapes of flowers.

Ernst H. F. Meyer: Geschichte der Botanik (1, 189–193, 1854).

X. GREEK GEOGRAPHY, GEOLOGY, AND METEOROLOGY

The Periplus of Scylax, if it be genuine, was written between 360 and 347. (See Scylax of Caryanda in the chapter devoted to the fifth century B. C.)

For Ephoros of Cyme (c. 350) see Section XII.

PYTHEAS

Pytheas of Massilia (Marseilles), Πυθέας, flourished c. 330. Sailed to Britain and farther north, possibly reaching the Arctic circle. Measured the maximum height of the sun at Massilia at the summer solstice. Noted the influence of the moon upon the tides. Pytheas is the earliest scientist of western Europe.

Text—Pytheae Massiliensis fragmenta, variis ex auctoribus collegit et commentariis illustravit Andreas Arv. Arvedson (36 p., Upsaliae, 1824). Pytheae quae supersunt fragmenta edidit Alfr. Schmekel (25 p., Merseburgi, 1848).

Commentaries—Joachim Lelewel: Pythéas et la géographie de son temps (75 p., 3 cartes, Paris, 1836). Max. Fuhr: Pytheas (Historisch-kritische Abh., 82 p., Darmstadt, 1842). Gustav Moritz Redslob: Thule. Die phönicischen Handelswege nach dem Norden insbesondere nach dem Bernsteinlande sowie die Reise des Pytheas (123 p., Leipzig, 1855). W. Bessell: Über Pytheas und dessen Einfluss auf die Kentniss der Alten vom Norden Europa's (282 p., Göttingen, 1858). Ch. E. de Ujfalvy: Le pays de Thulé (Communic. à la Soc. franç. de numismatique, 1873, 9 p., Paris, 1874). Georg Mair: Die Fahrten des Pytheas in der Ostsee (20 S., 1 Karte., Progr., Villach, 1893). Gustav Hergt: Die Nordlandfahrt des Pytheas (Diss., 78 p., Halle a. S., 1893). Franz Matthias: Über Pytheas und den ältesten Nachrichten von den Germanen (47 p., Progr., Berlin, 1901). Friedrich Kähler: Forschungen zu Pytheas' Nordlandsreisen (60 p., Halle a. S., 1903). Georg Mair: Pytheas und die mathematische Geographie (34 + 96 p., Progr., Marburg a. d. D., 1904–1906. According to Mair, Pytheas's interests were primarily astronomical and his expedition to the north was a real polar expedition undertaken with a purely scientific purpose!). Fridjof Nansen: In Northern Mists (vol. 1, 43–73, 1911). Paul Masson: Pythéas et le poumon marin (Ministère de l'instruction publique, Section de géographie, t. 28, 55–66, Paris, 1923. Pytheas's "sea-lung," πνεύμων, was a jelly-fish; Isis, VII, 177).

NEARCHOS

Νέαρχος, born in Crete, flourished in Amphipolis, Macedonia; he died after 323. Greek soldier. Admiral of Alexander's fleet, built on the Hydaspes in 327; he descended that river, then the Indus, and by way of the Arabian Sea and the Persian Gulf returned to Susa (325). Nearchos's account of his journey is preserved in Arrian's Indica (q. v., first half of second century).

DICAEARCHOS

Dicaearchos of Messina, Sicily (Δικαίαρχος, flourished in the second half of the century). Geographer and historian. Pupil of Aristotle, contemporary of Aristoxenos. Very learned and prolific writer. Wrote geographical treatises (περίοδος γῆς, with a map?, καταμετρήσεις τῶν ἐν Ἑλλάδι ὀρῶν) of which fragments remain. Measured the height of many mountains, using possibly a diopter. Estimated the length of the circumference of the earth to be 300,000 stades. Noted the influence of the sun upon the tides. His investigations prepared those of Eratosthenes. He wrote a history of Greek culture (Βίος Ἑλλάδος), treatises on politics, literature, philosophy, divination, etc., but only a few fragments of his work have come down to us.

Text—Dicaearchi Messenii quae supersunt composita, edita et illustrata a Maximiliano Fuhr (528 p., Darmstadt, 1841). Fragments published in C Müller: Geographi graeci minores (t. 1, 97–110, 1855), and in his Fragmenta historicorum graecorum (t. 2, 254 sq.).

Commentary—Ernst H. F. Meyer: Botanische Erläuterungen zu Strabons Geographie und einem Fragment des Dikäarchos (222 p., Königsberg, 1852. The fragment will be found on p. 185–192; it is a description of Mount Pelion). Very long article by Martini in Pauly-Wissowa (t. 9, 546–563, 1903). According to J. G. Frazer (translation of Pausanias, 2d ed., vol. 1, p. XLIII, 1913) the description of Greece ascribed to Dicaearchos must have been written at some time between 164 and 86 B. C. Frazer gives a paraphrase of Dicaearchos's description.

For the history of geology, refer to my note on Theophrastos in Section IX.

For the history of meteorology, refer to the notes on Aristotle and Theophrastos.

XI. GREEK ANATOMY, PHYSIOLOGY, AND MEDICINE

PRAXAGORAS

Praxagoras of Cos (Πραξαγόρας), flourished about 340–320. Physician, anatomist. Diocles's follower and successor as head of the Dogmatic school. The first to draw clearly the distinction between veins and arteries, holding that the former carry blood while the others are filled only with air. The body-warmth is not inherent but acquired. He made a deeper study of the pulse[r] and improved diagnosis and topical pathology.

PHILOTIMOS

Φιλότιμος, pupil of Praxagoras, flourished in the second half, and probably in the last quarter, of the fourth century B. C. He is quoted by Galen as one of the promoters of gymnastics, and as the author of treatises on diet and on the nature of a physician's work.

Short note by A. Hirsch, in Biographisches Lexicon (t. 4, 559, Wien, 1886).

MNESITHEOS

Μνησίθεος of Athens; pupil of Praxagoras; flourished in the second half, probably in the last quarter, of the fourth century B. C. Greek Hippocratic physician; one of the greatest of his time. He wrote a medical compendium containing original views on the classification of diseases and a treatise on diet and made anatomical investigations (on animals). He is quoted by Galen and Oribasios.

A. Hirsch, in Biographisches Lexicon (t. 4, 252, Wien, 1886).

MENON

Μένων, flourished probably in the second half of the fourth century B. C. Greek physician. Pupil of Aristotle. Author of a historical work describing in verse the pathological views of predecessors and contemporaries of Hippocrates.

Text—This work is of great importance, because it enables one to see the Hippocratic doctrines in a truer perspective. A student's note-book derived from it, dating from about the middle of the second century after Christ, was discovered in 1891 by Sir Frederic Kenyon, who brought it from Egypt to the British Museum (Papyrus 137). It was first published by Hermann Diels: Anonymi Londinensis ex Aristotelis iatricis Menonis et aliis medicis eclogae (Supplementum Aristotelicum, Vol. III, pars 1; 136 p., 2 pl., Berlin, 1893). German translation by Heinrich Beckh and Franz Spät: Anonymus Londinensis, Auszüge eines Unbekannten aus Aristoteles-Menons Handbuch der Medizin (Berlin, 1896).

Criticism—H. Diels: Über die Exzerpte von Menons Iatrika (Hermes, t. 28, 407–434, 1893); Medizin in der Schule des Aristoteles (Preussische Jahrbücher, t. 74, 412–429, 1893). Franz Spät: Die geschichtliche Entwicklung der sogenannten hippokratischen Medizin im Lichte der neuesten Forschung (Berlin, 1897).

XII. GREEK HISTORIOGRAPHY

EPHOROS

Ephoros of Cyme, Aeolis (Ἔφορος), flourished about the middle of the century. Historian, geographer. The first universal historian (if Herodotos is not considered as such), he is quoted here chiefly because of the importance he attached

---

[r] Little attention was paid to it in Hippocratic writings, though the Ebers papyrus already alludes to it. For further study of the pulse, see Herophilos, first half of third century B. C.

to geography and because of his philosophical views on the geographical basis of history. His history stops at the year 356–355; it was already available in 334.

Text—Ephori Cumaei Fragmenta collegit atque illustravit Meier Marx (322 p., Karlsruhe, 1815).

Commentary—Long article by Schwartz, in Pauly-Wissowa (t. XI, 1–16, 1907). Ernest Dopp: Die geographischen Studien des Ephorus (3 Gymn. Progr., Rostock, 1900, 1908, 1909). Josef Forderer: Ephoros und Strabon (Diss., 79 p., Tübingen, 1913).

THEOPOMPOS

Θεόπομπος, born at Chios c. 380; died in Egypt (?) after 323, possibly c. 305. Greek historian and orator.[a] He was very erudite and attached much importance to the analysis of characters, personal manners, and motives. He was in that respect a predecessor of Tacitus and the founder of psychological history. His main works were a Greek History in 12 books (Ἑλληνικαὶ ἱστορίαι or Σύνταξις Ἑλληνικῶν) continuing that of Thucydides from 410 to 398, and the History of Philip of Macedon (Alexander's father) in 58 books (Φιλιππικά), in fact, a history of the whole of Greece, continuing that of Xenophon, from 362 to 336.

Text—C. Müller: Fragmenta hist. graec. (t. 1, 278–333; t. 4, 643–645). R. H. Eyssonius Wichers: Fragmenta (308 p., Leyden, 1829). Eduard Meyer: Hellenika (Halle a. S., 1909). Bernard P. Grenfell and Arthur S. Hunt: Hellenica oxyrhynchia cum Theopompi et Cratippi fragmentis (180 p., Oxford, 1909).

Criticism—A. Croiset: Littérature grecque (t. 4, 2e ed., 662–674, 1900). Wilhelm Schranz: Theopompos Philippika (Diss., 78 p., Marburg, 1912).

XIII. HINDU AND ROMAN SOCIOLOGY AND LAW

For Roman law, see my note on Claudius Caecus in Section VIII.

KAUṬILYA

Or Cāṇakya, flourished toward the end of the century. Hindu statesman; minister to Candragupta, who founded the Maurya dynasty of Magadha about 321 and was the earliest emperor of India (c. 321 to c. 298). The Arthaśāstra, ascribed to Kauṭilya, is a treatise on government and administration, which is of considerable interest to the historian of science, for it contains information on medicine, mining, census-taking, meteorology, ships, surveying, etc., and affords glimpses into almost every aspect of Hindu life. In sharp contrast with the political writings of Plato and Aristotle, it is very concrete and practical, and reveals a very low morality. The statecraft taught by Kauṭilya is extremely cynical and unscrupulous.

The Arthaśāstra, if it is really genuine (and there is no serious reason for doubting this), is the oldest datable Sanskrit work.

Text—The Sanskrit text of the Arthaśāstra was edited for the first time by R. Shama Sastri (Mysore, 1909). English translation by the same (Bangalore, 1915). New Sanskrit edition, with English introduction, in the Trivandrum Sanskrit series (Trivandrum, 1924, etc.). German translation with notes and commentary by Johann Jacob Meyer, based upon the primary edition as emended by the translator (Hanover, 1925 sq.).

Criticism—Hermann Jacobi: Kultur-, Sprach- und Literar-historisches aus dem Kauṭilīya (Sitzungsber. d. Kgl. Preuss. Akad. d. Wiss., 954–973, Berlin, 1911);

[a] The earliest Greek writer to make any definite mention of Rome (Pliny, III, 9).

Über die Echtheit des Kauṭilīya (*ibidem*, 832–849, 1912. Jacobi maintains against Hillebrandt that the Kauṭilīya is authentic, and that it is really the work of Candragupta's famous minister). Narendra Nath Law: Studies in Ancient Hindu Polity based on the Arthaśāstra of Kauṭilya (Vol. I, 251 p., London, 1914.) With an introductory essay on the age and authenticity of the Arthaśāstra of Kauṭilya by Radhakumud Mookerji, reënforcing Jacobi's argument); Interstate Relations in Ancient India (Part I, 99 p., Calcutta, 1920; see J. R. Asiatic S., 614–616, 1921). Julius Jolly: Kollektaneen zum Kauṭilīya Arthaśāstra (Nachrichten von der Kgl. Gesellschaft der Wissensch. zu Göttingen, Philol. histor. Kl., p. 348–366, 1916. Jolly concludes from the study of technical details dealing with mining, the working of metals, and medicine, that the Arthaśāstra is of a much later time). George Melville Bolling: The Recension of Çāṇakya used by Galanos for his ἐκ διαφορῶν ποιητῶν (Studies in honor of Maurice Bloomfield, p. 49–74, New Haven, 1920). Julius Jolly: Das erste Buch des Kauṭilya Arthachastra (Z. d. deut. Morgenl. Ges., t. 74, 321–355, 1920). M. Winternitz: Geschichte der indischen Litteratur (Bd. 3, 509-524, passim, 1922). O. Stein: Megasthenes und Kauṭilya (340 p., Wien, 1922). E. O. von Lippmann: Technologisches und Kulturgeschichtliches aus dem Arthaśāstra (Chemiker Zeitung, 1925; reprint, 12 p.).

Oskar Kressler: Stimmen indischer Lebensklugheit. Die unter Cāṇakya's Namen gehende Spruchsammlung in mehreren Recensionem untersucht und nach einer Recension übersetzt (Diss., 195 p., Frankfurt a. M., 1904).

XIV. GREEK STUDY OF THE HISTORY OF SCIENCE

For Xenocrates (c. 339) see Section V; for Theophrastos (c. 332) see Section IX; for Menon (c. 325) see Section XI; for Eudemos (c. 320) see Section V.

CHAPTER VII

THE TIME OF EUCLID

(First Half of the Third Century B. C.)

I. Survey of Science in the First Half of the Third Century B. C. II. Development of the Jewish Scriptures. III. Greek and Chinese Philosophy. IV. Hellenistic Mathematics, Astronomy, and Physics. V. Hellenistic Anatomy, Physiology, Biology, and Medicine. VI. Hellenistic Technology. VII. Hellenistic, Hebrew, and Chinese Historiography. VIII. Greek Philology.

I. SURVEY OF SCIENCE IN FIRST HALF OF THIRD CENTURY B. C.

1. The period which we are now going to consider is widely different from the previous one. In the fourth century Athens was the greatest intellectual center of the world; by the beginning of the third century that center had already moved to Alexandria. Strictly speaking, the new period does not coincide with the first half of the third century, but began a little earlier, some time after the advent of the Ptolemies in Egypt. It can not have begun much earlier: Alexandria was founded only in 332, and the brilliant civilization which blossomed there can not have started at once—the material preparation required some time; we may assume that the activity of one generation was largely devoted to it. Strangely enough, we do not know the exact dates of three of the great men of this period—Euclid, Herophilos, and Manethon; we know only that they flourished under the first Ptolemy (Ptolemaeos Soter), who ruled Egypt from 323 to 285. Thus it is possible, and even probable, that some of their work was already done in the fourth century. Yet, as their activity was distinctly of the newer, Alexandrian (Hellenistic), type rather than of the older, Aristotelian, type, we feel justified in placing them in this chapter.

2. *Development of the Jewish Scriptures*—The Jewish Scriptures were not simply religious books in the narrow sense, but historical annals and codes of law and morality; put together, they formed a real encyclopaedia of Jewish wisdom and learning. It is thus worth while to watch their growth and coördination. A Greek translation was begun for the sake of the Alexandrian community, under the second Ptolemy (Philadelphos), king from 285 to 247. Aramaic and Samaritan traditions were developing at about the same time or even before.

3. *Greek and Chinese Philosophy*—The two greatest schools of philosophy of that time, the Lyceum and the Stoa, were fittingly represented, the one by Straton of Lampsacos (288), the other by Cleanthes of Assos (264). Straton was deeply interested in the more scientific problems of philosophy.

At the same time flourished in what is now the Chinese province of Anhui, the philosopher Chuang Tzŭ, one of the leaders of Taoism, author of the Nan Hua ching.

4. *Hellenistic Mathematics, Astronomy, and Physics*—The history of Hellenistic science begins admirably with Euclid, whose contributions to geometry were so great that even to-day, for a large number of people, the words Euclid and geometry

are almost synonymous. He stands almost[a] alone in that period, but he is so big that he fills it.

Astronomical observations were made in Alexandria by Aristyllos and Timocharis. The greatest astronomer of the age (and one of the greatest of all ages) was Aristarchos of Samos (c. 280), the "ancient Copernicus." He was the first to put forward the heliocentric hypothesis; he explained that the size of the earth and even of the sphere containing the earth's orbit was negligible as compared with the sphere of the fixed stars; he gave a method to measure the distances of the sun and moon. Aratos of Soli (c. 275) wrote an astronomical and meteorological poem which exerted considerable influence for a very long time.

Physical studies were carried on by Euclid and Aristarchos, not unnaturally in the field of optics, which touches both the mathematical and the astronomical fields. Euclid laid down some of the fundamental principles of geometrical optics.

At some time before or toward the middle of the century, a great institution for scientific research, the Museum, was established at Alexandria. It might be considered the earliest university and it was indeed a university in a truer sense than many modern colleges bearing that noble name, but wherein scientific research is entirely sacrificed to the lowest kind of expediency. The Museum will ever be famous, not so much because it afforded opportunities for research which had been hitherto unavailable anywhere, but because many great men were associated with it.

5. *Hellenistic Anatomy, Physiology, Biology, and Medicine*—Nicander of Colophon (c. 275) wrote various didactic poems on medical, zoological and agricultural subjects. The best known of them deals with poisonous animals, their venoms and the corresponding antidotes.

The newly born Alexandria saw the creation of a school of anatomy, illustrated by two of the greatest anatomists of all times, Herophilos and Erasistratos and their disciple Eudemos.

6. *Hellenistic Technology*—Sostratos of Cnidos built the lighthouse of Alexandria (c. 279).

7. *Hellenistic, Hebrew, and Chinese Historiography*—In no department of knowledge do the cosmopolitan tendencies of the age appear more clearly than in this. We witness the production within a short time of a number of historical works, most of them written in Greek, but very different otherwise, and dealing with many countries. Crateros compiled a collection of Athenian decrees; Megasthenes wrote an account of India; Manethon, the annals of Egypt; Berossos, those of Babylonia; Timaeos, histories of Sicily and of Pyrrhos's adventurous rule. Timaeos was the first (c. 264) to determine the sequence of events by systematic reference to Olympiads. The Parian chronicle dates from about the same time (c. 264). Great pains were thus taken during that period to establish exact chronologies, which are the very foundation of historiography. Note that these Hellenistic historians were each (as far as we can know) of a different nationality: Crateros was a Macedonian; Megasthenes, a Syrian; Manethon, an Egyptian; Berossos, a Babylonian; Timaeos, a Sicilian.

The Books of Chronicles, the Book of Ezra, and the Book of Nehemiah were probably edited at about that time; also the Book of Proverbs.

The Annals of the Bamboo Books (down to 298) are our safest chronological guide for the early history of China.

---

[a] I say almost, for Aristarchos too was a mathematician.

8. *Greek Philology*—Zenodotos of Ephesos, first librarian of the famous Alexandrian library (the greatest of antiquity), was the earliest scientific editor of the Iliad and the Odyssey and of Hesiod's Theogony, and he compiled a Homeric glossary.

9. *Conclusion*—The first half of the third century marks a great contrast with the preceding period. The age of magnificent, if premature, synthesis is already passed. Special investigations are now systematically carried on in many directions; men of science are no longer identified with philosophers, but are already divided into various esoteric groups. Great importance is attached in every field (even historiography) to technique and methods. These analytical tendencies of the Hellenistic age will be even more accentuated in the following periods, but they are obvious from the beginning. The Museum of Alexandria may be considered the symbol of a new departure in human progress.

II. DEVELOPMENT OF THE JEWISH SCRIPTURES

The Oral Targums—After the return from Babylon to Palestine, the majority of the Jews spoke Aramaic,[b] not Hebrew, and it had thus become necessary to interpret the Scriptures in Aramaic. Thus arose the so-called targums.[c] The earliest targums were purely oral, and it is thus obviously impossible to date them. They represent a tradition different from that of the Septuagint (and probably anterior to it) and also from that of the Hebrew scribes (Ṣopherim), which was not completely crystallized until the second century of our era. Written targums existed already in the first century of our era, but those which are now extant are all much younger (fourth and later centuries).

The Septuagint—The large colony of Jews established at Alexandria had gradually forgotten its Aramaic vernacular and spoke a Greek dialect (Judaeo-Hellenistic Greek). They needed a Greek version of the Scriptures. Such a version was undertaken during the reign of Ptolemaeos Philadelphos (King of Egypt from 285 to 247) by a group of Alexandrian (not Palestinian!) Jews, seventy-two (or seventy) in number. Hence the name *ἡ ἑρμηνεία κατὰ τοὺς ἑβδομήκοντα*, interpretatio septuaginta seniorum (or virorum), or, for short, *οἱ ο'*, the LXX.

This undertaking was at first limited to the Pentateuch and was approved by Aristeas, high priest at Jerusalem. The other books of the Old Testament were translated later; all those included in the Christian Bible were already available in Greek before 132 B. C. and all the Hebrew Scriptures, including the Apocrypha, before the beginning of our era. It should be noted that this Greek version was thus completed before the establishment of the standard Hebrew text of the Sopherim (first or second century after Christ). This was to be the source of endless controversies, for two separate Old Testament canons were thus constituted—a Christian canon based upon the Septuagint and a Jewish one based upon the official Hebrew text. The Septuagint was the earliest large work translated from another language.

The Samaritan Pentateuch—A fourth Old Testament tradition independent of the three already mentioned is represented by the Samaritan Pentateuch. This

---

[b] Anciently called "Chaldee." It is impossible to say exactly how fast and to what extent Hebrew was substituted by Aramaic.

[c] Targum, in Aramaic, means interpretation. The targums were formerly called "Chaldee paraphrase."

is probably older than the Septuagint; maybe it dates back to the end of the fifth century or to the fourth century. The text is Hebrew, but it is written in Samaritan character (an independent development of the old Hebrew-Phoenician script). This Samaritan-Hebrew Pentateuch should not be confused with a Samaritan-Aramaic Pentateuch (or Samaritan targum) dating from only the fourth century after Christ, or not much earlier.[d] The Samaritan Pentateuch was not discovered until 1616 (in Damascus). The earliest printed edition appeared in the Paris Polyglot, 1645; it was published also in the London Polyglot, 1657. Benjamin Blayney edited a transliteration of it in the square character in Oxford, 1790. A small remnant of the Samaritan community[e] still exists at Nablus (the ancient Shechem, near Mount Gerizim, their sanctuary).

H. B. Swete: Introduction to the Old Testament in Greek (603 p., Cambridge, 1900). Henry St. John Thackeray: The Septuagint and Jewish worship (London, 1921).

III. GREEK AND CHINESE PHILOSOPHY

STRATON

Straton of Lampsacos[f] (Στράτων ὁ φυσικός, flourished c. 288). Philosopher, scientist. Tutor of Ptolemaeos Philadelphos. Succeeded to Theophrastos as head of the Lyceum c. 288. He tried to reconcile the theories of Aristotle and Democritos. Mechanistic and deterministic explanation of the world. Even his psychology is mechanistic. Mainly interested in physics, he developed the most scientific parts of Aristotelian philosophy. His synthetical effort might have exerted a great influence upon the progress of science, but that it came too late, when analytic, empirical, and centrifugal tendencies were already triumphant.

G. Rodier: La physique de Straton (Thèse) 135 p., Paris, 1890. Very clear and comprehensive). H. Diels: Über das physikalische System des Straton (Sitzungsber. d. Kgl. Preuss. Akad. d. Wissensch., 101–127, Berlin, 1893. Followed by an improved text of the beginning of Heron's Pneumatics). M. Wellman: Über Träume (Archiv für Geschichte der Medizin, t. 16, 70–72, 1924).

CLEANTHES

Κλεάνθης, born at Assos in Troas, in 331–330; he died c. 232. Stoic philosopher. Successor of Zeno (q. v., second half of fourth century) as head of the Stoa (264 to 239). He wrote a hymn to Zeus which illustrates the pantheistic views of the school. He insisted upon strength of will (εὐτονία) as the fundamental moral quality. It is impossible to determine exactly Zeno's and Cleanthes's respective contributions to the Stoic world-conception. Cleanthes's scientific writings are lost.

Text—C. Wachsmuth: De Zenone et Cleanthe (2 Progr., Göttingen, 1874–75). A. C. Pearson: The Fragments of Zeno and Cleanthes (London, 1891). J. von Arnim: Stoicorum veterum fragmenta (vol. 1, Leipzig, 1905).

Criticism—J. von Arnim, in Pauly-Wissowa (t. 21, 558–574, 1921).

---

[d] There is also a Samaritan-Arabic Pentateuch dating from the eleventh century. In other words, the Samaritan script was used successively (as the vernacular of the people changed) to transliterate Hebrew, Aramaic, and Arabic. In the East much religious importance has always been attached to the script—sometimes more than to the language itself. See, for example, E. G. Browne: Literary History of Persia (t. 1, 8, 1908).

[e] About 170 souls c. 1909!

[f] On the Asiatic side of the Hellespont (Dardanelles).

CHUANG TZŬ

Chuang[1] Tzŭ[3] (2760, 12317), meaning the philosopher Chuang. His name was Chou[1] (2450) and his surname Chuang, hence he is sometimes called Chuang Chou. Born about 330, in the State of Wei[4] (12542), modern Anhui. Chinese philosopher. The greatest representative of Taoism and one of the most original thinkers of his country. He defended the doctrines of Lao Tzŭ, laying stress on the relativity of all things, the unreality of the tangible world, the value of spiritual freedom, the preëminence of wu-wei.[g] He wrote the work which is now generally called the Canon (or the Classic) of Nan Hua,[h] Nan[2] Hua[2] ching[1] (8128, 5005, 2122).

Text—Frederic Henry Balfour: The Divine Classic of Nan-Hua, with Copious Annotations in English and Chinese (Shanghai, 1881). Another English translation by James Legge in the Sacred Books of the East, vol. 39–40, 1891 (together with the masterly commentary by Lin[2] Hsi[1]-chung[1] (7159, 4031, 2875), dating from the first half of the seventeenth century). Musings of a Chinese Mystic. Selections edited by Lionel Giles in Wisdom of the East (112 p., London, 1906). Extracts translated into German by Richard Wilhelm (292 p., Jena, 1912; Isis, I, 119, 1919).

Criticism—H. A. Giles: Chuang Tzŭ, Mystic, Moralist, and Social Reformer (London, 1889); Chinese Biographical Dictionary 1898, 202–203).

IV. HELLENISTIC MATHEMATICS, ASTRONOMY, AND PHYSICS

EUCLID[i]

Εὐκλείδης, flourished in Alexandria probably under Ptolemy I, King of Egypt from 323 to 285. Mathematician and physicist. Probably trained in the Academy. He flourished after Plato's first pupils and before Archimedes. He systematized the mathematical knowledge of his time in the "Thirteen Books of Elements" (στοιχεῖα), which have remained until our day the basis of the teaching of elementary geometry. A great deal of these elements was probably his own contribution, and at any rate his work was not a mere compilation, but a synthesis of the highest grade in the elaboration of which he evinced considerable genius. To quote a single instance, the formulation of the postulates, and more particularly of the fifth one, was due to him. The innumerable attempts to prove this fifth postulate on the one hand and the development of the non-Euclidian geometries on the other are as many tributes to Euclid's wisdom. Leaving aside some undatable Pythagorean knowledge, Euclid discovered the earliest theorems of the theory of numbers, notably the existence of an infinitude of primes and that, if $p = \overset{n}{\Sigma}\, 2^n$ is prime, $2^n p$ is perfect.

Fundamental principles of geometrical optics: propagation of light in straight lines, laws of reflection.

---

[g] He has been compared to Heraclitos and also to Plato.

[h] Nan Hua being the name of a hill in Ts'ao[2]-chou[1] fu[3] (11636, 2444, 3682), Shantung, where he lived in retirement. This work bears said title only since its canonization, under the T'ang emperor Hsüan Tsung, in 742.

[i] Often mistaken by mediaeval writers and in the early printed editions for Euclid of Megara, Eleatic philosopher, one of the disciples of Socrates and the founder of a philosophic school (the Megaric, Dialectic, or Eristic) at Megara, almost halfway between Athens and Corinth.

Text and Translation—First printed edition of the Elements, Campanus's Latin translation from the Arabic, Venice, Ratdolt, 1482. See my note on Campanus, thirteenth century; see G. Valentin: Die beiden Euclid Ausgaben des Jahres 1482 (Bibliotheca Mathematica, p. 33–38, 1893). First Latin translation from the Greek, by Zamberti, q. v., fifteenth century (Venice, 1505). Revised edition of Campanus's Euclid by Pacioli, q. v., fifteenth century (Venice, 1509). Latin edition, containing both Campanus's and Zamberti's translations, by Jacques Lefèvre, q. v., fifteenth century (Paris, 1516). Editio princeps of the Elements, by Simon Grynaeus the elder (d. 1541), dedicated to Cuthbert Tonstall (Basel, 1533). Earliest complete edition of Euclid, by David Gregory, Greek and Latin (Oxford, 1703).

F. Peyrard: Les oeuvres d'Euclide (3 vols., Paris, 1814–18. Greek text, with Latin and French translations). Euclidis opera omnia ediderunt J. L. Heiberg et H. Menge (8 vols., Leipzig, 1883–1916, and a Supplement dated 1899). This is an excellent critical edition upon which all ulterior Euclid studies are based. It is divided as follows: Vols. I to IV (1883–1886) contain the thirteen books of "Elements," with Latin translation; Vol. V (1888), the so-called Books XIV (by Hypsicles) and XV (by a pupil of Isidoros in the sixth century), both with Latin translation, and abundant Greek scholia to the "Elements" (p. 71–738), the greatest part of these scholia being published for the first time; Vol. VI (1896), Euclid's "Data" (δεδομένα) in Greek and Latin with Marinos' commentary and ancient scholia; Vol. VII (1895), Euclid's "Optics" both in its genuine form and in the recension by Theon, and the "Catoptrics" ascribed to Theon (these three with Latin translation) and ancient scholia; Vol. VIII (1916), Euclid's "Phaenomena" and "Scripta Musica," and various fragments and scholia. The supplementary volume, edited by Maxim. Curtze (1899) contains Anaritius' (i. e., al-Nairīzī's) commentary to Books I to X of the "Elements" in the Latin Translation by Gherard of Cremona (Cod. Cracov., 569). J. L. Heiberg: Paralipomena zu Euklid (Hermes, t. 38, p. 46–74, 161–201, 321–356, Berlin, 1903). Sir Thomas L. Heath: The Thirteen Books of Euclid's Elements, translated from the text of Heiberg, with Introduction and Commentary (3 vols., Cambridge, 1908. Fundamental). Sir Thomas has recently published (Cambridge, 1920) the Greek text of Book I with commentary and notes, to be used in the schools; this is a most interesting undertaking. Giovanni Vacca has edited the Greek text of Book I, with Italian version and notes (140 p., Florence, 1916).

Ancient and Mediaeval Commentaries (outside of those already quoted):

(*A*) *Proclos*—Procli Diadochi in primum Euclidis elementorum librum commentarii ex recognitione God. Friedlein (515 p., Leipzig, 1873). Will. Barrett Frankland: The First Book of Euclid's Elements, with a Commentary based Principally upon that of Proclus Diadochus (155 p., Cambridge, 1905). For other Greek commentators see Heath (op. cit., I, ch. III, VI).

(*B*) *Arabic Editions and Commentaries*—Fr. Woepcke: Notice sur des traductions arabes de deux ouvrages perdus d'Euclide (Extrait du Journal Asiatique, 31 p., Paris, 1851. The two works alluded to are the treatises on divisions of figures and on the lever; see below). J. Chr. Gartz: De interpretibus et explanatoribus Euclidis arabicis (52 p., Halae ad Salam, 1823). The most important Arabic publications available to non-Arabic readers are al-Nairīzī's Commentary quoted above and the Codex Leidensis 399, 1. Euclidis elementa ex interpretatione al-Hadschdschadschii cum commentariis al-Narizii, edited in Arabic and Latin by R. O. Besthorn and J. L. Heiberg (Copenhagen, 1893 sq.[i]) See also Heath, op. cit., I, p. 75–90.

(*C*) *Mediaeval Translations and Editions*—See Heath (op. cit., I, ch. VIII).

[i] The first part of the Vol. III appeared in 1910; it contains the fourth book of the Elements.

General Studies—Heath's translation with commentary, of the Thirteen Books of Euclid's Elements (3 vols., Cambridge, 1908), is so complete and comprehensive that I need quote but very few of the previous publications.

J. L. Heiberg: Litterargeschichtliche Studien über Euklid (228 p., Leipzig, 1882. (I) Die Nachrichten der Araber; (II) Leben und Schriften Euklids; (III) Die verlorenen Schriften; (IV) Die Optik und Katoptrik; (V) Die alten Kommentatoren; (VI) Zur Geschichte des Textes). Paul Tannery: Les continuateurs d'Euclide (Bulletin des sciences mathématiques, t. XI, p. 86–96, Paris, 1887); Héron sur Euclide (*ibidem*, p. 97–108). Pietro Riccardi: Saggio di una bibliografia euclidea (published in 5 parts in 4to in the Memorie d. R. Accad. d. Sci., Bologna, 1887–1893). P. Tannery: Articles Euclide and Porisme in Grande Encyclopédie (c. 1893, c. 1900; Mémoires, III, 362–366, 374–377). Hultsch: Eukleides, in Pauly-Wissowa's Real-Encyclopädie (Bd. XI, col. 1003–1052, 1907). Heinrich Vogt: Die Lebenszeit Euklids (Bibliotheca Mathematica, t. XIII, p. 193–202, Leipzig, 1913). Vogt thinks that Euclid's life should be placed a little earlier than is generally done, that is, earlier than c. 300. According to Vogt, Euclid would have been born c. 365, flourished c. 325, and the Elements written between 330–320. Vogt's analysis is not based on any new fact and is not convincing. Nothing more positive can be said about Euclid's time than what I have said in my introductory paragraph. Hence one can place him and the Elements either at the end of the fourth or the beginning of the third century, as one wishes. I have given above my reason for choosing the latter alternative.

The Elements—Thomas L. Heath (op. cit., 1908, fundamental). P. Tannery: Sur l'authenticité des axiomes d'Euclide (Bull. des sci. mathém., VIII, p. 162–175, Paris, 1884; also Mémoires, t. II, p. 48–63); La technologie des éléments d'Euclide (*ibidem*, t. XI, p. 17–28, 1887); Sur la locution ἐξ ἴσου. Revue des études grecques (t. X, p. 14–18, 1897; also Mémoires, t. II, p. 540–544). Max Simon: Euclid und die sechs planimetrischen Bücher (Abhandl. zur Gesch. d. math. Wis., XI, 150 p., Leipzig, 1901). H. G. Zeuthen: Sur la constitution des livres arithmétiques des éléments d'Euclide et leur rapport à la question de l'irrationalité (Bull. de l'Acad. des sciences de Danemark, p. 395–435, 1910); Sur les définitions d'Euclide (Scientia, t. 24, p. 257–269, Bologna, 1918). Zeuthen's investigations have been analyzed by H. Bosmans in the Revue des questions scientifiques (11 p., Brussels, April, 1920). Enrico Rufini: La preistoria delle parallele e il postulato di Euclide (Periodico di matem., t. 3, 11–17, 1923).

Other works by Euclid:

(1) *The Pseudaria*—Exercises of elementary geometry. Lost.

(2) *The Data* (δεδομένα)—Also exercises of geometry. Ed. by H. Menge (1896, Opera Omnia, Vol. VI).

(3) *The Book on Divisions of Figures* (περὶ διαιρέσεων βιβλίον)—Raymond Clare Archibald: Euclid's Book on Divisions, with a Restoration based on Woepcke's (Arabic) text (see *supra*) and on the Practica geometriae of Leonardo Pisano (96 p., Cambridge, 1915).

(4) *The Porisms*—Three lost books dealing with higher geometry, namely, containing propositions belonging to the modern theory of transversals and to projective geometry. Michel Chasles: Les trois livres de Porismes d'Euclide rétablis pour la première fois d'après la notice et les lemmes de Pappus (334 p., Paris, 1860. These researches lead Chasles to the idea of anharmonic ratio).

(5) *The Surface-loci* (τόποι πρὸς ἐπιφανείαις)—This very likely included such loci as were cones, cylinders, and spheres. Lost.

(6) *The Conics*—Lost (see *supra* under Aristaeos the elder).

(7) *The Phaenomena*—A treatise on astronomy, or rather on spherical geometry, based upon Autolycos (q. v.). Edited by H. Menge (1916. Opera Omnia, Vol. VIII).

(8) *The Optics*—Edited by Heiberg (1895, Opera Omnia, Vol. VII). Jean de Pène: L'optique et la catoptrique d'Euclide. Trad. franc. de sa préface latine à l'ed. de 1555. In Albert de Rochas, La science des philosophes (2d ed., p. 217–233, Paris, 1912). H. Weissenborn: Zur Optik des Eukleides (Philologus, t. 45, p. 54–62, 1885). Sebastian Vogl: Über die (Pseudo) Euklidische Schrift de speculis (Archiv f. Gesch. d. Naturw., I, p. 419–435, 1909. A much later compilation, transmitted partly in Latin, partly in Hebrew, based upon Euclid and Heron, and frequently referred to by Roger Bacon). Giuseppe Ovio: L'ottica di Euclide (Milano, 1918).

(9) *Musical Writings*—Edited by H. Menge (1916, Opera Omnia, Vol. VIII). J. C. Wilson: Pseudo-Euclid. Introductio harmonica (Classical Review, t. 18, p. 150–151, 1904). Paul Tannery: Inauthenticité de la "division du canon" attribuée à Euclide (Acad. des Inscriptions, Comptes Rendus, t. 4, p. 439–445, 1904; Mémoires, III, 213). C. E. Ruelle: Sur l'authenticité probable de la division du canon (Revue des études grecques, t. XV, 1907).

The first treatise (*εἰσαγωγὴ ἁρμονική*) referred to was written by Cleonides, pupil of Aristoxenos; the second (*κατατομὴ κανόνος*, sectio canonis), dealing with the theory of intervals, is most probably genuine.

(10) *The Mechanical Writings* ascribed to Euclid by the Arabs are not genuine. A book of the Heavy and Light is mentioned in the Fihrist; it contains the notion of specific gravity in a form too clear to be pre-Archimedian. See Max. Curtze: Das Buch Euclids de gravi et levi (Bibliotheca Mathem., p. 51–54, 1900).

Two other mechanical fragments, in Arabic, deal with the lever and the balance. (The latter was mentioned by Woepcke in 1851, see *supra*.) See G. Vailati: Di una dimostrazione del principio della leva, attribuita ad Euclide (Bollet d. storia matem., I, p. 21–22, 1897). P. Duhem: Les Origines de la Statique (t. I, p. 62–79, 1905).

ARISTYLLOS

Ἀρίστυλλος, flourished in Alexandria at the beginning of the century. Astronomer. According to Ptolemy, Aristyllos and Timocharis, who worked at the same time in Alexandria, were about the only astronomers who made scientific observations of the stars before Hipparchos. Observations by Aristyllos were less numerous and less accurate than those of Timocharis. They referred to the declination of Capella and of the three stars in the tail of the Great Bear.

TIMOCHARIS

Τιμόχαρις, flourished in Alexandria at the beginning of the century. Timocharis's measurements were especially useful to Hipparchos for his determination of the precession of the equinoxes.

ARISTARCHOS

Aristarchos of Samos (Ἀρίσταρχος), flourished c. 280. Astronomer, mathematician. Pupil of Straton of Lampsacos. Made an observation of the summer solstice in 281–280. He taught the daily rotation of the earth about its axis. He was the first to put forward the heliocentric hypothesis. In order to reconcile the apparent immobility of the fixed stars with the revolution of the earth around the sun, he assumed that the sphere of the fixed stars was incomparably greater than that containing the earth's orbit. That is, the universe conceived by him was incomparably greater than that conceived by his predecessors. In his only extant treatise "on the sizes and distances of the sun and moon" he gave a scientific method to make these measurements. His results were grossly inaccurate, but the method was sound. This treatise is also of great mathematical interest because of its containing the calculation of ratios which are in fact trigonometrical ratios. Aristarchos added $\frac{1}{1623}$ of a day to Callippos's estimate of 365¼ days for the solar year; he estimated the length of the Great Year (luni-solar cycle) to be 2.484 years (he probably meant 2.434 years). The discovery of an improved sun dial (σκάφη, a concave hemispherical surface with a gnomon in the center) was ascribed to him. He wrote on vision, light, and colors.

Text—First edition in Latin by George Valla, together with Nicephorus's Logica and other treatises (1488, reprinted Venice, 1498). First independent Latin edition by Federigo Commandino, with Pappos's commentary (Pisauri, 1572). First edition of the Greek text, together with Commandino's translation of it and Pappos's commentary, by John Wallis (Oxford, 1688, reprinted in Wallis's Opera, 1695–1699, vol. 3, 565–594). Sir Thomas Heath: Aristarchus of Samos, the Ancient Copernicus. A History of Greek Astronomy to Aristarchus, together with Aristarchus's Treatise on the Sizes and Distances of the Sun and Moon. A New Greek Text, with Translation and Notes (433 p., Oxford, 1913. Fundamental).

Criticism—Of previous publications I quote only the following by Paul Tannery: Aristarque de Samos. Mémoires, de la soc. des sci. physiques et naturelles (t. V, p. 237–258, Bordeaux, 1883; Mémoires, I, 371–396); Scholies sur Aristarque (Revue de philologie, t. XI, p. 33–41, 1887; Mémoires, II, 332–334); La grande année d'Aristarque (Mém. de la soc. des sci. de Bordeaux, t. IV, p. 79–96, 1888; Mémoires, II, 345–366).

ARATOS

Aratos of Soli in Cilicia ("Αρατος), flourished about 275. Poet, scientist. Attended in Athens the Peripatetic and Stoic schools. Author of many books, chief among which is the Phaenomena (Φαινόμενα) a scientific poem (1,154 verses) written at the request of Antigonos Gonatas, King of Macedonia from 277 on. This poem contains three parts: the Phaenomena proper, then the common risings and settings of stars (συνανατολαί and συγκαταδύσεις), and finally the weather signs (προγνώσεις διὰ σημείων or διοσημεῖαι). The first two parts are based upon Eudoxos's Phaenomena, the third upon Theophrastos or upon an earlier common source.[k] This poem is important chiefly because of its influence upon contemporary and Roman thought.

Text—Princeps is in Astronomici Veteres, edited by Aldus Manutius (Venice, 1499). Aratus cum scholiis recognovit Imm. Bekker (Berlin, 1828). Arati Phaenomena recensuit et fontium testimoniorumque notis prolegomenis indicibus instruxit Ernst Maass, Berlin, 1893. Ernst Maass Aratea (Philologische Untersuchungen, XII, 416 p., Berlin, 1892). Ernst Maass: Commentariorum in Aratum reliquiae (821 p., 2 pl., Berlin, 1898).

English Translations—By Edward Poste: The Skies and Weather Forecasts, with notes (London, 1880); by Robert Brown jr. (London, 1885. With an attempt to show that Aratos's statements, wholly incorrect when applied to his own age, are quite applicable to the latitude of Babylon c. 2084 B. C.!); by C. L. Prince (London, 1895).

Criticism—Georg Thiele: Antike Himmelsbilder mit Forschungen zu Hipparchos, Aratos und seinen Fortsetzern und Beiträgen zur Kunstgeschichte des Sternhimmels (184 p., in 4°, 7 pl., 72 illustr., Berlin, 1898. Very important study inspired by Maass; the fourth and last chapter is entirely devoted to the zodiacal iconography of early Aratos MSS.). Julius Höpken: Über die Entstehung der Phaenomena des Eudoxos-Aratos (37 p., 3 pl., Progr., Emden, 1905).

---

[k] Cleostratos? See sixth century B. C.

The Museum of Alexandria

Theophrastos had established in Athens, in honor of Aristotle, a school of literature and art which was properly called τὸ Μουσεῖον (Museum), meaning a temple or place dedicated to the Muses. It is possible that other literary schools or clubs received the same appropriate name. However, the name Museum calls to one's mind the memory of another institution of a later time, of the very time with which we are now dealing, that established in Alexandria by the first or the second Ptolemy. The Alexandrian Museum was a sort of university, a combination of many research institutes, together with lecture-rooms, dining-halls, and cloisters. It was divided into four main departments dealing respectively with literature, mathematics, astronomy, and medicine. There was also a library, the largest by far of the ancient world (90,000 works, 400,000 volumes), so large that it was found necessary to move some of the books to another building, the Serapeium. The Serapeium library was destroyed by the bishop Theophilos c. 390. The main library subsisted until the Muslim conquest (640),[1] but its importance had gradually declined together with the pagan ideals.

Gustav Parthey: Das alexandrinische Museum (222 p., Berlin, 1838). Heinrich Hermann Göll: Das alexandrinische Museum (Progr., Plauen, 1868). Ludwig Weniger: Das alexandrinische Museum (32 p., Berlin, 1875).

V. HELLENISTIC ANATOMY, PHYSIOLOGY, BIOLOGY, AND MEDICINE

NICANDER

Nicandros of Colophon (Νίκανδρος). Born in Colophon, Ionia, flourished probably about 275. Greek didactic and bucolic poet, contemporary of Aratos and Theocritos. Priest of Apollo in Claros near Colophon. Pharmacist, toxicologist. Many writings in prose and verse are ascribed to him, among them a collection of cures (ἰάσεων συναγωγή), prognostics (προγνωστικά), treatises on agriculture (γεωργικά), on apiculture (μελισσουργικά), on snakes (ὀφιακά). The Theriaca (θηριακά) is a poem of 958 verses dealing with poisonous animals, the effects of their venoms, and their antidotes; the Alexipharmaca (ἀλεξιφάρμακα), a poem of 630 verses, deals with poisons in general, discusses 21 different poisons, and prescribes remedies. 125 plants are quoted in the two poems. Nicander was the first to speak of the therapeutic use of leeches.

Text—Aldine edition, Venice, 1499; again larger edition, also Aldine (Venice, 1523). Nicandrea. Theriaca et Alexipharmaca recensuit et emendavit, fragmenta collegit, commentationes addidit Otto Schneider. Accedunt scholia in Theriaca ex recensione Henrici Keil, scholia in Alexipharmaca ex recognitione Bussemakeri et R. Bentlei emendationes partim ineditae (478 p., Leipzig, 1856).

Translation in French verse by Jacques Grévin (90 p., Anvers, 1568). German translation, with commentary, by M. Brenning (Allgem. medizin. Zentral-L., t. 72, 58 p., 1904).

Commentary—Ernst H. F. Meyer: Geschichte der Botanik (t. 1, 244–250, 1854). Eugenius Abel et Rudofus Vári: Scholia vetera in Nicandri Alexipharmaca e codice Gottingensi edita. Adjecta sunt scholia recentia (120 p., Budapest, 1891). Georg Wentzel: Die Göttinger Scholien zu Nikanders Alexipharmaka (95 p., Abhdl. d. Kgl. Gesell. d. Wiss., t. 38, Göttingen, 1892). Friedrich Ernst Kind: Zu den Nikanderscholien (Hermes, t. 44, p. 624–625, Berlin, 1909). E. Bethe: Die

[1] See my note on the subject in Section II of Chapter XXV.

Zeit Nikanders (Hermes, t. 53, p. 110–118, Berlin, 1918). Three dates are given for Nicander: flourished c. 275, c. 225 to 200, c. 135. The first is the original dating, the two following represent a reaction. According to Bethe, there may have been two poets of the same name, but the pharmacist lived c. 275.

HEROPHILOS

Ἡρόφιλος. Born in Chalcedon[m] in the last third of the fourth century, flourished in Alexandria under Ptolemy I. The founder of anatomy as a scientific discipline; the greatest anatomist of antiquity; after Hippocrates and Galen the greatest physician of antiquity. Pupil of Praxagoras. He is said (by Galen) to have been the first to undertake (public?) human dissections. He made many new and correct anatomical observations and improved the technique and terminology of anatomy. Examples of his anatomical work: detailed description of the brain (cerebrum and cerebellum, meninges, calamus scriptorius, torcular Herophili); distinction between tendons and nerves, recognition of the nerves' function; good description of the optic nerves and of the eye, including the retina (ἀμφιβληστροειδής); description of the vascular system much improved; duodenum named; careful descriptions of the liver, salivary glands, pancreas, genital organs; observation of the chyliferous vessels. Clear distinction between arteries and veins (the arteries are six times as thick as the veins; they contain blood, not air, and are patent and empty after death).[n] Four forces control the organism: the nourishing, heating, perceiving, and thinking forces, seated respectively in liver, heart, nerves, and brain. The supremacy of the heart (still defended by Aristotle) is thus finally rejected. Herophilos improved Praxagoras's theory of the pulse, using a clepsydra to measure its frequency and diagnose fever. The strength of the pulse indicates that of the heart. His pathology was emphatically empirical; he improved diagnosis and prognosis. He introduced the use of many new drugs and recurred frequently to blood-letting. The embryo has only a physical, not a pneumatic life. Herophilos invented an embryotome widely used by ancient obstetricians in hopeless cases. He wrote a treatise in three books on anatomy, a smaller on the eyes, and a text-book for midwives (μαιωτικόν).

K. F. H. Marx: Herophilus (Karlsruhe, 1838; Göttingen, 1842). Hermann Schöne: Markellinos Pulslehre. Aus der Festschrift zur 49. Versammlung deutscher Philologen, 448–472, Basel, 1907. (This edition of Marcellinos's περὶ σφυγμῶν—a little treatise of no earlier date than the second century—is very important because of the detailed information it contains on Herophilos's quantitative theory of the pulse). Meyer-Steineg: Die Vivisektion in der antiken Medizin (Intern. Monatschrift, 1912). Article by Gossen, in Pauly-Wissowa (t. 15, 1104–1110, 1912). M. Wellman: Über Träume. Archiv für Geschichte der Medizin (t. 16, 70–72, 1924).

ERASISTRATOS

Ἐρασίστρατος, born c. 304 in Iulis, Ceos (one of the Cyclades), flourished in Alexandria c. 258–257. Younger contemporary of Herophilos. Pupil in Athens of Metrodoros, Aristotle's son-in-law, and of the younger Chrysippos. As an anatomist and physician, second only to Herophilos. As a physiologist, he was superior to Herophilos. Indeed, he may be called the founder of physiology as a

---

[m] Nearly opposite to Byzantium, in Bithynia.

[n] Herophilos called the pulmonary artery, arterial vein; and the pulmonary vein, venal artery; names which remained in use until the seventeenth century.

separate subject; he has been called also the founder of comparative and pathological anatomy. Practiced not simply human dissection but also (?) vivisection, and made many experiments upon animals. His main discoveries concern the brain, the nervous and vascular systems, and the heart. His physiology was the first to be based upon the atomistic theories as transmitted by the Dogmatic school (Praxagoras) and upon the axiom of the "horror vacui." He tried to explain everything by natural causes, and rejected any reference to occult causes. But for his conviction that the arteries are filled with air (πνεῦμα ζωτικόν, spiritus vitalis),[o] and for his pneumatic theories in general, he might have discovered the circulation of the blood; for instance, he suspected that the ultimate ramifications of veins and arteries were connected. He observed the chyliferous vessels in the mesentery. He realized that every organ is connected with the rest of the organism by a three-fold system of "vessels", artery, vein, nerve. He saw that there was a relation between the motion of the lungs and the pulsation of the heart and arteries. He improved the analysis of the vascular system. He described correctly the function of the epiglottis and of the auriculo-ventricular valves.[p] He recognized the motor and sensory nerves, improved Herophilos's description of the brain, distinguished more carefully between cerebrum and cerebellum and made experiments in vivo to understand their mechanism. Many pathological discoveries are ascribed to him. He was the first physician to discard entirely the humoral theory; the first also to distinguish between hygiene and therapeutics and to attach greater importance to the former. Hence his insistence upon diet, proper exercise, bathing, etc. He was opposed to violent cures, to the use of too many drugs, and to excessive blood-letting. He discovered the S-shaped catheter.

Erasistratos and Herophilos have both been accused of performing human vivisection. The accusation is made by Celsus in his de re medica (first half of first century) and violently repeated by the Latin father of the Church, Tertullian (born at Carthage c. 155; died after 220), and again later, by St. Augustine. Herophilos's practice of embryotomy is also reproved by Tertullian, whose hatred of paganism and of everything connected with it was intense. However, Galen does not say a word of these vivisections, and the accusation must be considered as non-proved.

Rob. Fuchs: Erasistratea quae in librorum memoria latent congesta enarrantur. (Diss., 32 p., Leipzig, 1892). Hermann Diels: Anonymous Londinensis (Berlin, 1893. Apropos of which see above my note on Menon, second half of fourth century B. C.; in Chapter XXXIII, l. 45–50, an interesting quantitative experiment anticipating Santorio, 1614!, is attributed to Erasistratos). M. Wellmann, in Pauly-Wissowa (1909). Galen on the Natural Faculties, I, 16 (p. 95 in Brock's translation, Loeb Library, 1916). C. Singer: Evolution of Anatomy (1925).

EUDEMOS OF ALEXANDRIA

Εὔδημος, flourished in Alexandria about the middle of the century. Anatomist; younger contemporary of Herophilos and Erasistratos. He made a deeper study of the nervous system, of the bones, and of the glands (pancreas), also of the female sexual organs and of embryology.

---

[o] That is, air as modified in the heart. The vital spirits are carried by the arteries to the brain, where they are further changed into animal spirits (πνεῦμα ψυχικόν, spiritus animalis).

[p] The one on the right was named by him τριγλώχιν = tricuspid.

VI. HELLENISTIC TECHNOLOGY

SOSTRATOS

Sostratos of Cnidos (Σώστρατος) flourished in the first half of the third century B. C. Architect of the lighthouse (φάρος, pharus) of Alexandria, which was completed under the reign of Ptolemaeos Philadelphos, c. 279. This was a landmark in the development both of navigation and of architecture.

Pliny XXXVI, 18. Edgar J. Banks: The Lighthouse of Alexandria (Art and Archaeology, t. 6, pp. 77–81, 4 illustr., Washington, 1917. Retracing also the later history of the pharus; its slow disintegration and disappearance from the seventh to the fifteenth century).

VII. HELLENISTIC, HEBREW, AND CHINESE HISTORIOGRAPHY

CRATEROS

Κρατερός; Macedonian who flourished about the beginning of the third century B. C. Greek historian. He compiled a collection of decrees of the Athenian people (Ψηφισμάτων συναγωγή). With commentary.

Text—C. Müller: Fragmenta historicorum graecorum (II, p. 617–622, 1841).

Criticism—Krech: De Crateri ψηφισμάτων συναγωγῆ et de locis aliquot Plutarchi ex ea petitis (Diss., 103 p., Berlin, Greifswald, 1888). A. Croiset: Litterature grecque (t. 5, 94, 1899).

MEGASTHENES

Μεγασθένης. Flourished about 300. Historian, geographer. Ambassador of Seleucus Nicator (King of Syria from 312 to 280) to the court of Candragupta in Pāṭaliputra (c. 302). His lost work on India (τὰ Ἰνδικά) was the chief authority on this country to the ancient world. The fragments transmitted to us contain valuable geographical and ethnographical information. Megasthenes's embassy took place, at least partly, before the end of the fourth century, but at any rate the knowledge accumulated by him could hardly have been published before the third century.

Text and Translation—Eugen Alexis Schwanbeck: Megasthenes Indica. Fragmenta collegit, commentationem et indices addidit (206 p., Bonn, 1846. The first part—81 pages—is a reprint of the author's thesis: de Megasthene rerum indicarum scriptore. Bonn, 1845). J. W. McCrindle: Ancient India as Described by Megasthenes and Arrian, with Introduction and Notes (235 p., Calcutta, 1877. English translation based upon Schwanbeck's text). O. Stein: Megasthenes und Kauṭilya (340 p., Wien, 1922).

MANETHON

Μανεθώς or Μανεθών, born in Sebennytos in the Nile Delta, flourished under Ptolemy I, Soter, King of Egypt from 323 to 285, and perhaps also under Ptolemy II, Philadelphos, King from 285 to 247. Egyptian historian. He wrote, in Greek, Annals of Egypt (Αἰγυπτιακά) in three books,[q] containing lists of kings which have been of considerable value in determining the chronology of the country.

Texts—The fragments have been edited by C. Müller in the Fragmenta historicorum graecorum. I. P. Cory: Ancient Fragments of Phoenician, Chaldean,

[q] The first dealt with predynastic history and the first ten dynasties; the second with dynasties XI to XIX (2160 to 1205); the third with dynasties XX to XXX (1200 to 332).

Egyptian, . . . and other writers (2d ed., London, 1832, with English translation); new edition by E. Richmond Hodges (London, 1876).

Criticism—See Histories of Egypt. J. T. Shotwell: History of History (62–64, 1922).

BEROSSOS

Βηρωσσός, also Βηρωσός, flourished under Antiochos I, Soter, King of Syria, from 281 to 262. Babylonian historian. He wrote in Greek a history of Babylonia in three books (Βαβυλωνικά, better than Χαλδαϊκά) from the creation down to Cyrus the Great (King of Persia from 558 to 529).[r]

Text—The original text is lost, but it can be partially reconstructed from the quotations from it made by Josephus and Eusebios. Editions by J. D. G. Richter (94 p., Leipzig, 1825); by C. Müller: Fragmenta historicorum graecorum (t. 2, Paris, 1848); by Paul Schnabel, Berosi Babyloniacorum libr. III quae supersunt (Leipzig, 1913). Isaac Preston Cory: Ancient Fragments of Phoenician, Chaldean, Egyptian, ... and other writers (with translation) 2d ed. London, 1832; new ed. by E. Richmond Hodges. London, 1876.

Criticism—François Lenormant: Commentaire des fragments cosmogoniques de Bérose d'après les textes cunéiformes et les monuments (576 p., Paris, 1871). Ernest Havet: Mémoire sur la date des écrits qui portent les noms de Bérose et de Manéthon (78 p., Paris, 1873. Concluding that both are apocryphal writings of the end of the second century B. C.). Schwartz, in Pauly-Wissowa (t. 3, 309–316, 1897). Paul Schnabel: Berossos und Kleitarchos (Diss., Jena, Leipzig, 1912); Berossos und die babylonisch-hellenistische Literatur (275 p., Leipzig, 1923). J. T. Shotwell: History of History (76–78, 1922).

TIMAEOS

Τίμαιος, born at Tauromenium, Sicily, about the middle of the fourth century, flourished fifty years in Athens, died in Sicily, probably at Syracuse, almost a centenarian. Greek historian. Extremely erudite, but with little experience of life, he insisted on the scientific side of historical research. He introduced the systematic dating by Olympiads. His main works are a History of Sicily (Σικελικά) in 45 books and a History of Pyrrhos (d. 272), continuing the latter down to 264.

Texts—C. Müller: Fragmenta historicorum graecorum (t. 1, 193–233).

Criticism—Johannes Geffcken: Timaios's Geographie des Westens (210 p., Philologische Untersuchungen, 13, Berlin, 1892). A. Croiset: Littérature grecque (t. 5, 109–115, 1899).

The Parian Chronicle (*or Marmor Parium*)—Greek inscription cut on a block of marble, discovered in the island of Paros (one of the larger of the Cyclades) and now at Oxford. It contains a Greek chronology from Cecrops to the archonship of Diognetos in 264–263, the interval amounting (according to the inscription) to 1,318 years. This places Cecrops in 1582 and the capture of Troy in 1209. This chronological scheme is older than that of Eratosthenes.

Text—Corpus inscriptionum graecorum (t. II, 293, No. 2374). Joseph Robertson (1726–1802): The Parian Chronicle or the Arundelian Marbles (233 p., London,

---

[r] The chronology was carried even 215 years further, to the death of Alexander (323–2). The three books dealt respectively with the following periods: (I) From the creation to the flood, 432,000 years; (II) From the flood to Nabonassar (747–6), 34,090 + 1,701 = 35,791 years; (III) From Nabonassar to Cyrus, 209 years; or to Alexander, 424 years. In all, 468,000 or 468,215 years. The first book and part of the second book were necessarily cosmological, hence the designation of Berossos as "the astrologer."

1788. Greek, Latin, and English). Marmor parium cum commentariis Car. Mülleri. Fragmenta historicorum graecorum (t. 1, 533–590, 1841. Greek and Latin). Chronicon parium, ed. by Joh. Flach (62 p., Tübingen, 1884. Greek). Greek edition by Felix Jacoby (Berlin, 1904).

Hebrew History

The two Books of Chronicles (65 chapters), the Book of Ezra (10 chapters) and the Book of Nehemiah[e] (13 chapters) were all written or edited by a single author toward the end of the fourth century or more probably in the third century. The Chronicles cover almost the same period as the other historical books of the Old Testament (Genesis to Second Kings; from the creation to 561)—for they tell the history of Judah from the time of Adam to the end of the Babylonian captivity, 538–536. The aim of the author is more limited, however, and his work has been called "the ecclesiastical chronicle of Jerusalem." It is based upon the other historical books of the Bible (chiefly upon Kings), but contains much additional matter derived from independent sources.

The Books of Ezra and Nehemiah are a continuation of the Chronicles; they deal with the period extending from 536 to 432. They are based essentially upon the original memoirs of Ezra and Nehemiah.

The Books of Proverbs[f] (also called the Proverbs of Solomon) was probably completed some time between 350 and 250, but it embodies much material of an earlier date. It forms a part of the Old Testament, both in the Jewish and in the Christian canon (31 chapters).

Arno Kropat: Die Syntax des Autors der Chronik verglichen mit der seiner Quellen (102 p., Giessen, 1909). Edward Lewis Curtis and Albert Alonzo Madsen: Commentary on Chronicles (550 p., New York, 1910).

Charles C. Torrey: Composition and Historical Value of Ezra-Nehemiah (65 p., Giessen, 1896). Loring W. Batten: Commentary on Ezra and Nehemiah (390 p., New York, 1913).

Crawford Howell Toy: Commentary on Proverbs (590 p., New York, 1899). Giacomo Mettacasa: Il libro dei Proverbi, studio sulle aggiunte greco-alessandrine (Roma, 1913).

Chinese Historiography

Our safest source for the earlier history of China, especially for the period anterior to 841 B. C., seems to be the so-called "Annals of the Bamboo Books," Chu[2]* shu[1] chi[4] nien[2] (2616, 10024, 922, 8301). The "Bamboo Books" is a collection of bamboo tablets said to have been discovered in 281 A. D. in the tomb of Hsiang[1] (4266), King of Wei[4] (12542 or 12567), who died in 295 B. C. This collection contained the text of the I[4] Ching[1] (5497, 2122) and of annals from the time of Huang Ti to 298 B. C.

Chinese scholars have generally preferred a chronology which is different from that of the Bamboo Annals, the chronology given by Pan Ku (q. v.) in the second half of the first century and repeated by later annalists. The Bamboo dates are generally later than those of the standard chronology, especially for the earliest times, when the difference reaches almost two centuries. The discordance decreases little by little as later times are considered, and ceases altogether by the year 841 B. C., the earliest exact date in Chinese history.

---

[e] See my notes on Ezra and Nehemiah, fifth century B. C.

[f] Mishlē.

Now, it was shown by Ed. Chavannes that the dates given by Ssŭ-ma Ch'ien (q. v., second half of second century B. C.) are closer to the Bamboo dates than to those of the standard chronology. This is a very serious reason to give credence to the Bamboo dates, for Ssŭ-ma Ch'ien was far more critical than Pan Ku, and the Shih-chi was composed almost two centuries earlier than the Ch'ien Han-shu. Besides, according to the standard chronology, the average length of the early reigns is incredibly long, 71 years(!), while the average length according to the Bamboo Annals is reduced to 43 years, a far more plausible figure.

Text—The Chinese text of the Bamboo Annals, together with an English translation, is given by James Legge in his Prolegomena to the Shu Ching (p. 105–183, Hongkong, 1865). French translation by Edouard Biot (Journal asiatique, Déc. 1841–Jan. 1842).

Criticism—Edouard Chavannes: Mémoires historiques de Se-Ma Ts'ien (t. 1, Paris, 1895, introduction; also t. 5, 446–479, 1905. Discussing their authenticity). Friedrich Hirth: Ancient History of China (New York, 1908). Léopold de Saussure: La chronologie chinoise (T'oung Pao, vol. 23, 287–346, 1924).

VIII. GREEK PHILOLOGY

Zenodotos of Ephesos (Ζηνόδοτος) c. 325 to c. 234. Greek philologist and lexicographer. First librarian of the great library of Alexandria early in the reign of Ptolemaeos Philadelphos, King of Egypt from 285 to 247. He was the earliest editor (διορθωτής) of the Iliad and Odyssey (before 274); this was a scientific edition, founded on numerous manuscripts, which aimed at restoring the original text. (It was probably the first scientific edition of any text.) He edited also Hesiod's Theogony and compiled a Homeric glossary (ἄτακτοι γλῶσσαι).

Adolf Römer: Über die Homer-recension des Zenodot (Abhdl. der bayer. Ak. d. Wiss., t. 17, 84 p., 1885). Sir John Edwin Sandys: History of Classical Scholarship (vol. 1^3, 119–121, 1921).

CHAPTER VIII

THE TIME OF ARCHIMEDES

(Second Half of the Third Century B. C.)

I. Survey of Science in Second Half of Third Century B. C. II. Development of Buddhism in India. III. Unification of China. IV. Chinese and Greek Philosophy. V. Greek Mathematics, Astronomy, and Physics. VI. Introduction of Greek Medicine in Rome. VII. Chinese and Hellenistic Technology. VIII. Greek and Roman Historiography. IX. Chinese Writing.

I. SURVEY OF SCIENCE IN SECOND HALF OF THIRD CENTURY B. C.

1. My outline of this period will seem at first a little strange, because, though by far the most important scientific work was done in two localities, Syracuse and Alexandria, events of considerable, but as yet undreamed of, pregnancy took place in other very distant countries, India and China. Hence a disharmony between the background and the principal action which would be very objectionable if my survey were restricted to this single period. In other words, the religious and cultural events which I explain briefly in this chapter do not form the background of the contemporary scientific activity, because they happen in other countries far too distant; yet the Historian of Science must know of them to obtain a full understanding of future developments. After all, my aim is simply to give a tableau of all the contemporary events of special interest to us; I do not think of suggesting that there must be a causal connection between them; in most cases there can not be. A palaeontologist, engaged in describing the fauna and flora of a definite horizon, does not claim that there is any family relationship between these organisms; their only relationship is that of simultaneity; but this is in itself of considerable interest and it implies that they may have a common past and common ancestors; it also implies various possibilities in the future. To use another comparison, my introduction into the same chapter of Aśoka, of the First Emperor, and of Archimedes is similar to the appearance of many disparate characters in the first scenes of a tragedy. Do not complain that they have nothing in common, but wait patiently; for aught we know, they themselves or their children will love or kill one another before the play is over. In this case, however, the tragedy occurs on a gigantic, superhuman scale; the actors are not puppets, but real men; the time of action is not counted in days, but in centuries; the scene is the whole world; the playwright is inscrutable Destiny.

2. *Development of Buddhism in India*—The earliest of the great missionary religions received a tremendous stimulus during the reign of the emperor Aśoka (269 to 232), the Constantine of Buddhism. His activity in that direction had begun already in 260, but became especially important toward the middle and in the second half of the century. In the years 240 to 232 he gathered the great Council of Pāṭaliputra, during the course of which the Tripiṭaka was established.

3. *Unification of China*—Shih Huang-Ti, the self-styled First Emperor (221 to 210) put an end to feudal anarchy and built up the foundation of Chinese unity. In 213 he ordered the Burning of the Books. He was responsible for the

building of the Great Wall and for many administrative reforms of a constructive and unifying type.

4. *Chinese and Greek Philosophy*—Hsün K'uang (d. after 238) maintained against Mencius the original depravity of man. He has deeply influenced Chinese thought.

Chrysippos of Soli, head of the Stoa from c. 233, completed the elaboration of the Stoic doctrine, paying special attention to logic and grammar.

5. *Greek Mathematics, Astronomy, and Physics*—The greatest man of the time (and one of the very greatest of all times), Archimedes, flourished in Syracuse until his death in 212. He dealt with a great number of mathematical, mechanical, and physical questions, leaving upon each the imprint of his genius. But above all he introduced into science what might be called the Archimedian spirit, a new way of submitting things to scientific analysis, the method (and point of view) of mathematical physics.

While Archimedes was working alone in Sicily, considerable work was being done in the Museum of Alexandria, especially by two men of genius, Eratosthenes of Cyrene (c. 244) and Apollonios of Perga (c. 222). Eratosthenes was the earliest mathematical geographer, and he gave an estimate of the size of the earth which was correct to an astonishing degree. Apollonios elaborated a complete theory of conics, which shows that he understood very well not only the main properties of each curve but also their relationships. Of course this wonderful work was not a spontaneous generation, but in part at least the development and systematization of previous investigations, for example, those of Conon of Samos.

6. *Introduction of Greek Medicine in Rome*—There is little to report upon this beyond the very interesting fact that the earliest professional physician on record in Rome was the Greek Archagathos, who was established there c. 219. Thereafter Roman medicine (that is, the most progressive part of it) was hardly more than a branch of Greek medicine.

7. *Chinese and Hellenistic Technology*—The general Mêng T'ien (d. 209) introduced the use of the writing brush. Li Ping engineered the irrigation of the Ch'êng-tu plain.

As evidence of Hellenistic technology we have a description of the immense floating palace constructed for the fourth Ptolemy (Ptolemaeos Philopator, 222 to 205).

8. *Greek and Roman Historiography*—The geographer Eratosthenes was deeply interested in chronology, and has been called the founder of the scientific chronology of ancient Greece (though we have seen in the previous chapter that work had been done in that line before him).

The earliest Roman historians appear in this time, Q. Fabius Pictor (c. 225 to 216) and L. Cincius Alimentus (c. 209), both dealing with the history of Rome, but it is significant that both of them wrote in Greek.

9. *Chinese Writing*—Toward the end of the century a new and simpler kind of Chinese writing was developed, the so-called "Lesser Seal," but it is difficult to say to whom this reform ought to be ascribed, Ch'êng Mo or Li Ssŭ. It is worth while to record this, because for a language of the isolating type, like Chinese, writing assumes a part of the importance attached to grammar in the case of inflectional languages. Thus it is not unfair to consider the introduction of the Lesser Seal as fully as important in its field as the elaboration of Greek grammar, with which I shall deal in the following chapter.

10. *Conclusion*—As far as actual achievements are concerned, this period was again almost exclusively Hellenistic. Geometry has already been carried to a high pitch of perfection. Above all towers the original genius of Archimedes. Who is it who said that every thinking man is either a Platonist or an Aristotelian? At any rate, this division is not exhaustive. Some of the greatest men of science throughout the ages, men like Leonardo, Stevin, Galileo, and Huygens, for example, represent another type, which might be called the Archimedian type. And it is largely because of the existence of that type that occidental science has become what it is.

In the meanwhile, a great king was promoting the gentlest philosophy of Asia. He too, like the Syracusan, was sowing seeds containing incalculable possibilities. Archimedes was the herald of western genius in its best and most characteristic mood. Aśoka was preparing the development of Buddhism and thus nursing the very soul of Asia. Archimedes was the father of European science, Aśoka the promoter of Asiatic art.

II. DEVELOPMENT OF BUDDHISM IN INDIA

The religion of the Buddha was considerably strengthened during the reign of Aśoka, the third king of the Maurya dynasty—one of the greatest men among kings. The dates are not absolutely certain, but we shall not be far wrong if we admit (with Vincent A. Smith) that Aśoka ruled the immense Maurya empire[a] from 273 (coronation in 269) to his death in 232. After his bloody conquest of the kingdom of Kalinga (along the eastern coast) in 261, he was so overcome with shame and sorrow that he devoted most of his energy to the propaganda of the Buddhist ideal. Thus Aśoka became the Constantine of Buddhism, and more than that, for he might be called also, not unjustly, the Saint Paul of Buddhism. His activity is witnessed by the most admirable set of inscriptions in the world: 257, 256, Fourteen Rock Edicts; 242, Seven Pillar Edicts; 240–232, Minor Pillar Edicts. (These inscriptions are distributed upon an immense area.)

Aśoka sent Buddhist missionaries not simply to the remotest parts of his empire, but also to Ceylon, to Kashmir, to Mysore, and to the Hellenistic kingdoms. (He was in relation with Antiochos II of Syria, with Ptolemaeos Philadelphos of Egypt, and with Antigonos of Macedonia.) Most of these missions failed as far as the main purpose was concerned, but the historian of civilization must take them into account. The mission to Ceylon was eminently successful; it took place in 251 or 250 under the rule of the Singhalese King Tissa and was conducted by Aśoka's younger brother, Mahendra (or Mahinda; d. in Ceylon in 204) and his sister Saṅghamitrā. This marks the beginning of a higher civilization in Ceylon. It is there that the sacred city of Anurādhapura was gradually built, which may be called the Buddhist Rome. Ceylon has remained to this day one of the greatest centers of Buddhist faith and learning.

Nor is this all, for it was also Aśoka who gathered (c. 240 to 232) the great Buddhist council of Pāṭaliputra (modern Patna), during the course of which the Buddhist Canon was established, or at least its nucleus, the so-called Three Baskets (Tripiṭaka): (1) Dialogues and narratives of the Buddha (Sūtra); (2) Discipline of the monks (Vinaya); (3) Philosophy (Abhidhamma).

---

[a] It included the whole Indian peninsula except the southern part (below, say 15° Lat. S.) and Ceylon.

Text—Inscriptions of Aśoka in the Corpus inscriptionum indicarum 1879 to 1888. Vincent A. Smith: The Edicts of Asoka (97 p., Broad Campden, 1909).

Criticism—L. A. Waddell: Discovery of the Exact Site of Asoka's Capital (Calcutta, 1892). Vincent A. Smith: Asoka (Oxford, 1901; 2d ed. 1909; 3d ed. enlarged, 278 p., Oxford, 1920). Edmund Hardy: Indiens Kultur in der blütezeit des Buddhismus (74 p., Mainz, 1902). Truman Michelson: Asokan Notes (Amer. Orient. Soc. Journal, v. 36, 205–212, 1916). E. Senart: Un nouvel édit d'Asoka à Maski (Journal asiatique, t. 7, 425–442, Paris, 1916; Isis, III, 452). James M. Macphail: Asoka (90 p., Calcutta, 1918). J. Przyluski: La légende de l'empereur Asoka (Asoka-avadana) dans les textes indiens et chinois (Annales du Musée Guimet, t. 32, 472 p., Paris, 1923; Isis, VII, 179).

III. UNIFICATION OF CHINA

SHIH HUANG-TI

Shih^{3} Huang^{2}-Ti^{4} (9982, 5106, 10942).[b] Born in 259; became king of Ch'in^{2} (2093) in 246; from 221 emperor of China; he died at Sha^{1}-chiu^{1} (9624, 2310), Chihli, in 210. One of the founders of Chinese unity. He is chiefly remembered as the builder of the Great Wall[c] to protect the empire against the Tartars. He introduced new copper coinage, the hair-pencil or brush (to replace the old stylus) and the use of silk instead of bamboo tablets; he ordered the standardization of weights and measures; he built a capital at Hsien^{2}-yang^{2} (4498, 12883) in Shensi, a canal,[d] and great roads; he divided the empire into 36 (30) provinces. The new script, the so-called Lesser Seal,[e] was introduced during his reign. In 213 he ordered the so-called Burning of the Books, that is, the destruction of all existing literature except the books on agriculture, medicine, and divination.[f]

H. A. Giles: Biographical Dictionary (401, 652–654, 657, 1898). Encyclopaedia Sinica, 511, 1917.

IV. CHINESE AND GREEK PHILOSOPHY

HSÜN K'UANG

Hsün^{2} K'uang^{4} (4875, 6412). Born in the Chao^{4} (498) State; flourished in the Ch'i^{2} (1074) and Ch'u^{3} (2662) States. Chinese philosopher. Author of a treatise, in 20 books, wherein he maintains against Mencius the original depravity of human nature. His doctrine, which is sometimes called pragmatical (vs. utopian) Confucianism, has deeply influenced Chinese thought. This influence seems to have been, on the whole, an evil one.

---

[b] His personal name was Chêng^{4} (692). The name Huang-Ti, chosen by him, is a proud allusion to the Yellow Emperor; Shih means first. Thus his name might be translated, the First Emperor.

[c] Wan^{4}li^{3}ch'ang^{2}ch'êng^{2} (12486, 6870, 450, 763) (the myriad li long wall). It is 1,500 miles long, its height varying from 15 to 30 feet. (Encyclopaedia Sinica, 1917, 218). It is the largest construction due to man's efforts; the only one, it has been remarked, which could be seen from another planet.

[d] The canal, 60 li (about 12 miles) in length, with 36 locks (?), was built through the mountainous country of Haiyang in Kuangtung, by the engineer Shih^{3} Lu^{4*} (9893, 7379).

[e] For which see my note on Ch'êng Mo at the end of this chapter.

[f] This was his simple way of making tabula rasa; they say that he wanted his rule to be an absolute beginning. Maybe he had already observed the excessive, pathological conservatism of his people. Some of the Classics were saved by devoted scholars, notably by K'ung Fu (d. c. 210), a descendant of Confucius in the ninth degree, the reputed author of memoirs of Confucius and his grandson K'ung Chi (q. v., fifth century B. C.) and of a vocabulary.

A. Wylie: Chinese Literature (1867, 1902, 82). H. A. Giles: Biographical Dictionary (315, 1898). L. Wieger: La Chine (65, 398, 1920); Histoire des croyances en Chine (268–276, 1922).

CHRYSIPPOS

Chrysippos of Soli, Χρύσιππος. Born at Soli[g] in Cilicia c. 280, died in 208–7. Stoic philosopher. Successor of Cleanthes as head of the Stoa (c. 233 to 208). He wrote many works, of which only a few fragments remain. His contributions to the Stoic philosophy were so great that he was considered the second founder of the school. ("Without Chrysippos, no Stoa.") He completed the formal elaboration of the Stoic doctrine, creating their logic and incidentally improving the definitions of Greek grammar.

Text—Johann von Arnim: Stoicorum veterum fragmenta (vol. 2, Chrysippi fragmenta logica et physica; vol. 3, Chrysippi fragmenta moralia. Fragmenta successorum Chrysippi. Leipzig, 1903).

Criticism—J. von Arnim, article in Pauly-Wissowa (vol. 6, 2502–2509,1899). Emile Bréhier: Chrysippe (Les grands philosophes) (304 p., Paris, 1910.)

V. GREEK MATHEMATICS, ASTRONOMY, AND PHYSICS

ARCHIMEDES

Ἀρχιμήδης, born about 287, died during the sack of Syracuse by the Romans in 212. The greatest mathematician, physicist, and engineer of antiquity. Extreme originality and directness of his work as compared with the work of Euclid and Apollonios. The geometry of Archimedes is chiefly a geometry of measurements, while that of Apollonios is rather a study of forms and situations. He realized quadratures of curvilinear plane figures and quadratures and cubatures of curved surfaces by a method more general than the method of exhaustion, and which can be regarded as an anticipation of the integral calculus. However, in his "Method" (discovered by Heiberg in 1906), Archimedes showed that the integrations effected by him could be avoided and replaced by solutions which seemed to him more rigorous. Study of paraboloids, hyperboloids, and ellipsoids. Summation of various series geometrically. For example,

$$3\,[a^2 + (2a)^2 + \ldots + (na)^2] = (n+1)\,(na)^2 + a\,(a + 2a + \ldots + na)$$

For $a = 1$, this gives $\sum_1^n n^2 = \frac{1}{6}n\,(n+1)\,(2n+1)$.

Solution of cubic equations by means of the intersections of two conics. His problem, to cut a sphere by a plane so that the two segments shall be in a given ratio, leads also to a cubic equation: $x^3 + c^2b = cx^2$. Use of immense numbers in the "sand reckoner" (ψαμμίτης). Cattle problem leading to a complicated system of indeterminate equations. Approximative calculation of square roots of very large numbers. By calculating the perimeters of inscribed and circumscribed regular polygons of 96 sides, Archimedes found that

$$3\tfrac{1}{7} > \pi > 3\tfrac{10}{71} \qquad (3{,}142 > \pi > 3{,}141).$$

If a circular cylinder, a circular cone, and a hemisphere have the same base and height, the volume of the hemisphere is twice larger than that of the cone, and the sum of their volumes is equal to the volume of the cylinder. Study of the (Archimedean) spiral that is, in modern notation, $r = a\vartheta$ or $\tan\varphi = \vartheta$.

---

[g] Not at Tarsos, but his father was of Tarsos.

Foundation of statics; theory of the lever, of the center of gravity. Centers of gravity of various surfaces determined. Foundation of hydrostatics; principle of Archimedes. Notion of specific gravity. Inventions of various machines ascribed to him (compound pulley, endless screw, hydraulic screw, orrery, burning-mirrors).

Text and Translations—First Latin (partial) edition by Tartaglia (Venice, 1543. This translation was actually made, not by Tartaglia, but by William of Moerbeke, q. v., second half of thirteenth century). First Greek edition by Thomas Gechauff (Venatorius), (Basel, 1544). Latin translation by F. Commandino (Venice, 1558. Based upon the Basel edition and Greek MSS.). Francois Peyrard: Oeuvres d'Archimède traduites littéralement avec un commentaire, suivies d'un mémoire du traducteur sur un nouveau miroir ardent, et d'un mémoire de J. B. J. Delambre sur l'Arithmétique des Grecs (650 p., in 4to, Paris, 1807). Archimedis Opera Omnia cum commentariis Eutocii iterum edidit J. L. Heiberg (3 vols., Leipzig, 1910–1915. This is the best edition of Archimedes; it was first published in 1880–81; it contains a Latin translation. Vol. I, 1910: De sphaera et cylindro; dimensio circuli; de conoidibus et sphaeroidibus. Vol. II, 1913: Fragmentum ab Angelo Mai editum (hydrostatics); de lineis spiralibus; de planorum aequilibriis; arenarius; quadratura parabolae; de corporibus fluitantibus; stomachion (loculus Archimedius); de mechanicis propositionibus ad Eratosthenem methodus (for transl. of this work see below); liber assumptorum; problema bovinum; fragmenta. Vol. III, 1915: Eutocios's commentaries, prolegomena, scholia, indexes. Thomas Little Heath: The Works of Archimedes, edited in Modern Notation, with Introductory Chapters (512 p., Cambridge, 1897. Important, though less comprehensive than Heath's studies on Aristarchos and Euclid; it is based on Heiberg's first edition of the text. Heath published later a separate translation of the "Method," see below). Fritz Kliem: Archimedes Werke mit modernen Bezeichnungen und mit einer Einleitung versehen (497 p., Berlin, 1914). Paul Ver Eecke: Les oeuvres complètes d'Archimède (612 p., 253 fg., Bruxelles, 1921. French translation based upon Heiberg's second edition; Isis, IV, 499). Various Archimedian texts in German translation have been included in the Ostwalds Klassiker (see e. g., Isis, V, 186; VI, 139, 140).

Archimedes's "Method"—A manuscript of this method (ἔφοδος) was discovered by Heiberg in Constantinople in 1906. As this is perhaps the most important discovery of an early scientific work made in modern times, many studies were devoted to it. The text was first published by Heiberg in Hermes (t. 42, p. 235–303, 1907); a first study and translation of it (in German) by J. L. Heiberg and H. G. Zeuthen appeared in Bibliotheca Mathematica (t. 7, p. 321–363, 1907).

Other translations of and commentaries on the "Method"—Wilh. Schmidt: Archimedes' Ephodikon (Bibliotheca Mathematica, t. I, p. 13–19, 1900). French translation by Th. Reinach, with introduction by Paul Painlevé (Revue générale des sciences 1907, 91 p.). H. Diels: Das neuentdeckte Palimpsest des Archimedes (Intern. Wochenschrift, I, 1907). Ch. S. Slichter: The Recently Discovered Manuscript of Archimedes (Bull. Amer. Math. Soc., 14, p. 382–393, New York, 1908). G. Milhaud: Le traité de la méthode (Revue scientifique, t. X, p. 417–423, Paris, 1908). Ant. Favaro: Intorno ad una scrittura inedita di Archimede. (Atti. d. Istit. Veneto, t. 67, pt. 2, p. 635–638, 1908. English translation by Lydia G. Robinson, with introduction by David E. Smith, in The Monist (Chicago, April 1909). English translation and commentary by Sir Thomas L. Heath (a supplement to his Works of Archimedes, 1897, Cambridge, 1912).

General Studies—J. L. Heiberg: Quaestiones Archimedeae. Inest de arenae numero libellus (205 p., Copenhagen, 1879); Neue Studien zu Archimedes (Zeitschrift für Mathematik und Physik, t. 34, Supplement, p. 3–84, Leipzig, 1890). P. Tannery: Article in Grande Encyclopédie, c. 1887 (Mémoires, III, 326). O.

Spiess: Archimed (Mitt. zur Gesch. d. Medizin, t. III, p. 224–246, 1904). P. Midolo: Archimede e il suo tempo (548 p., Siracusa, 1912). Ant. Favaro: Archimede (Profili, No. 21, 83 p., Genova, 1912); Archimede e Leonardo da Vinci (Atti del R. Istit. di scienze, t. 71, p. 2da, p. 953–975, Venezia, 1912). F. Arendt: Zu Archimedes (Bibliotheca Mathematica, t. 14, p. 289–311, 1915; Isis, III, 93). J. L. Heiberg: Le rôle d'Archimède dans le développement des sciences exactes (Scientia, t. 20, p. 81–89, 1916). Franz Winter: Der Tod des Archimedes (24 p., Berlin, 1924; Isis, VIII, 531).

Mathematics—H. G. Zeuthen: Note sur la résolution géométrique d'une équation du 3e degré par Archimède (Bibliotheca mathematica, p. 97–104, 1893). F. Hultsch: Die Näherungswerte irrationaler Quadratwurzeln bei Archimedes (Nachr. d. Ges. d. Wiss., p. 367–428, Göttingen, 1893). H. Becker: Die geometrische Entwicklung des Infinitesimalbegriffs im Exhaustionbeweise bei Archimedes (26 p., Insterburg, 1894). G. A. Gibson: The Treatment of Arithmetic Progressions by Archimedes (Proc. Math. Soc., t. 16, p. 2–12, Edinburgh, 1897) H. G. Zeuthen: Über einige archimedische Postulate (Archiv für Gesch. d. Naturw. u. Technik, I, 320–327; II, 321, 1909–1910).

On Spirals—Paul Tannery: Sur une critique ancienne d'une démonstration d'Archimède (Mém. de la société des sci. physiques, t. V, p. 49–61, Bordeaux, 1883; also Mémoires, I, 300–316; apropos of propos. 18 of the de helicibus). V. Sassoli: Trattato delle spirali. Versione italiana con note (112 p., Bologna, 1886).

The Cattle Problem—Paul Tannery: Sur le problème des boeufs (Bull. des sci. mathém., t. V, p. 25–30, 1881; Mémoires, I, 118–123). G. Fazzari: Il problema "de bovino" attributo ad Archimede (Il Pitagora, t. 9, p. 94–97, 1903). R. C. Archibald: The Cattle Problem of Archimedes (American Mathematical monthly, vol. 25, 411–414, 1918).

Measurement of the Circle—Paul Tannery: Sur la mesure du cercle d'Archimède (Mém. de la soc. des sciences physiques, t. IV p. 313–337, Bordeaux, 1882; Mémoires, I, 226–253). L. Maleyx: Etude sur la méthode suivie par Archimède pour déterminer approximativement le rapport de la circonférence au diamètre (36 p., Paris, 1886). Ferdinand Rudio: Archimedes, Huygens, Lambert, Legendre. Vier Abhandlungen über Kreismessung. Deutsch hrg. und mit einer Übersicht über die Geschichte des Problems von der Quadratur des Zirkels (174 p., Leipzig, 1892). F. Hultsch: Zur Kreismessung des Archimedes (Z. f. Math., t. 39, 1894, hist. Abt., 121–137, 161–172). Hermann Weissenborn: Die Berechnung des Kreisumfanges bei Archimedes und Leonardo Pisano (Berliner Studien für classische Philologie, t. 14, 3, 32 p., 1894). G. Fazzari: Archimede e la sua misura del cerchio (Il pitagora, t. 9, p. 31–32, 47–51, 1902). Edmund Hoppe: Die zweite Methode des Archimedes zur Berechnung von π (Archiv für Geschichte der Naturwissenschaften, t. 9, 104–107, 1922).

Physics—Statics and Center of Gravity—Giovanni Vailati: Del concetto di centro di gravità nella statica d'Archimede (Atti d. Accad. d. sci., t. 32, 19 p., Torino, 1897). La dimostrazione del principio della leva da Archimede (Atti congr. Roma, 1903, t. 12, p. 243–249). P. Duhem: Sur Charistion et sur le περὶ ζυγῶν d'Archimède (Origines de la statique, t. 2, 301–310, 1906). J. M. Child: Archimedes' Principle of the Balance and some Criticisms upon it (Studies in History of Science, Vol. 2, 490–520, 25 fig., Oxford, 1921. Discussion of Mach's interpretation).

Hydrostatics and Specific Gravity—H. Zotenberg: Traduction arabe du traité des corps flottants. Journal asiatique (t. 13, 509–515, 1879. (Arabic text with notes). P. Duhem: Archimède connaissait-il le paradoxe hydrostatique? Bibliotheca Mathematica (t. 1, p. 15–19, 1900). Wilh. Schmidt: Zur Textgeschichte der Ochumena (Bibliotheca Mathematica, t. III, p. 176–179, 1902). Eilhard Wiedemann: Über arabische Auszüge aus der Schrift des Archimedes über die schwimmenden Körper (Beiträge, VII, 152–162. Sitzb. d. Erlangen Soz., Bd. 38, 1906). Fr. Strunz: Die spezifische Gewichtsbestimmung von Archimedes (Chemiker Zeitung, Nr. 38, 1907). Edm. O. von Lippman: Die spezifische Gewichtsbestimmung bei Archimedes (Chemiker-Zeitung, p. 616, 1907; Abhandl. u. Vorträge, II, 168–170).

Optics—Wilh. Ludwig Oetinger: De speculo Archimedis quo classem Marcelli dicitur incendisse. (Diss., 29 p., Tübingen, 1725. Quoted faute de mieux).

Machines—H. Suter: Nachtrag zu meiner Uebersetzung des Matematiker-Verzeichnisses im Fihrist (Z. für Math. u. Physik, hist. Abt., t. 38, 126–127, 1893. Apropos of an Archimedian writing on water clocks). Carra de Vaux: Notice sur un manuscrit arabe traitant de machines attribuées à Héron, Philon et Archimède. (Bibliotheca Mathematica, t. I, p. 28–38, 1900).

Alia—Heinrich Suter: Der Loculus Archimedius oder das Syntemachion des Archimedes, zum ersten Male nach zwei arabischen Manuskripten der Königliche Bibliothek zu Berlin hrg. und übersetzt (Zeitschrift f. Mathem., t. 44, Suppl., M. Cantor's Festschrift, p. 491–499, 1899. This Loculus, Syntemachion or Stomachion is a sort of puzzle—in fact the earliest puzzle known to us. The genuineness of the writing describing it has been proved by two propositions of the recently discovered manuscript containing the ἔφοδος). Carl Schoy: Graeco-arabischen Studien (Isis, VIII, 35–40, 1926. Apropos of Archimedes's work on the regular heptagon).

ERATOSTHENES

Ἐρατοσθένης. Born in Cyrene c. 273, died in Alexandria c. 192. Mathematician, astronomer. The first great geographer of antiquity. Lived in Athens; arrived in Egypt c. 244; appointed librarian of the Museum of Alexandria in 235. Invented the so-called sieve of Eratosthenes (κόσκικον) to obtain the prime numbers, and an instrument to solve the duplication of the cube (μεσόλαβον). First scientific calculation of the circumference of the earth, based upon a measurement of the latitudes and distance of Syene and Meroe, supposed to be on the same meridian (result: length of the circumference, 252,000 stades or, if 1 st. = 157.5 m., 24,662 miles; corresponding diameter, 7,850 miles, only 50 miles less than the true value of the polar diameter!). New map of the world, partly based upon the work of Dicaearchos. Wrote a geographical treatise (Γεωγραφικά) in three books: (1) History of geography, (2) mathematical and physical geography, (3) preliminary data for the projection of the map, and descriptive geography, including economic and ethnographic notes. A book on stars (καταστερισμοί) to which a catalogue of stars was appended is also ascribed to him.

He was the founder of the scientific chronology of ancient Greece and was also a distinguished philologist.[h] His masterpiece in that line was a study on the old Attic comedy (περὶ τῆς ἀρχαίας κωμῳδίας).

General Studies—Eratosthenica composuit Godofr. Bernhardy (288 p., Berlin 1822, (I) Geographica, (II) Mercurius, (III) de mathematicis disciplinis, (IV) cubi duplicatio, (V) opera philosophica, (VI) de antiqua comoedia; de chronographiis). Ed. Hiller: Carminum reliquiae (140 p., Leipzig, 1872). Ernst Maass: Analecta Eratosthenica (Philologische Untersuchungen, VI, 153 p., Berlin, 1883. de Eratosthenis qui feruntur Catasterismis; de Eratosthenis Erigona; Epimetrum). Paul Tannery: Article in Grande Encyclopédie, c. 1893; Mémoires, III, 358–362).

Geography—Hugo Berger: Die geographischen Fragmente des Eratosthenes

[h] Technically he was the earliest philologist, for he was the first to assume the name φιλόλογος.

neu gesammelt, geordnet und besprochen (401 p., Leipzig, 1880). G. M. Columba: Eratostene e la misura del meridiano terrestre (72 p., Palermo, 1896). Assunto Mori: La misurazione eratostenica del grado ed altre notizie geographiche della Geometria di Marciano Capella (I. Rivista geograf. italiana, 18, p. 177–191, 1911). Willy Thonke: Die Karte des Eratosthenes und die Züge Alexanders. (Diss., 63 p., Strassburg, 1914). A. Thalamas: Etude bibliographique de la géographie d'Eratosthène (192 p.); La géographie d'Eratosthène (256 p., Paris, 1921; Isis, V, 422–426).

Mathematics—Ed. Hiller: Der Πλατωνικός des Eratosthenes (Philologus, Bd. 30, p. 60–72, 1870. That is the de mathematicis disciplinis of Bernhardy's edition).

Astronomy (or astronomical lore, the Catasterisms)—Carolus Robert: Eratosthenis Catasterismorum reliquiae. Accedunt prolegomena et epimetra tria (254 p., Berlin, 1878). Alessandro Olivieri: Pseudo-Eratosthenis catasterismi (Mythographi graeci, Vol. III, fasc. 1, 76 p.). Albert Rehm: Mythographische Untersuchungen über griechische Sternsagen (Diss. 50 p., München, 1896); Eratosthenis Catasterismorum fragmenta vaticana; de Catasterismorum recensionibus (Progr., 18 p., 44 p., Ansbach, 1899). H. Payn: The Well of Eratosthenes (The Observatory, vol. 37, 92–98, 1914; Isis, IV, 129).

CONON

Κόνων of Samos, died young, before Archimedes. Greek geometer and astronomer. Wrote seven books on astronomy containing the Chaldaean observations of eclipses, thus paving the way for Hipparchos. He compiled from his own observations in Southern Italy and Sicily, a parapegma, that is, a calendar giving the risings and settings of fixed stars and meteorological forecasts. He studied the intersections of conics. The fourth book of the "Conics of Apollonios" is based upon Conon's work. He named a constellation Coma Berenices (Berenice's locks) in honor of the wife of Ptolemy III, Evergetes, King from 247 to 222.

Article Conon in Grande Encyclopédie by P. Tannery, c. 1891 (Mémoires, III, 353–354).

APOLLONIOS

Apollonios of Perga, Pamphylia (Ἀπολλώνιος), flourished in Alexandria in the second half of the century; probably born c. 262. Mathematician. Younger contemporary of Eratosthenes and Archimedes. Wrote a treatise on conics (κωνικά), which is one of the greatest scientific books of antiquity. Of the eight books (387 propositions!) on conics, the first four contain a systematic account of the results previously obtained by Menaechmos, Aristaeos, and Euclid. Apollonios showed that all the conics could be considered as sections of the same cone; he introduced the names parabola, ellipse, hyperbola; he considered the two branches of the hyperbola as one single curve, thus evidencing the analogies between the three kinds of sections. Solution of the general equation of the second degree by means of conics. Main properties of conics established. Determination of the evolute of any conic. Construction of a conic by means of tangents. Three-line and four-line loci. The treatment of the whole subject is purely geometrical; these books might be called a geometrical algebra or geometrical analysis (as opposed to analytical geometry). Other mathematical books ascribed to Apollonios are quoted below. He originated the astronomical theory of epicycles and possibly also the theory of eccentrics. In his work entitled Quick delivery (ὠκυτόκιον) he is said to have given a closer approximation to the value of π than that given by Archimedes.

General Edition—Apollonii Pergaei quae graece extant cum commentariis antiquis. Edidit et latine interpretatus est J. L. Heiberg (2 vols., Leipzig, 1891–1893. This edition contains only the original Greek texts extant; for instance, of the Conics, only the first four books).

The Conics—Very poor Latin translation of Bks. I–IV published by Joannes Baptista Memus (Venice, 1537). Much better Latin edition by Commandinus, with Pappos's lemmas and Eutocios's commentary (Bologna, 1566). The first printed edition of Bks. V–VII was a Latin translation of the Arabic text by Abraham Ecchellensis and Giacomo Alfonso Borelli (Florence, 1661). Edmund Halley: Apollonii Conicorum libri octo et Sereni Antissensis de sectione cylindri et coni libri duo (Oxford, 1710. Splendid in folio edition, with Eutocios's commentaries and Pappos's commentaries and lemmas. Of the eight books on conics, seven only have survived, the first four in the original Greek, three in an Arabic translation. Halley's monumental edition contains the Greek text (editio princeps) of the first four books with Latin translation of the three following books and a conjectural restoration of Book VIII). H. Balsam: Des Apollonius sieben Bücher über Kegelschnitte nebst dem durch Halley wieder hergestellten achten Buche, deutsch bearbeitet. Anhang. Die auf die Geometrie der Kegelschnitte bezüchlichen Sätze aus Newton's Principia (Berlin, 1861). H. G. Zeuthen: Die Lehre von den Kegelschnitten im Altertum (Copenhagen, 1886). L. M. Ludwig Nix: Das fünfte Buch der Conica des Apollonius in der arabischen Übersetzung des Thabit ibn Corrah (48 p., Leipzig, 1890). Thomas Little Heath: Apollonius's Treatise on Conic Sections, Edited in Modern Notation with Introductions, including an Essay on the Earlier History of the Subject (426 p., Cambridge. The most convenient edition of the Conics, though less elaborate and comprehensive than Heath's translations of Euclid and Aristarchos; it is based upon the editions of Halley and Heiberg). Giov. Giovannozzi: La versione borelliana dei conici di Apollonio (Mem. Accad. Pontif., II, p. 1–31, Roma, 1916). Paul Ver Eecke: Les Coniques (French translation, 708 p., 419 fig., Bruges, 1924; Isis, VII, 178).

Other Works—Edm. Halley: Apollonii de sectione rationis libri duo ex arabico MSto latine versi; accedunt de sectione spatii libri duo restituti (222 p., Oxford, 1706). Wilhelm Adolf Diesterweg: Die Bücher de sectione spatii wiederhergestellt (162 p., 5 pl., Elberfeld, 1827); Die Bücher de sectione rationis nach dem Lateinischen des Edm. Halley frey bearbeitet (233 p., 9 pl., Berlin, 1824).

Joh. Wilh. von Camerer: Apollonii de tactionibus quae supersunt, ac maxime lemmata Pappi in hos libros graece nunc primum edita cum Francisci Vietae restitutione (176 p., Gotha, 1795).

Franz van Schooten: Apollonii Loca plana restituta (Exercitationum Mathematicarum liber III, p. 191–292, Leyden, 1656). Pierre de Fermat: Apollonii libri duo de locis planis restituti (Oeuvres de Fermat, t. I, p. 3–51, Paris, 1891. Reprinted from the Varia Opera Mathematica, Toulouse, 1679).

Samuel Horsley: Apollonii inclinationum libri duo (115 p., Oxford, 1770). Reuben Burrow: A Restitution of the Treatise on Inclinations (23 p., Oxford, 1779). Wilh. Ad. Diesterweg: Die Bücher des Apollonius wiederhergestellt von Sam. Horsley nach dem lateinischen frey bearbeitet (168 p., 19 pl., Berlin, 1823).

W. A. Diesterweg: Die Bücher des Apollonius de sectione determinata wiederhergestellt von Robert Simson und die angehängten Bücher des Letzeren (196 p., 18 pl., Mainz, 1822).

Franz Woepcke: Essai d'une restitution des travaux perdus d'Apollonius sur les quantités irrationelles d'après des indications tirées d'un manuscrit arabe (63 p., Paris, 1856; Mém. presentés à l'Académie des sciences, t. 14).

Special Studies—Paul Tannery: Quelques fragments d'Apollonius (Bull. des

[i] See Abū-l-Fatḥ of Ispahan (second half of tenth century).

sci. mathém., t. V, p. 124–136, Paris, 1881; Mémoires, I, 124–138); article Apollonius in Grande Encyclopédie, c. 1887; Mémoires, III, 322–325). Carra de Vaux: Note sur les mécaniques de Bédi ez-Zaman el-Djazari et sur un appareil hydraulique attribué à Apollonius (Annales internationales d' histoire, Congrès de Paris 1900, section V, p. 112–120, Paris, 1901). R. C. Archibald: Discussion and History of Certain Geometrical Problems of Heraclitus and Apollonius (Proc. Edinburgh Mathematical Society, vol. 28, p. 152–178, 1910). Carra de Vaux: Article Balīnūs, in Encyclopedia of Islam (t. 1, 620, 1913. Balīnūs, Bālīnās, Balīs, Abuluniyūs, thus was Apollonios called in Arabic, but in some cases these names referred to Apollonios of Tyana, first century). F. Arendt: Eine Interpolation des Eutokios in unserem Apolloniostext (Bibliotheca Mathematica, t. 14, p. 97–98, 1914). Ettore Bortolotti: Quando, come e da chi ci vennero ricuperati i sette libri delle coniche (Periodico di Matematiche, vol. 4, 12 p., 1924. Correcting very inaccurate statements on the subject in Ver Eecke's French translation, 1924; Isis, VII, 178).

VI. INTRODUCTION OF GREEK MEDICINE IN ROME

ARCHAGATHOS

'Αρχάγαθος; of Peloponnesian origin, flourished in Rome c. 219 B. C. Greek physician and surgeon. The first professional physician established in Rome.

Maurice Albert: Les médecins grecs à Rome (Paris, 1894). M. Wellmann, in Pauly-Wissowa (t. 2, 432, 1895. Ex Celsus, V, 19, 27).

VII. CHINESE AND HELLENISTIC TECHNOLOGY

MENG T'IEN

Mêng[2] T'ien[2] (7763, 11220) (originating through his ancestors from the Ch'i[2] (1074) State; in 221 he was appointed commander in chief of the army of the First Emperor; he was invited to commit suicide in 209). Chinese general. The invention of the harpsichord, chêng[1] (711), is ascribed to him, also that of the writing brush of hair. This was soon followed by the use of silk rolls. Up to the end of the Chou dynasty (255) writing was done with a bamboo pen and ink of lacquer made of tree-sap upon slips of bamboo or wood. That this transformation took place in the second half of the third century B. C. is proved by changes in the language. The word for chapter used after this time means "roll," the word for writing materials becomes "bamboo and silk" instead of "bamboo and wood." The use of seals (first mentioned in China c. 255 B. C.) became very general about the end of the third century. This was one of the practices which led by and by to the invention of printing.

H. A. Giles: Chinese Biographical Dictionary (584, Shanghai, 1898). Thomas Francis Parker: Invention of Printing in China (p. 2, New York, 1925; Isis, VIII, 361).

LI PING

Li[3] Ping[1] (6884, 9277). Flourished under the Ch'in[2] (?093) dynasty, B. C. 255–206. Chinese engineer. Prefect of the Shu[3*] (10057) district in Ssŭch'uan, he began the system of irrigation which transformed the immense Ch'êng[2]-tu[1] (762, 12050) plain into a region of extraordinary fertility.

Joshua Vale: Journal of the North China branch of the R. Asiatic Soc., vol. 33, 105–19, 1900; vol. 36, 36–50, 1905. Encyclopaedia sinica, 92, 311, 1917.

Hellenistic Technology

Fritz Caspari: Das Nilschiff Ptolemaios IV, 222 to 205 (Jahrbuch des K. deutschen archäologischen Instituts, Bd. 31, 1–74, Berlin, 1916; Isis, IV, 128).

VIII. GREEK AND ROMAN HISTORIOGRAPHY

For Greek historiography see my note on Eratosthenes in Section V.

PICTOR

Q. Fabius Pictor.[i] Grandson of the painter, flourished c. 225 to 216. Earliest Roman historian in prose. He wrote in Greek a history of Rome from the arrival of Aeneas in Italy down to his own time (second Punic war).

Eduard Heydenreich: Fabius Pictor und Livius (42 p., Freiberg, 1878).

ALIMENTUS

L. Cincius Alimentus (praetor in Sicily in 209). Roman historian. He wrote, in Greek, the Annals of Rome down to the second Punic war.

IX. CHINESE WRITING

Ch'êng[2] Mo[4]* (757, 7998[k]). Flourished under Shih Huang Ti, emperor from 221 to 210. Chinese grammarian who invented the Lesser Seal characters[l] and later the li[4] (7005) script, both forms being much simpler than the Old Seal, chuan[4], (2724) characters.

H. A. Giles: Biographical Dictionary (116, 1898). Bernhard Karlgren: Analytic Dictionary of Chinese. (Paris, 1923. Ascribes the invention to Li Ssŭ and discusses it: "The small seal was not a mere shortening and simplification of the earlier script; it was in fact to a large extent a new system of writing." The author indicates the characteristics of that new writing; Isis, VII, 567).

---

[i] The Pictor family of the Fabia gens derived its name from C. Fabius, surnamed Pictor, because of a painting made by him in the temple of Salus (c. 307–302)—the earliest Roman painting recorded.

[k] The character 7998 is colloquially pronounced miao[2].

[l] The invention of the Lesser Seal has been ascribed also to Li[3] Ssŭ[1] (6884, 10262), who died in 208, and is especially famous for having suggested the Burning of the Books to the First Emperor in 213. (See Giles, *ibidem*, 464.)

CHAPTER IX

THE TIME OF CATO THE CENSOR

(First Half of Second Century B. C.)

I. Survey of Science in First Half of Second Century B. C. II. Development of the Jewish Scriptures. III. Greek, Roman, and Chinese Philosophy. IV. Hellenistic and Chinese Mathematics. V. Hellenistic Astronomy. VI. Hellenistic Physics and Technology. VII. Hellenistic Geography. VIII. Roman Husbandry. IX. Hellenistic, Roman, and Chinese Medicine. X. Roman and Hellenistic Historiography. XI. Roman Law. XII. Greek Philology.

I. SURVEY OF SCIENCE IN FIRST HALF OF SECOND CENTURY B. C.

1. I entitle this chapter The Time of Cato the Censor, because, among the many figures of that complex and chaotic age, Cato's is probably the most impressive. It also has a symbolic value. Cato represents the last stand of the Romans against the Greeks, for it should not be supposed that Greece conquered Rome all at once. There were too many causes of incompatibility between the Roman and Greek temperaments to make this possible. The transitional character of the period might have been symbolized as well by a Greek personality, namely, by the most arresting of all, that of Polybios; but I wanted to emphasize, by means of a Latin name, that from now on Roman science and erudition, however inferior to Greek and Hellenistic, must be taken into account.

2. *Development of the Jewish Scriptures*—Ecclesiastes was probably composed at the end of the third century or in the first half of the second, before 168. Ecclesiasticus dates probably from the period 190 to 170. These two books are parts of the so-called Wisdom literature of the Old Testament and are among the most precious writings that have been handed down to us from ancient times. The Book of Daniel was written about the year 165.

3. *Greek, Roman, and Chinese Philosophy*—Ennius, with whom I shall deal presently (in Section X), wrote Latin poems explaining Pythagorean and Euhemeristic doctrines; he died in 169. In 156, Diogenes the Babylonian introduced into Rome that philosophy which was soon to become the Roman philosophy par excellence, Stoicism. Indeed, no system of thought was better adapted to the peculiar qualities of the Roman genius.

In the meanwhile, the Chinese philosopher K'ung An-kuo was reconstructing as much as possible the Classics destroyed during the Burning of the Books (213).

4. *Hellenistic and Chinese Mathematics*—The outstanding mathematician of the period was Hypsicles, who wrote the so-called XIVth book of Euclid, dealing with the regular icosahedron and dodecahedron. His treatise on the risings of stars is the earliest Greek work wherein the ecliptic is divided into 360 parts.

Much valuable work was done by various epigoni, whose dates are very uncertain: Zenodoros studied isoperimetric surfaces; Perseus, the spiric curves; Nicomedes, the conchoid and Hippias's quadratrix; Dionysodoros, toric surfaces; Diocles, the cissoid and the duplication of the cube. It is not at all certain that these mathematicians lived, all of them, in the first half of the second century; we know practically nothing about them, but their activities have so much in common that it seemed best to leave them together, as long as we have no positive grounds for dividing them. There can be no harm in this procedure if we do not forget its arbitrariness.

Chang Ts'ang, who died in 152, composed, or more probably edited, the most famous mathematical treatise of ancient China, the so-called "Arithmetical rules in nine sections." It deals essentially with arithmetic, but contains also some geometrical elements. One finds in it the earliest mention of a negative quantity.

5. *Hellenistic Astronomy*—Seleucos the Babylonian was bold enough to defend the heliocentrical system of Aristarchos, he being the last of the ancients to do so. He gave a lunar theory of the tides. Arrian the Meteorologist wrote on comets. Hypsicles, mentioned above, composed an astrological treatise. A student's note-book, dating from c. 192, the so-called Papyrus of Eudoxos, deals with astronomy and the calendar.

6. *Hellenistic Physics and Technology*—The mathematician Diocles wrote a book on burning-mirrors. Meteorological problems were dealt with by the astronomer Arrian. The greatest technician of that period (if he really belongs to it) was Ctesibios of Alexandria, who invented various mechanical and hydraulical contrivances. He was the earliest of those Hellenistic mechanicians who applied the knowledge and, to some little extent, the methods bequeathed to them by Archimedes to the solution of practical problems.

The historian of technology will find interesting information in Cato's de agricultura.

7. *Hellenistic Geography*—Crates of Mallos, who visited Rome in 168, constructed a terrestrial globe; he explained the theory of four land masses. Polemon Periegetes wrote various archaeological studies and historical guides for the use of travelers visiting Greece. Agatharchides wrote many geographical and historical works of which the most valuable deals with the Erythraean Sea and the countries surrounding it. The works of the historian Polybios are also of considerable geographical interest.

8. *Roman Husbandry*—Cato's treatise on husbandry was the earliest Latin work on the subject; it contains valuable information not only on husbandry, but on many other topics more or less related to it, for example, medicine. Of course husbandry may be taken to include the whole of domestic economy. A work like Cato's is thus a general guide for practical life, that is, an encyclopaedia of all the knowledge which is truly and immediately useful; the wish for other knowledge being from the stern Roman point of view a mere intellectual extravagance.

9. *Hellenistic, Roman, and Chinese Medicine*—The intellectual indigence of the age is nowhere more obvious than in the medical field. The only physician worth mentioning is Serapion of Alexandria, the founder of the empirical school, who carried his distrust of dogmatism so far as to adopt (by way of reaction) the most absurd popular remedies. Glimpses of Roman medicine may be obtained in the works of Cato.

The Chinese medicine of that time was represented by Shun Yü-i, born probably in 216.

10. *Roman and Hellenistic Historiography*—The poet Ennius, who died in 169, wrote annals of Rome in Latin verse. Yet the greatest historical work was still being done in Greek. The Arcadian Polybios, who has been called "the historian of the decline and fall of ancient Greece," is perhaps, all considered, the

greatest personality of that period. His work is certainly the best introduction to the understanding of the gigantic crisis which was then occurring, the intellectual conflict between Greece and Rome. The writings of the geographers Polemon and Agatharchides are almost as important from the historical as from the geographical point of view. Polemon was probably the earliest Greek epigraphist.

11. *Roman Law*—Sextus Aelius Paetus, consul in 198, composed the Tripartita or Jus Aelianum, based upon the Twelve Tables.

12. *Greek Philology*—The most important scientific work was perhaps that accomplished in the field of philology. We meet a number of eminent lexicographers, commentators, and grammarians. Aristophanes of Byzantium, librarian of the Museum from 195, systematized accentuation and punctuation and prepared better editions of the classics; Aristarchos of Samothrace, who succeeded him c. 180, improved the study of grammar; the archaeologist Demetrios of Scepsis, wrote Homeric commentaries; the philosopher Diogenes (see Section III) completed the elaboration of the Stoic grammar; finally, the geographer Crates (see Section VII) composed the first Greek grammar.

This efflorescence of grammatical studies was natural enough; it was a necessary result of the growing cosmopolitanism and polyglottism. There is no need of grammar as long as the acquisition of language is purely instinctive; but just as soon as this acquisition becomes an artificial process, as when a language is being learned by foreigners, the need of grammar, dictionaries, and other tools becomes very urgent. Some philosophers had been interested in grammar even before the Hellenistic mixture of peoples had begun, but this interest had remained largely speculative. But, since the time of Alexander, the number of foreigners, Jews, Romans, and others, wanting to study Greek had not ceased to increase. And not only that, but the Greek-speaking people (especially those residing in cosmopolitan cities like Alexandria) became less and less able to speak correctly without continuous effort; even the most educated realized that their language was very different from that of the classics; finally, the study of Homer and Hesiod stimulated philological inquiries in proportion as these texts became more remote. The days of linguistic innocence were now long over; self-consciousness had been introduced into the language and had come to stay. It is thus not surprising that this age, so poor in other respects, saw the birth of grammar.

Men of science should not think that this was a mean achievement. Of course, nowadays, to compile a grammar of a known language can hardly be considered a scientific work. But the creators of grammar, or those who, like Diogenes and Crates, were the first to systematize the results of a long evolution, were accomplishing a scientific task of considerable importance and merit. The discovery of the logical structure of language was as much a scientific achievement as the discovery of the anatomical structure of the body. But as linguistic self-consciousness appeared very gradually, the discovery was very slow and largely anonymous.

It should be noted also that scientific endeavors in other directions were bound to induce some sort of grammatical elaboration. Every scientific investigation entails sooner or later the use of special words and phrases; it introduces new thoughts which must be adequately expressed. It is not even sufficient for a scientist to use a correct language unconsciously, for he must know exactly the peculiarities and limitations of his tools, and language is one of them. He must be sure of his ability to express his thoughts with precision and without ambiguity. Further scientific progress involved necessarily a sufficient analysis and determination of the language. Grammatical work was thus an essential step in the development of science.

I suppose I need not apologize for having spoken of grammar at such length. I have done so because the subject is generally misunderstood by scientists. They but too often despise philological studies, not realizing how much they owe to the grammarians of old.

13. *Conclusion*—This period is still predominantly Hellenistic, but Alexandria is no longer the only center. Rome has become a focus of great importance; it is represented not simply by Romans like Ennius and Cato, but also by the outstanding personality of Polybios. Still another center, Pergamum, is brought to our attention. It reached the height of its splendor under Eumenes II, who ruled over it from 197 to 158. Its library, of which Crates was the head, seems to have rivaled at that time the library of Alexandria. Yet the most valuable scientific work, that of Hypsicles and Ctesibios, was still accomplished in Alexandria, and that city may boast of having been in those very days the cradle of grammar.

Outside of philology, the period is distinctly one of intellectual regression, but the climax previously reached, thanks to the genius of Archimedes and Apollonios, was perhaps abnormally high.

II. DEVELOPMENT OF THE JEWISH SCRIPTURES

It is impossible to date with any accuracy Ecclesiastes or the Preacher (Ἐκκλησιαστής), but the most probable date would be one included between say 250 and 168 B. C. (revolt of the Maccabees). It is included in both the Jewish and the Christian canon. It is a part of the Hebrew Wisdom literature, but a unique part in that it is a self-communion, suggesting comparisons with Marcus Aurelius and Pascal.

The Book of Ecclesiasticus (50 chapters) is another part of the Wisdom literature, though not included in the canon.[e] It is one of the most important Old Testament apocrypha. It was composed later than Ecclesiastes, probably about 190 to 170. Until 1896 it was known only through Greek and Syrian versions; large parts of the original Hebrew text were then and have since been discovered. Both Ecclesiastes and Ecclesiasticus are among the golden books of the world literature. In Ecclesiasticus we find allusions to the Empedoclean doctrine of opposites (coexistence in nature of two antagonistic moving forces) and to the Aristotelian notion that the heart is the seat of intelligence.

The Book of Daniel (in 12 chapters) was composed during the reign of Antiochos IV, Epiphanes, King of Syria from 175 to 164; more exactly, soon after the desecration of the Temple and the revolt of the Maccabees in 168. The apocalyptic

---

[a] The invention of parchment (charta pergamena, after Pergamum) is ascribed to this very king. On this subject see F. Cumont (Isis, VII, 565).

[b] It was joined later to that of Alexandria, having been presented by Antony to Cleopatra.

[c] In Hebrew, Qoheleth ("The Words of Qoheleth, Son of David, King in Jerusalem"). It contains 12 chapters.

[d] Also called the "Wisdom of Jesus, Son of Sirach", or the "Wisdom of Sirach." The Greek fathers called it Πανάρετος σοφία; the Talmudists, the Book of Ben Sira.

[e] That is, by the Jews and the Protestants. The Greek and Roman Catholic churches have included it.

visions of Daniel fall between 168 and 165, when the Temple was restored. This book is a part both of the Jewish and of the Christian canon. About half of it (from II, 4, to VII, 28) was written in Aramaic, the rest in Hebrew. Three additions to the original text are found in the Greek translation[f] and are accepted as canonical by the Roman Catholic and by the Greek Church, but not by the Protestant Churches.

George Aaron Barton: Critical Commentary on Ecclesiastes (226 p., Intern. crit. comm., New York, 1908).

A commentary on Daniel by Jephet ibn Ali the Karaite, edited and translated by D. S. Margoliouth (214 p., Oxford, 1889). John Dyneley Prince: Commentary on Daniel (Leipzig, 1899).

III. GREEK, ROMAN, AND CHINESE PHILOSOPHY

For Roman philosophy, see my note on Ennius in Section X.

DIOGENES THE BABYLONIAN

Διογένης ὁ Βαβυλώνιος. Born c. 240 in Seleucia on the Tigris, died before 150. Stoic philosopher. Disciple of Chrysippos (q. v., second half of third century B. C.), and at one time leader of the Stoa. Being sent to Rome in 156–5 as member of an Athenian embassy, he delivered lectures on Stoicism; this marks the introduction into the Roman world of a philosophy which was to become, during the following centuries, before the final triumph of Christianity, its supreme inspiration. He systematized Stoic views on grammar, and wrote on logic and divination. He considered the soul an exhalation (ἀναθυμίασις) of the blood. Stoicism stimulated scientific research in archaeology and grammar; it also influenced materially Roman jurisprudence.

M. Wellmann, in Pauly-Wissowa (t. 9, 773–776, 1903).

K'UNG AN-KUO

K'ung[3] An[1]-kuo[2]* (6605, 44, 6609). Flourished in the second century B. C. Descendant of Confucius in the twelfth degree and one of the earliest editors of the Confucian Classics. He discovered large portions of them in the house of K'ung Fu,[g] transcribed them into the li script,[h] and commented upon them.

H. A. Giles: Biographical Dictionary (397, 1896).

IV. HELLENISTIC AND CHINESE MATHEMATICS

HYPSICLES

Ὑψικλῆς. Flourished in Alexandria (?) in the beginning of the century. Mathematician. His father was an older contemporary of Apollonios. Hypsicles wrote the so-called XIVth book of Euclid's "Elements," which contains eight propositions dealing with the regular icosahedron and dodecahedron.

Polygonal numbers are defined as the sums of arithmetic progressions, the ratios of which are equal to the number of sides, less two, of the respective polygons. Further study of arithmetic progressions.

---

[f] The song of the three children; The history of Susannah: Bel and the Dragon.

[g] For whom, see footnote to my account of Shih Huang Ti (second half of third century B. C.).

[h] For which, see Ch'êng Mo (second half of third century B. C.).

He wrote an astrological treatise on the rising of stars (ἀναφορικός); this is the oldest Greek work wherein the (ecliptic) circle is divided into 360 parts; it is also the last vain attempt to solve exactly problems which can only be solved approximately by means of trigonometrical functions.

For text of and commentary on the XIVth book of Euclid, see Heiberg's Euclidis Opera Omnia (Vol. V), and T. L. Heath: The Thirteen Books of Euclid (Vol. 3, p. 512–519, Cambridge, 1908), and other Euclidian literature.

General study by Björnbo, in Pauly-Wissowa (vol. 17, col. 427–433, 1914).

K. Manitius: Des Hypsikles Schrift Anaphoricos nach Überlieferung und Inhalt kritisch dargestellt (Progr., 21 p., Dresden, 1888).

ZENODOROS

Ζηνόδωρος. Flourished in the second century. The dates of his life are very uncertain. He flourished after 200 B. C. and before 90 A. D., but probably not long after the former date. He wrote on isoperimetric plane surfaces (περὶ ἰσομέτρων σχημάτων) and showed also that of all solid figures the surfaces of which are equal, the sphere is the greatest in volume.

For the text of his treatise see: Zenodori commentarius de figuris isometris cum Pappi libro V collatus, in Fried. Hultsch: Pappi Alexandrini Collectionis quae supersunt (Vol. III, p. 1189–1211, Berlin, 1878; cfr. also *ibidem*, p. 1138–1165).

Sir Thomas Heath: History of Greek Mathematics (vol. 2, 207–213, 1921).

PERSEUS

Περσεύς. Flourished probably in the second century B. C. Mathematician, who lived before Heron and Geminos. He discovered and investigated the spiric curves, which were plane sections of surfaces generated by the revolution of a circle around an axis in its plane not passing through the center.

Perseus's dates are very uncertain. Heath (Greek mathematics, vol. 2, 1921, 204) would place him before Apollonios and near to Euclid.

NICOMEDES

Νικομήδης. Flourished probably in the second century B. C. Mathematician who lived after Eratosthenes and before Geminos. He invented the conchoid, investigated its properties, devised an instrument to trace it, and used it for the trisection of angles and the duplication of cubes. He investigated Hippias's quadratrix and used it to square the circle, whence its name.

DIONYSODOROS

Dionysodoros of Amisos, Pontos (Διονυσόδωρος). Lived probably in the second century B. C. Mathematician who wrote probably before Diocles. He solved the Archimedean problem concerning the division of a sphere by a plane in a given ratio—by means of the intersection of a parabola and an hyperbola. He wrote a book on tores (περὶ τῆς σπείρας) quoted by Heron. He is not to be mistaken for Dionysodoros of Melos, geographer, who lived after Eratosthenes and before Strabon.

Wilh. Schmidt: Über den griechischen Mathematiker Dionysodoros (Bibliotheca Mathematica, t. 4, 321–325, Leipzig, 1904).

DIOCLES

Διοκλῆς. Flourished probably in the second century B. C. Mathematician and physicist, who lived after Archimedes and before Geminos. He wrote a book on burning-mirrors (περὶ πυρείων); solved the problem of the division of a sphere in a given ratio by a plane section, invented the cissoid and applied it to the duplication of the cube.

CHANG TS'ANG

Chang[1] Ts'ang[1] (416, 11596). He died in 152 B. C., being more than a hundred years old. Mathematician. It is to him that we owe the text of the "Arithmetical rules in nine sections," Chiu[3]-chang[1] suan[4]-shu[4]* (2263, 390, 10378, 10053), the greatest arithmetical classic of China. The date of the original text can not be fixed; Chinese tradition ascribes it to the twenty-seventh century B. C.[i] Contents of the nine sections: (1) Mensuration of plane figures, fractions; (2) problems involving the rule of three; (3) partnership; (4) extraction of square and cube roots; (5) mensuration of solids; (6) alligation; (7) "excess and deficiency," using the rule of false position; (8) linear equations involving one or more unknown quantities, earliest known mention of a negative quantity;[j] (9) Pythagorean theorem; problems, one involving a quadratic equation, which is correctly solved. Value of π, 3.

Text—The text of the Chiu-chang suan-shu is included in the Tai[4]-chiao[4] suan[4]-ching[1] shih[2]*-shu[1] (10567, 1302, 10378, 2122, 9959, 10024), a collection of the ten oldest mathematical treatises edited in 1773 by Tai[4]-chên[4] (10567, 642). See L. Wieger: La Chine (399, 502, 525, 1920).

Criticism—For Chang Ts'ang's biography see Ssŭ-ma Ch'ien's Shih-chi (q. v., second half of second century B. C.). A. Wylie: Chinese Literature (113, (1867) 1902). A full account of the Nine Sections will be found in Yoshio Mikami; The Development of Mathematics in China and Japan (8–25, Leipzig, 1913). Shorter but complete account in D. E. Smith and Y. Mikami: History of Japanese Mathematics (11–14, Chicago, 1911).

V. HELLENISTIC ASTRONOMY

SELEUCOS

Seleucos the Babylonian (Σέλευκος). Flourished in Seleucia (?) on the Tigris about the middle of the century (?). Astronomer. One of the first and certainly the last of the ancients to take up Aristarchos's theory of the diurnal rotation of the earth and of its revolution around the sun. He was even more affirmative than his master on this question.[k] He explained the tides by the

---

[i] On the other hand, it may be as late as the Christian era! We do not know the original text. We only know its substance through the commentaries and elaborations of Liu Hui (q. v., second half of third century) and Li Shun-fêng (q. v., second half of seventh century). Li Shun-fêng's text was reconstructed after being extracted piecemeal from the Yung Lo ta tien (q.v., first half of fifteenth century).

[j] Called fu[4] (3743); the positive quantities being called chêng[4] (687).

[k] According to Plutarch (Quaest. Plat., VIII, 1) Aristarchos had introduced the heliocentrical system only as a hypothesis (ὑποτιθέμενος μόνον) but Seleucos had declared the theory to be true (καὶ ἀποφαινόμενος).

resistance opposed by the moon to the diurnal rotation of the atmosphere. He had discovered periodical inequalities in the tides of the Red Sea which he connected with the position of the moon in the zodiac (Strabon, III, 5, 9).

Sophus Ruge: Der Chaldäer Seleukos (23 p., Dresden, 1865). Sir Thomas Heath: Aristarchus (305–307, Oxford, 1913). Short article, very unsatisfactory, in Pauly-Wissowa (Zweite Reihe, 3, 1249, 1921).

ARRIAN THE METEOROLOGIST

'Αρριανός. Flourished after Eratosthenes and before Agatharchides, i. e., in the first half of the second century B. C. Meteorologist. Wrote a book on meteorology and a short monograph (*βιβλιδάριον*) on comets (*περὶ κομητῶν φύσεως τε καὶ συστάσεως καὶ φασμάτων*). His work was absorbed in Posidonios's writings and only three fragments of it remain.

William Capelle: Der Physiker Arrian und Poseidonius (Hermes, t. 40, 614–635, Berlin, 1905. Arrian's fragments have been transmitted to us by the polygraph Stobaeos, q. v., second half of fifth century).

THE "PAPYRUS OF EUDOXOS"

This Egyptian papyrus, preserved in the Louvre, is so called because an acrostic at the beginning gives the title: Εὐδόξου τέχνη (Eudoxi ars). It deals with astronomy and the calendar, and is probably a student's note-book. It dates from 193 to 190 B. C. The astronomical data correspond to the latitude of Alexandria.

Text—The first edition prepared by A. J. Letronne was published after his death by W. Brunet de Presle: Notices et Extraits (t. 18 (2), p. 1–76, 10 pl., 1865). New edition by F. Blass: Eudoxi Ars astronomica (25 p., Kiel, 1887, with Latin translation). French translation by P. Tannery: Recherches sur l'astronomie ancienne (p. 283–294, Paris, 1893).

Criticism—A. Boeckh: Über die vierjährigen Sonnenkreise der Alten (Berlin, 1863.) Article by Hultsch, in Pauly-Wissowa (t. 6, 949, 1907).

VI. HELLENISTIC PHYSICS AND TECHNOLOGY

CTESIBIOS

Ctesibios of Alexandria (Κτησίβιος). Flourished at the beginning of the second century (?). Mechanician, inventor. The earliest of the three great Hellenistic mechanicians: Ctesibios, Philon, and Heron. It is impossible to date their lives with any certainty, but it is probable that Ctesibios flourished about the end of the third or the beginning of the second century. Philon of Byzantium about the end of the second century and Heron of Alexandria about the beginning of the first century B. C.[1] His writings are lost. Invention of hydraulic clock, hydraulic organ (with keyboard?) and force-pump ascribed to him.

P. Tannery: L'invention de l'hydraulis (Revue des études grecques, t. 21, 326–340, 1908; Mémoires, III, 282. Posthumous paper completed by Baron Carra de Vaux). G. Speckhart: Das Räderwerk der wiedererstandenen Wasser-

[1] It is highly probable at any rate that the intervals of time elapsing between their lives were not much longer than my dating suggests; as this chronological discussion is centered upon Heron, refer for more information to the paragraph devoted to him.

uhr des Ktesibios (Deutsche Uhrmacherzeitung, J. 39, p. 157–169, 1915. Apropos of the reconstruction of Ctesibios's clock in the Deutsches Museum, Munich. This reconstruction is of very little value, for the works of the clock are of a modern type!) For further bibliography see under Philon of Byzantium.

VII. HELLENISTIC GEOGRAPHY

CRATES

Crates of Mallos in Cilicia (Κράτης). Flourished in Pergamum in the first half of the century. Philologist and grammarian, Stoic philosopher, head of the library of Pergamum. Commentator on Homer. According to Strabon (Geography, II, 5, 10), he constructed a terrestrial globe, the earliest recorded. He was the main exponent of the (Pythagorean) theory of four land masses, according to which the oikoumene is but one of four similar inhabited masses of land, separated from one another by two oceans, and antipodal, two by two. His comparison of Greek with Latin obliged him to analyze more deeply his own language and to compose the first formal Greek grammar. His visit to Rome in 168 may have affected the organization of the Roman public libraries.

Kurt Wachsmuth: De Cratete Mallota disputavit, adjectis ejus reliquis (78 p., Leipzig, 1860; for Strabon's fragment, see p. 66). Ern. Maas: De Cratete Mallota (Philologische Untersuchungen, H. 12, p. 165–207; chapter IV of the author's Aratea, Berlin, 1892). Sandys: History of Classical Scholarship (vol. 1^3, 156–160, 1921). W. Kroll, in Pauly-Wissowa (Bd. XI, 1634–1641, 1922; Isis, VI, 140).

POLEMON PERIEGETES[m]

Πολέμων ὁ περιηγήτης, of Troas, flourished in the first quarter of the second century B. C. Geographer and archaeologist. He had traveled all over Greece, copying inscriptions, and he wrote a number of books describing various parts of the country. He also wrote histories of the origins (κτίσεις) of many Greek cities. He published inscriptions (περὶ τῶν κατὰ πόλεις ἐπιγραμμάτων), and many monographs on other archaeological subjects.

Texts—Ludwig Preller: Polemonis fragmenta (Leipzig, 1838). C. Müller: Fragmenta historicorum graecorum (t. 3, 108–148).
Criticism—F. Susemihl: Griech. Litt. in der Alexandrinerzeit (t. 1, 665–676, 1891).

AGATHARCHIDES

Agatharchides of Cnidos (Ἀγαθαρχίδης). Flourished in the second quarter of the century in Alexandria. Geographer and historian. Peripatetician. The most important to us of his writings is the one on the Erythraean Sea (περὶ τῆς Ἐρυθρᾶς θαλάσσης), containing valuable geographic and ethnographic information on Aethiopia and Arabia, for example, accounts of the Aethiopian gold mines and of the Ichthyophagi of the Arabian coast. Among his other writings we may still mention his Geography and History of Asia in 10 books (τὰ κατὰ τὴν Ἀσίαν) and the Geography and History of Europe, in 49 books (Εὐρωπιακά).

Ernst H. F. Meyer: Geschichte der Botanik (t. 1, 311–313, 1854). H. Leopold: De Agatharchide Cnidio (Diss., Rostock, 1892). Article by Schwarz, in Pauly-Wissowa (t. 1, 739–741, 1894).

---

[m] There were quite a few "perigetae" in that time, a sort of guides whose business it was to explain ancient Greece to the increasing mass of travelers from abroad.

VIII. ROMAN HUSBANDRY

CATO THE CENSOR

Marcus Porcius Cato, (or Censorius, or Cato Major) born at Tusculum, 234, died in Rome 149. Roman statesman, moralist, farmer. Wrote in his old age a treatise on farming, gardening, fruit-growing, etc. (de agri cultura), the first book on the subject in Latin,[n] containing also valuable information on Roman medicine (empirical and magical). Violent antagonist of Greek medicine and philosophy (e. g., in his Praecepta ad filium). Among the facts incidentally quoted by Cato, we may mention the earliest recipe for ordinary mortar and the earliest description of a bain-marie.

Cato the Censor is so called to distinguish him from his equally illustrious great-grandson, Cato of Utica.[o] As the latter is one of the noblest figures of Roman times and will not be mentioned elsewhere in this Introduction, it is proper to say a few words about him in this place. Born in 95, bred as a Stoic, leader of the aristocratic party ultimately defeated by Caesar, his political career was outwardly a succession of failures, but he gave such admirable proofs of moral strength and virtue that his life will ever remain a source of inspiration. In 46, his task being accomplished, he committed suicide at Utica (hence his name) in order not to fall into the hands of Caesar. Cicero, Caesar, and Plutarch have told and discussed his life.

Text and Translation—Editio princeps of de agri cultura in Scriptores rei rusticae (Venice, Nic. Jenson, 1492). Heinrich Jordan: M. Catonis praeter librum de re rustica quae extant (245 p., Leipzig, 1860). Heinrich Keil: M. Porci Catonis de agri cultura liber, M. Terenti Varronis rerum rusticarum libri tres (3 vols., Leipzig, 1884–1897. Critical edition with ample commentary and index verborum). Fairfax Harrison: Cato's Farm Management. Eclogues from the de re rustica done into English, with notes of other excursions in the pleasant paths of agronomic literature by A Virginia Farmer (60 p., Chicago, 1910); Roman Farm Management. The treatises of Cato and Varro done into English, with notes of modern instances (379 p. New York, 1913). The second book contains the former in an improved form; Harrison's translation and commentary are most delightful and instructive.

Commentary—Heinrich Jordan: Quaestionum catonianarum capita duo (Diss., 85 p., Berlin, 1856). Paul Weise: Quaestionum catonianarum capita V (Chiefly philolog.; Diss., 172 p., Göttingen, 1886). Carlo Ricci: Catone nell' opposizione alla cultura greca e ai grecheggianti (46 p., Palermo, 1895). Edmund Hauler: Zu Catos Schrift über das Landwesen. (Progr., 29 p., Wien, 1896). Ferdinando Marcucci: Studio critico sulle opere di Catone il Maggiore (231 p., Pisa, 1902). Paul Reuther: De Catonis de agri cultura libri vestigiis apud Graecos (Diss., 53 p., Leipzig, 1903). Bern. Busch: De M. Porcio Catone quid antiqui scriptores aequales et posteriores censuerint (Diss., 82 p., Münster, 1911). Ed. Thrämer: Cato Censorius und die Griechenmedizin (Mitteil. zur. Gesch. d. Medizin, t. 14, p. 404–405, 1915. A short note to point out that the medical ideas which Cato opposed to the Greek ideas were probably also of Greek origin).

IX. HELLENISTIC, ROMAN, AND CHINESE MEDICINE

SERAPION

Serapion of Alexandria (Σεραπίων) flourished probably in the first half of the second century B. C. Founder of the empirical school of medicine. He rejected

[n] The earliest extant work in Latin prose. [o] Marcus Porcius Cato Uticensis.

every kind of medical dogmatism, even Hippocratism, and based his practice, firstly, upon experience and experiment (τήρησις); secondly, upon reliable clinical cases (ἱστορία); and thirdly, if necessary, upon analogy (ἡ τοῦ ὁμοίου μετάβασις). He wrote two works: the one against the medical sects (πρὸς τὰς διαιρέσεις) and the other on cures (a collection of cases?) (Curationes, Θεραπευτικά). His empiricism led him to try many popular remedies in spite of their absurdity.

Robert Fuchso in Puschmann: Geschichte der Medizin (t. 1, 310, 1902). Gossen, in Pauly-Wissowa (Zweite Reihe, t. 4, 1667, 1923).

For Roman medicine, see my note on Cato in the previous section.

SHUN YÜ-I[p]

Shun[4] Yü[2]-i[4] (10139, 13537, 5367). Born probably in 216 B. C.; flourished in Ch'i[2] (1074). Chinese physician. A collection of his medical writings, T'ai[4]-ts'ang[1]-kung[1]-fang[1] (10573, 11591, 6568, 3435), compiled by his disciples, is now lost.

Criticism—The Chapter of Ssŭ-ma Ch'ien's Shih-chi devoted to him has been translated by F. Huebotter, to appear in Mitt. der Deutschen Gesellschaft für Natur und Völkerkunde Ostasiens, Tokyo. F. Huebotter: Guide (15–16, Kumamoto, 1924).

X. ROMAN AND HELLENISTIC HISTORIOGRAPHY

ENNIUS

Quintus Ennius. Born of Greek race at Rudiae, Calabria, 239; flourished in Rome; died in 169. Poet, playwright and historian. The founder of Roman poetry, the forerunner of both Virgil and Lucretius. He translated Euripides into Latin. He wrote in verse Annals of Rome (Annalium libri XVIII) from the time of Aeneas to his own (c. 181). He wrote also two philosophical poems; Epicharmus, a summary of Pythagorean doctrine, and Euhemerus, a rationalistic interpretation of religious traditions.

Text—In Fragmenta poetarum veterum, edited by Robert and Henri Estienne[q] (Geneva, 1564). Fragmenta, edited by Hier. Columna (Naples, 1590). Paue Merula: Annalium lib. XIIX (Leyde, 1595). Joh. Vahlen: Ennianae poesis reliquiae (329 p., Leipzig, 1854; 1903). Lucian Müller: Carminum reliquiael (343 p., Petropoli, 1884). Luigi Valmaggi: I frammenti degli Annali (182 p., Torino, 1900). Edition by Ethel Mary Steuart (258 p., Cambridge, 1925).

Criticism—Lucian Müller: Der Dichter Ennius (29 p., Sammlung wiss. Vorträge, t. 8, Hamburg, 1893). Loura Bayne Woodruff: Reminiscences of Ennius, in Silvius Italicus (Univ. Michigan, Humanistic Studies, 4, 74 p., New York, 1910). Enrico Cocchia: I monumenti degli Scipioni e l'epigramma sepolcrale di Ennio (Acc. di Napoli, vol. 2, pt. 1, 201–221, 1913). Eleanor Shipley Duckett: Studies in Ennius (Bryn Mawr thesis, 78 p., 1915). William A. Merrill: Parallelisms and coincidences in Lucretius and Ennius (Univ. California publ. in Classical Phil., vol. 3, 249–264, 1918).

---

[p] Also called T'ai[4]-ts'ang[1]-kung[1] (10573, 11591, 6568).

[q] Called after two Sicilian philosophers respectively of the fifth century and the second half of the fourth century B. C. (see my notes devoted to them).

POLYBIOS

Πολύβιος. Born in Megalopolis, Arcadia, c. 207, died at the age of 82. Historian, geographer, Stoic. He might be called the first universal historian and, apart from style, he is one of the greatest. He wrote a "History of Greece and Rome" in 40 books, dealing chiefly with the period 220 to 146.[r] In his long introduction (Books I and II) he set forth the aim and theory of history. The aim is to establish the truth and to instruct, and the principal elements are (1) The study of the documents, (2) the study of geography, (3) the study of politics and military science. He attached considerable importance to physical geography, and showed the necessity of explaining the geographical background of human events. He had himself a very large amount of first-hand geographical knowledge, having traveled far and wide, and he was very learned. His work is an important landmark in the history of Greek thought; it is therein that the Greek spirit comes for the first time really into touch with the spirit of Rome.

Text and Translations—Earliest printed edition of Books I to V, Latin translation by Nicholas Perotti (Rome, 1473). First Greek text, de militia Romana, a fragment of Book VI, edited by A. J. Lascaris (Venice, 1529). First Greek edition of Books I to V by Vinc. Obsopaeus (Hagenau, 1530). First Greek edition with epitome of Books VI to XVII, by Arnoldus Arlenius of Brabant (Basel, 1549). The most important of later editions are: Joh. Schweighaeuser (8 vols. in 9 parts, Leipzig, 1789–1795), Ludwig Dindorf (4 vols., Leipzig, 1866–1868); Friedrich Hultsch (4 vols., Berlin, 1867–1872); and the last and best, Polybii Historiae, Editionem a L. Dindorfio curatam retractavit Theod. Büttner-Wobst (5 vols., 1882–1904).

Selections from Polybios, edited by James Leigh Strachan-Davidson (710 p., Oxford, 1888). These selections have been made from the point of view of the political and military historian. Two appendixes are of special interest to us, one dealing with the life and writings of Polybios, p. 642–648; the other with the astronomical indications of time (p. 15–21).

English translation from Hultsch's text by Evelyn S. Shuckburgh (2 vols., London, 1889). New edition with translation by W. R. Paton (6 vols., Loeb Classical Library, 1922, sq.).

French translation by Dom Vincent Thuillier (1685–1736), with commentary by the Chevalier de Folard (6 vols., Paris, 1727–1730); New edition (6 vols., Amsterdam, 1753–1774, 1 suppl. vol., 1777). Other French translation by Félix Bouchot (3 vols., Paris, 1847).

German translation by Haakh and Kraz (Stuttgart, 1858–1875).

Joh. Schweighaeuser and others: Lexicon polybianum (473 p., Oxford, 1822; new edition of vol. 8 of Schweighaeuser's Polybios).

Commentary—Fustel de Coulanges. Polybe ou la Grèce conquise par les Romains (Thèse, 109 p., Amiens, 1858. Quoted because of the personality of its author). E. F. Berlioux: La terre habitable vers l'équateur (108 p., 2 cartes. Paris, 1884). Rudolf von Scala: Die Studien des Polybios (360 p., Stuttgart, 1890). Otto Cuntz: Polybius und sein Werk (88 p., Leipzig, 1902). Richard Laqueur: Polybius (318 p., Leipzig, 1913). J. T. Shotwell: History of History (New York, 191–201, 1922). Fritz Taeger: Die Archaeologie des Polybius (Stuttgart, 1922).

---

[r] More exactly 220 to 168, but the story is continued down to 146. Books I to V are the only ones which are completely extant; extracts from Books VI to XVIII have come down to us in a single manuscript (Urbinas, 102). The remaining books are known only through extracts, classified by subject, in the historical encyclopaedia of Constantinos Porphyrogennetos (q. v., second half of tenth century).

XI. ROMAN LAW

AELIUS PAETUS

Sextus Aelius Paetus. Consul in 198, censor in 193. Roman jurist. Author of the Tripartita (or Jus Aelianum) containing a recension of the Twelve Tables (450 B. C.) with commentary.

XII. GREEK PHILOLOGY

ARISTOPHANES OF BYZANTIUM

Ἀριστοφάνης, flourished in Alexandria; born c. 257; died c. 180. Philologist and lexicographer. Perhaps the greatest philologist of antiquity. Successor of Eratosthenes, in 195, as librarian of the Museum of Alexandria. He systematized accentuation and punctuation, and improved the technique of textual criticism. He prepared a better edition of Homer and of Hesiod's Theogony, the first collected edition of Pindar, and recensions of Euripides and Aristophanes. He compiled a Greek dictionary (λέξεις) and made a study of grammatical analogies or regularities.

The *invention* of punctuation is sometimes ascribed to Aristophanes; I prefer to say *systematisation.* The most fundamental inventions are of necessity anonymous and almost unconscious in their early stages. Because of their very fundamentality, they must be obvious to many intelligent persons, though even those who conceive them most clearly can not possibly imagine their full pregnancy. Now, the invention of punctuation, accentuation, and similar devices (e. g., use of capital letters) was truly fundamental. Those who have been obliged to read texts without punctuation and capitals (e. g., in Arabic) will appreciate this more deeply. It is interesting to note that this great invention did not obtain any popularity for a considerable time. There are manuscripts even of the thirteenth century which are not punctuated. Punctuation was not generally adopted until the sixteenth century—seventeen hundred years after Aristophanes!—when it had been sufficiently advertised and stabilized by the printer's art.

Text—Fragmenta collegit et disposuit A. Nauck (Halle, 1848).

Criticism—T. O. H. Achelis: De Aristophane Byzantio (Diss., Jena, 32 p. Tübingen, 1913). Sandys: History of Classical Scholarship (vol. 1^3, 126–131, 1921).

ARISTARCHOS OF SAMOTHRACE

Ἀρίσταρχος; born c. 220; flourished in Alexandria; died in Cyprus c. 145. One of the greatest philologists of antiquity. He succeeded to Aristophanes c. 180 as librarian of the Museum of Alexandria. He wrote a large number of commentaries (ὑπομνήματα) and critical studies (συγγράμματα) on Greek literature. The comparison of the Homeric with the Attic writings obliged him to consider more carefully the grammatical structure of his language. He placed the study of grammar on a sound basis.[a]

Karl Fosman: De Aristarcho lexici Apolloniani fonte (129 p., Helsingfors, 1883). Wilhelm Bachmann: Die ästhetischen Anschauungen Aristarchs in der Exegese und Kritik der homerischen Gedichte (Progr., Nürnberg, 1902–1904). Ernst Lutz: Auf den Spuren Aristarchs (2. Ausg., 48 p., Erlangen, 1910). Adolph Roemer: Aristarch's Athetesen in der Homerkritik (Leipzig, 1912). Sandys: History of Classical Scholarship (vol. 1^3, 131–36, 1921, where Aristarchos is called "the founder of scientific scholarship").

---

[a] He was one of the first to recognize eight parts of speech: Noun (and adjective), verb, participle, pronoun, article, adverb, preposition, and conjunction.

DEMETRIOS OF SCEPSIS

Δεμήτριος, born not long before 200, lived probably until 130 or later, in Scepsis, Troas. Greek archaeologist. Author of a commentary on the Homeric Catalogue of Ships (Iliad, II, 816–877) which contained a large amount of information on Greek and Trojan archaeology (Τρωικὸς διάκοσμος).

Text—Richard Gaede: Demetrii quae supersunt (Diss., Greifswald, 1880).
Criticism—Franz Susemihl: Griech. Litt. in der Alexandrinerzeit (t. 1, 681–685, 1891). Schwartz, in Pauly-Wissowa (t. 4, 2807–2813, 1901).

CHAPTER X

THE TIME OF HIPPARCHOS

(Second Half of Second Century B. C.)

I. Survey of Science in the Second Half of the Second Century B. C. II. Chinese and Hellenistic Philosophy. III. Hellenistic and Chinese Mathematics and Astronomy. IV. Hellenistic and Chinese Physics and Technology. V. Hellenistic and Chinese Geography. VI. Chinese, Carthaginian, Roman, and Hellenistic Botany. VII. Hellenistic Medicine. VIII. Hellenistic and Chinese Historiography. IX. Sanskrit and Greek Philology.

I. SURVEY OF SCIENCE IN SECOND HALF OF SECOND CENTURY B. C..

1. In contrast with the third century, which was an age of Alexandrian science, the second century was an age of relative disintegration. Already during its first half, as we have shown in the previous chapter, instead of one intellectual center, there were many: Alexandria, Rome, Pergamum. This tendency is accentuated during the second half and, besides, there is a resurgence of activity in the East. Furthermore, the silk trade between China and the Roman Empire becomes more and more important and establishes a continuous, if indirect and very distant, contact between East and West.

2. *Chinese and Hellenistic Philosophy*—Huai Nan Tzŭ (d. 122) wrote a treatise on Taoist cosmology called the "Story of the Great Light."

Panaetios of Rhodes (d. 110) continued the teaching of Stoicism among the Romans and influenced them deeply through his writings, and later through Cicero's adaptations.

3. *Hellenistic and Chinese Mathematics and Astronomy*—By far the greatest scientist of the period was Hipparchos, and it is interesting to note that he flourished and made astronomical observations in Rhodes as well as in Alexandria. He was one of the greatest mathematicians and astronomers of all times. Unfortunately, he did not dare to follow the lead taken by Aristarchos, but developed instead a geocentrical system of astronomy. He founded trigonometry, both spherical and plane, and computed a table of chords; he used the stereographic projection. He discovered the precession of the equinoxes; this enabled him to distinguish between the sidereal and the tropical years. He compiled a catalogue of some 850 stars; in 134 he observed a nova. An astronomical inscription of about that time was found in Rhodes.

Nothing can show more clearly the immense contrast between Chinese and Greek science than a comparison of the very elaborate and efficient system of Hipparchos with the views of his younger contemporary Lo Hsia Hung, one of the computers of the Chinese calendar for the year 104.

4. *Hellenistic and Chinese Physics and Technology*—The mechanical lead taken by Ctesibios was followed by a number of technicians whose dates are unfortunately uncertain: Philon of Byzantium, who devised many pneumatic machines and possibly the so-called Cardan's suspension; Athenaeos, who wrote a book on siege-engines; Hermodoros, who built dry docks in Rome.

The Chinese statesman Chao-ts'o, who flourished in the period 156 to 141, invented a seismoscope. It is possible that the study of contemporary Taoist writings, such as those of Huai Nan Tzŭ, would provide information on the physical and chemical views of the Chinese of that time, but everything remains to be done in that direction, to begin with the publication of critical texts.

5. *Hellenistic and Chinese Geography*—Hipparchos improved Eratosthenes's geography and determined astronomically the geographical position of a number of places. On the other hand, Artemidoros of Ephesos (102) tried to determine the distances of places, and he paid special attention to physical geography.

Chang Ch'ien traveled to the west almost as far as the Caspian Sea, obtained information about countries still farther west, and paved the way for more regular intercourse between China and the Roman Orient (126–115).

6. *Chinese, Carthaginian, Roman, and Hellenistic Botany*—An important consequence of Chang Ch'ien's mission to the West was the introduction of various Central Asian plants to China, notably the alfalfa and the grapevine.

A Carthaginian work on agriculture of unknown date, ascribed to Mago, was translated from Punic into Latin by order of the Roman Senate soon after the destruction of Carthage (146). This work was extensively used by Latin writers. Attalos III, King of Pergamum from 138 to 133, also wrote a treatise on agriculture.

7. *Hellenistic Medicine*—For some reasons of his own, Attalos III was especially interested in poisonous plants; he might be called a toxicologist. Toward the end of the century flourished two distinguished physicians, the obstetrician Demetrios of Apamea and the surgeon Hegetor. Both wrote treatises on their respective arts, but only fragments of them remain.

8. *Hellenistic and Chinese Historiography*—Apollodoros of Athens wrote a chronology in Greek verse, down to 144.

By far the greatest historian of the period was the Chinese Ssŭ-ma Ch'ien, who became Grand Annalist to the imperial court in 110. He lived until at least the year 86, and it is probable that a part of his work was done in the first century, yet it seemed best to include him in our survey of the second century, because his famous "Historical Memoirs" (Shih-chi) extend only to the year 122. These memoirs are of considerable importance; they inaugurate fittingly the series of Dynastic Histories, which form, in their totality, the most imposing historical monument of the world's literature.

9. *Sanskrit and Greek Philology*—Patañjali, who flourished in northern India, probably toward the middle of the century and after, wrote an important commentary on Pāṇini's grammar.

The Athenian chronologist Apollodoros (c. 144) wrote commentaries on Homer and other classics. The Alexandrian Dionysios Thrax wrote the earliest Greek grammar extant. This work exerted a considerable influence upon the grammatical study not only of Greek, but of every European language.

10. *Conclusions*—The disintegration—or, considered from a different angle, the diffusion—of knowledge of which I spoke in the first paragraph is well illustrated by this summary. Of course, the greatest personality of all, Hipparchos, is a Greek-speaking Alexandrian. Philon too is an Alexandrian. But Hipparchos himself worked also in Rhodes, and so did Panaetios and Dionysios Thrax. And there were many other centers, even if one takes only the West into account: Rome, Ephesos, Pergamum, Athens. Two of the outstanding figures of this age were Chinese, Chang Ch'ien and Ssŭ-ma Ch'ien.

From now on we shall be almost constantly aware of the existence of great cultural centers, not only around the Mediterranean basin, but in India and China. These centers are not by any means isolated, but they are so distant that contacts are very restricted. Thus separate cultural evolutions are in full swing in each of these countries, and the very fact that the exchange of influences was limited for centuries to but a few hints, renders the comparison of these evolutions extremely instructive.

II. CHINESE AND HELLENISTIC PHILOSOPHY

HUAI NAN TZŬ[a]

Huai[2] Nan[2] Tzŭ[3] (5034, 8128, 12317). Grandson of the first Han emperor; he died in 122 B. C. Chinese Taoist and alchemist. His work called Hung[2] lieh[4*] chieh[3] (5269, 7086, 1515) (Story of the Great Light) is a treatise on cosmology embodying alchemical doctrines; it is a part of the Taoist canon.

H. A. Giles: Biographical Dictionary (488, 1898). L. Wieger: Taoisme (vol. 1, 185, No. 1170, 1911). A. Forke: The World-conception of the Chinese (for ex. p. 37, 1925; Isis, VIII, 373).

PANAETIOS

Panaetios of Rhodes (Παναίτιος). Born c. 180, flourished in Rome and abroad mainly in the company of Scipio Africanus, died 110–109. Stoic philosopher who lived for a time with Polybios in Rome and who is largely responsible for the diffusion of Stoicism among the Romans. He insisted upon the necessity of putting physics—that is, positive knowledge—at the basis of philosophy. He rejected astrology and manticism. His treatise on external duty (περὶ τοῦ καθήκοντος) is substantially reproduced in Cicero's "De officiis," Books I and II.[b] Cicero may have used other writings of Panaetios in the same way.

Harold N. Fowler: Panaetii et Hecatonis librorum fragmenta. (Diss., 66 p., Bonn, 1885). Joseph Kaussen: Physik und Ethik des Panätius (Diss., 49 p., Bonn, 1902).

III. HELLENISTIC AND CHINESE MATHEMATICS AND ASTRONOMY

HIPPARCHOS

Hipparchos of Nicaea, Bithynia. Ἵππαρχος. Flourished in Rhodes in the third quarter of the century. Astronomer, mathematician, geographer. Carried on astronomical observations in Rhodes, also in Alexandria, from 161 (or from 146) to 127. It is possible that all the Ptolemaic instruments, except the mural quadrant, had already been invented or used by him (e.g., dioptra, parallactic, and meridian instruments). He was the first Greek observer who divided the circles of his instruments into 360 degrees. He constructed the first celestial globe on record. He used and probably invented the stereographic projection. He made an immense number of astronomical observations with amazing accuracy. Nevertheless, the extreme conservatism and timidity of his mind prevented him from rejecting the geocentrical system, for the long predominance of which he is chiefly responsible. He applied the theories of epicycles and of

[a] This is his literary name, under which he is best known. He was prince of Huai Nan. His own name was Liu[2] An[1] (7270, 44).

[b] And is thus the earliest Stoic treatise of which we can have a complete idea.

eccentrics (the latter possibly introduced by him) to the explanation of the motions of the planets and, chiefly, of the sun and moon. His systematical and critical use of older Greek and Chaldean observations enabled him to discover the precession of the equinoxes, which he computed to be 36″ per year (instead of c. 50″). He distinguished between the sidereal and the tropical year and estimated the length of the latter to be $365^d\ 5^h\ 55^m\ 12^s$ (real value, 48^m 46). His use of Chaldean astronomy enabled him also to improve considerably the theory of the moon and the calculation of eclipses; average length of the synodic month $29^d\ 12^h\ 44^m\ 3\frac{1}{3}^s$ (real value, 2.7^s). He introduced a new cycle of 304 years (that is, four periods of Callippos), but this cycle does not exactly tally with the values of the tropical year and synodic month given by him. (It makes the year longer by 3.47^s and the month shorter by 0.78^s.) He estimated from the observation of eclipses the average distance of the moon and its diameter to be respectively equal to $33\frac{2}{3}$ and $\frac{1}{3}$ earth-diameters (real values, 30.2 and 0.27). He observed the apparition of a new star (nova) in the Scorpion in 134. He compiled a catalogue of stars, containing the celestial coördinates of not many more than 850 stars, together with their magnitudes.

He founded trigonometry, both spherical and plane, and computed a table of chords, practically equivalent to a table of natural sines. This would imply that he already knew the so-called Ptolemy's theorem about a quadrilateral inscribed in a circle, or a similar proposition.

He criticized Eratosthenes's geography and tried to fix astronomically the position of places on the surface of the earth by determining their latitude and longitude. The longitudes were to be determined by the observation of eclipses.

Text—Of the many writings of Hipparchos, the only complete text which is still extant is a comparatively insignificant work of his youth: In Arati et Eudoxi phaenomena commentariorum libri tres, edited in Greek with German translation by Karl Manitius (410 p., Leipzig, 1894). Hugo Berger: Die geographischen Fragmente des Hipparch, zusammengestellt und besprochen (128 p., Leipzig, 1869).

Commentary—Ernst Maass: Aratea (Philologische Untersuchungen, H. 12, 416 p., Berlin, 1892). A. Rehm: Zu Hipparch und Eratosthenes (Hermes, t. 34, p. 251-279, Berlin, 1898). Georg Thiele: Antike Himmelsbilder, mit Forschungen zu Hipparchos, Aratos und seinen Fortsetzern und Beiträgen zu Kunstgeschichte des Sternhimmels (196 p., in 4to, 7 pl., Berlin, 1898). F. Hultsch: Winkelmessungen durch die Hipparchische Dioptra (Abhdl. zur Gesch. d. Math., 9, p. 191–209, Leipzig, 1899); Hipparchos über die Grösse und Entfernung der Sonne (Ber. d. Sächs. Ges. d. Wiss., Phil. Kl., p. 169–200, 1900). Franz Xaver Kugler: Die babylonische Mondrechnung. Zwei Systeme der Chaldäer über den Lauf des Mondes und der Sonne (231 p., 13 pl., Freiburg i. Br., 1900. Fundamental contribution to the study of Chaldean influences upon Hipparchos. There is no doubt that Hipparchos took advantage of the Chaldean observations; on the other hand, the Chaldeans did not know the precession of the equinoxes). Franz Boll: Die Sternkataloge des Hipparch und des Ptolemaios (Bibliotheca Mathematica, II, p. 185–195, 1901). Karl Manitius: Hipparch's Theorie der Sonne nach Ptolemäus (Das Weltall, VI, 323–329, 340–349, 1906); Hipparchs Theorie des Mondes (*ibidem*, VIII, 1-9, 26–30, 45–54, 1907). A. Rehm. Hipparchos (Pauly-Wissowa, vol. 16, col. 1666–1681, 1913. The best general study of Hipparchos I know of, except that his mathematical work has been hardly touched upon). J. K. Fotheringham: The Secular Acceleration of the Sun as determined from Hipparchus's Equinox Observations, with a Note on Ptolemy's False Equinox (Monthly Notices, R. Astronomical Soc., vol. 78, p. 406–423, 1918); The New Star of Hipparchos (*ibidem*, v. 79, 162–167, 1919; Isis, IV, 129).

As it is not always easy to draw the line between Hipparchos and Ptolemy, it is not possible to study them independently. Hence refer to Ptolemy (first half of second century).

The Keskinto Inscription

An astronomical inscription, found in Keskinto, ancient Lindos, in the isle of Rhodes, dating probably from the period between 150 and 50 B. C.

Text—Hiller von Gaertringen: Inscriptiones Graecae insularum maris Aegaei (fasc. I, nr. 913, Berlin, 1895; Corrigenda, p. 207).

Commentary—Paul Tannery: L'inscription astronomique de Keskinto (Revue des études grecques, t. VIII, p. 48–58, 1895); Sur l'inscription, etc. (Comptes Rendus Ac. des Sci., t. 120, 363–365, 1895); Une inscription grecque astronomique (Bulletin astronomique, t. XII, p. 317–328, 1895. These papers have been reproduced in Tannery's Mémoires, t. II, p. 487–516).

LO HSIA HUNG

Lo^{4*} Hsia^{4} Hung^{2} (7328, 4230, 5281) flourished under the Western Han, c. 140–104. Chinese astronomer. He was one of the organizers of the famous calendar T'ai^{4} ch'u^{1} li^{4*} (10573, 2624, 6924) of the year 104 B. C.[c] In the same year he designed a celestial cupola according to the ancient system kai^{4}-t'ien^{1} (5784, 11208) (a hemisphere turning over the terrestrial plane).[d]

L. Wieger: La Chine (87, 321, 336, 388, 1920). A Forke: World-conception of the Chinese (10, 1925; Isis, VIII, 373). Says that Kêng Shou ch'ang constructed a sphere to measure degrees in the period 104 to 100 B. C.

IV. HELLENISTIC AND CHINESE PHYSICS AND TECHNOLOGY

PHILON

Philon of Byzantium, Φίλων, flourished about the end of the second century (?). Mechanician. Probably an older contemporary of Heron of Alexandria (q. v.). Author of a sort of encyclopaedia of applied mechanics (μηχανικὴ σύνταξις) of which only the fourth book and an epitome of the fifth are extant in Greek, and of a work on pneumatics and pneumatic machines (possibly a part of the preceding one?), also partly extant in Arabic and Latin. Invented many war engines, pneumatic machines, and possibly the so-called Cardan's suspension (suspension in gimbals). His pneumatics, e. g., his theory of the void, is a development of Straton's physics.

Text and Translations: Pneumatics—Wilh. Schmidt: Liber Philonis de ingeniis spiritualibus (Latin translation made from an Arabic version; with German translation) in Heronis Alexandrini Opera (vol. I, p. 458–489, Leipzig, 1899). French translation by Albert de Rochas: La science des philosophes et l'art des thaumaturges dans l'antiquité (Paris, 1912, first ed. 1882, p. 195–205). Baron Carra de Vaux: Le livre des appareils pneumatiques et des machines hydrauliques par Philon de Byzance, édité d'après les versions arabes d'Oxford et de Constantinople et traduit en français (Notices et extraits des MSS., t. 38, 211 p. Paris, 1902. This text is considerably longer than the fragment edited by Schmidt and translated by A. de Rochas; it contains the "Cardan's suspension" on p. 171, but this may be an interpolation).

---

[c] For which see chapter 21 of the Ch'ien Han-shu (Pan Ku, second half of first century).

[d] The calculations relative to that instrument were made by Hsien^{1}-yü^{2} Wang^{4}-jên^{2} (4467, 13537, 12503, 5624) and it was cast in bronze by Kêng^{3} Shou^{4} ch'ang^{1} (6009, 10019, 427) in 59 B. C. The same Kêng^{3} is said to have compiled moon tables.

Mechanics—Richard Schöne: Philonis mechanicae syntaxis libri quartus et quintus (Berlin, 1893. Reproducing the pagination of Thévenot's edition, Veterum Mathematicorum Opera, Paris, 1693. These two books deal only with fortifications, war engineering, war machines). Philons Belopoiika (viertes Buch der Mechanik) Griechisch und Deutsch von H. Diels und E. Schramm (68 p., 8 pl., Abh. d. Preuss. Akad. der Wiss., Berlin, 1919, Isis, IV, 130). French translation by Albert de Rochas d'Aiglun: Traité de fortification, d'attaque et de défense des places par Philon (with commentary, 258 p., Paris, 1872). Text and French translation of same in Charles Graux: Textes grecs (p. 173–227, Paris, 1886). Exzerpte aus Philons Mechanik, Bücher VII und VIII (vulgo fünftes Buch). Griechisch und Deutsch von H. Diels und E. Schramm (Abhdl. d. preuss. Akad. d. Wiss., philos. hist. Kl., 1919, 84 p., Berlin, 1920; Isis, IV, 396).

The little treatise on the seven wonders of the world (de septem orbis spectaculis) published in Rud. Herschel: Greek-Latin edition of Aelian (Paris, 1858) under Philon's name, is certainly apocryphal.

Commentary—Wilhelm Schmidt: Physikalisches und Technisches bei Philon (Bibliotheca Mathematica, II, p. 377–383, Leipzig, 1901). Th. Beck: Philon (Beiträge zur Geschichte der Technik, 2. Bd., p. 64–77. Berlin, 1910). Edm. O. von Lippmann: Geschichtlicher Beitrag zur Erkenntnis der Verbrennungsvorgänge (Z. f. angew. Chemie, v. 1, Dez. 1920. Shows that the ancients knew that air is indispensable to the process of combustion; deals chiefly with Philon).

ATHENAEOS

'Αθήναιος, flourished possibly about the end of the century. Mechanician who lived after Ctesibios and probably before Heron and Vitruvius. He wrote a book on siege engines (*περὶ μηχανημάτων*) which contains historical information on these engines.

Rochas d'Aiglun: Traduction du traité des machines d'Athénée (Mélanges Graux, p. 781–801, 12 fig., Paris, 1884).

HERMODOROS

Hermodoros of Salamis ('Ερμόδωρος). Flourished in Rome in the second half of the second century B. C. Architect of various Roman monuments and (according to Cicero, de Oratore, I, 62) of the navalia or dry docks.

See Fabricius, in Pauly-Wissowa (t. 15, 861, 1912).

CH'AO—TS'O

Ch'ao[2]-Ts'o[4]* (526, 11770). Flourished under Han Ching[3] Ti[4] (2143, 10942) emperor from 156 to 141. Chinese statesman and engineer. Invented various instruments, notably the first seismoscope.

The seismoscope is described by August Sieberg: Handbuch der Erdbebenkunde (p. 211, Braunschweig, 1904). The same invention is ascribed to Chang Hêng (q. v., first half of second century).

V. HELLENISTIC AND CHINESE GEOGRAPHY

ARTEMIDOROS

Artemidoros of Ephesos (Αρτεμίδωρος). Flourished about 104 to 100. Geographer. Ambassador of his native city to Rome. Traveled extensively and wrote a geography (*γεωγραφούμενα*) dealing with the whole "inhabited world" (*οἰκουμένη*). Attached much importance to physical geography and to the indications of distances. This last feature was partly a reaction against astronomical geography, considered utopian. He used extensively the works of his predecessors, especially of Agatharchides. Strabon often refers to him.

Rudolph Daebritz: De Artemidoro Strabonis auctore. (Diss., 70 p., Leipzig, 1905).

CHANG CH'IEN

Chang[1] Ch'ien[1] (416, 1692). Flourished in the second half of the second century B. C. Minister under the Emperor Wu[3] Ti[4] (12744, 10942) of the Han dynasty. Returned to China in 126 after a long journey to the western countries. He visited personally Ta-yüan (Ferghana), Ta-yüeh-ch'ih (Indoscythia), Ta-hsia (Bactria), and K'ang-chü (Soghdiana) and obtained knowledge of other countries such as An-hsi (Parthia), Li-hsien (Syria), T'iao-chih (Chaldea), T'ien Chu (India).[e] He introduced the alfalfa (a kind of lucern) and the grapevine and possibly other plants and animals from Central Asia into China. By 115 he had established regular intercourse between China and the West, and he may be said to have opened a new epoch in the development of Chinese civilization. Chang Ch'ien's mission was soon followed by the Chinese conquest of Eastern Turkestan, which helped to keep open a way to India and the Roman Orient for the increasing silk trade.

Friedrich Hirth: The Story of Chang K'ien, China's Pioneer in Western Asia (text and translation of chapter 123 of Ssŭ-ma Ch'ien's Shih-chi, Journal American Oriental Society, vol. 37, p. 89–152, New Haven, 1917. The first satisfactory translation of the main source (Chavannes' monumental translation of the Shih-chi having only reached ch. 47) with notes and elaborate index). T. W. Kingsmill: The Intercourse of China with Eastern Turkestan and the Adjacent Countries in the second century B. C. (Journal R. Asiatic Soc., t. 14, p. 74–104, 1882. To be used with caution). H. A. Giles: Chinese Biographical Dictionary (p. 12–13, Shanghai, 1898). Sir Henry Yule: Cathay and the Way Thither (New ed. rev. by Henri Cordier, Vol. I, London, 1915, passim).

For the introduction of plants into China, see Berthold Laufer: Sino-Iranica (Chicago, 1919; Isis, III, 299–302).

VI. CHINESE, CARTHAGINIAN, ROMAN, AND HELLENISTIC BOTANY

For Chinese botany, see my note on Chang Ch'ien above.

MAGO

Soon after the destruction of Carthage (146 B. C.) the Roman Senate ordered the translation into Latin of the famous work on agriculture of the Carthaginian Mago (date unknown). That work, written in Punic (a Phoenician dialect), was highly esteemed by the Romans and seems to have been extensively used by their agricultural writers. Columella called Mago the father of agriculture (pater rusticationis). The Punic and Latin texts are lost, but a few fragments of the Greek translation by Cassius Dionysius (q. v., first half of first century B. C.) are extant.

On Mago, see E. H. F. Meyer: Geschichte der Botanik (t. 1, 296–305, 1854).

---

[e] Ta[4]-yüan[1] (10470, 13720) Ta[4]-yüeh[4]*-ch'ih[2] (13781, 1983); Ta[4]-hsia[4] (4227); K'ang[1]-chü[1] (5908, 2987); An[1]-hsi[1] (44, 4031); Li[2]-hsien[1] (6942, 4474); T'iao[2]-chih[1] (11095, 1873); T'ien[1]-chu[2]* (11208, 2574).

ATTALOS

Attalos III, Philometor (Ἄτταλος ὁ Φιλομήτωρ). Born in 171, King of Pergamum from 138 until his death in the spring of 133. He studied botany, and agriculture. A treatise of his on agriculture was used by Varro, Columella, and Pliny. He was especially interested (for practical reasons) in poisonous plants; and he prepared poisons and experimented with them.

E. H. F. Meyer: Geschichte der Botanik (t. 1, 284–287, 1854). Wilcken, in Pauly-Wissowa (t. 4, 2175–2177, 1896).

VII. HELLENISTIC MEDICINE

DEMETRIOS OF APAMEA

Demetrios of Apamea (Bithynia), Δημήτριος, flourished at the end of the second or the beginning of the first century. Greek physician, specialized in obstetrics and gynaecology. He wrote treatises on obstetrics and semiotic (σημειωτικόν) and one on pathology (περὶ παθῶν) which contained at least 12 books. These works are known only through quotations made from them by Soranos (first half of second century) and Caelius Aurelianus (first half of fifth century).

M. Wellmann, in Pauly-Wissowa (t. 8, 2848, 1901).

HEGETOR

Ἡγήτωρ; he did not flourish before the end of the second century B. C. Greek surgeon of Herophilos's school. He wrote a book on the causes (of disease?) (περὶ αἰτιῶν). The only fragment extant deals with the dislocation of the hip. First description of the triangular ligament of the hip joint (ligamentum teres).

The fragment is quoted by Apollonios of Citium (23, 15), first half of first century B. C. See Gossen, in Pauly Wissowa (t. 7, 2613, 1912).

VIII. HELLENISTIC AND CHINESE HISTORIOGRAPHY

APOLLODOROS OF ATHENS

Ἀπολλόδωρος, flourished c. 144. Greek chronologist and archaeologist. Pupil of Aristarchos in Alexandria, which he left c. 146. He dedicated to Attalos II, King of Pergamum from 159 to 138, a Greek chronology in verse (Χρονικά), from the Fall of Troy to 144 (later extended to 119). This work superseded that (probably superior) of Eratosthenes (both are lost). He wrote commentaries on Homer and other authors, and studies on etymology, geography, and mythology (περὶ θεῶν).[f]

Texts—Felix Jacoby: Eine Sammlung der Fragmente (Philologische Untersuchungen, 16, 416 p., Berlin, 1902). Jules Nicole: Le procès de Phidias dans les chroniques d'Apollodore d'après un papyrus inédit de la collection de Genève (50 p., Genève, 1910).

Criticism—H. Gelzer: Sextus Julius Africanus und die byzantinische Chronologie (1898). Sandys: History of Classical Scholarship (vol. 1³, 137, 1921).

---

[f] The latter work should not be mistaken for the so-called Library (βιβλιοθήκη) of Apollodoros, the spirit and method of which were entirely different, and which was at least a century younger. The Library of Apollodoros was edited by Sir James George Frazer with an English translation (2 vols., London, Loeb Library, 1921).

SSŬ-MA CH'IEN

Ssŭ[1]-ma[3] Ch'ien[1] (10250, 7576, 1711). A native of Lung[2]-mên[2] (7479, 7751) in Shensi c. 145; after his father's death in 110 he succeeded him as grand astrologer or Grand Annalist[g] to the Chinese court; he died between 86 and 74. Chinese historian. One of the greatest historians of ancient times. He is sometimes called the Chinese Herodotos or the father of Chinese history. His "Historical Memoirs," Shih[3]-chi[4] (9893, 923), deal with Chinese history from the beginnings down to 122.[h] They have served as a model for every "Dynastic History" and are published at the head of the "Twenty-four Histories." They are divided into five sections (130 chapters), as follows:[i]

(1) Principal (imperial) annals, 12 chapters;[j] (2) Chronological tables, 10 chapters; (3) The eight treatises (rites, music, musical tubes, calendar, governors of heaven, sacrifices fêng[1] (3582) and ch'an[2] or shan[4] (348 and 9702), rivers and canals, commercial balance), 8 chapters; (4) Hereditary Houses (feudal annals), 30 chapters; (5) Monographs (biographies), 70 chapters.

Text—Chinese text published at the Chin[1]-ling[2] (2032, 7235) press (Nanking, 1878) (130 chüan[3] (3146) in 16 vol.). French translation, with long introduction and abundant notes by Edouard Chavannes: Les mémoires historiques de Se-ma Ts'ien (Paris 1895–1905; 5 volumes only have been published, carrying the translation to chapter 47, about the middle of the third section; the continuation of that work is highly desirable). The 24th biography of section 5, devoted to Chia[3]-i[2] (1181, 5354), was translated into German by Theodor Bönner (Diss., 31 p., Berlin, 1908).

Criticism—Giles: Biographical Dictionary (666–7, 672, 1898). Chavannes's Introduction (1895). G. Bezold: Sze-ma Ts'ien und die babylonische Astrologie (Hirths Festschrift, 42–49, Berlin, 1920. The Chinese became acquainted with Babylonian astrology probably before 523 B. C., and they adapted it to their own conceptions. Bezold makes a comparison between the Babylonian constellations and those quoted by Ssŭ-ma Ch'ien). Léopold de Saussure: Une interprétation du Che Ki. Le tableau calendérique de 76 années (Journal asiatique, t. 20, 105–135, 1922).

IX. SANSKRIT AND GREEK PHILOLOGY

PATAÑJALI

Flourished in northern India probably about 144 to 142 B. C.[k] Hindu grammarian. He wrote a commentary on Pāṇini's grammar, called the Great Commentary (Mahābhāshya), which is of very great importance because of the archaeological information it contains.[l]

---

[g] T'ai[4] Shih[3] Kung[1] (10573, 9893, 6568). I give the name of his office because it is sometimes used to designate himself.

[h] The work had been begun by his father, Ssŭ-ma T'an[2] (10656).

[i] I give this division because every Dynastic History is divided substantially in the same way.

[j] For the chronology of this first section see my note on Chinese historiography in the first half of third century B. C.

[k] According to V. A. Smith; History of India (118, 121, 1919) Patañjali was a contemporary of Pushyamitra (Pushpamitra), the first king of the Sunga dynasty, who ruled from 185 on. Pushyamitra had started a Brahmanical (anti-Buddhist) reaction. That dating is not inconsistent with mine.

[l] Whether this Patañjali or a relative of his is the author of the Yogaśāstra—the fundamental text of one of the six orthodox systems of philosophy—is a moot question. According to the latest English translator of the Yoga system, J. H. Woods (1914), this text dates only from the fourth or fifth century of our era (Isis, IV, 60).

Text—Lithographed edition (Benares, 1871). Photolithographic edition of the text and commentaries by Goldstücker (London, India Office, 1874). Critical edition by F. Kielhorn (3 vols., Bombay).

Criticism—J. Eggeling in his article Sanskrit. Encyclop. Brit. (180, 1911). Surendranath Dasgupta: The Study of Patañjali (213 p., Calcutta, 1920; Jour. Royal Asiatic Soc., 116, 1923).

DIONYSIOS THRAX

Denis of Thrace[m] (Διονύσιος), born c. 166, flourished in Alexandria and in Rhodes. Pupil of Aristarchos of Samothrace. Greek philologist and grammarian. Author of the earliest Greek grammar (τέχνη γραμματική)[n] extant. It remained the standard work on the subject for at least thirteen centuries. Latin grammar was modeled upon it and many technical terms still in use to-day (e. g., genitive, accusative, infinitive) are mistranslations of Greek technical terms. Dionysios wrote commentaries on Homer and on the "Works and Days" of Hesiod.

Text—J. Bekker: Anecdota graeca (II, 629–643, 1816). Better edition by Gustav Uhlig: Ars grammatica (224 p., Leipzig, 1883). Alfred Hilgard: Scholia in Artem grammaticam (703 p., Leipzig, 1901).

Translated into English by Thomas Davidson in Journal of Speculative Philosophy (16 p., St. Louis, 1874).

Criticism—Article in Pauly-Wissowa (t. 9, 977–983, 1903). Sandys: History of Classical Scholarship (vol. 1^3, 138–140, 1921).

---

[m] It seems that his father was a Thracian, not himself.

[n] There are rudiments of grammar in Aristotle's Categories and Rhetoric, but such can not be considered as constituting a grammar. Aristotle recognized only three parts of speech: the noun, the verb, and the rest. Crates of Mallos (q. v.) composed a formal grammar which is lost.

CHAPTER XI

THE TIME OF LUCRETIUS

(First Half of First Century B. C.)

I. Survey of Science in First Half of First Century B. C. II. Philosophical Background in the West. III. Hellenistic and Chinese Mathematics. IV. Hellenistic Astronomy. V. Hellenistic Physics and Technology. VI. Hellenistic Botany. VII. Hellenistic Medicine. VIII. Hellenistic and Roman Historiography. IX. Roman Writing.

I. SURVEY OF SCIENCE IN FIRST HALF OF FIRST CENTURY B. C.

1. During the present period, the more acute phase of the conflict between Greece and Rome is gradually ended, on the one hand by the firm establishment of Roman supremacy, on the other by a more complete assimilation of Greek knowledge. It is true, Egypt did not become a Roman province until the year 30 B. C., but the universal power of Rome was felt before that date all around the Mediterranean Basin and in western Europe. The greatest personality of the first half of the century and down to his assassination in 44 is of course that of Caesar, comparable only in the ancient world to that of Alexander. It is symbolic of the tremendous change which has gradually taken place in the western world. But while the Romans completed their conquests, they were brought to realize more keenly the superiority, if not of the Greek genius, which they could not really understand, at least of Greek knowledge. They assimilated that knowledge as far as they could. That was not very far, unfortunately, and the deepest parts of it, for example, the higher mathematics and astronomy, remained largely beyond their reach.

2. *Philosophical Background in the West*—Andronicos of Rhodes (c. 70) was the tenth successor of Aristotle at the head of the Lyceum and the first scientific editor of Aristotle's works. These have come down to us in the order established by him. The Stoic school was represented by a great man of science, Posidonios, who flourished mainly in Rhodes. Stoicism as taught by him was somewhat novel because of the Neoplatonic tendencies which tinged it. He influenced mediaeval thought to a considerable extent through his commentary on the Timaeos. All considered, Posidonios was the outstanding scientific personality of that time. Yet I have preferred to call it the time of Lucretius, not simply because the great philosophical poet is a more original figure, one which has captured more completely the imagination of men, but also because his Latin poem is a better symbol of the age than the Greek writings of Posidonios. Lucretius's poem is an amazing performance; it does not contain new scientific facts or theories, but sets forth Greek views in a wonderful manner, with many flashes of genius. It is a masterly exposition of the rationality and determinism of the universe. It marks the climax of Roman scientific thought. As compared with Lucretius, Cicero seems timid and second-hand, yet he contributed very substantially to the diffusion of Greek knowledge in the Latin world. I must mention one more philosopher, Figulus, a great man in his day, now almost forgotten.

"The Wisdom of Solomon," one of the Old Testament apocrypha, written in Greek at about that time, is an interesting product of Hellenistic Judaism.

3. *Hellenistic and Chinese Mathematics*—Toward the beginning of the century, the astronomer Theodosios of Tripolis was studying spherical geometry. A little later, Posidonios (c. 95) introduced new geometrical definitions. The astronomer Geminos (c. 70?) wrote a general treatise on mathematics of which only fragments remain, but which seems to have been quite important.

It is possible that the activity of Heron of Alexandria took place at about this time. This is far from certain, and I realize that some of the latest students of this moot question, notably, Sir Thomas Heath, favor a much later date—as late as the first half of the third century. Yet Sir Thomas's conclusions are not by any means convincing, nor is he convinced himself; the later date seems only a little more plausible to him. The only certain thing is that Heron lived after Archimedes and before Pappos; it is also tolerably certain that he lived after Hipparchos. I keep him at this place, if only to warn historians that they must take into account the possibility of the existence of the Heronian writings even at this time. There is certainly no internal reason precluding that possibility; everything contained in these writings might have been written in the first half of the first century B. C. Heron was a practical man; he was chiefly concerned with measurements; his best-known discovery is that of the formula giving the area of the triangle in function of its sides.

The Chinese mathematician Kêng Shou-ch'ang, who flourished in the second quarter of the century, prepared a new edition of the Arithmetic in Nine Sections.

4. *Hellenistic Astronomy*—Theodosios of Tripolis wrote three astronomical works included in the "Little Astronomy." Posidonios made new geodetic measurements and new estimates of the distance and size of the sun; he explained tides by the joint action of sun and moon. His disciple Cleomedes wrote a summary of Stoic astronomy and studied atmospheric refraction. Another disciple of Posidonios, but of uncertain date (possibly a direct disciple), Geminos of Rhodes, compiled a history of ancient astronomy, his own point of view being that of Hipparchos.

5. *Hellenistic Physics and Technology*—The most important work is, of course, that of Heron, but, as aforesaid, its date is very uncertain. Heron continued the mechanical tradition of Alexandria and invented (or described) many very ingenious devices. He proved that the total path of a reflected ray of light (before and after reflection) is a path of minimum length.

Asclepiodotos, probably a pupil of Posidonios, wrote a short treatise on tactics. The astronomer Cleomedes studied refraction.

6. *Hellenistic Botany*—Cratevas, physician to Mithridates, wrote a herbal which was at least partly illustrated. Cassius Dionysius of Utica (c. 88) translated Mago's agriculture into Greek and wrote a treatise on herbs or roots.

6 bis. *Hellenistic Geography and Geology*—In no scientific field did the genius of Posidonios shine more clearly than in this one. He collected a vast amount of geographical information and made interesting remarks on volcanoes and earthquakes. His explanation of tides has already been mentioned; he observed spring and neap tides.

7. *Hellenistic Medicine*—Mithridates Eupator, King of Pontos from 120 to 63, continued the tradition of Attalos III in his toxicological experiments. It suffices to recall the names of the botanists Cratevas and Cassius Dionysius. Until

relatively modern times the purpose of botanical research was either agricultural or medical. Both made investigations in materia medica.

Asclepiades of Bithynia, the earliest eminent physician in Rome (c. 84), developed new theories of disease, but despised anatomy. His disciple Themison of Laodicaea completed the elaboration of these theories and the constitution of the Methodical school of medicine. One important tenet of that school was insistence upon the dual qualities, striction and relaxation. Heraclides of Tarentum represented another school, the Empirical; he made many experiments with drugs, chiefly with opium, and wrote the earliest veterinary treatise. Glaucias of Tarentum (?) of the same school, wrote commentaries on Hippocrates and discovered a cure for erysipelas. Apollonios of Citium wrote a commentary on Hippocrates's book on articulations, which is of considerable iconographical interest, because a ninth century manuscript of it contains illustrations which may represent the ancient tradition.

8. *Hellenistic and Roman Historiography*—Posidonios continued Polybios's history, dealing with the period 144 to 82. Castor of Rhodes compiled synchronistic tables which are of great importance, as it is largely through them that the results of Greek research were transmitted to the Christian chronologists and indirectly to us.

The greatest historian of the period was undoubtedly Caesar, who wrote his Memoirs toward the end of it. They are among the most important historical works of the world's literature and the fact that they were written by the outstanding personality of that time increases considerably their human interest.

9. *Roman Writing*—It is worth while recording that M. Tullius Tiro, Cicero's secretary, invented a kind of shorthand.

10. *Conclusions*—This period is almost exclusively Hellenistic, or more exactly, Greco-Roman. The center of the western world is Rome. The outstanding personalities are Roman: Lucretius, Cicero, Caesar; Posidonios visited Rome and probably died there. But there are various secondary or provincial centers: at the court of Mithridates in Pontos; in Bithynia; in Rhodes, Alexandria, Athens, Tarentum. The western world is becoming Roman; knowledge too becomes Roman, but this means that it deteriorates. The love of truth for its own sake is fast disappearing and being replaced by utilitarian purpose and mean expediency. Yet this age produced the greatest philosophical poet of all ages, Lucretius; and Lucretius, be it said to the eternal glory of Rome, was a Roman.

II. PHILOSOPHICAL BACKGROUND IN THE WEST

ANDRONICOS

Andronicos of Rhodes (Ἀνδρόνικος) flourished in Athens c. 70 B. C. The tenth snccessor of Aristotle at the head of the Lyceum and the first scientific editor and commentator of his works. He arranged according to subjects the works of Aristotle and Theophrastos and these have been transmitted to us, as far as they are still extant, in the order established by him. Two writings ascribed to him (περὶ παθῶν and a paraphrase of the Nicomachean ethics) are apocryphal.

F. Littig: De Andronico (Diss., München, 1890); Andronikos v. Rhodos (Progr., 32, 35 p., Erlangen, 1894–1895. Including fragments of Andronicos). Article by Gercke: Andronikos 25, in Pauly-Wissowa (II, 2164–2167, 1894).

POSIDONIOS

Ποσειδώνιος, born in Apamea, Syria, c. 135, died at the age of 84, probably in Rome. Stoic philosopher with Neoplatonic tendencies, encyclopaedist, geographer, astronomer. Disciple of Panaetios in Athens, settled in Rhodes. He was the most eminent Stoic teacher of his time and exerted a deep influence upon Roman thought. He made a new measurement of the size of the earth, inferior, however, to that of Eratosthenes. His estimates of the diameter and distance of the sun are much better than those of Hipparchos (and Ptolemy!) but still very far from the truth. The most intelligent traveler of antiquity, he collected a large amount of geographical and anthropological information. He observed earthquakes and volcanoes, and recorded the elevation of a new volcanic islet among the Lipari islands. He was the first to explain the tides by the joint action of sun and moon and to call attention to the spring and neap tides. He gave new definitions of parallel lines and geometrical figures. He wrote on meteorology and on the ocean. He began in 74 the writing of a universal history, which continued that of Polybios; it deals with the period from 144 to 82. His commentary on the Timaeos affected philosophic ideas down to the end of the Middle Ages.

Two medical treatises attributed to a Posidonios, and which can not be ascribed to Posidonios the Physician (q. v., second half of fourth century), may well be his: the one deals with the plague, the other with the epiglottis.

Text—Posidonii Rhodii reliquiae doctrinae collegit atque illustravit Janus Bake. Accedit D. Wyttenbachii annotatio (304 p., Leiden, 1810).

Commentary—Friedrich Blass: De Gemino et Posidonio. (Diss., 25 p., Kiel, 1883). Franz Schühlein: Zu Posidonius Rhodius. Prüfung der Ueberlieferung bei Suidas. Allgemeine Untersuchungen über die Werke περὶ ὠκεανοῦ und ἱστορίαι (Progr., 35 p., Freising, 1891). Franz Malchin: De auctoribus quibusdam qui Posidonii libros meteorologicos adhiberunt (Diss., 57 p., Rostock, 1893). F. Hultsch: Poseidonios über die Grösse und Entfernung der Sonne (Abhdl. d. Ges. d. Wiss., Philol.-hist. Kl., I, 48 p., Göttingen, 1897). Franz Schühlein: Untersuchungen über des Posidonius Schrift περὶ ὠκεανοῦ (Progr., 99 p., Freising, 1900–1901). Robert Fuchs, in Puschmann: Geschichte der Medizin (t. 1, 314, 1902). Max. Arnold: Quaestiones Posidonianae (Diss., 72 p., Leipzig, 1903. Deals chiefly with Cleomedes). Wilhelm Capelle: Die Schrift von der Welt. Ein Beitrag zur Geschichte der Griechischen Popularphilosophie (Neue Jahrbücher für das klassische Altertum, t. 15, p. 529–568, Leipzig, 1905. Apropos of an anonymous book περὶ κόσμου, probably written in the first half of the second century after Christ, but reflecting the Posidonian ideas; interesting comparison between Posidonios and Giordano Bruno). Gust. Altmann: De Posidonio Timaei Platonis commentatore (Diss., 73 p., Berlin, 1906). Mathilda Apelt: De rationibus quibusdam quae Philoni Alexandrino cum Posidonio intercedunt (Diss., 141 p., Jena, 1907). G. D. Ohling: Quaestiones Posidonianae ex Strabone conlectae (Diss., 44 p., 1 pl., Göttingen, 1908). Wilhelm Gerhäusser: Der Protreptikos des Poseidonios (Diss., 75 p., München, 1912). W. Capelle: Zur Geschichte der meteorologischen Litteratur (Hermes, Vol. 48, 321–358, 1913). Karl Gronau: Poseidonios und die jüdischchristliche Genesisexegese (322 p., Leipzig, 1914. Important). Gunnar Rudberg: Forschungen zur Posidonios (Skrifter utgifna af K. Humanistika Vetenskaps-Samfundet, t. 20, 341 p., Upsala, 1918. (1) Zur Persönlichkeit; (2) Urzeit und Entwickelung; (5) Technik und Kunst). Karl Reinhardt: Poseidonios (475 p., München, 1921. Reviewed by Maurice Croiset in Journal des Savants, 145–152, 1922).

LUCRETIUS

Titus Lucretius Carus, born c. 98 or 95, died c. 55 B. C.; flourished in Rome. Roman philosopher and scientist, influenced chiefly by Empedocles and Epicuros. Author of "de natura rerum," the greatest philosophical poem of all times. It is an amazing account of the positive knowledge of his time (Greek knowledge of course) and of the atomic theory, together with a few prophetic views (e. g., vague anticipation of the theory of natural selection). Lucretius's chief purpose was to vindicate the rights of reason against superstition.

Text and Translations—Facsimiles of the two fundamental manuscripts, both of the ninth century and both kept in Leiden, have been published, with introductions by Em. Chatelain: Codex Vossianus oblongus (Leiden, 1908); Codex Vossianus quadratus (Leiden, 1913). Editio princeps, Brescia (c. 1473). First scientific edition, Lachmann (1850) and elaborate commentary by the same (3d ed. Berlin, 1866; 4th ed., 1871). An excellent edition is due to H. A. J. Munro (3 vols., 4th ed., London, 1905–1910; Vol. I, text; Vol. II, Notes; Vol. III, English translation. A full account of earlier editions will be found in Vol. I). I must also quote William A. Merrill's edition with introduction and notes (New York, 1907). Additional notes to this edition have been published by him in the University of California Publications in Classical Philology (Vol. III, p. 265–316, Berkeley, 1918). Various studies of Lucretius's text by Merrill have appeared *ibidem* (Vol. II, p. 93–150, 237–256, 1911–1914; Vol. III, p. 1–133, 1916, and finally a new edition of the whole text, *ibidem*, Vol. IV, 258 p., 1917).

Of the many *English translations*, besides Munro's, I will quote only that by Cyril Bailey, with notes and introduction (312 p., Oxford, 1910).

French Translations—The great poet Sully Prudhomme published a translation of Book I in verse, with long introduction (Paris, 1869). Text and translation by Alfred Ernout (2 vols. Collections des Universités de France, Paris, 1920; Isis, IV, 47).

Index—Johannes Paulson: Index Lucretianus (185 p., Gotoburgi, 1911). See also Reiley, below.

Main Studies—Constant Martha (1820–1895): Le poème de Lucrèce—Morale, Religion, Science. (1st ed. 1869; 5th ed., 418 p., Paris, 1896). John Masson: The Atomic Theory of Lucretius, Contrasted with Modern Doctrines of Atoms and Evolution (264 p., London, 1884); Lucretius, Epicurean and Poet (2 vols., 710 p., London, 1907–1909. This is the most elaborate study available; it deals with the life and times of Lucretius, his philosophic ideas and scientific knowledge, their sources, and their influence in later times down to our own).

Other Studies (*Life, Sources, Influence, Style*)—The most interesting publication provoked by Lucretius's poem is probably the Anti-Lucretius, sive de Deo et Natura libri novem (2 vols., Paris, 1747), by the Cardinal Marquis Melchior de Polignac (1661–1741). This long poem devoted to the criticism of Lucretius and even more of Bayle, was frequently republished in Latin, also in French, English, Italian, and Dutch translations. See C. A. Fusil: L'Anti-Lucrèce. Contribution à l'étude de la pensée philosophique et scientifique dans le premier tiers du XVIIIe siècle (Thèse, 164 p., Paris, 1918. Very elaborate).

Albert Bästlein: Quid Lucretius debuerit Empedocli (Progr., 21 p., Schleusingen, 1875). Wilh. Lohmann: Quaestionum Lucretianarum capita duo. (Diss., 60 p., Brunswick, 1882; c. II. De ratione quae intercedit inter Lucretium et Epicurum). Giacomo Giri: Il suicido di T. Lucrezio. La questione dell' emendatore ed editore della Natura (111 p., Palermo, 1895). George P. Eckman: Controversial elements in Lucretius (122 p., thesis, New York, 1899). Max Lehnerdt: Lucretius in der Renaissance (17 p., Königsberg, 1904). Will. A. Merrill: On the Influence of

Lucretius on Horace (Univ. of California Publ. on Classical philol., Vol. I, 111–129, Berkeley, 1905). Rob. Wreschniok: De Cicerone Lucretioque Ennii imitatoribus. (Diss., 62 p., Vratislaviae, 1907). Franz Jobst: Über das Verhältnis zwischen Lukretius und Empedokles. (Diss., 61 p., München, 1907). George Santayana: Three Philosophical Poets: Lucretius, Dante, and Goethe (223 p., Cambridge, Mass., 1910). Hans Rösch: Manilius und Lucrez (Diss., 117 p., Kiel, 1911). C. H. Herford: The Poetry of Lucretius (Bull. of the John Rylands Library, vol. 4, 26 p., Manchester, 1918). Ferd. Gabotto: Della fortuna di Lucrezio specialmente nelle traduzioni del suo poema (Prefaz. alla versione di C. Leardi, 26 p., Tortona, 1918). Will. A. Merrill: Parallels and coincidences in Lucretius and Virgil (Univ. of California Publ. in Classical Philol., Vol. III, 135–247, 1918); Parallelisms and Coincidences in Lucretius and Ennius (*ibidem*, p. 249–264). J. Mussehl: Über eine Aporie in der Lehre der Aggregatzuständen bei Lukrez (II, 444–477; Hermes, 53, 197–210, Berlin, 1918). H. Diels: Lukrez Studien (II–III, Sitzungsber. d Preuss. Akad. d. Wiss., 2–18, 1920). R. Reitzenstein: Das erste Prooemium des Lukrez (Nachr. der Ges. der Wiss., phil. Kl., Göttingen, 83–96, 1920). F. Jacobi: Das erste Prooemium des Lukrez (Hermes, vol. 56, 1–65, 1921).

On the subject of Cicero's edition of Lucretius's poem, see the paragraph devoted to Cicero.

Studies Specially Devoted to Lucretius's Scientific Ideas—J. B. Royer: Essai sur les arguments du matérialisme dans Lucrèce (151 p., Dijon, 1883). Hermann Schütte: Theorie der Sinnesempfindungen bei Lucrez (25 p., Danzig, 1888). Carlo Pascal: Studii critici sul poema di Lucrezio (224 p., Roma, 1903). Katharine C. Reiley: Studies in the Philosophical Terminology of Lucretius and Cicero. (Diss., 133 p., New York, 1909. The groups of terms specially considered are those relative to atoms, void, and space; universe; infinity of matter, of void, and of space). Egid Filek v. Wittinghausen: Die geographischen Anschauungen des Lucretius (Progr., 21 p., Wien, 1910). Adolf König: Lucretii de simulacris et de visu doctrina cum fontibus comparata (Diss., 106 p., Greifswald, 1917). Walther May: Lucrez und Darwin (Die Naturwissenschaften, t. 5, 276-279, 1917).

CICERO

Marcus Tullius Cicero. Born in 106 near Arpinum, Latium, murdered in 43. Roman statesman, lawyer, orator, writer. He popularized Greek philosophy and to a small extent Greek science for the Latin reader and, with Lucretius, he created the philosophical language of Rome. He translated Aratos's Phaenomena. The De natura deorum is a cosmogonical discussion, which contains much information on the scientific knowledge of the time and forms in that respect a valuable complement to Lucretius. Earliest statement of a teleological conception of the human body—the beginning of a tradition which is not yet entirely closed. In 75, being quaestor in Sicily, he discovered the tomb of Archimedes and restored it.

Bibliography—Pierre Deschamps: Essai bibliographique sur M. T. Ciceron (226 p., Paris, 1863).

Complete Works—Editio princeps by Alex. Minutianus (4 vol. fol., Milano, 1498–1499; vols. 1–2, 1498; vols. 3–4, 1499. Splendid volumes). The second edition prepared by P. Victorius and printed by the Juntas (4 vols. fol., Venice, 1534–1537) was far superior.

Collected Editions of the Opera philosophica—Princeps printed by Sweynheym and Pannartz (Rome, 1471, 2 vols. fol.). It includes: (I) De natura deorum; De divinatione; Officia; Paradoxa; De amicitia; De senectute. (II) Quaestiones Tusculanae; De finibus bonorum et malorum; De fato; De petitione consulatus; De philosophia; De essentia mundis; In Timeo Platonis; Quaestiones academicae;

De legibus. At least two other editions of Opera philosophica, less complete, however, appeared during the same year at Paris and Venice.

Lexica—C. G. Schütz: Lexicon ciceronianum (4 vols., Leipzig, 1817–1821). Hugo Merguet: Lexicon zu den Schriften Cicero's mit Angabe sämtlicher Stellen (7 vols., Jena, 1871–1894).

Translation of Aratos—Fragments of this translation will be found in Joh. Theoph. Buhle's edition of Aratos's Phaenomena (Leipzig, Vol. II, p. 3–30, 1801; also in Nisard's Latin-French edition of Cicero (t. IV, p. 631–643 (475 verses), Paris, 1881).

Gust. Sieg: De Cicerone, Germanico, Avieno, Arati interpretibus (Diss., 52 p., Halle, 1886). Johann Vogel: Scholia in Ciceronis Aratea aliaque ad astronomiam pertinentia e codice Mus. Brit. Harleiano 647 (Progr., Crefeld, 1887). Georg Kauffmann: De Hygini memoria scholiis in Ciceronis Aratum Harleianis servata scripsit, scholia apparatu critico et notis instructa et catalogum stellarum adhuc ineditum adjecit (180 p., Breslauer philologische Abhandl., t. III, 1888). Joh. Maybaum: De Cicerone et Germanico Arati interpretibus (Diss., 53 p., Rostock, 1889).

De natura deorum—To the editions above mentioned should be added many separate editions, of which the earliest is probably that of Reggio d'Emilia (1498), and the most elaborate that prepared by Joseph B. Mayor (3 vols., Cambridge, 1880–1885).

General Studies—Gaston Boissier: Cicéron et ses amis (Paris, 1865, 9th ed., 1892, English translation, 1897. A delightful book but containing nothing of special interest to the historian of science). Camille Thiaucourt: Les traités philosophiques de Cicéron et leurs sources grecques (Paris, 1885). Th. Zielinski: Cicero im Wandel der Jahrhunderte (1st ed., Leipzig, 1907; 2d, 1908; 3d, rev. 1912 379 p.). W. Warde Fowler: Social Life at Rome in the Age of Cicero (378 p., New York, 1909) Hannis Taylor: Cicero, a Sketch of his Life and Works followed by an Anthology of his Sayings (660 p., Chicago, 1916). Torsten Petersson: Cicero, a Biography (700 p., Berkeley, 1920).

Influence of Posidonios—De Posidonio Rhodio M. Tulli Ciceronis in Libro I. Tusc. Disp. et in somnio Scipionis auctore (Diss., 52 p., Bonn, 1878). P. H. Poppelreuter: Quae ratio intercedat inter Posidonii περὶ παθῶν πραγματείᾳ et Tusculanas disputationes Ciceronis (Diss., 40 p., Bonn, 1883).

Cicero and Lucretius—Karl Hartfelder: De Cicerone Epicureae doctrinae interprete (Diss., 48 p., Karlsruhe, 1875). Georg. Castellani: Qua ratione traditum sit M. T. Ciceronem Lucretii carminis emendatorem fuisse. (Diss., 19 p., Venice, 1894). Constant Martha: Lucrèce et Cicéron (Mélanges de Littérature ancienne, p. 157–177, Paris, 1896. Cicero probably edited Lucretius's poem?). William A. Merrill: Cicero's Knowledge of Lucretius's Poem (Univ. of California Publ. in Class. Philol., Vol. II, p. 35–42, Berkeley, 1909. Merrill doubts very much whether Cicero ever read the poem). Henry Wheatland Litchfield: Cicero's Judgment on Lucretius (Harvard Studies in Class. Philol., vol. 24, p. 147–159, Cambridge, Mass., 1913).

FIGULUS

Publius Nigidius Figulus. Contemporary and friend of Cicero, praetor in 59, died in exile in 44 B. C. Roman Pythagorean, astrologer, the most learned man of his time after Varro. His fame as an astrologer was considerable. Only fragments of his works remain: de diis, liber auguralis, de augurio privato, de extis, de somniis, de sphaera graecanica et barbarica, de vento, de hominum naturalibus, de animalibus, etc.

I quote Nigidius Figulus because of the relatively abundant literature devoted to him, but he seems to have obtained far more attention than he deserved.

Text—Alfr. Breysig: De Nigidii fragmentis apud scholiasten Germanici servatis (Diss., 44 p., Berlin, 1854). Ant. Swoboda: Nigidii operum reliquiae (143 p., Vienna, 1889. Text of all the fragments, notes, and introduction of 63 p.; the latter, entitled Quaestiones Nigidianae, also published in Dissert. philologae vindobonenses, Vol. II, 1890).

Commentary—Martinus Hertz: De P. Nigidii Figuli studiis atque operibus (50 p., Berlin, 1845). Armin Roehrig: De Nigidio (Diss., 70 p., Coburg, 1887. The first part is a study of Nigidius's sources). Alberto Gianola: Publio Nigidio Figulo, astrologo e mago (Biblioteca teosofica italiana, 38, 19 p., Roma, 1906).

THE WISDOM OF SOLOMON

The "Wisdom of Solomon" (*Σοφία Σαλωμῶνος*)[a] is one of the books of the Old Testament Apocrypha, second in importance only to Ecclesiasticus (first half of second century B.C.). It contains 19 chapters and belongs to the Wisdom literature. It is a typical product of Hellenistic Judaism. It was written directly in Greek some time after the publication of the Septuagint and before the Apostolic Age (let us say, some time between 150 B.C. and 40 A.D.). It contains allusions to the doctrine of the four elements and to the theory according to which the substance of the embryo is formed out of the catamenia, which cease to be discharged during pregnancy (Aristotle, de generatione animalium, I, 22).

III. HELLENISTIC AND CHINESE MATHEMATICS

HERON OF ALEXANDRIA

Ἥρων Ἀλεξανδρεὺς ὁ μηχανικός flourished at the beginning of the first century B.C. or later. Mechanician, physicist, mathematician. More interested in the applications of mathematics and mechanics than in the theories, he wrote a number of semi-popular books on these subjects. Surveying by means of the dioptra; determination of the distance between Rome and Alexandria by observation of the same lunar eclipse in both places and the drawing of the analemma for Rome. Formula giving the area of the triangle in function of the sides, $\sqrt{p\,(p-a)\,(p-b)\,(p-c)}$. Many expressions of areas and volumes (frustum of a pyramid, approximate value of frustum of a cone) and approximate square and cube roots. Algebraic solutions of equations of the first and second degree.

$$144\,x\,(14 - x) = 6720 \qquad \frac{11}{14}x^2 - \frac{29}{7}x = 212$$

Many pneumatic and other mechanic contrivances invented by him, e. g., siphons, Heron's fountain, fire engine, aeolipile, water-organ, thermoscope, various presses, contrivances using the force of steam, "penny-in-the-slot," and other automatic machines. The path of a reflected ray of light is a path of minimum length. Earliest statement of the problem concerning pipes filling a cistern.[c]

Text and Translations—Early editions—Federico Commandino: Pneumatica (Latin translation, Spiritalium liber, posthumously published, Urbino, 1575).

[a] Also called the "Book of Wisdom."

[b] A graphical method invented by Hipparchos or by Ptolemy. If it was invented by Ptolemy, and if this part of Heron's text is not an interpolation, Heron should be placed after Ptolemy.

[c] For a brief history of that old problem and its variants, see D. E. Smith, History of mathematics (vol. 2, 536–541, 1925).

First Greek edition by Thévenot in Veterum mathematicorum opera graece et latine edita (Paris, 1693).

Bernadino Baldi: Automata (περὶ αὐτοματοποιητικῆς). (Italian translation 1589; again Venice, 1601). First Greek edition by Thévenot (1693).

B. Baldi: Belopoiïca (first edition, Augsburg, 1616). Also in Thévenot (1693) and in Carle Wescher: Poliorcétique des Grecs (Paris, 1867).

Wilhelm Schmidt's critical edition with German translation (published in 5 vols., Leipzig, 1899–1914) supersedes all previous editions. Heronis Alexandrini opera quae supersunt omnia. Pneumatica et automata rec. W. Schmidt. Accedunt Heronis fragmentum de horoscopiis aquariis, Philonis de ingeniis spiritualibus, Vitruvii capita quaedam ad pneumatica pertinentia (Vol. I, 1899); Mechanica et catoptrica rec. L. Nix et W. Schmidt. Accedunt quaedam excerpta (Vol. II, fasc. 1, 1900); Rationes dimetiendi[d] et commentatio dioptrica[e] rec. Herm. Schoene (Vol. III, 1903); Heronis definitiones cum variis collectionibus, Heronis quae feruntur geometrica. Copiis W. Schmidt usus ed. J. L. Heiberg (Vol. IV, 1912); Heronis quae feruntur stereometrica et de mensuris ed. J. L. Heiberg (Vol. V, 1914).

French translation of the Pneumatics by Albert de Rochas in La science des philosophes et l'art des thaumaturges dans l'antiquité (Paris, 1882, new ed. 1912; cfr. Revue génér. des sci., t. 23, p. 870, 1912). English translation of the Pneumatics by Bennet Woodcroft (137 p., London, 1851). Baron Carra de Vaux: Les Mécaniques ou l'Elévateur de Héron d'Alexandrie publiées pour la premiere fois sur la version arabe de Qostâ ibn Lûqâ et traduites en français (Journal Asiatique, 9 série, t. I, p. 386–472, t. II, 152–269, 420–514, Paris, 1893. The same Arabic text is edited in volume 2 of Schmidt's edition; for Carra de Vaux's Introduction, see Journal Asiatique, t. I, p. 386–419). H. Diels und E. Schramm: Herons Belopoiika (Abhdl. der preuss. Ak., phil. kl., 56 p., 1918. Greek and German).

Chronological Studies—The date of Heron is very uncertain (see above, under Ctesibios). The only safe statement is that Heron lived after Archimedes and Apollonios and before Pappos; it is very probable that he lived after Hipparchos and that his writings appeared too late to be used by Vitruvius. Cantor (Vorlesungen, 3d ed.) and Tittel (Pauly-Wissowa, 1912) agree in placing him at the beginning of the first century B. C., but they do it with but little conviction. On the other hand, Hermann Diels (Ber. Akad., Berlin, 106, 1893) would place him in the second century after Christ or the beginning of the third, and Sir Thomas L. Heath (Encycl. Brit., 11th ed.) in the second half of the first century after Christ. In his Greek Mathematics (vol. 2, 298–306, Oxford, 1921), Sir Thomas places Heron even *later*, in the third century, and perhaps little if anything earlier than Pappos. Heiberg accepts this conclusion. Their argument is plausible but not convincing.

Wilhelm Schmidt: Wann lebte Heron? (Heronis Opera, Vol. I, p. ix–xxv, 1899; terminus post quem of Heron's Mechanics, 55 A. D. Heron lived before Ptolemy). Max Maass: Zur Heronischen Frage (Philologus, XIII, p. 605–609, 1900). Edmund Hoppe: Ein Beitrag zur Zeitbestimmung Herons (Progr., 9 p., Hamburg, 1902; end of second century B. C.). Rud. Meier: De Heronis aetate (Diss., 45 p., Leipzig, 1905. Heron did not flourish before 150 B. C., nor much after 50 A. D.). Tittel, in Pauly-Wissowa (vol. 15, col. 996–1000, 1912. It is certain that Heron flourished after 150 B.C. and before 250 A. D.; it is probable that he flourished in the beginning of the first century B. C.).

General Studies—The most recent and comprehensive study of Heron is Tittel's, in Pauly-Wissowa's Real Encyclopädie (vol. 15, col. 992–1080, 1912). Of previous studies I quote only Wilh. Schmidt: Leonardo da Vinci und Heron von Alexan-

---

[d] This is called more briefly the Metrica; this text was discovered only in 1896 in an eleventh or twelfth century manuscript at Constantinople by R. Schöne, the editor's father.

[e] First published in Italian by Venturi in 1814; first Greek edition by A. J. H. Vincent in Notices et extraits (t. 19 (2), 157–237, 1858).

dria (Bibliotheca Mathematica, III, 180–187, 1902). A. J. Letronne's Recherches critiques, historiques et géographiques sur les fragments d'Héron, crowned by the Académie des Inscriptions in 1816, but only published after his death in 1851, is of historical importance, because it initiated the scientific study of the subject. H. Martin's Reserches sur la vie et les ouvrages d'Héron, Paris, 1854, was equally fundamental.

Mathematics—Moritz Cantor: Die römischen Agrimensoren und ihre Stellung in der Geschichte der Feldmesskunst (Leipzig, 1875). P. Tannery: Sur les fragments de Héron conservés par Proclus (Bull. des sci. math., t. VI, p. 99–108, 1882; Mémoires, I, 156–167); L'arithmétique des Grecs dans Héron. Mém. de la soc. des sciences (t. IV, p. 161–194, Bordeaux, 1882; Mémoires, I, 189–225); La stéréometrie de Héron (t. V, p. 305–326, 1883; Mémoires, I, 397–421); Etudes héroniennes (t. V, p. 347–369, 1883; Mémoires, I, 422–448. Apropos of various approximative formulae used by the ancients to replace trigonometrical functions); Questions héroniennes (Bull. des sci. mathém., t. VIII, p. 329–344, 359–376, 1884; Mémoires, II, 137–178. On Egyptian and Greek fractions and approximate square roots); Οὐγκιασμὸς ὕδατος (école héronienne) (Revue archéologique, t. VI, p. 365–369, 1885; Mémoires, II, 202–210. Interpretation of a locus desperatus of de mensuris); Les définitions du pseudo-Héron (Bull. des sci. mathém., t. XI, p. 189–193, 1887); Héron sur Euclide (t. XI, p. 97–108, 1887); Un fragment des métriques de Héron (Z. f. Math. u. Physik, t. 39, p. 13–15, 1894; Mémoires, II, 447–450); Sur un fragment inédit des métriques de Héron (Bull. d. sci. math., t. 18, p. 18–22, 1894; Mémoires, II, 451–454). Max Curtze: Die Quadratwurzelformel des Heron bei den Arabern und bei Regiomontan und damit Zusammenhängendes (Z. f. Math., t. 42, hist. Ab., 145–152, 1897); Quadrat- und Kubikwurzeln bei den Griechen nach Heron's neu aufgefundenen Μετρικά (p. 113–120). G. Wertheim: Herons Ausziehung der irrationalen Kubikwurzeln (Z. f. Math., t. 44, hist. Abt., p. 1–3, 1–99). Wilh. Schmidt: Sind die heronischen Vielecksformeln trigonometrisch? (Bibliotheca Mathematica, I, p. 319–320, 1900). Gustav Eneström: Ueber die Geschichte der Heronschen Dreiecksformel im christlichen Mittelalter (Bibliotheca Mathematica, t. V, 311–312, 1904). P. Tannery: Notes critiques sur les Metrica de Héron (Revue de philologie, t. 28, 181–188, 1904; Mémoires, III, 196; Journal des Savants, mars 1903 et avril 1904; Mémoires, III, 203–211). J. E. Böttcher: Beweise für die Heronsformel aus zwei Jahrtausenden (Progr., 22 p., Leipzig, 1909). C. Sass: De Heronis quae feruntur definitiones geometricis (Diss., Greifswald, 1913).

Physics—Wilh. Schmidt: Heron, Konrad Dasypodius und die Strasburger astronomische Münsteruhr (Abh. zur Gesch. d. Math., t. VIII, p. 175–194, 1898); Heron im 17 Jahrhundert (*ibidem*, 195–214). F. Knauff: Die Physik des Heron (Progr., 23 p., Berlin, 1900). P. Duhem: Sur la résistance des matériaux (Études sur Léonard de Vinci, t. 1, 289, 1906); Sur les mécaniques de Héron (Origines de la statique, t. 2, 313–318, 1906). Th. Beck: Herons Mechanik (Beitr. zur Gesch. der Technik, t. I, p. 84–107, 1909). J. A. Repsold: Herons Dioptra (Astron. Nachr., nr. 4931, 1918). Hugo Theod. Horwitz: Ueber ein neueres deutsches Reichspatent und eine Konstruktion von Heron (Archiv f. Gesch. d. Naturw., t. 8, 134–139, Leipzig, 1918; Isis, III, 453). A. Rome: Le problème de la distance entre deux villes dans la Dioptra de Héron (Ann. de la soc. scientifique de Bruxelles, t. 42, 234–258, 1923; Isis, VI, 141).

Automata—Victor Prou: Les théatres d'automates en Grèce au IIe siècle avant l'ère chrétienne d'apres les αὐτοματοποιϊκά d'Héron (Mém. présentés à l'Académie des Inscriptions, t. IX, 162 p., Paris, 1881). Th. Beck: Herons Automatentheater (Beitr. zur Gesch. d. Technik, t. I, p. 182–199, Berlin, 1909).

War Engines—Rudolf Schneider: Herons Cheiroballistra (Mitt. d. deutschen Archäol. Instituts, t. 21, p. 142, Rome, 1906. The Cheiroballistra are a fragment of a technical lexicon). Th. Beck: Die altgriechische und altrömische Geschützbau nach Heron, Philon, Vitruv und Ammianus Marcellinus (Beitr. zur Gesch. d. Technik, t. 3, 163–184, Berlin, 1911).

Alia—Tittel: Das Weltbild bei Heron (Bibliotheca Mathematica, t. 8, p. 113–117, 1908). J. L. Heiberg: Der sogenannte Heronis liber geoponicus (Archiv f. Gesch. d. Naturwiss., I, 410–418, 1909. A book on husbandry of the Byzantine period; it was included in Hultsch's edition of 1864, Heronis geometricorum et stereometricorum reliquiae, p. 208–234; it is not included in Schmidt's edition).

KÊNG SHOU-CH'ANG

Kêng^{3} Shou^{4}-ch'ang^{1} (6009, 10019, 427). Minister of the emperor Hsüan^{1}-Ti^{4} (4805, 10942), who ruled from 73 to 49. Revised or enlarged the "Arithmetic in Nine Sections" previously revised by Chang Ts'ang (q. v., first half of second century B. C.).

See Yoshio Mikami, The Development of Mathematics in China and Japan (chapter 3, Leipzig, 1913).

IV. HELLENISTIC ASTRONOMY

THEODOSIOS

Theodosios of Bithynia (Θεοδόσιος) flourished about the beginning of the first century B. C., or possibly at the end of the second century B. C. Greek mathematician and astronomer. Three works of his are included in the collection of minor writings called ὁ μικρὸς ἀστρονομούμενος (τόπος): (1) Spherics (σφαιρικά), his main work, dealing with geometry on the surface of the sphere (no trigonometry). The substance of this book has been traced back to the fourth century B. C. (2) On days and nights (περὶ ἡμερῶν καὶ νυκτῶν). (3) On habitations (περὶ οἰκήσεων), giving the positions of the stars at various times of the year as seen from various parts of the earth. He invented a universal sun-dial (horologium πρὸς πᾶν κλίμα).

Texts and Translations—Ernest Nizze: Theodosii Tripolitae sphaericorum libri tres (198 p., Berlin, 1852. Greek text, Latin translation and notes; the Greek text is based upon that published by Jo. Pena, Paris, 1558). Nizze has also given a German translation: Die Sphärik des Theodosios (Stralsund, 1826), with notes. The original text of the other two works of Theodosios is still unpublished, but a Latin translation of both has been published by Joseph Auria (Rome, 1591). An outline of their propositions (without demonstrations) had appeared before in Dasypodius, Sphaericae doctrinae propositiones (Strasbourg, 1572). A critical edition of the works of Theodosios, with English translation and elaborate commentary, is much needed.

Commentary—A. Nokk: Über die Sphärik des Theodosius (Karlsruhe, 1847). Fr. Hultsch: Scholien zur Sphärik des Theodosius (Abh. d. Sächs. Gesell. d. Wiss., phil. Cl., t. 10, 381–446, Leipzig, 1888. Carra de Vaux: Remaniement des sphériques de Théodose par Jahia ibn Muhammed ibn Abī Schukr al-Maghrabī al-Andalusī (Journal Asiatique, t. 17, 287–295, 1891). Axel Anton Björnbo: Studien über Menelaos' Sphärik. Beiträge zur Geschichte der Sphärik und Trigonometrie der Griechen (154 p., Leipzig, 1902); Über zwei mathematische Handschriften (Bibliotheca Mathematica, t. 3, 63–75, 1902). Sir Thomas Little Heath: Greek Mathematics (1921).

CLEOMEDES

Κλεομήδης lived probably in the first century B. C. Disciple of Posidonios. He made interesting remarks on refraction (κατάκλασις), including atmospheric refraction. His work on the cyclical motion of celestial bodies (κυκλικὴ θεωρία μετεώρων) is a good summary of Stoic astronomy. Our information on the measurements of the earth by Eratosthenes and Posidonios are derived from this very work.

Text—First Latin edition (Venice, 1488). First Greek edition (Paris, 1539). Cleomedis de motu circulari corporum caelestium libri duo. New text by Hermann Ziegler, with Latin translation (264 p., Leipzig, 1891).

Commentary—Paul Tannery: Cléomède in Grande Encyclopédie (¾ of a column, ab. 1891; Mémoires, III, 351–353). Max. Arnold: Quaestiones Posidonianae (Diss., 72 p., Leipzig, 1903. Places Cleomedes in the second century after Christ). Alexis Boericke: Quaestiones Cleomedae (Diss., Leipzig, 84 p., Pegaviae, 1905. This author would place Cleomedes in the second century after Christ; he claims that Cleomedes had no access to Posidonios's books, but only to poor copies of them).

There are wide divergences on the date of Cleomedes. On this subject see E. Gerland, Geschichte der Physik (p. 125, 1913).

GEMINOS

Geminos of Rhodes (Γεμῖνος) flourished probably about 70 B. C. Mathematician, astronomer. Lived after Posidonios and before Alexander of Aphrodisias (c. 210). Stoic, influenced chiefly by Posidonios. Wrote introductory text-books on astronomy and mathematics; they are summaries made in a scientific way and with sound judgment. The introduction to astronomy is extant; it contains the most important doctrines of ancient astronomy, explained chiefly from Hipparchos's point of view. Only fragments remain of the introduction to mathematics. It was the main source of Proclos's commentary to the first book of Euclid, chiefly for the history of geometry. It contained a general definition and subdivision of mathematics (pure mathematics: arithmetic and geometry; applied mathematics: logistics, geodesy, harmonics, optics, mechanics, astronomy) and laid stress on the fundamental notions.

Text—Part of the text appeared as early as 1499 at the end of the Astronomi veteres edited by Aldus at Venice under the title Πρόκλου σφαῖρα. By 1620 more than 20 editions of this Proclos's "Sphere" had already appeared. It is a medieval compilation of extracts from Geminos's work. The whole work, Γεμίνου εἰσαγωγὴ εἰς τὰ φαινόμενα was edited for the first time by Edo Hildericus (Altdorf, 1590; again Leyden 1603). Scientific edition: Gemini elementa astronomiae ad codicum fidem recensuit, germanica interpretatione et commentariis instruxit Carolus Manitius (413 p., Leipzig, 1898).

Commentary—The most elaborate study of Geminos is that contributed by Karl Manitius to Pauly-Wissowa's Real-Encyclopädie (t. 13, col. 1026–1051, 1910).

Heinrich Brandes: Über das Zeitalter des Geographen Eudoxus und des Astronomen Geminus. 4. Jahresbericht des Vereins von Freunden der Erdkunde (Leipzig, 1866). Fried. Blass: De Gemino et Posidonio (Diss., 25 p., Kiel, 1883). Paul Tannery: Proclus et Geminus (Bulletin des sciences mathématiques, t. XX (1), p. 209–220, Paris, 1885); Le classement des mathématiques d'après Geminus (*ibidem*, p. 261–276); Sur l'époque où vivait Geminus (*ibidem*, p. 283–292). M. Steinschneider: Geminus in arabischer, hebräischer und zweifacher lateinischer Übersetzung (Bibliotheca Mathematica, (2), I, 97–99, Paris, 1887; IV, 107–108, 1890). Karl Manitius: Des Geminos Isagoge nach Inhalt und Darstellung kritisch beleuchtet (Commentationes Fleckeisenianae, p. 95–107, Leipzig, 1890).

Richard Schöne: Damianos Schrift über Optik, mit Auszügen aus Geminos griechisch und deutsch hrg. (45 p., Berlin, 1897). Paul Tannery: Le philosophe Aganis est-il identique à Geminus? (Bibliotheca Mathematica, II, p. 9–11, Leipzig, 1902; Mémoires, III, 37–41, 379).

Roman Astronomy

René Cagnat: Un très ancien calendrier romain (Journal des savants, t. 20, 37–40, 1922; published by Mancini in the Notizie degli Scavi, p. 73 sq., 1921; it dates from the beginning of the first century B. C.).

V. HELLENISTIC PHYSICS AND TECHNOLOGY

See the note on Heron of Alexandria in Section III.

ASCLEPIODOTOS

'Ασκληπιόδοτος, probably a pupil of Posidonios; if so, he flourished probably about the middle of the first half of the century. Greek student of meteorology and of military science.[f] He wrote a very succinct treatise (Τεχνὴ τακτική) of tactics in 12 chapters, illustrated by means of figures and diagrams.[g]

Text—Editio princeps by H. Köchly and W. Rüstow in their Griechische Kriegsschriftsteller (Leipzig, 1855). New edition, with English translation, by C. H. and W. A. Oldfather in Loeb Classical Library, Aeneas Tacticus, Asclepiodotus, Onasander, p. 229–340, 1923 (with technical glossary).

Criticism—W. A. Oldfather (American Journal of Philology, vol. 41, 127 sq. 1920.)

VI. HELLENISTIC BOTANY

CRATEVAS

Κρατεύας, flourished at the court of Mithridates Eupator, q. v. infra. Rhizotomist. Physician to Mithridates. Wrote a herbal (ῥιζοτομικόν) containing at least five books and *illustrated*. It is possible that his illustrations were the prototypes of those included in the famous sixth century Manuscript of Dioscorides, kept in Venice. Cratevas also wrote a Materia Medica wherein he showed much knowledge of the action of metals upon the body.

Max Wellmann: Krateuas (Abhdl. d. Kgl. Gesell. d. Wiss. zu Göttingen, Philol. hist. Kl., t. 2, 32 p., 2 pl., 1897). The plates reproduce two plants as represented in the above-mentioned and other manuscripts. Max Wellmann: Das älteste Kräuterbuch der Griechen in Festgabe für Franz Susemihl (Leipzig, 1898).

CASSIUS DIONYSIUS[h]

Cassius Dionysius of Utica. Flourished c. 88 B. C. Greek writer on botany and materia medica. He translated Mago's work into Greek,[i] c. 88 B. C., re-

---

[f] The oldest Greek military writer whose work is extant, after Aeneas Tacticos (q. v., first half of fourth century B. C.). Aeneas was an experienced soldier; Asclepiodotos, a "chair-strategist," a philosopher. It is possible that Asclepiodotos's little treatise is simply a summary of Posidonios's work on the same subject, also entitled Τεχνὴ τακτική.

[g] The tactician Aelian, who wrote in the time of Trajan, made extensive use of Asclepiodotos's work, without mentioning it.

[h] Κάσσιος Διονύσιος; the first word is Latin, the second, Greek. According to my system I ought to write Cassius Dionysios, but I prefer to be inconsistent.

[i] For the Latin translation, see my note on botany in the second half of the second century B. C. Was the Greek translation based upon the Latin, or were they both made from the Punic?

ducing[j] it from 28 to 20 books, but adding many excerpts from Greek literature. He composed a treatise on roots (ῥιζοτομικά). An illustrated pharmocopoeia was also ascribed to him.

Texts—A few extracts from Cassius's translation are quoted in R. Reitzenstein: De scriptorum rei rusticae qui intercedunt inter Catonem et Columellam libris deperditis (Diss., Berlin, 1884).
Criticism—M. Wellmann, in Pauly-Wissowa (t. 6, 1899, 1722).

VII. HELLENISTIC MEDICINE

MITHRIDATES EUPATOR

Μιθριδάτης, born in Sinope, 132, died in Panticapaeum, 63. King of Pontos from 120 to 63. He is quoted because of his pharmaceutical and toxicological investigations, the results of which were translated into Latin by order of Pompeius. He tried to produce immunity from poison by the administration of gradually increased doses of it and of the blood of ducks, supposed to be immune. He introduced new simples: Scordotis, Eupatoria, Mithridatia (?) and was first to give the formula of a universal antidote, called after him Mithridate (Μιθριδάτειος ἀντίδοτος).

Théodore Reinach: Mithridate Eupator, roi de Pont (510 p., illustr., Paris, 1890). An apparently exhaustive and very illuminating study of one of the most extraordinary personalities of ancient history; the scientific work of Mithridates is hardly discussed, but the fundamental facts are given p. 283–285. This book has been translated into German by A. Goetz (Leipzig, 1895). This is really a new edition, for the author has taken advantage of it to make many corrections and additions to the original text.

ASCLEPIADES

Asclepiades of Bithynia (Ἀσκληπιάδης) born c. 124 in Prusa, Bithynia. The first eminent Greek physician in Rome. Antagonist of the humoral theory of the Hippocratic school, he introduced the atomic ideas into medicine and based upon them new physiologic and therapeutic theories (solidism). Disease is a disturbance in the movements of the atoms which constitute the body; health a re-establishment of their normal movements. The most consistent advocate of the mechanistic point of view in medicine. The first to recommend tracheotomy. He despised anatomy.

Text and Translations—Christ. Gottlieb Gumpert: Asclepiadis Bithyni fragmenta (204 p., Vinariae, 1794). Gesundheitvorschriften des Asklepiades (ὑγιεινὰ παραγγέλματα) ed. by Robert Ritter von Welz (49 p., Greek, Latin and German, Würzburg, 1841. This writing of Asclepiades is not mentioned in Wellmann's list quoted below).
Commentary—G. M. Raynaud: De Asclepiade medico ac philosopho (Paris, 1862). Bruns: Quaestiones Asclepiadeae de vinorum diversis generibus (Parchim, 1884). M. Wellmann: Article Asklepiades 39, in Pauly-Wissowa (Real-Encyclopädie, t. 4, col. 1632–1633, 1896. Including a list of 17 writings ascribed to Asclepiades). Hans von Vilas: Der Arzt und Philosoph Asklepiades von Bithyn-

---

[j] This (or another) reduction is also ascribed to a contemporary writer, Diophanes (Διοφάνης) of Nicaea in Bithynia. Diophanes is said to have abridged Cassius's work for Deiotarus, King of Galatia, who died c. 42 B. C.

ien (82 p., Wien, 1903). Max Wellmann: Asklepiades von einem herrschenden Vorurteil befreit (Neue Jahrb. f. das klass. Altertum, 21. Bd., 684–703, Leipzig, 1908. Important; Wellmann claims that Asclepiades was not the first to base medicine upon atomism—he had been anticipated by one Aegimios (Αἰγίμιος) of Elis and by Erasistratos; neither was he a charlatan, as Pliny would have it).

THEMISON

Themison of Laodicaea (Θεμίσων) flourished about the middle of the first century B. C. Disciple of Asclepiades, he carried a little further and systematized the latter's doctrines, thus founding the Methodical school of medicine. Various medical writings are ascribed to him, also the introduction of many new drugs and of leeches. His pathology and therapeutics were based upon a classification of diseases into two main categories characterized, one by *στέγνωσις*, status strictus, the other by *ῥύσις*, status laxus, and corresponding each to a definite state of the pores of the body. Later, other categories (e. g., *τὸ μεμιγμένον*, status mixtus) were gradually added to the first two, when new clinical observations could no longer be accounted for in such a simple way.

Robert Fuchs: Aus Themison's Werke über die akuten und chronischen Krankheiten (Rhein. Mus. f. Philologie, t. 58, 67–114, 1903). Wellmann has shown that this writing is not Themison's work, but must be ascribed to Herodotos (q. v., second half of the first century after Christ). See Wellmann: Herodots Werk *περὶ τῶν ὀξέων καὶ χρονίων νοσημάτων* (Hermes, t. 40, 580–604, 1905).

HERACLIDES OF TARENTUM

Ἡρακλείδης, flourished about 75 B. C. The greatest physician of the Empirical school in ancient times. Disciple of the Herophilian physician Mantias. Made many pharmaceutical experiments (chiefly with opium) and wrote books on pharmacy, therapy, dietetics, etc., and Hippocratic commentaries. He was the author of the earliest veterinary treatise (*πρὸς τὰς χρονίους μυρμήκιας*).

See Gossen, in Pauly-Wissowa's Real-Encyclopädie (t. 15, col. 493–496, 1912), which contains a list of the 14 works ascribed to him; also article Hippiatrica by same (*ibidem*, t. 16, 1714, 1913).

GLAUCIAS

Γλαυκίας, of Tarentum (?), contemporary of Heraclides of Tarentum. Greek physician of the Empirical school. He wrote many commentaries on Hippocrates (e. g., on the sixth book of Epidemics and on the *περὶ χυμῶν*[k]) and a treatise on herbs, wherein he paid special attention to the thistle. He compiled an elaborate Hippocratic dictionary, which was used and quoted by Erotianos (q. v., second half of first century). He discovered a cure for erysipelas and invented a kind of bandage named after him spica Glaucii.

Gossen, in Pauly-Wissowa (t. 13, 1399, 1910).

APOLLONIOS OF CITIUM

Ἀπολλώνιος, flourished about the middle of the first century B. C. Alexandrian physician, disciple of Zopyros. He wrote a commentary on Hippocrates's book on articulations (*περὶ ἄρθρων*); two polemical treatises, one against Heraclides

[k] This work he ascribed to another Hippocrates.

of Tarentum (πρὸς τὰ τοῦ Ταραντίνου), the other πρὸς Βακχεῖον; and a collection of curationes, one of them dealing with epilepsy.

Text—Latin translation by Antonio Cocchi in his Graecorum chirurgici libri (Florence, 1754). The commentary on the περὶ ἄρθρων has been edited by F. R. Dietz: Scholiensammlung zum Hippokrates und Galen (t. 1, Königsberg, 1834). Separate edition by C. G. Kühn (Leipzig, 1838). Hermann Schöne: Illustrierter Kommentar zu der hippokrateischen Schrift περὶ ἄρθρων (75 p., 31 pl., Leipzig, 1896). This deals with the Codex Laurentianus LXXIV, 7, a Byzantine manuscript of the ninth century, containing very remarkable surgical illustrations here reproduced (e. g., with reference to reposition methods). There is a possibility that these illustrations represent a tradition contemporaneous with Apollonios. They were reproduced during the sixteenth century by il Primaticcio (1504 to 1570) and by Guido Guidi (Vidus Vidius, d. 1569). See Vidus Vidius: Chirurgia e Greco in Latinum a se conversa (Paris, 1544). Vidius's figures were in their turn reproduced by Ambroise Paré and Conrad Gesner (De chirurgia, scriptores optimi quique veteres et recentiores, Zürich, 1555). These illustrations represent thus possibly an iconographical tradition of more than sixteen centuries!

Criticism—M. Wellmann, in Pauly-Wissowa (t. 2, 149, 1895). Henri Omont: Collection de chirurgiens avec dessins attribués au Primatice (Paris, 1903).

VIII. HELLENISTIC AND ROMAN HISTORIOGRAPHY

See my note on Posidonios in Section II.

CASTOR

Castor of Rhodes (Κάστωρ) born or educated in Rhodes, flourished until after 61 B. C. Greek chronologist. His main work was a history (Χρονικά) in six books followed by synchronistic tables (from Belos and Ninos down to 61 B. C.). It was a link of great importance in the handing down of historical knowledge. It was through Castor indeed that most of the Greek research on that subject was transmitted to the Christian chronologists (especially Eusebios), thence to the Middle Ages and to us.

Text—Fragmenta collected by C. Müller in his edition of Herodotos (t. 2, 151–181, Paris (Didot), 1844. Greek and Latin).

Criticism—Franz Susemihl: Griechische Litteratur in der Alexandrinerzeit (t. 2, 365–372, 1892). Eduard Schwartz: Die Königslisten des Eratosthenes und Kastor, mit Excursen über die Interpolationen bei Africanus und Eusebius (Göttingen, Ges. der Wiss., t. 40, 1895). Kubitschek, in Pauly-Wissowa (t. 10, 2347–2358, 1919).

CAESAR

Gaius Julius Caesar. Born in 102 or 100, July 12; murdered in Rome 44 B. C., March 15. Statesman, soldier, historian. He is quoted here mainly because of the reform of the Roman calendar, accomplished by him with the technical assistance of Sosigenes,[l] and to which his name is attached. The essential feature of the Julian calendar is a cycle of 4 years, 3 of 365 days and 1 of 366; the mean length of the year being thus $365\frac{1}{4}$ days; the longer years (bissextile or leap years) were those the number of which was divisible by 4. The first Julian year began with the first of January, 45 B. C. (709 U. C.). To restore the vernal equinox to the 25th of March, the year 46 (annus confusionis) was extended to 15 months or 445 days. The Julian calendar held its own until 1582 in the Roman Catholic

[l] Σωσιγένης, Peripatetician, probably of Alexandria,

world, until 1572 in England; it was still in force in Russia until very recent times. Caesar is said to have written a book on astronomy (de astris) and a letter on surveying; both are lost. Also, he is said to have introduced the grammatical term ablativus, for which there was no analogy in the Greek language. He planned the surveying of the Roman empire and ordered Varro to organize a public library; both undertakings were interrupted by his death. Caesar's Memoirs (Commentarii) are among the masterpieces of historical literature (written c. 52 to 50).

Roman and Particularly Julian Calendar—Heinrich Matzat: Römische Zeitrechnung für die Jahre 219 bis 1 v. Chr. (308 p., Berlin, 1889). F. K. Ginzel: Handbuch der mathematischen und technischen Chronologie (II. Bd., Leipzig, Chapter X, p. 160–293, 1911, with abundant bibliography).

Sosigenes—Little is known about him. For his collaboration with Caesar see Pliny, Natural History (XVIII, 57; see also II, 6). Pliny says that Sosigenes wrote three treatises, continually corrected, on the calendar. Th. H. Martin: Sur deux Sosigène, l'un astronome, l'autre péripatéticien (Ann. de la fac. d. lettres de Bordeaux, t. 1, 174–187, 1879).

Geography—For the geographical knowledge contained in Caesar's Commentaries, see Alfred Klotz: Cäsarstudien nebst einer Analyse der strabonischen Beschreibung von Gallien und Britannien (First part: Geography, p. 1–148, Leipzig, 1910).

Historical Memoirs—Editio princeps, printed by Schweynheim and Pannartz (Rome, 1469), Commentarii cum A. Hirtii aliorumque supplementis, edited by Bernard Kübler (3 vols., Leipzig, 1893–1897). Edition by René Du Pontet (2 vols., Oxford, 1900–1901).

Latin text with English translation of the Gallic War by H. J. Edwards, Loeb Library (London, 1917).

Lexicons—Otto Eichart: Vollständiges Wörterbuch zu den Schriftwerken des C. J. Cäsar und seiner Fortsetzer (258 p., 8te Aufl., Hanover, 1883.) Rudolf Menge: Lexicon Caesarianum (1428 col., Leipzig, 1885–1890). Hugo Merguet: Lexicon (1146 p., Jena, 1886). Heinrich Meusel: Lexicon (2 vols. in 3, Berlin, 1887–1893).

General Criticism—Hermann Wesemann: Caesarfabeln des Mittelalters (Progr., 32 p., Löwenberg i. Schl., 1879). W. Warde Fowler: Julius Caesar and the Foundation of the Roman Imperial System (London, 1891; 1901). T. Rice Holmes: Caesar's Conquest of Gaul (888 p., London, 1899; 2d ed. entirely rev., 911 p., 1911); Ancient Britain and the Invasions of Julius Caesar (780 p., Oxford, 1907). G. Veith: Geschichte der Feldzüge C. J. Caesars (Wien, 1906, 46 maps). Adolf von Mess: Caesar (Leipzig, 1913).

Engineering—De bello gallico (IV, 17). August Rheinhard: Caesars Rhein-Brücke (16 p., Stuttgart, 1883). August Schleussinger: *Idem* (50 p., München, 1884). F. Zimmerhaeckel: *Idem.* Ein Rekonstruktions versuch. Statische Prüfung der Cäsarbrücke als leichte Kolonnenbrücke (24 p., Z. für math. und naturwiss. Unterricht, t. 29–30, 1899).

IX. ROMAN WRITING

TIRO

M. Tullius Tiro. Contemporary of Cicero, whom he survived. Cicero's freedman and secretary. He wrote a biography of his patron and preserved and edited part of his works and correspondence. He invented a kind of shorthand (notae tironianae).[m]

---

[m] The abbreviations found in medieval manuscripts down to the twelfth century are derived from these notae. Stenographers were called notarii, later excerptores.

Text—Tironiana et maecenatiana, sive M. Tullii Tironis et C. Cilnii Maecenatis operum fragmenta quae supersunt. Edited by Albert Lion (2d ed., 580 p., Göttingen, 1846; 1st ed. 1824).

Notae tironianae—Wilhelm Schmitz: Commentarii notarum tironianarum cum prolegomenis, adnotationibus criticis et exegeticis (132 p., Leipzig, 1893). Emile Chatelain: Introduction à l'étude des notes tironiennes (224 p., 18 pl., Paris, 1900). Paul Legendre: Etudes tironiennes (101 p., Bibl. école hautes études, sci. hist., 165, Paris, 1907). Louis Prosper Guénin et Eugène Guénin: Histoire de la sténographie dans l'antiquité et au moyen-âge (416 p., 8 pl., Paris, 1908).

CHAPTER XII

THE TIME OF VIRGIL

(Second Half of the First Century B. C.)

I. Survey of Science in Second Half of First Century B. C. II. Cultural Background in the West. III. Roman, Hellenistic, and Chinese Mathematics and Astronomy. IV. Roman Physics and Technology. V. Roman and Hellenistic Husbandry and Botany. VI. Roman, Hellenistic, and Chinese Geography and Geology. VII. Hellenistic, and Roman Medicine. VIII. Roman, Hellenistic, and Chinese Historiography. IX. Latin and Greek Philology.

I. SURVEY OF SCIENCE IN SECOND HALF OF FIRST CENTURY B. C.

1. It is sweet to invoke Virgil at the threshold of this chapter. It is sweet and it is fitting, for Virgil was undoubtedly the greatest figure of a time which was essentially Roman—the golden age of Rome.

2. *Cultural Background in the West*—Virgil dominates the period and his relative importance increased gradually as centuries went by. In medieval times he had become legendary, even as Aristotle.

About the year 37 B. C., C. Asinius Pollio founded the first Roman public library.

3. *Roman, Hellenistic, and Chinese Mathematics and Astronomy*—Upon Caesar's order, a much needed reform of the calendar was prepared by Sosigenes; the new (Julian) era began on the first of January 45 B. C. (709 U. C.).

Varro wrote various books on applied mathematics, including one on geometry, wherein he states that the earth is egg-shaped. Hyginus wrote a popular book on astronomy. Xenarchos wrote a treatise on the quintessence, wherein he criticized some of the fundamental principles of Peripatetic astronomy.

It is well to keep in mind that Heron of Alexandria (dealt with in the previous chapter) may have lived in this time.

Liu Hsin wrote a treatise on the calendar toward the end of the century.

4. *Roman Physics and Technology*—M. V. Agrippa accomplished great public works, for example, the aqueduct of Nîmes in 18 B. C. One of his collaborators, Cocceius, built the tunnel road lying between the Lacus Avernus and Cumae. The most famous engineer and architect of Roman times, Vitruvius, flourished under Augustus (emperor from 31 B. C. to 14 A. D.). Vitruvius's treatise on architecture is extremely important, because it is a real encyclopaedia of the physical and technical knowledge of those days; it is absolutely necessary to study it not only to understand Roman technique, but also to appreciate correctly the early Italian Renaissance, which was deeply influenced by it.

5. *Roman and Hellenistic Husbandry and Botany*—M. T. Varro wrote in his old age (c. 36) a treatise on agriculture which is extremely valuable. Virgil's "Georgics" were completed c. 31. C. J. Hyginus, second prefect of the Palatine Library, wrote treatises on agriculture and apiculture.

In the meanwhile, Nicholas of Damascus, friend of Herod the Great, King of Judaea from 40 to 4, wrote the treatise on plants often ascribed to Aristotle.

6. *Roman, Hellenistic, and Chinese Geography and Geology*—Caesar planned a general survey of the empire; this survey was completed by Agrippa (d. 12 B. C.)

and the results were shown upon a great map set up by order of Augustus in the Portus Octaviae in Rome. King Juba (d. 20 A. D.) made inquiries with regard to the Fortunate Islands (Canaries) and he had some knowledge of the Niger. The agriculturist Hyginus wrote a treatise on the geography of Italy.

The greatest geographer of that time and, all considered, one of the greatest of all times, was Strabon. He was not interested in mathematical geography, but rather in physical geography and what we would call to-day "human geography." His work was probably completed by the end of the century. It contains many observations of geological interest; for example, on earthquakes, volcanic phenomena, submarine explosions, sinking or rising of land, alluvial deposits, etc.

About the same time, Isidore of Charax wrote a description of the world, an account of a journey around Parthia and an itinerary from Antioch to the borders of India. Tu-ch'in described in 25 B. C., an itinerary from China to Kabul.

7. *Hellenistic and Roman Medicine*—Many Greek-speaking surgeons were flourishing in those days: Ammonios the lithotomist, Meges, Perigenes. Varro's "Agriculture" contains various items of medical interest, notably the idea of contagion by microorganisms. A part of this treatise was naturally devoted to animal diseases, their prophylaxy and cure. The most famous physician of Augustus was Antonius Musa, who recommended the use of cold baths. Aemilius Macer of Verona wrote poems on birds, snakes, and antidotes.

8. *Roman, Hellenistic, and Chinese Historiography*—Some of Varro's numerous writings were devoted to Roman history and archaeology, and we owe to him a great part of our knowledge of ancient Rome. Between the years 43 and 35, Sallust wrote an admirable series of historical monographs. Diodoros of Sicily completed, c. 30, a universal history, through which some valuable information has been transmitted to us. Juba II, King of Mauretania (d. 20 A. D.), wrote various histories, used by Pliny. Nicholas of Damascus, already mentioned, compiled a universal history. Dionysios of Halicarnassos composed for Greek readers an account of early Roman history. The geographer Strabon compiled also historical memoirs.

The greatest historian of that age was Livy, who wrote (c. 29 to 12 B. C.) a very elaborate history of Rome from the foundation to his own days. This work influenced historical thought very deeply until the nineteenth century.

The astronomer Liu Hsin established a chronology of prehistoric China. In spite of its scientific appearance, this work has no scientific value.

9. *Latin and Greek Philology*—Varro wrote a treatise which is of great value for the study of early Latin. The Alexandrian Didymos compiled many commentaries on the Greek classics. Dionysios of Halicarnassos took considerable pains to protect the Greek language against further adulteration. Toward the end of the century Verrius Flaccus compiled the earliest Latin dictionary.

10. *Conclusions*—As we would expect, Roman characteristics were even more accentuated in this age than in the previous one, and this implies a real intellectual deterioration. It is the golden age of Latin literature. It is also a great age from the technical point of view, the age of Vitruvius. Admirable monuments and public works and ambitious undertakings like the survey of the empire and the establishment of a new calendar are witnesses of Roman power and unity; they proclaim the Roman will to use knowledge for the public good. The age produced that miracle, Virgil; it produced Vitruvius and some great scholars like Varro, Strabon, Sallust, Livy; but we look in vain for a mathematician, for an

astronomer (Sosigenes seems to have been a practical man, not a real scientist), for a physicist, or a naturalist, even for a great physician. We look in vain also for a real philosopher; the first half of the century could still boast a Posidonios and a Lucretius; the deepest thinker of the second half is Horace, who has remained to this day the favorite "philosopher" of people who do not care particularly for philosophy.[a] It is an age of application, not one of scientific creation.

II. CULTURAL BACKGROUND IN THE WEST

VIRGIL

Publius Vergilius[b] Maro. Born in 70 near Mantova, died in 19 B. C., at Brindisi. The greatest Latin poet and one of the greatest poets of all times. Among his poems the "Georgica" are of special interest to us; this scientific poem was probably written (at a suggestion from Octavianus?) to draw the attention of the Romans to husbandry, which had become more and more neglected. The last lines were written at Naples, soon after Actium, 31. Virgil has apparently made use of all the sources of information available to him, traditional as well as literary. This poem, learned as it is, is exceedingly charming and beautiful.

Bibliography—Primo saggio di bibliografia virgiliana (R. Accad. Virgiliana, 31 p. Mantova, 1882. Additional annual bibliographies have appeared in the Atti e memoria of the same academy.) British Museum. Catalogue of Printed Books, Virgilius (74 col., 1882). W. A. Copinger: Incunabula virgiliana (Bibliogr. soc., transactions, II, 123–226, 1895).

Text—Two editions of Virgil appeared c. 1469, one at Rome, the other at Strasbourg. It is not possible to decide which is the princeps.

General Studies—André Bellessort: Virgile, son oeuvre et son temps (335 p., Paris, 1920; Isis, IV, 574). Tenney Frank: Vergil (207 p., New York, 1922). David Ansell Slater: Sortes vergilianae or Vergil and Today (29 p., Oxford, 1922). Norman Wentworth De Witt: Virgil's Biographia Litteraria (198 p., London, 1923). Terrot Reaveley Glover: Virgil (362 p., London, 1924; 1st ed. entitled Studies in Virgil, 1904; 4th ed. 1920).

Scientific Commentaries—A. J. Des Carrieres: Virgil's Description of the Ancient Roman Plough (29 p., London, 1788). Karl Brandt: De auctoribus quos in componendis Georgicon libris adumbravit Vergilius (Progr., 9 p., Salzwedel, 1884). André Le Breton: De animalibus apud Vergilium (Diss., Paris, 1895). Santi Consoli: Neologismi botanici nei carmi bucolici e georgici (152 p., Palermo, 1901). Paul Jahn: Eine Prosaquelle Vergils und ihre Umsetzung durch den Dichter (Hermes, t. 38, 244–264, 1903. Theophrastos). Otto Erdmann: Beiträge zur Nachahmungskunst Vergils in den Georgika (Diss., 64 p., Halberstadt, 1913). Celso Ulpiani (1866–1919): Le Georgiche (Annali d. R. Scuola d'agricoltura di Portici, vol. 14, 162 p., Portici, 1917). T. F. Royds: The Beasts, Birds and Bees of Virgil (126 p., Oxford, 1914; Isis, II, 205). John Sargeaunt: The Trees, Shrubs and Plants of Virgil (156 p., Oxford, 1920; Isis, III, 453; botanical criticism in Nature, t. 106, 825, 1921). See also under Varro and Lucretius.

Franc. Corazzini: La marina in Virgilio (412 p., Torino, 1898). Clifford Pease Clark: Numeral Phraseology in Virgil (Diss., 89 p., Princeton, 1913).

---

[a] I do not forget that Cicero died only in 43 and that some of his philosophical writings date only from the sixth decade of the century, but it seemed on the whole more correct to count him as a representative of the first half of the century.

[b] The spelling Vergilius is undoubtedly the better; witness early inscriptions and Greek transliterations; the form Virgilius does not occur before the fifth century. Yet I prefer to write Virgil instead of Vergil, in accordance with English usage and the usage of many other European languages.

Virgil in the Middle Ages—Virgil had become in the Middle Ages a sort of legendary figure—Aristotle and he were considered by many as necromancers, by others as men of superhuman wisdom—and one must be well informed on this subject to understand medieval thought. The main source is Domenico Comparetti's magistral study entitled Virgilio nel Medio Evo (2 vols., Livorno, 1872; 2d ed. 2 vols., Firenze, 1896; German translation, Leipzig, 1875; English translation by E. F. M. Benecke, 392 p., London, 1908). See also T. F. Royds: Vergil and Isaiah (Oxford, 1918. Virgil was considered for many centuries as one of the inspired prophets of Christ).

POLLIO

C. Asinius Pollio. Born at Rome, 76—died at Tusculum, near Rome, in 4 or 5 A. D. Roman writer, historian, critic and patron of letters. He founded in in 37 B. C. in the Atrium Libertatis the first Roman public library.[c] He protected Virgil, Horace, and other writers. He severely criticized Cicero, Caesar, Sallust, Livy.

F. A. Aulard: De Pollionis vita et scriptis (Paris, 1877).

III. ROMAN, HELLENISTIC, AND CHINESE MATHEMATICS AND ASTRONOMY

For Roman mathematics and astronomy refer to my notes on Heron and on Caesar in the previous chapter and on Varro and on Hyginus in Section V.

XENARCHOS

Ξέναρχος, of Seleucia in Cilicia, flourished in Alexandria, Athens, Rome, at the time of Augustus and Strabo. Greek philosopher. He wrote a treatise against the quintessence (*πρὸς τὴν πέμπτην οὐσίαν*) in which he criticized some of the fundamental principles of Peripatetic astronomy (the natural motions of celestial bodies are not exclusively circular, uniform, and homocentric).

Texts—The text is known only through Simplicios's quotations in his Comment. in Aristotelis IV libros de coelo.
Criticism—F. Susemihl: Griechische Litteratur in der Alexandrinerzeit (t. 2, 321, 1892). P. Duhem: Système du monde (t. 2, 61–67, 1914).

LIU HSIN

Liu[2] Hsin[1] (7260, 4576). Imperial prince who flourished under the Western Han and committed suicide in 22 A. D. Chinese scholar and astronomer. He succeeded his father Liu Hsiang[4] (4283) as imperial librarian in 7 B. C. In the following year he completed the catalogue Han[4] I[4]-wen[2]-chih[4] (3836, 5717, 12633, 1918) begun by his father.[d] He wrote a treatise on the calendar, called San[1]-t'ung[3]-li[4]* (9552, 12316, 6924). He did not know of the precession of the equinoxes and to reconcile the tropical and sidereal years he introduced an enormous period, like the Hindu Kalpa, a period of 23,639,040 years. He determined in the most artificial manner the chronology of prehistoric China; this fantastic chronology was readily accepted because of its scientific appearance.

L. Wieger: La Chine (87, 352, 516, 1920). Léopold de Saussure: La chronologie chinoise (T'oung Pao, vol. 23, 287–346, 1924).

---

[c] The library of Latin and Greek books of the Portus Octaviae was established after 33, and the Bibliotheca Palatina in 28 B. C. (See my note on Hyginus below.)

[d] Forming chapter 30 of the Ch'ien Han shu. See my note on Pan Ku (second half of first century). The San-t'ung-li forms chapter 21 of the Ch'ien Han shu.

IV. ROMAN PHYSICS AND TECHNOLOGY

AGRIPPA

Marcus Vipsanius Agrippa. Born in 63; died in 12 B. C. Roman soldier and statesman. He accomplished great public works (aqueducts, sewers) and completed the survey of the Roman Empire undertaken by Caesar[e] (q. v.). The results of this survey were shown in the great Map of the World, which after his death was set up by the order of Augustus in the Porticus Octaviae at Rome. He built the Pantheon in 27 B. C.; the magnificent aqueduct of Nîmes (Pont du Gard) in 18 B. C.

Criticism—P. Schreiner Frandsen: M. Vipsanius Agrippa; eine historische Untersuchung über dessen Leben und Werken (268 p., Altona, 1836). E. Schweder: Beiträge zur Kritik der Chorographie des Augustus (3 Teile., Kiel, 1876–1883). Friedrich Philippi: Zur Reconstruction der Weltkarte des Agrippa (25 p., 5 maps, Marburg, 1880). D. Detlefsen: Unters. zu den geograph. Büchern des Plinius. 1: Weltkarte des M. Agrippa (Progr., 17 p., Glückstadt, 1884); Ursprung, Einrichtung und Bedeutung der Erdkarte Agrippas (Quellen und Forschungen zur alten Geschichte und Geographie, 13, 123 p., Berlin, 1906). Franz Braun: Die Entwicklung des spanischen Provinzialgrenzen in römischer Zeit (*idem*, 17, 139 p., 1909).

COCCEIUS

L. Cocceius Auctus, one of the collaborators of Agrippa. Roman engineer who built the tunnel road of about 1,000 meters lying between the Lacus Avernus and Cumae (Grotta della Pace) and possibly also the tunnel of about 689 meters joining Naples and Puteoli (Grotta vecchia di Posilippo).

Fabricius and Stein, in Pauly-Wissowa (t. 7, 129, 1900).

VITRUVIUS

Marcus Vitruvius Pollio, flourished in the Augustan age. Roman architect, engineer, craftsman. He wrote ten books on architecture (de architectura libri decem) which form not simply a very comprehensive treatise on architecture, but also an encyclopaedia of the technical—and to a certain extent the scientific—knowledge of his day. Explanation of sound by a vibratory motion of the air; first study of architectural acoustics. Earliest recipe for hydraulic mortar. He paid attention to hygienic requisites and had some knowledge of lead poisoning. The study of Vitruvius is important for the understanding of the Early Renaissance.

Text, Translations, Index—Editio princeps, Rome c. 1486. The best edition of the text is by F. Krohn (310 p., Leipzig, 1912). A very elaborate edition with French translation and many plates has been given by Auguste Choisy (Paris, 1909, 4 vols.; Vol. I, analysis; Vols. II–III, text and translation; Vol. IV, plates). English translation by Morris Hicky Morgan, with illustrations prepared under the direction of H. L. Warren (Cambridge, Mass., 1914).

A study of the earlier editions with special reference to their illustrations will be found in Heinrich Röttinger: Die Holzschnitte zur Architectur und zum Vitruvius Teutsch des Walther Rivius (Studien zur deutschen Kunstgeschichte, 167, 53 p., 12 pl., Strassburg, 1914). Bodo Ebhardt: Die zehn Bücher der Archi-

---

[e] The work seems to have been directed by one head surveyor called Balbus, not to be mistaken for another surveyor of the first half of the second century bearing the same name (q. v.).

tektur und ihre Herausgeber seit 1484 (102 p., 100 ill., Berlin, Grunewald, after 1915. Elaborate bibliographic and iconographic study; Isis, IV, 575).

N. Nohl: Index Vitruvianus (158 p., Leipzig, 1876).

General Studies—A. Terquem: La science romaine à l'époque d'Auguste. Étude historique d'après Vitruve (Mém. de la soc. des sciences de Lille, 174 p., Paris, 1885). Victor Mortet: Remarques critiques sur Vitruve et son oeuvre (Revue archéologique, 3e. s., t. 41, p. 39–81, 1902; 4e. s., t. 3, p. 222–233, 382–393, 1904; t. 4, p. 265–266, 1904; t. 8, p. 268–283, 1906; t. 9, p. 75–83, 277–280, 1907). Ludwig Sontheimer: Vitruvius und seine Zeit (Diss., 135 p., Tübingen, 1908).

The first volume of Choisy's edition (1909) contains an analysis of Vitruvius's ideas, very brief and clear, but without historical and critical notes. It enables one to find out quickly what was Vitruvius's knowledge, say on geometry and astronomy, and as such is very useful. But that is only the first step toward a critical study of Vitruvius, which is very much needed. Such an investigation should be undertaken by one having a thorough knowledge of ancient technology, and its ultimate aim should be to explain the state of technical and scientific knowledge at the time of Christ and to account for it.

Sources—Max Thiel: Quae ratio intercedat inter Vitruvium et Athenaeum mechanicum (Diss., p. 277–328, Leipzig, 1895). Wilh. Schmidt: Haben Vitruv und die römischen Feldmesser aus Heron geschöpft? (Bibliotheca Mathematica, p. 297–318, 1900). Wilh. Poppe: Vitruvs Quellen im zweiten Buche de architectura (Diss., 65 p., Kiel, 1909). F. Krohn: De Vitruvio auctore commentarii qui inscribitur Ἀθηναίου περὶ μηχανημάτων (Progr., 24 p., Münster i. W., 1913).

Chronology—The dates of Vitruvius's life and activity are not positively established. Some scholars have gone so far as to consider his "Architecture" as a mediaeval imposture! It is very probable that it dates from the beginning of the Augustan age, i. e., about 27 B. C.

J. L. Ussing: Observations sur Vitruve et sur le temps où peut avoir été écrit l'ouvrage qui porte ce titre (D. Kgl. Danske Vidensk. Selsk. Skr., 6. R., hist. Afd., IV, 3, p. 95–160, Copenhagen, 1896. Written in Danish, but with a French summary, p. 149–160; there is also an English translation, 42 p., R. Institute of British archit., 1898. Concludes that Vitruvius is an imposter of the fourth or fifth century). Wald. Dietrich: Quaestionum Vitruvianarum specimen (Diss., 83 p., Leipzig, 1906. Vitruvius was already working on his book before 31 B. C.; he began writing it before 16 A. D.). H. Degering: Wann schrieb Vitruv sein Buch über die Architektur? (Berliner philologische Wochenschrift, 27 J., No. 43–49, 1907. The work dates from the beginning of the Augustan age; that is also Morgan's conclusion). Ludwig Sontheimer: Vitruvius und seine Zeit. (Diss., Tübingen, 1908. Vitruvius wrote his "Architecture" between 37 and 32 B. C.; he published it between 29 and 27).

Architectural Studies—Aug. Aurès: Nouvelle théorie du module déduite du texte même de Vitruve (55 p., Nîmes, 1862). Edw. Capps: Vitruvius and the Greek stage (studies in classical philol., Univ. of Chicago, Vol. I, 23 p., 1893). Jakob Prestel: Des Vitruvius Basilika zu Fanum Fortunae (57 p., 7 pl., Strassburg, 1900). Sackur: Des Vitruvius Basilika in Fanum und die neue Ausgabe (Krohn, 1912) der Decem libri de architectura (Repertorium für Kunstwissenschaft, t. 36, 1–40, Berlin, 1913). Adalbert Birnbaum: Vitruvius und die griechische Architektur (Denkschriften der Ak. der Wiss. in Wien, philos. Kl., t. 57, 63 p., 10 pl., 1914; Isis, IV, 575).

Other Studies—Friedrich Krohn: De M. Ceti Faventini epitoma (Diss., 43 p., Berlin, 1896). Morris H. Morgan: On the Language of Vitruvius (Proc. of Amer. Acad. Sci., vol. 41, 467–502, Boston, 1906); The Preface of Vitruvius (*ibidem*, vol. 44, 149–175, 1909); Notes on Vitruvius (Harvard Studies in Classical Philol., vol. 17, 14 p., 1906; vol. 21, 22 p., 1910). P. Duhem: Études sur Léonard de Vinci

(t. 1, 289, 1906, résistance des matériaux); Origines de la statique (t. 2, 310–312, 1906, statique). J. A. Jolles: Vitruvs Aesthetik (Diss., 101 p., Freiburg i. Br., 1906). E. Schramm: Erläuterung der Geschützbeschreibung bei Vitruvius, X, 10–12 (Sitzungsb. d. Preuss. Akad. d. Wiss., 718–734, 1917).

V. ROMAN AND HELLENISTIC HUSBANDRY AND BOTANY

VARRO

Marcus Terentius Varro. Born in Reate, near Rome, in the Sabine country, 116, died 27 B. C. Encyclopaedic writer of immense learning. Of his many writings, only two are extant: the de lingua latina (of importance for the study of early Latin) and the rerum rusticarum libri tres (of special interest to us), written at the age of eighty. Among the lost books I will quote only a book on mensuration (mensuralia), another on geometry, in which he stated that the earth is egg-shaped, one on arithmetic (Atticus sive de numeris) and finally an encyclopaedia (de disciplinis) divided into nine books as follows: (1) grammar; (2) dialectics; (3) rhetoric; (4) geometry; (5) arithmetic; (6) astrology; (7) music; (8) medicine; (9) architecture. Varro's historical and archaeological studies were of fundamental importance and much of what we know of ancient Rome is indirectly based upon them. His botanical knowledge was greater than Cato's. His book on farming contains interesting observations on the growth and movements of plants, also on prophylaxy and cure of animal diseases. Idea of contagion by microorganisms.[f]

General Studies—For a list of his writings see F. Ritschl: Die Schriftstellerei des M. T. Varro (Rheinisches Museum für Philologie, 6. J., 481–560, Frankfurt, 1848). Gaston Boissier: Etude sur la vie et les ouvrages de Varron (374 p., Paris, 1861. This is the only comprehensive study, and it is no longer up-to-date).

Text and Translations of the Rerum rusticarum libri—Editio princeps in Scriptores de re rustica (Venice, Nic. Jenson, 1472). Heinrich Keil (3 vols., see under Cato the Censor. The parts dealing with Varro are dated, the text 1884, the commentary 1891, the index 1902). Later edition by Georg Goetz (178 p., Leipzig, 1912).

English Translations—Varro on farming, translated with introduction, commentary, and excursus by Lloyd Storr-Best (391 p., London, 1912, based on Keil's text). By Fairfax Harrison (New York, 1913. See under Cato).

Commentaries on the Rerum rusticarum libri—Adolf Riecke: Varro, der römische Landwirth (64 p., Stuttgart, 1861). Franc. Zahlfeldt: Quaestiones criticae (33 p., Berlin, 1881). Heinrich Keil: Observationes criticae (Progr., 9 p., Halle, 1883). Hans Morsch: De Varrone Reatino auctore in Georgicis a Vergilio expresso (Progr., p. 65–78, Berlin, 1897). Guido Gentilli: De Varronis in libris rerum rusticarum auctoribus (Studi italiani di filologia classica, t. 11, 99–163, Firenze, 1903). Osc. Hempel: Quaestiones selectae (Diss., 93 p., Leipzig, 1908). E. Weiss: De Columella et Varrone rerum rusticarum scriptoribus (Diss., 43 p., Vratislaviae, 1911). Karl Engelke: Quae ratio intercedat inter Vergilii georgica et Varronis rerum rusticarum libros (Diss., 54 p., Blankenburgi, 1912). A. W. Van Buren and R. M. Kennedy: Varro's aviary at Casinum (Journal of Roman Studies, vol. 9, 59–66, 1919).

Historical Writings—Alwin Jacobson: Das Verhältnis des Dionys von Halicarnass zu Varro in der Vorgeschichte Roms. (Progr., 18 p., Dresden, 1895); De Varronis rerum divinarum libris I, XIV, XV, XVI ab Augustino in libris de

---

[f] Rerum rusticarum liber I, cap. 12.

civitate Dei IV, VI, VII exscriptis (Diss., 38 p., Leipzig, 1896). Reinhold Agahd: M. T. Varronis antiquitatum rerum divinarum libri I, XIV, XV, XVI. Praemissae sunt quaestiones Varronianae (Jahrbücher für classische Philologie, 24. Supp. Bd., 220 p., Leipzig, 1898). Rud. Ritter: De Varrone Vergilii in narrandis urbium populorumque Italiae originibus auctore (Dissertiones Philologicae Halenses, t. 14, 285–416, Halle, 1901). Heinrich Willemsen: De Varronianae doctrinae apud fastorum scriptores vestigiis (Diss., 43 p., Bonn, 1906). Plinio Fraccaro: Studi Varroniani De gente populi Romani libri IV (298 p., Padova, 1907).

Philological Writings—Editio princeps of De Lingua latina by Pomponius Laetus (Rome, 1471). Ad. Groth: De M. T. Varronis de lingua latina librorum codice florentino (Diss., 68 p., Strassburg, 1880). Victor Henry: De sermonis humani origine et natura M. T. Varro quid senserit (Thèse, Paris; Mém. de la soc. des sci. de Lille, t. XII, 94 p., 1883). Rob. Kriegshammer: De Varronis et Verrii fontibus quaestiones selectae (Diss., Jena, p. 73–126, Leipzig, 1903).

Other Studies—Charles Chappuis: Sentences de M. T. Varron et liste de ses ouvrages d'après différents manuscrits (124 p., Paris, 1856). Ernst Holzer: Varroniana (Progr., 19 p., Ulm, 1890). Ernst Samter: Quaestiones Varronianae (Diss., 86 p., Berlin, 1891). Georg Heidrich: Der Stil des Varro (Progr., 82 p., Melk, 1892). Paul Rusch: De Varrone Plinii in naturalis historiae libro VIII auctore commentatio (Gymn., 15 p., Stettin, 1900). Otto Probst: Celsus und Plinius in ihrem Verhältnis zum achten Buch der Encyclopädie Varros (Diss., 17 p., München, 1905). Peter Germann: Die sogenannten Sententiae Varronis (Studien zur Geschichte und Kultur des Altertums, III, 6, 99 p., Paderborn, 1910).

C. JULIUS HYGINUS

Born in Spain, flourished in Rome after 28 B. C., probably still living in 10 A. D. Roman polygraph. Second prefect of the Palatine Library founded in 28 B. C. Among his many works we must quote: (1) de agricultura (in 2 books, de agrorum cultu and de vitibus et arboribus, written soon after 37); (2) de apibus, the first Latin treatise on apiculture, possibly a part of (1); (3) a treatise on Italian geography (de situ urbium Italicarum); (4) an elementary treatise on astronomy dealing chiefly with the myths connected with the 24 constellations[a] (largely based on Aratos and Eratosthenes).

Texts—Fragments of (1) and (2) have been edited by R. Reitzenstein: De scriptorum rei rusticae libris deperditis (Berlin, 1884).

Poeticon astronomicon. Editio princeps (Ferrara, 1475). Second edition (Venice, Ratdolt, 1482, from which most later editions proceed). New text edited by Joh. Soter (Köln, 1534). German translation (Augsburg, 1491).

Modern edition by Bern. Bunte: Hygini astronomica (130 p., Leipzig, 1875). Emile Chatelain et Paul Legendre: Astronomica (Texte du Ms. tironien de Milan, Bibl. de l'Ecole des hautes études, sci. hist., 180, 50 p., 8 pl., Paris, 1909).

Criticism—E. H. F. Meyer: Geschichte der Botanik (t. 1, 375-377, 1854). Georg Kauffmann: De Hygini memoria scholiis in Ciceronis Aratum Harleianis servata (Breslauer philol. Abhd., 3, 176 p., Breslau, 1888). Georg Dittmann: De Hygino Arati interprete (Diss., 54 p., Leipzig, 1900). Tolkiehn, on Pauly-Wissowa (t. 10, 628–651, 1917).

NICOLAOS DAMASCENOS

Νικόλαος ὁ Δαμασκηνός, born in Damascus, 64 B. C., friend of Herod the Great, King of Judaea, 40 to 4 B. C., whom he survived. Greek historian and philosopher.

[a] It is entitled in various ways: de astrologia, de astronomia, astronomicon libri, de ratione sphaerae, de sideribus, etc. Also poeticon astronomicon. It is not certain that it is the same Hyginus who wrote (4) and the works previously named. This question is still very obscure.

Author of a universal history, a mediocre compilation in 144 books. The Aristotelian work de plantis is ascribed to him.

Text and Translations—The historical fragments are collected in the Fragmenta historicorum graecorum of C. Müller (t. III, 346 sq.) and in the Historici graeci minores of Dindorf (t. I, p. 1–156). E. H. F. Meyer: Nicolai Damasceni de plantis libri duo Aristoteli vulgo adscripti (Leipzig, 1841. The Greek original is lost; this is the Latin translation by one Alfredus Anglicus, made through Arabic and Syrian versions; see Singer's Studies, t. 2, 13).

Criticism—E. H. F. Meyer: Geschichte der Botanik (t. 1, 324–333, 1854). Paul Tietz: De Nicolai fontibus (Diss., Marburg, 1896). Wilh. Witte: De Nicolai fragmentorum romanorum fontibus (Diss., 50 p., Berlin, 1900). Rudolf Duttlinger: Untersuchungen über den historischen Wert des Βίος καίσαρος des Nicolaus Damascenus (Diss., Heidelberg, 153 p., Zürich, 1911). Paul Jacob: De Nicolai sermone et arte historica (Diss., 79 p., Goettingen, 1911). P. M. Bouyges: Sur le de plantis à propos d'un MS. arabe de Constantinople (Mélanges de l'Université St. Joseph t. 9, 71–89, Beyrouth, 1924. Manuscript of the translation made by Isḥāq ibn Hunain; Isis, VIII, 531).

VI. ROMAN, HELLENISTIC, AND CHINESE GEOGRAPHY AND GEOLOGY

For Roman geography, see my notes on Caesar in Chapter XI and on Agrippa, Juba, and Hyginus in Sections IV, VIII, and V of this chapter.

STRABON

Στράβων. Born in Amasia, Pontos, c. 63 B. C., died after 20 A. D. Greek historian and geographer. Stoic. His historical memoirs (ἱστορικὰ ὑπομνήματα) now lost, were a continuation of Polybios's history. His geography (γεωγραφικὰ sc. ὑπομνήματα), undertaken later, is the most comprehensive work of its kind in ancient times. This was the first attempt to write a geographical encyclopaedia, including mathematical, physical, political, and historical geography. The astronomical or mathematical part is comparatively neglected and is inferior to Eratosthenes's treatment of it. Strabon's geography is chiefly a philosophical and humane geography. He wrote for the statesman or the man of affairs rather than for the scientist. Yet he displays a very critical spirit and tries to explain in a scientific way various natural phenomena or geographical peculiarities which were the subject of legendary accounts. His work contains many historical and ethnographical notes and much information on trade and industries. There are also incidentally geological and biological observations. For example, he explains the formation of mountains by the action of internal pressures, and that of the famous Vale of Tempe (in Thessaly) by an earthquake. He continues to believe that volcanic phenomena are due to the force of winds pent up within the earth and he considers volcanoes as safety valves.[h] He attributes the formation of Mediterranean islands either to disruption from the mainland by quakes, or to volcanic action. He mentions submarine explosions among the Lipari Islands. He repeats very clearly the ancient philosophical belief that land and sea have been frequently interchanged. He notes a number of facts proving that there had been many sinkings or risings of lands, some of them local, others widespread. These movements of the earth's surface he ascribes to quakes. He

[h] His incorrect theory was apparently confirmed by observations connecting storms and volcanic eruptions in the Lipari islands. The conception of volcanoes as safety valves was repeated by James Hutton: Theory of the Earth (2d ed., vol. 1, 146, 1795).

conjectures that a similar sinking might destroy the isthmus of Suez and open a communication between the Mediterranean and the Red Sea. He relates many observations on the erosive power of water and on the alluvial deposits at the mouths of rivers or along their course. He gives information on the mining of salt and its extraction from salt-water springs.

According to Ettore Pais, the materials of his geography were collected in Alexandria and Rome, but the actual writing was done at Amasia c. 7 B.C., ulterior events being inserted in a revised edition prepared toward the end of his life.

Text and Translations of the Geography—First Greek edition, Aldine (Venice, 1516). A Latin translation by Guarino of Verona had appeared half a century before (Rome, c. 1470); this translation is important because it was made from better manuscripts than the Aldine edition, and these manuscripts are now lost. First scientific edition, Gust. Kramer (3 vols., Berlin, 1844–1852). Then, Aug. Meineke (3 vols., Leipzig, 1852–1853; new ed., 1866–1867, 1877). Greek and Latin ed. by C. Müller and F. Dübner (Paris 1853–1858).

English translation by H. C. Hamilton (Bks. I–VI) and W. Falconer (remainder, 3 vols., London, 1854–1857). By Horace Leonard Jones and J. R. S. Sterrett, with Greek text (Loeb Classical Library) 8 vols., London, 1917 etc.; Isis, III, 318).

French translation in 5 vols. by Laporte du Theil, A. Coray, J. A. Letronne, with notes by P. F. J. Gosselin (Paris, 1805–1819). German translation by Christoph Gottlieb Groskurd (4 vols., Berlin, 1831–1834. The notes of the French and German editions are important.)

Giuseppe Cozza-Luzi (1837–1905): Della geografia di Strabone, frammenti scoperti in membrane palimseste (7 parts, Roma, 1884–1898).

Henry Fanshawe Tozer: Selections from Strabo (in Greek), with Introduction and Notes (388 p., Oxford, 1893).

The introduction to H. L. Jones's edition (1917) contains a long bibliography, of which mine is independent, and wherein many more editions and translations are quoted.

Main Studies—The most elaborate study is Marcel Dubois: Examen de la géographie de Strabon. Etude critique de la méthode et des sources (416 p., Paris, 1891). The introduction to Tozer's "Selections" (53 p.) and the summaries connecting the extracts give one also a good view of the subject. For Ettore Pais's new theory, see his Ancient Italy (Ch. XXVI, Chicago, 1908. The time and place in which Strabon composed his historical geography, p. 379–430).

Other General Studies (*Composition, Sources, Style*)—Heinrich Butzer: Strabos Geographica, insbesondere über Plan und Ausführung des Werkes und Strabos Stellung zu seinen Vorgängern (Progr., 36 p., Frankfurt a. M., 1887). Franz Martin Schröter: Bemerkungen zu Strabo. (Progr., 17 p., Leipzig, 1887. The author contends that the Geography was not completed at any one time, but developed little by little, and that Strabon himself did not edit it). Wilh. Fabricius: Theophanes von Mytilene und Quintus Dellius als Quellen der Geographie des Strabon (Diss., 235 p., Strassburg, 1888). Paul Meyer: Straboniana (Progr., 34 p., Grimma, 1890. Für wenn wollte S. schreiben? er war gewiss ein weitgereister Mann; er hat seine Geographica nicht selbst herausgegeben). Eduard Stemplinger: Strabons litterarhistorische Notizen (Diss., 95 p., München, 1894). Rud. Daebritz: De Artemidoro Strabonis auctore (Diss., 70 p., Leipzig, 1905). Joseph Klein: Sprichwörter und paroemiographische Überlieferung bei Strabo (Diss., München, 40 p., Tübingen, 1909). Josef Forderer: Ephoros und Strabon (Diss., 69 p., Tübingen, 1913). J. G. C. Anderson: Some Questions Bearing on the Date and Place of Occupation of Strabo's Geography (Anatolian Studies presented to Sir William Mitchell Ramsay, 1–13, Manchester, 1923. Denying that Strabon's work was composed in Amasia; Isis, VIII, 531).

Special Studies Relative to Various Books of the Geography—I give at the same time briefly the contents of each book:

I–II. Prolegomena.

III. Spain: Rich. Zimmermann: Quibus auctoribus Strabo in libro tertio geographicorum conscribendo usus sit, quaeritur (Diss., 38 p., Halle, 1883). Wal. Ruge: Quaestiones Strabonianae (Diss., 107 p., Leipzig, 1883).

IV. Gaul: Herm. Wilkens: De Strabonis aliorumque rerum gallicarum auctorum fontibus (60 p., Marburg, 1886). Amédée Beretta: Les cités mystérieuses de Strabon dans la région Cavare (comtat Venaissin). L'Isaros et l'Isar (116 p., Lyon, 1906?). Alfred Klotz: Cäsarstudien. Nebst einer Analyse der strabonischen Beschreibung von Gallien und Britannien (267 p., Leipzig, 1910).

V. Northern and central Italy: Giulio Beloch: Le fonti di Strabone nella descrizione della Campania (Atti d. R. Accad. d. Lincei, serie terza, Memorie d. classe di sci. morali, stor. e filol., Vol. X, 429–448, Roma, 1882). Otto Steinbrück: Die Quellen des Strabo im fünften Buche (Diss., 76 p., Halle, 1909).

VI. Southern Italy and Sicily: Georg Hunrath: Über die Quellen des Strabo's im 6. Buche (Diss., 44 p., Marburg, 1879).

VII. Central and eastern Europe: E. von Stern: Bemerkungen zu Strabons Geographie der taurischen Chersonesos; mit einer Kartenskizze (Hermes, v. 52, 1–38, 1917).

VIII. Peloponnesus.

IX. Northern Greece.

X. The Greek islands.

XI. Northern and Central Asia: Karl Johann Neumann: Strabons Quellen im 11. Buche (1) Kaukasien. (Diss., 32 p., Leipzig, 1881).

XII. Asia Minor, Northern and central portions.

XIII. Asia Minor, Northwestern portion: Walter Leaf: Strabo on the Troad (Book XIII, ch. 1. Edited with translation and commentary, 400 p., Cambridge, 1923; Isis, VII, 179).

XIV. Asia Minor, Southwestern and southern portions.

XV. India: Aug. Vogel: De fontibus quibus Strabo in libro quinto decimo conscribendo usus sit (Diss., 54 p., Goettingen, 1874). Er. Schulz: De duobus Strabonis fontibus (Diss., 70 p., Rostock, 1909. Clitarchos and Polyclitos).

XVI. Southwestern Asia: Walt. Ruge: Quaestiones Strabonianae (Diss., Leipzig, 1888).

XVII. Egypt: Walt. Ruge (1888, quoted under XVI). Ferdinand Strenger: Strabos Erdkunde von Libyen (Quellen u. Forschungen zur alten Gesch. u. Geographie, 28, 140 p., Berlin, 1913).

Strabo's Scientific Observations—Ernst H. F. Meyer: Botanische Erläuterungen zu Strabons Geographie und einem Fragment des Dikäarchos (222 p., Königsberg, 1852). Albert Serbin: Bemerkungen Strabos über den Vulkanismus und Beschreibung der den Griechen bekannten vulkanischen Gebiete (Diss., Erlangen, 63 p., Berlin, 1893). Hans Rid: Die Klimatologie in den Geographica Strabos (Diss., Erlangen, 62 p., Kaiserslautern, 1903). Sir Archibald Geikie: The Founders of Geology (2d ed., 1905). P. Duhem: Etudes sur Léonard de Vinci (t. 2, 291, 1909. Geology).

Strabo's Historical Writings—Strabonis ἱστορικῶν ὑπομνημάτων fragmenta collegit et enarravit adiectis quaestionibus strabonianis Paulus Otto (Leipziger Studien zur class. Philol., XI, 350 p., Leipzig, 1889). Antonio Oddo: Gl'hypomnemata historika di Strabone come fonte di Appiano (41 p., Rassegna di antichità classica, 1900, Palermo, 1901). Karl Albert: Strabo als Quelle des Flavius Josephus (Diss., Würzburg, 48 p., Aschaffenburg, 1902).

ISIDORE OF CHARAX

Isidoros Characenos, Ἰσίδωρος ὁ Χαρακηνός. Born in Charax Spasini at the head of the Persian Gulf, flourished about the end of the first century B. C. Geographer. He wrote a "Description of the World" of which Pliny has transmitted a few fragments to us. A fragment of his "Journey around Parthia" (Παρθίας περιήγησις), dealing with pearls and pearl-fishing, is quoted by Athenaeos (III, 46). We have the complete text of his "Parthian Stations" (σταθμοὶ Παρθικοί), giving the itinerary of the caravan trail from Antioch to the borders of India.

Text and Criticism—Wilfred H. Schoff: Parthian stations of Isidore of Charax. An account of the overland trade route between the Levant and India in the first century B. C. Greek text with transl. and comment (47 p., Philadelphia, 1914). Article by Weissbach, in Pauly-Wissowa (t. 18, 2064–2068, 1916).

TU-CH'IN

Tu[4]-ch'in[1] (12043, 2114). Flourished under the Ch'ien[2] Han[4] (1737, 3836) c. 25 B. C. Chinese traveler. In 25 B. C. he wrote a detailed description of the itinerary from China to Kabul, via the Tarim and Upper Indus valleys and Peshawar.

L. Wieger: La Chine (439, 1920).

VII. HELLENISTIC AND ROMAN MEDICINE

AMMONIOS THE LITHOTOMIST

Ἀμμώνιος ὁ λιθοτόμος, flourished in Alexandria in the second half of the first century B. C., at any rate not later than the time of Augustus. Greek surgeon, who is supposed to have been the first to perform the operation of lithotomy. The compositions of a special styptic and of an eye-salve are also ascribed to him.

M. Wellmann, in Pauly-Wissowa (t. 1, 1867, 1894). E. Gurlt: Geschichte der Chirurgie (t. 1, 310, 1898).

MEGES

Μέγης, of Sidon, Phoenice, flourished in Rome toward the end of the first century B. C. Greek surgeon of the Methodist school. Many fragments of his works are quoted by Celsus, Scribonius, Pliny, Galen, and Oribasios, the most important of them dealing with fistulæ[1] (e. g., in rectum).

Text—Carol. Aug. von Bockelmann: De Megetis fragmentis (Diss., Gryphiae, 1844).

Criticism—E. Gurlt: Geschichte der Chirurgie (t. 1, 332–333, 1898).

PERIGENES

Περιγένης; flourished c. 60 to 30 B. C. Greek surgeon. He invented a kind of bandage for the head ("Fechterhelm") and another (cranes-bill) for the luxated humerus (Galen).

Criticism—J. Ch. Huber, in Biographisches Lexicon (t. 6, 958, 1888, 3 lines).

Other physicians and surgeons of the Alexandrian school, known only because of some quotation in later writings, are named in E. Gurlt: Geschichte der Chi-

---

[1] In Oribasios, bk. 44, first edited by Angelo Mai in vol. 5 of his Scriptorum veterum nova collectio e Vaticanis codicibus edita (10 vols., Roma, 1825–1838).

rurgie (t. 1, 1898, e. g., on p. 312); also in Albrecht von Haller: Bibliotheca chirurgica (t. 1, 20–22, 24–26), and in Franz Susemihl: Geschichte der griechischen Litteratur in der Alexandriner Zeit (t. 2, 414–447, 1892).

MUSA

Antonius Musa. Flourished at Rome under Augustus. Roman physician. The most famous of Augustus's physicians. He recommended the use of cold baths, and cured Augustus by that method in 23 B. C. His works on materia medica, quoted by Galen, are lost.

Text—Two Latin treatises, De herba vetonica and De bona valetudine, published under his name, are spurious. Edition of the first by Gabriel Hummelberger (Zurich, 1537). Edition of both (Venice, 1547).

Criticism—Edmond Spalikowski: Musa et l'hydrothérapie froide à Rome (Thèse, 42 p., Paris, 1896). M. Neuberger: Geschichte der Medizin (t. 1, 323, 333, 1906).

MACER

Aemilius Macer,[i] of Verona; died in Asia, c. 16 B. C. Roman poet. He wrote poems on birds, on snakes, and antidotes in imitation of Nicandros (q. v., first half of third century B. C.).

Ernst H. F. Meyer: Geschichte der Botanik (t. 1, 396–399, 1854).

VIII. ROMAN, HELLENISTIC, AND CHINESE HISTORIOGRAPHY

For Roman historiography, see my note on Varro in Section V. For Hellenistic historiography, see my notes on Nicholas of Damascus and on Strabon in Sections V and VI. For Chinese historiography, see my note on Liu Hsin in Section III.

SALLUST

Gaius Sallustius Crispus, born at Amiternum in the Sabine country in 86; flourished in Rome; died in 34. Roman historian; the earliest great one, his excellence being largely due to his style. He wrote what we would call historical monographs:[k] in 43–42, the conspiracy of Catilina (68); c. 40, the war of the Romans against Jugurtha, King of Numidia (111–106); c. 40 to 35, the Histories dealing with Roman events from 78 to 66 (lost).

Text—Princeps edition (Venice, 1470). Latin text with English translation by J. C. Rolfe (Loeb Library, London, 1921).

Otto Eicher: Vollständiges Wörterbuch (151 p., 3. Aufl., Hanover, 1881; 4. Aufl., 194 p., 1890).

Some manuscripts of Sallust's works contain a map of the world, probably to illustrate a passage of De bello Jugurthino. These maps represent a certain type of T–O maps, called the "Sallust maps" (J. K. Wright, Geographical lore, 68, 1924).

DIODOROS

Diodoros of Sicily, Διόδωρος Σικελιώτης, born at Agyrium in Sicily c. 90 to 80, flourished in Rome, died after 30 B. C. Greek historian. He completed c. 30,

[i] Not to be mistaken for Macer Floridus, for which see my note on Odo Magdunensis, second half of the eleventh century.

[k] "Res gestas populi Romani carptim, ut quaeque memoria digna videbantur, perscribere." (Catilina, IV, 2).

after thirty years of travel and study, a second-hand compilation of the most ambitious scope—a universal and encyclopaedic history from the beginnings to his time (Ἱστοριῶν βιβλιοθήκη, in 40 books, of which 15 are extant).[l] It is unphilosophical, unscientific, uncritical, yet very valuable because of the information preserved in it.

Texts—Latin translation by Poggio Bracciolini (Venice, 1496). Edition by L. Dindorf (5 vols., Leipzig, 1828–1831). Same text with additional fragments edited by C. Müller (2 vols., Paris, Didot, 1842–1844. Greek and Latin). New editions by L. Dindorf (5 vols., Leipzig, 1888–1906) and by Fr. Vogel (5 vol., Leipzig, 1888–1906).

French translation by Ferd. Hoefer (4 vols., Paris, 1865). German translation by Adolf Wahrmund (6 vols., Stuttgart, 1866–1869).

Criticism—Friedrich Wilhelm von Bissing: Der Bericht des Diodor über die Pyramiden (Bibl. I, 63, 2–64, 40 p., Berlin, 1901). F. Kanngiesser: Die Seuche im Lager der Karthager v. Syrakus (Medizin. Klinik, 677, 1912); Die attische Seuche bei Diodor (Münch. med. Wchscht., 375, 1912).

JUBA II

King of Mauretania, educated in Rome, restored to his kingdom in 29 B. C.; established his new capital in Caesarea;[m] died c. 20 A. D. Historian and archaeologist. One of the most learned kings. He wrote on the history of Rome; on Assyria, Arabia, Libya; on the art of painting (with biographies of artists); on the history of the theater. His works were one of the main sources of Pliny. Juba made inquiries with regard to the Fortunate Islands (Canaries), which he believed to be five in number. He knew the Niger. He originated some absurd theories about the Nile, for example, that it has its source in a mountain of Western Mauretania, not far from the ocean.[n]

Otto Hense: De Juba artigrapho (Philol. Ges., Acta, t. 4, 321 p., Leipzig, 1875). Hermann Peter: Über den Werth der historischen Schriftstellerei von Juba II. (Progr., 14 p., Meissen, 1879). E. H. Bunbury: Ancient Geography (vol. 2, 174–176, 201, 1879). Friedrich Reuss: De Jubae regis historia romana a Plutarcho expressa (Progr., 27 p., Wetzlar, 1880). Sandys: History of Classical Scholarship (vol. 1³, 294, 1921).

DIONYSIOS OF HALICARNASSOS

Διονύσιος, flourished in Rome from 30 to 8 B. C. Greek historian and philologist. He wrote a work on early Roman history (Ῥωμαϊκὴ αρχαιολογία) to explain Rome's greatness to the Greeks, and various commentaries, literary and grammatical studies. His activity contributed much to maintain a high standard of Atticism (vs. Asianism).

Text—Opera omnia, Greek and Latin, edited by Friedrich Sylburg (2 vols., Frankfurt, 1586; Leipzig, 1691). Edition by John Hudson (2 vols., Oxford, 1704). Edition variorum, Greek and Latin (6 vols., Leipzig, 1774–1775). Opera omnia (together with the fragments published by Angelo Mai in 1816, 6 vols., Leipzig, 1869–1883). Edition by Hermann Usener and Ludwig Radermacher (Leipzig, 1899–1904).

---

[l] It was divided into three sections: (I) Before the Trojan War (6 books); (II) From that war to Alexander's death (11 books); (III) From 323 to the beginning of Caesar's conquest of Gaul (58).

[m] Formerly Iol; now Cherchel (Zershell).

[n] This may have been the origin of another long-lived error, the belief in the connection between the Nile and the Niger.

Antiquitatum Romanorum libri X (Treviso, 1480); (Reggio d'Emilia, 1498). Modern edition by Karl Jacoby (4 vols., Leipzig, 1885–1905). Greek and Latin edition by Adolphe Kiessling and Victor Prou (Paris, Didot, 1886). English translation by Edward Spelman (4 vols., London, 1758). German translation by J. L. Benzler (2 vols., Lemgo, 1771–1772). Italian translation by Francesco Venturi (Venice, 1545; Verona, 1738).

Quae fertur Ars rhetorica edited by Hermann Usener (174 p., Leipzig, 1895).

De compositione verborum, Greek and English, by W. Rhys Roberts (371 p., London, 1910). The three literary letters, Greek and English, by W. Rhys Roberts (243 p., Cambridge, 1901).

Criticism—Alwin Jacobson: Das Verhältnis des Dionys von Halicarnass zu Varro in der Vorgeschichte Roms (Progr., 15 p., Dresden, 1895). Maximilian Egger: Denys d'Halicarnasse. Essai sur la critique littéraire et la rhétorique chez les Grecs au siècle d'Auguste (319 p., Paris, 1902). Franz Halbfas: Theorie und Praxis in der Geschichtsschreibung bei Dionys (Diss., 67 p., Münster, 1910). Franz Nassal: Aesthetisch-rhetorische Beziehungen zwischen Dionysius und Cicero (Diss., Tübingen, 1910). Sandys: History of Classical Scholarship (vol. 1^3, 279–287, 1921).

LIVY

Titus Livius, born at Padua in 59; flourished in Rome; died, probably at Padua, in 17 A. D. Roman historian. He wrote (c. 29 to 12 B. C.) an immense history of Rome from the beginning to his own time (Ab Urbe Condita, in 142 books, of which 35 are extant). This work had considerable literary merit and was the national history of Rome par excellence. Its influence upon modern historians and publicists (chiefly through Machiavelli) has been very great.

Text—Reproduction réduite du MS. en onciale, latin 5730 de la Bibliothèque Nationale (4 vols., Paris, 19—). Codex Vindobonensis lat. 15 phototypice editus. Praefatus est C. Wessely (Leyde, 1907, sixth century manuscript).

First edition appeared in Rome, c. 1469. Many other editions appeared before 1500.

Edition by Ant. Zingerle (6 vols., Leipzig, 1883–1901). By O. Riemann, E. Benoist, T. Homolle (3 vols., Paris, 1891–1911). By Robert Seymour Conway and William Charles Flamstead Walters (2 vols., Oxford, 1914–1919).

Criticism—Hippolyte Taine: Essai sur Tite Live (Paris, 1856). J. T. Shotwell: History of History (247–256, 1922).

IX. LATIN AND GREEK PHILOLOGY

DIDYMOS[o]

Δίδυμος; born c. 65 B. C.; flourished in Alexandria; died c. 10 A. D. Greek philologist, grammarian, lexicographer. He wrote many commentaries on Greek literature and edited Homer, Thucydides, and the Attic orators.

Texts—Opuscula ed. by Fr. Ritter (Köln, 1845). Fragmenta quae supersunt ed. Moritz Schmidt (Leipzig, 1854).

Aristarchs homerische Textkritik edited by Arthur Ludwich (2 vols., Leipzig, 1884–1885).

Lichtdrucke des Didymospapyros (Hrg. von der Verwaltung der Kgl. Museen., Berlin, 1904). De Demosthene commenta ed. by H. Diels and W. Schubart (64 p., Leipzig, 1904). Didymos Kommentar zu Demosthenes (Papyrus 9780) nebst

[o] Nicknamed Chalcenteros (χαλκέντερος, meaning of brazen bowels) because of his prodigious industry (Suidas).

Wörterbuch zu Demosthenes Aristocratea (Papyrus 5008) ed. by H. Diels and W. Schubart (148 p., Berlin, 1904).

Friedrich Hultsch: Heronis Alexandrini geometricorum et stereometricorum reliquiae. Accedunt Didymi Alexandrini mensurae marmorum, etc. (358 p., Berlin, 1864).

Criticism—Walther Florian: Studia Didymea historica ad saeculum quartum pertinentia (Diss., 86 p., Leipzig, 1908). Sandys: History of Classical Scholarship (vol. 1^3, 140–143, 1921).

FLACCUS

Verrius Flaccus. Flourished at Rome c. 10 B. C.; died at a very old age, under Tiberius. Roman lexicographer and grammarian. Author of the earliest Latin lexicon (de verborum significatu); this was apparently an encyclopaedic dictionary, for it contained much information upon the things themselves as well as upon the words.

Text—The text of Verrius's dictionary is lost, but it survives in an incomplete abridgment by Pompeius Festus (second century), which was in its turn abridged by Paulus Diaconus (c. 725–797). M. V. Flacci quae extant ex Sex. Pompei Festi de verborum significatione (Venice, 1560). Edition by André Dacier (Amsterdam, 1700); by A. J. Valpy (3 vols., London, 1826). Sexti Pompei Festi de verborum significatu quae supersunt cum Pauli epitome, ed. by Wallace M. Lindsay (600 p., Leipzig, 1913).

Criticism—Robert Kriegshammer: De Varronis et Verrii fontibus (Diss., Comment. phil. ienensium, t. 7, 73–126, 1903). Max Rabenhorst: Der ältere Plinius als Epitomator des Verrius Flaccus (Nat. hist., Bk. 7, 138 p., Berlin, 1907). Sandys: History of Classical Scholarship (vol. 1^3, 200, 1921).

See also my notes on Varro in Section V and on Dionysios of Halicarnassos in Section VIII.

CHAPTER XIII

THE TIME OF CELSUS

(First Half of First Century)

I. Survey of Science in First Half of First Century. II. Religious Background. III. Roman and Hellenistic Astronomy. IV. Hellenistic Alchemy. V. Roman Geography. VI. Roman and Hellenistic Medicine. VII. Roman Historiography.

I. SURVEY OF SCIENCE IN FIRST HALF OF FIRST CENTURY

1. The first half of the first century was even poorer than the previous period. Scientific activity reached a very distinct minimum. It was a time of suspense. The only great figure, not a very great one, was that of Celsus the physician.

2. *Religious Background*—And yet this was a time of immense and unique significance for a great part of the civilized world—the time of Christ. It is hardly necessary to enlarge on this.

While a new religion was thus ushered into existence, a philosopher of Alexandria, Philon the Jew, was making a great effort to reconcile the traditional wisdom of his people with Greek philosophy. Philon's personality is arresting. He is the forerunner of a great many philosophers and theologians—Jewish, Christian, Muslim—who will endeavor to harmonize religious faith and scientific knowledge.

3. *Roman and Hellenistic Astronomy*—The Stoic philosopher Manilius, who lived at the beginning of the century, is the only astronomer of note, and he is not a real astronomer, but rather an astrologer, though he had a scientific spirit.

The cycle of twelve animals, used throughout Central and Eastern Asia to designate twelve successive years (or months, days, double hours), originated probably in Egypt in the first century.

4. *Hellenistic Alchemy*—It is possible that Alexandrian alchemy dates from about the same time; it may be even earlier, or it may have developed in the following century. The earliest Greek writer on alchemy was probably Democritos (Pseudo-Democritos), but his own date is hardly more definite.

5. *Roman Geography*—The Spaniard Pomponius Mela (c. 43) the earliest Roman geographer, wrote a brief description of the world, probably based upon Greek models, but much inferior to them. He asserted the existence of antichthones and mentioned for the first time the Baltic Sea.

6. *Roman and Hellenistic Medicine*—The first official (Roman) school of medicine was established in Rome about the year 14. This organization was gradually perfected and extended to provincial centers. It lasted probably until the sixth century. At the beginning, medical teaching was imparted in Greek.

The greatest physician of the age was the encyclopaedist A. C. Celsus (flourished c. 14 to 37) who wrote an elaborate and beautiful medical treatise, which is the most impressive monument of Roman medicine. Another Roman, Scribonius Largus, compiled c. 47 a large collection of prescriptions. The freedman Menecrates dedicated to the emperor Claudius a Greek treatise on drugs, containing many novelties.

7. *Roman Historiography*—The only historian deserving mention is Quintus Curtius, who wrote, in a declamatory style, a history of Alexander the Great.

8. *Conclusion*—This age was almost exclusively Roman, and to a large extent Latin. Yet the New Testament was written in Greek; the deepest thinker of the time, Philon the Jew, wrote in Greek, and so did the early Alexandrian alchemists and the freedman Menecrates. But Manilius, Celsus, Mela, Scribonius, Curtius wrote in Latin.

II. RELIGIOUS BACKGROUND

The Birth of Christianity

No one can study the evolution of scientific thought at the beginning of our era without taking full account of the stupendous religious events which occurred at the same time. The birth of Christianity changed forever the face of the western world. It is not possible, however, nor is it necessary, to give here an adequate summary of that great subject.

It will suffice to refer to a few standard books and first of all, to the excellent dictionaries edited by James Hastings: The Dictionary of Christ and the Gospels (2 vols., Edinburgh, 1906–1908); Dictionary of the Apostolic Church (2 vols., Edinburgh, 1915–1918).

Edward Meyer: Ursprung und Anfänge des Christentums (Stuttgart, 1921). F. J. Foakes-Jackson and Kirsopp Lake: The Beginnings of Christianity (London, 1922 sq.).

For the Jewish point of view, see J. W. Lightley: Jewish Sects and Parties in the Time of Jesus (424 p., London, 1925), and Joseph Jacobs: Jesus as Others Saw Him (230 p., New York, 1925. An excellent work; Isis, VIII, 532).

An attempt is made to quote in the Critical Bibliography of Isis (under S. I) the most important publications relative to Jesus, the Apostolic Age, and the beginnings of Christianity.

The Christian era was introduced only in the first half of the sixth century by Dionysius Exiguus (q. v.). The purpose was to date all events with reference to the greatest of them, the Incarnation. However, it is now almost certain that Dionysius's computations were wrong. In other words, it is highly probable that Christ was born before Christ (c. 8 B. C.?). According to the latest discussion of the subject (in the Chronologie of E. Cavaignac, 14, 197–211, 1925) the Passion took place in April of the year 29, or even 28. Upon that basis (28), Paul's conversion occurred in 30, his first mission in 45–47, his second mission in 50. See also W. M. Calder: The Date of the Nativity (Discovery, I, 100–103, 1920; Isis, III, 453).

PHILON THE JEW

Philo Judaeus (Φίλων). Born in Alexandria c. 20 B. C., died after 40 A. D. Jewish philosopher, who wrote a large number of works (allegorical interpretations of the Old Testament, etc.) in Greek,[a] to reconcile Greek with Jewish wisdom. He had been deeply influenced by the Pythagoreans, by Plato, and by the Stoics, and in his turn he was a forerunner of Gnosticism, Neoplatonism, and of

[a] He knew Hebrew, but it is typical that he used the Septuagint without being aware of its disagreements with the Hebrew text. There has been much discussion about the authenticity of various writings ascbried to Philon.

the Greek fathers of the Church.[b] His influence upon the Jews was inconsiderable, for Hellenistic Judaism soon gave way to Palestinian Judaism.[c] He wrote a treatise on oneirology (in 5 books, 2 extant).

Texts—Princeps editions by A. Turnèbe (Paris, 1552. Very incomplete). Important edition by Thomas Mangey with Latin translation (2 vols., London, 1742). Since then new texts have been added, some being derived from Armenian versions. Edition by Leopold Cohn and Paul Wendland (6 vols., Berlin, 1896–1915).

English translation by C. D. Yonge (Bohn Library, 4 vols., London, 1854–1855). Commentaire allégorique des saintes lois après l'oeuvre des six jours. Texte grec, trad. française, introd. par Emile Bréhier (Paris, 1909).

General Criticism—Emil Schürer: Geschichte des jüdischen Volkes im Zeitalter Jesu Christi (2 vols., 1886). Edouard Herriot: Philon (385 p., Paris, 1898). M. Croiset: Littérature grecque, t. 5, 421–434, 1899). Jacob Zallel Lauterbach: Jewish Encyclopaedia (t. 10, 6–18, 1905). L'abbé Jules Martin: Philon (Les grands philosophes, Paris, 1907). Emile Bréhier: Les idées philosophiques et religieuses de Philon (350 p., Paris, 1908).

Special Criticism—Max Freudenthal: Die Erkenntnislehre Philos (Berliner Studien, t. 13, 77 p., 1891). Leopold Cohn: Einteilung und Chronologie der Schriften Philos. (Philologus, Sup. Bd. 7, 385–436, 1899). Jakob Horovitz: Philons und Platons Lehre von der Weltschöpfung (Diss., 114 p., Marburg, 1900). Henri Guyot: Les réminiscences de Philon chez Plotin (92 p., Paris, 1906). Mathilda Chr. M. Apelt: De rationibus quibusdam quae Philoni Alexandrino cum Posidonio intercedunt (Diss., Jena, 1907). P. Duhem: Études sur Léonard de Vinci (t. 2, 286–291, 1909. Apropos of the περὶ κόσμου or περὶ ἀφθαρσίας κόσμου falsely ascribed to Philon—Boetius is quoted in it!—chiefly from the geological point of view. Budé published a Latin version of that work in Paris, 1526). Karl Herzog: Spekulativ-psychologische Entwicklung der Grundlagen und Grundlinien des philonischen Systems (Diss., 127 p., Erlangen, 1911). H. A. A. Kennedy: Philo's contributions to religion (256 p., London, 1919). Thomas H. Billings: The Platonism of Philo Judaeus (114 p., Chicago, 1919; see Journal of Hellenic Studies, vol. 40, 134, 1920). Lynn Thorndike: History of Magic (vol. 1, 348–359, 1923).

III. ROMAN AND HELLENISTIC ASTRONOMY

MANILIUS

Marcus Manilius. Flourished about the end of the Augustan age. Author of a great astrological poem (Astronomicon libri quinque). A Stoic. Like Lucretius, he believed in the fixity of the laws of nature and the absence of miracles.

Text and Translations—Editio princeps by Regiomontanus (Nürnberg c. 1473). Ad. Cramer: Über die ältesten Ausgaben von Manilius' Astronomica (Progr., 30 p., Ratibor, 1893). Edition by Fr. Jacob (Berlin, 1846); by Theod. Breiter (2 vols., Leipzig, 1907–1908); by H. W. Garrod, liber II (265 p., Oxford, 1911, with English transl.). New critical edition by A. E. Housman, not yet completed: Book I appeared in London, 1903, Book IV in 1920. The Astronomica have also been edited by Jac. van Wageningen (222 p., Leipzig, 1915), and translated into Dutch by the same author (Leiden, 1914).

General Criticism—I. Woltjer: De Manilio poeta (Progr., 95 p., Gronigen, 1881). Gustave Lanson: De Manilio poeta ejusque ingenio (Thesis, 98 p., Paris, 1887).

---

[b] His influence may be traced as early as in the Fourth Gospel and in the Epistle to the Hebrews.

[c] Besides, he can hardly be called a representative of Hellenistic Judaism, for he had no Jewish disciples. He was an independent personality.

Aug. Kraemer: De Manilii qui fertur astronomicis. Inest de imperatoribus romanis in siderum numerum relatis (Diss., 73 p., Marburg, 1890). Malwin Bechert: De Manilio poeta (Progr., 20 p., Leipzig, 1891). Joh. Moeller: Studia maniliana (Diss., 58 p., Marburg, 1901). Edwin Müller: Zur Characteristik des Manilius (Philologus, t. 62, p. 64–86, Leipzig, 1903). Th. Breiter: Die Planeten bei Manilius (Philologus, t. 64, p. 154–158, 1905). Hans Rösch: Manilius und Lucrez (Diss., 117 p., Kiel, 1911). P. Duhem: Système du monde (t. 2, 303, 1914). Jacques van Wageningen: Commentarius in M. Manilii Astronomica (347 p., 10 pl., Amsterdam, 1921; Journal des Savants, 36, 1923).

Textual Criticism—Paul Thomas: Lucubrationes manilianae (Recueil de travaux de la Faculté de philos. et lettres de Gand, 61 p., Gand, 1888). Robinson Ellis: Noctes manilianae . . . , accedunt coniecturae in Germanici Aratea (271 p., Oxford, 1891). John Percival Postgate: Silva maniliana (80 p., Cambridge, 1897). Hermann Kleinguenther. Quaestiones ad astronomicon pertinentes (Diss., Jena, 59 p., Leipzig, 1905). A. Kraemer: De locis quibusdam qui in Astronomicon libro primo exstant, ab Housmano nuperrime corruptis (47 p., Francfurt a. M., 1906). Herm. Kleinguenther: Textkritische und exegetische Beiträge zum astrogischen Lehrgedicht des sogenannten Manilius (50 p., Leipzig, 1907).

Chronology—Berth. Freier: De Manilii quae feruntur astronomicon aetate (Diss., 90 p., Goettingen, 1880). A. Kraemer: Ort und Zeit der Abfassung der Astronomica (Progr., 27 p., Frankfurt a. M., 1904. The Astronomicon was written in Rome under Augustus).

The Cycle of Twelve Animals

In every Eastern country, from Turkestan to Japan, they use a cycle of twelve animals corresponding to twelve consecutive years. The animals are always placed in the same order: mouse or rat, ox, tiger or panther, hare, dragon or crocodile, snake, horse, sheep or goat, monkey, chicken, dog, pig or boar. The same animals are used also to designate twelve successive months, twelve days, or twelve double hours—just as in the Greco-Roman world successive hours, days, months, years, and epochs were placed under the domination of the seven planets and designated by them. According to F. Boll, this cycle of twelve animals originated in Egypt in the first century. If this is correct, it gives one a new proof of the immense influence exerted by the Hellenistic upon the Central Asian and Chinese civilizations.

See Franz Boll: Der ostasiatische Tierzyklus im Hellenismus (T'oung Pao, t. 13, 699–718, 8 pl., 1912). See my note on Abe Seimei in the second half of the tenth century.

IV. HELLENISTIC ALCHEMY

According to Ed. O. von Lippmann, "Entstehung und Ausbreitung der Alchemie" (Berlin, 1919), the earliest Greek writings on alchemy would date from the first century, and he devotes special paragraphs of his book to the following alchemists, who flourished presumably in the first century: Democritos (Pseudo-Democritos, see below), Pammenes, Maria, Cleopatra, Comarios. The actual authors of the works attributed to Hermes, Agathodaemon, Isis, Chimes, Ostanes, Petesis, Iamblichos, Moses, Joannes, also flourished probably some time at the beginning of our era (Isis, III, 302).

DEMOCRITOS

Pseudo-Democritos (Δημόκριτος). Flourished possibly in the first century or in the third? The earliest Greek writer on alchemy. His main work is the

Physica et Mystica (φυσικά καὶ μυστικά). Other alchemical writings ascribed to the philosopher Democritos are extant in Syriac.

Text and Translations—M. Berthelot et Ch. Em. Ruelle: Traités démocritains (Collection des anciens alchimistes grecs, t. I, Paris, 1887. Greek text, French translation and commentary). The Syriac texts have been published and translated into French by Rubens Duval and commented upon by M. Berthelot in the latter's La chimie au moyen âge (t. II, L'alchimie syriaque, Paris, 1893).

According to Berthelot, these Democritan treatises would be coeval with the Leyden Papyrus (third century); I place them in the first, following Lippmann.

Criticism—John Ferguson: On the First Editions of the Chemical Writings of Democritus and Synesius (Proc. Philos. Soc. of Glasgow, 11 p., 1884). E. O. von Lippmann: Entstehung der Alchemie (27–46, 327–333, 1919).

V. ROMAN GEOGRAPHY

MELA

Pomponius Mela. Born at Tingentera (?) Southern Spain; flourished under Claudius, c. 43 A. D. Earliest Roman geographer. His "De situ orbis libri III" is a short summary of descriptive geography, largely based upon Greek knowiedge, but containing new information as to details. It is much inferior to the work of Strabon. Mela asserts the existence of antichthones (ἀντιχθονοί) that is, people living in the southern temperate region beyond the torrid zone (not necessarily at the antipodes). His book was extensively used by Pliny. It contains the earliest mention of the Baltic Sea (Sinus Codanus).

Text and Translations—Editio princeps (Milan, 1471). Of the first modern editions we may quote those of Abraham Gronovius (Leiden, 1722, 1743, 1748.) French translation based upon this text by C. P. Fradin (2d ed., Paris, 1827, 3 vols., with abundant notes). Edition in 7 parts by Heinrich Tzschucke (Leipzig, 1806–1807). Louis Baudet: Géographie de Pomponius Mela (Texte et traduction, coll. Panckoucke, Paris, 1843). Text and French translation by J. J. N. Huot (Malte-Brun's editor and continuator), with geographical notes, in the Coll. Firmin-Didot, same volume as Macrobius and Varro (Paris, 1883). Gust. Parthey (280 p., Berlin, 1867). Karl Frick: Pomponii Melae de chorographia libri tres (120 p., Leipzig, 1880). German translation by Hans Philipp: Geographie des Erdkreises (Voigtländers Quellenbücher, 2 vols., Leipzig, 1912).

Criticism—D. Detlefsen: Die Geographie Afrikas bei Plinius und Mela und ihre Quellen (Quellen und Forschungen zur alten Gesch. u. Geogr., 14, 104 p., Berlin, 1908). Georg Wissowa: Die Abfassungszeit der Chorographie des Pomponius Mela (Hermes, v. 51, 89–96, 1916). Hugo Folmer: Stilistika studier öfver P. Mela (Uppsala, 1920).

VI. ROMAN AND HELLENISTIC MEDICINE

Roman Organization of Medical Studies

Asclepiades of Bithynia (q. v., first half of first century B. C.) had founded a medical school in Rome, but this was a private undertaking, the natural grouping of disciples around a famous master. Toward the end of the Augustan age (14 A. D.), however, various such schools combined, and thus was formed the first official school, the Schola medicorum. This organization was gradually improved, and under Vespasian (70 to 79) the medical teachers became civil servants; it reached its climax under Alexander Severus (222 to 235) and probably continued to exist until the death of Theodoric the Great (526). Provincial schools were established at Marseille, Bordeaux, Saragossa, etc. Medical teaching was given mainly in Greek, the use of Latin increasing gradually, but very slowly.

CELSUS

Aurelius Cornelius Celsus. Flourished under Tiberius, emperor from 14 to 37. In point of time, the third Roman encyclopaedist (Cato, Varro). The encyclopaedia entitled "Artes," which he wrote in the time of Tiberius, dealt with rhetoric, philosophy, law, military science, agriculture, and medicine. The medical part (de medicina libri VIII) only is extant. It is a masterly compilation, admirably written, our fundamental source for the history of Alexandrian medicine; the greatest medical work of antiquity after those of Hippocrates and Galen.[d] Books VII and VIII deal with surgery and contain many anatomical descriptions, including a complete account of the skeleton. Many surgical and medical descriptions have become classical: lateral lithotomy, operation of the cataract, plastic operations, removal of the tonsils, area Celsi (a skin disease), dental practice. Celsus's attitude was one of moderation between empiricism and methodism; theory and practice are equally indispensable.

His work was lost during the Middle Ages, being discovered in the first half of the fifteenth century.[e] It appeared in print before the writings of Hippocrates and Galen,[f] and its influence during the Renaissance was very great.

Text and Translations—Editio princeps (Florence, 1478). Text by Leonh. Targa (Patavia, 1769), often republished (for ex., Edward Milligan's ed., 2d ed. enlarged and improved, Edinburgh, 1831, with elaborate index), or translated. First scientific edition by Charles Daremberg (Leipzig, 1859)—all the translations quoted below are based upon it. Latest edition: Opera quae supersunt ed. Fr. Marx (Corpus medicorum latinorum, I) (600 p., Leipzig, 1915; Isis, III, 319).

French translation by A. Védrènes, preface by Paul Broca (810 p., Paris, 1876), with the Latin text and elaborate criticism, notes, indexes. Italian translation by Angiolo Del Lungo (Firenze, 1904). English translation by J. W. Underwood (2 vols., London, 1831). German translation by Eduard Scheller, with elaborate commentary, notes, indexes, and illustrations. This translation is based upon Daremberg's text revised by Walther Frieboes; it is introduced by R. Robert (2d ed., 904 p., Braunschweig, 1906). A partial translation, Über Grundfragen der Medizin (82 p.), has been edited by Theod. Meyer-Steineg for the Voigtländers Quellenbücher (Leipzig, 1912).

D. Barduzzi: Sui codici e sulle edizioni del libro De re medica (Rivista di storia critica delle scienze, t. I, p. 11–13, 1910).

Criticism (general)—Joh. Ilberg: Celsus und die Medizin in Rom (Neue Jahrb. f. d. Klass. Alt., t. 19, 377–412, 1907). Lorenzo Piazza: Il de re medica nella medicina romana (428 p., Catania, 1912). Max Wellmann: Celsus. Eine Quellenuntersuchung (Philol. Untersuchungen, 23. Heft, 142 p., Berlin, 1913. The Medicina might be simply the translation of a Greek work written by one Cassios between 14 and 26). Max Wellmann: Die Aufidius-Hypothese des neusten Celsus Herausgebers (Mitt. zur Gesch. d. Med. u. Naturw., t. 16, 269-300, 1917. Criti-

---

[d] It was probably adapted from a lost Greek original.

[e] By Guarino Veronèse in 1426. Better copies were discovered by Giovanni Lamola in 1427, and by Tommaso Parentucelli (Pope Nicholas V) in 1443, and the text was studied by Poliziano.

[f] Though later than the earlier commentaries of Jacopo da Forli on Hippocrates's Aphorisms (Venice, 1473) and on Galen's Tegne (Padua, 1475).

cism of Marx's edition; Isis, III, 319); Celsus (Archiv für Geschichte der Medizin, t. 16, 209–213, 1925).

Criticism (*special*)—E. Gurlt: Geschichte der Chirurgie (t. 1, 1898, 334–394). Joh. Lachs: Gynaekologisches von Celsus (Monatsch. f. Geburtshilfe u. Gynaek., t. 15, Ergänzungsheft, p. 451–485, Berlin, 1902). H. M. Church: Extracts from the Talmud and from Celsus Illustrative of the State of Gynaecological Science at the Beginning of the Christian Era (Medical and Surgical Journal, Jan. 1902). Otto Probst: Celsus und Plinius in ihrem Verhältnis zum achten Buch der Encyklopädie Varros (Diss., 17 p., München, 1905). Domenico Barduzzi: Celsiana Riv. di Storia delle scienze, 1919–1922 (passim).

SCRIBONIUS

Scribonius Largus. Flourished under Tiberius and Claudius. Roman pharmacologist. Published c. 47 the "Compositiones medicamentorum," a collection of 271 prescriptions. Many of the recipes are of popular origin and magical, but some are of greater scientific interest. This compilation contains, for example, the earliest account of the preparation of opium and recommends an application of an electric ray-fish for headache (electrotherapy!). Of the drugs mentioned by him, 242 were derived from plants, 36 from minerals, and 27 from animals.

Text and Translations—Scribonii Largi compositiones ed. Georg Helmreich (131 p., Leipzig, 1887). Wilhelm Schonack: Die Rezepte des Scribonius. Zum ersten Male vollständig ins Deutsche übersetzt und mit ausführlichen Arzneimittelregister versehen (214 p., Jena, 1913. A partial translation had been published by Felix Rinne, Halle, 1896).

Criticism—E. H. F. Meyer: Geschichte der Botanik (t. 2, 26–39, 1855). Wilh. Schonack: Die Rezeptsammlung des Scribonius (107 p., Jena, 1912. Important). Paul Jourdan: Notes de critique verbale sur Scribonius (Thèse, 107 p., Paris, 1919; Isis IV, 575). Fritz Trilk: Die zahnärztliche Pharmakotherapie in den Compositiones (Diss., 43 p., Leipzig, 1921; Isis, IV, 576).

MENECRATES

Menecrates of Zeophleta (Μενεκράτης).[g] Flourished under Claudius I, emperor from 41 to 54. Greek physician and druggist. He wrote and dedicated to Claudius a treatise on drugs (Emperor, unabridged book of worthy remedies; Αὐτοκράτωρ ὁλογράμματος ἀξιολόγων φαρμάκων) wherein the doses were indicated in full words to avoid confusion. He introduced various remedies, the name of one of which has survived until to-day, the emplastrum diachylum (διὰ χυλῶν = e sucis), an emplaster of litharge and herb juices.

Robert Fuchs, in Puschmann: Geschichte der Medizin (t. 1, 355, 1902). M. Neuburger: Geschichte der Medizin (t. 1, 323, 1906).

VII. ROMAN HISTORIOGRAPHY

CURTIUS

Quintus Curtius Rufus. Flourished probably during the reign of Claudius, emperor from 41 to 54. Roman rhetorician and historian. Author of a biography of Alexander the Great in ten books,[h] uncritical, but well written, in imitation of Livy and Seneca; a unique combination of Greek romance and Latin

---

[g] A freedman whose complete name was Claudius Quirina Menecrates.

[h] Books I and II are lost; the others, incomplete.

rhetoric. Curtius was apparently the first Roman historian to deal with an entirely foreign subject.

Text—Two editions of Curtius were published c. 1471 by G. Laver in Rome and Vindelin de Spira in Venice; it is not known which is the princeps. Edition by Erasmus in 1518.

Critical edition by Edmund Hedicke (Berlin, 1867; 414 p., Leipzig, 1908). Edition by S. Dosson (532 p., Paris, 1882); ninth printing revised by R. Pichon (Paris, 1912).

Englished by John Brende (London, 1553).

Spanish translation (Sevilla, 1518). Italian translations by P. Candido (Vinegia, 1531); by Tomaso Porcacchi (Vinegia, 1559).

Criticism—Alexis Chassang: Histoire du roman dans l'antiquité (Paris, 1862). Simon Dosson: Etude sur Quinte-Curce (383 p., Paris, 1887). Franz von Schwarz: Alexander des Grossen Feldzüge in Turkestan (München, 1893); article by same, in Pauly-Wissowa (vol. 8, 1871–1891, 1901). August Rüegg: Beiträge zur Erforschung der Quellenverhältnisse in der Alexandergeschichte des Curtius (Diss., 119 p., Basel, 1906). Georges Radet: La valeur historique de Quinte-Curce (C. R. de l'Acad. des Inscriptions, 356–365, 1924. Defending Curtius).

CHAPTER XIV

THE TIME OF PLINY

(Second Half of First Century)

I. Survey of Science in Second Half of First Century. II. Religious Background. III. Philosophical and Cultural Background. IV. Hellenistic Mathematics. V. Hellenistic and Chinese Astronomy. VI. Roman and Hellenistic Physics and Technology. VII. Roman and Hellenistic Botany. VIII. Roman, Hellenistic and Chinese Geography. IX. Hellenistic Medicine. X. Jewish, Roman, and Chinese Historiography. XI. Greek and Latin Philology.

I. SURVEY OF SCIENCE IN SECOND HALF OF FIRST CENTURY

1. The second half of the first century is a period of revival. A sharp recrudescence of intellectual energy can be witnessed in almost every field, as the following summary will clearly show.

2. *Religious Background*—The greatest personality of early Christendom (outside of the Master) was that of St. Paul. His activity began in the first half of the century, perhaps as early as the year 30, but it did not culminate, nor did it begin to tell, until the second half. It is easier, in this Introduction, to speak of Paul than of Christ. For one thing, the latter is almost above our reach and ken. And then, it is easier to consider Paul's endeavors in their proper perspective. They constitute an essential part not only of the religious, but also of the philosophical background. Paul was the first organizer of Christian doctrine; he it is who first assured its wordly triumph.

A new attempt to introduce Buddhism into China was probably made during the rule of Ming-Ti in 66, but it did not bear any fruit.

3. *Philosophical and Cultural Background*—Of the many emperors of this age—Claudius (41 to 54), Nero (54 to 68) and the three Flavian emperors (69 to 96), Vespasian (69 to 79), Titus, and Domitian—the one whom the historian of science will encounter most frequently is the infamous Nero, who organized the first persecution of the Christians in 64. Nero's teacher, Seneca, was the leading philosopher of the time; and his "Natural questions" contain abundant information on many scientific subjects, for example, the earliest detailed account of an earthquake (63). However, the greatest scientist in a general way was Pliny the Elder. He completed in 77 his "Natural History," an encyclopaedia of very wide scope, even wider than the title indicates. This work is of very great importance, not only as a mirror of contemporary knowledge, but also because it remained the main source of scientific information during a large part of the Middle Ages. Toward the end of the same period, a third author of encyclopaedic type, Plutarch, was writing a number of books in Greek. These three men, Seneca, Pliny, and Plutarch, were not very great, for they lacked originality, but they were men of considerable weight, who influenced the scientific and ethical development of mankind almost to our days. I shall not refer to them again in the following paragraphs of this survey, but it should be understood that

to investigate any subject relative to that time it is necessary first of all to consult the writings of these three men.

Contemporary Chinese philosophy was represented by the "heterodox" Wang Ch'ung, who died in 97.

4. *Hellenistic Mathematics*—The two mathematicians, Nicomachos and Menelaos, equally great in different fields, were probably contemporaries. The second flourished in Rome about 98; the date of the former can not be determined as neatly, but we shall not be far wrong if we place him too toward the end of the century. Both can be considered as the founders of separate branches of mathematics, in the sense that they were the first to recognize their relative independence: Nicomachos was the founder of arithmetic and Menelaos of trigonometry. Nicomachos made important investigations in the theory of numbers and Menelaos in spherical geometry.

5. *Hellenistic and Chinese Astronomy*—The mathematician Menelaos made astronomical observations and advanced the study of mathematical astronomy.

Chia K'uei improved the sphere of Kêng Shou-ch'ang.

6. *Roman and Hellenistic Physics and Technology*—Nero once appeared at the circus using a cut emerald as a lens. He ordered the piercing of the isthmus of Corinth. Onasandros composed, not long before 59, a treatise on the military art. All this is not very important, but the same age witnessed the activity of the greatest engineer of antiquity, Frontinus, who wrote a treatise on the water-supply of Rome. The mathematicians above mentioned must be again considered in this section, for Menelaos is said to have made some investigations on specific gravity, and Nicomachos wrote a treatise on harmony.

Information of chemical interest is contained in the work of Dioscorides.

7. *Roman and Hellenistic Botany*—The greatest botanist of the time was Dioscorides, but we shall deal with him in the medical section below. The Spaniard Columella wrote a treatise on agriculture. The Greek Pamphilos compiled a dictionary of plants.

8. *Roman, Hellenistic, and Chinese Geography*—Two important expeditions took place at about that time: the periplus of the Erythrean Sea, of which we have a Greek account, and the exploration of the Upper Nile (down to latitude 9° N.?) made during the reign of Nero, and briefly reported by Pliny and Seneca. Under Domitian (81 to 96), Dionysios Periegetes wrote in Greek verse a description of the world. This poem has but little scientific value, but it was one of the most popular sources of geographic knowledge in mediaeval times.

The historian Pan Ku included in his history of the earlier Han dynasty a complete and detailed geography of China, together with some information on foreign peoples.

9. *Hellenistic Medicine*—The foremost physician of the period was Dioscorides, a military doctor who flourished about the middle of the century. His great treatise on materia medica, containing descriptions of about 600 plants, remained, under various forms, the standard text-book on the subject for some fifteen centuries.

Athenaeos of Attalia founded in Rome the Pneumatic school of medicine; this school was developed by Agathinos. Demosthenes Philalethes wrote a treatise on eye diseases which exerted considerable influence, and another on children's diseases, the only one of its kind in antiquity. Andromachos the Elder and the Younger (father and son), Damocrates, and Xenocrates of Aphrodisias were especially interested in drugs. Herodotos and Thessalos, on the contrary, both belonging to the Methodist school, tried to develop general views on pathology. Many of these physicians were practicing in Rome, most of them had a Roman clientele, but it is noteworthy that all of them were Greek, and all of their works which are explicitly mentioned were written in Greek.

10. *Jewish, Roman, and Chinese Historiography*—The Jewish historian Flavius Josephus wrote in Greek many important works dealing with the history and antiquities of his people. It is through his writings that the fragments of Manethon and Berossos have been transmitted to us. His younger contemporary Tacitus, one of the greatest historians of all times, has left many works which are valuable not only for the history of Rome, but also for the early history of various European countries.

The great Chinese historian Pan Ku, who died in 92, wrote a history of the Earlier Han dynasty (the second of the twenty-four dynastic histories) which contains also a chronology of earlier times and a catalogue of the books published until his own time.

11. *Greek and Latin Philology*—Pamphilos of Alexandria compiled a Greek dictionary; the woman Pamphila wrote a history of Greek literature; Erotianos compiled a Hippocratic lexicon of great importance.

Palaemon of Vicenza wrote the earliest school-book on Latin grammar. His study of the subject was completed by the Syrian Valerius Probus, who was the first to apply the Alexandrian methods of criticism to the editing of Latin texts. The most famous teacher of the age was the Spaniard Quintilian. His work is important not only from the purely philological or rhetorical point of view, but also from the general pedagogical point of view. Education in ancient and medieval times was, of course, largely concerned with the teaching of language, and even to this day, when we speak of pedagogues, we think, first of all, of grammarians.

12. *Conclusions*—The contrast between this period and the previous one is enormous. Against the one outstanding personality of the first half of the century, the Roman Celsus, we can array in the second half, the Chinese Pan Ku and ten others in the West—Greeks, Romans, and Jews: Dioscorides, Demosthenes, Seneca, Flavius Josephus, Pliny, Plutarch, Nicomachos, Frontinus, Menelaos, and Tacitus! What is even more significant, we witness the creation, the recognition as independent subjects, of a series of new branches of learning—trigonometry, arithmetic, hydraulics, ophthalmology, pediatrics, Latin grammar. The apparition of the last subject is, of course, a cause of sadness rather than of joy, for it means that the golden age of Latin literature, the days of philological innocence, are already over and that the decadence has set in. It will be remembered that Greek grammar was not systematized until the first half of the second century B. C.; the evolution and crystallization of Latin grammar was much more rapid, because it was largely modeled upon the Greek example. In a way, one might say that the Roman writers, even those of the golden age, were never able to share the innocence of the Greek classics, because linguistic consciousness had been introduced in the meanwhile by the Alexandrian grammarians. If we leave this sad subject out of the picture—and it is sad only from the literary point of view—the achievements of this period are cheering enough. By the end of the century one has good reason to hope that the Roman power has not entirely destroyed the scientific spirit and one may look forward to a new period of scientific creation on a larger scale.

II. RELIGIOUS BACKGROUND

SAINT PAUL

Paul the Apostle (Παῦλος). Originally Saul. Born in Tarsos, Cilicia; his parents were Pharisees and Roman citizens; educated at Jerusalem; after his conversion to Christianity (in 30 or later) he flourished mainly at Antioch, but traveled extensively as a missionary—the first great missionary of Christ—in Asia Minor, Thracia, Greece; he was imprisoned at Caesarea c. 58 to 60, then taken to Rome; he was probably put to death under Nero, i. e. before 68. Greco-Jewish apostle, "The Apostle of the Gentiles." He is rightly called "the second founder of Christianity." He was the first Christian theologian, and he it was who first drew clean-cut distinctions between Judaism and Christianity and completed the transformation of a small Jewish sect into a universal religion. He is the supreme figure of the Apostolic Age (c. 30 to 100) and his Epistles are an essential part of the New Testament. Those of undisputed genuineness (Corinthians, Galatians, Romans) were probably written in 56–57.[a] His theological ideas[b] (on predestination, election, justification by faith) exerted a tremendous influence upon the development of Christian thought.

E. Renan: Saint Paul (650 p., Paris, 1869). Otto Pfeiderer: Der Paulinismus (1873; Englished, 1877); The Influence of Paul on the Development of Christianity (Hibbert lectures, 292 p., London, 1885). Auguste Sabatier: L'apôtre Paul (2[e] ed., 1881; Englished by G. G. Findlay, 1896). Sir W. M. Ramsay: Saint Paul the Traveler and the Roman Citizen (London, 1895). Karl Clemen: Paulus (Giessen, 1904). R. J. Knowling: Testimony of St. Paul to Christ (London, 1905). Adolf Harnack: Chronologische Berechnung des Tags von Damaskus (Berlin, Sitzungsber, Akad., 673–682, 1912); Ist die Rede des Paulus in Athens ein ursprünglicher Bestandteil der Apostelgeschichte? (100 p., Leipzig, 1913). W. H. P. Hatch: The Pauline Idea of Faith (Thesis, 97 p., Cambridge, Mass., 1917). Constant Toussaint: L'hellénisme et l'apôtre Paul (Thèse, Paris, 1921). Wilfred L. Knox: St. Paul and the Church of Jerusalem (424 p., Cambridge, 1925). Terrot Reaveley Glover: Paul (London, 1925).

KĀŚYAPA-MĀTAṄGA

Also written Kashiapmadanga. In Chinese Shê[4]*-mo[1]-t'êng[2] (9806, 7969, 10892) or Mo-t'êng. Flourished at Lo[4]*-Yang[2] (7328, 12883) in 67 and died not very long afterward. Hindu Buddhist, said to have returned into China with the mission sent in 66 by Ming[2]-Ti[4] (7946, 10942) (emperor of the Later Han dynasty from 58 to 76) to enquire about Buddhism. He settled at the Monastery of the White Horse[c] at Lo-yang and together with his countryman Gobharaṇa,[d] he began a Chinese translation of the Sūtra in forty-two sections,[e] Ssŭ[4] shih[2]* êrh[4] chang[1] ching[1] (10291, 9959, 3363, 390, 2122).

---

[a] It is now generally agreed that the Epistle to the Hebrews was not written by him.

[b] Represented by the general term Paulinism. It should not be forgotten, however, that this term is often used with reference to ideas ascribed to Paul or to misinterpretations of his ideas.

[c] Pai[2] ma[3] ssŭ[4] (8556, 7576, 10295); thus named much later, of course.

[d] In Chinese, Chu[2]* Fa[2]*-lan[2] (2574, 3366, 6721).

[e] This story is far from being certain, but I quote it because of the extreme importance of the introduction of Buddhism into China. According to Chinese tradition, Ming-Ti's was not the first, but the third, attempt to introduce Buddhism—two earlier ones having been

H. A. Giles: Biographical Dictionary (370, 753, 1898). Henri Maspero: Le songe et l'ambassade de l'empereur Ming-Ti. Bull. de l'école française d'Extrême Orient (95–130, 1910). O. Franke: Zur Frage der Einführung des Buddhismus in China (Mitt. des Sem. f. orient. Sprachen, Berlin, t. 13, 1910. Dealing with the mission of the year 2 B. C.; see E. Chavannes, in T'oung Pao, t. XI, 536–537, 697). R. F. Johnston: Buddhist China (135, London, 1913).

III. PHILOSOPHICAL AND CULTURAL BACKGROUND

NERO

Born at Antium in 37; Roman emperor from 54 to his self-inflicted death, near Rome, in 68. This infamous character is quoted because of three events which occurred during his reign: the exploration of the Upper Nile;[f] his use, at the circus, of a cut emerald as a lens;[g] the digging of a canal to cut the Isthmus of Corinth (interrupted in 68).[h]

Criticism—Among earlier works on Nero I quote for the sake of curiosity Girolamo Cardano (1501–1576): Neronis encomium (144 p., Amsterdam, 1640).

Adam Hendrik Raabe: Geschichte und Bild von Nero (Utrecht, 1872). Hermann Schiller: Geschichte des römischen Kaiserreichs unter Nero (728 p., Berlin, 1872). Fr. Wiedemeister: Der Cäsarenwahnsinn der Julisch Claudischen Imperatorenfamilie (Hanover, 1875). Gustav Nordmeyer: Der Tod Neros in der Legende (Gymnasium Festschrift, Moers, 1896). Bernard William Henderson: Life and Principate of Nero (544 p., 3 maps, 16 pl., London, 1903). John Nicholas Henry Jahn: Critical Study of the Sources of the History of Nero (Thesis, New York, 1920). Werner Schur: Der Orientpolitik des Kaisers Nero (Klio, Beiheft 15, Leipzig, 1923).

The great fire of Rome in 64—Nero has been accused of starting that terrible fire himself in order to be able to rebuild the city. This is hardly credible, but it is a fact that he organized the reconstruction of the city on an improved plan. He tried to throw the odium of this calamity on the Christians, many of whom were put to death on that account. The culpability of either Nero or the Christians, or of any Christian, can not be proved. Rome was a highly inflammable city at that time.

Carlo Pascal: L'incendio di Roma e i primi Cristiani (2d ed. con molte aggiunte, 41 p., Torino, 1900. Against the Christians). Vincenzo de Crescenzo: Un defensore di Nerone (28 p., Napoli, 1900. Against Pascal). Gabriele Cavazzi: Sull' incendio di Roma sotto Nerone (Roma, 1902. Against Pascal). Paul Allard: Les Chrétiens ont-ils incendié Rome? (62 p., Paris, 1904). Attilio Profumo: Le fonti ed i tempi dello incendio romano (758 p., Roma, 1905).

SENECA

Lucius Annaeus Seneca. Born at Cordova, Spain, 4 B. C., died in 65. Writer, philosopher, the leader of Stoicism in Rome, statesman, scientist. His "Quaestiones naturales" are a collection of physical, astronomical, geographical, geolog-

---

made in the third century B. C. and in the year 2 B. C. But Ming-Ti's attempt is the first for which there is some evidence. At any rate, Chinese Buddhism did not emerge from obscurity until the third century.

[f] For which see my note in Section VIII.

[g] Pliny's Natural History, book 37, ch. 16 (smaragdus). It is known that Nero was short-sighted.

[h] The modern canal, built in 1882–1893, follows exactly the same course as that planned by Nero's engineers. It is 6,300 meters long.

ical, and meteorological questions explained from the atomistic point of view. They contain hardly anything which is really original, but exerted a great influence throughout the Middle Ages. Special mention must be made of his account of the earthquake which did much damage in Campania on February 5, 63—the earliest detailed account of an earthquake. This led him to discuss earthquakes and volcanic phenomena. He distinguished three kinds of motion in quakes (succussio, inclinatio, and vibratio). Seneca was the first to express a belief in the progress of knowledge (not the progress of humanity); this idea of progress is unique in ancient literature. Earlier monographs of Seneca on India and Egypt and on earthquakes are lost.

Text and Translation—Editio princeps (Naples, 1475). Critical edition in 4 vols. by Hermes and others (Leipzig, 1898–1907; Vols. I–III republished 1905–1914; vol. II contains the Naturalium quaestionum libri VIII (only 7 books are extant) edited by Alfred Gercke, 326 p., 1907). English translation by John Clarke, with notes by Sir Archibald Geikie (422 p., London, 1910. Particularly interesting from the geological and meteorological standpoint).

Life of Seneca. General Criticism—Charles Aubertin: Sénèque et Saint Paul. Etude sur les rapports supposés entre le philosophe et l'apôtre (3e éd., 452 p., Paris, 1872; 1e éd., 1869). Eugen Westerburg: Der Ursprung der Frage dass Seneca Christ gewesen sei (52 p., Berlin, 1881). P. Hochart: Etudes sur la vie de Sénèque (300 p., Paris, 1885). Constant Martha: Sénèque (Lecture à l'Ac. des sci. morales, 1890; reprinted in Mélanges de littérature ancienne, 215–252, Paris, 1896). Alfred Gercke: Seneca Studien (Jahrbücher für classische Philol., Suppl. Bd. 22, 333 p., Leipzig, 1895; I, Die Überlieferung der Natur. Quaest.; II, Historisch biographische Untersuchungen über Seneca und seine Zeit). René Waltz: La vie politique de Sénèque (Thèse, 462 p., Paris, 1909). Francis Holland: Seneca (206 p., London, 1920). Paul Faider: Etude sur Sénèque (325 p., Gand, 1921). Richard Mott Gummere: Seneca the Philosopher and His Modern Message (166 p., Boston, 1922; Isis, V, 491).

Criticism of the Naturales Quaestiones—Wilh. Bernhardt: Die Anschauung des Seneca vom Universum (Progr., 28 p., Wittenberg, 1861). L. Crouslé: De Senecae naturalibus quaestionibus (Thèse, 160 p., Paris, 1863). Fr. Schultess: De Senecae naturalibus quaestionibus et epistulis (Diss., 52 p., Bonn, 1872). Georg Mueller: De Senecae naturalibus quaestionibus (Diss., 46 p., Bonn, 1886). Rud. Hartmann: De naturalium quaestionum libro septimo (Diss., 37 p., Münster i. W., 1911). Aug. Brennecke: Animadversiones ad fontes naturalium quaestionum (Diss., 52 p., Gryphiae, 1913). Joh. Hemsing: De naturalium quaestionum libro primo (Diss., 33 p., Münster i. W., 1913). H. Geist: De naturalium quaestionum codicibus (Diss., 64 p., Erlangen, 1914).

Criticism of Special Topics—Gott. Friedr. Drescher: Des Seneca 88. Brief an Lucilius oder dessen Ideen über das Verhältniss der wissenschaftlichen Bildung zur Sittlichen (61 p., Buedingen, 1830). Walter Ribbeck: Seneca und sein Verhältnis zu Epikur, Plato und dem Christentum (98 p., Hanover, 1887). Edw. Gaylord Bourne: Seneca and the Discovery of America (The Academy, London, 1893. Reprinted with some rearrangement in his Essays in Historical Criticism, p. 221–242, New York, 1901). Emil Badstübner: Beitr. zur Erklärung und Kritik der philosophischen Schriften Senecas (Progr., 28 p., Hamburg, 1901). Sir Archibald Geikie: Founders of Geology (2d ed., 1905). P. Stanislaus Strüber: Seneka als Psychologe (Diss., 84 p., Heiligenstadt, 1906). Charles Burnier: La morale de Sénèque et le néo-stoïcisme (Thèse, 105 p., Lausanne, 1908). Karl Preisendanz: De Senecae patris vestigiis in Senecae philosophi scriptis deprehendis (Diss., p. 68–102, Tübingen, 1908). Heinrich Schendel: Quibus auctoribus romanis Seneca in rebus patriis usus sit (Diss., 52 p., Gryphiae, 1908). Joan Marinescu: Die stoischen Elemente in der Pädagogik Senecas (Diss., 74 p., München, 1911). Charles Burnier: La pédagogie de Sénèque (95 p., Lausanne, 1914). Hermann Mutschmann: Seneca und Epikur (Hermes, vol. 50, p. 321–356, 1915). H. Dessau: Über die Abfassungszeit einiger Schriften Senecas (Hermes, vol. 53, 188–196, 1918). J. B. Bury: Idea of Progress (p. 13–15, London, 1920). Albert Rehm: Das siebente Buch des Naturales Quaestiones (Sitzungsber. der Bayer. Ak. der Wiss., 40 p., 1921). A. Bourgery: Sénèque prosateur (445 p., Paris, 1922).

PLINY

Pliny the Elder; Gaius Plinius Secundus. Born at Como in 23, died while observing the eruption of Vesuvius in 79. Writer, civil servant, soldier, scientist. His "Naturalis Historia" in 37 books, dedicated to Titus in 77, is a scientific encyclopaedia, often uncritical, but very elaborate and of great value. Pliny attached to each book the list of his authorities, 146 Roman and 327 Greek authorities being quoted. He explained that people may be living at the antipodes (II, 65),[i] and stated that the speed of light is greater than that of sound (II, 55). His History reveals to us many other bits of knowledge, old or new, too many to be quoted. It includes the oldest account of ancient art. Its influence throughout the Middle Ages was very great.

Text and Translations—Editio princeps (Venice, 1469). Editions by J. Harduin (10 vols., Paris, 1827–1832, vol. 10: Index by A. P. Delaforest); by Julius Sillig (8 vols., Hamburg and Gotha, 1851–1858); by L. Janus (6 vols., Leipzig, 1854–1865). Edition by D. Detlefsen (6 vols., Berlin, 1866–1882); also special edition of the geographical books (Berlin, 1904). Edition by Ludwig von Jan and Karl Mayhoff (5 vols., Leipzig, 1906–1909).

English translation with copious notes and illustrations by John Bostock and H. T. Riley (6 vols., Bohn's Classical Library, London, 1855–1857. This includes notes from the latest commentators, e. g., Cuvier).

Extracts translated into German, with notes by Friedrich Dannemann: Plinius und seine Naturgeschichte in ihrer Bedeutung für die Gegenwart (Klassiker der Naturwissenschaft, 251 p., Jena, 1921; Isis, IV, 501).

General Criticism—There is no complete and up-to-date study of Pliny's "Natural History." Such a study is badly needed. It would be extremely interesting and useful, not simply as a survey of scientific lore in the first century, but also as one of the fundamental sources of mediaeval thought.

We owe a very elaborate investigation of Pliny's sources to Friedrich Münzer: Beiträge zur Quellenkritik der Naturgeschichte des Plinius (444 p., Berlin, 1897). See also: Heinrich Brunn: De auctorum indicibus Plinianis (Bonn, 1856). Detlef Detlefsen: Untersuchungen über die Zusammensetzung der Naturgeschichte (96 p., Berlin, 1899). Otto Probst: Celsus und Plinius in ihrem Verhältnis zum achten Buch der Encyklopädie Varros (Diss., 17 p., München, 1905). Max Rabenhorst: Die Zeitangaben varronischer und capitolinischer Aera in der Naturalis Historia (Diss., 71 p., Berlin, 1905). Lynn Thorndike: History of Magic (vol. 1, 42–99, 1923). E. W. Gudger: Pliny's Historia naturalis (Isis, VI, 269–281, 1924. Survey of the editions showing the immense popularity of the work). Max Wellmann: Beiträge zur Quellenanalyse des älteren Plinius (Hermes, 59, 129–156, 1924).

For the sources of Pliny relative to special topics, see below.

Pliny's Influence—Karl Rück: Auszüge aus der Naturgeschichte in einem astronomisch-komputistischen Sammelwerke des 8. Jahrh. (Progr., München, 1888).

---

[i] See my note on Crates (first half of second century B. C.).

Karl Welzhofer: Beda's Citate aus der nat. hist. Abhdl. Wilh. v. Christ dargestellt (p. 25–41, München, 1891). J. W. Beck: Studia Gelliana et Pliniana (55 p., Leipzig, 1892). Joh. Keese: Quo modo Serenus Sammonicus a medicina pliniana ipsoque Plinio pendeat (Diss., 67 p., Rostock, 1896). K. Rück: Die Anthropologie der nat. hist. im Auszuge des Robert von Cricklade (Progr., 52 p., Neuburg a. D., 1905).

Astronomy—See above, Karl Rück (1888).

Chemistry—Edm. O. v. Lippmann: Die chemischen Kenntnisse des Plinius (Festschrift d. Naturfors. Ges. des Osterlandes, Altenburg, 1892; reproduced in Abhdl. u. Vortr., I, p. 1–46, 1906). K. B. Hoffmann: Notiz zur Gesch. des Wasserbades und Reagenzpapiers (Archiv f. Gesch. d. Naturw., III, 307–308, 1911). Kenneth C. Bailey: The Identity of "alumen" in Pliny (Nature, 115, 764, 1925).

Geology, Mineralogy—August Nies: Zur Mineralogie des Plinius (Progr., 27 p., Mainz, 1884). Elmer Truesdell Merrill: Notes on the Eruption of Vesuvius in 79 (American Jour. Archaeology, vol. 22, 304–309, 1918, t. 24, 262–268, 1920).

Botany, Husbandry—Max Brosig: Die Botanik des Plinius (Progr., 30 p., Graudenz, 1883). Joh. Georg Sprengel: De ratione quae in historia plantarum inter Plinium et Theophrastum intercedit (Diss., 63 p., Marburg, 1890). Hermann Stadler: Die Quellen des Plinius in 19. Buche (Diss., 104 p., Neuburg a. D., 1891). Ludwig Renjes: De ratione quae inter Plinii librum XVI et Theophrasti libros de plantis intercedit (Diss., 101 p., Rostock, 1893). Wilh. Schlottmann: De auctoribus quibusdam in Plinii libro XVIII (Diss., 45 p., Rostock, 1893). H. Stadler: Die Beschreibung des Reises (*Oryza sativa* L.) in der Naturgeschichte (Mitt. zur Gesch. d. Med., t. 12, 277–278, 1913).

Zoology—G. Montigny: Quaestiones in nat. hist. de anim. libros (Bonn, 1844). Friedrich Aly: Die Quellen des Plinius im 8. Buche (67 p., Marburg, 1882). Gustav Heigl: Die Quellen des Plinius in XI. Buche (45 p., Marburg, 1885). Fried. Aly: Zur Quellenkritik des Plinius (Progr., 21 p., Marburg, 1885). Paul Rusch: De Varrone Plinii in libro VIII auctore (Progr., 15 p., Stettin, 1900). D. Detlefsen: Verbesserungen und Bemerkungen zum XI. Buche (Hermes, t. 40, 571–579, 1905). August Steier: Aristoteles und Plinius (Studien zur Geschichte der Zoologie, 160 p., Würzburg, 1913; reprinted from Zoologische Ann., t. 4 and 5; see Isis, II, 202).

Geography—D. Detlefsen: Die geographischen Bücher mit vollständigen kritischen Apparat (300 p., Quellen u. Forsch. zur alten Gesch., 9, Berlin, 1904).

Gustav Oehmichen: Plinianische Studien zur geographischen und kunsthistorischen Literatur (240 p., Erlangen, 1880). Detlef Detlefsen: Die Masse der Erdteile nach Plinius (Progr., 16 p., Glückstadt, 1883); Untersuchungen zu den geogr. Büchern des Plinius. I. Die Weltkarte des M. Agrippa (17 p., *ibidem*, 1884). Otto Cuntz: De Augusto Plinii geographicorum auctore (Diss., 49 p., Bonn, 1888). D. Detlefsen: Die Beschreibung Italiens in der Naturalis Historia und ihre Quellen (Quellen und Forsch. zur alten Gesch., 1, 62 p., Leipzig, 1901). Alfred Klotz: Quaestiones Plinianae geographicae (Quellen und Forsch. zur alten Gesch., 11, 228 p., Berlin, 1906). D. Detlefsen: Die Geographie Afrikas bei Plinius und Mela und ihre Quellen. Die formulae provinciarum, eine Hauptquelle des Plinius (Quellen und Forsch., 14, 104 p., Berlin, 1908); Die Anordnung der geogr. Bücher des Plinius (Quellen und Forsch., 18, 177 p., Berlin, 1909).

Anthropology, Ethnology—See K. Rück (1905, see above). Max Rabenhorst: Der ältere Plinius als Epitomator des Verrius Flaccus. Eine Quellenanalyse des 7. Buches (138 p., Berlin, 1907).

History of Art—The elder Pliny's chapters on the history of art, translated by K. Jex-Blake, with commentary and historical introduction by Eugénie Sellers [Mrs. Arthur Strong] and additional notes by Heinrich Ludwig Urlichs (London, 1896).

Adolph. Brieger: De fontibus librorum XXXIII, XXXIV, XXXV, XXXVI, quatenus ad artem plasticam pertinent (Diss., 76 p., Gryphiae, 1857). Gustav Oehmichen: Plinianische Studien (248 p., Erlangen, 1880). Hugo Voigt: De fontibus earum quae ad artes pertinent partium naturalis historiae (Diss., 25 p., Halle, 1887). Hermann Koebert: Das Kunstverständnis des Plinius (Abhdl. Wilh. v. Christ dargebracht, München, p. 134–46, 1891). August Kalkmann: Die Quellen der Kunstgeschichte des Plinius (268 p., Berlin, 1898). Fried. Hauser: Plinius und das censorische Verzeichnis (Mitteil. k. d. archaeol. Instituts, t. 20, Rom., 1905). A. P. Laurie: Greek and Roman Methods of Painting. Some Comments on the Statements made by Pliny and Vitruvius about Wall and Panel Painting (130 p., Cambridge, 1910).

Medicine—Joh. Keese (1896, see above). E. Gurlt: Geschichte der Chirurgie (t. 1, 395–398, 1898). O. von Hovorka: Über Beziehungen zwischen den Lehren des Plinius und der dalmatischen Volksmedizin (XIII• Congrès intern. de médecine Paris, 1900). Max Wellmann: Xenocrates aus Aphrodisias (Hermes, t. 42, 614–629, 1907). Erich Strunz: Zahnheilkundliches in der Naturalis historia (Diss., 36 p., Leipzig, 1921). Léon Moulé: Le folklore médical de Pline (Bull. soc. d'histoire de la médecine, t. 17, 71–85, 1923).

Apocryphal Work—The so-called Medicina Plinii is a rearrangement a capite ad calcem of the medical contents of the Natural History. It was ascribed to Pliny or to one Plinius Valerianus. It dates probably from the second half of the fourth century and may have been used by Marcellus Empiricus.

Text—Medicinae plinianae libri quinque. Princeps edition by Pighinucci (Rome, 1509). Then in the collection entitled De re medica edited by Albanus Torinus (1 vol., Bale, 1528).

Criticism—E. H. F. Meyer: Geschichte der Botanik (Bd. 2, 1855, 398–412, with a list of plants). V. Rose: Über die Medicina Plinii (Hermes, t. 8, 19–66, 1874).

PLUTARCH

Πλούταρχος Χαιρωνεύς. Born at Chaeronea in Boeotia between 46 and 50. He spent some time in Rome and other places, but finally returned to Chaeronea, where he died between 120 and 125. Greek writer and moralist, chiefly famous for his Lives (Βίοι παράλληλοι). The rest of his writings (about 80 essays), some of which deal with scientific subjects, are arbitrarily collected under the title "Moralia" ('Ηθικά). Plutarch was an enthusiastic Platonist, a lovable moralist, himself a sincere lover of truth. His main scientific writing is the one "on the face which appears in the disk of the moon" (De facie in orbe lunae; the Greek title is uncertain), which is a summary of the knowledge of his day on the constitution of the moon. He explains correctly why the moon remains faintly visible during a lunar eclipse. One can not say that the earth is the center of the universe, for the latter, being infinite, has no center. The Placita philosophorum ascribed to Plutarch is one of our main sources (though itself second-hand) for the study of ancient philosophy. The Roman Questions (Quaestiones Romanae) are a very important source for the history of Roman religion. Plutarch may be considered one of the founders of the study of comparative religion.

Text and Translations—Editio princeps, Moralia (Aldine, 1507); Lives (Florence, 1517).

Modern editions of the Lives: by Theod. Doehner (Greek and Latin, Didot coll., 2 vols., Paris, 1846–1847); by Karl Sintenis (his 2d ed., 5 vols., Leipzig, 1852–1855, many different dates on different volumes); by Imm. Bekker (5 vols., Leipzig, 1855–1857). Greek text with Eng. translation by Bernadotte Perrin in the Loeb Classical Library (6 vols., London, 1914–1918).

Modern editions of the Moralia: by Fr. Dübner (2 vols., Didot coll., Greek and Latin, Paris, 1841); by G. N. Bernadakis (7 vols., Leipzig, 1888–1896). English translation by several hands (1684–1694), re-edited (Boston, 1870) in 5 vols., by William A. Goodwin with introduction by R. W. Emerson.

The Roman Questions, a new translation with introductory essays and a running commentary by H. J. Rose (220 p., Oxford, 1924. Very valuable work for the student of comparative religion). Isis et Osiris, traduction avec prolégomènes et notes par Mario Meunier (238 p., Paris, 1924; Isis, VIII, 165–167).

The French translation of Plutarch by Jacques Amyot (1513–1593)—Vies, 1559 or 1560; Oeuvres morales, 1572,—extensively used by Montaigne, is one of the greatest monuments of French literature in the sixteenth century.

The last volume of Didot's edition (Paris, 1855), contains "Fragmenta et spuria" edited by Fr. Dübner and an Index to the complete works of Plutarch compiled by Jakob Hunziher

General criticism—Richard Volkmann: Leben, Schriften, und Philosophie des Plutarch (2 vols., Berlin, 1869). Octave Gréard: La morale de Plutarque (3e éd., Paris, 1880). John Oakesmith: The Religion of Plutarch (258 p., London, 1902). Madame Jules Favre (1834 to 1896): La morale de Plutarque (451 p., Paris, 1909. With a biography and portrait of the author). Roger Miller Jones: The Platonism of Plutarch (Diss., Chicago, 153 p., Menasha, Wisc., 1916).

Special Criticism (Philosophic)—Eduard Rasmus: In Plutarchi librum qui inscribitur de stoicorum repugnantis coniecturae (Progr., 12 p., Brandenburg, 1880). Rich. Schmertosch: De Plutarchi sententiarum quae ad divinationem spectant origine. Accedit epimetrum de Plutarchi qui fertur περὶ εἱμαρμένης libello (Diss., 37 p., Leipzig, 1889). Wal. Abernetty: De Plutarchi qui fertur de superstitione libello (Diss., 100 p., Königsberg, 1911). Joh. Schroeter: Plutarchs Stellung zur Skepsis (Diss., Königsberg, 64 p., Greifswald).

Scientific Criticism—Adolf Dyroff: Die Tierpsychologie des Plutarchos (Progr., 59 p., Würzburg, 1897). Eduard Ebner: Geographische Hinweise und Anklänge in Plutarchs Schrift de facie in orbe lunae (Münchener geograph. Studien, 19, 101 p., München, 1906). Max. Adler: Quibus ex fontibus Plutarchus libellum de facie in orbe lunae hauserit (Dissertiones philologae vindobonenses, t. X, 85–180, Wien, 1910). A. O. Prichard: On the Face which Appears on the Orb of the Moon (translated with notes and appendix, 1911). P. Duhem: Système du Monde (t. 2, p. 293 sq., 359 sq., 1914. Speaking of the De facie in orbe lunae, Duhem remarks: "Ce petit traité est une oeuvre de génie"). H. J. Lulofs: Eubiotiek van Plutarchus (Bijdragen tot de geschiedenis der geneeskunde, 5, 237–247, 1925).

WANG CH'UNG

Wang[2] Ch'ung[1] (12493, 2924). Native of Shang[4]-yü[2] (9729, 13608) in Chekiang in 27; he died in 97. Chinese "heterodox" philosopher. His philosophy is a materialistic monism inviting comparison with that of Epicuros and Lucretius. He criticized freely the superstitions of his day and even the doctrines of Confucius and Mencius. His main work is called the Lun-hêng.[i]

Text—Alfred Forke: Lun-Hêng. Philosophical and Miscellaneous Essays of Wang Ch'ung (2 vols., Leipzig, 1907–1911. Part I appeared in the Mitt. des Seminars für orient. Sprachen, Berlin, Jahrg. 9–11, 1906–1908; part II, in the Beiband zum Jahrg. 14, of the same publication).

Criticism—H. A. Giles: Biographical Dictionary (818, 1898). A. Forke: World-conception of the Chinese (15, 22, 31, 1925; Isis, VIII, 373).

---

[i] Lun[4] (7475) means essay or discussion; hêng[2] (3912), weighing things, considering them.

IV. HELLENISTIC MATHEMATICS

NICOMACHOS

Nicomachos of Gerasa (Νικόμαχος). Born at Gerasa, Arabia Petraea (?), flourished some time between 30 and 150, say toward the end of the first century. Neo-Pythagorean mathematician. His introduction to arithmetic (εἰσαγωγὴ ἀριθμητική) is the earliest treatise extant in which arithmetic is considered as an autonomous discipline. It deals with the general properties of numbers, containing, e. g., an elaborate theory of polygonal numbers and of ratios and medieties. Cubic numbers are the sums of the successive odd numbers: $1 + (3 + 5) + (7 + 9 + 11) + (13 + 15 + 17 + 19) + \ldots = 1^3 + 2^3 + 3^3 + 4^3 + \ldots$. He quoted the first four perfect numbers: 6, 28, 496, 8128,[k] and noted that the last figure was either 6 or 8.

This book was soon translated into Latin by Apuleius (second half of second century) and later by Boetius and, through the latter's version, its influence through the Middle Ages was very great. From now on, arithmetic received increasingly more attention, at the expense of geometry. Nicomachos wrote also a manual of harmony (ἐγχειρίδιον ἁρμονικῆς) which is our oldest source for Pythagorean music, and other Pythagorean books used by Iamblichos.

Text and Translations—Theologumena arithmeticae . . . , Nicomachi Gerasini institutio arithmetica, ed. by Fried. Ast. 344 p., Leipzig 1817 (the first named treatise, τὰ θεολογούμενα τῆς ἀριθμητικῆς, is now generally ascribed to Iamblichos, first half of fourth century). Nicomachi introductionis arithmeticae libri II, ed. by Ric. Hoche (211 p., Leipzig, 1866). Introduction to Arithmetic. Englished by Martin Luther D'Ooge. With studies in Greek arithmetic by Frank Egleston Robbins and L. C. Karpinski (318 p., New York, 1926; important, Isis, IX).

For the manual of harmony, see Karl von Jan, Musici scriptores greci (p. 209–282, Leipzig, 1895). For Boetius's translation, see Boetius, first half of sixth century.

Criticism—Of the old commentaries I quote only that by Joh. Philoponos of Alexandria (first half of sixth century), published, by Ric. Hoche (46 p., Berlin, 1867). On this subject see: Paul Tannery: Les commentaires sur Nicomaque (Archives et missions scientifiques, t. 13, 1888; reprinted in Tannery's Mémoires, t. 2, p. 302–310).

Paul Tannery: Sur la sommation des cubes entiers dans l'antiquité (Bibliotheca mathematica, t. 3, 257–258, 1902; Mémoires, III, 116–118; Isis, IV, 340); article Nicomaque, in Grande Encyclopédie, t. 24, 1068, Mémoires, VII, 315–317. Max Simon: Die ersten 6 Kapitel der Institutio Arithmetica des Nikomachos (Archiv. f. Gesch. d. Naturw., I, 455–463, 1909). George Johnson: The Arithmetical Philosophy of Nicomachus of Gerasa (52 p., Lancaster, Pa., 1916).

MENELAOS

Menelaos of Alexandria (Μενέλαος). He made astronomical observations in Rome in 98. Greek mathematician, astronomer, and physicist. He wrote six books (lost) on the calculation of chords and three on spherics, extant in Arabic, Hebrew, and Latin translations. The books on spherics, in contrast to Theodosios's work, are in fact a treatise on spherical trigonometry. That is, Menelaos was the first to disengage trigonometry from stereometry and astronomy. The first book of the

[k] The fifth was not given until about fourteen centuries later in a manuscript dated 1456, 1461 (Cod. lat. Monac. 14908): 33550336. (L. E. Dickson. History of the Theory of Numbers, vol. 1, 1919, 6.)

spherics contains the definition of spherical triangles (τρίπλευρον) and the explanation of their fundamental properties. Two propositions of Book III are particularly noteworthy: III, 1, is equivalent to the so-called "theorem of Menelaos" relative both to spherical and plane triangles (also called in the first case, regula sex quantitatum); III, 5, implies a knowledge of the projectivity of duplicate ratios of chords upon a sphere. He made investigations on specific gravity.[1]

Text and Translations—The Spherics have come down to us through the Arabic translation made by Isḥāq ibn Ḥunain (q. v., second half of ninth century). That translation was probably revised by Thābit ibn Qurra (q. v., second half of ninth century). Other revisions of the Arabic text were due to al-Māhānī (q. v., second half of ninth century), and Aḥmad ibn abī Sa'īd abū-l-Faḍl al-Harawī (time unknown; manuscript dated 1144–1145), Abū Naṣr Manṣūr (q. v., second half of tenth century), Naṣīr al-dīn al-Ṭūsī (second half of thirteenth century), Muḥammad ibn abī-l-Shukr al-Maghribī (probably the father of Muḥyī al-dīn al-Maghribī, q. v., second half of thirteenth century).

This Arabic text was translated into Latin by Gerard of Cremona (q. v., second half of twelfth century) and into Hebrew by Jacob ben Machir ibn Tibbon (Prophatius, q. v., second half of thirteenth century).

The first printed edition was a Latin edition by Maurolycus (Messina, 1558); this is a very poor edition, based on an imperfect manuscript and full of interpolations. Another Latin edition was given by Marin Mersenne: Universae geometriae mixtaeque mathematicae synopsis (Paris, 1644). A posthumous edition by Edmund Halley (1656–1742): Menelaei Sphaericorum libri III (120 p., Oxford 1758, with preface by George Costard; largely derived from the Hebrew text but with reference to Arabic manuscripts). The first truly complete edition was given in German, by A. A. Björnbo in the Studien quoted below (1902).

Criticism—Axel Anthon Björnbo: Studien über Menelaos' Sphärik. Beiträge zur Gesch. der Sphärik und Trigonometrie der Griechen (Abhdl. zur Gesch. d. math. Wiss., 14. Heft., 162 p., Leipzig, 1902; exhaustive study, very important). A. A. Björnbo: Hat Menelaos einen Fixsternkatalog verfasst? (Bibliotheca mathematica, II, 196–212, 1901. Important). Sir Thomas Heath: Greek Mathematics (II, 260–273, 1921).

Criticism—Axel Anthon Björnbo: Studien über Menelaos' Sphärik. Beiträge zur Gesch. der Sphärik und Trigonometrie der Griechen (Abhdl. zur Gesch. d. math. Wiss., 14. Heft., 162 p., Leipzig, 1902; exhaustive study, very important). A. A. Björnbo: Hat Menelaos einen Fixsternkatalog verfasst? (Bibliotheca mathematica, II, 196–212, 1902. Important). Sir Thomas Heath: Greek mathematics (II, 260-273, 1921).

V. HELLENISTIC AND CHINESE ASTRONOMY

For Hellenistic astronomy see my note on Menelaos in the previous section.

CHIA K'UEI

Chia[3] K'uei[2] (1181, 6505).[m] Flourished c. 89 to 101. Chinese astronomer, who improved the sphere of Kêng Shou-ch'ang (for which see my note on Lo Hsia Hung, second half of the second century B. c.) and added the ecliptic.

A. Forke: World-conception of the Chinese (10, 1925; Isis, VIII, 373).

---

[1] According to the Fihrist and to al-Khāzinī. He had composed a treatise called De cognitione quantitatis discretae corporum permixtorum. (See H. Suter, Mathematiker der Araber, 226, 1900.)

[m] The tone of character 1181 is not indicated in Giles's Dictionary; it is probably 3.

VI. ROMAN AND HELLENISTIC PHYSICS AND TECHNOLOGY

For Nero's lens and the piercing of the isthmus of Corinth, see my note on Nero in Section III.

For the investigations of Menelaos on specific gravity and of Nicomachos on harmony, see Section IV.

ONASANDER

'Ονάσανδρος.[n] Flourished about the middle of the first century. Greek military writer. He composed, not long before 59, a treatise in 42 chapters entitled "The General," Στρατηγικός (sc. λόγος), explaining the broad principles of generalship (στρατηγικαὶ ὑφηγήσεις). It is the earliest military treatise[o] wherein so much stress is laid upon the commander's duties, the morale of the troops, the ethical side of warfare. It enjoyed much popularity in the Renaissance.

Text—Editio princeps by Nicolaus Rigaltius (Paris, 1598 and 1599, with Latin translation). Arminius Koechly: Onosandri de imperatoris officio liber (Leipzig, 1860, Greek and Latin). New edition by W. A. Oldfather, A. S. Pease, J. B. Titchener (Loeb Classical Library, 1923, Greek and English, with an elaborate bibliography).

First Latin edition by Nicolaus Sagundinus (Rome, 1494), included in the well-known collection Rei militaris scriptores; only the 1494 edition, however, contains Onasander. First Spanish translation by Al. de Palencia (c. 1495, s.a., s.l.). First German translation (anonymous, Mainz, 1524, 1532). First French translation by Jean Charrier (Paris, 1546) together with Machiavelli. First and only Italian translation by Fabio Cotta (Venezia, 1546, 1548). First English translation (and the only one except that of the Loeb Library) by Peter Whvtehorne (London, 1563, from Cotta's Italian translation).

FRONTINUS

Sextus Julius Frontinus. Born c. 40, died in 103. Roman soldier and engineer. Appointed in 97 superintendent of the aqueducts of Rome (curator aquarum). He wrote a work in two books on the water-supply of the city of Rome (De aquis urbis Romae), the most important ancient work on engineering; and a treatise on military stratagems (Strategematon). A treatise on land-surveying is also ascribed to him. He knew that the speed of outflow is dependent upon the height of the water above the outlet.

Text and Translation—First edition of the Strategemata in the same volume with Aelian, Vegetius, and Modestus, Roma, 1487; reprinted 1494, 1497. Other edition Bologna, 1495. Ten more editions in the sixteenth century, and six or seven more in the seventeenth. First edition of De aquis, together with Vitruvius, by Pomponius Laetus and Sulpicius, Rome, 1484–1492. First complete edition of Frontinus by Scriverius, Leyden, 1607.

De aquae ductibus urbis Romae liber, ed. by And. Dederich with notes by Karl Fried. Heinrich, and Chr. Ludwig Schultz and German translation (354 p., Vesaliae, 1841). De controversiis agrorum libellus, edited by K. Lachmann (2 Progr., Berlin, 1844–1845). Frontini Strategematicon libri IV eiusdem de aquae ductibus urbis Romae, edited by And. Dederich (173 p., Leipzig, 1855). Franc. Buecheler: De aquis urbis Romae libri II (68 p., Leipzig, 1858). Karl Thulin: Corpus agri-

---

[n] Better than 'Ονόσανδρος or 'Ονήσανδρος.

[o] For earlier Greek treatises see my note on Aeneas Tacticos (first half of fourth century B. C.) and Asclepiodotos (first half of first century B. C.).

mensorum romanorum. I, 1, Opuscula agrimensorum veterum (Leipzig, 1913, with illustrations from the manuscripts). A splendid edition with English translation is due to Clemens Herschel (322 p., 23 pl., many illustrations, Boston, 1899; republished London, 1913). It contains a facsimile reproduction of the only fundamental manuscript, a Montecassino manuscript of the twelfth or thirteenth century, and is accompanied by an elaborate commentary (p. 103–296), especially valuable from the technical point of view, the author being himself an hydraulic engineer. Edition by F. Krohn (66 p., Leipzig, 1922). The Stratagems and the Aqueducts of Rome, with English translation by Charles E. Bennett (d. 1921) (Loeb Library, London, 1925).

Criticism—Moritz Cantor: Die römischen Agrimensorem und ihre Stellung in der Geschichte der Feldmesskunst (Leipzig, 1875). E. Stöber: Die römischen Grundvermessungen nach dem lat. Texte des gromatischen Codex, insbes. des Hyginus, Frontinus, und Nipsus (München, 1877). Paul de Tissot: Étude sur la condition des agrimensores (174 p., Paris, 1879). Clemens Herschel: Frontinus (Lecture, Cornell University, 40 p., Ithaca, N. Y., 1894). Kappelmacher: Iulius Frontinus, in Pauly-Wissowa (t. 19, 591–606, 1917).

Siegfried Loeschcke: Lampen aus Vindonissa. Ein Beitrag zur Geschichte von Vindonissa und des antiken Beleuchtungswesen (358 p., 23 pl., Zürich, 1919. Description of about 11,000 lamps of the first century found in Vindonissa = Windisch; Isis, IV, 397).

VII. ROMAN AND HELLENISTIC BOTANY

The greatest botanist of the age was Dioscorides, but his aim being exclusively medical, I shall deal with him below in Section IX.

COLUMELLA

Lucius Junius Moderatus Columella. Born at Gades, Cadiz; flourished about the middle of the first century.[p] Writer on agriculture. He wrote "De re rustica" twice, but only one book of the first version, De arboribus, is extant. The 12 books "De re rustica" contain much miscellaneous information, more or less connected with the main subject, e. g., on surveying, on contagious diseases among animals. His mathematics are derived from Heron of Alexandria (or from a common source).

Text and Translations—Editio princeps (Venice, 1472). The best complete edition is by J. G. Schneider (Leipzig, 1794–1797). A new text is being edited in Upsala by Wilh. Lundström. I have seen only 3 parts (Part 1, De arboribus, 1897; Part 6, De re rustica, Book 10, 1902 (that is the book written in hexameters, upon the model of the Georgics); Part 7, De re rustica, Book 11, 1906). German translation by Heinrich Oesterreicher (2 vols., Stuttgart, 1914).

Criticism—E. H. F. Meyer: Geschichte der Botanik (t. 2, 58–80, 1855). V. Barberet: De Columellae vita et scriptis (Thèse, Paris, 129 p., Nantes, 1887). Wilh. Becher: (same title, 82 p., Leipzig, 1897). Gelasius Kraus: Die Quellen des De arboribus (Progr., 50 p., Heiligenstadt). Hermann Gummerus: De Columella philosopho (Öfversigt af Finska vetenskaps-societetens förhandlingar, t. 52, Afd. B., 55 p., Helsingfors, 1910). Ernest Weiss: De Columella et Varrone rerum rusticarum scriptoribus (Diss., 43 p., Breslau, 1911). Michael Ahle: Sprachliche kritische Untersuchungen zu Columella (Diss., Würzburg, 62 p., München, 1915. Chiefly philological, but the introduction contains a bibliography

[p] Columella's exact date is difficult to determine. He speaks of Celsus and Seneca as contemporaries. On the other hand, the Res rustica seems to have been written or completed in the sixties.

and a note on the manuscripts). Article by Kappelmacher, in Pauly-Wissowa (t. 19, 1054–1068, 1917). Lizzie B. Marshall: L'horticulture antique et le poème de Columelle (Thèse, 162 p. Paris, 1918).

PAMPHILOS THE BOTANIST

Πάμφιλος. Flourished about the end of the first century.[q] Greek botanist. He compiled a dictionary of plants (εἰκονες (τῶν βοτανῶν) κατὰ στοιχεῖον; περὶ βοτανῶν).

Ernst H. F. Meyer: Geschichte der Botanik (2.Bd., 23, 137–148, 1885). Robert Fuchs, in Puschmann: Geschichte der Medizin (t. 1, 358).

VIII. ROMAN, HELLENISTIC, AND CHINESE GEOGRAPHY

Periplus of the Erythrean Sea

This circumnavigation of the Indian Ocean is a manual for sailors and merchants, written in Greek, by an anonymous author. It is an important source for the history of geography and trade in the first century. It dates probably from the second half of the century. It contains some information about countries beyond India and mentions the region of Thin at the eastern end of the earth (first use of the word China).[r]

Text and Translations—Editio princeps, (under the title Arriani et Hannonis periplus, etc. Bale, 1533). Of the modern editions, let us quote first that by William Vincent: The Commerce and Navigation of the Ancients in the Indian Ocean (2 vols., London, 1807; Vol. I, The voyage of Nearchus; Vol. II, The Periplus . . . . in two parts; Greek text with English translation and valuable notes). English translation by the same (Oxford, 1809). Greek and Latin edition by Karl Müller in the Geographi graeci minores of the coll. Didot (Paris, 1855). English translation by J. W. McCrindle (Calcutta, 1879). The best edition is that by B. Fabricius (Leipzig, 1883; new Greek text with German translation, notes, and lexicon). Wilfred H. Schoff: The Periplus of the Erythrean Sea. Travel and Trade in the Indian Ocean, by a merchant of the First Century (English translation, 323 p., London, 1912, with very elaborate commentary and various appendixes, the text itself covering only 28 p. The writer has made full use of all the previous researches).

Criticism—E. H. F. Meyer: Geschichte der Botanik (t. 2, 81–92, 1855). Of course the main publication is Schoff's English translation quoted above. See also by the same, First Century Intercourse between India and Rome (The Monist, t. 22, 138–149, 637–638, Chicago, 1912); The Date of the Periplus (Journal R. Asiatic Society, 827–830, 1917. The journey was made between 65 and 80, the work written in the last quarter of the century; Isis, IV, 397); J. Kennedy: (*ibidem*, 1918; Isis, IV, 397). P. Zenetti: Über den Periplus (Natur und Kultur, Jahrgang 1920–1921, 18 p. Not seen).

Travel in the first century—Caroline A. J. Skeel: Travel in the First Century after Christ, with special Reference to Asia Minor (169 p., Cambridge, 1901. A useful compilation, clearly written).

---

[q] Not to be confused with other men bearing the same name and living at about the same time, the grammarian, for example (see below in Section XI) or that druggist (μιγματοπώλης) who made a fortune in Rome selling a salve for sycosis. A portrait of the botanist is included in the famous Dioscorides's codex of Venice (see first half of the sixth century).

[r] The word Sinim (Ṣinīm) in Isaiah 49, 12, refers to an unknown country, most probably not China. The LXX translates "Persians."

Exploration of the Upper Nile

Under the reign of Nero (emperor from 54 to 68) two centurions were ordered to ascend the Nile above Syene and find its source. They did not, of course, find its source, but they seem to have reached the great marshes on the course of the White Nile,[a] above its junction with the Sobat (latitude 9° N.). That point was not rediscovered until almost eighteen centuries later, by the Egyptian expeditions of 1839–1840. Unfortunately, the account which has come down to us of the early expedition is very meager (Pliny, Natural History, VI, 184–186 and Seneca, Naturales Quaestiones, VI, 8).

E. H. Bunbury: History of Ancient Geography (vol. 2, 346–48, 1879).

DIONYSIOS PERIEGETES

Διονύσιος ὁ περιηγητής. Flourished some time in the first or second century, probably under Domitian, emperor from 81 to 96. Author of a geographic poem describing the world (οἰκουμένης περιήγησις) in 1187 hexameters. Its scientific value is very small, but it exerted a great influence during the Middle Ages through the translations in Latin verse by Avienus (second half of fourth century) and Priscianus (first half of sixth century) and through the elaborate commentary by Eustathios of Thessalonica (second half of twelfth century).

Text—Editio princeps (Venice, 1477). God. Bernhardy: Dionysius Periegetes, graece et latine (2 vols., 1114 p., Leipzig, 1828. Contains the text of Avienus's and Priscianus's translations, Eustathios's Greek commentary, other scholia and paraphrases, abundant notes, and indexes). This text is reprinted in Volume II of the Geographi graeci minores edited by K. Müller (Coll. Didot, Paris, 1861).
Criticism—Ulrich Bernays: Studien zu Dionysius Periegetes (Diss., München, 73 p., Heidelberg, 1905). Article by Knaack, in Pauly-Wissowa (t. 9, 915–924, 1903).

For Chinese geography, see my note on Pan Ku in Section X.

IX. HELLENISTIC MEDICINE

DIOSCORIDES

Pedanios Dioscorides of Anazarbos, near Tarsos, Cilicia. (Πεδάνιος Διοσκορίδης.) Flourished under Claudius and Nero, about the middle of the first century. Botanist, pharmacologist, military physician. Dioscorides wrote an encyclopaedia of materia medica in five books (περὶ ὕλης ἰατρικῆς) which embodied the results of Greek research in pharmacy and applied botany and was far better arranged and more complete than the earlier compilations. This work remained authoritative for more than fifteen centuries, at the cost, however, of continual interpolations and of changes of all kinds. About 600 plants are described in it and their medical properties explained. The study of Dioscorides is of great interest from the point of view of the still very imperfectly known history of botanic iconography and of book illustration in general. Dioscorides's work is of importance also for the history of ancient chemistry, as it describes simple chemical preparations (for example, to obtain mercury from cinnabar, or potash from

[a] Seneca states that they reached inextricable marshes. His brief but clear description can only apply to the marshes above mentioned, for there is nothing like them below.

tartar), mentions the earliest reaction of wet analysis, the detection of iron vitriol by means of gall-nut juice, and quotes many chemical substances.

Text—First Latin edition, Colle, 1478. Editio princeps, Aldus Manutius, Venice, 1499. Second Greek edition by Franc. Asulanus, Venice, 1518. The third and fourth Greek editions appeared in the same year, prepared respectively by Marcellus Vergilius (Cologne, 1529) and by Ianus Cornarius (Basel, 1529). Fifth edition by Jacques Goupyl, Paris, 1549; sixth edition, Francfort, 1598; the latter prepared by Ianus Saracenus was by far the best early edition.

Pedanii Dioscoridis Anazarbei de materia medica libri quinque. Edited with Latin translation by Kurt Sprengel in K. G. Kühn's Medicorum graecorum opera quae exstant (vol. 25, Leipzig, 1829). Volume 26, 1830, of the same collection contains the other Dioscoridean writings and an extensive commentary on the texts edited in both volumes. The texts included in volume 2 are now generally admitted to be apocryphal. A better text of Dioscorides's Materia Medica has been edited by Max Wellmann in 3 volumes (Berlin, Vol. I, 1907; Vol. II, 1906; Vol. III, 1914). Appended to Volume III: Cratevas, Sextii Nigri fragmenta, Dioscoridis liber de simplicibus. A German translation with commentary has been published by J. Berendes (572 p., Leipzig, 1902. See Hermann Stadler: Deutsche Dioskuridesübersetzungen, Blätter für das Gymnasialschulwesen, 39, 543–549). Berendes has also translated some of the apocryphal writings: Hausmittel (*περὶ εὐποριστων ἁπλῶν τε καὶ συνθέτων φαρμάκων*) (Janus, t. XII, passim, 136 p., 1907); Über Gifte und Gegengifte (*περὶ δηλητηρίων φαρμάκων*), Über die giftigen Tiere und den tollen Hund (*περὶ ἰοβόλων*). (Apothekerzeitung, nr. 89–94, 1905). Hermann Stadler: Dioskurides Longobardus (Cod. Lat. Monacensis, 337). (Vollmöllers Romanische Forschungen, t. X–XIV, Erlangen, 1899–1903, passim. The text of this ninth century manuscript is of special interest to the student of Romance philology). Two Arabic manuscripts of Dioscorides are described by Hartwig Derenbourg: Notes critiques sur les manuscrits arabes de la bibliothèque nationale de Madrid (p. 19, 30–31, Paris, 1904). For the genealogy of the early manuscripts and a list of them see C. Singer: Studies (Vol. II, 63–66, Oxford, 1921).

Commentary—L. Leclerc: De la traduction arabe de Dioscorides et des traductions arabes en général (Journal asiatique, t. 9, 5–38, 1867). Max Wellmann: Sextius Niger. Eine Quellenuntersuchung zu Dioscorides (Hermes, t. 24, 530–569, Berlin, 1889). Max Wellmann: Die Schrift des Dioscurides *περὶ ἁπλῶν φαρμάκων* (Ein Beitrag zur Gesch. d. Medizin. Berlin, Weidmann, 1914. Proving the authenticity of this work). Rudolf Mock: Pflanzliche Arzneimittel bei Dioskurides die schon im Corpus Hippocraticum vorkommen (Diss., 44 p., Tübingen, 1919. Not seen). Guido M. Piccinini: La rinomanza di Dioscoride e la denominazione materia medica (Riv. di storia delle scienze, 68–82, 101–116, 1920). Lynn Thorndike: History of Magic (vol. 1, 605–612, 1923).

History of Botanic Iconography—Codex Aniciae Iulianae picturis illustratus nunc Vindobonensis Med. Gr. 1 phototypice editus. Moderante Iosepho de Karabacek praefati sunt Antonius de Premerstein, Carolus Wessely, Josephus Mantuani (Codices Graeci et Latini photographice depicti duce Scatone De Vries, t. X–XI, 2 vols., in folio, Leyden, 1906). This manuscript, kept first in Constantinople, then in Vienna, now in St. Mark's Library, Venice, and dating from about 512, is of immense importance for the history of plant illustration. The introduction to this splendid facsimile reproduction is also the most elaborate study of the subject; it has been published separately (490 p., Leyden, 1906). Karl Wessely deals with the palaeographic problems, and Joseph Mantuani considers the miniatures from the artistic point of view; the latter study is interesting for the historian of science also, for it will help him to determine the degree of lifelikeness and originality of these illustrations. The most important part of the introduction, however, is the one contributed by Ant. von Premerstein, in which Greek herbals are thoroughly discussed. See also my note on Cratevas (first half of first century B. C.).

Edmond Bonnet: Essai d'identification des plantes médicinales mentionées par Dioscoride d'après les peintures d'un mns. de la Bibliothèque nationale de Paris (mns. Grec 2179. IXe siècle, Janus, t. 8, p. 169–177, 225–232, 281–285, 1903). J. de M. Johnson: A Botanical Papyrus with Illustrations (Arch. für Gesch. d. Naturw., t. IV, 403–408, 2 pl., 1913. A terminus ante quem is supplied by the hand of the copyist, a medium-sized semi-uncial of the second century, but this text might be anterior to Dioscorides).

Chemistry—Edm. O. von Lippmann: Die chemischen kenntnisse des Dioskorides. Zeitschrift für angewandte Chemie (p. 1209, 1905). Reprinted in his Abhandl. u. Vorträge, Vol. I, 1906, p. 47–73.

ATHENAEOS OF ATTALIA

Athenaeos of Attalia, Pamphylia (?) (Ἀθήναιος). Flourished in Rome under Claudius (41–54) and Nero (54 to 68). Founder of the Pneumatic school of medicine, a development of Stoic physics. He wrote a comprehensive treatise on medicine in at least 30 books (entitled περὶ βοηθημάτων?) containing many definitions (ὅροι), and highly praised by Galen. Interesting fragments of it deal with the study of food and drink, the influence of air (in different places and at different times), the education of children and women, etc.

Max Wellmann: Die pneumatische Schule bis auf Archigenes (Philol. Untersuch., XIV, 1895). See also his summary, in Pauly-Wissowa (t. 4, 2034–2036, 1896). M. Neuburger: Geschichte der Medizin (t. 1, 332, 1911).

AGATHINOS

Claudios Agathinos (Κλαύδιος Ἀγαθεῖνος), of Sparta, flourished in the second half of the century. Physician, disciple of Athenaeos, and master of Archigenes. Founder of the Eclectic (or Episynthetic; ἐπισυνθετικοί) school of medicine, a development of the Pneumatic school. He wrote a treatise on the pulse (περὶ σφυγμῶν); another on the action of hellebore, partly based on experiments; and recommended the use of cold (vs. warm) baths.

Short article by M. Wellmann, in Pauly-Wissowa (t. 1, 745, 1894). M. Neuburger: Geschichte der Medizin (t. 1, 332, 1911).

DEMOSTHENES

Demosthenes Philalethes. Δημοσθένης φιλαλήθης, flourished under Nero. One of the greatest ophthalmologists of antiquity, the most distinguished representative of the later Herophilian school; established in Zeuxis, near Laodicea, Phrygia. He wrote a book on ophthalmology (Ὀφθαλμικός or περὶ ὀφθαλμῶν) which has been the main source of all later writings on the subject, and which was still extant in the tenth to fourteenth centuries. He also wrote three books on the pulse (περὶ σφυγμῶν) and a treatise on children's diseases.[t]

Criticism—Max Wellmann: Demosthenes περὶ ὀφθαλμῶν (Hermes, t. 38, p. 546–566, 1903). See also Wellmann's notice in Pauly-Wissowa (t. 9, 189–190, 1903). Julius Hirschberg: Die Bruchstücke der Augenheilkunde des Demosthenes (Archiv für Geschichte der Medizin, t. XI, 183–188, 1919).

---

[t] The only one in ancient times (K. Sudhoff: Geschichte der Medizin, 3te Auflage, 214, 1922).

ANDROMACHOS THE ELDER

Ἀνδρόμαχος of Crete; physician to Nero, emperor from 54 to 68. Greek physician and druggist. He is famous because he composed a theriaca[u] which completely superseded the Mithridate.[v] He described it in a poem of 174 lines.[w]

ANDROMACHOS THE YOUNGER

Son of the preceding. Also a physician and specially interested in drugs. He wrote a treatise on the preparation of drugs (περὶ φαρμάκων σκευασίας) in three books: (1) external drugs (τὰ τῶν ἐκτὸς φάρμακα); (2) internal (τὰ τῶν ἐντός); (3) ocular.

Text—Bussemaker: Poetarum de re physica et medica reliquiae (Paris, 1851). J. L. Ideler: Physici et medici graeci minores (t. 1 138–143, 1841).

Criticism—E. H. F. Meyer: Geschichte der Botanik (t. 2, 39–42, 135–137, 1855). M. Wellmann, in Pauly-Wissowa (t. 2, 2153, 1894). M. Neuburger: Geschichte der Medizin (t. 1, 323, 1906).

DAMOCRATES

Servilius Damocrates (Δαμοκράτης),[x] of Athens, flourished under Nero and Vespasian. Greek physician who wrote pharmacological poems in iambic trimeter, t is said, to avoid the substitution of numbers by copyists.

Text—Damocratis Servilii quae supersunt carmina medicinalia, edited by Harless (Bonn, 1833). U. C. Bussemaker, in Poetae bucolici et didascalici (Paris, 1851). Studemund is preparing a critical edition, see Index lectionum Vratislaviensium (1888–9).

Criticism—Ernst H. F. Meyer: Geschichte der Botanik (t. 2, 42–44, 1855). M. Wellmann, in Pauly-Wissowa (t. 8, 2069, 1901). Rubert Fuchs, in Puschmann: Geschichte der Medizin (t. 1, 357, 1902).

XENOCRATES OF APHRODISIAS

Ξενοκράτης, flourished in Rome c. 70. Greek physician. Wrote many books on food and drugs, of special interest for the history of ancient superstition. His περὶ τῆς ἀπὸ τοῦ ἀνθρώπου καὶ τῶν ζῴων ὠφελείας is a source of Pliny's Natural History, Books 28–30. His best-known writing is on the food derived from aquatic animals (περὶ τῆς ἀπὸ τῶν ἐνύδρων τροφῆς).

Text and Translation—Editio princeps in Greek and Latin by the Bishop Janus Dubravius (Zürich, 1559). Text of the last-mentioned work in J. L. Ideler: Physici et medici graeci (Vol. I, 121–133, Berlin, 1841).

Criticism—E. H. F. Meyer: Geschichte der Botanik (t. 2, 55–58, 1855). Gustav Oehmichen: Plinianische Studien zur geographischen und Kunsthistorischen Literatur (Erlangen, 1880). M. Wellmann: Xenokrates aus Aphrodisias (Hermes, t. 42, 614–629, Berlin, 1907).

---

[u] That is, originally at least, an antidote against snake-bites. Andromachos's theriaca was called γαλήνη, meaning sea-calm, and included 61 constituents.

[v] For which see my note on Mithridates Eupator (first half of first century B. C.). The galene's success was so great that under Antoninus (138 to 161) it was prepared by the Roman State.

[w] Galen deals with it too, in his περὶ ἀντιδότων, 14.

[x] Or Δημοκράτης. His name Servilius, under which he is often quoted, was given to him when he was freed by the consularis M. Servilius (3 A. D.) whose daughter he had healed (Pliny, Bk. XXIV, 28; XXV, 49).

HERODOTOS

Ηρόδοτος, flourished in Rome under the Flavian emperors, 69 to 96. Physician. Pupil of Agathinos, but with stronger leanings toward Methodism.[1] He elaborated very strict therapeutic prescriptions. He distinguished in any disease the four following stages: ἀρχή, ἐπίδοσις, ἀκμή, παρακμή. Description of smallpox (?) and recognition of its contagious nature.

[1] Max Wellmann: Herodotos, in Pauly-Wissowa (t. 15, 990–991, 1912. Contains a list of his writings); Zu Herodots Schrift περὶ τῶν ὀξέων καὶ χρονίων νοσημάτων (Hermes, t. 48, p. 141, 1913).

THESSALOS

Thessalos of Tralles, Caria (Θεσσαλός), flourished under Nero and Trajan. Greek physician of the Methodist school, practicing in Rome. Completed the work of Themison (q. v., first half of first century B. C.). Introduced clinical teaching and new methods of treating chronic affections (cyclus metasyncriticus or recorporativus, cyclus resumptivus).

Theod. Meyer-Steineg: Thessalos von Tralles (Archiv für Gesch. d. Medizin, t. 4, 89–108, 1910).

Max Neuburger: Medizinisches aus dem Epos des C. Silius Italicus (26 to 101) "Punica" (Monatschrift Eesti Arst, No. 9, 215–220, Dorpat, 1924).

X. JEWISH, ROMAN AND CHINESE HISTORIOGRAPHY

JOSEPHUS

Flavius Josephus.[y] Ἰώσηπος, later Ἰώσηφος. Born at Jerusalem in 37–8; after the fall of the city in 70 he resided chiefly in Rome; he died under Trajan, that is, after 98. Jewish historian. His main works are (1) the History of the Jewish War (66–70), Περὶ τοῦ Ἰουδαϊκου πολέμοῦ, in seven books, written first in Aramaic,[z] then in Greek, between 70 and 79; (2) the Jewish Antiquities, Ἰουδαϊκὴ ἀρχαιολογία, in 20 books[a] dealing with Jewish history from the creation to 66 A. D., completed in 94; (3) his Autobiography, written c. 97, a sort of appendix to (2); (4) a defense and glorification of the Jewish people (vs. the Greek) called Against Apion[b] (Ἀντιρρήσεις πρὸς Ἀπίωνα, or more correctly, πρὸς τοὺς Ἕλληνας). The last-named work contains the only fragments of Manethon and Berossos which have come down to us. Josephus's influence has been far greater upon the Christians than upon the Jews.

---

[y] He took the name Flavius when the Emperor Vespasian (T. Flavius Sabinus) gave him the freedom which he had lost in the Jewish War.

[z] The Aramaic text is lost. His other writings are in Greek.

[a] Books I to X told the story down to the Babylonian captivity (586), then the account became fuller and fuller, e. g., four books (XIV to XVII) being devoted to the reign of Herod the Great (40 to 4 B. C.) The early history was based chiefly upon the Septuagint, but one should remember that the Greeks and Romans were extremely ignorant of Jewish history; they could hardly believe that such a civilization had existed so near the Mediterranean Sea! This shows the importance of Josephus's work. Its title and subject were probably suggested by the Ῥωμαϊκὴ ἀρχαιολογία of Dionysios of Halicarnassos (second half of first century B. C.).

[b] Apion (Ἀπίων) was a Greek grammarian of Alexandria (flourished c. 38), who had attacked and insulted the Jews in his work on Egypt (Αἰγυπτιακά).

Texts—First edition of the Latin translation (Augsburg, 1470). First Greek edition by Arnoldus Peraxylus Arlenius (Bale, 1544). There are also Hebrew translations, at least of Against Apion.

Greek edition by Bened. Niese (7 vols., Berlin, 1887–1895); by S. A. Naber (6 vols., Leipzig, 1888–1896).

Latin text of Against Apion edited by Karl Boysen in Corpus script. ecclesiast. lat. (t. 37, Wien, 1898).

English translation by William Whiston (1667–1752), London, 1737 (often reprinted). Revised by A. R. Shilleto (5 vols., Bohn Library, London, 1889–1890).

Oeuvres complètes traduites en français sous la direction de Théodore Reinach (t. 1–3. Paris, 1900–1904).

Criticism—M. Croiset: Littérature grecque (t. 5, 434–445, 1899). Karl Albert: Strabo als Quelle des F. Josephus (Diss., 48 p., Würzburg, 1902). Samuel Krauss: Jewish Encyclopedia (vol. 7, 247–281, 1904). Eugen Täubler: Die Parther-Nachrichten bei Josephus (Diss., Berlin, 65 p., 1904). Alexander Berendts: Die Zeugnisse vom Christentum im slavischen de bello judaico (79 p., Leipzig, 1906). Paul Durrieu: Les Antiquités Judaïques et le peintre Jean Foucquet (MS. Bibliothèque Nationale; 132 p., 27 pl.; Paris, 1908). Heinrich Luther: Josephus und Justus von Tiberias (Diss., Halle, 90 p., 1910). Hölscher, in Pauly-Wissowa (t. 18, 1934–2000, 1916. Important). Max Neuburger: Die Medizin im F. Josephus (74 p., Bad Reichenhall, 1919). J. T. Shotwell: History of History, 119–127, 1922).

TACITUS

Cornelius Tacitus. Born c. 55, died c. 120. Roman historian. One of the greatest historians and writers of all times. His life of Agricola (his father-in-law) c. 98, contains valuable information on Brittany and England and his Germania, c. 99, on early Germany. The Histories and Annals are later works.

Texts and Translations—De vita et moribus Julii Agricolae: Edited by Alfred Gudemann (Berlin, 1902). By William Francis Allen (with the Germania, 188 p., Boston, 1913). By Cesare Annibaldi (70 p., Torino, 1917).

Germania: Facsimile reproduction of the Codex Leidensis with preface by Georg Wissowa (Codices graeci et latini photographice depicti, suppl. IV, Leyde, 1907). Edited by H. Schweizer-Sidler (6. ed., Halle, 1902). By Edward Wolff (2. ed., Leipzig, 1907). By Cesare Annibaldi (Torino, 1916).

Oxford translation revised (Bohn collection, London, 1854). English translation of Dialogus, Agricola, and Germania (the last two by Maurice Hutton) in Loeb Classical Library (London, 1914). Arthur Charles Howland: The Early Germans (as Described by Caesar, Tacitus, Josephus, and Ammianus Marcellinus) (Translations and Reprints, VI, 3, 2d ed., Philadelphia, 1901).

Lexicons—Philippe Fabia. Onomasticum Taciteum (775 p.; Annales de l'Université de Lyon, Paris, 1900). Arnold Gerber and A. Greef: Lexicon Taciteum (1802 p., 1877–1902, Leipzig, 1903).

Criticism—Karl Müllenhoff: Die Germania erläutert (775 p., Berlin, 1900. Deutsche Altertumskunde, IV). Gaston Boissier: Tacite (and other essays) (Paris, 1903. English translation, London, 1906). Giovanni Ferrara: La forma della Britannia secondo la testimonianza di Tacito (Rend. dell'Istituto Lombardo (2), t. 37, 1905). Robert Pöhlmann: Die Weltanschauung des Tacitus (90 p., Bayer. Ak. der Wiss., phil. Kl., München, 1910; improved ed. 1913). Eduard Norden: Die germanische Urgeschichte in Tacitus Germania (Leipzig, 1920). Georg Wilke: Archäologische Erläuterungen zur Germania (84 p., 74 ill., Leipzig, 1921; Isis, IV, 576). J. T. Shotwell: Introduction to the History of History (257–272, 1922).

PAN KU

Pan[1] Ku[4] (8595, 6204). Chinese historian. His father, Pan Piao[1] (9112), was a native of An[1]-ling[2] (44, 7235) in Shensi; Pan Ku died in prison in 92. He wrote a history of the Earlier (or Western) Han Dynasty (206 B. C. to 24 A. D.) called Ch'ien[2] Han[4]-shu[1] (1737, 3836, 10024) which is the second of the twenty-four dynastic histories. This work, interrupted by his death, was completed by his sister Pan Chao[1] (473). A chapter of it, the Lü[4*] li[4*] chih[4] (7548, 6924, 1918) gives a chronology of earlier times. This chronology has been followed by all later annalists and is, so to say, the official chronology of China.[c] Chapter 28 is a complete and detailed geography of the empire. Chapter 30, the Han I-wen-chih, is a catalogue of some 590 early Chinese works, most of which are now lost.[d] The Ch'ien Han-shu contains very valuable information on foreign peoples, e. g., on the Huns, Koreans, the peoples of Central Asia. Pan Ku wrote also a cosmogonical treatise called Pai[2] hu[3] t'ung[1] (8556, 4920, 12294) which contains strange notions on many subjects, e. g., on physiology. Earliest Chinese mention of amber (imported from Kashmir).

Text—Chinese text printed at the Chin-ling press (Nanking, 1869, 120 chüan, in 16 vols.).

Criticism—Wylie: Notes on Chinese Literature (17, 159, 1902). Giles: Biographical Dictionary (608, 611, 1898). L. Wieger: La Chine (493, 1920). Léopold de Saussure: La chronologie chinoise et l'avènement des Tcheou (T'oung Pao, vol. 23, 287–346, 1924).

XI. GREEK AND LATIN PHILOLOGY

PAMPHILOS

Pamphilos of Alexandria (Πάμφιλος), flourished in 50 A. D. Greek lexicographer. He compiled a work in 95 books on rare and difficult words (περὶ γλωσσῶν ἤτοι λέξεων) (lost).

Sandys: History of Classical Scholarship (vol. 1^3, 295, 1921).

PAMPHILA

Pamphila (Παμφίλη), flourished at Epidaurus in the time of Nero. Greek philologist. She compiled a work in 33 books on the history of literature (Ὑπομνήματα ἱστορικά).

Maurice Croiset: Histoire de la littérature grecque (t. 5, 405–407, 1899).

EROTIANOS

Ἐρωτιανός flourished in the time of Nero. Greek philologist and lexicographer. He compiled one of the most important lexicons of ancient times, one especially important to us, for it was devoted to Hippocrates (τῶν παρ' Ἱπποκράτει λέξεων συναγωγή).

---

[c] But Western scholars (Chavannes, Hirth) are inclined to give more credence to the Bamboo chronology, for which see my note on Chinese historiography in the first half of the third century B. C.

[d] This catalogue had been compiled by Liu Hsin, for which see my note in the second half of the first century B. C.

Text—Erotiani vocum Hippocraticarum conlectio ed. by Joseph Klein (132 p., Leipzig, 1865). New edition by Ernst Nachmanson (187 p., Göteborg, 1918).

Criticism—Article by Cohn, in Pauly-Wissowa (t. XI, 544–548, 1907). Ernst Nachmanson: Erotianstudien (590 p., Upsala, 1917).

PALAEMON

Quintus Remmius Palaemon. Born at Vicenza in northern Italy, yet of Greek origin, for his name is obviously Greek (Παλαίμων), flourished c. 35 to 70. Roman grammarian; the foremost teacher of the subject in Rome at his time. His Ars grammatica (c. 67 to 77) was the first school-book on Latin grammar.

Text—Ars grammatica secunda in Grammatici illustres (36 to 40, 1516).

The De ponderibus et mensuris formerly ascribed to Palaemon (e. g., in the edition of it appended to Celsus, De re medica, Haganoae, 1528) is a later work,[e] hence the notion of specific gravity contained in that book can not be credited to Palaemon.

Criticism—De Q. R. Palaemonis libris grammaticis (Diss., 85 p., Leipzig, 1885). Sandys: History of Classical Scholarship (vol. 1^3, 200, Cambridge, 1921).

VALERIUS PROBUS

M. Valerius Probus. Of Beyrut, flourished in Rome c. 56 to 88. Roman grammarian, the foremost of his time.[f] He wrote various grammatical works and prepared scientific editions of Plautus (?), Terence, Lucretius, Virgil, Horace, and Persius, using critical symbols (21 in number) like those invented by the Alexandrian scholars.

Text—De interpretandis romanorum litteris (Venice, 1499. With other treatises by other authors). In Virgilii Bucolica et Georgica commentarius, edited by H. Keil (Halle, 1848). Appendix ad Probi Artem minorem in Joseph von Eichenfeld, Analecta grammatica . . . . (437, 1837); edited also by Wendelin Foerster, in Wiener Studien (t. 14, 278–322, 1892). L'Appendix Probi (pt. III) e il glossarietto latino-greco del papiro Sault (9 p., Roma, 1904).

Criticism—Oskar Froehde: V. Probi de nomine libellum Plini Secundi doctrinam continere demonstratur (Jahrb. für class. Phil., Supp. Bd. 19, 157–203, 1892). Karl Ullmann: Die Appendix Probi (Romanische Forsch., t. 7, 145–226, 1893). Wilhelm Heraeus: Die Appendix Probi (text of 3d part with notes, Archiv f. lat. Lexicographie, t. XI, 34 p., 1899). J. E. Sandys: History of Classical Scholarship (vol. 1^3, 204–206, 1921).

QUINTILIAN

Marcus Fabius Quintilianus; born at Calagurris[g] in Spain, c. 35; died c. 96. Roman rhetorician, philosopher, educator. His main work is the De Institutione Oratoria Libri XII, which exerted a powerful influence.[h] It is the most

---

[e] Probably of the fourth or fifth century. See Friedrich Hultsch: Metrologicorum scriptorum reliquiae (t. 2, Scriptores Romani, 26, Leipzig, 1866). It has been ascribed also to Priscianus (second half of fourth century), e. g., in Lucas Paetus's edition of 1573.

[f] Says Sandys (loc. cit., 206): "To these two writers (Pliny the Elder and Probus) and to Palaemon, may be ascribed the main outlines of the traditional Latin grammar."

[g] Calahorra, near the Ebro.

[h] A century before, rhetorical teaching in the Roman Empire was still almost entirely in the hands of the Greeks. Quintilian's influence was lost in the early Middle Ages, but it was felt anew long before the time of Poggio (q. v., first half of fifteenth century), for example, in the schools of Bec and Chartres (twelfth century). Poggio's discovery of a complete manuscript of Quintilian in 1416 stimulated tremendously the humanistic revival.

elaborate treatise on education, as it is the most important monument of literary criticism, of ancient times.

Text—Complete works, edited by Peter Burmann (Leyden, 1720).

Institutio Oratoria, first edition, by Campano, Rome, 1470. Later editions by G. L. Spalding, completed by C. T. Zumpt and Eduard Bonnell (6 vols., Leipzig, 1798–1834; last volume, lexicon and index); by Charles Halm (Leipzig, 1868–1869); W. Peterson (Oxford, 1891). First book edited by F. H. Colson (306 p., Cambridge, 1924, with long introduction).

Translations—Englished by H. E. Butler in Loeb Classical Library (London, 1921).

French translation in Collection Didot (Paris, 1865).

Criticism—Giov. Bat. Gerini. Le dottrine pedagogiche di Cicerone, Seneca, Quintiliano et Plinio il Giovine (200 p., Torino, 1894). M. Cantor: Geschichte der Mathematik (vol. 1^3, 549–550, 1907. On a passage in Bk. I, of mathematical interest). Johann Michel Hofer: Die Stellung des D. Erasmus und des J. L. Vives zur Pädagogik des Quintilians (Diss., Erlangen, 1910). B. Appel: Das Bildungs- und Erziehungsideal Quintilians (Donauwörth, 1914).

CHAPTER XV

THE TIME OF PTOLEMY

(First Half of Second Century)

I. Survey of Science in First Half of Second Century. II. Religious Background. III. Hellenistic Philosophy. IV. Roman and Hellenistic Mathematics. V. Hellenistic and Chinese Astronomy. VI. Roman, Hellenistic, and Chinese Physics and Technology. VII. Hellenistic Geography. VIII. Hellenistic, Roman, and Hindu Medicine. IX. Roman and Hellenistic Historiography. X. Roman Law. XI. Chinese and Greek Philology.

I. SURVEY OF SCIENCE IN FIRST HALF OF SECOND CENTURY

1. The scientific revival which had begun in such promising manner during the previous period developed fully, up to the highest expectations, within the course of the second century. Indeed, that century may be considered the golden age of Greco-Roman science.

2. *Religious Background*—There is nothing important to report from our point of view about the evolution of Judaism and Christianity in those days, except perhaps that the edition and translations of the Old Testament and of the Gospels, with which I shall deal in the next chapter, were gradually prepared and completed. In particular Aquila's Jewish Greek version dates from c. 128.

In the meanwhile, Buddhism was undergoing radical changes. It is noteworthy that the patriarch Aśvaghosha, who flourished under the rule of Kanishka (c. 120 to c. 162?), has been called the founder of Mahāyāna Buddhism. Whether this appellation is correct or not, Aśvaghosha, who was one of the greatest Buddhist and Sanskrit poets, reveals a doctrine and feelings which are as different from those of early Buddhism as the teachings and feelings of the New Testament are different from those of the Old Testament.

3. *Hellenistic Philosophy*—One of the noblest representatives of Stoicism, Epictetos, delivered in his old age, at Nicopolis, the discourses or sayings which the historian Arrian took down in writing and published. Arrian's relation to Epictetos was very similar to that of his model Xenophon, to Socrates. Contemporary Peripateticism, much influenced by Stoicism, was represented by Adrastos.

Polemon's treatise on physiognomy, the earliest of its kind outside of the one ascribed to Aristotle, gives us an entirely different insight into the Greek thought of that time.

4. *Roman and Hellenistic Mathematics*—Roman mathematics remained always on a very low level; they were essentially restricted to the needs of accounting and surveying. Two distinguished surveyors, Balbus and Hyginus, flourished under Trajan (emperor from 98 to 117).

Theon of Smyrna (c. 130) wrote an elementary treatise on general mathematics. The only mathematical work of real importance was that of the astronomer Ptolemy, who continued the elaboration of trigonometry and perfected it as far as it could be done without sines. He had a remarkable knowledge of geographical projections.

5. *Hellenistic and Chinese Astronomy*—Theon of Smyrna made observations of

Venus and Mercury between 127 and 132 and revived the Heraclidean theory. The greatest astronomer of antiquity and one of the greatest of all times, Ptolemy, wrote the Almagest, which remained the fundamental authority in its field for at least fourteen centuries. He discovered the evection and tried to give a mathematical account of it. He compiled a catalogue of 1,028 stars. He carried mathematical astronomy to the very limit of the mathematical and astronomical possibilities of his time.

Chang Hêng, who died in 139, wrote the Ling-hsien and constructed a celestial hemisphere; he seems to have known a great number of stars.

6. *Roman, Hellenistic, and Chinese Physics and Technology*—For Roman physics, I must refer once more to the surveyors, whose activity implied the use of some physical instruments. Balbus and Hyginus are dealt with in Section IV. The time of Trajan (98–117), to which they belonged, marked the culmination of Roman engineering, and the greatest engineer of that time was Apollodoros of Damascus, who built the forum and the aqueduct of Trajan and, in 105, a permanent bridge across the Danube. A year later, a bridge was built across the Tagus by C. Julius Lacer. The mathematician Theon of Smyrna included the theory of music in his above-mentioned text-book. A treatise ascribed to Ptolemy contains an experimental study of refraction, which is the most remarkable experimental investigation of antiquity.

In 105, the eunuch Ts'ai Lun made a report to the emperor on paper-making. The invention of real paper is traditionally ascribed to him. It is certain that pure rag paper was made in China by the middle of the second century; this is the most certain and the most complete of Chinese inventions. The astronomer Chang Hêng invented a seismometer or perfected Ch'ao-Ts'o's invention.

7. *Hellenistic Geography*—Marinos of Tyre, who flourished probably not long before Ptolemy, was a very great geographer. But we know nothing of his work, except through Ptolemy, who praises him very highly. Marinos attempted to reconstruct the map of the world upon a scientific basis. Ptolemy was the greatest geographer, even as he was the greatest astronomer, of antiquity, and his "Geography" was almost as authoritative as the "Almagest." It is essentially a mathematical geography; it constituted the main foundation of cartography until about the sixteenth century. It is difficult to determine to what extent the maps themselves were made by Ptolemy; it is possible that some, at least, of the maps were drawn by him or by his immediate pupils; Agathodaemon may have been one of these.

The historian Arrian compiled in 131 an account of the coasts of the Black Sea.

8. *Hellenistic, Roman, and Hindu Medicine*—This was a great medical age. Archigenes of Apamea, who belonged to the Eclectic School, elaborated the theory of the pulse. The Pneumatic School was represented by two famous surgeons, Antyllos and Heliodoros. Marinos of Alexandria wrote an important treatise on anatomy, based upon personal observation. Anatomical tradition can be completely traced from him down to Galen. Rufus was also a great anatomist and the greatest physician of Roman times after Galen. The most remarkable of the many observations ascribed to him is the correspondence between the pulse and heart-beat and the systole. Soranos was the greatest gynaecologist of antiquity; he gave an admirable description of the womb. The woman physician Metrodora, who was also a specialist of female complaints, may have lived at about the same time; the real date of her activity is unknown.

The Kashmirian physician Caraka wrote a medical treatise expounding the views of the school of Ātreya.

9. *Roman and Hellenistic Historiography*—Suetonius wrote in 120 a series of biographies of the Twelve Caesars (from Julius Caesar to Domitian), largely based upon original documents. Arrian, Epitectos's editor, wrote an account of Alexander's expedition and of Nearchos's voyage.

The astronomer Ptolemy drew up with considerable care a list of kings from 747 B. C. to 137 A. D. This list is important because it was used considerably by later chronologists and because it helps us to connect Greek and Babylonian dates.

10. *Roman Law.*—Julian completed in 131 a code of praetorian law. He compiled a Digest in 90 books.

11. *Chinese and Greek Philology*—Hsü Shên completed c. 120 the Shuo-wên, the earliest Chinese dictionary arranged by radicals; it contains some 10,500 characters classified under 540 radicals and is still the fountain-head for the study of Chinese etymology.

Apollonios Dyscolos continued the work of the Alexandrian grammarians; he introduced the study of syntax. Aelios Dionysios compiled a Greek lexicon. Nicanor investigated punctuation. Hephaestion wrote a treatise on Greek prosody.

12. *Final Remarks*—The internationalism of this age is very striking. To be sure, the dominating personality, that of Ptolemy, is Greek. And it would be difficult to find in the whole range of history a more imposing personality than his. Just think that astronomy and geography submitted to his authority for some fourteen centuries, that he carried out physical investigations of fundamental importance, and that his chronological inquiries have remained valuable unto this day. Galen, of whom I shall speak in the next chapter, dominated one branch of science for a millennium and half, but Ptolemy dominated two of them and left his mark upon various others. The Greco-Roman civilization of those days produced many other distinguished men: Epictetos and his disciple Arrian, Marinos the Geographer and Marinos the Anatomist, Rufus, and Soranos. But they must share the burden and the glory of advancing knowledge with men of other races—the Chinese Chang Hêng and Hsü Shên, the Kashmirian Caraka. And the greatest technical advance, the invention of paper—almost as pregnant as the invention of printing—was made, not in the West, but in China.

II. RELIGIOUS BACKGROUND

AŚVAGHOSHA

In Chinese, Ma^3-ming^2 (7576, 7960). Born in Sāketa; flourished in the reign of the Kushān king Kanishka.[a] Hindu Buddhist teacher. Twelfth Western patriarch. Author of various Sanskrit works which have exerted a deep influence

[a] The date of Kanishka is not yet established. Some would place him in the first century B. C.; the latest date is the first half of the second century of our era (c. 120 to c. 162). I place him tentatively there following Vincent A. Smith (Oxford History of India, 1919), who is not categorical about it. (Smith is more categorical in the second edition of his History, 126, 1923). The chronological uncertainty is now reduced to a period of 40 years; "Did Kanishka come to the throne in A. D. 78 or about 40 years later." Kanishka contributed perhaps as much to the diffusion of Buddhism abroad as Aśoka had contributed to its progress in India. He has been called a second Aśoka.

upon Mahāyāna Buddhism. He is often called the founder of Mahāyāna. This is misleading, however, because the Buddhist Council of Kashmir in which Aśvaghosha took part was still Hīnayāna. Moreover, it is hardly possible to assign the foundation of such a heterogeneous group of systems as the Mahāyāna to any single man.

The most important of his works are a metaphysical treatise called the Awakening of Faith,[b] and a poetical biography of the Buddha called the Buddhacarita (Doings of the Buddha).[c]

Text—The Fo-sho-hing-tsan-king, translated from Sanscrit into Chinese by Dharmaraksha in 420 and from the Chinese into English by Samuel Beal. Sacred Books of the East (vol. 19, 1879). The Buddha-karita edited by E. B. Cowell (190 p., Oxford, 1893). Translation by the same in the Sacred Books of the East (vol. 49). Translation from the Chinese version by T. Suzuki (174 p., Chicago, 1900). Carlo Formichi: Açvaghosa, poeta del Buddhismo (424 p., Bari, 1912. Italian translation with commentary; see Isis, I, 115). First German translation of the Buddha-charita, by Richard Schmidt (126 p., Hagen, 1923).

The "Awakening of Faith," translated from Sanscrit into Chinese by Paramārtha and from Chinese into English by Timothy Richard (Shanghai, 1907, with the Chinese text). For a criticism of Richard's translation see his biography by Wm. E. Soothill (London, 315–319, 1924).

Vajra-sūchī or the Needle adamant. Translated from Sanscrit into English by W. Morton (6 p., Appended to Vrajamohana Deva. On the Supreme God, 1843). Die Vajrasūcī. Eine buddhistische Streitschrift über die Irrigkeit der Ansprüche der Brāhmana-Kaste. In Albrecht Weber: Indische Streifen (t. 1, 186–209, 1868. This work ascribed to one Aśvaghosha is a refutation of the caste system).

Criticism—M. Anesaki, in Encyclopaedia of Religion and Ethics (vol. 2, 159, 1910). Else Wolgemuth: Über die chinesische Version des Buddhacarita (Diss., Leipzig, Berlin, 1916?). M. Winternitz: Geschichte der indischen Litteratur (Bd. 2, 201–214, 1920).

III. HELLENISTIC PHILOSOPHY

EPICTETOS

Ἐπίκτητος, born about the middle of the first century at Hierapolis, Phrygia; flourished at Rome, first as a slave then as a freedman until 94,[d] when he moved to Nicopolis in Epirus. He died during the reign of Hadrian, 117–138. One of the greatest Stoic philosophers. One of his disciples in Nicopolis was Arrian, to whom we owe the publication of his teachings.

Texts—Editions by Trincavelli (Venice, 1535). By John Upton, with Latin translation (2 vols., London, 1739–1741). By Johann Schweighaeuser, with Latin translation and Simplicios's commentary (5 vols., Leipzig, 1799–1800). By Fr. Dübner (Paris, Didot, 1842. Together with M. Aurelius). By Heinrich Schenkl (844 p., Leipzig, 1894; re-edited in 1916).

The Discourses and Manual, together with fragments, translated by P. E. Matheson (2 vols., Oxford, 1916).

---

[b] In Chinese, Ch'i³-hsin⁴-lun⁴ (1070, 4587, 7475).

[c] Translated into Chinese between 414 and 421, under the title Fo²*so³-hsing² tsan⁴ (3589, 10211, 4624, 11532). It is not certain that the two works quoted by me were written by the same man, for Chinese and Tibetan sources mention many Aśvaghosha, who may be identical or not. The Buddhist patriarch wrote the Buddhacarita.

[d] When philosophers were expelled from Italy by Domitian.

Criticism—M. Croiset: Littérature grecque (t. 5, 457–66, 1899). Adolf Bonhöffer: Epiktet und das Neue Testament (Giessen, 1911).

ADRASTOS

Adrastos of Aphrodisias (in Caria). Ἄδραστος. Flourished about the beginning of the second century. Peripatetic philosopher who wrote commentaries on Aristotle (ethics, logic, physics), on Theophrastos (ethics), and on Plato's Timaeos. His commentary on the Timaeos dealt with mathematical and astronomical questions and was partly based upon Posidonios. He wrote a treatise upon the order of the Aristotelian writings (περὶ τῆς τάξεως τῶν Ἀριστοτέλους συγγραμμάτων).

Criticism—Gercke, in Pauly-Wissowa (t. 1, 416, 1894). P. Duhem: Études sur Léonard de Vinci (t. 1, 58, 1906. On the equilibrium of the ocean).

POLEMON OF LAODICEA

Polemon Laodicensis, Πολέμων Λαοδικεύς, born at Laodicea, flourished at Smyrna under Hadrian and Antoninus, 117 to 138, 138 to 161. Greek sophist. Author of the earliest treatise on physiognomy (φυσιογνωμονικά), outside of the Pseudo-Aristotelian one.[e] It consists of seventy chapters.

Text—Poor edition by J. G. F. Franz: Scriptores physiognomoniae veteres (Altenburg, p. 169–310, 1780. Greek and Latin; the text is here divided into two books, of 23 and 27 chapters respectively). Critical edition by Georg Hoffmann, in the Scriptores physiognomonici edited by Richard Foerster (vol. 1, 93–294, 1893. Latin and Arabic; see indexes at the end of vol. 2, 1893).
Criticism—Richard Foerster: De Polemonis Physiognomonicis (Progr., 27 p., Kiel, 1886).

IV. ROMAN AND HELLENISTIC MATHEMATICS

BALBUS

Flourished in the reign of Trajan, at the beginning of the second century. Roman surveyor. After the first (or the second) Dacian war he dedicated to one Celsus a book on surveying: Balbi ad Celsum expositio et ratio omnium formarum (mensurarum?), based upon Heron's work or upon common sources. He is, with Frontinus and Hyginus, one of the best Roman gromaticians or surveyors. (Not to be mistaken for another Balbus, to whom the survey of the empire was entrusted by Agrippa, q. v., second half of first century B. C.)

Text and Translations—Friedrich Blume, Karl Lachmann, A. Rudorff: Die Schriften der römischen Feldmesser hrg. u. erläutert (2 vols., Berlin, 1846–1852). Friedrich Hultsch: Metrologicorum scriptorum reliquiae (Vol. II, Leipzig, 1866). The opuscule de asse minutisque eius portiunculis is apocryphal, and posterior to 222 A. D.).
Criticism—Gensel, in Pauly-Wissowa (t. 4, 2820–2822, 1896).

HYGINUS

Flourished probably under Trajan, emperor from 98 to 117. Roman surveyor (gromaticus). He wrote, probably at the time between the two Dacian wars, c. 103, a treatise on surveying, De limitibus (constituendis), wherein he describes, among other things, three different methods of determining the east-west direction.

---

[e] For which see my note on Aristotle's apocrypha.

Text—Gromatici veteres (vol. 1, 166–208, 1848). New edition by Charles Thulin: Corpus agrimensorum romanorum (vol. 1, 71–98, 1913. With many illustrations from various manuscripts: De limitibus; de condicionibus agrorum; de generibus controversiarum).

Criticism—M. Cantor: Geschichte der Mathematik (t. 1³, 535, 553, 599, 601, 1907).

THEON OF SMYRNA

Θέων. Flourished c. 127–132, probably in Smyrna. Platonic philosopher. He wrote a compilation entitled, "On the Mathematical Knowledge which is Needed to Read Plato" (*περὶ τῶν κατὰ τὸ μαθηματικὸν χρησίμων εἰς τὴν Πλάτωνος ἀνάγνωσιν*) and containing five parts: (1) Arithmetic, (2) plane geometry, (3) stereometry, (4) astronomy, (5) music. Parts 2 and 3 are lost, as also part 5, dealing with the harmony of the spheres, but we have his mathematical study of music, appended (in the Byzantine edition) to part 1. In 127, 129, 130, 132 he made observations of Mercury and Venus, which are recorded by Ptolemy. Mercury and Venus rotate around the sun (cfr. Heraclides); the earth is the center of the universe, but the sun is its heart. n^2 or n^2-1 is divisible by 3, by 4 or by both 3 and 4; if n^2 is divisible by 3 and not by 4, then n^2-1 is divisible by 4. Earliest suggestion of a magic square (excepting the Chinese tradition).

Theon's arithmetic is independent from that of Nichomachos (q. v., second half of first century). It will be recalled that the latter's date is uncertain. Nicomachos and Theon may have been contemporaries; they used the same sources.

Text and Translations—First edition, with Latin translation by Ism. Bullialdus (Boulliau) (Paris, 1644, containing the arithmetic and music); by J. J. de Gelder, with Latin translation (Leiden, 1827, arithmetic only). First edition of the astronomical part, with Latin translation, and commentary by Th. H. Martin (480 p., Paris, 1849). First complete edition by Ed. Hiller (224 p., Leipzig, 1878). An excellent edition with French translation by J. Dupuis (432 p., Paris, 1892. Hiller's text with small modifications, abundant notes, and a long appendix on Plato's geometrical number).

Criticism—Julius Lippert: Theon in der orientalischen Litteratur, in Studien auf dem Gebiete der griechisch-arabischen Übersetzungslitteratur (p. 39–50, Braunschweig, 1894). Paul Tannery: Note sur les problèmes musicaux dits d'Aristote (Revue des études grecques, t. 5, 51–52, 263, 1892); Sur Théon de Smyrne (Revue de philologie, t. 18, 145–152, 1894); Sur un passage de Théon (*ibidem*, t. 19, 67–69, 1895. See also Tannery's Mémoires, t. 2, 440–441, 455–465, 466–469). P. Duhem: La théorie de l'équilibre des mers selon Aristote, Adraste (d'Aphrodisie!) et Théon de Smyrne (Etudes sur Léonard de Vinci, t. 1, p. 58–62, 1906). Sir Thomas Heath: Greek Mathematics (t. 2, 238–244, 1921)

For Ptolemy's mathematical contributions, see the note devoted to him in the following section.

V. HELLENISTIC AND CHINESE ASTRONOMY

The observations of Venus and Mercury made by Theon of Smyrna from 127 to 132 have been mentioned in the previous section.

PTOLEMY

Claudios Ptolemaeos, Πτολεμαῖος, born in Egypt, flourished in Alexandria in the second quarter of the second century, died after 161. Astronomer, mathematician, geographer, physicist, chronologist. His influence upon later times (until the middle of the sixteenth century) is second only to that of Aristotle, for it was supreme in at least three great fields of knowledge. It was due largely to his masterly exposition of his subjects and his mathematical treatment of them. Ptolemy was a man of the Euclidean type. Assuming that the bulk of his facts, methods, and principles was derived from Hipparchos (q. v.)—in most cases Ptolemy admits it himself—the credit of this perfect exposition must remain to him, and this credit is very great. It seems difficult to conceive two men separated by almost three full centuries as close collaborators, yet their fame is inseparable.

Ptolemy's main work is his great Mathematical Treatise (*ἡ μαθηματικὴ σύνταξις*, or *μεγάλη σύνταξις τῆς ἀστρονομίας*, hence, by contraction of the first two words of the second title the name Almagest[f]) which is an encyclopedia of astronomy. It remained authoritative until 1543. Most of it is based upon Hipparchos. Ptolemy's own recorded observations extend from 127 to 151; he was apparently a poor observer. His chief contributions seem to be his very elaborate theory of the planets (notion of equant) and his discovery of a second inequality in the moon's motion (now named evection). He fixed the amount of the evection at 1°19′30″. He accounted for this inequality by the simultaneous use of eccentrics and epicycles, and a small oscillation of the epicycle (*πρόσνευσις τοῦ ἐπικύκλου*). Ptolemy's system is strictly geocentrical. The elaboration of trigonometry—that is, the substitution of diagrams by calculations—completed the establishment of astronomy as a mathematical discipline. Ptolemy's catalogue of 1,028 stars was probably dependent to a large extent upon Hipparchos's catalogue; but the latter being lost, Ptolemy's is the most ancient accurate description of the heavens, in fact the only one until the fifteenth century, and is therefore of inestimable value.

Books IX and XI of the "Almagest" contain a splendid exposition of trigonometry, spherical and plane. In Book IX, Ptolemy explains how to construct a table of chords, and gives one for every half degree from 0° to 180°. The so-called theorem of Ptolemy, about the quadrilateral inscribed in a circle, gives him a formula equivalent to ours relative to sin $(a \pm b)$. Sexagesimal division of the radius (partes *minutae* primae, partes minutae *secundae;* thence our words, minutes, seconds). Ptolemy's trigonometry introduced the use and appreciation of approximate calculations, the basis of applied mathematics. Ptolemy attempted to prove the fifth postulate of Euclid.

The "Geographical Treatise" (*γηωγραφικὴ ὑφήγησις*) is second in importance only to the "Almagest;" it influenced the progress of geography as deeply and as long as the latter influenced the progress of astronomy and mathematics. It is more the work of an astronomer than of a geographer, most of it being a table of the latitudes and longitudes of the most important places of the world. First technical use of the terms parallels and meridians. For his geographical information, Ptolemy admits his dependence upon Marinos of Tyre (q. v.). The astronomical location of places was greatly vitiated by his having adopted Posidonios's wrong estimate of the size of the earth, by his bad determination of the prime meridian (Fortunate Islands), and by very imperfect observations of the latitudes and even more of the longitudes. Yet his overestimate of the extent in longitude of Eurasia was one of the factors of Columbus's discovery. Methods of projection

---

[f] For further information on this derivation, see my note on the al-Ḥajjāj ibn Maṭar (first half of ninth century).

(orthographic, stereographic) remarkably advanced; in fact, far ahead of his knowledge of geographical facts. His maps were at least as influential as his tables, but it is impossible to know exactly to what extent those transmitted to us by mediaeval draftsmen represent those drawn by him or under his own supervision.

The Optics ascribed to Ptolemy contains an experimental study of refraction, and also an elaborate study of atmospheric refraction. It is the most remarkable experimental research of antiquity. Ptolemy found that the angles of incidence and refraction are proportional, which is approximately correct in the case of very small angles.

For the minor works of Ptolemy, or those ascribed to him, see the bibliography.

The Complete Works

(1) *Text and Translation*—Greek edition with French translation and elaborate notes, appendixes, etc., by the Abbé Nicolas B. Halma (Paris, 1816–1820), the various volumes of which are quoted below. A complete edition is in course of publication in Leipzig, but only the "Almagest" and the "Opera astronomica minora," both edited by Heiberg, have thus far appeared (3 vols., 1898–1907).

(2) *General Criticism*—There is no general study devoted to Ptolemy. The nearest approach to it is an excellent sketch in the Encyclopedia Britannica (11th edition, before 1911, 15 cols.) by G. J. Allman, Sir E. H. Bunbury and C. R. Beazley.

The Almagest

(3) *Tradition*—Commentaries by Pappos (second half of third century), Theon of Alexandria (second half of fourth century), Proclos (second half of fifth century) Latin translation by Boetius, lost. Translation into Arabic under al-Ma'mūn revised at the end of the ninth century by Thābit ibn Qurra. Translation from the Greek into Latin c. 1160 by an anonymous Sicilian author (this translation was long forgotten). Translation from the Arabic into Latin in 1175 by Gerard of Cremona. New translation from the Greek into Latin by George of Trebizond in 1451 (the first direct translation to be printed, 1528, see below).

Moritz Steinschneider: Die arabischen Bearbeiter des Almagest (Bibliotheca mathematica, p. 53–62, 1892). J. L. Heiberg: Eine mittelalterliche Übersetzung der Syntaxis (Hermes, t. 45, p. 57 sq., 1910; t. 46, 207–216, 1911). Charles H. Haskins and Dean Putnam Lockwood: The Sicilian Translators of the Twelfth Century and the First Latin Version of Ptolemy's Almagest (Harvard Studies in Classical Philology, t. 21, 75–102, 1910). For the Arabic Almagest, see H. Suter: Encyclopedia of Islam (t. 1, 313, 1913).

(4) *Text and Translation*—First edition of an epitome of the Almagest begun by Purbach and completed by Regiomontanus: Epytoma in Almagestum Ptolemei (Venice, 1496). First complete edition by P. Liechtenstein (Venice, 1515. A Latin translation from the Arabic). First Latin translation from the Greek by George of Trebizond (Venice, 1528). First Greek text by Simon Grynaeus (Basel, 1538. Based upon the manuscript once in the possession of Regiomontanus, now lost).

Greek and French text by Halma, notes by Delambre (2 vols., Paris, 1816). Syntaxis mathematica ed. J. L. Heiberg (Pars I, libros I–VI continens, 552 p., Leipzig, 1898; Pars II, libros VII–XIII continens, 612 p., 1903). Karl Manitius: Des Ptolemäus Handbuch der Astronomie (2 vols., Leipzig, 1912–1913. German translation with notes; essentially based upon Heiberg's text) There is no English translation!

(5) *Scientific Criticism*—A. Wittstein: Bemerkung zu einer Stelle im Almagest

(Z. f. Mathem. t. 32, hist. Abt., 201–208, 1887). Franz Boll: Beiträge zur Ueberlieferungsgeschichte der griechischen Astrologie und Astronomie (Sitzungsber. d. Akad. d. Wiss., philos. hist. Classe, p. 77–140, München, 1899. Überlieferungsgesch. einiger Schriften des Ptolemaios; Syntagma Laurentianum; eine illustrierte Prachthdsch. der astronomischen Tafeln des Ptolemaios). A. Häbler: Die Lehren des Ptolemaios von den Bewegungen der Planeten (Z. f. Mathem., t. 45, hist. Abt., 161–198, 1900). Karl Manitius: Die Parallaxen des Mondes und seine Entfernung von der Erde nach Ptolemaeus (Das Weltall, t. 10, No. 3–6, 1909). Paul Boelk: Darstellung und Prüfung der Mercurtheorie des Ptolemaeus (Diss., 40 p., Halle, 1911). J. K. Fotheringham and Longbottom: The Secular Acceleration of the Moon's Mean Motion as Determined from the Occultations in the Almagest (Monthly Notices of the R. Astron. Soc., vol. 75, 377–394, 1915; Isis, IV, 132).

(6) *Catalogue of Stars*—A splendid edition of this catalogue (in Almagest, Bks. VII and VIII), edited by Chr. H. F. Peters and Edw. Ball Knobel, was published in 1915 by the Carnegie Institution of Washington (207 p., Isis, II, 401). The result of this painstaking research confirms Tycho Brahe's view that this catalogue was deduced from Hipparchos's catalogue by the addition of a constant to the longitudes. The true epoch of the catalogue, so obtained, is the year 58, which proves that it can not be the fruit of Ptolemy's own observations. Peters and Knobel's book contains information on the previous editions, the manuscripts, etc. Franz Boll: Die Sternkataloge des Hipparch und des Ptolemaios (Bibliotheca mathematica, t. 2, 185–195, 1901). A. A. Björnbo: Hat Menelaos aus Alexandria einen Fixsternkatalog verfasst? (*ibidem*, 196–212. Björnbo concludes that although it contains c. 200 more stars, Ptolemy's catalogue is much inferior to that of Hipparchos, for it is an uncritical collection of heterogeneous material). J. L. E. Dreyer: On the Origin of Ptolemy's Catalogue (Monthly Notices of the R. Astron. Soc., vol. 77, 528–539; vol. 78, 343–349, 1917–1918. Defending the originality of Ptolemy's catalogue, Isis, IV, 131).

The Geography

(7) *Text and translations*[g]—For the manuscripts, see § 10. First Latin edition (Vincenza, 1475), a later edition (Bologna, 1482) was believed to be the first because of a misprint, "LXII". First Greek edition by Erasmus (Bale, 1533). For more information on the early editions see: Justin Winsor: A Bibliography of Ptolemy's Geography (Harvard Bibliographical Contributions No. 18, 42 p., 1884). Wilberforce Eames: A List of Editions of Ptolemy's Geography (45 p., New York, 1886. 50 copies printed). Henry N. Stevens: Ptolemy's Geography. A Brief Account of All the Printed Editions down to 1730, etc.; 2d edition, 70 p., London, 1908) Philip Lee Phillips: List of Geographical Atlases (4 vols., Washington, 1909–1920; Isis, IV, 40–43).

Best Greek edition, by C. F. A. Noble (3 vols., Leipzig, 1843–1845, with index). Greek and Latin edition (Didot collection) by Charles Müller and C. Th. Fischer (Paris, 1883–1901, with abundant notes). Hans von Mžik: Afrika nach der arabischen Bearbeitung der Γεωγραφικὴ ὑφήγησις von Muḥammad ibn Mūsā al-Hwārizmī, herausgegeben, übersetzt und erklärt von Joseph Fischer (Akad. der Wiss., phil. Kl., Denkschriften, t. 59, 4, Wien, 1916; Isis, V, 208). No English translation!

(8) *General Criticism*—Thomas Glazebrook Rylands: The Geography of Ptolemy elucidated (117 p., 4to, 20 plates, Dublin, 1893. An elaborate study of Ptolemy's methods and errors). Vidal de la Blache: Les voies de commerce

[g] More information on the early printed editions will be found in my chapter on Geography in the fifteenth century.

dans la Géographie de Ptolémée (Comptes Rendus de l'Acad. des inscriptions, 456–483, 1896. With three maps; important). Theod. Schoene: Die Gradnetze des Ptolemäus im ersten Buche seiner Geographie. Übersetzung der Kapitel 21–24 nebst Anmerkungen, und Figuren. (Progr., 28 p., Chemnitz, 1909). Otto Cuntz: Die Geographie des Ptolemaeus (232 p., 3 maps, Berlin, 1923. Important; Isis, VIII, 735).

(9) *Criticism Restricted to Special Parts of the World*—William Plate: Ptolemy's Knowledge of Arabia, especially of Hadhramaut and the Wilderness el-Ahqāf (Classical Museum, No. 8, 11 p., London, 1845). D. G. Hogarth: Penetration of Arabia (chapter 1, 1904).

Albrecht Roscher: Ptolemaeus und die Handelstrassen in Central-Africa (122 p., 1 map, Gotha, 1857).

Georg Holz: Über die germanische Völkertafel des Ptolemaeus (80 p., 1 pl., Halle a. S., 1894). Anton Gnirs: Das östliche Germanien und seine Verkehrswege in der Darstellung des Ptolemaeus (43 p., 1 map, Prag, 1898). C. Mehlis: Ptolemaeus über Grossgermanien (Geographischer Anzeiger, 22 J., 200–206, 1921); Die Städte und Verkehrswege im Südosten der Germania megale (Archiv für Anthropologie, Bd. 19, 147–165, 1923).

Col. G. E. Gerini: Researches on Ptolemy's Geography in Eastern Asia. Further India and Indo-Malay Peninsula (Asiatic soc. monographs, 1, 967 p., 11 tables, 2 maps, London, 1909. A study on an immense scale, fundamental but monstrous; see a review of it by Ed. Chavannes in T'oung Pao, vol. 11, 296–299). Wilh. Volz: Südost-Asien bei Ptolemäus (Geographische Zeitschrift, vol. 17, 31–44, Leipzig, 1911).

(10) *Maps*—Reproduction photolithographique du MS. grec du monastère Vatopédi au mont Athos, edited with introduction by Victor Langlois (Paris, 1867). This manuscript dates from c. 1250. Father Jos. Fischer is preparing a facsimile edition of an earlier atlas, the Urbinas 82 of c. 1200.

Joseph Fischer: Die handschriftliche Überlieferung der Ptolemäuskarten (Petermanns geogr. Mit., p. 61–63, 1912). Gudmund Schütte: Der Ursprung der hdschr. Ptolemäuskarten (Mit. zur. Gesch. d. Medizin, vol. 13, 573–577, 1914; Isis, III, 320). L. O. Th. Tudeer: On the Origin of the Maps Attached to Ptolemy's Geography (Journal Hellenic Studies, vol. 37, 62–76, London, 1917). Gudmund Schütte: Ptolemy's Maps of Northern Europe, a Reconstruction of the Prototypes (200 p., Copenhagen, 1917; Isis, III, 422). Jos. Fischer: Die Stadtzeichen auf den Ptolemäuskarten (Kartographische und schulgeogr. Zeit., 7. Jahr., 49–52, Wien, 1918; Isis, IV, 131); Pappus und die Ptolemäuskarten (Z. d. Gesell. f. Erdkunde, 336–358, Berlin, 1919; Isis, IV, 131); Ptolemäus und Agathodämon (Akad. d. Wiss. in Wien, phil. Kl., Denkschriften, vol. 59, 4 p., 71–93, 1916; Isis, V, 206. Fischer concludes that the maps of separate countries were made by Ptolemy, but that his map of the world was superseded by that of Agathodaemon).[h] I. A. Richmond: Ptolemy's Map of Denmark, a Study in Conflicting Evidence (Scottish Geographical Magazine, vol. 39, 99–102, 1923). Edward Heawood: The Wilton Codex of Ptolemy Maps (Geographical Journal, vol. 64, 237–240, 1924; Isis, VII, 180).

The Optics

(11) *Text*—The text of the Optics is known only through a twelfth-century Latin translation from the Arabic, and of its five books, the first is entirely lost, and we have only extracts from the fifth. Is this Ptolemy's own work? or an Arabic forgery? The fact that it was commented upon as early as the fifth century refutes the sec-

[h] On Agathodaemon, see also Berger, in Pauly-Wissowa (vol. 1, 747, 1894). Agathodaemon was of Alexandria, but his time is unknown.

ond hypothesis; on the other hand, it is very strange that the "Almagest" contains no allusion to it or to refraction.

Gilberto Govi: L'ottica di Tolomeo da Eugenio, ammiraglio di Sicilia, scrittore del secolo XII, ridotta in latino sovra la traduzione araba di un testo greco imperfetto (222 p., 9 tav., Torino, 1885; see Bibliotheca Mathematica, 1888, 91–92. Ptolemy's optics contains an allusion to the principle of conservation of energy: Cursus naturae in conservandis actibus virtutis).

(12) *Criticism*—A. Favaro's review of Govi's publication, in Boncompagni's Bullettino (t. 19, 115–120, 1886). Henri Narducci: Sur l'optique de Ptolémée (Bibliotheca Mathematica, p. 97–102, 1888).

MINOR WRITINGS

(13) Apparitions of Fixed Stars and Collection of Prognostics: (φάσεις ἀπλανῶν ἀστέρων καὶ συναγωγὴ ἐπισημασιῶν), edited by Halma, with French translation, (Vol. III, Paris, 1819); by Heiberg, Opera astronomica minora (1–68, Leipzig, 1907).

G. Hellmann: Ueber die ägyptischen Witterungsangaben im Kalender von Ptolemaeus (Sitzungsber. d. preuss. Akad. d. Wiss., 332–341, 1916).

(14) Planetary Hypothesis (ὑποθέσεις τῶν πλανωμένων). A summary of the planetary theories of the Almagest. Edited by Halma, with French translation (Vol. IV, Paris, 1820); by Heiberg, Op. astronom. minora, (69–145, 1907. Book I is published in Greek and German; Book II, lost in the original, is translated from the Arabic into German by Ludwig Nix.)

(15) Inscriptio Canobi, edited by Heiberg, *ibidem*, 147–155.

(16) Manual Tables (προχείρων κανόνων διάταξις καὶ ψηφοφορία). A summary of the tables of the Almagest; edited by Heiberg (*ibidem*, 159–185).

(17) The Analemma (περὶ ἀναλήμματος), A Treatise on gnomonics; orthographic projection. Only fragments of the Greek text remain. Edited by Fed. Commandino, a Latin version from the Arabic (Rome, 1562). New edition by J. L. Heiberg (Abhdl. zur Gesch. d. Mathematik, VII, 1–30, Leipzig, 1895. In Latin, but with the text of the Greek fragments. Reprinted with few changes in the Op. astron. min., 187–223).

(18) Planisphaerium (called by Suidas, ἅπλωσις ἐπιφανείας σφαίρας) contains a theory of stereographic projection. Greek text lost. Latin version from the Arabic edited by Commandino (Venice, 1558). Reëdited by Heiberg, Op. astr. min. (225–259). A German translation of Heiberg's text by J. Drecker will appear in Isis, Vol. IX or X.

The Opera astronomica minora edited by J. L. Heiberg, in 1907, contain the works dealt with in §13 to 18, and also a few fragments (p. 263–270). For criticism of these astronomical writings refer to §5 (criticism of the Almagest).

(19) Tetrabiblon or Quadripartitum (τετράβιβλος). An astrological treatise to which is generally joined another one, the Centiloquium (καρπός). Greek and Latin edition by Camerarius (Nürnberg, 1535) and Melanchton (Bale, 1553). Ptolemy's Tetrabiblos or Quadripartite being four books on the influence of the stars. Newly translated into English from the Greek paraphrase of Proclus. . . . with notes, etc., by J. M. Ashmand, followed by the Centiloquy (272 p., London, 1822. It is typical that this is the only work of Ptolemy of which an English translation is available!) Tetrabiblos Buch III und IV. Nach der von Philip Melanchton besorgten und mit einer Vorrede versehenen selten Ausgabe griechisch und lateinisch (Ins Deutsche übertragen von M. Erich Winkel, 158 p., Berlin, 1923).

Fr. Foll: Studien über Ptolemäus. Ein Beitrag zur Gesch. d. griech. Philosophie und Astrologie (Jahrb. f. klass. Phil., supp. Bd. 21, p. 51–243, Leipzig, 1894. Boll is convinced that the Tetrabiblon is genuine and the Carpos apocryphal). See also

§5. J. K. Fotheringham: Ancient Observations of Coloured Stars (The Observatory, vol. 43, 191–192, 1920; Isis, IV, 132).

(20) Table of Reigns (κανὼν βασιλειῶν). Chronological tables of Assyrian, Persian, Greek, and Roman kings from Nabonasar to Antoninus Pius. Greek and French edition by Halma (Paris, 1819). E. Cavaignac: Chronologie (chapter 6, p. 35–40, Paris, 1925, containing a summary and discussion of Ptolemy's Canon).

(21) Treatise on Music (ἁρμονικά). Greek and Latin edition by John Wallis (Oxford, 1682; reprinted with Porphyry's commentary in Wallis's Opera mathematica, Vol. III, Oxford, 1699).

(22) On Judgment and Hegemony of the Soul (περὶ κριτηρίου καὶ ἡγεμονικοῦ), edited by Fr. Hanow (15 p., Leipzig, 1870). Friedrich Lammert: Zur Erkenntnislehre der späteren Stoa (Hermes, vol. 57, 171–188, 1922).

CHANG HÊNG

Chang[1] Hêng[2] (416, 3912). Born in Nan[2]-yang[2] (8128, 12883) in 78; died in 139. Chinese astronomer. Minister to the Han emperors, An[1]-Ti[4] (44, 10942) and Shun[4]-Ti[4] (10143). He constructed a celestial hemisphere turning above an equatorial plane.[i] He seems to have known a great number of stars. In addition to the sun and moon, the five planets, and the 28 solar mansions, he enumerates 124 ever-visible stars, 320 stars with names, 2,500 bigger and 11,520 (?!) smaller stars unnamed (Forke). A kind of seismometer (?) is also ascribed to him.[j] He wrote the Ling[2]-hsien[4] (7222, 4547), a book of cosmology and astronomy. His value of π was equivalent to $\sqrt{10}$. He corrected the calendar in 123.

H. A. Giles: Chinese Biographical Dictionary (p. 22, Shanghai, 1898). Yoshio Mikami: The Development of Mathematics in China and Japan (p. 46–47, Leipzig, 1913). Encyclopaedia Sinica (1917) article seismology. Arthur Waley: Chinese Painting (29, 1923). L. Wieger: La Chine (108, 405, 1920. Wieger says that Chang constructed his celestial sphere in 169; this does not tally with the date of death given by Giles and reproduced by me). A. Forke: World-conception of the Chinese (9, 10, 18–19, 1925; Isis, VIII, 373). The very interesting text from the Hou Han-shu, for which, see my note on Fan Yeh, first half of fifth century, relative to the seismometer, is quoted and translated on p. 19.

VI. ROMAN, HELLENISTIC, AND CHINESE PHYSICS AND TECHNOLOGY

For Roman physics, see my notes devoted to the surveyors Balbus and Hygiuns in Section IV.

APOLLODOROS OF DAMASCUS

Ἀπολλόδωρος. Flourished under Trajan, emperor from 98 to 117, put to death by Hadrian. One of the greatest architects of antiquity. The time of Trajan marked the culmination of Roman engineering and Apollodoros carried out many of Trajan's great ideas. In 105, he constructed a permanent bridge across the Danube in Dacia (at the modern Turnu Severin, near the Iron Gate)[k]; he also built the forum and aqueduct, named after Trajan, and several roads. He wrote a book on poliorcetics and possibly other technical works, which are lost.

See Fabricius. in Pauly-Wissowa (vol. 2, 2896, 1894). For a list of the public works accomplished under Trajan (and other emperors), see Curt Merckel: Die

---

[i] Similar spheres had been constructed before, i. e., see my note on Lo Hsia Hung (second half of second century B. C.) and Chia K'uei (second half of first century).

[j] See my note on Ch'ao-Ts'o, second half of second century B. C.

[k] The bridge across the Tagus near Alcantara was built at about the same time (105–6) by another architect of Trajan's, C. Julius Lacer.

Ingenieurtechnik im Altertum (p. 642, Berlin, 1899). On the Reign of Trajan, see Heinrich Francke: Zur Geschichte Trajan's und seine Zeitgenossen (2te Ausg., 754 p., Quedlinburg, 1840. Public Works, science, and arts p. 566 to the end). C. de la Berge: Essai sur le règne de Trajan (Bibliothèque de l'école des hautes études, sci. philol. et hist., 32, 360 p., Paris, 1877). Maurice Pellisson: Rome sous Trajan (300 p., Paris, 1886).

A part of the mathematical manual compiled by Theon of Smyrna was devoted to the scientific study of music, see my note in Section IV.

A treatise on optics, ascribed to Ptolemy (q. v., in Section V), contains an experimental study of refraction of very great importance.

TS'AI LUN

Ts'ai[4] Lun[2] (11519, 7464). Native of Kuei[4]-yang[2] (6461, 12883) in Kueichou; flourished at Lo[4*]-Yang[2] (7328, 12883); died in 114. Chinese engineer and inventor, inspector of public works. Chief eunuch under the emperor Ho[2] Ti[4] (3945, 10942). The invention of real paper made of "tree bark, hemp, rags, and fish nets," is traditionally ascribed to him. (It is probable that some near-paper made of silk fiber was already made in the first century.)[l] In 105 he made a report to the emperor on the process of paper-making. "From this time (says Fan Yeh) paper has been in use everywhere and is called the paper of Marquis Ts'ai." The tradition that paper was manufactured at about that time has been amply confirmed by the discovery of fragments of pure rag paper dating from c. 150, in a watch tower of a western spur of the Great Wall.[m] The manufacture of paper was quickly and steadily improved after Ts'ai Lun's time. Thus the invention of paper may be said to be the most certain and the most complete of Chinese inventions. Its cultural value can hardly be exaggerated; it was one of the essential conditions of the accumulation of knowledge, and thus of its progress. Other writing materials like wood or bamboo were too cumbrous and too heavy, or, like silk (or parchment in the West), too expensive.

Friedrich Hirth: Die Erfindung des Papiers in China (T'oung Pao, vol. 1, 1–14, 1890). Augustin Blanchet: Essai sur l'histoire du papier (Paris, 1900). H. A. Giles: Biographical Dictionary (751, 1898). Ed. Chavannes: Les livres chinois avant l'invention du papier (Journal asiatique, t. 5, 5–75, 1905). Thomas Francis Carter: Invention of Printing in China (1925; Isis, VIII, 361. Contains the original account of the invention as written by Fan Yeh, q. v. first half of fifth century, in his History of the Eastern Han dynasty).

For the Chinese discovery of the seismometer, see my note on Chang Hêng in Section V.

VII. HELLENISTIC GEOGRAPHY

MARINOS

Marinos of Tyre. Μαρῖνος. Flourished probably not long before Ptolemy. Greek geographer, whom we know only through Ptolemy.[n] Most of the geo-

---

[l] For a previous stage in the history of Chinese writing, see my note on Mêng T'ien (second half of third century B. C.).

[m] The discovery was made by Sir Aurel Stein in 1911. These fragments consist of 9 letters written in the Sogdian language and a few written in Chinese. See facsimile in Carter's work opposite p. 5.

[n] His work was still extant in the tenth century, for Mas'ūdī declares having seen it (Livre de l'Avertissement, p. 53).

graphical information contained in the latter's Geography is derived from Marinos. This enables us to judge how much geographical knowledge had increased from the time of Strabon and Pliny to the time of Marinos, especially with regard to Asia and Africa. This great increase of knowledge obliges us to place him at the beginning of the second or the end of the first century. Ptolemy praised Marinos's knowledge and method in the highest terms. Marinos's aim was to correct the map of the world, both with regard to its contents and to its mathematical construction. His method was still very crude: he took the parallel of 36° (Gibraltar, Rhodes) as the foundation of his map, and set off the degrees of longitude along this, according to their proportion to those of latitude (at that latitude); he made no attempt to preserve correct proportions along the other parallels. The meridians and parallels were then represented by two sets of straight lines perpendicular to each other.[a]

E. H. Bunbury: History of Ancient Geography (vol. 2, 519–545, 1879. Places Marinos much earlier).

For Ptolemy's geography, see my note on Ptolemy in Section V.
For Arrian's periplus of the Black Sea (131), see my note on Arrian in Section IX.

VIII. HELLENISTIC, ROMAN, AND HINDU MEDICINE

ARCHIGENES

Archigenes of Apamea, Syria. Ἀρχιγένης. Flourished in Rome under Trajan. Physician, the most famous disciple of Agathinos. He distinguished the four following stages in the development of disease (see Herodotos): ἀρχή, ἀκμή, παρακμή, ἄνεσις. Classification of fevers: κατόξεις, ὀξεῖς, χρόνιοι, βραχυχρόνιοι. His was the most elaborate theory of pulse in ancient times. Refinement of diagnosis. Description of leprosy; of Hindu therapeutics. Used a speculum uteri.

Max Wellmann: Archigenes (Pauly-Wissowa, Vol. III, 484–486, 1895); Die pneumatische Schule bis auf Archigenes (Philol. Untersuch., XIV, 1895). E. Gurlt: Geschichte der Chirurgie (vol. 1, 411–414, 1898).

ANTYLLOS

Ἄντυλλος. Flourished in the first half of the second century; he quotes Archigenes and is quoted by Galen. Greek physician of the Pneumatic school, famous as a surgeon. Only fragments of his work remain (chiefly through Oribasios); they deal with balneology, medical climatology; he prescribed physical exercises. He made a study of venesection, cupping, and leeching, of styptic agents. He gave elaborate surgical directions (e. g., tracheotomy, cataract, plastic operations). Therapeutics of real and traumatic aneurysms.

Text and Translations—Fragments collected by A. Lewy and Landsberg in Janus (Vol. II, Breslau, 1847); also in Bussemaker and Daremberg: Oeuvres d'Oribase (4 vols., 1851–1862). Antyllos's main works were his Remedies, περὶ βοηθημάτων and his surgery, χειρουργούμενα). The very important text relative to aneurysm will be found in Vol. IV, p. 52, and a German translation of it has been given by Gurlt: Geschichte der Chirurgie (vol. 1, p. 483–484, 1898).

Criticism—E. Gurlt: Geschichte der Chirurgie (vol. 1, 474–486, 1898). M. Wellmann, in Pauly-Wissowa (vol. 2, 2644–2645, 1894). J. Hirschberg: Die Star-

---

[a] Ptolemy used the same network for his maps of particular countries.

Operation nach Antyllos (Zentralblatt f. praktische Augenheilkunde, vol. 30, 97–100, 1906).

HELIODOROS

Ἡλιόδωρος; probably of Egyptian origin,[p] flourished at Rome in the time of Trajan. Greek surgeon of the Pneumatic school. His main work is a treatise on surgery (χειρουργούμενα) in five books. He is possibly the author of two other treatises on articulations (ἡ περὶ ἄρθρων πραγματεία) and on luxations (ἡ περὶ ὀλισθημάτων πραγματεία).

Text—The writings of Heliodoros are known through the fragments preserved in the works of Oribasios (q. v. second half of fourth century) and in Nicetas's collection (q. v., second half of ninth century). Georg Fr. Th. Lenz: De Heliodori fragmentis (Diss., Gryphiae, 1846).

For a few fragments on papyri see Crönert, in Archiv für Papyrusforschung (vol. 2, 480 sq.), and Ilberg (*ibidem*, vol. 4, 273).

Henry E. Sigerist: Die Cirurgia Eliodori (Archiv für Geschichte der Medizin, Bd. 12, 1–9, 1920); Die Lecciones Heliodori (*ibidem*, Bd. 13, 145–156, 1921; Isis, VII, 181).

Criticism—E. Gurlt: Geschichte der Chirurgie (vol. 1, 414–421, 1898). Max Neuburger: Geschichte der Medizin (Bd. 2, 51, 1911). Article by Gossen, in Pauly-Wissowa (vol. 8, 41–42, 1912).

MARINOS THE ANATOMIST

Μαρῖνος, flourished at Alexandria about the beginning of the second century. Greek anatomist highly praised by Galen. He wrote a comprehensive treatise an anatomy in twenty books, which we know through the outline of it given by Galen. This work was based upon personal observation. Marinos determined accurately the foramina of skull and vertebrae. He improved the technique of bone drilling.

Irrespective of his own merits, which were apparently great, Marinos is an important personality in the history of anatomy, because it helps one to reconstruct the tradition which culminated in Galen's immense endeavor. This tradition can be summarized as follows: Marinos was the teacher of Quintos (Κοΐντος) who flourished at Pergamum, Alexandria, and Rome and died at Pergamum. Three of Quintos's disciples influenced Galen, to wit, Satyros (Σάτυρος), who taught at Pergamum, Numisianos, who taught at Corinth, and Lycos (Λύκος) the Macedonian. Pelops (Πέλοψ), who taught at Smyrna, was a distinguished pupil of Numisianos. Now Galen studied under Satyros, Numisianos, and Pelops.

The works of Marinos and of his disciples are lost. Almost everything we know of him and of them is derived from Galen's writings and chiefly from the anatomical books which have come down to us through a ninth century Arabic translation. See Max Simon's Arabic and German edition of them (2 vols., Leipzig, 1906; see chiefly, vol. 2, 167). On Satyros, see brief note in Pauly-Wissowa, Zweite Reihe (vol. 3, 235, 1921, by Kind).

RUFUS

Rufus[q] of Ephesus. Ῥοῦφος. Flourished under Trajan, in Rome and in Egypt. Greek anatomist and physician; the greatest Greek physician of the Roman

---

[p] The name Heliodoros was fairly common in Egypt.

[q] The transcription Rhuphos would seem more natural, but I give the one most generally adopted. Rufus was an extraordinarily common name in Rome—meaning red-haired (French, roux).

Empire after Galen.[r] His work was largely based upon the works of Herophilos and Erasistratos (e. g., theory of nerves) but he had made elaborate anatomical researches upon monkeys and pigs. First description of the optic chiasma; much improved description of the eye (he mentions the lens, lentil-shaped, φακοειδής).[s] He understood the difference between sensory and motor nerves, and saw the immense functional importance of the nervous system. He described the oviduct of the sheep. He wrote on the diseases of the urinary organs and on many other anatomical and medical subjects. The most important of his extant writings is an elementary treatise of anatomy, the earliest treatise on anatomical nomenclature (περὶ ὀνομασίας τῶν τοῦ ἀνθρώπου μορίων). Another work of his on the anatomy of the human body (περὶ ἀνατομῆς τῶν τοῦ ἀνθρώπου μορίων) contains the earliest description of the liver as five-lobed.[t] His short treatise on the pulse (Σύνοψις περὶ σφυγμῶν)[u] is very important because it contains a good definition of the pulse, and the wonderful remark that the pulse and heart-beat correspond to the systole (not to the diastole).[v] This treatise represents the earliest attempt to base pathology upon anatomy and physiology. Many diseases or symptoms are described by him for the first time (e. g., bubo), and he gave good hygienic advice (e. g., to boil suspicious water before using it). The most interesting part of his surgery is his description of haemostatic methods.

Text and Translations—Rufi Ephesi de vesicae renumque morbis, de purgantibus medicamentis, de partibus corpis humani, nunc iterum typis mandavit Gul. Clinch (London, 1726). The best edition is that by Charles Daremberg, completed by Ch. Emile Ruelle, with French translation (Paris, 1879). It contains all the Greek works extant and fragments collected from Greek and Arabic authors. German translation by Robert von Töply: Anatomische Werke des Rhuphos und Galenos (Anatomische Hefte, 1. Abt., t. 25, Wiesbaden, 1904. Translation of the περὶ ὀνομασίας).

Criticism—E. Gurlt: Geschichte der Chirurgie (vol. 1, 421–428, 1898). Article by Gossen, in Pauly-Wissowa, Zweite Reihe (vol. 1, 1207–1212, 1914. Contains a catalogue of 36 works of Rufus; only 12 are extant, some of them incompletely.) M. Menestrier: A propos du Traité du pouls attribué à Rufus et de la sphygmologie des anciens (Bull. soc. franç. hist. méd., 18, 97–98, 1924. In praise of this treatise, which is probably anterior to Rufus; Isis, VII, 180).

SORANOS OF EPHESUS

Σωρανός. Born in Ephesus, flourished in Rome under Trajan and Hadrian, (i. e., 98–138). Greek anatomist and physician, the greatest representative of the Methodist school (methodicorum princeps), the greatest gynaecologist of antiquity. His main work is a treatise on women's diseases, obstetrics, and pediatrics

---

[r] The Muslims had a very high regard for him.

[s] This is the earliest reference to the real form of the crystalline lens. Says Singer (Typewritten Notes to Illustrate the History of Anatomy, p. 28, 1923), "The structure and function of the lens was misunderstood until the seventeenth century, save for this one passage of Rufus (in his περὶ ὀνομασίας). It was entirely misrepresented by both Leonardo and Vesalius."

[t] That is, he describes a pig's liver. This gross mistake remained in force until the time of Vesalius!

[u] At first only known through a twelfth century Latin translation and published by Chartier (vol. 8, 330 sq.) as a work of Galen. First Greek edition by Daremberg. Traité sur le pouls (Paris, 1846, with Greek translation). Daremberg considered it unauthentic but contemporary.

[v] This was forgotten, however, and had to be rediscovered in the seventeenth century by Harvey, being the first step toward the latter's great discovery.

(περὶ γυναικείων παθῶν), containing elaborate descriptions of many diseases and rational therapeutic advice. Admirable description of the womb. Use of speculum (δίοπτρα), of obstetric chair (δίφρος μαιωτικός), and of an instrument to make injections into the womb (μητρεγχύτης). We owe to Soranos the earliest life of Hippocrates.[w]

Text and Translations—Editio princeps by F. R. Dietz: De arte obstetricia morbisque mulierum quae supersunt (Königsberg, 1838). Greek and Latin edition by Fr. Z. Ermerins: De muliebribus affectionibus (427 p., Utrecht, 1869). Greek edition by Val. Rose (Leipzig, 1882), with the Gynaecia Muscionis (444 p.). German translation by H. Lüneburg with notes by J. Chr. Huber (München, 1894). French translation by F. J. Herrgott: Soranus d'Ephèse (Nancy, 1895). English translation of the description of the womb, in J. S. McKay: History of Ancient Gynaecology (London, 1901).

The book on fractures (περὶ σημείων καταγμάτων, De signis fracturarum) was edited by Ant. Cocchi (1695–1758) in his Graecorum chirurgici libri (p. 45–51, Florence, 1754), also by J. L. Ideler: Physici et medici minores (t. 1, 1841, with other fragments).

The book on acute and chronic diseases (περὶ ὀξέων καὶ χρονίων παθῶν) is known only through Caelius Aurelianus, De morbis acutis et chronicis, which is almost a translation of it.

Criticism—J. Chr. Huber: Nachträge zu Soranus (Münchener medicinische Wochenschrift, 44. J., 365–366, 1897). E. Gurlt: Geschichte der Chirurgie (vol. 1, 400–407, 1898). Johann Lachs: Die Gynäkologie des Soranus (Volkmann's Sammlung klinischer Vorträge, Leipzig, 1902). Joh. Ilberg: Die Überlieferung der Gynäkologie des Soranos (Abhdl. d. philol. hist. Kl. d. Sächs. Ges. d. Wiss., vol. 28, 122 p., Leipzig, 1910). A. H. F. Barbour: Soranus on gynaecological anatomy. XVIIth International Congress of Medicine, 1913, historical section, (p. 269–283, London, 1914).

Ludw. Scheele: De Sorano Ephesio medico etymologico (Dissertationes philologicae argentoratenses, Vol. VIII, 177–254, Strasburg, 1884). Hermann Stadler: Neue Bruchstücke der Quaestiones medicinales des Pseudo-Soranus (Archiv f. latein. Lexicographie, XIV, 361–368, 1905).

Max Wellmann: Der Verfasser des Anonymus Londinensis (Hermes, vol. 57, 396–429, 1922). Apropos of the London papyrus 137 discovered by F. G. Kenyon and published by H. Diels: Anonymi Londinensis ex Aristotelis iatricis Menoniis et aliis medicis eclogae (Berlin, 1893, Suppl. Arist.), Wellmann concludes that it is a fragment from the Soranos Isagoge.

Gynaecological Illustrations—See my note on iconographic traditions apropos of Moschion (first half of sixth century). Also J. Ilberg: Eine Zeichenkünstlerin Olympias? (Archiv für Geschichte der Medizin, Bd. 2, 426–428, 1909).

METRODORA

This is perhaps the best place to say a few words about this woman physician of whom nothing is known, except that she wrote a Greek treatise on the diseases of the womb, which seems quite valuable. This treatise is found in a single manuscript of the Laurentiana, Florence (Plut. LXXV, a manuscript of the twelfth century, f. 4 to 33), entitled: Ἐκ τῶν Μητροδώρας περὶ τῶν γυναικείων παθῶν τῆς μήτρας. This treatise is probably the earliest extant medical treatise written by a woman.

---

[w] It should be noted that the influence of Soranos upon the progress of medieval medicine was exerted only in an indirect way, through Moschion's (q. v., first half of sixth century) Latin adaptation.

G. A. Costomiris: Revue des études grecques (t. 3, 147, 1890). Skevos Zervos: Das unveröffentliche medizinische Werk der Metrodora (Archiv für Geschichte der Medizin, Bd. 3, 141–144, 1909).

HINDU MEDICINE

CARAKA

Born in Pañcanada, Kashmir, flourished under the Indoscythian King Kanishka,[1] who reigned probably c. 120 to 162. Kashmirian physician who wrote a compendium (Caraka saṃhitā) which represents Ātreya's system of medicine (see sixth century B. C.) as handed down by his pupil Agniveśa. (The Agniveśa samhitā itself is lost.)

Text—The Caraka-saṃhitā has been edited by J. Vidyāsāgara (2. ed., Calcutta, 1896); by Gupta (Calcutta, 1897); by C. Dutta (Calcutta, 1892–1893); etc.

Translation by A. C. Kaviratna (Calcutta, 1891–1912).

Criticism—A. F. Rudolf Hoernlé: Studies in the Medicine of Ancient India (Part I, Oxford, 1907); The Authorship of the Charaka Samhita (Archiv für Geschichte der Medizin, Bd. 1, 29–40, 1907. Left incomplete). M. Winternitz: Geschichte der indischen Litteratur (Bd. 3, 545, 1922).

IX. ROMAN AND HELLENISTIC HISTORIOGRAPHY

SUETONIUS

Caius Suetonius Tranquillus. Born under Vespasian, emperor from 69 to 79; flourished at Rome; died c. 160. Roman historian and polygraph. He compiled a miscellany, called the Meadows (Prata), dealing chiefly with Roman antiquities and natural sciences (laws; customs; winds; seas; animals; plants; minerals); a collection of lives of great men (De viris illustribus) and, in 120, biographies of the Twelve Emperors (Vitae duodecim Caesarum). His fame rests entirely upon this last work, which is completely extant (the Prata are lost, and only a few of the lives of great men remain). It is based, to a large extent, upon original documents.

Texts—Editio princeps (Rome, 1470). Quae supersunt omnia, edited by C. L. Roth (Leipzig, 1858; again 1875, 1882, 1886). Opera, ed. by Maxim. Ihm (Leipzig, 1907).

Latin text with English translation by J. C. Rolfe (Loeb library, 2 vols., 1914).

Albert Andrew Howard and Carl Newell Jackson: Index verborum C. Suetonii Tranquilli stilique ejus proprietatum nonnullarum (273 p., Harvard Press, Cambridge, Mass., 1922).

Criticism—Walter Dennison: The Epigraphic Sources of Suetonius (American Journal Archaeology, vol. 2, 25–70, 1898). Alcide Massé: Essai sur Suétone (Bibl. des écoles franç. d'Athènes et de Rome, 82, 454 p., Paris, 1900). John Carew Rolfe: Suetonius and his Biographies (Amer. Philos. Soc., vol. 52, 206–225, Philadelphia, 1913).

ARRIAN

Arrianus Flavius, Ἀρριανός. Born in Nicomedia, Bithynia, at the end of the first century, he was still living in 171. Historian. Governor of Cappadocia 131 to 137. Pupil and editor of Epictetos (Ἐπικτήτου διατριβαί, Ἐγχειρίδιον). He wrote a history of Alexander's expedition (Ἀλεξάνδρου ἀνάβασις), followed by a relation of the voyage of Nearchos (Ἰνδική). In 131, he compiled for Hadrian

[1] **According to the Chinese version of the Tripiṭaka, Caraka was Kanishka's physician.**

a Periplus of the Euxine (Περιπλόυς Εὐξείνου πόντου). He is generally well informed, clear, critical. He was not improperly called the "new Xenophon."

Text and Translations—Arrian's Anabasis et Indica ed. F. Dübner, Reliqua Arrianis et scriptorum de rebus Alexandri M. fragmenta coll. Car. Müller (Greek and Latin edition, Paris, 1846). Arriani quae exstant omnia ed. A. G. Roos (Vol. I, Anabasis, 480 p., Leipzig, 1907). Scripta minora ed. Rud. Hercher (232 p., Leipzig, 1885, Indica; Cynegeticus; Acies contra Alanos; Periplus; Tactica). Τῶν μετ' 'Αλέξανδρον libri septiml ed. Ric. Reitzenstein (Breslauer philolog. Abhdl., III, 36 p., 1888). German translation by C. Cless (4 vols., Stuttgart, 1862–1865).

Anabasis, ed. by Roos (1907). English translation with notes by E. J. Chinnock (London, 1884, also 1893, Bohn Library).

Indica, English translation with Greek text, by William Vincent (Oxford, 1809). J. W. McCrindle: Ancient India as Described by Megasthenes and Arrian (234 p., Calcutta, 1877). The Commerce and Navigation of the Erythraean Sea, being a translation of the Periplus Maris Erythraei, by an anonymous writer, and of Arrian's account of the voyage of Nearkhos (reprinted with add. from the Indian antiquary, 238 p., Calcutta, 1879).

Periplus: Voyage around the Euxine Sea, translated by Wil. Falconer (Oxford, 1805). Arriani periplus Ponti Euxini, Anonymi periplus Ponti Euxini qui Arriano falso adscribitur, Anonymi periplus Ponti Euxini et Maeotidis paludis, Anonymi mensura Ponti Euxini, Agathemeri hypotyposes geographiae, etc., cum notis variorum. Edited in Greek and Latin by Sam. Wilh. Hoffmann (415 p., Leipzig, 1842).

Criticism—E. H. F. Meyer: Geschichte der Botanik (Bd. 2, 158–160, 1855). Schwartz, in Pauly-Wissowa (vol. 3, 1230–1247, 1895). Carl Patsch: Arrians Periplus (Klio, vol. 4, 68–75, Leipzig, 1904).

For Ptolemy's chronology, see my note on Ptolemy (Minor Works, 20) in Section V.

X. ROMAN LAW

JULIAN

Salvius Julianus; flourished under Hadrian, Roman emperor from 117 to 138. Roman jurist. Author of a consolidation of praetorian law called Edictum Perpetuum, ratified by a senatusconsultum in 131. His main work was the Digesta in 90 books.[v]

Text—The original text is lost, but has been reconstructed as much as possible from later codes. A. A. F. Rudorff: De jurisdictione edictum. Edicti perpetui quae reliqua sunt (292 p., Leipzig, 1869). Otto Lenel: Das Edictum Perpetuum, ein Versuch zu dessen Wiederherstellung (Leipzig, 479 p., 1883; 2d edition, 1907). Translated into French by Peltier (2 vols., 1901–1903).

Criticism—Heinrich Buhl. Salvius Julianus (Heidelberg, 1886). C. P. Sherman: Roman Law (vol. 1, 98, Boston, 1917). M. Cantor: Geschichte der Mathematik (Bd. 1^3, 562, 1907: Interesting problem of inheritance). D. E. Smith: History of Mathematics (vol. 2, 54, 1925. For a brief history of inheritance problems).

XI. CHINESE AND GREEK PHILOLOGY

HSÜ SHEN

Hsü[3] Shên[4] (4761, 9846). Native of Shao[4]-ling[2] (9777, 7235) in Honan; died c. 120. His tablet was placed in the Confucian temple in 1875. Chinese lexi-

[v] Justinian's Digest contains 456 extracts and 620 citations from Julian's works.

cographer. He wrote commentaries on the Classics, but is chiefly known for his great work entitled Shuo[1]* wên[2] chieh[3] tzŭ[4] (10164, 12633, 1515, 12324), the earliest Chinese dictionary arranged by radicals.[z] It was presented to the emperor An[1] Ti[4] (44, 10942), in 121, by the son of the author, Hsü[3] Ch'ung[1] (4761, 2908). It contains some 10,500 characters, written in the Lesser Seal script, hsiao[3] chuan[4] (4294, 2724), classified under 540 radicals, and the graphic origin of each character is explained. To show the importance of the Shuo wên, it will suffice to recall that all modern etymological research is ultimately based upon it.[a] It has remined the canon of Chinese writing.

Text—The Shuo wên was printed for the first time between 984 and 988. The text which has come down to us has been altered and improved by later commentators chiefly by the two brothers Hsü[2] Ch'ieh[1] (4748, 1576) (920–74) and Hsü[2] Hsüan[3] (4748, 4799) (916–91). It is possible that the pronunciations indicated in the original text were different from those transmitted to us; it is possible also that the original form of script was different.

Criticism—H. A. Giles: Biographical Dictionary (309, 300, 314, 1898). John Chalmers: An Account of the Structure of Chinese Characters under 300 Primary Forms; after the Shwoh-wan and the Phonetic Shwoh-wan (208 p., London, 1882). Frank H. Chalfant: Early Chinese Writing (35 p., Pittsburgh, 1906). Encyclopaedia sinica (299, 513, 633, 1917). Bernhard Karlgren: Analytic Dictionary of Chinese (1923. Shows the importance of Hsü Shên's work for the history of Chinese phonology; Isis, VII, 567).

APOLLONIOS DYSCOLOS

Ἀπολλώνιος Δύσκολος,[b] flourished in Alexandria, probably at the time of Hadrian. Greek grammarian. He and his son, Herodian, were the foremost grammarians of the imperial age; they centralized and systematized the results accumulated by the Alexandrian grammarians. He was the inventor of syntax and might be called the founder of scientific grammar. His work remained authoritative down to the fifteenth century.[c]

Text—Apollonii Dyscoli quae supersunt edited by Richard Schneider and Gustav Uhlig (3 vols., Leipzig, 1878–1910). German translation by Alexander Buttmann (Berlin, 1877).

Criticism—Emile Egger: Apollonius. Essai sur l'histoire des théories grammaticales dans l'antiquité (350 p., Paris, 1854). Sandys: History of Classical Scholarships (vol. 1³, 319–321, 1921).

DIONYSIOS

Aelios Dionysios, Αἴλιος[d] Διονύσιος. Flourished in the time of Hadrian, emperor from 117 to 138. Greek lexicographer. He compiled a lexicon of Attic words in 10 books, containing many examples of the use of each word.

---

[z] It is called Shuo wên for short, meaning a treatise of written character. The full title might be translated (Work in which the author) shows the figurative characters and explains the composed characters.

[a] For example, L. Wieger's great work on Chinese characters (English edition, 1915) is essentially derived from the Shuo wên.

[b] Meaning crabbed, ill-tempered.

[c] It influenced the Latin grammars of Donatus (first half of fourth century) and Priscian (first half of sixth century) and thus indirectly almost every European grammar.

[d] I give this Greek transcription because it occurs, but Aelius is originally a Latin name.

Text—Ern. Schwalbe: Aelii Dionysii et Pausaniae Atticistarum fragmenta (290 p., Leipzig, 1890).
Criticism—Heinrich Heyden: Quaestiones de Aelio Dionysio et Pausania Atticista etymologici magni fontibus (Leipzig, 1885).

NICANOR

Νικάνωρ[e] flourished in Alexandria probably under Hadrian. Greek grammarian. He wrote a work on punctuation (περὶ στιγμῆς) of which he distinguished eight varieties.

Text—Περὶ Ἰλιακῆς στιγμῆς, edited by Ludwig Friedlaender (Königsberg, 1850). Περὶ Ὀδυσσειακῆς στιγμῆς, edited by Otto Carnuth (68 p., Berlin, 1875).
Criticism—Sandys: History of Classical Scholarship (vol. 1^3, 322, 1921).

HEPHAESTION OF ALEXANDRIA

Ἡφαιστίων flourished in Rome about the end of the first half of the second century. Greek grammarian. Tutor of L. Verus (130–169), who shared the imperial power with M. Aurelius from 161 to 169. He wrote a great work on meter (in at least 48 books), known only through his own manual of it (Ἐγχειρίδιον περὶ μέτρων), the main source of our knowledge on Greek meters.

Text—Enchiridion (First edition, Florence, 1526). Editions by J. C. de Pauw (Utrecht, 1726); Thomas Gaisford (Oxford, 1810, again 1855); Heinrich zur Jacobsmuehlen (Strassburg, 1886). Hephaestionis Enchiridion cum commentariis veteribus, edited by Max. Consbruch. Accedunt variae metricorum graecorum reliquiae (462 p., Leipzig, 1906).
Criticism—Sandys: History of Classical Scholarship (vol. 1^3, 328, 1921).

---

[e] Nicknamed ὁ στιγματίας, the punctuator.

CHAPTER XVI

THE TIME OF GALEN

(Second Half of the Second Century)

I. Survey of Science in Second Half of Second Century. II. Religious Background. III. Hellenistic, Roman, and Chinese Philosophy. IV. Roman and Chinese Mathematics. V. Syrian and Chinese Astronomy. VI. Hellenistic Natural History. VII. Hellenistic and Roman Geography. VIII. Hellenistic and Chinese Medicine. IX. Hellenistic, Roman, and Chinese Historiography. X. Roman Law. XI. Greek Philology.

I. SURVEY OF SCIENCE IN SECOND HALF OF SECOND CENTURY

1. The second half of the second century is still a period of great activity, but in almost every field, except medicine, the heyday is already over. The time of Galen, as compared with the time of Ptolemy, is a period of regression.

2. *Religious Background*—The Hebrew text of the Old Testament was finally and completely edited in the second century, but that text, the so-called Text of the Ṣopherim, was purely consonantal: vowel-points and accents were not indicated. As it was realized that the Greek text of the Septuagint did not always tally with the Ḥebrew text, various new translations into Greek were made. The oldest Latin version was probably made at about the same time in Carthage. The oldest Syriac version (the Pěshīṭtā) may be a little earlier. There were also Coptic versions. It is important to know as well as possible when each of these translations was compiled, not only for religious, but also for linguistic reasons. Each is a cultural landmark; in many cases it marks the beginning of a new literature, of a new civilization.

Similar remarks apply of course to the Gospels. A Greek combination of the four Gospels, the Diatessaron, was composed by Tatian about the middle of the century. This was translated into Syriac c. 170. Syriac translations of the separate Gospels appeared toward the end of the century, but did not supersede the Diatessaron for more than two hundred years.

Soon after 150, Justin Martyr wrote an apology of Christianity, wherein he tried to reconcile the Christian ideals with those of Greek philosophy; a little later, c. 160, he wrote another apology against the Jews. His disciple Tatian, the author of the Greek Diatessaron, wrote apologetic works of the same kind. Their activity is similar to that of Philon in the first half of the first century; even as Philon tried to harmonize Jewish and Pagan ideals, they try to adjust Christian and Pagan duties. Their contemporary Irenaeos was more concerned with the definition of Christian orthodoxy against the heresies of his time, especially against Gnosticism; his work is of considerable value for the history of Christian doctrine. On the other hand, the Platonician Celsos wrote a defense of Paganism against Christianity. It is interesting to note that all of these philosophers and theologians hailed from the Near East.

The Jewish patriarch Judah ha-Nasi, who transferred the Sanhedrin to Beth She'arim, was the main editor of the Mishnāh.

3. *Hellenistic, Roman, and Chinese Philosophy*—Throughout ancient and mediaeval times, much importance was attached to the study of dreams. I shall not attempt to explain the evolution of this special "science," but it is well to keep in mind its existence, and to consider it as forming a part of the general intellectual background. The main treatise on the subject, in ancient times, was that of Artemidoros, who flourished under the Antonines (c. 138 to 180).

A very characteristic figure, typical of the intellectual decline which is steadily going on, is that of Apuleius; his works are of great interest for the history of superstition. Philosophy proper was represented in the first place by the noble figure of Marcus Aurelius, whose Meditations are the swan song of Stoicism. Numenios, who tried to reconcile Pythagoraeism with Platonism and with various oriental philosophies is also a very typical product of the age; he is a forerunner of the Neoplatonists. The writings of Bardesanes show the same syncretic tendencies, but Bardesanes was a Christian; his message contained the seed of Manichaeism. The main Sceptical philosopher, Sextos Empiricos, took pleasure in exposing the relativity of knowledge, the doubts and difficulties of almost every subject, and the conflicting opinions expressed about it; his works are a real mine of information on ancient doctrines.

Observe that Apuleius was an African, Aurelius a Roman, Numenios and Bardesanes Syrians, Sextos a Greek.

The Confucian scholar Hsün Yüeh wrote the Shên-chien, a treatise on government and morality.

4. *Roman and Chinese Mathematics*—Apuleius composed the first translation of Nicomachos's arithmetic into Latin.

Toward the end of the second century or the beginning of the third Hsü Yüeh wrote an arithmetical treatise.

5. *Syrian and Chinese Astronomy*—The philosopher Bardesanes wrote a treatise wherein he proved that the world would last only 6,000 years.

Liu Hung seems to have had some notion of the precession of the equinoxes.

6. *Hellenistic Natural History*—The original Greek Physiologos, a collection of Christian moralities based upon the real or legendary characteristics of animals, was probably edited at Alexandria toward the end of the second century or the beginning of the third.

The writings of Marcellos of Side, on fishes, and of Philumenos, on animal poisons, though primarily medical, may offer some zoological interest.

7. *Hellenistic and Roman Geography*—The Greek traveler Pausanias wrote, c. 160 to 174, a "Description of Greece" which contains very valuable and abundant information, especially with regard to ancient Greek topography. But Pausanias speaks also of many other things, e. g., Chinese silkworms and sericulture. It is interesting to note in this connection that the first known travelers from Rome to China were envoys sent by Marcus Aurelius (166).

8. *Hellenistic and Chinese Medicine*—By far the greatest personality of this age was that of Galen, the most famous physician of antiquity after Hippocrates. Galen made some very remarkable physiological experiments. He came very close to discovering the circulation of the blood. He systematized the anatomical and medical knowledge accumulated unto his time in such masterly way that his works remained the supreme authority down to the sixteenth century.

Aretaeos, who flourished about the same time, was perhaps as great a physician as Galen (possibly even a greater one), but he was less dogmatic and could not impose himself as Galen did. He gave very clear descriptions of diseases. Menodotos tried to syncretize the views of the Empirical and Sceptical schools. Marcellos of Side wrote on lycanthropy and on the medical use of fishes; Philumenos, on animal poisons and their antidotes; Leonides, on various surgical operations; Marcellinos, on the pulse.

The medical school of Edessa may already have been in existence in that time, though it did not attain any considerable importance until much later. An elaborate medical treatise in Syriac may be an early product of this school of Edessa, but at any rate it is a translation from the Greek, thus simply a reflection of Hellenistic medicine.

The greatest Chinese physician of the time was Chang Chung-ching or Chang Chi (c. 200), who wrote a treatise on dietetics, wherein many plants are mentioned, and another on fevers which was exceedingly popular, almost until our own days, both in China and in Japan.

9. *Hellenistic, Roman, and Chinese Historiography*—Tatian's apology (dealt with in Section II) contains chronological information which was embodied in the works of the early Christian chronologists. Appian wrote a history of Rome in Greek (c. 160). Aulus Gellius compiled, in Athens, a Latin miscellany, which is valuable, as all such works are, because of the many fragments of ancient lore which it has helped to transmit. Pausanias's Description, referred to in Section VII, is as important from the archaeological as from the geographical point of view.

The philosopher Hsün Yüeh wrote a history of the Western Han Dynasty.

10. *Roman Law*—One of the greatest jurists, Gaius, wrote an elementary treatise on Roman law (Institutes), which is of very great importance, not only because of its excellence, but also because of the information on earlier law which it contains and because of its own influence upon later works of the same kind, e. g., Justinian's.

11. *Greek Philology*—Pausanias the Atticist compiled a Greek dictionary; Herodian—whom historians of mathematics remember chiefly on account of the so-called "Herodianic numerals"—wrote many works on grammatical subjects; Phrynichos and Pollux compiled more dictionaries, the need of lists of Attic words increasing as the language was more adulterated.

12. *Final Remarks*—The work of this period was predominantly Greco-Roman, but a few contributions were made by Chinese scholars. The reign of Marcus Aurelius gave us two clear instances of contact between China and the Roman Empire (see section 7). Marcus Aurelius himself was the greatest man of that time, though in a history of science we must, of course, give the first place to Galen. Galen was undoubtedly a man of science of the very first order and, if we are to judge him by the influence which he exerted, one of the very greatest in the whole past.

II. RELIGIOUS BACKGROUND

Old Testament

The most important text of the Old Testament is the one prepared by Jewish scribes (ṣopherim) of Palestine. This is the so-called "Text of the Ṣopherim," accepted as a standard by the Rabbis. It was completed in the second century and has remained unchanged ever since.[a] It was then faithfully copied and inter-

[a] This text was, however, purely consonantal; vowel-points and accents were not added until the seventh century.

preted by other scribes called Massorites.[b] The Mishna[c] also was fairly well developed. One may say that by the end of the second century Judaism had already assumed essentially its final form.

While the standard Hebrew text was being established, the Christians realized more and more the many differences between that text and their own Septuagint. The necessity of a new Greek translation of the Hebrew text became equally obvious to Christians and to Jews. Not less than six new translations of the standard texts were thus made during the second century. It will suffice to enumerate them:

The Version of Aquila—Aquila was born at Sinope in Pontus; he flourished at Jerusalem c. 128 and was successively converted to Christianity and to Judaism and his version was much approved by the Rabbis. It is pedantically accurate. '

Joseph Reider: Prolegomena to a Greek-Hebrew Index to Aquila (Thesis, Philadelphia, 1916).

The Version of Theodotion—Theodotion was a Jew of Ephesus (or of Sinope?); he flourished probably under Marcus Aurelius (161 to 180). His version is more idiomatic than Aquila's.

The Version of Symmachos—Symmachos was a Samaritan (?) converted to Judaism; a younger contemporary of Theodotion. His translation was apparently both literary and accurate.

The three other versions are called respectively the Quinta, the Sexta, and the Septima. Origen found a manuscript of the Quinta in 231; a manuscript of the Sexta (or Septima) was found in 217. (It is thus possible that these three versions date from the beginning of the third century.)

The Versions of Aquila, Theodotion, and Symmachos were edited by Origen (q. v., first half of third century) in his Hexapla[d] together with the text of the Septuagint as revised by him.

The Old Latin Version (Vetus Itala), derived from the Greek text, dates from the middle of the second century. It was probably made at Carthage.

Toward the end of the same century the Septuagint was translated also into at least two Coptic dialects (Bohairic and Sahidic). Versions into other Egyptian dialects appeared later.

The oldest Syriac Version was made probably at Edessa about the middle of the second century or before, from the Hebrew. It is called the Pĕshīṭtā (mappaqtā pĕshīṭtā, the simple or plain version). It was made by Christians with the collaboration of Jews. It is clear that the Pĕshīṭtā was revised with reference to the Septuagint, for the Syriac text shows many traces of Greek influence.

This Syriac version was followed by others (notably the Philoxenian in 505 or 508[e] and the Syriac Hexapla in 615 and 617), but it is not here the place to examine these. It is with the earlier translations that we are naturally most concerned, as these early translations often mark the beginning of new languages and of new civilizations. Besides, the Pĕshīṭtā was not entirely displaced by

---

[b] Massora means tradition.

[c] That is, the oral law, the instruction of the rabbis. The most important Mishna collection was that of Galilee.

[d] The Hexapla contained also occasional references to the Quinta and the Sexta.

[e] The Heraclean version of 616 is a revision not of the whole Philoxenian Bible, but only of the New Testament.

the new versions. These were made by Jacobites (Monophysites), while the Nestorians remained largely faithful to the old Pěshīṭtā.

Syriac Versions of the New Testament[f]

The oldest form of the Syriac New Testament is represented by the Diatessaron. This work was written in Greek, probably at Rome, about the middle of the second century, by Tatian (q. v.). This explains many similarities with the Vetus Itala. It was translated into Syriac c. 170, that is, before Tatian's death. Tatian may have been his own translator.[g] The original text of the Diatessaron is lost, but it is possible to reconstruct it from St. Ephraim's Armenian commentary, and an Arabic translation, ascribed to the Christian physician Ibn al-Taiyib (q. v., first half of eleventh century),[h] is extant. The Diatessaron was used by the Syrians until the fifth century, when it was superseded by the separate Gospels.

Text—Theodor Zahn: Forschungen zur Geschichte des neutestamentlichen Kanons (1. Teil., Tatians Diatessaron, Leipzig, 1881. Its reconstruction from St. Ephraim and other sources). Augustinus Ciasca: Tatiani Evangeliorum Harmoniae arabice (Roma, 1888, Arabic and Latin). Samuel Hemphill: The Diatessaron, a Harmony of the Four Gospels (London, 1888, English). Latin and Old High German texts edited by Edward Sievers (Paderborn, 1872; again 1892).

Criticism—Arthur Hjelt: Die altsyrische Evangelienübersetzung und Tatians Diatessaron (Diss., 170 p., Helsingfors, 1901; again Leipzig, 1903). See also my note on Tatian, below.

About the very end of the second century appeared, then, the earliest Syriac translation of the separate Gospels. This was called the Evangelion da-měpharrěshē.[i] It was based upon the Greek text in use at Antioch, but the translator availed himself also of the Diatessaron, thus introducing fragments of the occidental tradition. The New Testament Pěshīṭtā is a later revision of the Evangelion da-měpharrěshē.

Text—Wm. Cureton: Remains of a Very Ancient Recension of the Four Gospels in Syriac (London, 1858). Robert L. Bensly, Rendel Harris and Crawford Burkitt: The Four Gospels in Syriac, Transcribed from the Sinaitic Palimpsest (Cambridge, 1894). Agnes Smith Lewis: Some Pages of the Four Gospels Retranscribed from the Sinaitic Palimpsest (London, 1896). Adalbert Merx: Die vier kanonischen Evangelien nach ihrem ältesten bekannten Texte, Übersetzung und Erläuterung der syrischen im Sinaikloster gefundenen Palimpsesthandschrift (Berlin, 1897–1905). F. Crawford Burkitt: Evangelion da-mepharreshe. The Curetonian Version of the Four Gospels with the Readings of the Sinai Palimpsest and Early Syriac Patristic Evidence (2 vols., Cambridge, 1904).

---

[f] This subject is very difficult, and there are many moot questions which it is not possible to discuss here. I simply summarize F. C. Burkitt's conclusions (1904) after R. Duval: Littérature syriaque (37–42, 1907).

[g] Diatessaron derives from Τὸ διὰ τεσσάρων εὐαγγέλιον. It is called in Syriac Dia-ṭessarōn or Evangelion da-měhallěṭē, the "Gospel of the Mixed," because it is a combination of the four Gospels.

[h] It is possibly earlier than the eleventh century, however. See P. Cheikho: Journal asiatique (p. 301–307, Sept., 1897).

[i] It is also called the Curetonian version. The text of the Sinai palimpsest is essentially the same.

JUSTIN MARTYR

Ἰουστῖνος. Born c. 100, into a Pagan family, at Flavia Neapolis[i] in Samaria; he flourished in Ephesus and Rome, and died a martyr of the Christian faith c. 163–167. He tried to reconcile the new ideals of Christianity with those of Greek philosophy. Not long after the year 150 he wrote, in Rome, an Apology[k] (Ἀπολογία) of Christianity against the Pagans. Some time later, c. 160, he wrote another apology against the Jews under the form of a dialogue with the Jew Tryphon (Πρὸς Τρύφωνα). Justin was probably acquainted with the Synoptic Gospels (the first three), but he did not know any canon of the New Testament.

Text—Princeps edition by Robert Estienne (311 p., Paris, 1551). J. K. F. Otto: Opera omnia (Greek and Latin, 3 t. in 5, Jena, 1848–1876. Containing many apocryphal works). English translation by G. J. Davie (Oxford, 1861; also in the Anti-Nicene Christian Library, II, Edinburgh, 1868).

Die Apologien des heiligen Justinus übersetzt von P. A. Richard (Kempten, 1871). Apologies, textes grec et français, par Louis Pautigny (Paris, 1904). The Apologies, Greek edition by A. W. F. Blunt (212 p., Cambridge, 1911).

Dialogue avec Tryphon. Textes grec et français, introduction et notes par Georges Archambault (2 vols., Paris, 1909).

Criticism—Karl Clemen: Die religionsphilosophische Bedeutung des stoisch-christlichen Eudämonismus in Justins Apologie (Leipzig, 1890). Thomas Maria Wehofer: Die Apologie Justins in literarhistorischer Beziehung (Rom, 1897). Ernst Lippelt: Quae fuerint Justini ἀπομνημονεύματα quaque ratione cum forma Evangeliorum syrolatina cohaeserint (Dissert. philolog. halenses, 15, 1–103, 1901). Adolf Harnack: Diodor von Tarsus; vier pseudojustinische Schriften als Eigentum Diodors nachgewiesen (Leipzig, 1901). Edgar Johnson Goodspeed: Index apologeticus sive Clavis Justini Martyris operum aliorumque apologetarum pristinorum (306 p., Leipzig, 1912). Karl Hubik: Die Apologien des hl. Justinus (Wien, 1912). Adolf Harnack: Ist die Rede des Paulus in Athen ein ursprünglicher Bestandteil der Apostelgeschichte? (100 p., Leipzig, 1913). Walther Jehne: Die Apologie Justins. (Diss., Leipzig, 1914). Marie Joseph Justin: Saint Justin (2e edition, Paris, 1914). Article by Lietzmann, in Pauly-Wissowa (vol. 20, 1332, 1919). Erwin Rainsdell Goodenough: The Theology of Justin Martyr (Jena, 1923).

TATIAN

Τατιανός. Born in Assyria; flourished in Rome where he was influenced by Justin Martyr and converted to Christianity; c. 173, he became a heretic. He wrote the Diatessaron (about which see my note on the Syriac New Testament) and various apologetic works, of which one only is extant, a defense of Christianity against the Pagans (c. 150 to 165) (Λόγος πρὸς τοὺς Ἕλληνας, Oratio ad Graecos). Chronological information contained in this work was used by the Christian chronologists: Julios Africanos, etc.

Text—Oratio ad Graecos, Greek and Latin edition by J. K. F. Otto (Jena, 1851). Greek text by Eduard Schwartz (Leipzig, 1888). German translation by Adolf Harnack (54 p., Giessen, 1884). French translation with commentary, by Aimé Puech (165 p., Paris, 1903).

Criticism—Richard Cornelius Kukula: Tatian's sogenannte Apologie (Leipzig, 1900). Joseph Feuerstein: Die Anthropologie Tatians (Diss., Münster i. W.,

---

[i] Ancient Sichem; now Nablus.

[k] With a subsequent supplement, which is sometimes considered a second apology.

1906). Friedrich Köhler: Zur Frage der Entstehungsweise der althochdeutschen Tatianübersetzung (Diss., Leipzig, 1911).

ST. IRENAEOS

Irenaeus Lugdunensis, Εἰρηναῖος. Born in Asia Minor, possibly near Smyrna c. 130; bishop of Lyons from c. 178 until his death, which is said to have occurred during the reign of Septimius Severus, emperor from 193 to 211. Christian theologian. He wrote in Greek, c. 180, a treatise on Christian theology and against the Christian heresies of his day, especially against the Valentinians (the most important of the Gnostic systems). (Ἔλεγκος καὶ ἀνατροπὴ τῆς ψευδωνύμου γνώσεως, Refutation and overthrow of Gnosis; often called Contra omnes haereses, Against all the heresies.)[1] This work contains valuable historical information and a great many New Testament quotations which are a witness to the New Testament text long prior to any extant manuscript; it is the first systematic exposition of Christian theology. Another work of his, "In Proof of the Apostolic Teaching," the earliest Christian catechism, has been preserved in an Armenian translation.

Text—Editio princeps by Erasmus (Basel, Froben, 1528). Edition by the Benedictine René Massuet (Paris, 1710; Venice, 1734, reprinted in Migne's Greek Patrology, vol. 5, 1857). Modern editions by Adolph Stieren (2 vols., Leipzig, 1848–1853) and by W. Wigan Harvey (2 vols., Cambridge, 1857, with Syriac fragments).

Novum Testamentum Sancti Irenaei Lugdunensis. Old Latin biblical texts, No. 7. Edited by the late William Sanday (1843–1920) and Cuthbert Hamilton Turner (Oxford, 1923. Sanday's life-work, begun in 1884; the first proof of part of it was sent out by the Clarendon Press in 1893, the book finally appearing thirty years later!).

English translation by Alexander Roberts and W. H. Rambaut (in the Anti-Nicene Library; 2 vols., Edinborough, 1868–1869).

Irenaeus gegen die Häretiker, Buch IV und V in armenischer Version entdeckt von Karapet Ter Mekerttschian hrg. von Erwand Ter-Minassiantz (272 p., Leipzig, 1910).

Des heiligen Irenaeus Scrift zum Erweise der apostolischen Verkündigung Εἰς ἐπίδειξιν τοῦ ἀποστολικοῦ κηρύγματος (Armenian text, with German translation by the same, 146 p., Leipzig, 1907). Armenische Irenaeus Fragmente mit deutscher Übersetzung nach W. Lüdtke, zum Teil erstmalig hrg. und untersucht von Hermann Jordan (230 p., Leipzig, 1913). Démonstration de la prédication apostolique. Traduite de l'arménien et annotée par Joseph Barthoulot avec une introduction et des notes par J. Tixeront (72 p., Paris, 1917). Demonstratio apostolicae praedicationis, ex Armeno vertit, prolegomenis illustravit notis locupletavit Simon Weber (Freiburg i. B., 1917). English translation of the same work by J. Armitage Robinson (163 p., London, 1920).

Criticism—Ernst Klebba: Die Anthropologie des hl. Irenaeus (199 p., Münster i. W., 1894). Adolf Harnack: Die Pfaff'schen Irenäus Fragmente als Fälschungen Pfaffs nachgewiesen (148 p., Leipzig, 1900). Albert Dufourcq: Saint Irénée (Paris, 1904).

CELSOS

Κέλσος. Flourished in the Near East, probably in Egypt, about the years 178 to 180. Platonician who wrote the first systematic criticism of Christianity.

---

[1] The Greek text is lost, but there is an old Latin translation (fourth century or earlier?) which is extremely literal. It is strange to think that Erasmus thought that this work was originally written in Latin!

His treatise, called the True Word ('Ἀληθὴς λόγος), is known only through the refutation of it which Origen composed in 248 (Κατὰ Κέλσου, in eight books).[m] It is a document of great importance.

Text—Reconstruction of the text in German by Theodor Keim: Celsus wahres Wort (Zürich, 1873). Reconstruction in French by Benjamin Aubé: Histoire des persécutions de l'Église. La polémique païenne à la fin du IIe siècle (2e éd. 531 p., Paris, 1878). John Patrick: The Apology of Origen in Reply to Celsus (350 p., Edinburgh, 1892). K. J. Neumann: Κέλσου ἀληθὴς λόγος. Der literarische Kampf des Heidentums gegen das Urchristentum (Scriptores Graeci qui Christianam impugnaverunt religionem, 1).

Criticism—K. J. Neumann, in Pauly-Wissowa (t. 3, 1884, 1899). Maurice Croiset: Littérature grecque (t. 5, 693, 1899). J. F. S. Muth: Der Kampf des heidnischen Philosophen Celsus gegen das Christentum (Mainz, 1899). Lynn Thorndike: History of Magic (vol. 1, 436–461, 1923).

JUDAH HA-NASI

Judah[n] ha-Nasi, or Judah I, or Rabbi Júdah ha-Nasi,[o] born c. 135; flourished in Galilee, chiefly at Beth She'arim; died at Sepphoris c. 220. Jewish Patriarch. He transferred the seat of the patriarchate and of the academy to Beth She'arim. He was the principal redactor of the Mishnāh,[p] an elaboration of the Tōrāh, and probably one of the main contributors to it.

Article by W. Bacher, in Jewish Encyclopaedia (vol. 7, 333–337, 1904).

III. HELLENISTIC, ROMAN, AND CHINESE PHILOSOPHY

ARTEMIDOROS

'Αρτεμίδωρος of Ephesus; surnamed Daldianos after Daldis in Lydia, his mother's native place; flourished under the Antonines, i. e., c. 138 to 180. Author of a treatise on oreirology in five books ('Ονειροκριτικά), which is the most important of the ancient treatises on the subject; it is based largely upon earlier literature,[q] but also on his own experience. It is an important source for the history of ancient superstition. It is interesting to note that the same man wrote treatises on auspices (Οἰωνοσκοπικά, divination based upon the observation of birds) and on chirognomy (Χειροσκοπικά, palmistry); these treatises are lost.

Text—Aldine edition of the Greek text (Venice, 1518). Latin translation by Janus Cornarius (Basel, 1539). Greek and Latin edition by Nicolas Rigault (Rigaltius) (Paris, 1603). Critical edition by Rudolf Hercher (Leipzig, 1864. Containing information on early editions).

Early Italian translation by Pietro Lauro (Venice, 1547; 1558). German translation by Krauss (Vienna, 1881).

Criticism—Walther Reichardt: De Artemidoro librorum onirocriticorum auctore (Diss., Jena, 44 p., Leipzig, 1893). Riess, in Pauly-Wissowa (vol. 1, 1334, 1895). Hans Fischer: Ad artis veterum onirocriticae historiam symbola (Diss., 50 p., Jena, 1899). Lynn Thorndike: History of Magic (vol. 2, 290, 1923).

---

[m] According to K. J. Neumann, at least nine-tenths of the work of Celsos are thus known, and three-fourths of that is known literally.

[n] Or Jehuda.

[o] Meaning, the Prince. He was also called "Rabbi," the master par excellence (thus always in the Mishnāh), or Rabbenu, our master.

[p] For which, see my note on the Talmud, second half of fifth century.

[q] See my notes on Democritos (fifth century, B. C.) and on Aristotle.

APULEIUS

Lucius Apuleius.[r] Born in Madaura, Numidia, c. 125; flourished chiefly in Carthage. Platonic sophist; a clever writer whose curiosity was encyclopaedic. The first translator of Nicomachos's arithmetic; this translation is lost. His scientific writings are also lost, excepting—if it be genuine—his "De mundo." His most important work for us (more particularly for the historian of medicine) is his book on Magic ("De magia or apologia"); then his "Metamorphoses," generally named the "Golden Ass." These books are typical of their time; it is not by accident that they are coeval with the first alchemic writings.

Text and Translations of the Complete Works—Editio princeps (Rome, 1469). Opera omnia ed. by F. Oudendorp (3 vols., Leiden, 1786–1823); by G. F. Hildebrand (2 vols., Leipzig, 1842). Latin and French edition by Victor Bétolaud (Nouv. éd., 2 vols., Paris, 1891). Apulei Platonici Madaurensis opera quae supersunt (3 vols., Leipzig, 1905–1910); Vol. I: Metamorphoseon libri XI, rec. Rud. Helm, 304 p., 1907, new ed. 1913; Vol. II: (1) Pro se de magia liber, rec. R. Helm, 120 p., 1905, new ed. 1912; Vol. II (2) Florida, rec. R. Helm, 105 p., 1910; Vol. III: De philosophia libri, rec. Paul. Thomas, 218 p., 1908 (the order is the same as that followed in Alex. Goldbacher's previous ed., Vienna, 1876, to wit: de deo Socratis; Asclepius; de Platone et eius dogmate; de mundo. But Thomas has added the liber περὶ ἑρμηνείας, ed. by Goldbacher in 1885. Some of these writings are apocryphal, see below). A complete English translation has been published in the Bohn Classical Library (London, 1853). William Adlington's translation of the Golden Ass (1566) has been republished in the Loeb Classical Library (London, 1915).

General Criticism—Schwabe, in Pauly-Wissowa (vol. 3, 246–258, 1895).

Text and Translation of the Apologia—H. E. Butler and A. S. Owen: Apulei Apologia, with Introduction and Commentary (274 p., Oxford, 1914). The claims of the authors that the Apologia has found no modern commentator is incorrect. English translation of the Apologia and Florida by H. E. Butler (Oxford, 1909).

Criticism of the Apologia—Adam Abt: Die Apologie und die antike Zauberei (Religionsgeschichtliche Versuche und Vorarbeiten, vol. 4, 75–345, Giessen, 1908; published as a Diss., 1907). Paul Vallette: L'apologie (Thèse, 338 p., Paris, 1908).

Apocryphal Writings—(*a*). De mundo, an adaptation of the Peripatetic treatise περὶ κόσμου is possibly apocryphal. Heinrich Becker: Studia Apuleiana, 2. De mundo librum falso adhuc Apuleio attributum esse demonstratur (p. 54–92, Berlin, 1879).

(*b*). Asclepius, Latin text of a dialogue between Asclepios and Hermes Trismegistos. Excellent critical edition by P. Thomas (1908). New edition with abundant commentary in Walter Scott's Hermetica (4 vols., Oxford, 1924 sq.; Isis, VIII, 343).

(*c*). Herbarium or De herbarum virtutibus (medicaminibus) by Apuleius Platonicus or Barbarus; dates from about the fifth century. The earliest edition of it appeared in Rome soon after 1480; it contained the earliest printed illustrations of plants. An Anglo-Saxon translation dates from the first half of the eleventh century; it belongs to the school of Aelfric Grammaticus (q. v., second half of tenth century). The manuscript (British Museum) contains a number of illustrations derived from older illustrations, which might possibly be traced back to Cratevas? (q. v., first half of first century B. C.). The Anglo-Saxon text was edited by Oswald Cockayne in his Leechdoms (vol. 1, 1864, Rolls Series). Herm. Koebert: De

---

[r] The spelling Appuleius was more common in ancient times, but I write Apuleius in accordance with modern usage.

Pseudo-Apulei herbarum medicaminibus. (Diss., München, 60 p., with 3 plates, Baruth, 1888). Hugo Berberich: Das Herbarium Apulei nach einer früh-mittelenglischen Fassung hrg. (Anglistische Forschungen, 5, 140 p., Heidelberg, 1902). Pseudo Apulei libellum de medicaminibus herbarum ex codice Lucensi 296 descripsit, prolegomenis auxit Aug. Mancini (Atti d. R. Accad. di scienza, t. 32, 51 p., Lucca, 1903). The herbal of Apuleius Barbarus, from the early twelfth century manuscript, formerly in the Abbey of Bury St. Edmunds (MS. Bodley 130). Described by Robert T. Gunther (Roxburghe Club, London, 1925).

Ernst H. F. Meyer: Geschichte der Botanik (vol. 2, 1855, 316–328).

(*d*) De remediis salutaribus, containing medical prescriptions. First edition by Jul. Sillig, in Plini Naturalis historia (vol. 5, p. xv–xli, Hamburg, 1851).

(*e*). Physiognomonia, edited by R. Förster in his Scriptores physiognomonici (Vol. II, 3–145, Leipzig, 1893). Ferd. Maier: De anonymi physiognomonia Apuleio falso adjudicata. (Progr., 24 p., Bruchsaliae, 1880). Edm. Keller: Apulei quae fertur physiognomonia quando composita sit (Diss., 50 p., Kiel, 1890. Concluding that it dates from the fourth century).

Karl Sudhoff: Die Fragmenta Emmeranensia des Pseudo-Apuleius in München und der Leidener Sammelkodex Cod. Voss. lat. Q. 9 (Archiv für Geschichte der Medizin, 8, 446–449).

Hosidius Geta's tragedy Medea. A Vergilian cento. Latin text with metrical translation by Joseph J. Mooney; with an outline of ancient Roman magic (96 p., Birmingham, 1919). (Geta flourished about the end of the second century; he is mentioned by Tertullian.)

AURELIUS

Marcus Aurelius Antoninus. Born at Rome in 121, died in Pannonia in 180. Roman emperor from 161 to 180. One of the wisest and best of men. His autobiographical notes or Meditations, in Greek (Τὰ εἰς ἑαυτόν), are one of the golden books of universal literature. It is also the greatest monument of the Stoic philosophy, and should be studied to understand the scientific attitude of the Stoics. After the time of M. Aurelius, the influence of Stoicism diminished very rapidly, and Stoicism was finally submerged by the coming tide of Christianity. Some of the Stoic precepts became an integral part of the Christian teaching, but Stoic monism disappeared altogether until the time of Spinoza.

The first travelers from Rome to China were envoys of the Emperor "An Tun," who came by sea to Tongking in 166, and thence went overland to the capital Lo-yang.

Text—First edition by Xylander (Zürich, 1558). Later editions by Casaubon (London, 1643); by Thomas Gataker (Cambridge, 1652, with Latin translation); by Johann Stich (240 p., Leipzig, 1882); by J. H. Leopold (152 p., Oxford, 1908); by Heinrich Schenkl (Leipzig, 1913).

English translation by Meric Casaubon, with notes; re-edited by W. H. D. Rouse (London, 1900; correspondence of M. Aurelius and Fronto, p. 185–203). Greek text with English translation by C. R. Haines (Loeb Library, London, 1916).

German translation by F. C. Schneider (Breslau, 1857). Greek text with Persian translation by Hammer-Purgstall (Vienna, 1831).

Criticism—E. Renan: Marc-Aurèle et la fin du monde antique (754 p., Paris, 1882. Important). Leonard Alston: Stoic and Christian in the Second Century (156 p., London, 1906). Henry Dwight Sedgwick: Marcus Aurelius (309 p., New Haven, 1921; Isis, V, 148).

E. H. F. Meyer: Geschichte der Botanik (t. 2, 166–176. 1855. Des Marcus Aurelius Verzeichniss steuerpflichtiger Waaren).

NUMENIOS

Νουμήνιος of Apamea, in Syria, flourished about the middle of the second century. Pythagorean philosopher; forerunner of the Neoplatonists. He tried to reconcile the doctrine of Pythagoras with that of Plato and also with various Oriental philosophies (Hebrew, Hindu, Persian, and Egyptian).

Texts—Fragments of Numenios are preserved in Eusebios's Praeparatio Evangelica.

Criticism—Johann Friedrich Thedinga: De Numenio philosophico platonico (71 p., Bonn, 1875). Kenneth Sylvan Guthrie: Numenius the father of Neo-Platonism (Thesis, Columbia, 1914; 219 p., London, 1917).

BARDESANES

Bar-Daiṣān. Born in Edessa 154; died in Anium, Armenia, 222. Christian philosopher, the last of the Gnostics and the earliest Syriac writer (except the translators of the Bible). The founder of Syriac poetry. Historian, astrologer. He wrote a treatise on astronomy (lost), wherein he proved that the total duration of the world was 6,000 years. Some time in his mature years he ceased to believe in many astrological and Gnostic theories. Not long after 196 he wrote a dialogue on destiny,[a] which contains no trace of Gnosticism. It is possible that this work was not written by himself, but by one of his disciples; it is a sort of Platonic dialogue wherein Bardesanes is the chief speaker; it undoubtedly reflects his teaching. The writings of Bardesanes are of special interest because they were the main source of Manes's thought (q. v., second half of third century).

Text—Bardesanis Syri fragmentum adversus astrologos, ed. by J. C. Orelli in his Alexandri Aphrodisiensis, etc., de Fato quae supersunt graece (Zürich, 203–219, 1824, Greek and Latin).

Smaller texts are quoted by F. Nau (1910, see below).

Syriac text of the book on destiny edited by Wm. Cureton: Spicilegium syriacum (London, 1855). German translation by Merx (1863) in work quoted below. New edition with French translation by F. Nau (1899, see below).

Criticism—Adalbert Merx: Bardesanes (131 p., Halle, 1863). Adolf Hilgenfeld: Bardesanes, der letzte Gnostiker (Leipzig, 1864). E. Renan: Marc Aurèle (Paris, 1882). E. Amelineau *in* Grande Encyclopédie ($2\frac{1}{4}$ col., 1888, with bibliography). François Nau: Une biographie inédite de Bardesane l'astrologue, tirée de l'histoire de Michel le Grand, patriarche d'Antioche (1126–1199) (20 p., Paris, 1897); Bardesane l'astrologue (Journal Asiatique, t. 14, p. 12–19; 1899); Les conjonctions des planètes d'après Bardesane (*ibidem*, t. 16, 209–219, 1910); Le livre des lois des pays (Paris, 1899). The abbé Nau insists that Bardesanes was less a Gnostic than an astrologer, a scientist; his was a scientific heresy; it is because of this that I have included him. Rubens Duval: La littérature syriaque (3e éd., 235–240, Paris, 1907). Felix Haase: Zur bardesanischen Gnosis (Texte und Untersuchungen zur Geschichte der altchristlichen Literatur, vol. 4, 98 p., Leipzig, 1910). Eugène de Faye: Gnostiques et gnosticisme. Etude critique des documents du gnosticisme chrétien au IIe et IIIe siècles. (491 p., Paris, 1913; Bibliothèque de l'école des hautes études, sci. relig., 27; see P. Monceaux. Les Gnostiques. Journal des savants, t. 16, 12–26, 69–82, 140–152, Paris, 1918.) Article Ibn Daiṣān by Cl. Huart, in Encyclopedia of Islam (vol. 2, 370). F. C. Burkitt: The Religion of the Manichees (Cambridge, 1925; Isis, VIII, 647).

[a] Syriac title: Kĕthābhā dhĕ-nāmōsē dh'athrawāthā, meaning The book of the laws of the countries. According to Bardesanes, man is influenced by nature, by fate, and by his own will. Fate is determined by the position of the stars at the moment of his birth. Astrology is limited to the study of this second agent only, fate.

SEXTOS EMPIRICOS

Σέξτος Ἐμπειρικός flourished about the end of the second or the beginning of the third century. Physician of the Empirical School (hence his name). Sceptical philosopher. His works are the most elaborate witness of Sceptical philosophy. He wrote a shorter treatise in 3 books, Pyrrhonian sketches (Πυρρώνειοι ὑποτυπώσεις) and a larger one in 11 books, Sceptical commentaries (Ὑπομνήματα σκεπτικά). The larger work is of special interest because of the information it gives us on the different sciences it aims at destroying, and on the encyclopedic outlook (ἐγκύκλια μαθήματα) of the time. The author's scepticism is, to some extent, a guaranty of impartiality. This work is divided into two parts, the first (Bks. I–V) being a discussion of dogmatic philosophy (πρὸς δογματικούς; logic, physics, and ethics), the second (Bks. VI–XI) a discussion of the sciences (πρὸς μαθηματικούς; grammar, rhetoric, geometry, arithmetic, astrology, and music).

Texts—Greek and Latin edition by Henri Estienne (Cologne, 1621). Greek and Latin edition by J. A. Fabricius (735 p., Leipzig, 1718; revised edition, 2 vols., Leipzig, 1840–1841). Greek text only edited by Emmanuel Bekker (819 p., Berlin 1842). By Hermann Mutschmann (2 vols., Leipzig, 1912–1914).

Criticism—Mary Mills Patrick: Sextus and Greek scepticism, with a translation of the first book of the Pyrrhonic sketches. (Thesis, Bern; Cambridge, 1899.) M. Croiset: Littérature grecque (t. 5, 701–703, 1899). Emil Issel: Quaestiones sextinae et galenianae (Diss., Marburg, 1917).

HSÜN YÜEH

Hsün^{2} Yüeh^{4*} (4875, 13776). Born in 148; flourished at the court of Hsien^{4}-ti^{4} (4530, 10942) last emperor of the Eastern Han, 189–220; died in 209. Chinese Confucian (anti-Taoist) scholar and historian. Curator of the Imperial Library. Author of a brief history, Han^{4} chi^{4} (3836, 922), of the Western (Earlier) Han dynasty and of a treatise, Shên^{1} Chien^{4} (9816, 1644), on government and morality, which is one of the noblest Confucian writings.

H. A. Giles: Biographical Dictionary (316, 1898). L. Wieger: La Chine (398, 486, 493, 1920); Histoire des croyances religieuses (340–341, 1922).

IV. ROMAN AND CHINESE MATHEMATICS

For Roman mathematics, see my note on Apuleius in Section III.

HSÜ YÜEH

Hsü^{2} Yueh^{4*} (4748, 13366). Flourished at the end of the second century, or the beginning of the third. Chinese mathematician of the Han dynasty. Author of the Shu^{4}-shu^{4*} chi^{4}-i^{2} (10075, 10053, 922, 5440), commented upon by Chên-luan (q. v., second half of sixth century), containing arithmetical problems and possibly the earliest trace of suan^{4}-p'an^{2} (10378, 8620), i. e., abacus arithmetic (Hsü Yüeh speaks of chu^{1}-suan^{4} (2549, 10378), i. e., ball arithmetic).

Yoshio Mikami: The Development of Mathematics in China and Japan (p. 43–44, 57–58, 111, Leipzig, 1913).

V. SYRIAN AND CHINESE ASTRONOMY

For Syrian astronomy, see my note on Bardesanes in Section III.

LIU HUNG

Liu[2] Hung[2] (7270, 5252). Flourished under the Later Han, c. 196. Chinese astronomer. He showed that the equator and the ecliptic do not coincide, that the solstitial points are not fixed, and that the length of the tropical year is not exactly 365¼ days. This is an important landmark in the history of the Chinese calendar.

[1]L. Wieger: La Chine (108, 352, 1920).

VI. HELLENISTIC NATURAL HISTORY

For the writings of Marcellos of Side on fishes and of Philumenos on animal poisons, see the notes devoted to them in Section VIII.

The Physiologos

The Physiologos, a collection of Christian allegories based upon the marvelous peculiarities of animals, was probably composed, or rather edited, in Alexandria, toward the end of the second century (after Justin Martyr and before Aelian). The fortune of this work throughout the Middle Ages was amazing. It was translated from the Greek in Aethiopian, Armenian, Syriac, Latin (fifth century), Arabic, Old High German, Anglosaxon, Icelandic, Rumanian, Slavonic, etc. As this subject concerns medieval thought in general rather than the special period which we are at present considering, I propose to deal with it more fully in my chapter on mediaeval bestiaries.

Various Texts (*incomplete list, exempli gratia*)—Gustav Heider: Nach einem Handschrift des XI. Jahrhunderts (45 p., pl., Wien, 1851). Emile Legrand: Poème en grec vulgaire (Paris, 1873). Th. Möbius: Icelandic text, in Analecta norroena (2d ed., Leipzig, 1877). Fritz Hommel: Aethiopische Übersetzung (Leipzig, 1877). Verner Dahlerup: Icelandic text (Aarboger for nordisk old-kyndighed, vol. 4, 199–290, 1889). K. Ahrens: Syriac text (Kiel, 1892). Max Goldstaub and Richard Wendriner: Italian text (Halle a. S., 1892). Albert Stanburrough Cook: The Old English Elene, Phoenix and Physiologus (New Haven, 1919); The Old English Physiologus (New Haven, 1921). William Rose: The Epic of the Beast (London, 1924).

Criticism—Karl Ahrens: Zur Geschichte des Physiologus (Progr., 23 p., Ploen, 1885). Friedrich Lauchert: Geschichte des Physiologus (325 p., Strassburg, 1889). C. Krumbacher: Byzantinische Literatur (874–877, 1897). Josef Strzygowski: Der Bilderkreis des griechischen Physiologus (138 p., 48 pl., Leipzig, 1899). M. F. Mann: Zur Bibliographie des Physiologus (Mitt. aus dem gesamten Gebiete der englischen Sprache., vol. 10, 214–287, 1900). Maxmilian Goldstaub: Der Physiologus und seine Weiterbildung besonders in der lateinischen und in der byzantinischen Litteratur (Philologus, Supp. Bd. 8, 337–404, 1901).

Abundant bibliography in Krumbacher.

VII. HELLENISTIC AND ROMAN GEOGRAPHY

I have referred to the Roman embassy which was sent to the Chinese court via Tongking, in 166, in my note on Marcus Aurelius (section III).

PAUSANIAS

Παυσανίας. Flourished under Hadrian, Antoninus Pius and Marcus Aurelius, i. e., some time between 117 and 180; born probably in Lydia, near Mount Sipylus. Greek traveler and antiquarian. His "Description of Greece" in ten books

(Περιήγησις τῆς Ἑλλάδος) was primarily a guide book for educated travelers; it was written between c. 160 and c. 174. It is our fundamental source on ancient Greek topography and it contains invaluable information on Greek art (incl. the lost paintings), also on folklore and superstitions. "Without Pausanias, the ruins of Greece would be for the most part a labyrinth without a clue" (Frazer). We find in his work a few descriptions of natural curiosities, and an account of Chinese silkworms (σήρ) and sericulture (end of Bk. VI).

Text and Translations—Edition princeps, Aldine (1516). Editions by K. God. Siebelis (5 vols., Leipzig, 1822–1828); by Joh. H. Chr. Schubart and Chr. Walz (3 vols., Leipzig, 1838–1839). Greek and Latin edition by L. Dinsdorf (Paris, 1845). New edition by J. H. C. Schubart (2 vols., Leipzig, 1853–1854. Often republished). The best editions are the monumental editions by Herm. Hitzig and Hugo Bluemner (3 large vols., Leipzig, 1896–1910, with abundant notes); and the smaller edition by Fried. Spiro (3 vols., Leipzig, 1903).

An English translation with abundant commentary has been published by J. G. Frazer (6 vols.; Vol. I, translation based on Schubart's text, 1854; Vols. II–V, commentary; Vol. VI, index and maps, London, 1898; 2d edition, 1913). A more modest translation by W. H. S. Jones, to be completed in 6 vols., is appearing since 1918 in the Loeb Classical Library. It is based in the main upon Spiro's text.

Criticism—A. Kalkmann: Pausanias der Perieget. Untersuchungen über seine Schriftstellerei und seine Quellen (303 p., Berlin, 1886). William Gurlitt: Über Pausanias (506 p., Graz, 1890). Max Bencker: Anteil der Periegese an der Kunstschriftstellerei der Alten (77 p., München, 1890). Rudolf Heberdey: Die Reisen des Pausanias in Griechenland. (Abhdl. des arch.-epigr. Seminares der Universität Wien, 10, 116 p., Wien, 1894). J. G. Frazer: Pausanias and other Greek Sketches (London, 1900. The essay on Pausanias p. 1–160 is simply a reprint of Frazer's introduction to his translation, but without the notes). Carl Robert: Pausanias als Schriftsteller (348 p., Berlin, 1909). H. Blümner: Karte von Griechenland zur Zeit des Pausanias sowie in der Gegenwart (Bern, 1911). Sir James George Frazer: Sur les traces de Pausanias (372 p., Paris, 1923).

VIII. HELLENISTIC AND CHINESE MEDICINE

GALEN

Γαληνός. Born in Pergamum 129; died at the age of 70. Anatomist, physician, philosopher. The greatest physician of antiquity after Hippocrates. He dissected numerous animals, but very few human bodies; discovered a large number of new facts in the fields of anatomy, physiology, embryology, pathology, therapeutics, pharmacology. He made various physiological experiments, e. g., to determine the mechanism of respiration and pulsation, the function of the kidneys, of the cerebrum, and of the spinal cord at different levels. He proved experimentally that arteries contain and carry blood; that it suffices to divide even a small artery to drain away all the blood of the body in half an hour or less;[r] that the right auricle outlives the rest of the heart. He gave a semi-rational (physiological) interpretation of dreams and had some notion of their medical interest.

His chief merit consists in having systematized and unified Greek anatomical

---

[r] Harvey was clever enough to give as much credit as he could to Galen; it is astounding to realize how close Galen came to the discovery of the circulation of the blood, at least as far as some of the main facts were concerned. See Harvey: De motu cordis (1628, Chapter VII and passim).

and medical knowledge and practice. He was a very prolific, clear, and vigorous writer. He strove to establish medicine at once on an experimental and on a rational basis, but failed to realize the narrow limitations of the deductive method in the field of biology. Yet he was a careful observer and experimenter. His immense learning, his intelligence, his facility of expression, his dogmatism contributed to maintain his authority unimpaired until the sixteenth century. He was bent upon teleological explanations and established more strongly the vitalistic ideas of Aristotelian philosophy. He is one of the greatest medical philosophers.

General Editions and Translations—First Latin edition, Venice, 1490; first Greek edition, in five folio vol., Aldine, 1525. The latest complete edition—Greek text with Latin translation—is the one edited by Karl Gottlob Kühn (20 vols., Leipzig, 1821–1833), forming the first twenty volumes of the collection "Medicorum graecorum opera quae exstant," edited by himself. The 20th volume is an index compiled by Fr. Will. Assmann. Three volumes of Scripta minora have been edited, the first by Joh. Marquardt, 1884; the second by Iw. Mueller, 1891; the third by Georg Helmreich, 1893, Leipzig. A new complete critical edition is in course of publication since 1914, as part of the Corpus medicorum graecorum edited under the joint auspices of the academies of Berlin, Copenhagen, and Leipzig.

Fried. Reinh. Dietz: Apollonii Citiensis, Stephani, Palladii, Theophili, Meletii, Damasii, Ioannis, aliorum scholia in Hippocratem et Galenum (2 vols., Königsberg, 1834).

For the translations into Arabic, see L. Leclerc: Médecine arabe (t. 1, 242–252, 1876); for the Galenic tradition—Byzantine and Arabic—"the XVI Books of Galen" (see *ibidem*, 38–55). G. Bergsträsser: Ḥunain ibn Isḥāq über die syrischen und arabischen Galen-Übersetzungen (Leipzig, 1925. Very important; 129 Galenic works are mentioned; elaborate analysis by M. Meyerhof in Isis, VIII, 685–724, 1926).

I do not know any complete translation in a modern language. See Charles Singer: Scheme for a Complete Translation into English of the Entire Works of Galen (Annals of Medical History, vol. 1, p. 433–434, New York, 1917). Ch. V. Daremberg: Oeuvres anatomiques, physiologiques et médicales de Galien (2 vols., Paris, 1854–1857). Robert Ritter von Töply: Anatomische Werke des Rhuphos und Galenos (Wiesbaden, 1904).

Of the Manuscripts, I will quote only: Miniaturen der lateinischen Galenos-Handschrift der Kgl. Bibliothek in Dresden, Db 92–93 in phototypischer Reproduction. Einleitung und Beschreibung von E. C. van Leersum und W. Martin (Leiden, 1910, Codices graeci et latini photographice depicti. Suppl. VIII). The 116 Flemish miniatures contained in this manuscript, representing chiefly medical subjects and dating from the end of the fifteenth century, are very interesting documents for the study of the medical life of that time.

Biographical and General Studies—W. Crönert: Klaudios Galenos (Mitt. zur Gesch. d. Medizin und Naturw., I, p. 3–4, 1902. The gentile name Claudius is apocryphal; Crönert suggests that it may have been suggested by Ptolemy's name). I. Bloch: Einführung in das Studium des Galenos, mit einer Galen-Bibliographie (Berlin, 1908). J. Zimmerman. Material zur Würdigung Galens als Geschichtsschreiber der Medizin, Forscher und Commentator (Diss., 50 p., Berlin, 1902). L. Meunier: Essai sur Galien et le galénisme (Janus, IX, 270–284, 313–324, 1904). J. Ilberg: Aus Galens Praxis. Ein Kulturbild aus der römischen Kaiserzeit (Neue Jahrbücher f. d. Klass. Altertum, vol. 15, 276–312, 1905). Julius Pagel: Galenforschung im letzten Jahrzehnt (Mitt. zur Gesch. d. Medicin, Vol. VI, p. 225–229, 1907). Jul. Wiberg: Galen og den galenske laegevidenskab og laegekunst (243 p., Odense, 1910. In Danish: Galen and the Medical Art and Science; see Janus, p. 143, 1911). J. Mewaldt: Galenos (Pauly-Wissowas Real-Encyclopädie, vol.

13, col. 578–591, 1910). Theodor Meyer-Steineg: Ein Tag im Leben des Galen (63 p., Jena, 1913; Isis, II, 204).

Sources of Galen; His Influence—Hermann Schoene: De Aristoxeni περὶ τῆς Ἡροφίλου αἱρέσεως libro tertio decimo a Galeno adhibito (Diss., 32 p., Bonn, 1893). Wilh. Westermann: De Hippocratis in Galeno memoria quaestiones (Diss., 50 p., Berlin, 1902). Bachmann: Neugalenismus, eine auf biologischen Anschauungen aufgebaute Krankheitslehre, deren Grundzüge mit der altklassischen Medizin, besonders des Galenus, übereinstimmen (23 p., München, 1907; see also Janus, Vol. VII, p. 455–459, 1902). Heinrich Heinrichs: Die Überwindung der Autorität Galens durch Denker der Renaissancezeit (Diss., 50 p., Bonn, 1913). Emil Issel: Quaestiones Sextinae et Galenianae (58 p., Marburg, 1917. Sextos Empiricos is quoted in a pseudo-Galenic contemporary writing, but not in Galen's own works). Justus Niedling: Die mittelalterlichen und frühneuzeitlichen Kommentare zur Techne des Galenos (Diss., 29 p., Paderborn, 1924; Isis, VII, 181). K. Sudhoff: Eine Liste von Galenschriften aus dem Anfang des 15. Jahrhunderts (Archiv für Geschichte der Medizin, 17, 140, 1925).

Special Criticism: Anatomical and Medical—E. Gurlt: Geschichte der Chirurgie (t. 1, 428–474, 1898). Friedrich Meyer: Beitrag zur Therapie des Galen (Diss., 30 p., Berlin, 1899). Joh. Lachs: Die Gynäkologie des Galen (Abhdl. zur Gesch. d. Medizin, 4) (87 p., Breslau, 1903). Hans Erich Blaich: Das Wasser bei Galen (34 p., Stuttgart, 1906). Theodor Beck: Die galenischen Hirnnerven in moderner Beleuchtung (Archiv für Geschichte der Medizin, Bd. 3, 110–114, 1909). Karl Kassel: Galens Lehre von der Stimme (Zeits. f. Laryngologie, Rhinologie, usw., 1911). Jul. Wiberg: Hjaerneanatomien hos Galen og Ali Abbas (Anatomy of the Brain according to Galen and 'Alī ibn 'Abbās) (Copenhagen, 1913). Theod. Meyer-Steineg: Studien zur Physiologie des Galenos (Archiv für Geschichte der Medizin, 5, 172–224; 6, 417–48, Leipzig, 1911–1913. Important). John S. Milne: Galen's Knowledge of Muscular Anatomy (XVIIth Congress of Medicine, Histor. Section, 389–400, London, 1914). Karl Sudhoff: Vom Pestsamen des Galenos (Mitt. zur Gesch. d. Med., vol. 14, p. 227–229, 1915; Isis, III, 320). Herm. Schöne: Τὸ τοῦ Τραϊανοῦ γυμνάσιον bei Galenos (Hermes, vol. 52, 105–111, 1917; Isis, IV, 132). Friedrich Ullrich: Die anatomische und vivisektorische Technik des Galenos (Diss., 54 p., Werdau i. Sa., 1919; Isis IV, 577).

Special Criticism: Alia—Karl Joachim Marquardt: Galeni locus qui est de horologiis veterum emendatus et explicatus (Progr., 11 p., Gotha, 1865). Eric Pernice: Galeni de ponderibus et mensuris testimonia (64 p., Bonn, 1888. Important contribution to the study of ancient metrology; synoptic tables on p. 34–35). F. Brenner: Die Seelenlehre des Galenos (Die Seele des Menschen, Pflanzenseele, Die Seele der Gestirne). (Primitiae Czernovicienses, p. 65–86, Czernowitz, 1909). J. Mewaldt: Galenos über echte und unechte Hippocratica (Hermes, vol. 44, p. 111–134, Berlin, 1909). Hermann Schöne: Verbesserungen zum Galentext (Sitzungsber. d. preuss. Ak. der Wiss., 15, 94–106, 1924). I do not generally quote philological studies, except those whose aim it is to help in the reconstruction and elucidation of the original scientific texts—but one can not understand Galen's personality if one does not consider him also from a pure literary point of view. He was a man of letters, an Atticist, a lexicographer. Hence I must mention: Will. Herbst: Galeni Pergameni de atticissantium studiis testimonia (Leipzig, 1911; partly published in 1910 as a Marburg Diss.).

Editions and Translations of Separate Texts and Criticism Relating to Them—I quote only the writings about which I have some information to offer.

Galen's studies of his own writings.

Περὶ τῆς τάξεως τῶν ἰδίων βιβλίων. De ordine librorum suorum. Greek text, Latin translation and notes by Iwan Mueller (Progr., 27 p., Erlangen, 1874). New critical text by same editor, Scripta minora (II, 80–90, 1891).

Περὶ τῶν ἰδίων βιβλίων. De libris propriis. Greek text ed. by I. Mueller: Scripta Minora (II, 91–124, 1891).

MEDICAL PHILOSOPHY AND DEONTOLOGY.

Περὶ αἱρέσεων τοῖς εἰσαγομένοις. De sectis ad eos qui introducuntur. Greek text edited by Georg Helmreich: Acta seminarii philologici Erlangensis (Vol. II, 239–310, Erlangen, 1881); also by same, in Scripta minora (III, 1–32, 1893).

Περὶ τῆς ἀρίστης διδασκαλίας. De optima doctrina, edited by Joh. Marquardt, in Scripta minora (I, 82–92, 1884).

"Ὅτι ὁ ἄριστος ἰατρὸς καὶ φιλόσοφος. Quod optimus medicus sit quoque philosophus, edited by Iw. Mueller, in Scripta minora (II, 1–8, 1891).

Προτρεπτικὸς ἐπὶ τὰς τέχνας. Oratio suasoria ad artes, edited by Joh. Marquardt, in Scripta minora (I, 103–129, 1884). Protreptici quae supersunt, edited by Georg Kaibel (72 p., Berlin, 1894). Adam Rainfurt: Zur Quellenkritik von Galens Protreptikos (Diss., 60 p., Freiburg i. B., 1904).

"Ὅτι ταῖς τοῦ σώματος κράσεσιν αἱ τῆς ψυχῆς δυνάμεις ἕπονται (or ὅτι τὰ τῆς ψυχῆς ἤθη ταῖς τοῦ σώματος κράσεσιν ἕπεται). Quod animi mores corporis temperamenta sequantur, edited by I. Mueller, in Scripta minora (II, 32–79, 1891).

Περὶ τῶν ἰδίων ἑκάστῳ παθῶν καὶ ἁμαρτημάτων τῆς διαγνώσεως. De propriorum animi cujusque affectuum et vitiorum diagnosi et curatione, edited by Joh. Marquardt, in Scripta minora (I, 1–81, 1884). Joh. Marquardt: Observationes criticae, in Galeni περὶ ψυχῆς παθῶν (46 p., Leipzig, 1870). Otto Hennicke: Same title. (Diss., Erlangen, 61 p., Berlin, 1902). Alessandro Olivieri: Osservazioni sopra un' opera morale di Galeno (Atti d. R. Accad. di Archeologia, Napoli, I, 2da parte, 95–109, 1910). Wilko De Boer: In Galeni περὶ ψυχῆς παθῶν (Diss., 56 p., Marburg, 1911). Robert Van Der Elst: Traité des passions de l'âme et de ses erreurs (Trad. franç. avec notes, lexique, etc., 144 p., Paris, 1914).

Περὶ τῆς ἰατρικῆς ἐμπειρίας. H. Schöne: Eine Streitschrift Galen's gegen die empirischen Aerzte (Sitzungsber. d. Kgl. Preuss. Ak. d. Wiss., 1255–1263, Berlin, 1901. First publication of the Greek text of this work known previously only in a Latin translation entitled "Sermo adversus empiricos medicos"). A. Brinkmann: Zu Galens Streitschrift gegen die Empiriker (Rheinisches Museums für Philologie, vol. 59, 317–320, Frankfurt a. M., 1904).

Ὑποτύπωσις ἐμπειρική. De subfiguratione empirica. The Greek text is lost. The Latin version by Nicolas of Rhegium has been edited by Max Bonnet (Diss., 80 p., Bonn, 1872).

Περὶ τῶν τῆς ἰατρικῆς μερῶν. De partibus artis medicativae. Hermann Schöne: Galenus, De partibus artis medicativae. Eine verschollene griechische Schrift in Übersetzung des 14. Jahrhunderts (39 p., Griefswald, 1911. Text of Nicolas of Rhegium's Latin version).

PHILOSOPHY.

Εἰσαγωγὴ διαλεκτική. Institutio logica, edited by Karl Kalbfleisch (Leipzig, 1896. The same author proved the genuineness of this book in Jahrb. f. Klass. Philol., Suppt. 23, 679–708, 1897).

Περὶ ἀποδείξεως. De demonstratione by Iw. Mueller: Über Galens Werk vom wissenschaftlichen Beweis (München, 1895. Only fragments of it remain).

Περὶ τῶν παρὰ τὴν λέξιν σοφισμάτων. De captionibus quae per dictionem fiunt, edited by Karl Gabler (Diss., 36 p., Rostock, 1903).

"Ὅτι αἱ ποιότητες ἀσώμαται. De qualitatibus incorporeis, edited by Joh. Westenberger (48 p., Marburg, 1906).

HIPPOCRATIC COMMENTARIES.

Περὶ φύσεως ἀνθρώπου. De natura hominis commentaria III, edited by Joh. Mewaldt in Corpus medicorum graecorum (v. 9, 1., Leipzig, 1914); Die editio princeps von Galenos in Hippocratis de natura hominis (Sitzungsber. d. Kgl. Preuss. Akad. d. Wiss., p. 892–903, 1 pl., 1912).

Περὶ διαίτης ὀξέων. De victu acutorum comm. IV, edited by G. Helmreich, in Corp. med. graec. (v. 9, 1, 1914).

Περὶ τῆς Ἱπποκράτους διαίτης ἐπὶ τῶν ὀξέων νοσήματων. De diaeta Hippocratis in morbis acutis, edited by Joh. Westenberger, in Corp. med. graec. (v. 9, 1, 1914).

Εἰς τὸ προρρητικὸν Ἱπποκράτους. Prorrheticum I comm. III, edited by Hermann Diels, in Corp. med. graec. (v. 9, 2, 1915). H. Diels: Die handschriftliche Überlieferung (41 p., Abhand. philos-hist. Kl., Kgl. Pr. Ak. d. Wiss., Berlin, 1912).

Περὶ τοῦ παρ' Ἱπποκράτει κώματος. De comate apud Hippocratem, edited by Joh. Mewaldt in Corp. med. graec. (v. 9, 2, 1915). Joh. Mewaldt: Eine Fälschung Chartiers in Galens Schrift über das Koma (Sitzungsber. d. Kgl. Preuss. Akad. d. Wiss., p. 256–270, 1913). Hermann Schöne: Zu Galens Schrift περὶ τοῦ παρ' Ἱπποκράτει κώματος (Rheinisches Museum f. Philol., vol. 71, 388–405, 1916).

Εἰς τὸ προγνωστικὸν Ἱπποκράτους. Prognosticum comm. III, edited by Jos. Heeg, in Corp. med. graec. (v, 9, 2, 1915).

Περὶ ἄρθρων. De articulis. Hermann Schöne: Eine Blattversetzung bei Galen (Rheinisches Museum f. Philol., vol. 57, 627–629, 1902).

Κατ' ἰητρεῖον. De officina medici. Siegfried Vogt: De Galeni in libellum κατ' ἰητρεῖον commentariis (Diss., 52 p., Marburg, 1910).

Περὶ ἑβδομάδων, De septimanis. Pseudogaleni in Hippocratis de septimanis commentarium ab Hunaino q.f. arabice versum ex codice Monacensi primum edidit et germanice vertit Gotthelf Bergstraesser. (Corp. med. graec., XI, 2, 11, Leipzig, 1914. Arabic and German texts.)

Ἱπποκράτους γλωσσῶν ἐξήγησις. G. Helmreich: Handschriftliche Verbesserungen zu dem Hippokratesglossar des Galen (Sitzungsber. d. preuss. Akad. d. Wiss., 197–214, 1916).

Ernest Wenkebach: Pseudogalenische Kommentare zu den Epidemien des Hippokrates (Abh. d. preuss. Ak. d. Wiss., philos. Kl., 62 p., 1917. This text is a cento of the seventeenth or eighteenth century; Isis IV, 132); Das Proömium der Kommentare Galens zu dem Epidemien des Hippokrates (Ibidem, 55 p., 1918); Eine alexandrinische Buchfede um einen Buchstaben in den hippokratischen Krankengeschichten. Ein unveröffentliches Galenkapitel (Sitzungsber. d. preuss. Ak. d. Wiss., 241–253, 1920).

Anatomy and Physiology.

Περὶ χρείας τῶν ἐν ἀνθρώπου σώματος μορίων. De usu partium corporis humani libri XVII, edited by Georg Helmreich (2 vols., Leipzig, 1907–1909). German translation by Nöldeke (Oldenburg, 1805).

Περὶ τῶν ἀνατομικῶν ἐγχειρήσεων. De anatomicis administrationibus libri XV. The Books IX to XV exist only in Arabic; they have been edited in Arabic with German translation by Max Simon: Sieben Bücher Anatomie des Galen (2 vols., Leipzig, 1906. With an admirable Arabic-Greek-German vocabulary of technical terms).

Περὶ τῶν καθ' Ἱπποκράτην καὶ Πλάτωνα δογμάτων. De Hippocratis et Platonis placitis libri IX, edited by Iw. Mueller, with Latin translation (836 p., Leipzig, 1874). Karl Kalbfleisch: In Galeni de placitis Hippocratis et Platonis libros observationes criticae (Diss., 50 p., Berlin, 1892). Maxim. Pohlenz: Quemadmodum Galenus Posidonium in libris de placitis Hippocratis et Platonis secutus sit (Diss., Berlin, 44 p., Leipzig, 1898).

Περὶ τῶν καθ' Ἱπποκράτην στοιχείων. De elementis secundum Hippocratem, edited by Georg Helmreich (Erlangen, 1878). Idem. Observationes criticae . . . . Acta seminarii philologici Erlangensis (vol. I, p. 49–78, 1878).

Περὶ κράσεων. De temperamentis libri III, edited by Georg Helmreich (142 p., Leipzig, 1904).

Περὶ φυσικῶν δυνάμεων. De facultatibus naturalibus libri III, edited by Georg Helmreich, in Scripta minora (III, 101–257, 1893). Galen on the Natural Faculties, with an English translation by Arthur John Brock (Loeb Classical Library, London, 1916. The text is essentially the same as that of Helmreich's edition).

Περὶ χρείας ἀναπνοῆς. De usu respirationis, edited by Rudolph Noll (Diss., 75 p., Marburg, 1915).

Εἰ κατὰ φύσιν ἐν ἀρτηρίαις αἷμα περιέχεται. An in arteriis natura sanguis contineatur, edited by Friedrich Albrecht (83 p., Marburg, 1911).

Εἰ ζῷον τὸ κατὰ γαστρός. An animal sit, id quod in utero est (apocryphal), edited by Hermann Wagner (77 p., Marburg, 1914).

J. Hirschberg: Galen und seine zweite Anatomie des Auges (Berl. Klin. Wochenschr., p. 610–612, 620–623, 1919).

HYGIENE.

Ὑγιεινά. De sanitate tuenda libri VI. Otto Hartlich: De Galeni ὑγιεινῶν libri quinti argumento ac dispositione (Diss., 59 p., Marburg, 1913).

Περὶ ἀρίστης κατασκευῆς τοῦ σώματος. De optima corporis nostri constitutione, edited by Georg Helmreich (40 p., Progr., Hof, 1901).

Περὶ εὐεξίας. De bono habitu, edited by Helmreich, together with the preceding work (Hof, 1901).

Περὶ ἔθους (or περὶ ἐθῶν). De consuetudine, edited by Iw. Mueller, in Scripta minora, II, 9–31, 1891).

Πότερον ἰατρικῆς ἢ γυμναστικῆς ἐστι το ὑγιεινόν. Utrum medicinae sit an gymnastices hygieine, edited by Georg Helmreich, in Scripta minora (III, 33–100, 1893).

Περὶ τοῦ διὰ τῆς σμικρας σφαίρας γυμνασίου. De parvae pilae exercitio, edited by Joh. Marquardt, in Scriptora minora (I, 93–102, 1884). Wilh. Schaefer: De Galeni qui fertur de parvae pilae exercitio libello (Diss., 50 p., Bonn, 1908. This contains a new edition of the text).

THEORY OF THE PULSE.

Σύνοψις περὶ σφυγμῶν. Synopsis de pulsibus. Joh. Gossen: De Galeni libro qui σύνοψις περὶ σφυγμῶν inscribitur (39 p., Berlin, 1907).

DIETETICS.

Περὶ λεπτυνούσης διαίτης. De victu attenuante. First Greek edition by Karl Kalbfleisch (70 p., Leipzig, 1898). German translation (Über die säfteverdünnende Diät) by W. Frieboes and F. W. Kobert (Abhdl. zur Gesch. d. Medizin, 5, 52 p., Breslau, 1903).

Περὶ τροφῶν δυνάμεως. De alimentorum facultatibus libri III. Herman Schöne: Ein Palimpsestblatt des Galen aus Bobbio (Sitzungsber. d. Kgl. Preuss. Ak. d. Wiss., p. 441–417, 1902). G. Helmreich: Galen περὶ τῶν ἐν ταῖς τροφαῖς δυνάμεων, I, 13 (Philologus, vol. 63, 310, 1904). Ed. of Book III, ch. 21–41, by G. Helmreich (Progr., 36 p., Ansbach, 1909).

PHARMACY.

Περὶ κράσεως καὶ δυνάμεως τῶν ἁπλῶν φαρμάκων. De simplicium medicamentorum temperamentis et facultatibus libri XI. See M. Wellmann, in Hermes (vol. 38, p. 292–304, 1903).

Περὶ συνθέσεως φαρμάκων. De compositione medicamentorum (τῶν κατὰ γένη, secundum genera libri VII; τῶν κατὰ τόπους secundum locos libri X).

Περὶ τῆς θηριακῆς. De theriaca. Rudolf Beer. Galenfragmente im Codex Pal. Vindobonens. 16. (Wiener Studien, 34, 97–108, 1912. This manuscript contains two fragments of De theriaca and De compositione medicamentorum).

Περὶ ἀντεμβαλλομένων. De remediis parabilibus. H. Schöne: Fragment einer alten Galenhandschrift im Vatikan (Mitt. zur Gesch. d. Med. u. Naturw., I, 141–143, 1902).

PATHOLOGY.

Περὶ τῶν συνεκτικῶν αἰτίων. De causis continentibus. Lost in Greek, edited for the first time in Latin from Nicolas of Rhegium's translation by Karl Kalbfleisch (24 p., Marburg, 1904).

Περὶ δυσπνοίας. De difficultate respirationis libri III. Albrecht Minor. De Galeni περὶ δυσπνοίας (Diss., 63 p., Marburg, 1911).

Περὶ τῶν παρὰ φύσιν ὄγκων. De tumoribus praeter naturam. German translation by Paul Richter: Über die krankhaften Geschwülste (26 p., Klassiker der Medicin, 21, Leipzig, 1913). Paul Richter: Über die altägyptische Vorlage zu dieser Schrift (Archiv für Geschichte der Medizin, 10, 189–199, 1917).

THERAPEUTICS.

Περὶ φλεβοτομίας θεραπευτικόν. De curandi ratione per venaesectionem. Short note by G. Helmreich, in Mitt. zur Gesch. d. Medizin (vol. 17, 167–168, 1918).

SUMMARY OF GALENIC MEDICINE.

Τέχνη ἰατρική. Ars medica. The so-called Microtechne (Ars parva) which enjoyed considerable popularity. Text in Kühn's edition (vol. 1, 305–412). Arthur Müller-Kypke: Über die Ars parva (Diss., Berlin, 1893).

ALIA AND APOCRYPHA.

Oeconomica. Theodor Trotz: Der Inhalt der Dresdener lateinischen Galenhandschrift aus dem Anfange des 15. Jahrhunderts; Erster Abdruck der "Oeconomica Galeni" (Diss., 14 p., Leipzig, 1921; Isis IV, 398).

Mass. Cardini: Galeno e la patomimia (Riv. de storia delle scienze, 513–515, 1918. Italian version of Galen's text: Come si possono riconescere i simulatori di malattie).

Hugo Reich: Die pseudogalenischen Schriften de usu farmacorum und de clisteribus et colica (Diss., 8 p., Leipzig, 1921; Isis, IV, 576). The second of these treatises is generally ascribed to one Severos, Σευήρου ἰατροσοφιστοῦ περὶ ἐνετήρων ἤτοι κλυστήρων. It was first published by F. Reinhold Dietz: Severi de clysteribus liber (Diss., 56 p., Königsberg, 1836). In its present form it is of a late period, and its author Severos (Σευῆρος) may have lived some time between the fifth and seventh centuries. But it is equally possible that the original treatise was much earlier; it might be ascribed to one famous physician, Severus, of the Augustan age. This Severus was chiefly known as an oculist and otologist (See Kind's article, in Pauly-Wissowa, Zweite Reihe, vol. 2, 2010–2011, 1923).

Ernest Wickersheimer: A Note on the liber de medicinis expertis attributed to Galen (Annals of Medical History, vol. 4, 323–7, 1922; Bull. soc. histoire médecine, t. 17, 19–27, 1923; Isis, V, 537; VI, 204).

ARETAEOS

Aretaeos of Cappadocia. Ἀρεταῖος. Flourished after Archigenes and before Alexander of Aphrodisias, that is, some time between 120 and 200. Greek physician of the Eclectic school, with strong leanings toward Pneumatism. Though far less prolific and influential than his contemporary Galen, he came much nearer than he to the true Hippocratic spirit and greatness. Two treatises of his have remained (each in four books), one, on the causes and indications of acute and chronic diseases (περὶ αἰτιῶν καὶ σημείων ὀξέων καὶ χρονίων παθῶν), the other on the treatment of the same diseases (περὶ θεραπείας etc.). They are admirably written, and typically enough in Ionic dialect (Hippocrates's language). He drew extensively upon the work of Archigenes of Apamea (q. v., first half of second century). His descriptions of diseases are very methodical and truthful (e. g., first description of diabetes; description of pleuritis with empyema, pneumonia, phthisis with haemoptysis, asthma, various paralytic conditions, tetanus, epilepsy with the premonitory aura, hysteria (also in man!), gout, dropsy, leprosy, elephantiasis). Clear differentiation between cerebral and spinal paralysis. Under the influence of Pneumatic ideas, he attached great importance to cardiac pathology, and his therapeutics was very simple; his prescriptions were largely restricted to physical agents and to dietetic regulations (e. g., use of cow milk).

Text and Translations—First Latin edition (Venice, 1552); first Greek edition (Paris, 1554). A Greek edition with Latin translation and the notes of previous commentators was published by Hermann Boerhaave, who admired Aretaeos very much (Leiden, 1731; 1735). First modern edition by C. Gottl. Kühn: Medicorum graecorum opera (t. 24, Greek and Latin, 1066 p., Leipzig, 1828). Later edition by F. Z. Ermerins (1847). Greek text with English translation by Francis Adams, published by the Sydenham Society (530 p., London, 1856). Aretaeus, edited by Carolus Hude (Corpus medicorum graecorum, II, 208 p., Leipzig, 1923).

Criticism—H. Locher: Arataeus aus Cappadocien (Zürich, 1857). M. Wellmann, in Pauly-Wissowa (vol. 3, 669–670, 1895). E. Gurlt: Geschichte der Chirurgie (vol. 1, 407–11, 1898). Hans Pohlmeyer: Zahnärztliches bei Rufos, Soranos und Aretaios (Diss., 20 p., Leipzig, 1922).

MENODOTOS

Menodotos of Nicomedia (Μηνόδοτος). Flourished probably c. 150. Greek physician, the first, or one of the first, to syncretize the ideas of Empirical and Sceptical medicine. Galen wrote one of his works against Menodotos.

Criticism—The date of his activity is not fixed with certainty. Sudhoff (Pagels Einführung, 1915, p. 86), following Sprengel, would place him at the end of the first century. Robert Fuchs, in Puschmann: Geschichte der Medizin (vol. 1, 314, 1902). Albert Favier: Un médecin grec du IIe siècle, précurseur de la méthode expérimentale moderne; Ménodote de Nicomédie (387 p., Paris, 1906).

MARCELLOS OF SIDE[u]

Μάρκελλος Σιδήτης. Flourished under Marcus Aurelius, emperor from 161 to 180. Greek physician. Author of a medical treatise (Ἰατρικά) in 42 books, of which a fragment on lycanthropy and a poem (101 lines) on fishes (περὶ ἰχθύων) are extant. About 75 fishes are mentioned; the purpose is medical.

Text—Fed. Morelli: Iatrica de piscibus, graece et latine (Paris, 1591). Medicina ex piscibus, in Joh. Alb. Fabricius (Bibliotheca graeca, Hamburg, p. 14–20, 1705). Schneider: Marcelli Sidetae medici fragmenta (Leipzig, 1888).

Criticism—E. H. F. Meyer: Geschichte der Botanik (vol. 2, 161, 1855). Robert Fuchs, in Puschmann: Geschichte der Medizin (vol. 1, 371, 1902).

PHILUMENOS

Φιλουμένος. Probably a younger contemporary of Galen. Greek physician of the Eclectic school. A compiler who quoted his sources, and whose work was used extensively by Oribasios (second half of fourth century) and Aëtios of Amida (first half of sixth century). His main extant work deals with animal poisons and their remedies (περὶ ἰοβόλων ζῴων καὶ τῶν ἐν αὐτοῖς βοηθημάτων).

Text and Translations—Theod. Puschmann: Nachträge zu Alexander Trallianus. Fragmente aus Philumenus und Philagrius . . . (Berliner Studien für class. Phi-

---

[u] Or Marcellos Sidetes. Side was a city on the coast of Pamphylia, a little west of the river Melas.

lologie, v. 2, 189 p., Berlin, 1887. The fragments are given in Latin, the Greek text being lost, with a German translation: De reumate ventri; De dysenteria reumatica; De coeliacis; De tenesmo). Philumeni de venenatis animalibus eorumque remediis capita XXXVII, first edition, by Max. Wellmann (80 p., Leipzig, 1908. This was the first part of the great Corpus medicorum graecorum to appear).
Criticism—Max. Wellmann: Philumenos (Hermes, vol. 43, 373–404, Berlin, 1908. Important study; my dating of Philumenos is derived from it. Wellmann says he flourished c. 180; he had previously said c. 250. See Puschmann's Handbuch, Vol. I, p. 339, 1902). Ernest Fr. Kind: Zu Philumenos (Hermes, vol. 44, p. 621–624, 1909. Pointing out similarities in Philumenos and Nicander of Colophon). Edm. O. von Lippmann: Ein Vorläufer des papinschen Dampfstopfes (Chemiker Zeitung, p. 1097, 1909; reprinted in Lippmann's Abhandlungen, t. II, 201–202. Apropos of two passages in Puschmann's edition quoted above, p. 42, 46, describing a Papin's digester, without safety-valve).

LEONIDES

Λεωνίδης, of Alexandria; flourished in Rome at the end of the second century and the beginning of the third century. Greek surgeon. Fragments of his works relative to various special operations are quoted by Caelius Aurelanius, Aëtios and Paul Aegineta.

E. Gurlt: Geschichte der Chirurgie (vol. 1, 486–492, 1898).

MARCELLINOS

Μαρκελλῖνος, flourished in the second century or later.[v] Greek physician; eclectic, but with dogmatic tendencies (chiefly pneumatic). He wrote a treatise on the pulse (περὶ σφυγμῶν) which is of historical importance.[w]

Hermann Schöne: Markellinos' Pulslehre (Festschrift zur 49. Versammlung deutscher Philologen, 448–472, Basel, 1907. Critical edition of the Greek text with introduction and notes).

Various additional notes on anatomy, physiology, and medicine in the second half of the second century.
Greek—J. D. Rolleston: Lucian and Medicine (Janus, vol. 20, 83–108, Leyde, 1915; Isis, IV, 397).
Jewish—Emanuel Rosenbaum: Une conférence contradictoire religieuse et scientifique sur l'anatomie et la physiologie des organes génitaux de la femme à l'école de Rami, fils de Samuel et de Rabbi Yitsaac, fils de Rabbi Yehoudou à la fin du IIe siècle (90 p., Francfort, 1901. Interesting in many respects, e. g., for the study of menstruation).
Roman—P. Foucart: Rescrit d'Antonin relatif à la circoncision et à son application en Egypte (Journal des Savants, IX, p. 5–14, 1911. Unknown date, before 155).
Syriac—E. Wallis Budge: Syrian Anatomy, Pathology, and Therapeutics, or the Book of Medicines (2 vols., Oxford, 1913). This long treatise is obviously the Syriac translation of a series of lectures on human anatomy, pathology, and therapeutics, originally written in Greek by a physician who (according to his own testimony) had studied in Alexandria. These lectures are partly based upon per-

---

[v] He quotes many physicians, but not Galen, and may have flourished before the latter. His language seems to point to a later date, however.

[w] See my note on Herophilos (first half of third century B. C.). Our knowledge of ancient sphygmology is based on writings of Galen, on others ascribed to Galen, Rufus, and Soranos, and on Marcellinos.

sonal experiences; the spirit pervading them is very distinctly Hippocratic. However, the form of the prescriptions is curiously reminiscent of the Ebers Papyrus. This compilation may date from the second century, but it is possibly of a later period—fourth century or later still. A medical college is thought to have been in existence at Edessa in the second century.

Since writing the above, I have read C. Brockelmann's elaborate examination of Budge's edition (Z. d. deutschen morgenl. Ges., vol. 68, 185–203, 1914). Brockelmann proves that the most valuable part of this text is plagiarized from Galen's *περὶ τῶν πεπονθότων τόπων*. We know that that text was translated into Syriac by Sergios of Resaina (first half of sixth century). It is possible that the text published by Budge is posterior to Sergios's translation and derived from it.

CHANG CHUNG-CHING

Chang^{1} Chung^{4}-ching^{3} (416, 2876, 2143), also called Chang^{1} Chi^{1} (416, 787) or Chi Chung-ching. He was born either in Nan^{2}-yang^{2} (8128, 12883), Honan, or in Tsao^{3}-yang^{2}-hsien^{4} (11623, 12883, 4545), Hupeh, and flourished at the end of the second century. Chinese physician, the greatest of his time. He wrote a treatise on dietetics, wherein many plants are enumerated, the Chin^{1} kuei^{4} yü^{4*} han^{2} yao^{4} lüeh^{4*} fang^{1} lun^{4} (2032, 6465, 13630, 3812, 12889, 7565, 3435, 7475).[a] He wrote also a treatise on fevers entitled Shang^{1}-han^{2}-lun^{4} (9742, 3825, 7475), which enjoyed as long a popularity in the Far East as Galen's works in the West. It is divided into ten chüan, of which the first deals with the pulse and the others with various fevers and suitable prescriptions.

These two treatises were among the very first Chinese medical works to be imported into Japan, their Japanese names being respectively Kin-ki and Sho-kanron. The other Chinese works upon which Japanese medicine was primarily founded are the Su^{4}-wên^{4} (10348, 12650) (Questions of internal medicine), the Ling^{2} ch'u^{1} ching^{1} (7222, 10092, 2122) (Classic of the marvelous pivot) ascribed to the Yellow Emperor (Huang Ti), and the Nan^{2}-ching^{1} (8135, 2122) (Classic of difficulty). I have already dealt with these works in my notes on Chinese medicine in the fifth and the first half of the fourth century B. C. I may add here that the Japanese names of these three works are respectively So-mon, Rei-sui, and Nan-kyō.

Texts—The text of the Chin Kuei which has come down to us is probably very remote from the original. A collection of prescriptions lent itself admirably to interpolations and additions. The earliest commentary was made by Wang^{2} Shu^{2*}-ho^{2} (12493, 10039, 3945) of the Chin^{4} (2069).

There are a great many Chinese and Japanese editions of the Shang-han-lun.

Commentary—E. Bretschneider: Botanicon sinicum (Part I, 41, Shanghai, 1882). Puschmann: Geschichte der Medizin (Bd. I, 38, 1902, B. Scheube). M. Courant: Catalogue des livres chinois de la Bibliothèque Nationale (t. 2, 81–83, 109, 1910). Berthold Laufer: Sino Iranica, 205, 1919 (Isis, III, 301). F. Huebotter: Guide (16–18, Kumamoto, 1924; Isis, VII, 259).

IX. HELLENISTIC, ROMAN, AND CHINESE HISTORIOGRAPHY

For the works of Tatian and Pausanias, see the notes devoted to them in Sections II and VII.

---

[a] Often abbreviated to Chin kuei yao lüeh, or even to Chin Kuei.

APPIAN

Ἀππιανός. Born in Alexandria about the end of the first century; flourished at Rome until the beginning of M. Aurelius's reign, that is, until after 161. Roman historian. He wrote c. 160, in Greek, a "History of Rome" in 24 books (Ῥωμαϊκά), arranged, not chronologically but ethnographically—from the origins to the end of Trajan's reign (117).

Texts—Partial Latin editions (Venice, 1472, etc.). Greek princeps edition by Charles and Robert Estienne (Paris, 1551). Joh. Schweighaeuser: Greek and Latin texts (3 vols., Leipzig 1785–1795). New fragments discovered by Angelo Mai, edited by him in his Scriptorum veterum nova collectio (t. 2, Rome, 1825). New edition including these fragments (Paris, Didot, 1840). Greek text by Em. Bekker (2 vols., Leipzig, 1852–1853). By Ludwig Mendelssohn (2 vols., Leipzig, 1879–1881).

Greek text with English translation by Horace White (Loeb Library), 4 vols., London, 1912–1913.

Criticism—M. Croiset: Littérature grecque (t. 5, 672–678, 1899). Antonio Oddo: Gl'hypomnemata historika di Strabone, come fonte di Appiano (Rassegna di antichità classica, 41 p., 1900).

GELLIUS

Aulus Gellius. Born c. 130; died after 180. Roman scholar. He wrote at about the age of thirty, in Athens, an erudite and pedantic miscellany in 20 books, called Noctes Atticae. It contains much information on various archaeological, grammatical, and lexicographical subjects, but its chief value lies in the many fragments of lost works which are preserved in it.

Text—Editio princeps, Rome, 1469 (with Theod. Gaza's collaboration). Edition by Martin Hertz, 2 vols., Berlin, 1883–1885 (Supplementum apparatus Gelliani by same in Jahrb. für classische Philologie, Supp. Bd. 21, 1–48, 1894). Hertz's edition, revised by Carl Hosius. 2 vols. Leipzig, 1903.

Attic nights, translated by William Beloe. 3 vols. London, 1795.

Criticism—J. W. Beck: Studia gelliana et pliniana (55 p., Jahrb. f. class. Philol., Sup. Bd., 19, 1892). Sandys: History of classical scholarship (vol. 1^3, 1921, 210–213). Mousson-Lanauze: La médecine dans Aulu-Gelle (Paris médical, 7 oct. 1922, 9–13). Max Neuburger: Die Medizin in den Noctes atticae (Archivio di storia della scienza, 6, 1–17, 1925).

The philosopher Hsün Yüeh, dealt with in Section III, wrote a brief history of the Earlier Han dynasty.

X. ROMAN LAW

GAIUS

Flourished under Hadrian and Commodus, thus at least from 138 to 180. One of the greatest Roman jurists. He was considered by the Valentinian Law of Citations (426) as one of the five fundamental jurists[y] and much use was made of his writings in the compilation of the Digest. His main work is the "Institutes," an elementary treatise of Roman law, of unsurpassed excellence, in four books,[z] upon which Justinian's treatise was largely based. Gaius's "Institutes"

---

[y] The four others being Papinian, Paulus, Ulpian, and Modestinus (all of the first half of the third century). Sir Henry Maine considered Gaius a higher authority than Ulpian (Ancient Law, 1861). The Digest contains 535 extracts from Gaius.

[z] (I) Persons; (II) Things, wills; (III) Interstate successions, obligations; (IV) Actions and their forms.

are of considerable importance because of the historical information which they contain.

Text—The "Institutes" were probably used as a text-book down to the time of Justinian. Yet they were discovered only in 1816 by B. G. Niebuhr in a Verona palimpsest: Gai Codex rescriptus in bibliotheca capitularia ecclesiae cathedralis Veronensis cura et studio eiusdem bibliothecae custodis phototypice expressus (Leipzig, 1909, fifth century manuscript).

First edition by I. F. L. Goeschen in 1820. Edition by Paul Krueger and Wilhelm Studemund (Berlin, 1877; 5th edition, 275 p., 1905). By Emil Seckel and others (2d edition, 301 p., Leipzig, 1908). By Ferdinand Kniep (369 p., Jena, 1911).

James Muirhead: The Institutes of Gaius and Rules of Ulpian. With translation, Notes and Alphabetical Digest (654 p., Edinburgh, 1880). Latin and English texts by Edward Poste, with commentary (Oxford, 1871; 3d edition 1890; 4th edition, 723 p., 1904).

Criticism—Sir Henry Maine: Early History of Institutions (chapter 9, 1888). See Histories of Roman Law.

Théodore Reinach: Un code fiscal de l'Egypte romaine: le gnomon de l'Idiologue (Nouv. revue hist. du droit, 583–636, 1919; 5–136, 1920. Apropos of an important Berlin papyrus, dating from c. 161; first published by W. Schubart, Berlin, 1919; Isis, V, 492).

XI. GREEK PHILOLOGY

PAUSANIAS ATTICISTA

Pausanias the Atticist, Παυσανίας Ἀττικιστής. Flourished under Antoninus Pius and possibly also under M. Aurelius, that is, some time between 138 and 180. Greek lexicographer who wrote a lexicon of about the same size as that of Aelios Dionysios (q. v., first half of second century), but containing fewer examples.

Text—Ern. Schwalbe: Aelii Dionysii et Pausaniae atticistarum fragmenta coll. (290 p., Leipzig, 1890).

Criticism—Heinrich Heyden: Quaestiones de Aelio Dionysio et Pausania atticistis etymologici magni fontibus in Leipziger Studien (vol. 8, 171–264, 1885). Sandys: History of Classical Scholarship (vol. 1^3, 323, 1921).

HERODIAN

Aelios Herodianos (Ἡρωδιανός). Nicknamed ὁ τεχνικός. Flourished at Rome under Marcus Aurelius. Son of Apollonios Dyscolos (q. v., first half of second century). Greek grammarian. He wrote a work in 21 books (Καθολικὴ προσῳδία) dealing with accentuation, quantities, breathings, and enclitics. He wrote also on other grammatical subjects and orthography. His treatise on exceptional words (περὶ μονήρους λέξεως) is extant.

One of the many works ascribed to him, a treatise on numbers (περὶ ἀριθμῶν) contains a description of the so-called "Herodianic" signs. It is misleading to call them numerals, for they are not real numerals, but simply the first letters of the number words. These signs were already used in the text of Solon's laws, and instances of them are found in Attic inscriptions from 454 to c. 95 B. C. The ordinary Greek alphabetic numerals date from a somewhat later period, the earliest known example of their use being a Halicarnassian inscription of c. 450 B. C.

Text—Ἐπιτομὴ τῆς καθολικῆς προσῳδίας Ἡρωδιανοῦ rec. Maur. Schmidt (Jena. 1860). Herodiani Technici reliquiae, edited by August Lenz (2 vols., Leipzig,

1867–1870). The περὶ ἀριθμῶν is published in appendix to Henri Estienne's Thesaurus linguae graecae (VIII, 345, ed. Didot).

Criticism—Article by H. Schultz, in Pauly-Wissowa (vol. 15, 955–973, 1912). Sandys: History of Classical Scholarship (vol. 1^3, 321, 1921). Sir Thomas Heath: History of Greek Mathematics (vol. 1, 30, 1921).

PHRYNICHOS

Φρύνιχος, flourished in Bithynia? under M. Aurelius and Commodus, that is, some time between 161 and 192. Greek lexicographer. He compiled a vast lexicon of Attic words in 37 books, called "the rhetorical magazine" (Σοφιστικὴ προπαρασκευή), and partly founded on the work of Aelios Dionysios. He composed also a shorter work of the same kind, named the Atticist (Ἀττικιστής or Ἐκλογὴ ῥημάτων καὶ ὀνομάτων Ἀττικῶν).

Text—Imm. Bekker. Anecdota graeca (t. 1, 1–74, 1814).

First edition of the Atticist (Rome, 1517). Later editions by J. C. de Pauw (Utrecht, 1739); by C. A. Lobeck (Leipzig, 1820); by W. G. Rutherford (London, 1881).

Criticism—Moritz Naechster: De Pollucis et Phrynici controversiis (Diss., Leipzig, 1908). Joh. von Borries: Phrynici sophystae praeparatio sophistica. (Diss., Strassburg, 1911). Sandys: History of Classical Scholarship (vol. 1^3, 323, 1921).

POLLUX

Julius Pollux. Ἰούλιος Πολυδεύκης of Naucratis in Egypt, flourished in Athens under Commodus, died at the age of 58 before 193. Greek lexicographer. He compiled, before 177, a collection of Attic words and phrases (Τὸ ὀνομαστικόν), in 10 books, divided by subjects. It is far more than a glossary, though less than an encyclopedic dictionary.

Text—Ἑρμηνεύματα καὶ καθημερινὴ ὁμιλία, publiés pour la première fois d'après les MSS. de Montpellier et Paris par A. Boucherie (Notices et extraits, t. 23 (2), 277–494, 1872).

Onomasticon (Venice, 1502; Florence, 1520; Bale, 1536). Greek and Latin edition by J. H. Lederlin and Tib. Hemsterhuis (683 p., Amsterdam, 1706). By Guil. Dindorf (5 vols., Leipzig, 1824). By Imm. Bekker (Berlin, 1846). By Erich Bethe (Leipzig, 1900).

Criticism—Reinhold Michaelis: Quae ratio intercedat inter Julii Pollucis Onomasticon et Aristotelis de republica atheniensium (Progr., 12 p., Berlin, 1902). Sandys: History of Classical Scholarship (vol. 1^3, 327, 1921).

CHAPTER XVII

THE TIME OF ALEXANDER OF APHRODISIAS

(First Half of Third Century)

I. Survey of Scientific Research in First Half of Third Century. II. Religious Background. III. Hellenistic and Chinese Philosophy. IV. Chinese and Hellenistic Mathematics. V. Hellenistic, Roman, Chinese, and Jewish Astronomy. VI. Hellenistic and Roman Natural History. VII. Roman and Chinese Geography. VIII. Hellenistic, Roman, Hindu, Chinese, and Jewish Medicine. IX. Hellenistic Historiography. X. Roman and Jewish Law.

I. SURVEY OF SCIENTIFIC RESEARCH IN FIRST HALF OF THIRD CENTURY

1. This chapter is dedicated to Alexander of Aphrodisias, who was, undoubtedly, the greatest scientific thinker of the time, but it should be noted that, as far as we know, Alexander flourished only at the beginning of the century. With regard to chronological considerations, it would be more correct to call the first half of the third century the time of Origen, for Origen died in 254. Origen was certainly a great man, as great as Alexander, if not greater, and he was steeped in Greek philosophy; but he was primarily a theologian, while Alexander continued the Aristotelian tradition.

2. *Religious Background*—The radical transformation of Buddhism, of which I have already spoken in Chapter XV apropos of Aśvaghosha, had continued and was already very advanced by the beginning of the third century. Nāgārjuna's nihilism was the most striking development. Nāgārjuna was apparently an original thinker of great learning; various medical and alchemical treatises are ascribed to him.

I shall deal in Section III with St. Hippolytos, who wrote a refutation of Christian heresies on the main ground that they were not really the fruits of Christian doctrine but of Greek philosophy and superstition. The greatest theologian of the day was the Alexandrian Origen, an encyclopaedic mind who used his deep knowledge of Greek philosophy and of the Scriptures to produce the first systematic exposition of Christian theology. He edited the earliest polyglot Bible, the so-called Hexapla. He wrote in 248 a refutation of Paganism, against Celsos.

Jewish theology was developing too. Abba Arika ("Rab") founded the Academy of Sura and Mar Samuel the Academy of Nehardea, which became two of the greatest intellectual centers of Israel and emancipated Babylonia from Palestinian guidance. The Babylonian Talmud contains abundant proofs of the activity of these two men.

3. *Hellenistic and Chinese Philosophy*—Diogenes Laërtios was the first to write a history of all the Greek schools of philosophy. Alexander of Aphrodisias, who became the head of the Lyceum some time between 198 and 211, was the greatest commentator of Aristotle, the commentator *κατ' ἐξοχήν*. He strove hard to preserve Peripatetic teachings from Stoic and Neoplatonic contaminations. His influence upon mediaeval philosophy, through Syriac and Arabic channels, was perhaps more considerable than has been hitherto realized. Philostratos wrote

a life of Apollonios of Tyana (before 217) and lives of the sophists. Ammonios, Plotin's teacher, is often considered the founder of Neoplatonism. The refutation of Christian heresies composed by Hippolytos contains, by way of introduction, a history of Greek philosophy; it is a valuable source for the study of ancient magic and superstition.

Liu Shao edited the "Classic of Filial Piety" and wrote a treatise on anthropology.

4. *Chinese and Hellenistic Mathematics*—Sun Tzŭ, of uncertain date but possibly of the beginning of the third century, wrote an arithmetical treatise which contains the solution of indeterminate equations of the first degree.

Heron of Alexandria may have been flourishing at this time. The "Embroidered Girdles" of the historian Sextos Julios Africanos give one some idea of contemporary Roman mathematics. The works of the Roman jurists have also some mathematical interest, the most notable instance being Ulpian's earliest mention of the probable duration of life.

5. *Hellenistic, Roman, Chinese, and Jewish Astronomy*—Achilles Tatios wrote a commentary on Aratos's "Phaenomena." The chronology of Sextos Julios Africanos contains information on the calendar. The Roman Censorinus wrote an important astrological treatise in 238.

Lu Chi, who died before 220, constructed a celestial map.

Mar Samuel improved the Jewish calendar.

5 bis. *Hellenistic and Chinese Physics and Technology*—A kind of optical telegraphy is explained in the "Girdles" of Sextos Julios Africanos.

Sun Tzŭ determined the density of various substances (?).

6. *Hellenistic and Roman Natural History*—Aelian wrote a treatise on the nature of animals which is distinguished by the same moralizing tendencies as the Physiologos. Florentinos wrote a treatise on agriculture in Greek, and Gargilius Martialis another one in Latin.

7. *Roman and Chinese Geography*—Perhaps the most interesting scientific feature of this age was the development of itineraries, both in the written and in the painted form. The "Itinerarium provinciarum Antonini Augusti," an itinerary of the first kind, dates back probably to the second decade of the century. The "Tabula Peutingeriana" is the only itinerary of the second kind extant. The drawing was probably made after 226 and before 273.

How much would one not give to know exactly which were the trade routes along which Chinese silk—and various other things—were carried from the Far East to the Roman Empire? The only document giving some information on the subject is to be found in the Wei lüeh, a text dating from the middle of the third century.

8. *Hellenistic, Roman, Hindu, Chinese, and Jewish Medicine*—Cassios the Iatrosophist compiled a collection of medical and physical problems. Serenus Samonicus composed in verse a series of prescriptions for ailments arranged from head to foot. Philostratos wrote a treatise on gymnastics.

The Greek and Latin writers on husbandry mentioned in Section VI are also interesting from the medical point of view; Florentinos studied the medical action of plants; Martialis wrote a veterinary treatise.

Contemporary Hindu medicine is possibly represented by treatises ascribed to Nāgārjuna, but the subject has not yet been investigated. It is possible also that Nāgārjuna prepared an edition of the Suśruta-saṃhitā.

Hua T'o wrote an important medical treatise, the Chung-ts'ang-ching. Hua produced anaesthesia by means of a certain wine.

Mar Samuel took pains to rationalize Jewish medicine.

9. *Hellenistic Historiography*—Aelian compiled a collection of historical anecdotes in fourteen books. Herodian wrote a history of the Roman Empire from 180 to 238. Athenaeos of Naucratis edited the "Banquet of the Learned," a mediocre miscellany, which has some value because of the many fragments of ancient lore which it has helped to preserve. Sextos Julios Africanos compiled a chronology extending from the creation of the world in 5499 B. C. to 221 A. D.; he has been rightly called the father of ecclesiastical chronology. Dion Cassios published a Roman history from the origins down to 229. All of these men wrote in Greek.

10. *Roman and Jewish Law*—This was the golden age of Roman law. The two greatest jurists were Ulpian and Paulus; excerpts from their writings form respectively one-third and one-sixth (together one-half) of Justinian's "Digest." Much important juridical work was done also by their contemporaries Papinian and Modestinus.

Jewish law being inseparable from Jewish religion, the outstanding theologians, two of whom were dealt with in Section II, were of necessity the outstanding jurists.

11. *Final Remarks*—If one excepts law and possibly geography, the scientific production of this age was mediocre. There were some great men, such as Nāgārjuna, Alexander of Aphrodisias, Origen, Ulpian, Hippolytos, but these men were not concerned with science proper. This would seem to prove that the scientific mediocrity must be ascribed largely to the age itself; good men were not lacking, but the main interests enforced upon them were not scientific, but theological, legal, at best philosophical. The most important works were composed in Greek, but the age was truly international and many notable works were written in Latin, Hebrew, Sanskrit, and Chinese.

II. THE RELIGIOUS BACKGROUND

NĀGĀRJUNA

Flourished, probably in the kingdom of Kōsala, at the end of the second century and the beginning of the third century. Hindu Buddhist philosopher. The fourteenth Western patriarch of Buddhism. One of the creators of Mahāyāna Buddhism, and more particularly founder of the Mādhyamika school, characterized by absolute negativism. A rigorous logical analysis led him to the conclusion that the world not only has no existence in absolute truth, but has even no phenomenal existence. This is the so-called doctrine of vacuity (śūnyatā).

An edition of Suśruta's medical treatise (q. v., sixth century B. C.) is ascribed to Nāgārjuna. According to Chinese tradition, Nāgārjuna wrote two medical treatises and had a good knowledge of herbs, astrology, and alchemy. A treatise on rasa (metallic preparations having marvelous curative properties) is also ascribed to him. However, it is probable that these ascriptions refer not to the Buddhist patriarch, but to other Hindus of the same name: e. g., the author of a Rasaratnākara who flourished in the seventh or eighth century, and a Nāgārjuna of Daihak near Somanāth who, according to al-Bīrūnī, wrote a Rasāyana treatise and lived about a century before him (Winternitz, op. cit., 3, 552).

Text—Mādhyamikasūtra, avec la Prasannapadā, commentaire de Candrakīrti, publié par L. de la Vallée-Poussin (St. Pétersburg, 1903. Candrakīrti's commentary dates probably from the first half of the seventh century). Max. Walleser: Die Mittlere Lehre (Mādhyamikaśāstra) des Nāgārjuna, nach der tibetischen

Version übertragen (296 p., Heidelberg, 1911); *idem*, nach der chinesischen Version übertragen (204 p., 1912. Forming parts 2 and 3 of Walleser. Die Buddhistische Philosophie in ihrer geschichtlichen Entwicklung, 1904–1912).

L. de la Vallée-Poussin: Pañcakrama (72 p., Gand 1896. "Peut passer pour un résumé des doctrines nihilistiques de Nāgārjuna, doctrines qui sont à la base de la discipline tantrika").

Criticism—P. Cordier: Nāgārjuna et l'Uttarantra de la Suçrutasamhita (Anantarivo, 1896). M. Winternitz: Geschichte der indischen Litteratur, (vol. 2, 250–254; vol. 3, 552 and passim, 1920–1922). A. B. Keith: Buddhist Philosophy (1923, chiefly chapter 13, 235–241. M. Walleser: Die Lebenszeit des Nāgārjuna (Z. f. Buddhismus, vol. 9, 97 sq.; Italian translation in Alle fonti delle religioni, vol. 2, 2, Roma, 1923).

For St. Hippolytos's Refutation of Christian heresies, see my note in Section III.

ORIGEN

Ὠριγένης, born probably in Alexandria c. 185; flourished and taught mainly in Alexandria, Caesarea of Palestine, and Tyrus; died at Tyrus in 254. Greek theologian, exegete, encyclopaedist. He tried to establish Christian theology upon the whole of Greek knowledge. His treatise on principles (περὶ ἀρχῶν), composed at Alexandria before 231, is the first systematic exposition of Christian theology. He edited six different texts of the Bible in parallel columns (τὰ ἑξαπλᾶ)[a] and published many Biblical commentaries. The best known perhaps of his works is his "Refutation of Celsos" in 8 books (Κατὰ Κέλσου), composed in 248. It is a very able defense of Christianity against paganism; he insists that Greek philosophy is too learned a doctrine for the great mass of the people.

Texts—Benedictine edition by Charles and C. V. de La Rue (4 vols., folio, Paris, 1733–1759), reproduced in Migne's Patrologia graeca (t. 11–17, Paris, 1857–1860). Edition by C. H. E. Lommatzsch (25 vols., Berlin, 1831–1848). By Paul Koetschau and others (7 vols., Leipzig, 1899–1921. Die griechischen christlichen Schriftsteller).

English translation by Frederick Crombie (2 vols., Edinburgh, 1869–1872. Ante-Nicene Christian Library, 10, 23).

Hexaplorum quae supersunt, edited by Bernard de Montfaucon (2 vols., Paris, 1713); edition revised by C. F. Bahrdt (2 vols., Leipzig, 1769–1770).

For his refutation of Celsos, see my note on Celsos, second half of second century.

Criticism—August Kind: Teleologie und Naturalismus in der altchristlichen Zeit. Der Kampf des Origenes gegen Celsus um die Stellung des Menschen in der Natur (38 p., Jena, 1875). M. Croiset: Littérature grecque (t. 5, 845–855, 1899). F. Prat: Origène (Paris, 1907). Adolf von Harnack: Der kirchengeschichtliche Ertrag der exegetischen Arbeiten des Origenes (2 vols., Leipzig, 1918–1919). Shotwell: History of History (289–299, 1922). Eug. de Faye: Origène (254 p., Bibl. de l'Ecole des Hautes Etudes, Paris, 1923; Isis, VII, 181).

ABBA ARIKA[b]

Born into a Babylonian family, he was educated in Palestine; he returned to Babylonia in 219, settling first at Nehardea, then at Sura on the Euphrates; he

---

[a] The Hebrew text and its transliteration into Greek; the text of the Septuagint, first half of third century B. C., and three other Greek translations by Aquila, Symmachos, and Theodotion (see my note on religion in second half of second century).

[b] Generally called Rab.

died very old at Sura in 247. Jewish teacher and leader. Founder of the Academy of Sura, which flourished for nearly eight centuries and became one of the greatest intellectual centers of Israel. It soon made Babylonia independent from Palestine and gave it a predominant position in the Jewish world. A large part of the Babylonian Talmud[c] is constituted by the opinions of Rab and of his immediate disciples.

Article by W. Bacher, in Jewish Encyclopaedia (vol. 1, 29, 1901).

MAR SAMUEL[d]

Born c. 165 at Nehardea, Babylonia, where he flourished and died c. 257. Jewish educator, physician, astronomer, and jurist. He became the director of the Academy of Nehardea, which, together with the greater academy of Sura, emancipated Babylonia from Palestinian guidance.[e]

He opposed the medical superstitions of his day and introduced more rational methods.[f] His astronomical interest was centered upon the calendar, which he improved.[g] He was the most eminent teacher of Jewish law in his day, and he established the principle that the law of the country in which the Jews are living is binding upon them. Many of his maxims and rules are scattered through the Talmud, upon which his influence was probably considerable.

Article by Rabbi J. Z. Lauterbach, in Jewish Encyclopaedia (Vol. XI, 29–31, 1905).

III. HELLENISTIC AND CHINESE PHILOSOPHY

DIOGENES LAËRTIOS

Διογένης Λαέρτιος, of Laërte, Cilicia, flourished probably about the beginning of the third century. Greek historian of philosophy. He was the first to write the history not of one school, but of all Greek schools. This work is called "The Lives, Doctrines, and Maxims of Famous Philosophers" (Περὶ βίων, δογμάτων καὶ ἀποφθεγμάτων τῶν ἐν φιλοσοφίᾳ εὐδοκιμησάντων) and is divided into 10 books. It is superficial, but contains valuable information.

Text—Latin editions (Venice, 1475, etc.). Editio princeps (Bale, 1534). Greek and Latin editions by Heinrich Gustav Huebner (2 vols., Leipzig, 1828–1831); by Carel Gabriel Cobet (Paris, Didot, 1850).

English translation by C. D. Yonge (Bohn Library, 496 p., London, 1853).

Criticism—M. Croiset: Littérature grecque (t. 5, 1899, 806–813). Spyridion P. Lambros: Ἀνέκδοτα ἀπανθίσματα Διογένους τοῦ Λαερτίου (Mélanges Nicole, 639–651, Genève, 1905). Hans Schmidt: Studia laërtiana (Diss., 43 p., Bonn, 1906).

ALEXANDER OF APHRODISIAS

Alexander of Aphrodisias, in Caria (Ἀλέξανδρος). Flourished in Athens during the reigns of Septimius Severus and Caracalla, 193–217. Peripatetic philosopher who became the head of the Lyceum some time between 198 and 211. The

---

[c] For which see my note below, second half of fifth century.

[d] Also called Samuel Yarḥina'ah, because of his familiarity with the calendar (yeraḥ meaning month).

[e] After Rab's death, the academy of Nehardea was for a time the foremost Babylonian academy.

[f] An eye-salve was named after him the "quillurin (κολλύριον) of Mar Samuel."

[g] A further improvement was due to the Patriarch Hillel II (330–365).

greatest commentator of Aristotle (he was called the exegete, ὁ ἐξηγητής). His commentaries are extensive and very valuable; many are still extant, others are partly known through later commentaries or Arabic translations. Alexander tried to free the Aristotelian doctrine from Neoplatonic syncretism and Stoic tendencies. The most important of his original contributions are one on fate and free will (περὶ εἱμαρμένης) against the Stoics, another on the soul (περὶ ψυχῆς), in which he denies its immortality, a third one (περὶ κράσεως καὶ αὐξήσεως or περὶ μίξεως), wherein he contends against the Stoic doctrine of the interpenetration of bodies. He was apparently acquainted with the distillation of sea-water.

The Commentaries on Aristotle—Commentarius in libros metaphysicos, ed. Herm. Bonitz (Berlin, 1847). The following have appeared in the great collection Commentaria in Aristotelem graeca, published in Berlin: Analyticorum priorum liber I (1883), libri VIII topicorum (1891), Sophistici elenci (1898), by Max. Wallies; Metaphysica (1891), and Meteorologica (1899), by Mich. Hayduck; De sensu (1901), by Paul Wendland.

Original Writings—Hugo Grotius included the text of the treatise on fate in his Philosophorum sententiae de fato et de eo quod in nostra est potestate collectae partim et de graeco versae (348 p., Amsterdam; 1648). Praeter commentaria scripta minora, edited by Ivo Bruns (Supplementum aristotelicum, II, Part I, De anima liber cum mantissa 1887; Part II, Quaestiones, de fato, de mixtione 1892). Alexandri Aphrodisiensis, Ammonii Hermiae, Plotini, Bardesanis Syri, et Georgii Gemisti Plethonis de fato quae supersunt, edited by Jos. Conr. Orelli, with Latin translation (Zürich, 1824). Jean Félix Nourrisson: Essai sur Alexandre d'Aphrodisias suivi du traité du destin et du libre pouvoir (344 p., Paris, 1870).

Apocryphal Writings—Problemata per Giorgum Vallam in latinum conversa (Venice, 1488, with the problems of Aristotle and Plutarch). Greek and Latin edition of De febribus libellus by Franc. Passow (Breslau, 1822). The Latin translation is Valla's; reprinted in Passow's Opuscula academica (p. 521–611, Leipzig, 1835). Edition of the Greek text of both writings by Jul. Lud. Ideler in his Physici et medici graeci (Vol. I, p. 3–106, 1841). According to Wellmann (Puschmann's Handbuch der Gesch. der Medizin, I, 482), the author of these writings was a physician of the Pneumatic school, who lived after the second century.

Criticism—J. F. Nourrisson: Essai sur Alexandre d'Aphrodisias, etc. (Paris, 1870). Otto Apelt: Die Schrift des Alexander von Aphrodisias über die Mischung (Philologus, vol. 45, 82–99, Goettingen, 1886). C. E. Ruelle: Alexandre d'Aphrodisias et le prétendu Alexandre d'Alexandrie (Revue des études grecques, t. 5, 103–107, Paris, 1892). Gercke, in Pauly-Wissowa (Vol. I, 1453–1455, 1894). Georges Volait: Die Stellung des Alexander von Aphrodisias zur aristotelischen Schlusslehre (100 p., Halle a. S., 1907). P. Duhem: Le Système du Monde (t. 2, p. 293 sq., 1914; principes de l'astrologie, partisans de la contigence; t. 3, 1916, p. 376, théorie de l'intelligence humaine).

A general study of Alexander's work from our special point of view, and of the transmission of his thought through Syriac, Arabic, and Latin intermediaries is badly needed. It would be worth while also to determine exactly his influence upon medieval philosophy, his doctrine being to some extent an anticipation of nominalism.

PHILOSTRATOS

Φιλόστρατος, born in Lemnos; flourished at Athens,[h] then at Rome at the court of the Empress Julia[i]; he was still living under Philippus, emperor from 244 to 249.

---

[h] Hence his surname, the Athenian. He is also called Flavius.
[i] Wife of Alexander Severus, emperor from 222 to 235.

Greek scholar. Author of a "Life of Apollonios of Tyana"[i] (dedicated to the empress Julia, who died in 217), chiefly devoted to a description of his travels; of the "Lives of the Sophists," from the fifth century B. C. to his own time, and of a treatise on gymnastics which contains information on ancient athletics.

Texts—First edition (Venice, 1502). By C. L. Kayser (Zürich, 1842–1846). By Antoine Westermann: Greek and Latin Text (Paris, Didot, 1822; 1849). C. L. Kayser (2 vols., Leipzig, 1870–1871). O. Bendorf and C. Schenkl (Leipzig, 1893).

Life of Apollonius, with an English translation by F. C. Conybeare (2 vols., Loeb Library, 1912). Philosotratus and Eunapius; the Lives of the Sophists, with an English translation by Wilmer Cave Wright (Loeb Library, London, 1922). Traité sur la gymnastique, Greek and French, by Ch. Daremberg (Paris, 1858). Philostratos über Gymnastik, edited by Julius Jüthner (332 p., Leipzig, 1909, with German translation).

Criticism—M. Croiset: Littérature grecque (t. 5, 761–770, 1899).

AMMONIOS[k]

Ἀμμώνιος; of Alexandria; teacher of Plotin c. 232–242. Greek philosopher. Born a Christian, he reverted to Hellenism; of course, there were many points of contact between the Platonizing Christians of those days and the as yet undeveloped Neoplatonists. In spite of the fact that no writings can be specifically ascribed to Ammonios, he is often called the founder of Neoplatonism. He was probably the first organizer of those Neoplatonic tendencies which would find full expression in the works of his pupil, Plotin. It is plausible to assume that the teachings of Ammonios are reflected in the philosophical "Hermetica," a collection of writings dating mainly from the third century.

Pauly-Wissowa (vol. 1, Sp., 1863, 1894, by Freudenthal). Edward Zeller: Ammonius und Plotinus (Archiv für Gesch. der Philos., vol. 7, 295–312, 1894). Walter Scott: Hermetica. The Ancient Greek and Latin Writings which Contain Religious or Philosophic Teachings Ascribed to Hermes Trismegistus (4 vols., Oxford, 1924, sq.; Isis, VIII, 343–346).

ST. HIPPOLYTOS

Ἱππόλυτος. Taught at Rome until 235, when he was deported to Sardinia, where he probably died. Bishop of Portus Romanus. Roman theologian, exegete, chronologist. His main work is entitled Philosophical Subjects (τὰ φιλοσοφούμενα), in 10 books, probably composed soon after 222, the aim being to refute all heresies and to show that they derive from Greek philosophy and superstition. Book I is a history of Greek philosophy, and Books II and III (lost) dealt with pagan mysteries, astrology, and magic. Hippolytos exposed the frauds of the magicians and the irrationality of magic and astrology.[l]

Text—Until 1842, only Book 1 was known, and it was ascribed to Origen. In 1842, Minoïdes Minas discovered Books 4 to 10 in an Athos manuscript; Books 2 and 3 are still missing.

---

[i] Apollonios traveled to Babylonia and India within the years 39–47, and died in 97–8 (Isis III, 319). He was considered as having supernatural wisdom and was later opposed to Christ, but this was not Philostratos's intention.

[k] Nicknamed Saccas, Σακκᾶς, the porter.

[l] In this he followed closely Sextos Empiricos. He may have been influenced also by Celsos. In other words, he made full use of pagan arguments against pagan superstitions.

The Philosophumena have been edited by E. Miller (Oxford, 1851); L. Duncker and F. G. Schneidewin (Göttingen, 1859. Reproduced in Migne's Patrologia, vol. 16, with Origen's works). New edition by H. Diels: Doxographi graeci (t. 1, Berlin, 1879). English translation by F. Legge (2 vols., London, 1921. See J. R. A. S., 468–472, 1922).

An extract of the Philosophumena (Bk. 4, c. 4) dealing with the physical tricks of magicians is translated in Albert de Rochas. La science des philosophes et l'art des thaumaturges dans l'antiquité (Paris, 241–250, 1912?).

Adolf Bauer: Die Chronik des Hippolytos im Matritensis graecus 121. Nebst einer Abhandlung über den Stadiasmus maris magni von Otto Cuntz (290 p., 4 facsim., Leipzig, 1905).

Canones S. Hippolyti Arabice e codicibus romanis cum versione latina, edited by D. B. de Haneberg (125 p., München, 1870). German translation by Valentin Gröne (48 p., Kempten, 1874). Canones, die "Ägyptische Kirchenordnung" und die entsprechenden Stücke der Const. apost. VIII in Hans Achelis, Die ältesten Quellen des orientalischen Kirchenrechtes (1891).

For other works see P. A. de Lagarde: Hippolyti romani quae feruntur omnia graece (Leipzig, 1858). Complete edition by G. N. Bonwetsch, Hans Achelis, und Paul Wendland (3 vols., Griech. christl. Schriftsteller, Leipzig, 1897–1916).

Criticism—H. Staechelin: Die gnostischen Quellen Hippolyts in seiner Hauptschrift gegen die Häretiker, with appendixes by Adolf Harnack (Leipzig, 1890). Hans Achelis: Hippolytstudien (Leipzig, 1897). M. Croiset: Littérature grecque (t. 5, 843–845, 1899). Karl Johannes Neumann: Hippolytus in seiner Stellung zu Staat und Welt (Leipzig, 1902). Richard Ganschinietz: Hippolytos's Capitel gegen die Magier (Refut. haer., IV, 28–42; 77 p., Leipzig, 1913). Lynn Thorndike: History of Magic (vol. 1, 466–469, 1923).

LIU SHAO

Liu^2 Shao^4 (7270, 9773). Born at Han^2-tan^1 (3781, 10610) in Chihli; flourished as a high official in 224. Chinese scholar and anthropologist (?). He edited the "Classic of Filial Piety," Hsiao^4-ching^1 (4334, 2122),[m] one of the secondary classics, and wrote a treatise entitled Jên^2-wu^{4*}-chih^4 (5624, 12777, 1918), dealing with the division of mankind into classes according to their dispositions as revealed by their outward characteristics.

A. Wylie: Chinese Literature (158, 1867 [1902]). H. A. Giles: Biographical Dictionary (520, 1898).

IV. CHINESE AND HELLENISTIC MATHEMATICS

SUN-TZŬ

Sun^1-Tzŭ^3 (10431, 12317). Flourished about the end of the first century, more probably as late as the beginning of the third. Chinese mathematician. The Sun-Tzŭ Suan^4-ching^1 (10378, 2122) (arithmetical classic of Sun-Tzŭ) is an elaborate and methodical treatise of arithmetic in three books. Solution of indeterminate equations of the first degree. Information on Chinese metrology. Decimal number system. Density of various substances.

Text—The text now extant was extracted piecemeal from the Yung^3-Lo^{4*} Ta^4-tien^3 (13504, 7331, 10470, 11177) (q. v., first half of fifteenth century).

Criticism—A. Wylie: Chinese Literature (114–115, 1867, 1902). Yoshio

---

[m] Hsiao^4 is much more than "filial piety;" it is humanity; it has a political as well as a domestic acception.

Mikami: The Development of Mathematics in China and Japan (chapter 4, p. 25–33, Leipzig, 1913). L. Wieger: La Chine (394, 521, 1920).

For Hellenistic mathematics, see my note on the historian Sextos Julios Africanos in Section IX and on the jurist Ulpian in Section X.

It is possible that Heron of Alexandria flourished at this time.

V. HELLENISTIC, ROMAN, CHINESE, AND JEWISH ASTRONOMY

ACHILLES TATIOS

Ἀχιλλεὺς Τάτιος.[n] Flourished probably toward the end of the second century or some time during the third century. Greek astronomer. One of the many commentators on the Phaenomena of Aratos (q. v., first half of third century B. C.). This commenatry, entitled "On the Sphere" (Περὶ σφαίρας) is preserved only in a fragmentary condition.

Text—First Greek edition (together with Hipparchos and others) by Petrus Victorius, Florence, 1567. New edition with Latin translation in the Uranologium of Dionysius Petavius (Denis Petau), Paris, 1630, p. 121–169; Amsterdam, 1703.

Criticism—Ernst Maas. Aratea. Berlin, 1892. Schaefer, in Pauly-Wissowa, vol. 1, 1894, 247.

For the Hellenistic calendar see my note on Sextos Julios Africanos in Section IX.

CENSORINUS

Roman astrologer. He composed in 238 a treatise on the birthday (De die natali), which is an important astrological summary; in great part extant. There remain also some small mathematical, astronomical, and musical fragments.

Text and Translations—Edition by Otto Jahn (137 p., Berlin, 1845). By Fried. Hultsch (111 p., Leipzig, 1867). By Joh. Cholodniak (83 p., St. Petersburg, 1889). Edition with French translation and notes by J. Mangeart (133 p., Paris, 1843).

Criticism—Wissowa, in Pauly-Wissowa (vol. 3, col. 1908–1910, 1899). Alfred Hahn: De Censorini fontibus (Diss., 46 p., Jena, 1905).

Jean Mascart: Le plus vieil instrument d'astronomie nautique (15 p., 8 fig., Lyon, 1923. A bronze instrument contained in a wooden box, found in the remains of a ship sunk near the isle of Antikythera; Isis, VIII, 534).

LU CHI

Lu[4]* Chi[1]* (7432, 832). Native of Kiangsu; died before 220, at 32. Chinese mathematician and astronomer. He constructed a celestial map and wrote a commentary on the I[4] Ching[1] (5497, 2122), the Lu[4]*-Shih[4] Chou[1]-i[4] Shu[4]* (7432, 9978, 2450, 5497, 10054).

H. A. Giles: Biographical Dictionary (538, 1898). L. Wieger: La Chine (361, 509, 1920).

For the Jewish calendar, see my note on Mar Samuel in Section II.

VI. HELLENISTIC AND ROMAN NATURAL HISTORY

For zoological works continuing the tradition of the Physiologos, see my note on the historian Aelian in Section IX.

---

[n] Suidas writes Στάτιος and confuses him with the Alexandrian author of an erotic romance (Τὰ κατὰ Λευκίππην καὶ Κλειφῶντα) who lived probably in the sixth century.

FLORENTINOS[a]

Flourished under the reign of Alexander Severus, 222–235. He wrote a large treatise on agriculture in Greek (γεωργικά). He was especially interested in the medical applications of agriculture (the medical action of plants and fruits) and in horticulture.

E. H. F. Meyer: Geschichte der Botanik (vol. 2, 218–220, 1855). Eugen Oder, in Rheinisches Museum (vol. 45, 83–87, 1890). Wilhelm Gemoll: Untersuchungen über die Quellen der Geoponica (Berliner Studien, Bd. 1, 1–280, 1884). M. Wellmann, in Pauly-Wissowa (vol. 6, 2756, 1909).

MARTIALIS

Gargilius Martialis. Flourished under Alexander Severus, 222–235. Author of writings on husbandry, on the medical virtues of fruits and herbs, and on veterinary art, which were much appreciated during the middle ages.

Text and Translations—Text of the Curae Boum in J. M. Gesner: Scriptores rei rusticae veteres latini (t. III, 455–458, 1787). Angelo Mai published in 1828 the first edition of De arboribus pomiferis and of De pomis seu medicina ex pomis. Classici auctori e Vaticanis codicibus (t. I, p. 391–413, t. III, p. 416–426. Both reprinted in Luneburg, 1832, in his Gargilii Martialis quae supersunt e codicibus Neapolitano et Vaticanis, which contains also the Curae Boum). A better edition of the latter text is appended to Ern. Lommatzsch's edition of Vegetius's Mulomedicina (Leipzig, p. 307–310, 1903). Edition by Val. Rose (Leipzig, 1875).

Criticism—E. H. F. Meyer: Geschichte der Botanik (vol. 2, 228–236, 1855).

VII. ROMAN AND CHINESE GEOGRAPHY

Roman Itineraries

From the Map of Agrippa (q. v., second half of first century B. C.) and from its commentary developed slowly two kinds of geographical summaries, called itineraries. From the map were derived the "Itineraria picta," from the commentary the "Itineraria adnotata." Very remarkable examples of each belong to the third century.

The Itinerarium provinciarum Antonini Augusti is an itinerary of the second kind. Its date can not be exactly determined; it is in its present state a heterogeneous document, the oldest parts of which date back probably to Antoninus Caracalla (211–217), with additions of the time of Diocletian (284–305) and of the beginning of the fourth century.

Itinerarium Antonini Augusti et Hierosolymitanum, edited by Gust. Parthey and Moritz Pinder (443 p., Berlin, 1848). A. Aurès: Concordance des vases Apollinaires et de l'itinéraire de Bordeaux à Jérusalem et comparaison de ces textes avec l'itinéraire d'Antonin et la table théodosienne (Mémoires de l'Académie du Gard, 132 p., Nimes, 1868).

The Tabula Peutingeriana (called after its former owner, the archaeologist Konrad Peutinger of Augsburg, 1465–1547; now in the Palatine Library in Vienna) is the only itinerary of the first kind extant. It was drawn probably after 226 and before 273, with the restriction that some parts of it may be of an earlier or a later date. The existing copy of it was made by a monk in Colmar in 1265, who appears in the main to have faithfully transcribed the older map, which he had

[a] Possibly identical with the Roman jurist of the same name.

before him.[p] It has been frequently published and is often included in atlases of ancient geography.

I quote the following editions: Franz Chr. v. Scheyb: Peutingeriana tabula itineraria (Vienna, 1753). Mat. Pet. Katancsich: Orbis antiquus . . . . (Budae, 1824–1825). Ernest Desjardins: La table de Peutinger précédée d'une introduction historique et critique (Liv. 1–14, Paris, 1869–1874; no more published). Konrad Miller: Weltkarte des Castorius (Ravensburg, 1887–8. Miller concludes that Castorius, a Roman cosmographer often quoted by the Ravenna geographer, q. v., second half of seventh century, was the author of the Peutinger table); Mappaemundi (Vol. VI, 36, 1898); Itineraria Romana (p. xxvi–xxxvi, 1916).

Anton Elter: Itinerarstudien (76 p., Bonn, 1908. Deals with both kinds of itineraries).

A topographical document, as interesting as unusual, was found by Franz Cumont in 1923 at Sālihīyeh (ancient Dura-Europos) on the Euphrates; it is a fragment of the shield of a Roman soldier, bearing a list of stopping places. It must date from the first half of the third century. See Franz Cumont: Fragment d'un bouclier portant une liste d'étapes (15 p., Syria, 1925; Isis, VII, 564; VIII, 533, 735)

Chinese Itineraries

The only Chinese text giving precise information on the itineraries of Chinese merchants across the Ta⁴-ch'in² (10470, 2093) (the Roman East) was contained in the Wei⁴ lüeh⁴* (12567, 7564), dating from the middle of the third century. This work is lost, but the fragment of interest to us was inserted in 429 at the end of chapter 30 of the San Kuo chih (for which see my note Ch'ên Shou in the following chapter).

Paul Pelliot: Note sur les anciens itinéraires chinois dans l'orient romain (Journal asiatique, t. 17, 139–145, 1921; Isis, V, 492).

VIII. HELLENISTIC, ROMAN, HINDU, CHINESE, AND JEWISH MEDICINE

CASSIOS THE IATROSOPHIST

Κάσσιος ὁ ἰατροσοφιστής. Flourished probably at the beginning of the third century. Unknown Greek physician and author of a collection of 84 medical and physical problems (*ἰατρικαὶ ἀπορίαι καὶ προβλήματα φυσικά*), very similar to those ascribed to Alexander of Aphrodisias[q] and to Adamantios (q. v., first half of fourth century). Cassios's point of view is sometimes that of the pneumatic school, sometimes that of the methodist school.[r]

Text—First edition by G. de Sylva (Paris, 1541). New edition with Latin translation by Conr. Gesner (Zürich, 1562).

Latest edition in J. L. Ideler: Physici et medici graeci (vol. 1, 144–167, 1841).

Criticism—E. Gurlt: Geschichte der Chirurgie (vol. 1, 331–332, 1898). M. Wellmann, in Pauly-Wissowa (vol. 3, 1679, 1899).

SERENUS SAMONICUS

Quintus Serenus Samonicus (or Sammonicus). Flourished in Rome at the beginning of the third century; murdered by command of Caracalla, in 212.

---

[p] H. F. Tozer: History of Ancient Geography (310–312, 1897).

[q] See my note on Alexander's apocryphal writings.

[r] Byzantine editors have put together Cassios's problems and those of the pseudo-Aristotle and of the pseudo-Alexander.

Author of a medical poem extending to 1,115 hexameters, De medicina praecepta saluberrima.[a] It is chiefly a collection of popular prescriptions for various ailments, arranged a capite ad calcem. It contains much information, mostly derived from earlier writers, on natural history, medicine, and superstition.

Text and Translations—The text of this poem has been often published, together with Celsus's works. For example: Aldine of 1528 by G. B. Egnazio (Giov. Cipelli); another edition of the same year in Hanau; Volpi's edition (Padova, 1750). First critical edition: Liber medicinalis by F. Vollmer, in Corpus med. latin. (II, 3; 106 p., Leipzig, 1916; Isis, III, 320). Translated into French, together with Macer and Marcellus, by Louis Baudet, with the Latin text (Paris, 1845).

Criticism—E. H. F. Meyer: Geschichte der Botanik (vol. 2, 209–218, 1855). Gnüg: Sprachliches zu Serenus (Progr., 73 p., Hildburghausen, 1906). F. Vollmer: Nachträge zur Ausgabe des Serenus Liber medicinalis (Philologus, vol. 75, 128–133, 1919. Philological).

For the treatise on gymnastics written by Philostratos, see my note devoted to him in Section III. It will be necessary to refer also to my notes on Florentinos and Martialis in Section VI.

I do not know whether the following notes refer to the first or to the second half of the third century.

Victor Deneffe: Etude sur la trousse d'un chirurgien gallo-romain du IIIe siècle (66 p., 9 pl., Anvers, 1893); Les oculistes gallo-romains au IIIe siècle (185 p., 5 pl., Anvers, 1896. Important studies, the more so that the late Professor Deneffe had contributed considerably to make of the collection of ancient surgical instruments of the University of Ghent one of the first, if not the first, in the world. Professor Deneffe had traveled extensively to complete it).

Joseph Offord: A Magical and Medical Papyrus of the Third Century (American Antiquarian and Oriental Journal, vol. 26, 271–272, Chicago, 1904. Apropos of the Demotic magical papyrus of London and Leyden, ed. by F. L. Griffith and Herbert Thompson).

V. Bugiel: Les détails médicaux dans un roman grec du IIIe siècle (Bull. soc. franç. hist. méd., t. 18, 320–338, 361–392, 1924. Medicine in the Story of Apollonios of Tyre).

For the Hindu medical works which may have been composed at this time, see my note on Nāgārjuna, in Section II.

For Jewish medicine see my note on Mar Samuel, in the same section.

HUA T'O

Hua[2] T'o[2] (5005, 11346) or Yüan[2] (13744). Born in Po[4]*-hsien[4] (9399, 4545), Anhui; flourished probably c. 190–265. Chinese surgeon. The work published under his name, the Hua T'o Chung[1]-ts'ang[4]-ching[1] (2875, 11601, 2122), is certainly not his in its present form. The present edition was prepared by Têng[4] Ch'u[3] Ch'ung[1] (10870, 2660, 2875) during the Sung dynasty. Chapters 1 to 11 deal with the pulse and physiology; chapters 12 to 49 with pathology; then follows special therapeutics. Hua produced general anaesthesia by means of a wine of unknown composition called ma[2]-fei[4]-san[4] (7591, 3490, 9559) or ma[2]-yao[4] (12958).

Text—The text is included in the great encyclopaedia Ku[3]-chin[1] t'u[2]-shu[1] chi[2]*-ch'êng[2], 1726 (6188, 2027, 12128, 10024, 906, 762). Revised edition by the Japanese physician Genko Hori, c. 1750.

---

[a] Unless the author be his son, bearing the same name. There is no way of deciding the matter.

Criticism—Biography translated from Chinese sources by F. Huebotter. To appear in Mitt. der Deutschen Gesellschaft für Naturkunde Ostasiens, Tokyo (information received in Nov., 1924). F. Huebotter: Guide (18–21, Kumamoto, 1924).

IX. HELLENISTIC HISTORIOGRAPHY

AELIAN

Claudios Aelianos. Αἰλιανός. Born at Praeneste, Latium. Flourished in Rome under Septimius Severus, 193–211, and probably outlived Elagabalus, who died in 222. Roman compiler and moralist. His most important works were a collection of historical anecdotes in 14 books (ποικίλη ἱστορία) and another on the peculiarities or nature of animals (περὶ ζῴων) in 17 books. One might call the latter a "moral" zoology. It is a series of zoological facts told with an ethical purpose, many being quoted from earlier writers. The beginning of his historical collection deals also with natural history.

Text and Translation—First complete edition by Conrad Gesner, with Latin translation and illustrations (Zürich, 1556). Greek and Latin edition by Rud. Hercher (Paris, 1858; in 2 vols., Leipzig, 1864–1866). There is an English translation of the "Registre of hystories" by Abraham Fleming (London, 1576), but none of the zoology. Complete German translation by Wunderlich and Jacobs (9 vols., 1126 p., Stuttgart, 1839–1842).

Criticism—M. Wellmann, in Pauly-Wissowa (Vol. I, 486–488, 1894. Containing a list of Aelian's sources).

HERODIAN

Ἡρωδιανός, born c. 170, flourished in Italy, died after 250. Roman historian. He wrote, c. 250, a history of the empire from the death of M. Aurelius in 180 to 238 (Τῆς μετὰ Μάκρον βασιλείας ἱστορίαι), in eight books.

Text—Princeps edition (Venice, 1503). Greek and Latin edition by Johann Schweighaeuser (Bale, 1781); also by T. G. Irmisch (5 vols., Leipzig, 1789–1805). Greek text by Emm. Bekker (Leipzig, 1826); by Ludwig Mendelssohn (Leipzig, 1883).

English translation by J. Hart (London, 1749). French translation by Léon Halévy (Paris, 1860).

Criticism—Erich Baas: De Herodiani fontibus et auctoritate (Berlin Diss., 81 p., 1909). J. C. P. Smits: Herodianus en zijne bronnen (Leiden, 1913).

ATHENAEOS OF NAUCRATIS

Athenaeos of Naucratis (Egypt). Ἀθήναιος, lived at the end of the second century and at the beginning of the third, probably until after 228. Author of a very learned but poor compilation, the "Banquet of the Learned"[t] (Δειπνοσοφισταί) in fifteen books,[u] wherein extracts from many hundred ancient writers are quoted on almost every conceivable subject, though chiefly on gastronomy. First account of a rain of fishes.

Texts and Translations—First edition, by Marcus Musurus (Aldine, 1514). Edition by J. Bedrotus (Bale, 1535). Latin translation (Bale, 1556). Greek edition by Isaac Casaubon with Latin translation by Jacques Dalechamps (Heidelberg, 1597. The Commentary by Casaubon announced on the title page was not published until 1600, 648 p., in Lyon).

---

[t] Probably completed after 228.
[u] Books I, II, III, XI, XV are only partly known.

Greek-Latin edition by Joh. Schweighaeuser (14 vols. Strasbourg, 1801–1807; vols. 1–5, text, 1801–1805; vols. 6–13, commentary, 1801–1805; vol. 14, index, 1807). Greek editions by Wilhelm Dindorf (3 vols., Leipzig, 1827); by August Meineke (4 vols., Leipzig, 1858–1867); by Georg Kaibel (3 vols., Leipzig, 1887–1890).

English translation by Charles Duke Yonge (1812–1891) (3 vols., Bohn's Collection, London, 1854). French translation by Lefebvre de Villebrune (5 vols., Paris, 1789–1791).

Criticism—Joh. Meyer: Emendationes et observationes in Athenai novissimam editionem. (Progr., 40 p., Regensburg, 1897). Article by Wentzel, in Pauly-Wissowa's Real-Encyclopädie (t. 2, 2026–2033). Wilhelm Franzmeyer: Kallixenos' Bericht über das Prachtzelt und den Festzug Ptolemaeus II (Athenaeus V, cap. 25–35; Diss., 70 p., Strassburg, 1904). Friedrich Hackmann: De Athenaeo quaestiones selectae (Diss., 70 p., Berlin, 1912. De Aeliano Athenaei compilatore; de nonnullis libris ab Athenaeo ipso lectis; quatenus Athenaeus aequalium vitam mores studia respexerit). Karl Mengis: Die schriftstellerische Technik im Sophistenmal des Athenaios (Studien zur Geschichte und Kultur des Altertums, X, 5, 140 p., Paderborn, 1920. Chapter 4 examines the influence exerted by Athenaeos upon Macrobius).

I know of no study of Athenaeos from our point of view, save a short chapter on his botanical knowledge in Ernst H. F. Meyer: Geschichte der Botanik (vol. 2, 197–202, 1855), and a notice on the fishes by Wellmann (Hermes, vol. 23, 179–193, 1888).

JULIOS AFRICANOS

Sextos Julios Africanos, born in Jerusalem, flourished under Alexander Severus, emperor from 222 to 235, in Emmaüs, Palestine, later in Alexandria. Christian chronologist and encyclopaedist. The father of ecclesiastical chronology. His Chronology (Chronographia) extended from the creation of the world in 5499 B. C. to 221 A. D. It contains information on the calendar. The encyclopaedia entitled "Embroidered Girdles" (Κεστοί, Cesti) dealt with agriculture, medicine, natural history, applied mathematics, etc., e. g., chapter 31 deals with measurements of heights and distances by means of similar right-angled triangles; chapter 76 explains a kind of optical telegraphy.

Text and Translations—Fragments of the Cesti published in Thévenot's edition of the Mathematici veteres (Paris, 1693), also in the Geoponica. See also the texts published by Vincent (1842, 1858) as quoted by Cantor (Vol. I, 3d edition, p. 438, 440).

Criticism—E. H. F. Meyer: Geschichte der Botanik (vol. 2, 220–226, 1855). Heinrich Gelzer: Sextus und die byzantinische Chronographie (3 vols., Leipzig, 1880–1898). M. Cantor: Geschichte der Mathematik (vol. 1^3, 438–440, 1907). Kroll and Sickenberger, in Pauly-Wissowa (vol. 19, 116–125, 1917. Important; deals also with various other writings of Julios Africanos).

DION CASSIOS

Dion Cassios Cocceianos, Δίων Κάσσιος, born at Nicaea, Bithynia, not long before 155; flourished in Rome; died in Bithynia c. 230 to 240. Roman statesman and historian. After twenty years of preparation (c. 200–221) he began the publication of his Roman History (Ῥωμαϊκὴ ἱστορία) in 80 books, from the time of Aeneas to his own (229). Only books 36 to 60 are extant, dealing with the period 68 B. C. to 47 A. D.; also parts of books 79 and 80, dealing with the beginning of the third century. Of the rest of the work we can judge only by fragments and Byzantine abridgments and compilations (see my notes on Xiphilinos, second half of eleventh century, and Zonaras, first half of the twelfth century).

Text—Cassii Dionis hist. rom. lib. LXXIX, LXXX quae supersunt. Codex vaticanus graecus 1288 (Facsimile edition, preface by P. P. Franchi de' Cavalieri. Leipzig, 1908).

Princeps edition by R. Estienne (Paris, 1548). Edition by Ludwig Dindorf (5 vols., Leipzig, 1863–1865). By Johann Melber (2 vols., Leipzig, 1890–1894). By U. P. Boissevain (3 vols., Berlin, 1895–1901).

Greek text with English translation, by Earnest Cary (9 vols., Loeb Library, London, 1914–1917).

Criticism—M. Croiset: Litérature grecque (t. 5, 806–13, 1899).

X. ROMAN AND JEWISH LAW

PAPINIAN

Aemilius Papinianus, possibly of Syrian birth, flourished possibly at Beyrut, then at Rome; murdered by Caracalla in 212. One of the greatest Roman jurists. One of the five authorities mentioned in the Valentinian Law of Citations; his advice was preponderant. There are 601 extracts from his works and 153 citations in the "Digest." His main works are the Quaestiones (37 books) and the Responsa (19 books). He wrote one legal treatise in Greek.

Giuseppe Mantellini: Papiniano (2d edition, Roma, 1885; Sentenze, p. 113–116). Emilio Costa: Papiniano (4 vols., Bologna, 1894–1899).

ULPIAN

Domitius Ulpianus. Born near Tyre, Phoenicia, or of Tyrian origin, murdered in Alexander Severus's palace, in 228. The greatest Roman jurist. Excerpts from his works form about one-third of the "Digest" (see Justinian, first half of sixth century). The contributions of his contemporary Julius Paulus are second in importance to his and form about one-sixth of the "Digest." First mention of a probable duration of life (based on a table?[v]).

Text—Ulpiani liber singularis regularum, Pauli libri quinque sententiarum, fragmenta minora saeculorum p. Chr. n. secundi et tertii, edited by Paul Krueger (Collectio librorum iuris anteiustiniani, ed. P. Krueger, Theod. Mommsen, Wil. Studemund, tomus alter, Berlin, 1878). The Institutes of Gaius and Rules of Ulpian, with Translation, Notes, etc., by James Muirhead (654 p., Edinburgh, 1880).

PAULUS

Julius Paulus. Flourished at Rome under the Severi; he survived Ulpian, who died in 228. One of the greatest Roman jurists, and at any rate the most prolific after Ulpian. He was one of the five jurists to whom the Law of Citations, enacted by Theodosius II and Valentinian III in 426, gave special authority. A great number (70) of law books are ascribed to him; his Sententiae are abstracted in Alaric's "Breviary" (first half of sixth century), and various other fragments of it are extant. His largest work was the "Ad Edictum," in 80 books. The Digest contains 2,081 extracts from Paulus's works.[w]

Text—The Regulae Sententiae are included in Volume II of Krueger, Mommsen and Studemund's Collectio librorum juris ante-Justiniani (Berlin, 1878).

---

[v] Ad legem Falcidiam, XXXV, 2, 68 (as quoted in Cantor's Geschichte, vol. 1^3, 561). The writings of the Roman jurists offer other points of special interest to us; for instance, see my note on Julian (first half of second century).

[w] That is, more than from any other works, Ulpian's excepted, and more than a sixth of the whole Digest.

MODESTINUS

Herennius Modestinus. Originating from one of the Greek-speaking provinces, possibly from Dalmatia, died after 244. Roman jurist. Pupil of Ulpian. One of the five authoritative jurists mentioned in the Law of Citations. The "Digest" contains 344 extracts from his writings. His chief works are the "Responsa" (19 books), the Pandecton (12 books), the Regulae (10 books), the Differentiae (9 books), the Excusationes (6 books in Greek!), and the Punishments (4 books).

C. J. A. Kriegel: Antiqua versio latina fragmentorum e libro De excusationibus in digestorum lib. XXVI in integrum restituta (Diss., 85 p., Leipzig, 1830).

For Jewish Law, see my notes on Abba Arika and Mar Samuel.

CHAPTER XVIII

THE TIME OF DIOPHANTOS

(Second Half of Third Century)

I. Survey of Science in Second Half of Third Century. II. Religious Background. III. Hellenistic and Chinese Philosophy. IV. Hellenistic and Chinese Mathematics. V. Hellenistic and Chinese Chemistry and Physics. VI. Hellenistic, Roman, and Chinese Natural History. VII. Roman, Hellenistic, and Chinese Geography. VIII. Chinese Medicine. IX. Chinese Historiography. X. Roman Law. XI. Chinese and Greek Philology.

I. SURVEY OF SCIENCE IN SECOND HALF OF THIRD CENTURY

1. If Diophantos flourished in the second half of the third century, he was undoubtedly the greatest scientist of that time; indeed, he would have been one of the greatest of any time. This dating is plausible, but there is only one witness to establish it positively, and that a late one, the Byzantine scholar Psellos. It is well to keep this in mind when one speaks, as we do, of the time of Diophantos.

2. *Religious Background*—The outstanding religious fact of that age was the birth of Manichaeism. Mānī began his preaching in 242 and continued it until his execution in 276. Our interest in Manichaeism, though indirect, is very great. For a thousand years the persecuted Manichees roamed from one place to another, finding no peace anywhere except in Central Asia. Their religion was thus an important vehicle, a living connection between East and West. Its relative importance will increase probably as more of the documents discovered (or to be discovered) in the deserts of Central Asia are deciphered. The historian who is bent upon explaining the continuity of human progress must try to determine all cultural contacts between East and West; from that point of view the history of Manichaeism is full of significance.

3. *Hellenistic and Chinese Philosophy*—Neoplatonism was finally established as a definite doctrine by the great philosopher Plotinos. His "Enneads" were written in Rome, after 254, in the Greek language. It is not too much to say that Neoplatonism transformed the intellectual atmosphere; in so far as it displaced Peripateticism and Stoicism it impeded the progress of science. That transformation was radical but very gradual; both Peripateticism and Stoicism had been contaminated by Neoplatonizing tendencies long before the time of Plotinos and they continued to exist after his time. For example, the greatest of Plotinos's disciples, Porphyry, wrote an introduction to Aristotelian logic which was exceedingly popular during the Middle Ages.

The Seven Sages of the Bamboo Grove, who were flourishing at about that time, influenced considerably Chinese thought.

4. *Hellenistic and Chinese Mathematics*—This age witnessed a sort of mathematical renaissance both in China and even more distinctly in the West. Diophantos, one of the greatest mathematicians, flourished probably in that time. He might be called the father of algebra; he introduced various algebraic symbols, discovered new properties of numbers, and solved many kinds of determinate and undeterminate equations ("Diophantine Analysis"). Anatolios of Alexandria wrote

various mathematical treatises. The geometrical collection compiled by Pappos contains much information on ancient Greek geometry and a number of new conceptions and propositions, some of which of great originality (e. g., involution of points). It is possible that Heron of Alexandria flourished in the same period, shortly before Pappos. Sporos of Nicaea, who lived at the end of the century, wrote a mathematical compilation which has some historical interest.

Wang Fan found that a circumference is to its diameter as 142 to 45, which is equivalent to putting $\pi = 3.155$. Liu Hui wrote, in 263, a commentary on the "Arithmetic in Nine Sections" and he composed the "Sea-Island Arithmetic." He used red and black computing rods for positive and negative quantities.

4 bis. *Chinese and Hellenistic Astronomy*—Wang Fan replaced the celestial hemisphere used by Chang Hêng by a complete sphere.

The mathematician Anatolios wrote a treatise on the determination of Easter.

5. *Hellenistic and Chinese Chemistry and Physics*—Zosimos, the earliest writer on alchemy who can be identified and whose writings are extant, flourished probably about the end of the third century. The famous chemical papyri of Leyden and Stockholm date from about the same time.

There may be some alchemical lore in the Taoist writings of the same period, but the subject has not yet been investigated. (We know practically nothing of Chinese alchemy or chemistry.)

Porphyry wrote a commentary on Ptolemy's treatise on music. Pappos studied various mechanical problems; his calculation of the area and volume of revolutes by the centrobaric method is one of the finest fruits of ancient mathematics.

6. *Hellenistic, Roman, and Chinese Natural History*—Nemesianus wrote poems on fishing and hunting. One Caelius, who flourished probably about this time, was the author of the famous Roman treatise on cooking and confectioning called Apicius; that treatise is of some interest to the historian of botany.

The earliest mention of tea is found in the work of the historian Ch'ên Shou, who died in 297. The earliest Chinese treatise on plants, of a purely botanical character, dates also from the end of this century. It is an account of the flora of Southern China, describing some 80 species, written by Chi Han.

7. *Roman, Hellenistic, and Chinese Geography*—Solinus's compilation was one of the most popular sources of geographical information during the Middle Ages. A geography written by the great mathematician Pappos is unfortunately lost.

Tu Yü wrote a topographical commentary on Confucius's Spring and Autumn. Pei Hsiu formulated the fundamental principles of Chinese cartography, which may be said to begin with him.

8. *Chinese Medicine*—Huang Fu wrote a treatise on acupuncture, which is a fundamental branch of Chinese medicine. This treatise has been the basis of all ulterior works on the subject. Wang Shu-ho wrote a famous treatise on the pulse.

9. *Chinese Historiography*—Hsün Hsü was the main editor of the old Bamboo Annals discovered in 281; Ch'ên Shou edited the official history of the Three Kingdoms (220–80).

10. *Roman Law*—The Syrian Gregorius compiled the collection of imperial statutes called after him Codex Gregorianus.

11. *Chinese and Greek Philology*—The Chinese lexicographer Sun Yen invented the spelling system called fan ch'ieh, probably under Hindu influence.

Timaeos compiled a Platonic lexicon.

12. *Final Remarks*—If we restrict ourselves to the purely scientific subjects, this period is characterized in the first place by a magnificent mathematical activity, Diophantos and Pappos being two men of considerable genius; in the second place by a very remarkable Chinese supremacy in various other fields—botany, geography, medicine, history, philology. Indeed, this was the first time that Chinese endeavors surpassed contemporary efforts made in the West. But for the fact that Diophantos was such an outstanding personality, one that has influenced the development of mathematics down to this day, it would have been proper to give to this chapter a Chinese title. Finally, during this period a new link has been added which helped to some extent to hold together the dispersed members of mankind—Manichaeism; this was a strange link, but it worked, however humbly and secretly, for a thousand years.

II. RELIGIOUS BACKGROUND

MANI

Mānī the Zindīq;[a] Manes. Born at Hamadān? in 215–6; of Persian nationality and perhaps of Persian race, though he spoke mainly Syriac; he attended the Coronation of Shāpūr I on March 20, 242, at Seleucia-Ctesiphon and began, there and then, his preaching; he traveled extensively in India and other Eastern countries; he was executed during the reign of Bahrām I, in 276, at Gundē-Shapur. Founder of Manichaeism, a syncretistic, ascetic, cosmopolitan faith, which was essentially a kind of Christian Gnosticism colored by Mazdaism. The prophets who in Mani's opinion had preceded him were Hermes Trismegistos, Plato, the Buddhha, Zoroaster, and Jesus, this last being the most important, for Mani called himself the Apostle of Jesus Christ. The main sources of his thoughts were the writings of Bardesanes (q. v., second half of second century) and those of another Gnostic, Marcion, perhaps the most original Christian doctor of the second century.[b] Various other elements were included in the original Manichaeism (e. g., Babylonian elements) or were added to it in the course of time (e. g., Buddhist accretions, in Turkestan).

One essential feature of Manichaeism was the recognition of two eternal principles, Light and Darkness, the world in which we live being due to the mixture of both. It is because of this dualism that this religion has been sometimes considered a sort of a Christianized Mazdaism, but the Christian elements in it are undoubtedly far more important than the Zoroastrian. We must not forget that the problem of evil, the consciousness of evil in the world and in ourselves, leads easily enough to dualistic views. Whatever Christian theologians might say, it is certain that the average Christian of not so long ago, who believed in a personal devil as firmly as in a personal God, was a practical dualist. This attitude was not due, of course, to any Zoroastrian or Manichaean influence, but to an uneschewable and unexplainable fact, the existence of good and evil everywhere.

Mani composed seven theological works, six of them in Syriac, and one, the Shaburqān or Shāhpuhrakān, in Pahlawī. All were written in a peculiar script

---

[a] Zindīq is probably a variant of the Arabic al-Ṣiddīq, meaning the truthful, the faithful, a title given to fully initiate Manichees (Aramaic, Saddīqai; Persian, Zandīk.).

[b] Marcion of Sinope (southern shore of the Black Sea), flourished in Rome c. 150. On himself and Marcionism see article by N. McLean in Dictionary of Religion and Ethics (vol. 8, 407–409, 1916).

invented by himself.[c] These writings are known indirectly through various criticisms of them written in Greek, Latin, Syriac, and Arabic and directly through many fragments found in Chinese Turkestan. These fragments are written in Soghdian (a kind of Middle Persian), Early Turkish, and Chinese. All of the Soghdian and most of the Turkish documents can be identified immediately, for they are written in Manichaean script.

The influence of Manichaism was considerable for a thousand years. The Manichees were equally execrated by Jews, Zoroastrians, Christians, and Muslims. This was possibly due to their syncretism and even more to their extreme asceticism, for the world has never been able to bear patiently with people who took their religion too seriously. Whatever the cause of the persecutions, these contributed to spread the Manichees over an immense area, and the hated religion thus became a vehicle of civilization, a new link between East and West. I will quote a few facts, among many, to illustrate the extent of Manichaeism in space and time, and its importance as a transmitting agency.

St. Augustine (q. v., first half of the fifth century) was a Manichee from 373 to 382, and some traces of Manichaean influence may be found even in his later writings. The Buddhist tradition contained in the famous story of Barlaam and Ioasaph (q. v., my note on John of Damascus, first half of the eighth century) reached the West through a Manichaean channel. (A. von Le Coq, in Sitzungsberichte of the Prussian Academy, 1909). Ibn al-Nadīm (q. v., second half of the tenth century) gives a long account of Mani and his writings in the Fihrist (988); he knew three hundred Manichees in Bagdad alone. Al-Bīrūnī (q. v., first half of the eleventh century) declares that "most of the Eastern Turks, of the people of China and Tibet, and some of the Hindus, adhere to Mani's law and doctrine." We know from other sources that Manichaeism was the state religion of the Uighurs, whose capital was in Turfan; it is there that so many Manichaean fragments have been discovered. Early printed editions of the Taoist canon (for which see my note on Fêng Tao, first half of the tenth century) contain two books of the Manichaean scriptures! The Albigensian heresy (q. v., twelfth century) was influenced to some extent by Manichaeism. It is in Central Asia that the Manichees were most influential, and it is especially for the understanding of all cultural exchange involving Central Asia, that one must take full account of that religion, but the examples which have been given show that it really extended from China to France.

The purely scientific interest of Manichaean literature seems very small. Their cosmological views were very crude. In the Khuastuanift, a Turkish Manichaean writing, relatively recent, discovered by Sir Aurel Stein in Tung-Huang, animals are subdivided into five kinds: men, quadrupeds, animals that fly in the air, animals that live in the water, and lastly, those that creep on the earth. (Augustine knows the same classification.)

Texts—Prosper Alfaric: Les écritures manichéennes (2 vols., Paris, 1918; Isis, V, 304). The best guide as far as it goes, but various texts have been published since; for example, A. von Lecoq: Dr. Stein's Turkish Khuastuanift, being a confession prayer of the Manichaean auditores (Journal R. Asiatic Soc., 1, 277–314, 1911. Text edited with translation, notes, glossary and facsimile).

Commentary—Isaac de Beausobre: Histoire critique de Manichée et du Mani-

[c] I have already indicated the great religious importance attached to script (vs. language) by Eastern peoples. See my note on the Jewish Scriptures in first half of third century B. C.

chéisme (2 vols., Amsterdam, 1734–1739. Monumental work now superseded). Gustav Flügel: Mani, seine Lehre und seine Schriften. Aus dem Fihrist im Text nebst Übersetzung, Commentar und Index (Leipzig, 1862). Alexius Geyler: Das System des Manichaeismus und sein Verhältnis zum Buddhismus (Diss., 62 p., Jena, 1875). E. G. Browne: Literary History of Persia (vol. 1, 154–166, 1908). Em. De Stoop: La diffusion du Manichéisme dans l'empire romain (Gand, 1909). F. Cumont et A. Kugener: Recherches sur le Manichéisme (Bruxelles, 1908–1912). A. A. Bevan: Article Manichaeism (Dictionary of Religion and Ethics, vol. 8, 394–402, 1916). Sigurd Lindquist: Manikeismens religions-historiska ställning (Upsala, 1921). A. von Lecoq: Die Buddhistische Spätantike im Mittelasien (Berlin, 1922–1924, Isis, VIII, 790). F. C. Burkitt: The Religion of the Manichees (138 p., Cambridge, 1925; Isis, VIII, 647; the author lays stress upon the Christian sources of Mani).

III. HELLENISTIC AND CHINESE PHILOSOPHY

PLOTINOS

Πλωτῖνος. Born at Lycopolis in Egypt c. 203; he came to Rome in 244; died in 270 in Campania. Greek philosopher. Founder of the Neo-Platonic school (in Rome!). His 54 books, written after 254, were arranged by Porphyry in six Enneads (six sets of nine). His work contains little of direct interest to the scientist, but it transformed the scientific atmosphere.

Text and Translations—Enneades cum Marsilii Ficini interpretatione castigata iterum edid. Fried. Creuzer et G. H. Mozer. Primum accedunt Porphyrii et Procli institutiones et Prisciani philosophi solutiones (Paris, 1896). English translation by Kenneth Sylvan Guthrie, with the biographies by Porphyry, Eunapios, and Suidas and various commentaries (4 vols., London, 1918). The Ethical Treatises (first ennead), with Porphyry's Life and the Preller-Ritter Extracts forming a Conspectus of the Plotinian System (translation by Stephen MacKenna, London, 1917); translation of the fourth ennead by the same (160 p., London, 1924). French translation by M. N. Bouillet (3 vols., Paris, 1857–1861). Greek text with French translation by Emile Bréhier (Paris, 1924; Isis, VII, 534). German translation (selections) by Otto Kiefer (1905).

General Criticism—There is a very abundant literature on Plotinos, especially on his esthetics. I quote only a few general studies. Arthur Drews: Plotin und der Untergang der antiken Weltanschauung (352 p., Jena, 1907). Will. Ralph Inge: The Philosophy of Plotinus (2 vols., 553 p., London, 1918; second edition, 1923). H. F. Müller: Dionysios, Proklos, Plotinos: ein historischer Beitrag zur neuplatonischen Philosophie (Beitr. zur Gesch. d. Philos. d. Mittelalters, 20, Münster i. W., 1918).

Special Criticism—P. Duhem: Système du Monde (t. 2, p. 309, 1914, ses idées astrologiques: les astres ne sont pas des causes mais des signes; p. 318; t. 4, 1916, p. 376, théorie de l'intelligence humaine). Franz Cumont: Comment Plotin détourna Porphyre du suicide (Revue des études grecques, t. 32, 113–120, 1919). Fritz Heinemann: Plotin. Forschungen über die Plotinische Frage; Plotins Entwicklung und seine System (332 p., Leipzig, 1921).

PORPHYRY

Πορφύριος, alias Malchos. Born in 233 either in Batanea in Palestine or at Tyre, came to Rome in 264 and flourished there until his death c. 304. Pupil of Plotinos; Neoplatonic philosopher. Wrote commentaries upon Plotinos, upon Ptolemy's treatise on music, upon Aristotle's Categories. The latter, translated into Latin by Boetius, was a popular vehicle of Aristotelian logic during the Middle Ages. He wrote lives of Pythagoras and Plotinos.

Text and Translations—There is no complete edition or translation of Porphyry's work. I quote here a few separate writings, reserving his "Isagoge" for the following paragraph. The Pythagorae vita was edited by Westermann in Greek and Latin and appended to Diogenes Laertios: De clarorum philosophorum vitis (II, 87–101, 1850). The In harmonica Ptolemaei commentarius was edited for the first time by John Wallis, in his Opera mathematica (III, 183 sq., 1695, with Latin translation).

Introduction to Aristotle's Categories—Boethii in isagogen Porphyrii commenta, edited by Georg Schepss and Samuel Brandt: Corpus scriptorum ecclesiasticorum latinorum (vol. 48, 509 p., Vienna, 1906). Various other commentaries have been published in the Commentaria in Aristotelem graeca, all edited by Ad. Busse: Ammonios son of Hermias (end of fifth century) (Vol. IV, 3, 1891); Elias Philosophos (sixth century?), (Vol. XVIII, 1, 1900); David Thessalonicensis (Vol. XVIII, 2, 1904).

Adolf Busse: Die neuplatonischen Ausleger der Isagoge des Porphyrius (Progr. 23 p., Berlin, 1892). Fred. Cornwallis Conybeare: A Collation with the Ancient Armenian Versions of the Greek Text of Aristotle's Categories, ... and of Porphyry's Introduction (Anecdota oxoniensia, Vol. I, 6, 224 p., Oxford, 1892). Anton Baumstark: Syrisch-arabische Biographien des Aristoteles. Syrische Commentare zur εἰσαγωγή des Porphyrios (Leipzig, 1900).

General Criticism—Marcus Gazensis: Vita Porphyrii episcopi gazensis (Leipzig, 1895. English translation by G. F. Hill, Oxford, 1913). J. Bidez: Vie de Porphyre (250 p., Gand, 1913. Very elaborate, with many texts quoted in full in the appendices).

Special Criticism—Bruno Mommert: Porphyrii sententiae ad intelligibilia ducentes (*ἀφορμαὶ πρὸς τὰ νοητά*) (Diss., 34 p., Leipzig, 1907. That is, Porphyry's commentary upon Plotinos). P. Duhem: Système du Monde (t. 4, p. 376, 1916. Théorie de l'intelligence humaine).

Tradition—The Isagoge was translated into Syriac at least three times between the middle of the fifth and the middle of the seventh century. The earliest Syriac commentaries are independent from that of Ammonios (q. v., first half of sixth century). On this Syriac tradition, see R. Duval: Littérature syriaque (3e ed., 246, 1907).

For the Muslim tradition of the εἰσαγωγή see the article īsāghūdjī in the Encyclopedia of Islam (vol. 2, 527, 1921), by Moh. ben Cheneb. Many translations and adaptations of it were published in Arabic.

CHI K'ANG

Chi[1] K'ang[1] (884, 5908). Born in Anhui 223, executed in 262. Taoist philosopher and "alchemist." One of the "Seven Sages of the Bamboo Grove," Chu[2]* lin[2] ch'i[1]* hsien[2] (2616, 7157, 1055, 4513), who flourished in Yüan[2] wu[3] (13700, 12744), Honan, the others being Juan[3] Chi[2]* (5713, 899), Shan[1] T'ao[1] (9663, 10833), Hsiang[4] Hsiu[4] (4283, 4675), Liu[2] Ling[2] (7270, 7200), Juan[3] Hsien[2] (5713, 4498), and Wang[2] Jung[2] (12493, 5746). The philosophy of these men was a matter of temperament rather than doctrine; they were distinguished by extreme individualism combined with quietism. To call them "alchemists" is misleading, unless one takes the term in a very broad acception as Chinese (and Muslims) often did. We might say that their concern was the alchemy of happiness.[d] Their attitude influenced Chinese thought and art considerably.

H. A. Giles: Chinese Biographical Dictionary (p. 119, 1898); History of Chinese Literature (p. 125, 1901). Delightful details on the Seven Sages, and especially

---

[d] I use the Arabic phrase: Kīmīyā-l-sa'ādati.

on Chi K'ang, may be found in Agnes E. Meyer: Chinese Painting (74–81, New York, 1923. This includes a translation of the famous letter addressed by Chi K'ang to another of the Seven Sages, Shan T'ao, severing their friendship; Isis, VII, 145–147).

IV. HELLENISTIC AND CHINESE MATHEMATICS

DIOPHANTOS

Diophantos of Alexandria. Διόφαντος. Flourished in the second half of the third century.[e] Greek mathematician; the greatest Greek writer on algebra; one of the greatest algebraists of all times. He might be called the father of algebra. His main work was the Arithmetica, of which we have 6 of the original 13 books; we have also part of his tract on Polygonal Numbers; his Porisms are lost. His "Arithmetica" is a collection of problems leading, some of them, to determinate equations of the first degree with as many as four variables, to determinate quadratic equations and even to one cubic equation;[f] the greatest number, however, lead to indeterminate equations (hence indeterminate analysis is often called Diophantine analysis). Diophantos solved (in rational numbers) indeterminate equations of the second, third, and fourth degrees and even one (an easy one) of the sixth degree. He introduced symbols for minus (⁄|\), for the unknown quantity, called ἀριθμός (ς), and for its powers up to the fourth. Various new properties of numbers were discovered by him: e. g., the difference between two cubes can be resolved into the sum of two cubes; no number of the form $8n + 7$ can be the sum of three squares; if $2n + 1$ is to be the sum of two squares, n must not be odd.

Text and Translations—Many problems of Diophantos were translated in Bombelli's Algebra (1572). First Latin translation of Diophantos by Xylander (Wilh. Holtzmann, Bale, 1575). First Greek edition by Bachet de Méziriac (Paris, 1621); a bad reprint of this text (Toulouse, 1670) is of great value because of the notes added to it by P. de Fermat (reprinted in the Oeuvres de Fermat, ed. by P. Tannery, Vol. I, 1891). Scientific edition by Paul Tannery, with Greek commentaries and Latin translation (2 vols., Leipzig, 1893–1895). First English translation with commentary, by Sir Thomas Heath (1885); new edition vastly enlarged and improved (1910, see below). G. Massoutié: Le traité des nombres polygonaux de Diophante (Trad. française avec une introduction, 32 p., Paris, 1911). German translation of all of Diophantos's works, by G. Wertheim, with notes (356 p., Leipzig, 1890).

General Criticism—The following book is fundamental. Sir Thomas L. Heath: Diophantus of Alexandria. A Study in the History of Greek Algebra. Second edition with a supplement containing an account of Fermat's theorems and problems connected with Diophantine analysis and some solutions of Diophantine problems by Euler (395 p., Cambridge, 1910). This study is so exhaustive that it is superfluous to quote other studies anterior to it. I should mention, however, that many papers on Diophantos by Paul Tannery, dating from 1879 to 1892, will be found in his Mémoires (Vol. I, 62–73; Vol. II, 64–90, 269–301, 367–399, 418–439; Vol. III, 355–358; Isis, I, 114, 509; IV, 338). See also F. Hultsch, in Pauly-Wissowa (vol. 5, 1052–1073, 1903) and G. Milhaud: Etude sur Diophante (Revue générale des sciences, t. 22, 749–752, 1911. Apropos of Heath's book). C. Büchel: Die Arithmetica des Diophant (Progr., 38 p., Hamburg, 1912).

---

[e] According to Psellos, Anatolios's treatise on the Egyptian method of reckoning was dedicated to Diophantos; our dating of Diophantos's activity is based upon this single fact.

[f] $x^3 + x = 4x^2 + 4$.

Special Criticism—Much historical information on particular problems will be found in L. E. Dickson: History of the Theory of Numbers. Vol. II. Diophantine analysis. (Carnegie Inst. Washington, 830 p., 1920; Isis, IV, 107.)

ANATOLIOS

Anatolios of Alexandria. Ἀνατόλιος. Greek chronologist and mathematician. Professor of Aristotelian philosophy in Alexandria, then, in 269, Bishop of Laodicea, in Syria. He wrote a manual of arithmetic (ἀριθμητικαὶ εἰσαγωγαί) in 10 books; he wrote also on mathematics in general; on the determination of Easter; on the Egyptian method of reckoning.

Text and Translations—Fragments of his arithmetic are preserved in the Θεολογούμενα τῆς ἀριθμητικῆς (edition by Friedrich Ast, Leipzig, 1817). Anatolius sur la décade et les nombres qu'elle comprend (περὶ δεκάδος καὶ τῶν ἐντὸς αὐτῆς ἀριθμῶν), edited by J. L. Heiberg with French translation and notes by Paul Tannery (Congrès d'histoire des sciences, p. 27–57, Paris, 1900; Mémoires, III, 12–31, with two appendixes).

Criticism—P. Tannery, in Grande Encyclopédie (c. 1887; Mémoires, III, 321–322). Hultsch, in Pauly-Wissowa (vol. 2, col. 2073–2074, 1894). G. Borghorst: De Anatolii fontibus (Diss., Berlin, 1904. Not seen).

It is possible that Heron of Alexandria, whom I placed tentatively in the first half of the first century B. C., flourished as late as the second half of the third century after Christ, but before Pappos.

PAPPOS

Pappos of Alexandria. Πάππος. Flourished probably under Diocletian, who ruled from 284 to 305. Greek geometer. His main work is his "Mathematical Collection" (συναγωγή) in eight books (the greatest part of Books II to VIII is extant), a systematic account of previous research, equally valuable for the historical information it contains and for the additional explanations. New propositions on the quadratrix and on curves of double curvature. Focus of the parabola. Definition of conic sections by means of the directrix. Involution of points. Problem of Pappos: given several straight lines in a plane, to find the locus of a point such that when straight lines are drawn from it to the given lines at a given angle, the product of certain of the segments shall be in a given ratio to the product of the remaining ones. Theory of the seven simple machines. Theory of the center of gravity, including the centrobaric method of calculating area and volume of revolutes (improperly called Guldin's properties).[g] Pappos wrote many other books which are lost, e. g., a geography (χωρογραφία οἰκουμενική), commentaries on Euclid's elements (the commentary to Book X exists in Arabic), and on Ptolemy's Almagest and Harmonics.

Text and Translations—First Latin edition by Commandino (Pesaro, 1588). First complete Greek and Latin edition by Fr. Hultsch (3 vols., Berlin, 1876–1878, with notes). There are also a few partial editions, e.g., in Commandino's Latin editions of Apollonios (Bologna, 1566) and Aristarchos (Pesaro, 1572); also in John Wallis's edition of Aristarchos (Oxford, 1688; reprinted in Vol. III of his Opera mathem., 1695). There is no complete translation in any modern language, but C. I. Gerhardt has published a German translation of Books VII and VIII (Halle, 1871). See also Michel Chasles: Les trois livres de porismes d'Euclide rétablis pour la

[g] They were rediscovered by Habakkuk (Paul) Guldin and published in his Centrobaryca 1641 (Vienna, 1635–1641).

première fois d'après la notice et les lemmes de Pappos (333 p., Paris, 1860). Heinrich Suter: Der Kommentar des Pappus zum X. Buche des Euklides aus der arabischen Übersetzung des Abū 'Othmān al-Dimashqī (q. v., first half of tenth century) (German translation. Abhdl. zur Gesch. der Naturwiss., Heft 4, 9–78, Erlangen, 1922; Isis, V, 492). An English translation of Pappos's works, with full commentary, is very much needed.

Criticism—See N. Khanikoff's edition of Al Khāzinī's Book of the Balance of Wisdom (Journal Am. Or. Soc., vol. 6, 1–128, 1860). It contains many references to Pappos, including the suggestion that Pappos invented the areometer. (This invention was made probably in the third century.) Paul Tannery: L'arithmétique des Grecs dans Pappus (Mém. de la soc. des sciences physiques de Bordeaux, t. 3, 351–371, 1880; Mémoires, t. 1, 80–105). S. Günther: Über eine merkwürdige Beziehung zwischen Pappus und Kepler (Bibliotheca mathematica, 81–87, 1888). J. S. MacKay: Pappus on the Progressions (Proc. Math. Soc. of Edinburgh, vol. 6, 48–58, 1888). P. Tannery: Note sur le problème de Pappus (Oeuvres de Descartes (Adam et Tannery), t. 6, 721–725, 1902; Mémoires, III, 42–50). J. H. Weaver: Pappus (Bull. Amer. Math. Soc., vol. 23, 127–135); On Foci of Conics (*ibidem*, 357–361, 1916–7. Important). Jos. Fischer: Pappus und die Ptolemäuskarten (Zeit. d. Ges. f. Erdkunde zu Berlin, 336–358, 1919. Important; Isis IV, 131).

SPOROS

Sporos of Nicaea. *Σπόρος*. Flourished toward the end of the third century. Greek mathematician. Author of a compilation, called *'Αριστοτελικὰ κηρία*, containing information on the quadrature of the circle and the duplication of the cube.

P. Tannery: Sur Sporos de Nicée (Annales de la faculté des lettres de Bordeaux, t. 4, 257–261, 1882; Mémoires, t. 1, 178–184). Sir Thomas L. Heath: History of Greek Mathematics (t. 1, 1921).

WANG FAN

Wang[2] Fan[2] (12493, 3392). Born c. 229, murdered after 264. Flourished in the Kingdom of Wu. Chinese astronomer and mathematician; Buddhist. If the circumference of a circle be 142, then the diameter should be 45 (equivalent to taking $\pi = 3.1555$). Wang's chief merit was to replace the celestial hemisphere still used by Chang Hêng (q. v., first half of second century) by a complete celestial sphere, the earth being in its center and the equator and ecliptic differentiated. This was a natural development of the ideas of Liu Hung (q. v., second half of second century).

Y. Mikami: Development of Mathematics in China and Japan (p. 46–7, 57, Leipzig, 1913). L. Wieger: La Chine (127, 457, 1920). A. Forke: World Conception of the Chinese (20, 1925; Isis, VIII, 373).

LIU HUI

Liu[2] Hui[1] (7270, 5160). Flourished in the Kingdom of Wei[h] toward the end of the period of the Three Kingdoms (221 to 265). Chinese mathematician. In 263 he wrote a commentary on the "Arithmetic in Nine Sections" (Chiu-chang suan-chu), and he composed himself the "Sea-Island Arithmetical Classic," Hai[3]-tao[3] suan[4]-ching[1] (3767, 10790, 10378, 2122),[i] so-called because its first

---

[h] Or in Wu? (Wieger: La Chine (127, 352, 1920)).

[i] It is probable that this was originally a part of the preceding commentary. It was commented upon by Li Sh'un-fêng (q. v., second half of seventh century).

problem deals with the measurement of an island from a distance. The problems of this book imply some knowledge of algebra. He used red computing rods for the positive (chêng) quantities and black rods for the negative (fu).[j]

Text—The text of the Hai-tao, even as that of the Chiu-chang, was reconstructed after being extracted piecemeal from the Yung Lo Ta-tien.

Criticism—A. Wylie: Chinese Literature (1867, 113, 1902). Y. Mikami: Development of Mathematics in China (chapter 5, 1913).

V. HELLENISTIC AND CHINESE CHEMISTRY AND PHYSICS

ZOSIMOS

Zosimos of Panopolis, Upper Egypt. Ζώσιμος. Flourished about the end of the third century or possibly in the fourth. He quotes Porphyry and is quoted by Synesios. Greek author of alchemical, magical, and mystical writings. His main work was an encyclopaedia of the chemical arts in 28 books. He is the earliest writer on alchemy of whom we have genuine writings and whom we can identify, but his encyclopaedia was at least in part an amalgamation of older writings. For example, his description of distillatory apparatus is borrowed from Cleopatra or from some contemporary of hers. A book on beer-brewing is also ascribed to him.

Text and Translations—The whole of Berthelot and Ruelle's Collection des anciens alchimistes grecs, Seconde livraison (Paris, 1888, Greek text, French translation and notes) is devoted to Zosimos. See also Berthelot and Duval's L'alchimie syriaque (La chimie au moyen age, t. II, Paris, 1893).

For the treatise on beer-brewing, see Chr. Gott. Gruner: Zosimi de zythorum confectione fragmentum, nunc primum graece ac latine editum. Accedit historia zythorum sive cerevisiarum quarum apud veteres mentio fit (128 p., Sulzbach, 1814).

Criticism—M. Berthelot: Les origines de l'alchimie (Paris, 1885). Ed. O. von Lippmann: Über das erste Vorkommen des Namens Chemie (Chemiker Zeitung, p. 685, 1914); the first to use the term χημεία or an equivalent was not Firmicus Maternus, but Zosimos (see Isis, III, 321; Alchemie 1919, p. 75–93, 337–339). Mrs. Ingeborg Hammer-Jensen: Die älteste Alchemie (Danish Ac. of sciences, 1921; Isis IV, 523–530).

EARLY CHEMICAL PAPYRI

Two chemical papyri formerly owned by Johan d'Anastasy and now respectively kept in Leyden and Stockholm are of fundamental importance. They have the same origin and date of the same time, probably the third century. They contain various chemical and technical recipes—which may be much older—and give one a good idea of the Egyptian knowledge of chemistry or alchemy in Roman times.

Text and Translations: Leyden Papyrus—Conrad Leemans: Papyri graeci musei antiquarii publici Lugduni-Batavi (Tomus II, Leyden, 1885. Edited with Latin translation, notes and indexes. Our papyrus is "Papyrus X" (read eks, not ten); it is published and translated on p. 204–249; notes, p. 250–259). Translation into French with long commentary by Marcellin Berthelot and Ch. Em. Ruelle: Collection des anciens alchimistes grecs (t. 1, p. 3–73, Paris, 1887).

---

[j] Thus following probably an older tradition. See my note on Chang Ts'ang (first half of second century B. C.). The computing rods are called by the Chinese ch'ou[2] (2493); the Japanese call them sangi.

Stockholm Papyrus—Otto Lagercrantz: Papyrus graecus Holmiensis (P. Holm.). Recepte für Silber, Steine, und Purpur (248 p., Upsala, 1913, text p. 3–42, followed by an elaborate commentary and indexes).

Criticism—Hermann Diels: Eine Inkunabel der Chemie (Deutsche Literaturzeitung, 34, 901–906, 1913). Mme. Ingeborg Hammer-Jensen: Deux papyrus à contenu d'ordre chimique (Bull. de l'académie des sciences, 279–302, Copenhague, 1916; Isis, IV, 398). Ed. O. von Lippmann: Über chemische Papyri des 3. Jahrhundertes nr. Chr. (Chemiker Zeitung, 933 sq., Cöthen, 1913; p. 589 sq., 1917; Isis, III, 320; V, 492); Entstehung und Ausbreitung der Alchemie (p. 1–27, Berlin, 1919).

See also my notes on Chemistry in the first half of the first century. For the papyri Kenyon and Africanus see Lippmann (op. cit., p. 73–75).

For Chinese "alchemy," see my note on Chi K'ang in Section III.

For Hellenistic physics, see my notes on Porphyry and Pappos in Sections III and IV.

VI. ROMAN, HELLENISTIC, AND CHINESE NATURAL HISTORY

NEMESIANUS

Marcus Aurelius Olympius Nemesianus, of Carthage, flourished at the court of the emperor Carus, 282–83. Roman poet. Author of poems upon fishing and hunting. A fragment of the latter (Cynegetica, 325 hexameters) is extant.

Text—E. Baehrens: Poetae lat. min., 1879. The eclogues of Calpurnius Siculus and M. A. O. Nemesianus, edited by C. H. Keene (London, 1887). Calpurnii et Nemesiani bucolica, edited by Caesar Giarratano (Naples, 1910).

Criticism—Marthe Conor: Un texte de Némésien de Carthage sur la pathologie canine (rage et piroplasmose) (Archives de l'Institut Pasteur de Tunis, p. 131–135, 1912). Donnis Martin: The Cynegetica of Nemesianus (Thesis, with text, Cornell University, 1917).

CAELIUS

Unknown author of a treatise on cooking and confectioning named "Apicius," after a famous gourmet, M. Gabius Apicius, who flourished under Tiberius (14 to 37). This treatise, divided into ten books (with Greek titles), can hardly be earlier than the third century. It offers some scientific interest, for example from the botanical point of view.

Text—Caelii Apicius de opsoniis et condimentis sive de arte (de re) coquinaria. Princeps by Guilelmus Signerte (Milano, 1498). Edition by Blasius Lancilotus (Venice, 1503). Edition with commentary by Gabriel Hummelberger (Zurich, 1542). Edition with commentary by Martin Lister (245 p., London, 1705); this commentary reprinted in the edition of Theod. Jans van Almeloveen (295 p., Amsterdam, 1709). New editions by Chr. Theophil. Schuch (202 p., Heidelberg, 1867), and by Cesare Giarratano and Fr. Vollmer (96 p., Leipzig, 1922; Isis, V, 491).

Criticism—J. H. Dierbach: Flora apiciana (83 p., Heidelberg, 1831). E. H. F. Meyer: Geschichte der Botanik (vol. 2, 236–49, 1855, including a list of plants). M. Wellmann, in Pauly-Wissowa (vol. 5, 1254, 1897). C. Giarratano: I codici dei libri De re coquinaria de Celio (18 p., Naples, 1912). Friedrich Vollmer: Studien zu dem römischen Kochbuche von Apicius (Sitzungsber. der Bayer. Akad. der Wiss., 47 p., 1920).

CHI HAN

Chi[1] Han[2] (884, 3818). Minister of state under the Western Chin emperor Hui-Ti, who ruled from 290 to 307. Chinese botanist. Author of the earliest

Chinese work dealing with plants and bearing a purely botanical character. It is called Nan[2] fang[1] ts'ao[3] mu[4]* chuang[4] (8128, 3435, 11634, 8077, 2756) (Account of the Flora of the Southern Regions) and contains accounts of 80 species known at that time in South China. They are classified into four groups—herbs, forest-trees, fruit-trees, and bamboos.

E. Bretschneider: Botanicon sinicum (Part I, Journal, N. China branch of R. A. S., vol. 16, 38–39, 1881, including a list of many of the plants described).

For Ch'ên Shou, whose work contains the earliest mention of tea, see Section IX.

VII. ROMAN, HELLENISTIC, AND CHINESE GEOGRAPHY

SOLINUS

Caius Julius Solinus. Flourished in the third century, probably in the third quarter. Author of a geographical compilation, mainly derived from Pliny and Mela. It is of very little value, but it exerted a great influence during the Middle Ages (for example, upon Isidore of Seville and Brunetto Latini). Its original title was "Collectanea rerum memorabilium," but the Middle Ages knew it under the title "Polyhistor seu de mirabilibus mundi," given to it by a sixth century editor. Solinus is the only ancient writer who mentions the English Isle of Thanet (Tanatus insula).

Text and Translations—Theodosios the Younger, Roman Emperor of the East until his death in 450, engrossed himself a copy of Solinus's work. Many incunabula editions, the first being probably that of Venice, 1473 (there are at least two undated editions which may be earlier). Critical edition by Th. Mommsen (Berlin, 1864; revised, 382 p., 1895). English translation by Arthur Golding (1587).
Criticism—The bulky commentary by Claude de Saumaise: Plinianae exercitationes in Solini polyhistora (Paris, 1629; also 1689) may still be of use. E. H. F. Meyer: Geschichte der Botanik (vol. 2, 249–252, 1855). Fragments of an index to Solinus have been published by Friedrich Lederer (Gymn. Progr., Bayreuth, 1901, 1902, 1909, 1910). Fried. Rabenald: Quaestiones solinianae (Diss., 137 p., Halle a. S., 1909. On Solinus's sources and his method of compilation).

For Pappos's Geography, see my note on Pappos in Section IV. That work is lost, but we can form some idea of it through another, which was largely based upon it, the geography ascribed to Moses of Chorene (q. v., first half of the fifth century).

TU YÜ

Tu[4]-Yü[4] (12043, 13675). Born at Tu[4]-ling[2] (12043, 7235), Shensi, 222, flourished under the first Chin[4] (2070) emperor, Wu[3] Ti[4] (12744, 10942); died in 284. Chinese scholar. Author of the Ch'un[1] Ch'iu[1] shih[4]*-li[4] t'u[3]-ti[4] ming[2] (2854, 2302, 9983, 7006, 12099, 10956, 7940), a topographical commentary on the Ch'un Ch'iu.[k]

H. A. Giles: Biographical Dictionary (785, 1898). L. Wieger: La Chine (440, 532, 1920).

PEI HSIU

Pei[2] Hsiu[4] (8831, 4675). Born in 224; died in 271. Chinese statesman and geographer. The father of scientific cartography in China. He was the first in his country to formulate the fundamental principles of cartography. In 267 he was appointed minister of public works to the first Chin emperor.

[k] The Annals of Lu from 722 to 481 B. C. See Confucius (sixth century B. C.).

Ed. Chavannes: Les deux plus anciens spécimens de la cartographie chinoise (Bull. de l'Ecole franc. d'Extrême-Orient, t. 3, 214–247, 3 maps, Hanoi, 1903; see p. 241 sq.; with a translation of the relevant text, ch. 35 of the Chin Shu in which these principles are explained). I quote briefly these principles, using Chavannes's own words: "Pour dresser une carte il y a six principes: 1° les divisions rectilignes; 2° l'orientation exacte; 3° les li de route; 4° le haut et le bas; 5° les angles droits et les obliques; 6° les courbes et les droites."

VIII. CHINESE MEDICINE

HUANG FU

Huang^2 Fu^3 (5106, 3624), also called Shih^4 An^1 (9992, 44). Flourished under the Chin^4 (2070) dynasty, c. 215 to 282. Chinese physician. Confucianist. His most famous work is a treatise on acupuncture, called Chia-i-ching[l] which became the fountain-head of all ulterior works on the subject; it was based itself upon older works. It is divided into 128 chapters and 12 chüan^4 (3146) as follows: (1, 2) Anatomy, physiology; (3) the 354 spots for acupuncture; (4) pulse, etc.; (5) places where acupuncture is forbidden; (6–12) pathology, ending with women's and children's diseases.

F. Huebotter: Guide (21–2, Kumamoto, 1924).

WANG SHU-HO

Wang^2 Shu^{2*}-ho^2 (12493, 10039, 3945). Flourished under the Western Chin^4 (2070) dynasty, 265 to 317. Chinese physician. Author of a celebrated treatise on the pulse Mo^{4*} Ching^1 (8011, 2122) in ten books.[m]

Text—German translation in course of preparation (Nov., 1924) by Franz Huebotter.

Criticism—A. Wylie: Notes on Chinese Literature (1867, 2d edition, Shanghai, 1902, p. 97). F. Huebotter: Guide (23–24, Kumamoto, 1924).

IX. CHINESE HISTORIOGRAPHY

HSÜN HSÜ

Hsün^2 Hsü^{4*} (4875, 4740). Born at Ying^3-chou^1 (13336, 2444) in Anhui; flourished under the Wei^4 (12567) dynasty and under the Emperor Wu^3 Ti^4 (12744, 10942) of the Chin^4 (2070); died in 289. Chinese scholar. Main editor of the Annals of the Bamboo Books discovered in 281.[n] He also edited the Mu^{4*} t'ien^1-tzŭ^3-ch'uan^2 (8082, 11208, 12817, 2740), purporting to be an account of the visit of the Chou emperor Mu^{4*} Wang^2 (8082, 12493) (d. 946 B. C.) to the Royal Lady of the West, Hsi^1 Wang^2 Mu^3 (4031, 12493, 8067).

H. A. Giles: Biographical Dictionary (314, 1898). L. Wieger: La Chine (398, 512, 530, 1920).

---

[l] The full title reads: Huang^2-ti^4 chên^1-chiu^3 chia^{3*}-i^{4*}-ching^1 (5124, 10942, 615, 2275, 1167, 5341, 2122).

[m] Revised and published in 1068 by Lin^2 I^4 (7157, 5368). Often reprinted. Another treatise on the same subject, but more popular, has been mistaken for the Mo ching and wrongly ascribed to Wang Shu-ho. A Ming revision of this second treatise, translated by Father Hervieu, was included in J. B. Du Halde's Description de la Chine, 1735.

[n] For which see my note on Chinese historiography in the first half of the third century B. C.

CH'ÊN SHOU

Ch'ên[2] Shou[4] (658, 10019). Native of Ssŭch'uan, born in 233; died in 297. Chinese historian. Under the Chin dynasty he edited the official history of the Three Kingdoms (220–80).[o] This work, called San[1] kuo[2*] chih[4] (9552, 6609, 1918), is the fourth of the Twenty-four Histories. It contains the earliest mention of tea.[p]

Text—Chinese edition (Nanking, 1870, 65 chüan in 8 vols.).
Criticism—Wylie: Chinese Literature (18, 1902). Giles: Biographical Dictionary (100, 1898).

X. ROMAN LAW

GREGORIUS

Professor at the law school of Beirut (?), about the end of the third century. Roman jurist. Author of a collection of imperial statutes (constitutiones) from Hadrian to Diocletian, called the Codex Gregorianus.

Text—Fragments edited by Krüger in the Collectio Juris Antejustiniani (vol. 3, 236 sq., Berlin, 1895).

XI. CHINESE AND GREEK PHILOLOGY

SUN YEN

Sun[1] Yen[2] (10431, 13069) or Sun Shu[2*]-jan[2] (10039, 5551).[q] Native of Lo[4*]-an[1] (7331, 44), Shantung; flourished in the third century, probably c. 270. Chinese lexicographer. Under the influence of Sanskrit learning,[r] he introduced the spelling system called fan[3] ch'ieh[4*] (3413, 1552). This is a way of representing the pronunciation of a character by means of two others indicating respectively the initial and final sounds. He wrote commentaries on the Classics.

H. A. Giles: Biographical Dictionary (694, 1898). L. Wieger: La Chine (391, 1920).

TIMAEOS

Τίμαιος. Flourished probably about the end of the third century. Greek lexicographer. Author of a lexicon to Plato (Τιμαίου σοφιστοῦ περὶ τῶν παρὰ Πλάτωνι λέξεων).

Text—The Lexicum vocum platonicarum was edited by David Ruhnkenius for the first time (Leyden, 1754; again in 1789. Third, posthumous, edition by the same, London, 1824. Fourth edition, Leipzig, 1828.)

---

[o] That is, Shu[3*], Wei[4], and Wu[2] (10057, 12567, 12748). Shu was in the west (modern Ssŭch'uan), and had its capital at Ch'êng[2]-tu[1] (762, 12050). It lasted less than the other kingdoms (221–64), yet is generally considered the legitimate successor of the Han dynasty and is called, because of that, the Minor Han. Wei (220–65) in the center and north had its capital at Lo[4*]-Yang[2] (7328, 12883). Wu (229–80), south of the Yangtze, had its capital at Nanking.

[p] In the biography of Wei[2] Chao[1] (12527, 473) who died in 273. (He is called in that biography Wei[2] Yao[4] (12954). Chao was his original name, but it happened to be also the name of Ssŭ-ma Chao, the father of the first emperor of the Chin dynasty. Hence to show reverence for the emperor, Wei Chao's name was changed by the author of the San kuo chih to Wei Yao). Tea did not become generally known in North China until about the tenth century. First mention in European literature, 1588.

[q] Yen was his official name; Shu-jan, his private name. It is better to call him Sun Yen.

[r] There are other evidences of Hindu learning in China at that time. For example, about the middle of the century, the Sogdian Sêng[1] Hui[4] (9617, 5184) translated Buddhist tales into Chinese; he was thus one of the first to introduce Hindu folk-lore into the Far East. His biography is included in the Kao[1] sêng[1] ch'uan[2] (5927, 9617, 2740), written by Hui[4] Chiao[3] (5193, 1305) in 519. Text in the Tokyo edition of the Tripiṭaka (vol. 35). Translated by Ed. Chavannes in T'oung Pao (10, 199–212, 1909).

CHAPTER XIX

THE TIME OF IAMBLICHOS

(First Half of Fourth Century)

I. Survey of Science in First Half of Fourth Century. II. Religious Background. III. Hindu, Hellenistic, Latin, and Chinese Philosophy. IV. Hellenistic and Roman Mathematics and Astronomy. V. Hellenistic and Chinese Physics and Chemistry. VI. Roman Husbandry. VII. Hellenistic and Chinese Medicine. VIII. Hellenistic Historiography. IX. Roman Law. X. Chinese, Gothic, Latin, and Egyptian Philology.

I. SURVEY OF SCIENCE IN FIRST HALF OF FOURTH CENTURY

1. If the date of Chalcidius had been more certain than it is, this chapter would have been fittingly dedicated to him. But as the date is conjectural, there is no alternative but to call this time by the name of Iamblichos. To be sure, Iamblichos was no true scientist, but on the contrary, a mystic philosopher, a wonder-worker. Yet he was as good a representative of the Hellenic side of his age as Chalcidius was of the Latin side; both men are almost on the same intellectual level. Both misunderstood the true nature of science, yet they were deeply interested in it.

2. *Religious Background*—An event of considerable importance for the future history of the world occurred at the beginning of the century (c. 315 to 320)—the birth of Christian monasticism. There had been before that date Christian hermits led by St. Anthony, but St. Pachomios was the first to establish a real Christian monastery, to create a Christian religious order. Before the end of the century, various forms of monasticism had already spread from one end of the Roman Empire to the other. The Council convoked at Nicaea in 325 by the emperor Constantine, to define the Catholic faith, confirmed the condemnation of Arianism. But a few years later, after Constantine's death in 337, Arianism was for a short time the orthodox doctrine. Ulfilas, apostle of the Goths, being consecrated in 341, during that very time, it followed that the Teutonic tribes became Christians of the Arian kind, while Latin Christianity remained Catholic. A religious wall was thus unfortunately built across the young, undeveloped, Europe.

A new translation of the Bible from Hebrew into Latin had been made by Lucian before 312. On the other hand, the historian Eusebios completed the edition of Origen's revision of the Septuagint. Ulfilas translated the Bible from Greek into Gothic, and thus Gothic was the first Barbarian vernacular to assume the dignity of a literary language.

The elaboration of Buddhist philosophy was continued by Asaṅga and his younger brother Vasubandhu.

3. *Hindu, Hellenistic, Latin, and Chinese Philosophy*—The earliest extant treatise on Sāṃkhya philosophy was probably composed by Īśvarakṛishṇa about the beginning of this century.

Iamblichos, pupil of Plotinos, carried Neoplatonism a step further away from its Platonic source, exaggerating, on the contrary, the mystical tendencies inherited from the Pythagorean sect and from various Greek and Oriental mysteries. Thus was the decomposition of Greek thought considerably accelerated. The Latin writer Chalcidius, who lived probably at the same time, translated the Timaeos into Latin and discussed it. The historical value of this work is considerable because, down to the twelfth century, it was almost the only channel through which Platonic knowledge reached the Latin West. It should be noted that Chalcidius's sources were anterior to Plotinos.

The Taoist philosopher Kuo P'o is said to have originated the application of fêng shui to the determination of the best location for graves. Fêng shui is a pseudo-science which had (and still has) as much popularity in China as astrology in the West. Another Taoist philosopher, Ko Hung, is mentioned below.

4. *Hellenistic and Roman Mathematics and Astronomy*—Iamblichos wrote various mathematical works. His interest in number mysticism led him to investigate the theory of numbers. He mentioned the first pair of amicable numbers, 220 and 284. Serenos wrote treatises on the sections of the cone and the cylinder, showing that they are not essentially different, and stated implicitly the fundamental property of a harmonic pencil.

The main works of astronomical interest are Chalcidius's commentary on the Timaeos and the great astrological treatise of Firmicus Maternus (c. 335).

5. *Hellenistic and Chinese Physics and Chemistry*—The alchemical treatise ascribed to Iamblichos is probably apocryphal. The physician Adamantios wrote a treatise on winds which reflects Peripatetic views on the subject. The treatise on optical theories ascribed to Damianos is probably a production of this time.

Fêng shui is a perverse application of physical and meteorological knowledge; the student of Chinese physics must take full account of it, even as the student of Western astronomy must take full account of astrology. It is just as comprehensive as astrology and a history of fêng shui would touch the history of Chinese science on every side. Thus it is fitting to recall in this place the name of Kuo P'o. Another Taoist, Ko Hung, seems to have actually made alchemical experiments for which he needed cinnabar.

6. *Roman Husbandry*—Palladius, the last of the Roman agriculturists, wrote a treatise which contains interesting views on grafting and on drainage and fertilization of the soil.

7. *Hellenistic and Chinese Medicine*—Apsyrtos wrote a treatise on the veterinary art which had considerable influence. He gave a clear description of glanders. The physician Adamantios wrote a summary of Polemon's treatise on physiognomy.

The Taoist philosopher Ko Hung wrote at least two medical works.

8. *Hellenistic Historiography*—Eusebios, the Father of Church History, wrote not only a church history (down to 323) but also a universal history (down to 325), which was the greatest chronological work of antiquity and the basis, to a very large extent, of all ulterior publications.

9. *Roman Law*—Hermogenianus compiled, before 324, a collection of imperial statutes, principally those of Diocletian. He is the latest Roman jurist represented in the Digest.

10. *Chinese, Gothic, Latin, and Egyptian Philology*—The Taoist philosopher Kuo P'o edited a dictionary of ancient terms called the "Hill and Water Classic."

Ulfilas systematized the Gothic language by his translation of the Bible (c. 350).

Donatus wrote a Latin grammar which obtained an immense success throughout the Middle Ages and the Renaissance.

The date of Horapollon's activity is difficult to ascertain, but we shall not be far wrong if we place him tentatively about the middle of the fourth century. He wrote in Coptic a treatise on hieroglyphics, which in spite of its fantastic features, remained authoritative until the seventeenth century.

11. *Final Remarks*—We have seen (in Chapters IX and X) that the conflict between Roman and Greek ideals was most acute during the second century B. C.; indeed, the intellectual life of that century was dominated by it. Then a slow process of diffusion took place. Romans and Greeks learned to know each other better and their differences were gradually adjusted. But their wounds were not yet entirely healed when a new crisis, even deeper than the first, was already preparing. The clash between Pagan and Christian ideals was at first restricted to relatively few individuals and localities, but after the conversion of Constantine the Great (312), the adoption of the Christian faith by the Roman state, and the Council of Nicaea (325), it became at once more general and more intense. The crisis increased considerably during the following period, then it gradually subsided because of the decay and submergence of the Pagan spirit.

Among the personalities quoted in this chapter (I leave out of account the theologians dealt with in Section II), the following were Christians: Chalcidius, Eusebios, Donatus; Firmicus Maternus was converted c. 346. Adamantios was a Jew. The only Pagan philosopher was Iamblichos; he was also one of the last. The gradual ending of Roman times is also manifested by the following facts: Palladius and Hermogenianus were respectively the last Roman geoponist and jurist.

If our chronology of Hindu facts is correct, a similar crisis was taking place at the same time in India. The development of Buddhist thought entailed necessarily a conflict between that new philosophy, which under Mahāyāna influences was becoming more and more religious, and the older systems, notably the Sāṃkhya.

The Chinese philosophers of this period were Taoists, but the heyday of Chinese Buddhism was approaching, and China would soon be rent by a crisis very similar to that of the West. The conflict between Taoist and Buddhist ideals is indeed comparable to that between Pagan and Christian ideals, but it was complicated by the presence of a third philosophy, Confucianism, and the victory of Buddhism was never as complete as that of Christianity.

II. RELIGIOUS BACKGROUND

CHRISTIAN MONASTICISM

Monasticism is not a Christian invention. That type of organization satisfies too well two fundamental needs of the human heart—asceticism and mysticism—not to have been discovered wherever those needs, normally latent, asserted themselves. Thus Buddhist monasticism can be traced back to the very time of the Buddha. Another form of the same institution existed also among the Jews. The Essenes led a full monastic life in Judea before the time of Christ; the monastic habits of the Therapeutae established near Alexandria were already described by Philon (first half of first century). The Christian form of monasticism appeared first in Egypt not before the second half of the third century. It is not necessary to admit that it was at all influenced by Buddhist or Jewish examples, for similar causes must needs produce everywhere similar fruits.

According to Egyptian traditions, St. Anthony (born in Egypt c. 250, died about the middle of the following century in the monastery called after him, Der Mar Antonios, upon the mountain of the same name near the Red Sea), was the father of Christian monasticism. He lived for many years as a hermit, but his fame attracted many disciples to him and he was finally obliged to help and lead them. These Antonian communities were hardly organized, however; they were essentially of an eremitical type. This form of monasticism prevailed in Northern and Middle Egypt.

Another form of monasticism was established in Southern Egypt by St. Pachomios (born c. 292 at Esna, Upper Egypt, died c. 346). He founded at Tabennisi, near Dendera, c. 315 to 320, the first Christian coenobium or monastery in the true sense of the word. That is, he was the first to organize a (one sex) community life, exalted by Christian devotion and careful discipline. He attached considerable importance to manual work, so that every monastery became a sort of agricultural colony. It is interesting to note that the monasteries founded by St. Pachomios formed a religious order. That is, they were not independent one from another. The abbot of the head monastery was the superior-general of the whole order, and a general chapter was held each year in the mother house. St. Pachomios was thus anticipating a type of organization which was not reestablished until the first half of the tenth century.

Egyptian monasticism did not last very long; it began to wane about the end of the following century, and the Muslim conquest gave it a crushing blow from which it never recovered. Meanwhile, however, the monastic ideal had been carried to Syria and other parts of the Near East. Before the end of the fourth century it had already spread into Arabia, Persia, and Mesopotamia.

St. Basil (q. v., next chapter) introduced Pachomian monasticism into the Eastern Roman Empire. He insisted upon the importance of labor and the vanity of excessive asceticism. His influence was so deep that Greek and Slavonic monasticisms are still essentially based upon the foundations established by him.

St. Athanasios (born in 293, probably at Alexandria, where he died in 373; Bishop of Alexandria since 326) went to Rome c. 340 and introduced monasticism—unfortunately of the Antonian (eremitical) type—into the West. From Rome it spread throughout Italy, and also into Gaul and North Africa.[a] This type of monasticism was doubly unsound in the West, where neither the climate nor the character of the people harmonized with it. Thus by the end of the fifth century, Western monasticism had already begun to ebb. Its further decline was happily halted by St. Benedict (q. v., first half of sixth century).

One can not lay too much stress on the importance of Christian monasticism. It was for many centuries the strongest and steadiest influence for charity and justice—the greatest civilizing power amidst periodic anarchy and general corruption. Monasteries were the natural depositories of much knowledge which otherwise would have perished; they became the sanctuaries of many men and women[b] upon whom the mission of transmitting and increasing that knowledge had devolved and who would have been utterly handicapped and ruined, in a barbarous age, by their very nobility of soul and spirit.

---

[a] The first monastery in Gaul was founded by Martin of Tours in 360 at Ligugé near Poitiers. He founded another soon afterward at Marmoutier, near Tours. About 400, Honoratus founded the still more famous monastery of Lérins on an island near Toulon. By the end of the fifth century, monasteries had been established in nearly all the provinces of the Roman empire (C. H. Robinson: Conversion of Europe, p. 9, 1917).

[b] Monasteries for women were possibly older than those for men. The sisters of each of the three great founders, Pachomios, Basil, and Benedict, organized communities for women modeled upon the communities ruled by their brothers.

The literature devoted to this subject is very great. I will simply refer, for general orientation, to Adolf Harnack: Das Mönchtum, seine Ideale und seine Geschichte (Giessen, 1881; 6th edition, 63 p., 1903; Englished, London, 1901), and to the excellent article on monasticism in the Encyclopaedia Britannica (1911, 10 col.) by the Right Rev. Edward Cuthbert Butler, O. S. B.

ARIOS

"Αρειος. Born c. 280, educated at Antioch, presbyter at Alexandria, died at Constantinople in 336. It is extremely difficult to reconcile the notions of monotheism and Trinity, and many controversies agitated the early church concerning the relations of the "persons" of the Trinity to one another. Being steeped in Aristotelian philosophy, Arios tried to solve the difficulty with logical rigor, and was led to deny the divinity of Christ. He began to explain his doctrine (Arianism) about the year 318. He was deposed by the synod of Alexandria in 321 and emigrated with his supporters to Palestine. His deposition was confirmed at the first oecumenical council which had been convoked by Constantine in Nicaea (Bithynia) in 325, and he was banished to Illyricum. To prevent the recurrence of other misunderstandings, the council then proceeded to define the Catholic faith (Nicene symbol). This definition was naturally the origin of new controversies which have no interest for us, except in showing to what extent theological perversity can go. For a while the protagonists were Eusebios of Nicomedia and Athanasios; the latter's activity in defense of the Nicene symbol was so intense that the symbol came to be known (incorrectly) after him ("Athanasian Creed"). The main issue brought into being by the council rested upon the words ὁμοούσιος (consubstantial, unius substantiae) and ὁμοιούσιος (of similar essence, οὐσία); that is, it rested upon a single iota. Are the Father and Son consubstantial, the same person (Athanasios), or are they only of a similar essence without being abolutely identical (Eusebios)?

To return to Arianism. After the death of Constantine (337), the new emperor Constantios reversed the decision of the council of Nicaea and Arianism became momentarily (until 378) the orthodox doctrine. Further vicissitudes do not concern us. The point of interest is that Ulfilas, apostle of the Goths, was consecrated bishop by Eusebios in 341, during the Arian supremacy. Because of this initial accident, the Goths were and remained Arians,[c] and other Teutonic tribes —Suevi, Vandals, Burgundians, Lombards—were either Arians from the beginning or became so because of the Gothic example. Thus Teutonic Christianity was Arian, while Latin Christianity was Catholic. Both religions were essentially the same, but there was enough theological difference to add some religious rancor to racial enmities. No international hatred is truly perfect unless the self-righteousness of both parties is enhanced by a feeling of religious superiority. In this case, the theologians of Nicaea had provided the necessary touch of perfection; a single iota made the whole difference between good people and others.

This state of affairs lasted until the sixth century. The Franks were the first Germanic tribe to become Catholic, in 496; by the middle of the sixth century, the greatest part of Gaul was Catholic;[d] the Visigoths of Spain were converted in 589; etc.

---

[c] The Goths were Arians for two centuries, their time of prosperity; they were established in Italy, Gaul, and Spain.

[d] Arian tendencies lingered here and there, especially in Southern France; they help to explain the religious unrest toward the end of the twelfth century.

Godefroy Hermant: La vie de St. Athanase qui comprend encore l'histoire de plusieurs autres saints avec la naissance et le progrès de l'Arianisme (2 vols., Paris, 1671). Louis Maimbourg: Histoire de l'Arianisme . . . . avec l'origine et le progrès des Sociniens (Paris, 1673; again 1686). Henry Melvill Gwatkin: The Arian Controversy (187 p., London, 1889); Studies of Arianism (2d ed., 340 p., Cambridge, 1900; first edition 1882). Article by F. J. Foakes-Jackson, in Dictionary of Religion and Ethics (vol. 1, 775–786, 1908). Hans von Schubert: Staat und Kirche in den arianischen Königreichen und im Reiche Chlodwigs (214 p., München, 1912). James Hay Colligan: The Arian Movement in England (184 p., Manchester, 1913). H. Idris Bell: Jews and Christians in Egypt. The Jewish Troubles in Egypt and the Athanasian Controversy (152 p., 5 pl., London, 1924; Isis, VIII, 534).

See also histories of religion. I have used G. F. Moore's excellent history (vol. 2, 1919).

ULFILAS[e]

Born in 311 or 313 among the Transdanubian Goths, flourished at Constantinople in 332 and the following years; ordained Bishop of the Goths in 341, he lived among his flock; he died at Constantinople in 383. Apostle of Arian Christianity to the Goths. Father of the Teutonic literatures. He translated the Bible from Greek into Gothic, which was thus the earliest barbarian tongue to become a literary language (c. 350).

Text—Fragments of Ulfilas's Bible have often been edited, editions by H. F. Massmann (904 p., Stuttgart, 1857. Gothic, Greek, Latin); by Ernst Bernhardt (725 p., Halle, 1875. Gothic, Greek). New edition by the same: Die gotische Bibel des Vulfila nebst der Skeireins, dem Kalendar und den Urkunden (Halle, 1884. With glossary). G. H. Balg: First Germanic Bible and other Remains of the Gothic Language (Milwaukee, 1891. With syntax and glossary). F. L. Stamm: Ulfilas oder die uns erhaltenen Denkmäler der gothischen Sprache neu herausgegeben. Text und Wörterbuch von Moritz Heyne, Grammatik von Ferdinand Wrede (9. Aufl., Paderborn, 1896). Der Wulfila des Bibliotheca Augusta zu Wolfenbüttel herausgegeben v. Hans Henning (8 pl., Hamburg, 1913).

Criticism—C. A. Scott: Ulfilas (London, 1885). Curt Rollfuss: Wulfilas Schriftsprache (Progr., Dresden, 1913). Leo Wiener: Contributions toward a History of Arabico-Gothic Culture (New York, 1917. According to Wiener, the early Gothic documents would be forgeries of a later time betraying Arabic influences). C. H. Robinson: The Conversion of Europe (241–257, London, 1917).

LUCIAN

Λουκιανός. Flourished at Antioch, martyred on January 7, 312. Translator of the Bible from Hebrew into Greek. Lucian revised previous Greek translations to such an extent that his version may be considered a new one. It is both accurate and idiomatic. The Philoxenian Syriac, Gothic, and Slavonic versions are derived from it. He revised the Antiochean text of the New Testament.[f]

For Eusebios, see my note below, in Section VIII.

---

[e] Or Wulfila, little wolf.

[f] By the beginning of the fourth century, the New Testament was represented by three great recensions corresponding to the three great provinces of the church in the East: the Alexandrian (revised by Hesychios), the Antiochean, and the Caesarean (revised by Pamphilos). The western recension was not revised.

ASAṄGA

Or Āryāsaṅga, or Vasubandhu Asaṅga. Born into the Brahmin family Kauśika in Purushapura (i. e., Peshawar in Kandahar), flourished at Ayodhyā (i. e., Oudh), probably about the beginning of the fourth century. Buddhist philosopher who elaborated a systematic theory of the mind. Even as Nāgārjuna (q. v., first half of the third century) was the founder of the Mādhyamika school, Asaṅga was the founder of the Yogācāra school of Mahāyāna Buddhism (Buddhist idealism). His main works are the Yogācārabhūmiśāstra (of which only a part, the Bodhisattvabhūmi is extant in Sanskrit) and the Mahāyāna-sūtrālaṃkāra.

The Buddhist sect based upon his philosophy is called dharmalakshaṇa, meaning the wisdom which shows us the true nature of all phenomena. It is represented now only in Japan and in the Buddhist academy of Nanking.

Texts—Asaṅga's works are included in the Chinese Tripiṭaka, being ascribed to Maitreya, the future Buddha. Mahāyāna-sūtrālaṃkāra, esposé de la doctrine du Grand Véhicule selon le système Yogācāra. Edité et traduit par Sylvain Lévi (2 vols., Paris, 1907–1911).

Criticism—Asaṅga, by M. Anesaki, in Dictionary of Religion and Ethics (vol. 2, 62, 1910). M. Winternitz: Indische Litteratur (t. 2, 255, 1920).

VASUBANDHU

Younger brother of Asaṅga. One of the greatest Buddhist philosophers. He died probably c. 350.[g] His main work, the Abhidharmakośa, dealing with ethics, psychology and metaphysics, is lost in Sanskrit, but is known through Chinese and Tibetan versions and also through the Abhidharmakośavyākhyā, a commentary composed by Yaśomitra. The oldest Chinese version was made by Paramārtha (q. v., second half of sixth century) between 563 and 567; a second one was made by Hsüan Tsang (q. v., first half of seventh century) c. 651 to 654. Vasubandhu wrote also a collection of proverbs, Gāthāsaṃgraha. It should be noted that the two works mentioned belong to the Hīnayāna doctrine, though the former is considerably used by Chinese and Japanese Mahāyānists. Late in life, he was converted to Mahāyāna by his brother Asaṅga; after the latter's death, he wrote a number of commentaries on Mahāyāna sūtras. A treatise against the Sāṃkhya philosophy called Paramārthasaptati (seventy [verses] on the highest truth) is also ascribed to him; this seems to be a refutation of the work of Īśvarakṛishṇa.

Theodor Stcherbatzky: The Soul Theory of the Buddhists (Bull. Acad. des sciences de Russie, 823–958, 1919. Contains a translation of the appendix to the eighth chapter of Vasubandhu's Abhidharmakośa; see J. R. A. S., 128, 1925).

The Life of Vasubandhu by Paramārtha (499–569) is contained in the Chinese Tripiṭaka. See Japanese edition (vol. 24, part 9, p. 115v to 118r; Cfr. Bunyiu Nanjio's Catalogue No. 1463). English translation by J. Takakusu in T'oung Pao (5, 259–296, 1904; see F. W. Thomas in J. R. A. S., 748–751, 1914). No dates can be extracted from that biography, but it is said that Vasubandhu died at the age of 80 in Ayodhyā.

Noël Peri: A propos de la date de Vasubandhu. Bulletin de l'Ecole française

[g] The date of his activity has been much discussed. The Japanese scholars Takakusu and Wogihara, also Sylvain Lévi, place him much later, in the fifth century. I adopt the very plausible dating given by N. Peri (1911). It would seem that Vasubandhu lived in the reigns of Candragupta I (acc. 320) and of Samudragupta (acc. c. 330).

d'Extrême-Orient (t. XI, 339–390, 1911. Important). M. Winternitz: Indische Litteratur (vol. 2, 256–259, 379, 1920). Article Vasubandhu by U. Wogihara, in Dictionary of Religion and Ethics (vol. 12, 595–596, 1922). A. B. Keith: Buddhist Philosophy (1923).

III. HINDU, HELLENISTIC, LATIN, AND CHINESE PHILOSOPHY

ĪŚVARAKRISHNA

Flourished at an unknown time, probably c. 300 or before.[h] Hindu philosopher. Author of the Sāṃkhyakārikā, which is the earliest extant treatise on Sāṃkhya philosophy, one of the six orthodox systems of Hindu philosophy.[i] This work is one of the most remarkable not simply of the Sāṃkhya but of the whole scholastic philosophy of India. A commentary by Māṭhara, the Māṭharavṛitti, was devoted to it, and both the original text and this commentary were translated into Chinese by Paramārtha, between 557 and 569.[j] Al-Bīrūnī (q. v., first half of eleventh century) derived his knowledge of Sāṃkhya, from a later commentary by Gauḍapāda, which seems to be hardly more than a summary of the Māṭharavṛitti, but superseded it.

Text—Sanskrit text, together with Gauḍapāda's and another commentary, edited by Bechanarāma Tripāṭhī (Benares Sanskrit series, 9, 1883).

English translation by H. T. Colebrooke, together with a translation of Gauḍapāda's commentary by H. H. Wilson (Oxford, 1837; again Bombay, 1887). A later translation by John Davies (Trübner's Oriental Series, London, 1881; reprinted in 1894). German translation, in P. Deussen: Allgemeine Geschichte der Philosophie (vol. 1, 413–466, Leipzig, 1894).

Criticism—Richard Garbe: Die Sāṃkhya philosophie. Eine Darstellung des indischen Rationalismus (355 p., Leipzig, 1894). J. Takakusu: La Sāṃkhyakārikā étudiée à la lumière de sa version chinoise (Bull. Ec. franç. Extrême Orient, t. 4, 1–65, 978–1064, 1904). M. Winternitz: Geschichte der indischen Litteratur (3, 452, 651, 1920). A. B. Keith: Buddhist Philosophy (139, 1923).

IAMBLICHOS

Ἰάμβλιχος. Born in Chalcis, Coele Syria, in the second half of the third century, died probably about the end of Constantine's reign, 306 to 337. Neoplatonic philosopher and thaumaturgos, pupil of Anatolios and Porphyry. He elaborated the more mystical side of Neoplatonism. His main work was an encyclopaedia of Pythagorean doctrine (συναγωγὴ τῶν Πυθαγορείων δογμάτων), in nine books, of which four or five remain: (1) Pythagoras's life (περὶ τοῦ Πυθαγορικοῦ βίου); (2) exhortation to philosophy (προτρεπτικὸς εἰς φιλοσοφίαν); (3) on mathematics in general (περὶ τῆς κοινῆς μαθηματικῆς ἐπιστήμης); (4) arithmetical introduction (ἀριθμητικὴ εἰσαγωγή or περὶ τῆς Νικομάχου ἀριθμητικῆς); (5) arithmetical theology (τὰ θεολογούμενα τῆς ἀριθμητικῆς).[k] In his mathematical books, number

[h] There has been much discussion about the probable date of his activity. Some have placed him as late as the beginning of the fifth century, this being almost the upper limit, because of the Chinese translation mentioned below. It would seem, however, that Vasubandhu knew of his work and we are now tolerably sure that Vasubandhu flourished in the first half of the fourth century. See my note on Vasubandhu above.

[i] Probably the oldest system. Its foundation is ascribed to Kapila, who may have lived before the Buddha. The Sāṃkhya is a rationalistic and dualistic philosophy; it probably influenced both Jainism and Buddhism.

[j] The Sanskrit original of the Māṭharavṛitti was recently discovered by S. K. Belvalkar.

[k] This contains probably the substance of Book VII.

mysticism is carried to the extreme. He developed Thymaridas's ἐπάνθημα, extending this method to other indeterminate problems.

He mentions the first pair of amicable numbers 220 and 284, but they must have been known before, as the Pythagoraeans were deeply interested in the properties of numbers. The second pair of amicable numbers was not discovered until about thirteen centuries later by Fermat, in 1636, namely 17,296 and 18,416 (L. E. Dickson. History of the Theory of Numbers, vol. 1, 38, 40, 1919).

Text and Translation—Greek and Latin edition of De vita Pythagorica and other writings, by Theoph. Kiessling (2 vols., Leipzig, 1815–16). Edition of the same book by Augustus Nauck (455 p., Petrograd, 1884. Accedit epimetrum de Pythagorae aureo carmine). Edition of the Protrepticos, by Herm. Pistelli (184 p., Leipzig, 1888). Edition of De communi mathematica scientia, by N. Festa (163 p., Leipzig, 1891). Edition of the Introduction to Nicomachos, by Herm. Pistelli (204 p., Leipzig, 1894). Edition of the Theologumena arithmeticae, by Fried. Ast, with Nichomachos's introduction (344 p., Leipzig, 1817). A summary of Books V, VI, VII, by Psellos (second half of eleventh century) has been edited by Paul Tannery: Psellus sur les nombres (Revue des études grecques, t. 5, 269–274, 1892; Mémoires, IV, 343; Isis, IV, 342).

The life of Pythagoras has been translated into English by Thomas Taylor (London, 1818).

Criticism—Fried. Blass: De Antiphonte sophista Iamblichi auctore (17 p., Kiel, 1889). Fr. Hultsch: Erlaut. zu den Berichte des Iamblichos über die vollkommenen Zahlen (Nachr., Gesell. d. Wissensch., phil.-hist. Classe, 246–255, Göttingen, 1895). K. Töpfer: Die sogenannten Fragmente des Sophisten Antiphon im Protreptikos des Iamblichos (Progr., 14 p., Gmunden, 1911). Wilh. Bertermann: De Iamblichi vitae Pythagoricae fontibus (Diss., 77 p., Koenigsberg, 1913). G. Mau and Kroll, in Pauly-Wissowa (vol. 17, 645–651, 1914). P. Duhem: Système du Monde (t. 4, 376, 1916, on his theory of human intelligence; t. 1, p. 333, 1913, his theory of space). Thomas Whittaker: The Neoplatonists (second edition, Cambridge, 1918). J. Bidez: Le philosophe Jamblique et son école (Revue des études grecques, t. 32, 29–40, 1919).

Apocryphal Writings—De mysteriis, considered by Proclos as genuine, is certainly a product of Iamblichos's school, if not his own work. Translated into English by Alex. Wilder (London, 1911). Karl Rasche: De Iamblicho libri qui inscribitur de mysteriis auctore (Diss., 82 p., Münster i. W., 1911. A philological study concluding that De mysteriis is probably genuine).

There is no sufficient reason for ascribing to this Iamblichos the alchemical text edited and translated into French by M. Berthelot in his Collection des anciens alchimistes grecs (3e livraison, p. 285–289, 274–278, 1888; Procédés de Jamblique) from the Paris Greek manuscript 2327, fol. 266–267. See M. Berthelot: Origines de l'alchimie (72–144, 1885); E. O. von Lippmann: Alchemie (68, 1919).

The letters to Iamblichos ascribed to the emperor Julian and on which account it was claimed that Iamblichos must have lived until almost the middle of the century, are certainly apocryphal. See Franz Cumont: Sur l'authenticité de quelques lettres de Julien (Gand, 1889). Oeuvres de Julien traduites par J. Bidez (t. 1 (2), 233–245, 1924; Isis, VII, 534).

CHALCIDIUS

Flourished probably in the first half of the fourth century. Christian. Latin translator and commentator of the Timaeos.[1] His astronomical knowledge was derived from Adrastos (first half of second century) and other pre-Plotinian

[1] This translation was dedicated to a Christian named Osius, possibly the Osius who was bishop of Corduba c. 296 to 357. It was restricted to the first fifty-three chapters.

sources. His work is of great importance, because, until the end of the twelfth century, Plato was known in the West almost exclusively through him.

Text—Editio princeps, by Aug. Justinianus (Paris, 1520). Later editions by Meursius (Leyde, 1617); Fabricius (Hamburg, 1718). Scientific edition by F. W. A. Mullach: Fragmenta philosophorum graecorum (t. 2, 185 sq., Paris, 1867).

Criticism—Article by Kroll, in Pauly-Wissowa (vol. 6, 2042, 1899). Eduard Steinheimer: Untersuchungen über die Quellen des Chalcidius (Progr., Aschaffenburg, 1912). P. Duhem: Système du monde (t. 2, 417–426, 1914, physics; t. 3, 47 sq., 1915, motion of Venus and Mercury around the sun).

KUO P'O

Kuo[1]* P'o[4]* (6617, 9443). Born in Wên[2]-hsi[3] (12651, 4073), Ho[2]-tung[1] (3936, 12248), in 276; murdered in 324. Taoist philosopher, astrologer, occultist, lexicographer. He is the reputed founder of fêng[1] shui[3] (3554, 10128) (i. e., wind and water); at any rate, he became famous as a soothsayer and the practice of fêng shui, especially its application to the determination of the best location for tombs, was probably systematized by him. Fêng shui is a development of the oldest cosmogonical ideas of the Chinese, a new application of their immemorial dualism, symbolized by Yang[2] and Yin[1] (12883, 13224), the positive and negative, male and female, principles of universal life. It is "the art of adapting the residence of the living and the dead so as to cooperate and harmonize with the local currents of the cosmic breath" (H. Chatley). It is misleading to translate fêng shui by geomancy; it is comparable to western astrology, though very different; it is a complicated and very comprehensive pseudo-science which obtained as much prestige in the Far East as astrology in the West. There are two collections of Kui P'o's predictions, the Tung[4]-lin[2] (12266, 7157) and the Hsin[1]-lin[2] (4574, 7157).

Kuo P'o edited the Book of Mountains and Seas (the so-called Hill and Water Classic), Shan[1]-hai[3] ching[1] (9663, 3767, 2122), and explained the difficult terms contained in that geographical treatise. He also wrote commentaries on the Êrh-ya (q. v., fifth century B. C.) and on the Fang[1] yen[2] (3435, 13025), a treatise on Chinese dialects written by Yang[2]-hsiung[2] (12876, 4699), c. 14 B. C.[m]

H. A. Giles: Chinese biographical dictionary (Shanghai, p. 408–409, 1898); History of Chinese Literature (138, London, 1901). S. Couling: Encyclopaedia sinica (175, 1917, article fêng shui).

IV. HELLENISTIC AND ROMAN MATHEMATICS AND ASTRONOMY

For Iamblichos and Chalcidius, see my notes in Section III.

SERENOS[n]

Σέρηνος 'Αντινοέως. Flourished in the fourth century, probably after Pappos and before Theon of Alexandria. Greek mathematician. Two treatises of his are extant: περὶ κυλίνδρου τομῆς, De sectione cylindri (33 problems); περὶ κώνου τομῆς, De sectione coni (69 problems). In the first he showed that the transverse sections of a cylinder are not essentially different from those of a cone. Property of harmonic pencil implicitly stated.

[m] L. Wieger: La Chine (472, 492, 1920).

[n] The ancient editors call him, erroneously, Serenus Antissensis ('Αντισσαῖος). His birthplace was not Antissa in Lesbos, but Antinoeia or Antinoopolis, a Roman town in Middle Egypt.

Text and Translations—His writings have been published with those of Apollonios by Commandino (Bologna, 1566, Latin translation only) and by Edmund Halley (Oxford, 1710, Greek and Latin). New edition by J. L. Heiberg (Leipzig, 322 p., 1896). German translation by E. Nizze (Progr., Stralsund, 1860–1861).

Criticism—Paul Tannery: Serenus d'Antissa (Bull. d. sci. math., t. 7, 237–244, 1883; Mémoires, I, 290–299). J. L. Heiberg: Über den Geburtsort des Serenus (Bibliotheca mathematica, p. 97–98, 1894). M. Cantor: Geschichte der Mathematik (t. 1[3], 489–491, 1907). Orinsky, in Pauly-Wissowa (second series, vol. 4, 1677, 1923).

Michigan mathematical papyrus No. 621. This papyrus, which is anterior to the Akhmīm papyrus (q. v., second half of the sixth century) may be placed tentatively in the fourth century. For a partial publication of it see L. C. Karpinski (Isis, V, 20–25, 1 facsimile, 1923). It contains numerical problems entirely similar to those found in the ancient Egyptian treatises and in the Akhmīm papyrus. "The document is of real importance in considering the development of Greek arithmetical computation (logistica), of which science little has come down to us. The absolute dependence upon Egyptian arithmetic is established beyond doubt."

FIRMICUS MATERNUS

Iulius Firmicus Maternus. Born in Sicily, he flourished there during the first half of the fourth century. Astrologer. Neoplatonist. He composed, between 334 and 337, the most comprehensive text-book of astrology of ancient times: Matheseos libri VIII. It deals with the whole subject from the elements up to the mysteries of the sphaera barbarica. After his conversion to Christianity he wrote, c. 346, a violent attack on paganism, "De errore profanarum religionum."

Text and Translations—De navitatibus (Venice, 1497); Scriptores astronomici veteres (Venice, 1499). Matheseos libri VIII edited by Wilhelm Kroll and Franz Skutsch (2 vols., Leipzig, 1898–1913). De errore profanarum religionum, edited by Konr. Ziegler (Leipzig, 1907).

Criticism—Clifford H. Moore: Firmicus der Heide und der Christ (Diss., 54 p., München, 1897). Theod. Friedrich: In de errore . . . . libellum (Diss., 56 p., Bonn, 1905). Alfons Müller: Zur Ueberlieferung der Apologie des Firmicus (Diss., 94 p., Tübingen, 1908, with long bibliography). Boll, in Pauly-Wissowa (vol. 12, 2365–2379, 1909. Very elaborate discussion). Edm. O. von Lippmann: Ueber das erste Vorkommen des Namens Chemie (Chemiker Zeitung, p. 685, 1914; Isis, III, 321). P. Duhem: Système du Monde (t. II, p. 324, 1914. Les astres sont causes secondes des évènements sublunaires). Lynn Thorndike: History of Magic (vol. 1, 525–538, 1923. Discussing the dates of the Mathesis given above).

V. HELLENISTIC AND CHINESE PHYSICS AND CHEMISTRY

For the alchemical treatise ascribed to Iamblichos, see my note in Section III. For Adamantios's treatise on winds, see my note in Section VII.

DAMIANOS

A treatise on optical theories has been ascribed to one Damianos, son or pupil of Heliodoros of Larissa. It has been published by Richard Schöne: Damianos, Schrift über Optik, mit Auszügen aus Geminos (Griechisch und Deutsch, 44 p., Berlin, 1897.) It is entitled: *Δαμιανοῦ τοῦ Ἡλιοδώρου Λαρισσαίου κεφάλαια τῶν ὀπτικῶν ὑποθέσεων*. Heliodoros is older than Theon of Alexandria, hence this treatise dates possibly of the fourth century. The whole question is very obscure.

Paul Tannery: Les hypothèses optiques de Damianos et Ange Vergèce (Rapport sur une mission en Italie en 1886, Ch. IV. Archives et missions scientifiques, t. 13,

p. 409–455, 1888; Mémoires, II, 319–324). Hultsch, article Damianos, 3, in Pauly-Wissowa (vol. 8, 2054, 1901).

For Kuo P'o, see my note in Section III.

KO HUNG

Ko[2]* Hung[2] (6069, 5252). Style name, Chih[4] Ch'uan[1] (1871, 2728). Born at Chiang[1]-ning[2]-fu[3] (1208, 8327, 3682) in Kiangsu. Flourished probably c. 281 to 361. Chinese Taoist, alchemist and physician. He asked the Emperor Yüan[2]-ti[4] (13744, 10942), some time after 326, to be sent to Kou[1]-lou[4] (6135, 7360), because cinnabar, which he needed for his experiments, could be obtained there from Cochin-China. He wrote two medical works, the Chin[1]-kuei[4] yao[4]-fang[1] (2032, 6465, 12958, 3435) in 100 chüan and the Chou[3]-hou[4]-pei[4]-chi[2]*-fang[1] (2474, 4025, 8804, 892, 3435) in 8 chüan. Of his other works, I shall quote only the Pao[4]-p'o[4]*-tzŭ[3] (8709, 9416, 12317), a treatise on Taoist alchemy, dietetics, and magic. He influenced considerably the development of Taoist doctrines and superstitions.

Text—Yüan edition of the Chou-hou-pei chi-fang by Tuan[4] Ch'êng[2] Chi[3] (12140, 762, 921). Modern editions are derived from a Ming reprint.
Criticism—A. Wylie: Chinese Literature (219, (1867), 1902). H. A. Giles: Biographical Dictionary (978, 1898). L. Wieger: Le canon Taoïste (1911, passim); La Chine (322, 514, 1920). Histoire des croyances (385–406, 1922; analysis of Ko's work). F. Hübotter: Guide (24, Kumamoto, 1924). A. Forke: World Conception of the Chinese (16, 20, 21, 1925; Isis, VIII, 373).

VI. ROMAN HUSBANDRY

PALLADIUS[a]

Rutilius Taurus Aemilianus Palladius. Flourished in the fourth century, probably in the first half. Roman writer on medicine and agriculture. The last of the Roman geoponists. His main work is the "De agricultura," a farmer's calendar, chiefly based upon Gargilius Martialis (q. v., first half of third century). Of the 14 books of this work, the first is introductory; Books II to XIII deal with the duties of each month, beginning with January; Book XIV is a poem upon the art of grafting (De insitione). Account of the artificial drainage of soil and of the use of various sea-weeds to fertilize it.

Text and Translations—Princeps (Venice, 1472). Palladii viri inlustris opus agriculturae, edited by J. C. Schmitt (284 p., Leipzig, 1898). Latin text with French translation by Cabaret-Dupaty (Paris, 1843).
Middle-English translation of Palladius De re rustica, edited with critical and explanatory notes by Mark Liddell (Part 1, text 299 p., Berlin, 1896). Palladius on husbondrie. From the unique manuscript of ab. 1420 A. D. in Colchester castle, edited by Barton Lodge (Early English Text Society, 2 parts, London, 1873–1879).
Criticism—Ernst H. F. Meyer: Geschichte der Botanik (vol. 2, 328–333, 1855). M. Sirch: Die Quellen des Palladius (Progr., 55 p., Freising, 1904). Max Wellmann: Palladius und Gargilius Martialis (Hermes, vol. 43, 1–31, 1908). J. H. Schmalz: Sprachliche Bemerkungen zu des Palladius opus agriculturae (Glotta, VI, 172–190, 1915).

---

[a] This is really a Greek name (Παλλάδιος).

VII. HELLENISTIC AND CHINESE MEDICINE

APSYRTOS

Ἄψυρτος, of Prusa or Nicomedia in Bithynia, flourished under Constantine the Great, c. 332 to 334. Greek veterinary surgeon. He wrote a treatise (in two books) on the veterinary art,[p] which was used considerably by later authors (such as Theomnestos, Pelagonios, and chiefly Hierocles) and is one of the main sources of the Hippiatrica. Apsyrtos gave a very clear description of glanders, a highly contagious and dangerous disease affecting horses.[q]

Text—Simon Grynaeus: Veterinariae medicinae libri duo a Joanne Ruellio olim quidem latinitate donati nunc vero ijdem sua hoc est graeca lingua primum in lucem editi (Basel, 1537). An edition of the Hippiatrica is being prepared by Eugen Oder.

Criticism—K. Sprengel: De Apsyrto Bithynio (Halle, 1832). M. Wellmann, in Pauly-Wissowa (vol. 3, 286, 1895; only a few lines). Eugen Oder: De hippiatricorum codice cantabrigiensi (Berlin, 1896).

ADAMANTIOS

Adamantius Sophista. Ἀδαμάντιος, flourished at Alexandria in the fourth century, probably in the first half. Jewish physician and sophist (ἰατρικῶν λόγων σοφιστής). He compiled an epitome of Polemon's treatise on physiognomy (q. v., first half of second century).[r] A treatise on winds (περὶ ἀνέμων) is also ascribed to him; it reflects the views of Peripatetic meteorology. Various medical fragments of his are extant.

Text—First edition (Greek, Paris, 1540). Edition with Janus Cornarius (Basel, 1544). Edition with Aelian (Rome, 1545). Poor edition of the Physiognomy, in J. G. F. Franz: Scriptores physiognomoniae veteres (311–448, Altenburg, 1780, Greek and Latin). New edition in Richard Foerster: Scriptores physiognomonici (vol. 1, 295–431, 1893. Adamantii Physiognomonica cum epitomis Matritensi et Pseudopolemonis, the three Greek texts are printed on the same pages).

Treatise on winds published by Valentin Rose in Anecdota graeca (t. 1, 29, 1864).

Criticism—M. Wellmann, in Pauly-Wissowa (vol. 1, 343, 1894). S. Krauss (Jewish Encyclopaedia, vol. 1, 183, 1901). Iwan Bloch, in Puschmann: Handbuch der Geschichte der Medizin (vol. 1, 522, 1902).

VARIA

Karl Sudhoff: Zwei weitere amtsärztliche Atteste unter den griechischen Papyri aus Oxyrhynchos (Archiv für Geschichte der Medizin, vol. 3, 104–109, 1909). Apropos of two documents of the year 316, bearing Nos. 896 and 983 in B. P. Grenfell and A. S. Hunt's Oxyrhynchus papyri (1896–1924).

Karl Sudhoff: Hat das Konzil von Ankyra (314) Absonderungsvorschriften für Leprakranke erlassen? (Archiv für Geschichte der Medizin, vol. 4, 379–383, 1911).

For Ko Hung see my note in Section V.

---

[p] Partly based upon the work of Eumelos, Εὔμηλος (c. 200 A. D.).

[q] Also asses and mules. The microorganism producing it, *Bacillus mallei*, was first obtained in pure culture and accurately studied by Loeffler and Schutz in 1882.

[r] This epitome was dedicated to the Emperor Constantius. But which? Constantius I ruled in 305–6; Constantius II from 337 to 361, being succeeded by Julian. Medicaments introduced by Adamantios are quoted by Oribasios.

VIII. HELLENISTIC HISTORIOGRAPHY

EUSEBIOS

Eusebios Pamphilou—meaning, disciple of Pamphilos. Εὐσέβιος Παμφίλου, born in Palestine c. 265, bishop of Caesarea in Palestine from 313 to his death in 340. Greek historian and theologian; father of church history. His main works are a universal history (Παντοδαπὴ ἱστορία) down to 325, and a church history (Ἐκκλησιαστικὴ ἱστορία) down to 323. The former is divided into two parts: the chronography (Χρονογραφία) and tables of synchronisms called the canon (Κανὼν χρονικός). This was the greatest chronological work of ancient times; all later works were built directly or indirectly upon it. Eusebios completed the edition of Origen's revision of the Septuagint, begun by Pamphilos (martyred c. 308).[a]

Texts—Opera in Migne: Patrologia graeca (vol. 19–24). New edition by Dindorf (4 vols., Leipzig, 1867–1871).

Universal History—Only fragments of the Greek text remain. There is an Armenian version of the whole text edited by J. B. Aucher (Venice, 1818), together with the Greek fragments and a Latin translation. German translation of the Armenian text by Joseph Karst in "Die griechischen christlichen Schriftsteller der ersten drei Jahrhunderten" (Leipzig, 1911). Alfred Schoene: Chronicorum libri duo (2 vols., Leipzig, 1866–1875).

The second part had long been known through St. Jerome's Latin version (and continuation to 378). There are many early editions of this part: Milan, c. 1476, Venice, 1483, etc. Later edition by I. I. Scaliger (Leyden, 1606). Modern edition by Rudolf Helm (Leipzig, 1913). The Bodleian manuscript of Jerome's version reproduced in collotype, with an introduction by J. K. Fotheringham (Oxford, 1905). Eusebii Pamphili Chronici Canones, latine vertit, adauxit, ad sua tempora produxit S. Eusebius Hieronymus, edited by Joannes Knight Fotheringham (387 p., London, 1923).

Church History—The Greek text exists entirely and is published in Migne's and Dindorf's editions quoted above. There are also Latin and Armenian versions, both of the fifth century. The former, by Ruffinus, was published in Mantua, 1479, Strassburg, 1500, etc. W. Wright and Norman McLean: The Ecclesiastical History, in Syriac, edited from the manuscripts, with a collation of the ancient Armenian version by A. Merx (436 p., Cambridge, 1898).

Greek and Latin edition by Henri de Valois (3 vols., Paris, 1659–1673). Greek and French editions by Emile Grapin (3 vols., Paris, 1905–1913). English translation by A. C. McGiffert, in Nicene and Post-Nicene Fathers (vol. 1, 81–403. New York, 1904).

Criticism—Heinrich Gelzer: Julius Sextus Africanus (vol. 2, 23–107, 1885). Anton Halmel: Die Entstehung der Kirchengeschichte (64 p., Essen, 1896). M. Croiset: Littérature grecque (t. 5, 908–914, 1899). A. K. I. Schöne: Die Weltchronik des Eusebius in ihrer Bearbeitung durch Hieronymus (293 p., Berlin, 1900). James T. Shotwell: Introduction to the History of History (300–313, New York, 1922).

IX. ROMAN LAW

HERMOGENIANUS

Flourished in the Eastern Empire about the beginning of the fourth century. Roman jurist. Author (before 324) of a collection of imperial statutes, prin-

[a] This was the fifth column of the Hexapla. It is known as Eusebios's edition (or the Palestine edition, or Origen's edition) of the Septuagint.

cipally those of Diocletian (284–305). It is called after him Codex Hermogenianus. The latest Roman jurist from whom there is an extract in the Digest.

Text—Edited by Krüger, in Collectio librorum Juris Ante-Justiniani (Vol. III, 242–245, Berlin, 1895).

X. CHINESE, GOTHIC, LATIN, AND EGYPTIAN PHILOLOGY

For Chinese philology, see my note on Kuo P'o, in Section III.
For Gothic philology, see my note on Ulfilas, in Section II.

DONATUS

Aelius Donatus. Flourished at Rome about the middle of the fourth century. Teacher of St. Jerome. Latin grammarian. Author of a Latin grammar (Ars grammatica) which has come down to us in two editions (a smaller and a larger one). The success of that book throughout the Middle Ages was phenomenal. It was one of the earliest books to be printed; a large number of editions appeared in close succession. In Old French and English the word donat (donet) came to mean grammar. The Ars grammatica was translated into Greek by Maximos Planudes (q. v., second half of thirteenth century). Donatus wrote commentaries on Terence and Virgil.

Text—Donati Ars Grammatica tribus libris comprehensa, edited by F. Lindemann, in Corpus gramm. latin. (Leipzig, 1831).
For bibliography of earlier editions see Paul Schwenke: Die Donat- und Kalender-type. Nachtrag und Übersicht . . . . mit einem Abdruck des Donattextes nach den ältesten Ausgaben (50 p., 7 pl., Mainz, 1903).
Criticism—Remigius Antissiodorensis in artem Donati minorem commentum, edited by W. Fox (Leipzig, 1902). Pauly-Wissowa (vol. 10, 1545–1547, 1905).
Most of the modern studies on Donatus are devoted to his commentary on Terence.

HORAPOLLON

Ὡραπόλλων Νειλῷος, of Nilopolis, flourished probably in Egypt in the fourth century, certainly not before. Egyptian archaeologist and occultist, who wrote in Coptic a treatise on hieroglyphics, in two books.[t] He knew at least some hieroglyphics, but could not read the script and invented mystical and fantastic explanations of individual characters. His work contains much animal lore such as is found in Aelian (q. v., first half of third century). The seventeenth century knowledge of hieroglyphics[u] was still based upon that of Horapollon!

Text—Princeps edition. Vita et fabellae Aesopi, etc., Ori Apollinis Niliaci Hieroglyphica, etc. (Venice, 1505). J. Mercer (Paris, 1548, 1551); David Hoeschel (Augsburg, 1595); Johan. Corn. de Pauw (412 p., Utrecht, 1727). Best editions by Conrad Leemans (Amsterdam, 1835). Text with English translation by Alexander Turner Cory (186 p., London, 1840).
Other Translations—Joh. Herold Heyden-Weldt (Basel, 1554). Pietro Vasolli (Venezia, 1548). Jean Baptiste Réquier (Amsterdam, 1779, in French).
Criticism—Roeder, in Pauly-Wissowa (vol. 8, 2313–2319, 1913). Lynn Thorndike: History of Magic (vol. 1, 331–334, 1923).

---

[t] We know it only through a poor Greek translation (Ἱερογλυφικά) made by one Philippos, probably in the fifth or sixth century, but possibly later (before 1419).

[u] As represented by the works of Pierio Valeriano; Lorenzo Pignoria, 1605, 1608; Athanasius Kircher, 1650, 1652, 1672. The earliest correct interpretations of hieroglyphics were due to the Dane Jörgen Zoega (d. 1809) and to Champollion.

CHAPTER XX

THE TIME OF ORIBASIOS

(Second Half of Fourth Century)

I. Survey of Science in Second Half of Fourth Century. II. Religious Background. III. Hellenistic and Hindu Philosophy. IV. Hellenistic, Roman, Jewish, and Chinese Mathematics and Astronomy. V. Roman and Chinese Technology. VI. Roman and Hellenistic Natural History and Husbandry. VII. Roman and Hellenistic Geography. VIII. Hellenistic and Roman Medicine. IX. Roman Historiography. X. Roman Law.

I. SURVEY OF SCIENCE IN SECOND HALF OF FOURTH CENTURY

1. The conflict between Pagan and Christian ideals, of which I spoke in the last chapter, is admirably reflected in the soul of the emperor Julian—Julian the Apostate. The personality of Julian is equally fascinating for the historian and the psychologist, but we can not place it in the center of our picture. Julian was, at most, as it was his ambition to be, a philosopher; he could not be called a scientist; indeed he was not particularly interested in science. But his age, so poor in other respects, was one of great medical activity, and the most prominent physician was undoubtedly Oribasios, Julian's friend. It is thus very appropriate to call it the Age of Oribasios.

2. *Religious Background*—Some of the greatest Fathers of the Church belong to this period. The council of Nicaea (325)—the first oecumenic council—had considerably stimulated the activity of theologians, and the acknowledgment and fear of heresies had naturally accelerated the systematization of Christian doctrine. The Christian Fathers were not genuinely interested in science, but they were obliged to obtain a sufficient amount of scientific information in order to refute the Pagan arguments and to interpret the first chapter of Genesis. It was necessary to justify the Biblical cosmology and therefore to assimilate Greek knowledge as far as it was compatible with the Christian dogmas. The "Hexaëmeron" of Basil the Great exerted a deep influence upon Patristic literature and contributed powerfully, if indirectly, to shape the thought of the Middle Ages. Another Greek Father, Epiphanios, completed a critical study of some eighty heresies and wrote a little treatise, which became the model of Christian lapidaries. The contemporary Latin Fathers were St. Ambrose and St. Jerome; St. Augustine belongs rather to the following century. St. Jerome composed a Latin translation of the Bible, the so-called Vulgate, and he adapted Eusebios's chronicles to the needs of Latin readers, extending them down to 378.

The development of Buddhist logic by Dignāga will be considered below. The Pure Land (or Lotus) school of Buddhism was founded in China about the year 373 by Hui Yüan. The point of view represented by that school—the Amidist point of view—obtained considerable popularity in the Far East. Buddhism was introduced about this time also into the three Korean Kingdoms: into Koma, in 372; into Kudara, in 384; into Shiragi in 424.

3. *Hellenistic and Hindu Philosophy*—The most impressive personality is, of course, that of the emperor Julian, who made a last but fruitless stand against

Christianity in the name of Greek philosophy. That philosophy continued to exist, but henceforth it was tolerated only to the extent of its own submission to the theological dictates. One of the latest philosophers of the ancient type was the Peripatetician Themistios, who flourished in Constantinople. Themistios was not a Christian, but was prudent enough to show a great deal of religious toleration.

Dignāga, who flourished in Telingāna (Madras Presidency) introduced formal logic into Buddhist philosophy. His influence throughout Buddhist Asia is comparable to that of Aristotle's logic in the West.

4. *Hellenistic, Roman, Jewish, and Chinese Mathematics and Astronomy*—The main mathematician of the period was Theon of Alexandria, Hypatia's father, who wrote a commentary on the "Almagest," and explained the arithmetical treatment of sexagesimal fractions. His fame was great in mediaeval time, for he was thought to be the main author of Euclid's geometry!

Paul of Alexandria wrote a treatise which contains the oldest astrological chorography extant. Another astrological treatise was written at about the same time by Hephaestion of Thebes. The Roman geographer Avienus translated Aratos's Phaenomena and Prognostica into Latin.

The Jewish patriarch Hillel II fixed the calendar for the whole Diaspora in 358 (?). Chiang Chi corrected the Chinese calendar in 385.

5. *Roman and Chinese Technology*—Vegetius wrote a treatise on military and naval arts, which contains valuable information on the technical knowledge of those days.

The invention of real black ink, the so-called "India ink," was made (or remade) in China some time in the fourth or fifth century.

6. *Roman and Hellenistic Natural History and Husbandry*—Ausonius of Bordeaux wrote various didactic poems in Latin; one of them gives an account of a trip up the Moselle from Bingen to Treves and contains descriptions of some sixteen species of fishes.

Anatolius of Beirut and Didymos of Alexandria wrote or edited Greek writings on agriculture.

7. *Roman and Hellenistic Geography*—Avienus wrote Latin poems, of which one is a free translation of Dionysios's description of the world, and another an account of the Mediterranean shores.

Various Roman and Hellenistic itineraries, continuing the tradition of which I have spoken in Chapter XVII, date from the fourth century; one of them, the Bordeaux-Jerusalem itinerary, dates from the first half of the century (333), but I did not separate it from the others, which date more probably from the second half, in order not to disintegrate my material too much. It did not seem worth while to speak of that itinerary alone; in all probability that tradition was unbroken at least from the time at which I first mentioned it (first half of the third century).

8. *Hellenistic and Roman Medicine*—It was in the medical field that the scientific activity of this age was greatest. The names of a number of prominent physicians have come down to us. There is, first of all, one Theodoros who attended King Shāpūr II and wrote a medical compendium in Pahlawī. Hierocles was a famous veterinary surgeon. Oribasios wrote a large medical encyclopaedia, prepared the Galenic supremacy, and fought against superstition. The brothers Philagrios and Posidonios made many original observations; Philagrios was especially interested

in spleen diseases; Posidonios was mainly a psychiatrist—he made a first attempt to localize functions of the brain—but he investigated various other diseases. Nemesios, bishop of Emesa, wrote a book on the nature of man which has some physiological interest.

All of these physicians wrote in Greek, but Latin treatises were published at the same time by Vindicianus, Priscianus, and Vegetius. The former two deal with general medicine and female disorders, the latter with the veterinary art. Placitus compiled a treatise on drugs of animal origin. The so-called "Medicine of Pliny" is a medical treatise, arranged from head to foot, which dates probably from this same period.

9. *Roman Historiography*—The historical works of this time were exclusively Latin: Ammianus Marcellinus compiled a history of Rome (from 96 to 378), which is honest and full of information; Sulpicius Severus wrote a summary of Christian history (down to 400) and a life of St. Martin of Tours, which is important, because of the great influence it exerted upon mediaeval historians.

10. *Roman Law*—I find only one legal work to report, but it is one of special interest, one of the earliest studies of comparative law—an anonymous Latin comparison of Jewish with Roman Law, published after 390 and before 428.

11. *Final Remarks*—This age was predominantly Greco-Roman, but not strictly Mediterranean; a greater part of the world is gradually appearing upon the intellectual map. Julian traveled over a great part of Europe. Ausonius flourished in Bordeaux and explored the Moselle. Sulpicius Severus flourished in Bordeaux, Toulouse, and Tours. Of course, the imperial capital, Constantinople, assumes more and more importance; Oribasios and, later, the Paphlagonian Themistios, were working there. The best mathematician of the age, Theon, and the astrologer Paul were in Alexandria; Nemesios, in Emesa; Anatolius, in Beirut; Philagrios, in Thessalonica.

Little is done in the East; but the progress of Buddhist philosophy in India and of Buddhist propaganda in China and Korea prepares new developments.

II. RELIGIOUS BACKGROUND

Fathers of the Christian Church

There is an abundant literature dealing with the Fathers of the Church in a general way. Some of the most important works are quoted below (in this and following chapters) apropos of individual fathers.

I quote here a few publications devoted to the study of Patristic literature from our special point of view.

O. Zöckler: Geschichte der Beziehungen zwischen Theologie und Naturwissenschaft mit besonderer Rücksicht auf Schöpfungsgeschichte (vol. 1, Gütersloh, 1877). F. E. Robbins: The Hexaëmeral Literature (Thesis, Chicago, 1912).

For their cosmological views, see P. Duhem: Système du Monde (t. 2, 393–501, 1914). Salvatore Ciarcià: Il sistema cosmografico e i Padri della Chiesa (117 p., Messina, 1923; Isis, VIII, 212).

For their anatomical, physiological, and medical views see M. Neuburger: Geschichte der Medizin (vol. 2, 75–80, 1911).

BASIL

St. Basil; Basil the Great. Βασίλειος. Born at Caesarea, Cappadocia, c. 331; bishop of Caesarea from 370, died in 379. One of the Greek fathers of the church. The most interesting of his many writings is his "Hexaëmeron" (Ἑξαήμερον), nine popular sermons on Genesis I, which he made toward the end of his life. It was not the first work of the kind, but certainly the best; it exerted a deep influence upon patristic literature and remained an unsurpassed model during the Middle Ages. Such a subject involves naturally cosmological theories and scientific explanations. Basil's "Hexaëmeron" reveals a great deal of scientific curiosity and is an excellent source for the study of the popular knowledge of his time. Basil explained by lunar action not only the water tides, but also atmospheric tides.

Texts—Benedictine edition by Julien Garnier (3 vols., Paris, 1721–1730). Migne: Greek Patrology (vol. 29–32, Paris, 1857). English translation in The Nicene and Post-Nicene Fathers (2d series, edited by Wace and Schaff, 1890–1900; for the Hexaëmeron, see vol. 8). Anglo-Saxon version of the Hexaëmeron, or Be Godes six daga weorcum . . . . edited by H. W. Norman (2d edition, 77 p., London, 1849).

Criticism—M. Croiset: Littérature grecque (t. 5, 929–939, 1899). Karl Weiss: Die Erziehungslehre der drei Kappadozier (95 p., Diss., Freiburg i. B., 1903). Paul Plass: De Basilii et Ambrosii excerptis ad historiam animalium pertinentibus (Diss., 56 p., Marburg, 1905). Theodore Leslie Shear: The Influence of Plato on St. Basil (Thesis, 62 p., Baltimore, 1906). E. F. Morison: St. Basil and his Rule (162 p., London, 1912). W. K. Lowther Clarke: St. Basil the Great (185 p., Cambridge, 1913). Lynn Thorndike: Early Christianity and Natural Science (Biblical Review, vol. 7, 322–356, 1922. Forming ch. 21 of his History of Magic, 1923).

EPIPHANIOS

St. Epiphanios. Ἐπιφάνιος. Born in Palestine c. 315; abbot of the monastery of Eleutheropolis, near Jerusalem; from 367 on, bishop of Constantia in Cyprus, where he died in 403. One of the Greek fathers of the church. Theologian and historian. His book called the "Bread Basket" (Πανάριον;[a] in Latin, Contra haereses) composed c. 374 to 377, is a criticism of eighty heresies (20 of them being anterior to Christ). For example, it contains abundant information on Manichaeism. He wrote after 392 a treatise "on the twelve gems in the breastplate of the Hebrew high priest" (περὶ τῶν ιβ' λίθων ἐν τῷ λογίῳ τοῦ ἱερέως ἐμπεπηγμένων, Liber de XII gemmis rationali summi sacerdotis Hebraeorum infixis), which is one of the earliest Christian lapidaries.

Texts—Opera omnia, Greek and Latin edition by D. Petavius (2 vol. folio, Paris, 1622). The text of the Christian lapidary will be found in vol. 1, p. 333–334. The part of the Panarium relative to the Greek philosophers is included in Diels's Doxographi graeci (Berlin, 1879). Ancoratus und Panarion, edited by Karl Holl: Die griechischen christlichen Schriftsteller der ersten drei Jahrhunterte, vol. 25 and 31 (Leipzig, 1915-1922).

Criticism—M. Croiset: Littérature grecque (t. 5, 928, 1899). Karl Holl: Die handschriftliche Überlieferung des Epiphanius (100 p., Leipzig, 1910). Lynn Thorndike: Early Christianity and Natural Science (Biblical Review, vol. 7, 332–356, 1922. Reprinted in his History of Magic, ch. 21, 1923).

AMBROSE

St. Ambrose. Born c. 337 to 340 in Treves, where his father was the Roman prefect of Gallia Narbonensis; educated in Rome; baptized in 374 and consecrated

[a] It is interesting to note that this is not a genuine Greek word, but simply a transliteration of the Latin word panarium.

bishop of Milan a few days later; he died in 397. Christian theologian, one of the fathers of the church. He struggled with indomitable energy against paganism and Arianism. He wrote various works on theology and biblical commentaries ("Hexaëmeron," etc.), which interest the historian of science only in a very indirect way. Yet St. Ambrose cut too great a figure in the intellectual life of the second half of the fourth century to be neglected.

Text—Migne: Latin Patrology (vols. 14 to 17). Modern edition by Carl Schenkl: Opera (Pars I–VI, Vienna, 1896–1919. Corpus scriptorum ecclesiasticorum latinorum, 32, 62, 64).

Criticism—Guido Maria Dreves: Aurelius Ambrosius, der Vater des Kirchengesanges (151 p., Freiburg i. Br., 1893). Raymond Thamin: Ambroise et la morale chrétienne au IVe siècle; étude comparée des traités "Des devoirs" de Cicéron et d'Ambroise (492 p., Paris, 1895. Annales de l'Université de Lyon, t. 8). Ambrosiana, Scritti varii pubblicati nel XV centenario dalla morte di S. Ambrogio, con introduzione d'Andrea C. cardinale Ferrari (693 p., Milano, 1897). Paul Plass: De Basilii et Ambrosii excerptis ad historiam animalium pertinentibus (Diss., 56 p., Marburg, 1905. Ambrose used the writings of Basil). Peter Asslaber: Die persönlichen Beziehungen der drei grossen Kirchenlehrer, Ambrosius, Hieronymus, und Augustinus (Wien, 1908). David Heinrich Müller: Die Deutungen der hebräischen Buchstaben bei Ambrosius (27 p., Kais. Akad. d. Wissensch., Sitzungsber., phil. Klasse, vol. 167, 2, Wien, 1911).

JEROME

St. Jerome; Hieronymus. Born at Strido,[b] Dalmatia, c. 340 to 350; his period of greatest activity began with his residence in Bethlehem, c. 386, where he lived until the end, 420. One of the Latin fathers of the church. Historian and theologian. His main works from our point of view are his Latin translation of the Bible, his translation and adaptation of Eusebios's Chronicles, and their extension down to 378. He wrote the latter work probably in 379 to 381 at Constantinople.[c] He began a revision of the Latin versions of the Bible in 384, at Rome, with reference to the best Greek manuscripts. However, he soon realized the insufficiency of the Septuagint and the necessity of referring also (for the Old Testament) to the Hebrew and Aramaic texts.[d] The greatest part of his Latin translation (the so-called Vulgate) was done in Bethlehem between 386 and 404.[e]

Texts—Opera omnia, edited by Erasmus (9 t. in 4 vols., Bale, 1565). The most important texts are published in Migne: Patrologia latina (vol. 27 to 29), and in Corpus script. eccl. lat. (t. 59, 1913).

Eusebius Pamphili: Chronicon a sancto Hieronymo latine versu, et ab eo, Prospero et Matthaeo Palmerio usque ad annum 1481 continuatun (Venice, 1483). Hieronymi Chronicorum codicis floriacensis fragmenta leidensia, parisina, vaticana, phototypice edita: praefatus est Lud. Traube (Leyden, 1902).

Ernest A. Wallis Budge: The Paradise or Garden of the Holy Fathers, being

---

[b] Near the modern town Grahovo.

[c] The West knew Eusebios's Chronology only through Jerome's translation The latter's importance in European historiography is thus truly fundamental.

[d] Jerome was apparently the first Latin father who knew Hebrew and realized its importance.

[e] The Vulgate is the only Latin version which the Roman Catholic Church considers authentic. The Douai (or Douay) Bible is the English version of the Vulgate (N. T., Rheims, 1582; O. T., Douai, 1609–1610).

Histories of the Anchorites, Recluses, Monks, Coenobites, and Ascetic Fathers of the Deserts between 250 and 400, compiled by Athanasius, Palladius, St. Jerome, etc., translated out of the Syriac, with Notes and Introduction (2 vols., New York, 1909; pref. 1907).

Palestinae descriptiones ex saeculo IV, V, et VI, edited by Titus Tobler (St. Gallen, 1869. Including the Peregrinatio S. Paulae). The pilgrimage of the Holy Paula, translated by Aubrey Stewart, with notes by Sir C. W. Wilson (Palestine Pilgrims' Text Soc., London, 1885).

Criticism—According to Labriolle, the most important study of Jerome is that by G. Grützmacher: Hieronymus (3 vols., Leipzig, 1901–1908). Jakob Ecker: Psalterium juxta Hebraeos Hieronymi in seinem Verhältnis zu Masora, Septuaginta, Vulgata mit Berücksichtigung der übrigen alten Versionen untersucht (Trier, 1906). Peter Asslaber: Die persönlichen Beziehungen der drei grossen Kirchenlehrer, Ambrosius, Hieronymus, und Augustinus (Wien, 1908). Joh. Nep. Brunner: Hieronymus und die Mädchenerziehung auf Grund seiner Briefe an Laeta und Gaudentius (56 p., München, 1910). Arthur Stanley Pease: Medical Allusions in the Works of St. Jerome (Harvard Studies in Classical Philology, vol. 25, 73–86, Cambridge, 1914). P. de Labriolle: Littérature latine chrétienne (445–500, table 7, 1920). Ferdinand Cavallera: Saint Jérome, sa vie et son oeuvre (2 vols., 344 et 229 p., Louvain, 1922; Isis, VII, 534).

Progress of Buddhism

The development of Buddhist logic by Dignāga is considered in the following section.

HUI YÜAN

Hui[4] Yüan[3] (5193, 13743), surnamed Chia[3] (1181). Native of Yen[4]-mên[2] (13137, 7751) Shansi; born in 333; flourished at Lu[2]-fêng[1] (7402, 3564), Hupeh, from 373 until his death in 416. Chinese Buddhist. Founder of a Buddhist school, the Ching-t'u tsung;[f] which is exceedingly popular in China and Japan. It has influenced every form of later Buddhism in spite of the fact that it is quite separate from, and almost antagonistic to, the higher Mahāyāna thought. The Ching-t'u is not really a sect or school, but rather a point of view. There are no pure Amidists, except among the uneducated, but every Buddhist is more or less of an Amidist. The favorite scriptures of the Amidists are the Pure Land (or Lotus) sūtras.[g]

H. A. Giles: Chinese Biographical Dictionary (342, 1898). R. F. Johnston: Buddhist China (London, 1913, passim).

Introduction of Buddhism into Korea

In the fourth century Korea was still divided into three kingdoms, san-kan, or San[1] han[2] (9552, 3827): the kingdoms of Koma, Kudara, and Shiragi.

Koma (also called Kōrai, Shin Kan, or Ch'ên[2] Han[2] (656, 3827), or Ko-gur-yu) was the first to receive the gospel of Buddhism, in 372, from a priest of Hsin[1]-an[1]-fu[3] (4574, 44, 3682).

Twelve years later, in 384, a Hindu priest called Masananda brought Buddhism to Kudara (Hakusai; Ben-Kan or Pien[4] Han[2] (9197, 3827); Pakche).

---

[f] Ching[4]-t'u[3]-tsung[1] (2176 or 2177, 12099, 11976) meaning the Pure Land school. It is also called Lien[2] tsung[1] (7115, 11976) (Lotus school), Hêng[2] ch'ao[1] (3915, 506) (the Short Cut), and Amidism. The corresponding Japanese sect is called Jōdo-shū (second half of twelfth century).

[g] For which see my note on Chih-i (second half of sixth century).

Finally, Shiragi (Shinra, Silla, Ba-Kan, or Ma[3] Han[2], 7576, 3827) was evangelized by a missionary from Koma, in 424.

Frederick Starr: Korean Buddhism (123 p., Boston, 1918).

III. HELLENISTIC AND HINDU PHILOSOPHY

JULIAN THE APOSTATE

Flavius Claudius Julianus, nephew of Constantine the Great; born at Constantinople in 331; exiled from 337 to 343 at Macellum in Cappadocia; flourished then for a time at Nicomedia and Athens; raised to the Caesarship in 355 at Milan, he spent the years 355 to 359 pacifying Gaul; proclaimed emperor in 359, he ascended the throne at Constantinople in 361. He died on the battlefield during a campaign against the Persians, at Maranga, east of the Tigris, not far from Ctesiphon, in 363. Roman emperor; Greek philosopher. Brought up as a Christian, he became more and more convinced of the superiority of ancient philosophy. He attempted vainly to restore the Hellenic traditions jeopardized by the success of Christianity.[h] His main works are a treatise Against the Christians (Κατὰ Χριστιανῶν, largely lost) and a satire on the inhabitants of Antioch, called the Beard-hater (Μισοπώγων), both written at Antioch c. 362–363. These and other works of Julian (including many letters) are of great importance for the history of thought. Idea of determinism and of the molding action of soil and climate upon men.[i] Description of Lutetia (Paris) (in Misopogon). Julian's works contain autobiographical effusions, such as are rarely found in ancient or mediaeval literature.[j]

Text—Opera quae quidem reperiri potuerunt omnia, edited by S. Cramoisy (977 p., Paris, 1630. Greek and Latin). Edition by F. C. Hertlein (2 vols., 650 p., Leipzig, 1875–1876). Edition by Wilmer Cave Wright, with English translation (Loeb Library, 3 vols., London, 1913–1923). Oeuvres complètes, texte et traduction française par J. Bidez (Paris, 1924 sq.; Isis, VII, 534).

Librorum contra Christianos quae supersunt, edited by K. J. Neumann (252 p., Leipzig, 1880). Epistulae, leges, poematia, fragmenta varia, edited by J. Bidez and F. Cumont (Paris, 1922; Isis, V, 493).

Bücher gegen die Christen, German translation by K. J. Neumann (52 p., Leipzig, 1880). Georg Mau: Die Religionsphilosophie Kaiser Julians in seinen Reden auf König Helios und die Göttermutter (Leipzig, 1907, with German translation of both). Philosophische Werke übersetzt von Rudolf Asmus (230 p., Leipzig, 1908).

Augusto Rostagni: Giuliano l'Apostata. Saggio critico con le operette politiche e satiriche, tradotte e commentate (Torino, 1920).

Criticism—Charles William Kind: Julian the Emperor, containing Gregory Nazienzen's Two Invectives and Libanius's Monody with Julian's extant theosophical works (302 p., London, 1888). Alice Gardner: Julian and the Last Struggle of Paganism against Christianity (384 p., Heroes of the Nations, New York, 1895). Wilhelm Koch: Julians Jugend und Kriegsthaten bis zum Tode des Kaisers Constantinius (331–361). Jahrbuch für classische Philologie (Supp. Bd. 25, 329–

---

[h] It is well to insist that this was not by any means a struggle of rationalism against unreasoned faith. It was rather a fight between Hellenic and Neoplatonic traditions and superstitions on the one hand and Jewish and Christian beliefs and customs on the other.

[i] In Contra Christianos, Neumann's edition (p. 185–186). Talbot's French translation (p. 332–333).

[j] They suggest comparisons with St. Augustine and al-Ghazzālī.

488, 1899). T. R. Glover: Life and Letters in the IVth Century (47–76, 1901). Gaetano Negri: Giuliano (2d edition, revised, 542 p., Milano, 1902: Englished by the Duchess Litta-Visconti-Arese, 2 vols., 670 p., New York, 1905). Richard J. H. Gottheil: Selection from the Syriac Julian Romance (Syriac, with English and German Glossary. 112 p., Leiden, 1906). Paul Allard: Julien (3e éd. revue, 3 vols., Paris, 1906–1910). Joh. Geffcken: Kaiser Julianus (Das Erbe der Alten, 8, Leipzig, 1914). Edward J. Martin: Julian, and Essay on his Relations with the Christian Religion (128 p., London, 1919). J. Bidez: Evolution de la politique de Julien en matière religieuse (Bull. Ac. de Belgique, lettres, 406–461, 1914; Isis, IV, 133); La jeunesse de Julien (*ibidem*, 197–216, 1921; Isis, IV, 398); L'apostasie de Julien (Bull. de l'Association G. Budé, No. 7, 9–14, 1925). R. Anthony: Julien et la question du déterminisme morphologique en biologie (Revue anthropologique, Janv. 1919. Reprinted in his book Le déterminisme et l'adaptation morphologiques en biologie animale. I. 49–57, Paris, 1922. Anthony's claim, that Julian was a forerunner of the theory of evolution, of Lamarckianism, seems a little extravagant. See Isis, V, 456).

The extraordinary drama of Julian's life was bound to tempt artists. It will suffice to recall Henrik Ibsen's play Emperor and Galilean (1873) and the historic novel written by Dmitriĭ Sergieevich Merezhkovskiĭ, Julian the Apostate (also entitled, in another English translation, the Death of the Gods).

THEMISTIOS

Θεμίστιος, born in Paphlagonia, flourished mainly in Constantinople. Philosopher, educator. Tutor of Arcadios (b. 383), emperor of the East from 395 to 408. He wrote paraphrases of Aristotle (Later Analytics; Physics; de Anima). His paraphrase of the Metaphysics, book Λ, was translated into Arabic (ninth century), thence into Hebrew (1255) and Latin (1576). His official orations (Πολιτικοὶ λόγοι) are remarkable because of their religious tolerance.

Texts—Opera omnia, hoc est Paraphrases et Orationes, edited by Victor Trincavellius (Venice, 1534).

Paraphrasis in Posteriora Aristotelis, in Physica, etc. (Venice, 1499). Commentaria in Posteriora, in Physica, in libros De Anima (Venice, 1520). Paraphrases Aristotelis librorum quae supersunt, edited by Leon. Spengel (2 vols., Leipzig, 1866, in Greek).

The following texts have been published in the Commentaria in Aristotelem graeca, Berlin: In Analyticorum priorum librum I ed. by Maxim. Wallies (1884); In De Anima, by Ric. Heinze (1899); In Physica, by Heinrich Schenkl (1900); In Analyticorum posteriorum, by Maxim. Wallies (1900); In De Caelo, hebraice et latine, by Samuel Landauer (1902); In Parva naturalia, by Paul Wendland (1903); In Metaphysicorum librum Λ, hebraice et latine, by Samuel Landauer (1903).

The Orationes have been edited by Dionysius Petavius (Paris, 1618, Greek and Latin), and by G. Dindorf (Leipzig, 1832).

Criticism—P. Duhem: Système du monde (t. 4, 383 sq., 1916). Sandys: History of Classical Scholarship (vol. 1³, 352, 1921).

Theodore Haarhoff: The Schools of Gaul. A Study of Pagan and Christian Education in the Last Century of the Western Empire (284 p., Oxford, 1920; Isis, IV, 398).

DIGNĀGA

Ācārya Dignāga. He was nicknamed, because of his dialectical strength, the Bull in discussion (Sanskrit, Tarka-puṅgava). His Tibetan name is Phyogs-glaṅ. Of Brāhman caste; born near Kāñci, modern Conjeeveram in the Madras

Presidency; he flourished in Andhra, modern Telingāna in the Madras Presidency; he is said to have died in a solitary wood in Orissa. He was a pupil of Vasubandhu (q. v., previous chapter), and thus he flourished probably in the second half of the fourth century. Buddhist philosopher. He it is who introduced formal logic into Buddhism. His works, so far as they are extant, are preserved in Tibetan translation in the Tanjur.[k] His influence throughout Buddhist Asia is comparable to Aristotle's influence upon Western logic.[l]

Criticism—Satis Chandra Vidyabhusana: Dignāga and his Pramāṇa-samuccaya (Journal Asiatic Society of Bengal, vol. 1, 1905); History of the Mediaeval School of Indian Logic (78–101, Calcutta, 1909, with a portrait (!) taken from the Tanjur and the analysis of his main works); Influence of Aristotle on the Development of the Syllogism in Indian Logic (Journal R. Asiatic Society, 469–488, 1918).

A. B. Keith: Indian Logic and Atomism (Oxford, 1921); Buddhist philosophy (p. 305–307, Oxford, 1923). P. Masson-Oursel: Philosophie comparée (105–138, Paris, 1923).

IV. HELLENISTIC, ROMAN, JEWISH, AND CHINESE MATHEMATICS AND ASTRONOMY

THEON OF ALEXANDRIA

Flourished under Theodosios the Great, 378 to 395, and before c. 365 to 372. Greek astronomer and mathematician. Teacher at the Museum of Alexandria. Father of Hypatia (q. v., next chapter). Editor of Euclid. It was thought for a long time during the Middle Ages that Euclid had simply enounced the geometrical propositions but that Theon had proved them! His most important work is his (incomplete) commentary on the "Almagest" and on other writings of Ptolemy. Multiplication, division, and approximate extraction of square roots of sexagesimal fractions. The genuineness of the scholies to Aratos, ascribed to him, is uncertain. Theon mentions the precession of the equinoxes, and accepts the Ptolemaic value of it (one degree per century).[m] He tells us that according to some astronomers the precession was not progressive, but restricted to an oscillation along an arc of 8°.

Text and Translations—See the critical edition of Ptolemy, also earlier editions, Halma's for instance.

Criticism—Julius Lippert: Theon in der orientalischen Literatur (Studien auf dem Gebiete der griechisch-arabischen Übersetzungsliteratur, p. 39–50, Braunschweig, 1894). Eduard Scheer: Theon und Sextion (19 p., Progr., Saarbrüchen, 1902). J. L. E. Dreyer: Planetary Systems (203, 276, 1906). H. Bürger und K. Kohl: Geschichte des Transversalensatzes (Abhdl. z. Geschichte der Naturwiss., Heft 7, 41–4, Erlangen, 1924; Isis, VIII, 799).

PAUL OF ALEXANDRIA

Παῦλος, flourished c. 378. Greek astrologer. Wrote c. 378 an astrological introduction (Εἰσαγωγὴ εἰς τὴν ἀποτελεσματικήν) which contains the oldest astrological chorography extant.

---

[k] One of these texts at least is translated from a Chinese version of the Sanskrit original. Two of his works had been translated from Sanskrit into Chinese c. 557–569.

[l] It was Dignāga's logic which Hsüan Tsang carried with him to China in 645, and which the Japanese monk Dōshō, a disciple of Hsüan Tsang, transmitted to Japan c. 658. See S. Sugiura: Hindu Logic as Preserved in China and Japan (38–41, Philadelphia, 1900).

[m] This is very remarkable, because, outside of Ptolemy, Hipparchos's great discovery was never mentioned by ancient writers except by Proclos (q. v., second half of fifth century), who denied it!

Text published by Schato (Witebergae, 1586). Franz Cumont: La plus ancienne géographie astrologique (Klio, t. 9, 263–273, 1909).

HEPHAESTION OF THEBES

Hephaestion of Thebes, Egypt. Ἡφαιστίων. Flourished c. 381. Greek astrologer. Author of an astrological compilation entitled Ἀποτελεσματικά, in three parts: (1) Astronomical introduction; (2) genethlialogy proper; (3) doctrine of καταρχαί (i. e., the right beginnings).

See A. Engelbrecht: Hephaestion von Thebes und sein astrologisches Compendium (102 p., Wien, 1887). Boll, in Pauly-Wissowa (t. 15, 309, 1912).
For a translation of Aratos by Avienus, see my note in Section VII.

HILLEL II

Jewish patriarch from 330 to 365. Reformer of the Jewish calendar. Political persecutions making it impossible for the dispersed Jewish communities to communicate each year with the Judean Sanhedrin for the determination of fasts and feasts, Hillel II fixed the calendar for the whole Diaspora and for all time to come, in 358[n] (= 670 Sel.).

See article Calendar by Cyrus Adler (Jewish Encyclopedia, vol. 3, 498–501, 1902), and article Hillel II by Rabbi S. Mendelsohn (*ibidem*, vol. 6, 400, 1904). F. K. Ginzel: Handbuch der mathematischen Chronologie (2. Bd., 70–80, 1911. Discussing the whole question of the reform of the Jewish calendar; that Hillel was the author of the reform is doubtful; the oldest instances of the use of the modern Jewish calendar dating respectively from A. D. 717, 846, 929).

CHIANG CHI

Chiang[1] Chi[4*] (1233, 843). Flourished under the Eastern Chin, c. 385. Chinese astronomer. He corrected the calendar in 385 and explained moon eclipses.

L. Wieger: La Chine (142, 325, 1920).

V. ROMAN AND CHINESE TECHNOLOGY

VEGETIUS

Flavius Renatus Vegetius. Flourished at some time between 383 and 450, possibly under Theodosios, 379 to 395. Author of the "Epitoma rei militaris, sive institutorum rei militaris libri quinque," a compilation on military and naval art, which is of interest to the historian of technology (e. g. description of the onager, of the Roman navy, of a system of military telegraphy).

Text and Translations—Ed. princeps (Utrecht c. 1473). The abundance of manuscripts and the prompt publication of translations in the vernacular languages prove the popularity of this book. A German translation by Ludwig Hohenwang appeared in Augsburg (1476).[o] An English translation through the French was printed by Caxton (Westminster, 1489. The book of fayttes of armes of Chrystyne of Pyse). See also L'art de chevalerie par Jean de Meun, and Li

---

[n] Date generally but not unanimously accepted. The Jewish year exceeds the Gregorian year by about 6m. 40s.

[o] This was the first technical book to appear in German. It was illustrated by means of plates taken from the first edition of Valturio, q. v., second half of fifteenth century (Verona, 1472). These illustrations of machines remained unique in Germany for eighty years (see Feldhaus: Die Technik (1914, article Hohenwang).

abrejance de l'ordre de chevalerie, both texts edited by Ulysse Robert and published by the Société des anciens textes français (2 vols., Paris, 1897). Scientific edition by Karl Lang (Leipzig, 1869). English translation by John Clarke (London, 1767).

Criticism—See my note on P. R. Vegetius, probably identical with F. R. Vegetius, in Section VIII. Max Jähns (Gesch. d. Kriegswissenschaften, 1889).

Invention of Real Black Ink

The invention of real ink occurred in China most probably some time in the fourth or fifth century. It is ascribed to a man named Wei² Tan⁴ (12527, 10644), but this ascription is made rather late, by Lu⁴*-yu³ (7432, 13429) of the Yüan dynasty (as quoted in the Tz'ŭ² yüan² (12402, 13704) dictionary, under the word mo⁴* (8022), ink). Before the fourth century the Chinese did not use real ink, but a lacquer (called ch'i¹*, 1023) made of tree sap. The new ink was made of lamp black; our modern "India ink" (more correctly "encre de Chine") is essentially similar to the original one. It is peculiarly indelible and the best ink, even to this day, for use with wooden blocks, but it is not satisfactory for taking impressions from metal, and a new kind of ink (an oily ink) had eventually to be invented to make western typography possible.

I said in the title of this note "black ink," for another kind of ink—red ink—had been used in China at least since the Han dynasty. That red ink was made simply of cinnabar (mercury sulphide), which exists in China (province of Kueichou) in the natural state. Red ink was soon restricted to imperial use; the same happened in Constantinople c. 470.

It should be noted that both lampblack ink and cinnabar were used by the Egyptians long before the Chinese; they would seem to have been invented independently in both countries. The invention is important because of its cultural value, but it is a very simple one.

See Samuel Couling: Encyclopaedia sinica (250, 1917). T. F. Carter: Invention of Printing in China (New York, 1925; Isis, VIII, 361). Berthold Laufer: History of Ink in China (in the course of preparation; end 1925).

Since writing the above, Laufer's capital study on Chinese ink has appeared in Frank B. Wiborg: Printing ink (New York, 1926: Isis, IX). According to Laufer, the discovery of ink occurred earlier than I said, as early as the first half of the third century, because Wei Tan (or Wei Chung-tsiang), who was in all probability the inventor, flourished during the Wei dynasty (220–264).

VI. ROMAN AND HELLENISTIC NATURAL HISTORY AND HUSBANDRY

AUSONIUS

Decimus Magnus Ausonius. Born at Bordeaux c. 310; tutor to Gratian; consul in 379; died near Bordeaux[p] c. 390. Roman teacher and poet. Author of many didactic and other poems. The most interesting of them, as well as the most pleasing, is the Mosella, a description of the river Moselle apropos of a journey (c. 370) from Bingen on the Rhine up the Moselle to Treves. This contains recognizable descriptions of some sixteen species of fishes (brook and salmon trout, etc.).

---

[p] Probably at Lucaniac (St. Emilion). The "Château Ausone," "Premier des grands crus de St. Emilion," is thus named because the vineyard producing this special "cru"—well known to amateurs of Bordeaux wine—is traditionally supposed to be located upon the very grounds of Ausonius's villa. I discovered this during the course of a pilgrimage to St. Emilion which I made on September 11, 1925.

Text—Opera. First edition, Venice, 1472. Later editions Venice, 1494, 1496; Parma, 1499, etc.

Opera omnia edited by A. J. Valpy (2 vols., London, 1823). Opuscula recensuit Carolus Schenkl (Berlin, 1883).

Latin edition with English translation by Hugh G. Evelyn White (Loeb Library, 2 vols., 1919–1921).

Mosella: Edition of the Mosella, with German translation and ichthyological commentary by Oken (Isis, 5–44, 1845). Critical edition with French translation, introduction, facsimile of early editions by Henri de La Ville Mirmont (Bordeaux, 1889). Carl Hosius: Mosella, hrg. und erklärt. Anhang. Die Moselgedichte des Venantius Fortunatus (Marburg, 1894; again 1909).

Criticism—Terrot Reaveley Glover: Life and Letters in the Fourth Century (102–124, Cambridge, 1901). René Pichon: Les derniers écrivains profanes (Paris, 1906). Albert Delachaux: La latinité d'Ausone (Thèse, Lausanne, Neuchâtel, 1909). Percival Richard Cole: Later Roman Education in Ausonius, Capella, and the Theodosian Code, with Translations and Commentary (39 p., New York, Teachers' College, Columbia, 1909). Pierre de Labriolle: Un épisode de la fin du paganisme; la correspondance d'Ausone et de Paulin de Nole (63 p., Paris, 1910). Henri de La Ville de Mirmont: Le MS. de l'ile Barbe (Cod. leidensis Vossianus latinus III) et les travaux de critique sur le texte d'Ausone, l'oeuvre de Vinet et l'oeuvre de Scaliger (3 vols., Bordeaux, 1917–1921).

ANATOLIUS OF BERYTOS

Vindonius Anatolius of Berytos (i. e., Beirut in Syria), flourished in the fourth or fifth century.[q] He compiled a collection of Greek writings on agriculture, in 12 books (Συναγωγὴ γεωργικῶν ἐπιτηδευμάτων), which was one of the main sources of the Byzantine geoponica.[r] This collection was translated into Syriac by Sergios of Resaina (q. v., first half of sixth century); and the Syriac version was in its turn the basis of an Arabic adaptation by Qusṭā ibn Lūqā (second half of ninth century).

Text—See the edition of the Geoponica by Joa. Nic. Niclas (Leipzig, 1781) and Paul de Lagarde: Geoponicon in sermonem Syriacum versorum quae supersunt (Leipzig, 1860).

Criticism—E. H. F. Meyer: Geschichte der Botanik (vol. 2, 258–261, 1855). Wilhelm Gemoll: Untersuchungen über die Quellen der Geoponica (Berliner Studien, Bd. 1, 1883). Eugen Oder: Beiträge zur Geschichte der Landwirthschaft bei den Griechen (Rheinisches Museum, vol. 45, 212–222, 1890). M. Wellmann, in Pauly-Wissowa (vol. 2, 2073, 1894).

DIDYMOS

Δίδυμος. Of Alexandria. Flourished at the same time as Anatolios, that is, in the fourth or fifth century. Agriculturist and physician. He compiled an agricultural treatise called Γεωργικά, in 15 books. This was one of the main sources of the Byzantine geoponica. He wrote also a medical treatise in 8 books (Ὀκτάτομος); it contained a number of wonderful remedies (φυσικά), for example, against hiccups.

[q] If he is identical with the jurist and civil servant, Anatolius of Berytos, nicknamed Azutrio, the date can be given with greater precision, for Azutrio flourished under Julian the Apostate and died in 360–61.

[r] For which see my note on Constantinos Porphyrogennetos (q. v., second half of tenth century.

Same references as the preceding note, plus M. Wellmann, in Pauly-Wissowa (vol. 9, 445, 1903).

VII. ROMAN AND HELLENISTIC GEOGRAPHY

AVIENUS

Rufus Festus Avienus. Flourished in the second half of the fourth century. Roman poet and geographer. Wrote a translation of Aratos's Phaenomena and Prognostica, and a paraphrase of the Περιήγησις of Dionysios (second half of first century), Descriptio orbis terrae—both in hexameters. He composed a description of the shores of the Mediterranean, Caspian, and Black Seas in iambic trimeters, "Ora maritima," of which only a fragment is extant. This poem contains the only account of the Carthaginian expedition along the Western coast of Europe under Himilco in the fifth century B. C.[a]

Text and Translations—Edited by J. C. Wernsdorf in the Poetae latini minores (Vol. V, without the Aratea). Edited by Alfred Holder (Ad Aeni Pontem, 1887). Aratea edited by Alfr. Breysig (102 p., Leipzig, 1882). Latin text with French translation by E. Despois and Ed. Saviot (Paris, 1843). Antonio Blasquez y Delgado-Aguilera. Avieno. Ora maritima. Edicion critica y estudio geográfico (Bol. de la R. Soc. geog., t. 44, 1923–24).

Criticism—Wilh. von Christ: Avien und die ältesten Nachrichten über Iberien und die Westküste Europa's (Abhdl. d. bayer. Akad., cl. I, t. 11, München, 1865). Gustavus Sieg: De Cicerone Germanico Avieno Arati interpretibus. (Diss., 52 p., Halle, 1886). C. Ihlemann: De Avieni in vertendis Arateis arte et ratione. (Diss., 94 p., Goettingen, 1909). Joh. Frank: Beiträge zur geographischen Erklärung der Ora Maritima (Diss., Würzburg, 85 p., Sangerhausen, 1913, with map and bibliography).

ITINERARIES AND OTHER GEOGRAPHICAL WORKS

For the "Iterinarium Antonini Augusti" and the "Tabula Peutingeriana," see my note on Geography in the first half of the third century.

Itineraries in General—Titus Tobler: Palestinae descriptiones ex saeculo IV, V, et VI (149 p., St. Gallen, 1898. Ed. with notes of the following texts: Itin. Burdigala Hierusalem usque; S. Paulae perigrinatio auctore S. Hieronymo; S. Eucherii epitome de aliquibus locis sanctis; Theodori liber de situ Terrae Sanctae). Paul Geyer: Itinera Hierosolymitana saeculi IIII–VIII (Corpus scriptorum ecclesiasticorum latinorum, t. 39, Vienna, 1898).

The Bordeaux-Jerusalem Itinerary—Written by a Christian in 333 A. D.: Itinéraire de Bordeaux à Jérusalem d'après un manuscrit de la bibliothèque du chapitre de Vérone, ... publié par Anatole de Barthélemy (Revue archéologique, t. 10, 98–112, 1864). Itinerary from Bordeaux to Jerusalem translated by Aubrey Stewart, annotated by Sir C. W. Wilson (Palestine Pilgrims' Text Society, 5, 80 p., London, 1887).

Charles Clermont-Ganneau: Observations sur quelques points des côtes de la Phénicie et de la Palestine d'après l'Itinéraire (Bull. de la Soc. de géogr., 43–54, juillet 1883).

The Pilgrimage of Etheria—This pilgrimage was made by Etheria (or Silvia) of Aquitania to Jerusalem in 385. An account of it was found by G. F. Gamurrini in Arezzo, 1884, and published by him (Rome, 1887). According to some, the Peregrinatio Aetheriae dates only from the sixth century. German translation by

---

[a] But this expedition is briefly mentioned by Pliny. See my note on Geography in the fifth century B. C.

Hermann Richter (110 p., Essen, 1919; Isis, IV, 399); English translation by M. L. McClure and C. L. Feltoe (London, 1920).

Apropos of this and other contemporary pilgrimages to Palestine, see T. R. Glover: Life and Letters in the Fourth Century (chapter 6, Women pilgrims, 125–147, 1901).

Expositio totius mundi et gentium—Latin translation of a Greek text which is lost. Description of the Roman Empire at the time of Constantius, 337 to 361; the only one, said Mommsen (Römische Geschichte, vol. 5, p. 461) in which industrial conditions were considered.

Text published by C. Müller in the Geographi graeci minores (II, 513–518, 1861); also by Alex. Riese in the Geographi latini minores (104–126, 1878), finally, with abundant notes, by Giacomo Lumbroso (90 p., Roma, 1903).

Ludwig Hahn: Die Sprache der sogenannten Expositio (Diss., Erlangen, 98 p., 1898).

Stadiasmus maris magni—The most important of the ancient Periploi, dating from the fourth or fifth century or even later. The title is: Σταδιασμὸς ἤτοι περίπλους τῆς μεγάλης θαλάσσης or Stadiasmus maris magni.

Ed. princeps by Iriarte (1769). Text, Latin translation and notes by C. Müller in his Geographi graeci minores (Vol. I, 427–514, CXXIII–CXXVIII, Paris, 1855).

Konrad Kretschmer: Die italienischen Portolane des Mittelalters (159–163, Berlin, 1909).

VIII. HELLENISTIC AND ROMAN MEDICINE

THEODOROS

Theodoros or Theodosios. Flourished in Persia under Shāpūr II, king from 309 to 379.[4] Greek Christian physician. Wrote a compendium of medicine in Pahlawī, which was later translated into Arabic (lost, but mentioned in the Fihrist).

Leclerc: Médecine arabe (t. 1, p. 24, 1876). E. G. Browne: Arabian medicine (p. 20, 1921).

HIEROCLES

Ἱεροκλῆς. Flourished about the middle of the fourth century or later. Greek veterinary surgeon, one of the greatest of antiquity. He wrote a work in two books on the care of horses (περὶ ἵππων θεραπείας).

Text—The text of Hierocles's work is included in the Hippiatrica, compiled probably during the reign of Constantinos Porphyrogennetos (q. v., second half of tenth century). First Latin edition by Jean Ruelle of Soissons (Paris, 1530). First edition of original Greek text by Simon Grynaeus (Basel, 1537). Italian translation (Venice, 1543); French translation (1563).

A new edition is being prepared by Eugen Oder.

Criticism—Gossen, in Pauly-Wissowa (vol. 16, 1489, 1713–1715, 1913. Containing information on Hippiatrica in general and mentioning various ancient authors whom I could not consider in this Introduction),

ORIBASIOS

Ὀρειβάσιος or Ὀριβάσιος. Born c. 325 at Pergamum, died about the beginning of the following century. Eminent Greek medical encyclopaedist. Friend and physician of Julian the Apostate. He wrote a vast medical encyclopaedia in 70

---

[4] The length of Shāpūr's reign is accounted for by the fact that he was solemnly crowned while still in his mother's womb, the crown being placed upon her body. Theodoros being explicitly mentioned as Shāpūr's physician and friend, we may assume that he flourished toward the middle or in the second half of the century.

books (Ἰατρικαὶ συναγωγαί), of which only one-third is still extant, a summary of it (σύνοψις), and a book of home medicine (εὐπόριστα, Remedia parabilia). This work has considerable historical value, because Oribasios quoted his authorities with great care, often verbatim. His frequent commendation of Galen prepared the latter's immense popularity. He fought courageously against the rising tide of superstition.

Text and Translations—Greek text with French translation by Bussemaker and Daremberg, in six large volumes (Paris, 1851–1876. Collection des médecins grecs et latins).

Criticism—E. H. F. Meyer: Geschichte der Botanik (vol. 2, 261–273, 1855). Hermann Hagen: De Oribasii versione latina Bernensi (Progr., 24 p., Berne, 1875). E. Gurlt: Geschichte der Chirurgie (vol. 1, 527–544, 1898). Bernh. Faust: De machinamentis ab antiquis medicis ad repositionem articulorum luxatorum adhibitis. Commentarius in Oribasii librum XLIX (Diss., Greifswald, 1912). Willy Heinecke: Zahnärztliches in den Werken des Oreibasios (Diss., 21 p., Leipzig, 1922; Isis, V, 207).

PHILAGRIOS

Φιλάγριος. Born in Epirus, flourished in Thessalonica in the second half of the fourth century. Greek physician and medical writer. Many medical observations and discoveries were made by him. He is chiefly famous for his diagnosis and treatment of diseases of the spleen.

Text and Translations—Latin text (the Greek being lost), with German translation published by Theod. Puschmann: Nachträge zu Alexander Trallianus (p. 74–129, Berlin, 1886).

Iwan Bloch, in Puschmann: Geschichte der Medizin (vol. 1, 489–490, 1902; also 372).

POSIDONIOS THE PHYSICIAN

Ποσειδώνιος, brother of Philagrios.[u] Greek physician, psychiatrist. He made a deep study of brain diseases and a first attempt of localization of functions in the brain. Among the phenomena of which he gave descriptions, together with therapeutic indications, were phrenitis, lethargy (λήθαργος and κάρος), coma, catalepsy, giddiness, nightmare (ἐφιάλτης), epilepsy, melancholy, hydrophobia (λύσσα). His investigations were partly based upon those of the great physicians of the second century,[v] but largely upon his own observations.

Texts—Only fragments are extant. A. Lewy and Landesberg: Über die Bedeutung des Antyllus, Philagrius, und Posidonius (Henschel's Janus, vol. 2, 758–771, 1847; vol. 3, 166–184, 1848).

Criticism—Iwan Bloch, in Puschmann: Geschichte der Medizin (vol. 1, 489–490, 1902). Max Neuburger: Geschichte der Medizin (vol. 2, 54–56, 1911).

NEMESIOS

Νεμέσιος. Flourished in Emesa, Syria, at the end of the fourth or the beginning of the fifth century. Christian philosopher. Bishop of Emesa. Author of a book on the nature of man (περὶ φύσεως ἀνθρώπου) which was very much appreciated during the Middle Ages,[w] and contains interesting views on human physiology.

---

[u] Their father was Philostorgios, also a physician, living at the time of Valens (364 to 378) and Valentinianus II (375–92).

[v] Archigenes, Rufus, Aretaeos, Galen.

[w] It was formerly ascribed to Gregory of Nyssa (c. 332 to 395).

Text and Translations—Ed. princeps with Latin translation (Antwerp, 1565). Best edition, Greek and Latin, by Chr. Friedr. Matthaeus (538 p., Halle, 1802). Latin translation by Alfanus, edited by C. Holzinger (Leipzig, 1887); by Burgundio of Pisa in 1159, edited by C. I. Burkhard (134 p., Progr., Wien, 1891–1902); by N. Alfanus, Archbishop of Salerno, edited by C. I. Burkhard (166 p., Leipzig, 1917). English translation by Geo. Wither (London, 1636), German translation by Osterhammer (Salzburg, 1819). French translation by J. B. Thibault (Paris, 1844).

Criticism—Bol. Domanski: Die Psychologie des Nemesius (Beitr. zur Gesch. d. Phil. des Mittelalters, vol. 3, Münster, 1900). Hans Krause: Studia neoplatonica (Diss., Leipzig, 1904). We. Wi. Jaeger: Nemesios. Quellenforsch. zum Neoplatonismus (Berlin, 1914). Heinrich A. Koch: Quellenforschungen zu Nemesios (Diss., 52 p., Berlin, 1921).

VINDICIANUS

Born in Africa, flourished under Valentinian I, 364 to 375. Roman physician. Wrote "Gynaecia" and "De expertis remediis;" extracts from the former book remaining. Much admired by Priscianus and by his friend St. Augustine, who states that Vindicianus did not believe in astrology.

Text and Translations—See Priscianus. Joseph Schipper: Ein neuer Text der Gynaecia aus einer Münchener Hds. des 12. Jahrhundertes (Diss., Leipzig, 29 p., Erlangen, 1911; Isis, IV, 577). Christoph Ferckel: Ein deutscher anatomischer Vindiciantext (Archiv für Geschichte der Medizin, vol. 7, 306–318, edition and commentary).

Criticism—Karl Sudhoff: Zur Anatomie des Vindicianus. Handschriftenstudie (Archiv für Gesch. der Medizin, Bd. 8, 414–423, 1915); Ein neues deutsches anatomisches Vindizianfragment und anderes Medizinische in einer Basler Handschrift des 14. Jahrhundertes (*ibidem*, Bd. 9, 168–171, 1916).

PRISCIANUS

Theodorus Priscianus. Physician to Gratianus, 367 to 383. Roman physician, disciple of Vindicianus. Author of a book of medicine, the Euporiston or Medicinae praesentaneae, chiefly a collection of therapeutic prescriptions (Book I, Faenomenon deals with external ailments a capite ad calcem; Book II, Logicus, with internal medicine; Book III, Gynaecia, with female disorders. Fragments of the so-called Physica contain popular remedies.

Text and Translations—Theodori Prisciani Euporiston libri III cum physicorum fragmento et additamentis Pseudo Theodoreis, edited by Val. Rose, accedunt Vindiciani Afri quae feruntur reliquiae (Leipzig, 1894). German translation by Theod. Meyer-Steineg: Theod. Priscianus und die römische Medizin (352 p., Jena, 1909; Mitt. zur Gesch. d. Medizin, Vol. IX, 163–166).

Criticism—E. H. F. Meyer: Geschichte der Botanik (vol. 2, 286–299, 1855, with a list of plants).

VEGETIUS

Publius Renatus Vegetius. Probably the same individual as Flavius dealt with in Section V. Author of a work on veterinary art called Mulomedicina.

Text and Translations—P. Vegetii Renati digestorum artis mulomedicinae libri, edited by Ern. Lommatzsch. Accedit Gargili Martialis de curis boum fragmentum (385 p., Leipzig, 1903).

Criticism—Christoph Schöner: Studien zu Vegetius (Progr., 44 p., Erlangen, 1888. Concluding that the same individual was the author of the Epitoma and the Mulomedicina, and lived in the second half of the fourth century, probably in Austria).

The Mulomedicina Chironis is the main source of Vegetius's Mulomedicina. It is a translation in rustic Latin by one Claudius Hermerus of a Greek original ascribed to Chiron "the Centaur" and Apsyrtos (q. v., first half of fourth century). Apsyrtos's book was published c. 334. The text of the Mulomedicina Chironis has been edited by Eug. Oder (504 p., Leipzig, 1901, with elaborate indexes). Max Niedermann: Proben aus der sogenannten Mulomedicina Chironis (Buch II und III) (Sammlung vulgärlateinischer Texte, 3, 78 p., Heidelberg, 1910).

Ernst Lommatzsch: Zur Mulomedicina Chironis (Archiv f. lat. Lexicographie, 12, 401–410, 551–559, 1901–1902). Helge Ahlquist: Studien zur spätlateinischen Mulomedicina Chironis (148 p., Upsala, 1909. Grammatical studies). Einar Löfstedt: Zur Mulomedicina Chironis (Glotta, vol. 3, 19–33, 1910).

PLACITUS

Sextus Placitus Papyriensis. Also called Sextus Philosophicus Platonicus. Flourished probably in the second half of the fourth century. Author of the Liber de medicina ex animalibus, in 34 chapters, dealing with various drugs of animal origin.

Text—Editio princeps, Nuremberg, 1538. Second or third edition, De medicina animalium, bestiarum, pecorum et avium, with scholia by Gabriel Hummelberger (122 p., Zürich, 1539). Also in Ackermann (Parabil. med. script. 1, Nürnberg, 1788).

Anglo-Saxon partial version De quadrupedibus in Cockayne's Leechdoms (vol. 1, 326–373, 1864). New edition of the Medicina de quadrupedis by Joseph Delcourt, with translation and glossary (Thèse, Paris, Anglistische Forschungen, 40, 91 p., Heidelberg, 1914).

Criticism—August Hirsch, in his Biographisches Lexicon (vol. 5, 1887, 378), puts him in the sixth century. Julius Pagel, in Puschmann: Handbuch (vol. 1, 622, 1902).

For the Medicina Plinii, see my note on Pliny in the second half of the first century.

IX. ROMAN HISTORIOGRAPHY

AMMIANUS

Ammianus Marcellinus. Born in Antioch, Syria, c. 325–330; still living in 391. Roman historian. Author of a history from Nerva to Valens's death (96–378), Rerum gestarum libri XXXI (only the last 18 books, covering the years 353 to 378, are extant). Valuable because of its honesty and because of the many geographic and scientific digressions (earthquakes, plague, rainbow, etc.). But for his lack of style, Ammianus would have been a great historian.[1]

Text—Editio princeps (incomplete) by Sabinus (1474); completed by Accursius (1533). Scientific edition by V. Gardthausen (2 vols., Leipzig, 1874–1875). Heinr. Nissen: Fragmenta marburgensia (Berlin, 1876). Latest edition by Charles Upson Clark, Ludw. Traube, and Wilh. Heraeus (2 vols., Berlin, 1910–1915). English translation by C. D. Yonge (Bohn Collection, London, 1862).

Criticism—Max Büdinger: Ammianus und die Eigenart seines Geschichtswerkes (Denkschr. d. K. Akad. d. Wiss., Wien, Philos. hist. Classe, vol. 44, 1895). Léon Dautremer: Ammianus (248 p., Travaux de l'université de Lille, 23, Lille, 1899). T. R. Glover: Life and Letters in the Fourth Century (20–46, 1901). Mary Jackson Kennedy. The Literary Work of Ammianus (Diss., Chicago, 65 p., Lan-

[1] See Gibbon's brief but impressive encomium of him in the Decline and Fall (Bury's edition, vol. 3, p. 128).

caster, Pa., 1912). Walter Klein: Studien zu Ammianus (Klio, 13. Heft, 136 p., Leipzig, 1914). Wilhelm Ensslin: Zur Geschichtsschreibung und Weltanschauung des Ammianus (Klio, Beiheft 16, 106 p., Leipzig, 1923).

SULPICIUS SEVERUS

Born in Aquitania c. 360, flourished in Bordeaux, Toulouse, Tours; died in the beginning of the fifth century. Christian historian.[y] Author of a "Chronica," a summary of Christian history from the creation to 400. He owed his popularity mainly to his "Life of St. Martin"[z] (at whose feet he had sat in Tours), written in 397 (additional Dialogues published in 403–4).

Text—Migne: Latin Patrology (vol. 20, 95–248). Edition by Carl Halm in Corpus script. eccl. lat., I (Vienna, 1866).

Chronica, with French translation by Lavertujon (2 vols., Paris, 1896–1899). Vita Martini edited by Dübner-Lejay (Paris, 1890).

Criticism—Heinrich Gelzer: Sextus Julius Africanus (vol. 2, 107–121, 1885). T. R. Glover: Life and Letters in the Fourth Century (278–302, Cambridge, 1901). P. de Labriolle: Littérature latine chrétienne (508–516, 1920).

X. ROMAN LAW

The Collatio legum Mosaicarum et Romanorum[a] is an anonymous compilation made probably soon after 390, certainly before 428, the aim of which is to compare Mosaic law as set forth in the Pentateuch with the Roman law of the time. It is one of the earliest monuments of comparative law.

Edited by Krüger and Mommsen in the Collectio Juris Antejustiniani (vol. 3, 137–198, Berlin, 1895). P. F. Girard: Textes de droit romain (3e éd., p. 543–577, 1903). M. Hyamson: Latin text with English translation (Oxford, 1913).

---

[y] Scaliger called him "ecclesiasticorum purissimus scriptor."

[z] The influence of the Vita Martini is attested by the many conscious or unconscious imitations of it in the mediaeval Latin biographies (see Max Manitius: Lateinische Literatur des Mittelalters, vols. 1–2, 1911–1923, passim).

[a] Or Lex Dei quam praecipit Dominus ad Moysen.

CHAPTER XXI

THE TIME OF FA-HSIEN

(First Half of Fifth Century)

I. Survey of Science in First Half of Fifth Century. II. Religious Background. III. Hellenistic and Roman Philosophy IV. Hellenistic, Hindu, and Chinese Mathematics and Astronomy. V. Hellenistic and Chinese Alchemy, Physics, and Technology. VI. Chinese and Armenian Geography. VII. Roman, Hellenistic, Hindu, and Korean Medicine (including Botany and Biology). VIII. Hellenistic, Roman, Armenian, and Chinese Historiography. IX. Roman and Barbarian Law. X. Armenian and Greek Philology.

I. SURVEY OF SCIENCE IN FIRST HALF OF FIFTH CENTURY

1. It may seem strange to give a Chinese title to this chapter, but this will help the reader to remember that China was becoming one of the most important provinces of mankind. Also the name of Fa-hsien suggests Buddhism, which was then in one of its most vigorous phases—a civilizing power equal to Christianity and already spread over an immense area. Moreover, the monk Fa-hsien was one of the greatest travelers of all ages. There is, however, an essential difference between him and the Christian missionaries who roamed across Europe at the same time; they went out to teach, he went out to learn.

2. *Religious Background*—The tendency which I mentioned at the end of my survey of the previous period—the diffusion of Mediterranean culture into the interior of Europe—was considerably accelerated in the fifth century by the activity of Christian missionaries. Their main concern was to announce the Gospel and to teach savages the love of God and man; this was in itself, however humble their success, an immense step forward; but outside of that, they could not help carrying with them a part of Roman civilization. The most remarkable of these apostles was St. Patrick, thanks to whose activity Ireland became an important secondary center of cultural diffusion.

Christianity influenced the progress of civilization in another way, by causing the publication of new translations of the Bible into Ethiopic, Armenian, and Georgian. Thus was the fundamental struggle against illiteracy—a primary tillage of the ground, so-to-say—carried into new territories.

And still in a third way did Christianity promote the intellectual advance. The innate jealousy and irritability of theologians is a centrifugal force which continuously tends to drive out and to drive farther and farther away those of them whose intellectual submission and conformity are not absolute. The cultural diffusion is thus accomplished not only by missionaries, but also by religious refugees and exiles, by those who have been cast out, by heretics. The Nestorian heresy, which originated in 431, is one of these great centrifugal forces due to theological hatred; it pushed Christianity across the mountains and the deserts as far as China and thus became a very important link between East and West.

Another heresy, Pelagianism, started at the same time, but it remained restricted to Western Europe and its cultural importance is very small.

The greatest theologian of the age was St. Augustine. His main works were written during the latter part of his life, that is, in the first quarter of the fifth century. He developed the idea of potential creation, thus reconciling (more than 1,400 years before there was a theological need for it) the Christian idea of creation and the scientific idea of evolution. A number of Christian historians flourished in those days, but I shall deal with them in my historical section below.

Under the leadership of Rabbi Ashi (d. 427), Sura became once more the intellectual center of Babylonia. He was one of the main editors of the Talmud.

The patriarch Kumārajīva translated various Buddhist sūtras from Sanskrit into Chinese. In the meanwhile, Buddhist doctrine was magnificently rounded out by Buddhaghosa, the greatest representative of Buddhist scholasticism. Buddhaghosa flourished in Anurādhapura, Ceylon, and wrote in Pāli.

3. *Hellenistic and Roman Philosophy*—The main philosophers of this age were Neo-Platonists: Synesios, the alchemist; Macrobius, whose commentary on Cicero's Dream of Scipio was one of the main sources of Platonism in the Christian world before the middle of the twelfth century; finally, Syrianos, who became the head of the Academy and wrote commentaries on Aristotle and Plato. The writings of Macrobius are of special interest to us, because of the many scientific glimpses which they afford.

4. *Hellenistic, Hindu, and Chinese Mathematics and Astronomy*—The daughter of Theon of Alexandria, Hypatia, wrote commentaries on Apollonios, Ptolemy, and Diophantos. Her murder at Alexandria in 415 by a Christian mob is a date in the history of thought. Greek science, which had once been supreme and had made of Alexandria a second Athens, was no longer tolerated.

The Hindu Siddhāntas date possibly from the first half of the fifth century. They are largely based upon Greek mathematics and astronomy, but contain some original views. The most important of these—indeed, its importance can hardly be overestimated—is the introduction of the notion of sine, in the place of the clumsy chords used by Ptolemy.

Two Chinese astronomers of that time deserve to be named, Ch'ien Lo-chih and Ho Ch'êng-t'ien.

5. *Hellenistic and Chinese Alchemy, Physics, and Technology*—Bishop Synesios, in a letter to his teacher Hypatia, mentions a kind of hydrometer. He composed a very important alchemical writing, a commentary on Pseudo-Democritos. Another alchemical treatise was written by the historian Olympiodoros.

The manufacture of glass, which had been practiced for a considerable time in Egypt, was introduced into China, at once in the North and in the South, during this period.

6. *Chinese and Armenian Geography*—The most arresting personality of this age was that of the Chinese Buddhist Fa-hsien. He accomplished, between 399 and 414, one of the most remarkable journeys on record. To obtain Buddhist scriptures he traveled from Central China to India, crossing the Gobi Desert and the Hindu Kush Mountains, and returned home by sea by way of Ceylon and Java. The account of his journey is an eloquent witness of the progress of Buddhism in those days.

The Armenian historian Moses of Chorene wrote a geography which was largely based upon the lost treatise of Pappos, and is especially valuable with regard to the chorography of Armenia and neighboring countries.

7. *Roman, Hellenistic, Hindu, and Korean Medicine (including Botany and Biology)*—Marcellus Empiricus of Bordeaux wrote, c. 410, a book of medicaments the scientific level of which is very low. Cassius Felix, who flourished a little later, probably in Carthage, wrote a medical treatise derived largely from Galen. Caelius Aurélianus, another African, probably a contemporary of Cassius Felix, translated a lost treatise of Soranos. The botanico-medical treatise ascribed to Apuleius, and also based upon Greek models, dates probably from the same time. To complete this account of Roman (or Latin) medicine and biology, I might recall here Augustine's theory of potential creation above mentioned.

The only Greek-writing physician was Palladios the Iatrosophist, who flourished in Alexandria, and wrote a treatise on fevers and Hippocratic commentaries.

The Bower Manuscript, dating from c. 450, contains two medical tracts. It is of importance as a help in determining the chronology of Sanskrit medicine.

It would seem that Korean physicians were called to Japan, the earliest in 414, another c. 468. This would be one of the earliest links between the Chinese and Japanese civilizations.

8. *Hellenistic, Roman, Armenian, and Chinese Historiography*—It is convenient for our synthetic purpose to divide the Western historians into two groups—the Pagan and the Christian; these two groups are almost evenly balanced.

To the first group belong Eunapios, who wrote a history of his time (from 270 to 404) and a series of biographies of Neoplatonic philosophers; Zosimos, who wrote a history of the Roman Empire down to the sack of Rome by Alaric in 410; and the alchemist Olympiodoros, who wrote a history of the Western Empire from 407 to 425.

The Christian historians were Socrates of Constantinople, who completed Eusebios's work down to 439; Sozomen and Theodoretos, these three writing in Greek; and the Spaniard Orosius, who composed the earliest Christian universal history.

Moses of Chorene, Mesrop's pupil, wrote an account of Armenian history down to 440.

Fan Yeh compiled the official annals of the Eastern Han Dynasty (25 to 220).

9. *Roman and Barbarian Law*—The Codex Theodosianus, so-called after Theodosius II, Emperor of the East from 408 to 450, was promulgated in January 439. It exerted a deep influence upon ulterior legislation, Roman and Barbarian. The Codex Arcerianus, the substance of which dates probably from the middle of the fifth century, is a collection of administrative documents which is of great interest for the history of Roman surveying and of kindred subjects.

The most important document of ancient Irish law is the so-called Senchus Mór, which was edited in 438.

10. *Armenian and Greek Philology*—The translations of the Bible into Ethiopic, Armenian, and Georgian dealt with in Section II, are, of course, of considerable philological interest—each marks the beginning of a new language, of a new conscious type of civilization. The case of Armenia is the most significant. Mesrop, who died in 440, not only translated the Bible into his national language, but invented a new Armenian alphabet, the first successful one. He fully deserves to be called the Father of Armenian Literature.

Two Hellenistic lexicographers must be named—Orion, who compiled an etymological dictionary, and Hesychios, whose lost work is said to have been the most extensive Greek dictionary of antiquity.

11. *Final Remarks*—This was an age, not of scientific conquest, but rather of in-

tellectual tilling, of cultural diffusion. The crops are few, but it is a time of intense and widespread sowing; the crops will come later. So many were the tillers and sowers, and they worked with such enthusiasm in so many fields, that the spectacle is truly impressive. To consider only the protagonists, St. Patrick in Ireland, Eunapios and Syrianos in Athens, Zosimos, Socrates, and Sozomen in Constantinople, Augustine and the Spaniard Orosius in Hippo, Synesios in Cyrenaica, Hypatia in Alexandria, Nestorios in Upper Egypt, Mesrop and Moses in Armenia, Ashi in Sura, Theodoretos in Syria, and farther away still, Buddhaghosa in Ceylon and Kumārajīva in Nanking!

Europe and the Near East are slowly but steadily conquered by Christianity; the murder of Hypatia in 415 is one of the last blows to Paganism. In the meanwhile, Eastern Asia is conquered by Buddhism, and Fa-hsien, in his astounding journey, encompasses the Buddhist world even as Paul, about three and a half centuries before, had encircled the newly born Christian world of his days.

The greatest scientific advance of this time has not yet been taken into account in this final summary, because its date is uncertain and because it is anonymous. I refer to the introduction of the notion of sine. This seed was apparently of no great moment, like a mustard seed, but falling upon the fertile ground of Greek geometry, it helped to constitute one of the most useful branches of mathematics, trigonometry.

II. RELIGIOUS BACKGROUND

Christianization of Europe

A complete history of science should give brief but full information on the gradual process of Christianization because, in spite of some obscurantist tendencies (which did not become conspicuous until much later), Christianism was the vehicle by means of which civilization was introduced into the greatest part of barbarous Europe.[a] To name all the missionaries who carried the Gospel into every country, the founders of the first monasteries, and some of the early bishops of every see, would take me too far out of my way. A general account, clear and well ordered, will be found in Charles Henry Robinson's "The Conversion of Europe" (664 p., London, 1917, with select bibliography and good index).

In this note I shall simply draw the reader's attention, for the sake of example, to a missionary whose influence was exceptionally great. St. Patrick (born in Great Britain c. 389; studied under St. Martin at Tours; died at Saul in 461)[b] was not the first missionary into Ireland, but he was by far the greatest and became its patron saint. He wrote in Latin and caused Latin to become the ecclesiastical language of Ireland, a fact of great consequence.

Irish monasticism dates back to the days of St. Patrick. Its development was remarkably vigorous, and Ireland soon became one of the most civilized countries of the West and the nursery of many missionary activities into almost every large district of northern or central Europe. No country did a larger share in the Christianization of the world at that time than did that little island.

Antoine Fréderic Ozanam: La civilisation au Ve siècle (2d. ed., 2 vols., Paris, 1862); English translation by A. C. Glyn (2 vols., London, 1868. Strong Roman Catholic bias). Kuno Meyer: Learning in Ireland in the Fifth Century and the Transmission of Letters (29 p., Dublin, 1913).

[a] See my note on Christian monasticism in the first half of the fourth century.

[b] Dates according to J. B. Bury; see Robinson, op. cit., 56.

TRANSLATIONS OF THE BIBLE

An Ethiopic version was first made in the fifth or sixth century. The Armenian version appeared before the middle of the fifth century; it was begun by Mesrop (q. v., in Section X) and completed by Moses of Chorene (q. v.). We owe to Mesrop, also a Georgian, or Iberian version. The Ethiopic, Armenian, and Georgian versions were all derived from the Septuagint. But the Ethiopic represented purely the Greek tradition of the Scriptures, while the Armenian and Georgian texts, being based upon Origen's investigations, embodied as well fragments of the Hebrew tradition.

J. Oscar Boyd: The Text of the Ethiopic Version of the Octateuch (30 p., Bibl. abessinica, Princeton, 1905).

Fréderic Macler: Le texte arménien de l'Evangile d'après Matthieu et Marc. (Annales du Musée Guimet, 719 p., Paris, 1919).

NESTORIANISM

The Syrian priest Nestorios, born at Germanicia, near Mount Taurus, was consecrated patriarch of Constantinople in 428. His intelligence and excessive zeal, more than doctrinal differences, caused him to become the victim of jealousies and intrigues and he was brutally deposed at the council of Ephesus in 431. Nestorios retired into a monastery of Antioch; in 435 he was banished to Petra in Arabia, and later to the Great Oasis in Upper Egypt and suffered many more vicissitudes; he died after 450. The heretical doctrine imputed to him consisted in denying the complete mergence of the divine and human natures into one person in Christ, and in claiming that Mary, the Mother of Christ, ought not to be called the Mother of God (θεοτόκος). It would seem, however, that the heresy called Nestorianism does not represent Nestorios's thought, but is a distortion of it.

The Nestorians emigrated eastward and many of them went to Edessa, where a school of medicine had been flourishing for centuries. The school of Edessa became the center of Nestorian influence until 489, when it was closed by order of the emperor Zeno. This caused a further dispersion of the Nestorians, who had considerable missionary zeal and carried their doctrines throughout the whole length of Asia. The Nestorian heresy is thus very important, even if one is not at all interested in the theological discussions involved, because it was for many centuries one of the main links between East and West.

The seat of the Nestorian catholicos was transferred in 498 to Seleucia-Ctesiphon on the Tigris, and in 762 to Bagdad. The rapid diffusion of Nestorianism is attested by the presence of Nestorian bishoprics as far as Merv and Herat before the end of the fifth century (Paul Pelliot: T'oung Pao, vol. 15, 624). "In almost every site excavated by the German expedition in Turkestan, remains of Christian churches were found, with manuscripts in Syriac and Persian as well as in Chinese and the languages of Central Asia. Even the correspondence of some of these priests with their mother churches in Syria has been unearthed." (T. C. Carter: Invention of Printing in China, 90, 1925, wherein other instances of Nestorian penetration may be found.) See also my note on the Nestorian monument of 781 in the chapter dealing with the second half of the eighth century. Marco Polo found Nestorian churches all along the main roads as far as Pekin.

The medical school, to which I alluded above, was succeeded by the school of Nisibis in Mesopotamia (then under Persian rule), noticed by Cassiodorus, and by the school of Jundīshāpūr (q. v., first half of sixth century). Many Greek works on mathematics and medicine were translated into Syriac during the fifth century, and the Nestorians had a large share in this. It is true no translator of that time was of outstanding importance, except perhaps Probos and Ibas, with whom I shall deal in the next chapter. This activity continued until the ninth century, becoming gradually more and more important. The later translations were made into Arabic, but generally with the help of Syriac versions. The point which I wish to emphasize here is that most of those translators were Christians, in all probability Nestorians. This is certainly the case with regard to the translations of Galen's works, as shown by Ḥunain ibn Isḥāq (q. v., second half of the ninth century). These Nestorians were especially well fitted for that task because of their polyglottism; they all knew Greek, Syriac, and (after the Muslim conquest) Arabic; some of them knew Persian.

Nestorios wrote in Greek an apology curiously entitled the "Book or the Bazaar[c] of Heraclides of Damascus." It is extant only in a Syriac version, which was edited by Paul Bedjan (674 p., Leipzig, 1910), and translated into French by François Nau (432 p., Paris, 1910) and into English by G. R. Driver and Leonard Hodgson (460 p., Oxford, 1925; Isis, IX).

See also Abbé Jérôme Lambert: Le Christianisme dans l'empire perse sous la dynastie sassanide (224–632) (Thèse., Paris, 1904). James Franklin Bethune-Baker: Nestorius and his Teaching (250 p., Cambridge, 1908). Friedrich Loofs: Anordnung der Fragmente des Nestorius (160 p., Halle, 1904); Nestorius and His Place in the History of Christian Doctrine (140 p., Cambridge, 1914).

It is interesting to note that there are still Nestorians (or East Syrians) to-day, in spite of continuous attempts on the part of other Christian churches (Roman Catholic, Orthodox, and Protestant) to win their allegiance. They are located in Persia and Turkey, in a district limited by the lakes of Urmia and Van, and Mosul.

Justin Perkins: A Residence of Eight Years in Persia, among the Nestorian Christians (530 p., Andover, 1843); Missionary Life in Persia (Boston, c. 1861). William Walker Rockwell: The Pitiful Plight of the Assyrian Christians in Persia and Kurdistan (2d ed., 72 p., New York, 1916).

Pelagianism

As it is not my purpose to write a history of the church, I deal only with those heresies which affected materially cultural exchanges. From this, our point of view, Nestorianism is extremely important. Another heresy of the same time, Pelagianism, was far less important—though it raised a considerable stir among western theologians. It will suffice to say a few words about it. The British (Irish?) theologian Pelagius went to Rome early in the fifth century and later (c. 409 to c. 415) to Palestine. He strongly opposed the Augustinian theory of predestination and of original sin; he claimed that man is endowed with a free will and that his sins are entirely his own ("If I ought, I can"). He was accused of heresy, but absolved by Palestinian synods; the accusation being repeated by the African church, he was condemned at Carthage in 418, and this condemnation was confirmed at the council of Ephesus in 431. However, as the extreme doctrines of St. Augustine never obtained any currency in the Greek and Oriental

[c] The Greek word was probably πραγματεία, which means study, philosophical argument, or treatise, but also business. Hence the Syriac mistranslation which was reproduced in English by means of the Persian word bazaar!

churches, the Pelagian controversy remained restricted to the West. It caused a good deal of theological rancor, but did not affect the course of civilization.

Heinrich Zimmer: Pelagius in Ireland (358 p., Berlin, 1901). Article by Marcus Dodds in Encyclopaedia Britannica (4 cols., 1911).

ST. AUGUSTINE

Aurelius Augustinus. Born in Tagaste, Numidia, 354; died during the siege of Hippo, 430. One of the greatest Fathers of the Church. Successively a Manichaean, a Neoplatonist, a Christian. He developed the idea of potential creation, which implies a theory of evolution. Augustine taught that the fetus is besouled during the second month and besexed during the fourth, and that premeditated abortion is equivalent to homicide. This view influenced law to a considerable extent. Two of his works which belong to the latter part of his life have become classics of the world literature: the "Confessions" and "The City of God" (De civitate Dei, begun c. 413, completed in 428). We find in them a unique combination of ancient thought, Christian faith, and modern psychology. The tremendous success of Platonism in the West was largely due to Augustine "The City of God" may be considered the first Christian philosophy of history.

Text and Translations—Benedictine edition of his works, newly published (11 vols., Paris, 1836–1839). Edition of the Vienna Academy (Corpus scriptorum ecclesiasticorum latinorum, Vienna, 1887–1913). It is noteworthy that 33 new sermons of St. Augustine were discovered and published during the war by Dom Germain Morin (O. S. B.): Sancti Aureli Augustini tractatus sive sermones inediti ex codice Guelferbytano (Wolfenbüttel) 4096 (Kempten im Schwaben, 1917). English translation edited by Philip Schaff (Vols. I–VII, Buffalo 1886–New York, 1888).

General Criticism—R. T. Glover: Life and Letters in the Fourth Century (194–215, 1901). Georg von Hertling: Augustin. Der Untergang der antiken Kultur (Weltgeschichte in Karakterbildern) (112 p., 50 illustr., Mainz, 1902. From the Roman Catholic point of view, interesting illustrations). Joseph McCabe: St. Augustine and his Age (516 p., London, 1902. Agnostic point of view). W. Montgomery: St. Augustine. Aspects of his Life and Thought (London, 1914). Prosper Alfaric: L'évolution intellectuelle de Saint Augustin. Du Manichéisme au Néoplatonisme (566 p., Paris, 1918. The most elaborate study as far as it goes; see Journal des Savants, 241–253, 1920).

Special Criticism—I do not know any comprehensive study of Augustine from our point of view. For his ideas on creation and evolution, see Henry Fairfield Osborn: From the Greeks to Darwin (p. 71–74, New York, 1894). S. Angus: The Sources of the First Ten Books of Augustine's De civitate Dei (281 p., Thesis, Princeton, 1906). Ed. O. von Lippmann: Der heilige Augustin über den Ätzkalk (Chemiker Z., 304, 1896; also Abhdl. und Vorträge, I, 77–80. Apropos of the beginning of the Bk. 21 of the De civitate Dei, written c. 415). Thomas Jones Parry: Augustine's Psychology during his First Period of Literary Activity, with Special Reference to his Relation to Platonism (Diss., Strassburg, 87 p., Borna-Leipzig, 1913). Th. Lamb. Haitjema: Augustinus' Wetenschapsidee; bijdrage tot de kennis van de opkomst der idee eener christelijke wetenschap in die antieke wereld (Diss., Utrecht, 1917). John Neville Figgis: The Political Aspect of Augustine's City of God (136 p., London, 1921). Johannes Hessen: Die Begründung der Erkenntnis nach dem heil. Augustinus (Beiträge zur Geschichte der Philosophie des Mittelalters, vol. 19, 2, 130 p., Münster, 1916). Charles Boyer:

L'idée de vérité dans la philosophie de St. Augustin (272 p., Paris, 1920, Catholic; Isis, VI, 143).

For the Christian historians, see Section VIII.

ASHI

Born in 352; flourished at Sura; died in 427. Jewish teacher and editor of the Talmud. He reestablished the Academy of Sura[d] and was its director for 52 years. Under Ashi's direction, Sura became again the leading intellectual center of Babylonia. Ashi did for the Gemārā what Judah ha-Nasi (second half of second century) had done for the Mishnāh, thus completing the Talmud. He revised the Gemārā twice. A final revision of the Talmud was made by Rabina (Rabina II., b. Huna), who was director of the Academy of Sura in 474 and died in 499.

See article by Wilhelm Bacher, in Jewish Encyclopaedia (vol. 2, 187, 1902).

KUMĀRAJĪVA

In Chinese: Chiu[1] Mo[1] Lo[2] (2267, 7969, 7291). Born probably at Kucha in the Tarim basin, Eastern Turkestan, of a Kashmirian family. He flourished from 383 to 401 in Kansu, then at the court of Yao[2]-ch'in[2] (12935, 2093) of the later (Eastern) Chin[4] (2070 or 2069) dynasty. He died c. 412. The nineteenth of the western patriarchs of Buddhism.[e] He translated the Lotus and Vimalakīrti sūtras into Chinese and dictated commentaries on them; he also translated the Satya siddhi śāstra and introduced into China the works of two main schools of Buddhist philosophy, the Sautrāntika and the Śūnyavāda. He wrote biographies of Aśvaghosha and Nāgārjuna, which were translated into Chinese in the fifth century. His translation of the Diamond sūtra (Prajñāpāramitā), printed in China in 868, is the earliest printed book extant.[f]

H. A. Giles: Biographical Dictionary (389, 1898).

BUDDHAGHOSA[g]

Born at Budh Gayā,[h] in northern India, c. 390, flourished there and in Anurādhapura, Ceylon. The greatest representative of Buddhist scholasticism. His main work is an encyclopaedia of Buddhist doctrine, in Pāli, "the Way of Purity" (Visuddhimagga).[i] During his stay in the Great Minster of Anurādhapura he translated the Buddhist commentaries from Singhalese into Pāli; he wrote commentaries on each of the four great collections or Nikāyas, wherein are recorded the very teachings of the Buddha. Commentaries on the whole of the canonical literature are ascribed to him, but it is likely that some of them, notably the Dhammapada commentary, are not his own work.

---

[d] Which had been closed since 309.

[e] Also called one of the Four Suns of Buddhism.

[f] See my note on Technology in the second half of the ninth century.

[g] "Voice of the Buddha."

[h] Near the Great Bodhi Tree (or Bo-tree, Tree of Wisdom) under which Gotama attained the supreme enlightenment.

[i] It is interesting to note that this work was written in Anurādhapura at about the same time that St. Augustine was writing the "Confessions" and the "City of God," in Hippo.

Texts and Translations—I do not attempt to quote all the editions, some of which appeared in India, Ceylon, and Burma.

The Visuddhi magga was edited by C. A. F. Rhys Davids (2 vols., Pāli text soc., London, 1920–1921). English translation by Pe Maung Tin (Part 1, Of virtue, or morals, 102 p., Pāli text soc., Oxford, 1922).

The Aṭṭhasālinī (The expositor). Buddhaghosa's commentary on the Dhammasaṅgaṇi, edited by Edward Müller (Pāli text soc., London, 1897). English translation by Maung Tin and Mrs. Rhys Davids (*idem.*, 2 vols., London, 1920–21; J. R. A. S., 127–132, 1922).

Sutta-nipāta commentary being Paramatthajotikā II, edited by Helmer Smith (*idem.*, London, 1916–1918).

Sumaṅgala-vilāsinī commentary on the Dīgha nikāya, edited by T. W. Rhys Davids and J. Estlin Carpenter (*idem.*, London, 1886).

Dhammapadaṭṭhakathā. Commentary on the Dhammapada, edited by H. C. Norman (5 vols., in 6, *idem.*, London, 1906–1915). Eugen Watson Burlingame: Buddhist Legends from the Dhammapada Commentary (3 vols., Harvard Press, 1921; Isis, V, 270).

Papañcasūdanī. Commentary on the Majjhima nikāya, edited by J. H. Woods and D. Kosambi (*idem.*, London, 1922).

Criticism—Mahāmaṅgala: Buddhaghosuppatti, or the historical romance of the rise and career of Buddhaghosa, edited by James Gray (84 p., London, 1892. English translation by same (London, 1892. An uncritical biography by a Burmese author of the fifteenth (?) century). The most reliable information on Buddhaghosa is derived from the Mahāvamsa (ch. 37 in Turnour's edition, Colombo, 1837), for which see my note on Mahānāma in the next chapter.

T. W. Rhys Davids: Article in Dictionary of Religion and Ethics (vol. 2, 881–885, 1910). Louis Finot: La légende de Buddhaghosa. Cinquantenaire de l'Ecole des Hautes Etudes (Mélanges, 101–119, Paris, 1921; reviewed in T'oung Pao, vol. 21, 243–244, by Paul Pelliot, and by Maung Tin in J. R. A. S., 265–269, 1923). Bimala Charan Law: The Life and Work of Buddhaghosa (200 p., Calcutta, 1923).

III. HELLENISTIC AND ROMAN PHILOSOPHY

For Synesios, see Section V below.

MACROBIUS

Ambrosius Theodosius Macrobius. Of Greek parentage, flourished probably under Honorius, 395 to 423, possibly before. Roman Neo-Platonist. Author of two works, the Saturnalia and a commentary on Cicero's Somnium Scipionis (in Book VI of De republica), both of which contain many incidental remarks on physics, astronomy, geography, mathematics. It gives one an idea of the scientific knowledge of an educated man of his time. The commentary on the Somnium was the main source of Platonism in the Latin West, before the middle of the twelfth century, outside of Chalcidius (q. v., first half of the fourth century).

Text and Translations—Ed. princeps (Venice, 1472). Edition by L. von Jan (Leipzig, 1848–1852). By F. Eyssenhardt (Leipzig, 1868; republished, 1893). Latin text with French translation by Henri Descamps and others (3 vols., Paris, 1845–1847).

Criticism—Hugo Linke: Quaestiones de Macrobii Saturnaliorum fontibus (56 p., Breslau, 1880). C. Biuso: Varroniana nonnulla ex antiquitatibus derivantia quae in Macrobii Saturnaliorum libris inveniuntur (63 p., Florence, 1882). R. T. Glover: Life and Letters in the Fourth and Fifth Century (171–193, 1901). Mat.

Schedler: Beiträge zur Philosophie des Macrobius (Diss., Freiburg i. B., 34 p., Münster i. Westf.; reprinted in the Beitr. zur Gesch. d. Philos. d. Mittelalters, vol. 13, 1916). See also P. Duhem: Système du Monde (t. 3, p. 47, 1915, on the motions of Venus and Mercury; p. 62, on his influence upon mediaeval thought). Thomas Whittaker: Macrobius, or Philosophy, Science and Letters in the Year 400 (110 p., Cambridge, 1923). Max Neuburger: Die Medizin im Macrobius und Theodoretus (Janus, 28, 155–172, 1925; Isis, VIII, 534).

SYRIANOS

Συριανός. Born in Alexandria c. 380; died in Athens c. 450. Neo-Platonic philosopher; teacher of Proclos. Head of the Academy, before Domninos and Proclos. Commentator of Aristotle (chiefly of his Metaphysics) and of Plato.

Text—In Metaphysica commentaria ed. Guil. Kroll (Comment. in Aristotelem graeca, VI, 1, Berlin, 1902).

Criticism—P. Duhem: Système du Monde (t. 1, p. 333, on place, 1913; t. 2, p. 99, on the value of astronomical hypotheses, 1914).

IV. HELLENISTIC, HINDU, AND CHINESE MATHEMATICS AND ASTRONOMY

HYPATIA

Ὑπατία. Born in Alexandria, flourished there at the end of the fourth and the beginning of the fifth century, murdered by a Christian mob in 415. Mathematician, astronomer, Neo-platonic philosopher. Daughter of Theon of Alexandria (q. v.). Wrote commentaries on Diophantos, Apollonios, and the Canon of Ptolemy (all lost). Scientific correspondence with Synesios (q. v.) between 404 and 407.

Criticism—Stephan Wolf: Hypatia, nach den Quellenschriften dargestellt (42 p., Wien, 1879). Paul Tannery: L'article de Suidas sur Hypatia. Annales de la Faculté des lettres de Bordeaux (t. 2, 197–201, 1880; Mémoires, I, 74–79). Guido Bigoni: Ipazia Alessandrina (Atti d. Istituto veneto, t. 5, 397–437, 495–526, 681–710, Venice, 1887). Praechter in Pauly-Wissowa (vol. 17, 242–249, 1914).

Hypatia as a Martyr of Science—The murder of Hypatia is the chief source of her immortality. Many writings have been inspired by it. I mention for the sake of curiosity John Toland's pamphlet entitled "Hypatia or the History of a most beautiful, most virtuous, most learned, and every way accomplish'd Lady; who was torn to pieces by the clergy of Alexandria, to gratify the pride, emulation and cruelty of their archbishop, commonly but undeservedly styled St. Cyril" (36 p., London, 1753, with a portrait of Hypatia!) and Charles Kingsley's famous novel, "Hypatia." Hedwig Bender: Märtyrer des freien Denkens aus alter und neuer Zeit (Sammlung gemeinverständlicher wissenschaftlicher Vorträge, Heft 132, vol. 6, 415–440, Hamburg, 1891).

The Siddhāntas

The earliest Hindu scientific works dealing with astronomy are the so-called siddhāntas. These are real treatises, largely theoretical, as opposed to works of a more practical nature called karaṇas, and to tables and commentaries. There were five Siddhāntas, as follows: the Sūrya-Siddhānta, the Paitāmaha-Siddhānta, the Vāsishṭha-Siddhānta, the Pauliśa-Siddhānta, and the Romaka-Siddhānta; but only the first one, the Sūrya, is extant in its original form. It is impossible to date them with any precision, and there are enough differences between them to justify the assumption that they were composed at different times. For example, they show many traces of Greek influence, but in different degrees, this influence being least conspicuous in the Paitāmaha and most conspicuous in the Romaka. We do not know through which channels Greek astronomy reached them, but they are very probably post-Ptolemaic. On the other hand, they were already well known when Varāhamihira wrote his Pañcasiddhāntikā in 505. They antedate also Āryabhaṭa. I place them tentatively in the first half of the fifth century.

The Sūrya-Siddhānta is the only one which seems to be completely extant. It is written in ślokas (epic stanzas) divided into 14 chapters. According to al-Bīrūnī, it was composed by Lāṭa, but it is probable that Lāṭa wrote simply a commentary upon it as he did (so says Varāhamihira) upon the Pauliśa and Romaka Siddhāntas. According to the text itself (introductory verses), it was written by Sūrya, the Sun God, in Romaka (Rome?, Alexandria?). The main astronomical doctrines are Greek, but the author, whoever he was, has obviously tried to preserve as much of the old Hindu astronomical lore as was possible without gross inconsistency; for example, it contains references to the conjunctions of planets with the nakshatras (Hindu zodiacal constellations), to the enormous periods of time beloved of the Hindus (yuga = 4,320,000 years; kalpa = 1,000 yugas, etc.), to the mountain Meru situated at the North Pole, etc. The most important feature of this comprehensive treatise is the consistent use of sines (jyā) instead of chords. It also contains the earliest mention of a versed sine (utkramājyā).[i]

The Pauliśa Siddhānta is equally important. We know it only through Varāhamihira and Varāhamihira's commentator, Bhaṭṭotpala (see my note in the first half of the sixth century). Al-Bīrūnī quotes it quite often under the name Pulisa, which, he says, is the name of a Greek who flourished in Saintra (Alexandria?). This has suggested an identification with Paul of Alexandria (q. v., second half of the fourth century), but it is impossible to substantiate it. The Pauliśa may be considered the foundation of Hindu trigonometry, a very original development of Greek geometry. It introduces the notion of sine and contains a table of 24 sines (and versed sines) progressing by intervals of 3° 45′. The table was constructed in the following manner. The sine of 3° 45′ (or 225′) was considered equal to the arc of 225′ (called kramajyā). The other sines up to sin 86° 15′ were calculated by means of a rule which we would express as follows:

$$\sin (n+1)\alpha = 2 \sin n\alpha - \sin (n-1)\alpha - \frac{\sin n\alpha}{\sin \alpha}$$

wherein $\alpha = 225' = \sin \alpha$.

The Romaka-Siddhānta contains even more traces of Greek influence than the two preceding ones. The length of the year is calculated as done by Ptolemy. The author speaks of a yuga of 2,850 solar years, unknown to Hindu tradition. This text differs so much from that of the Sūrya that one must admit that the authors of the Sūrya and the Romaka used different Greek sources. Perhaps the title of this siddhānta, the word Romaka, is itself of Greek origin.

There is less to say about the two-remaining Siddhāntas. The Paitāmaha seems to have been the least developed from the scientific point of view, the Vāsishṭha shows a better knowledge of astronomical facts.

Text and Translations—First printed edition of the Sūrya Siddhānta (Meerut, India, c. 1867; facsimile of a page in D. E. Smith: History of Mathematics,

---

[i] Or utramadjyā. In a circle of unit radius versin $a = 1 - \cos a$.

vol. 2, 625, 1925). The Sūrya Siddhānta, an ancient system of Hindu astronomy, with Ranganātha's exposition, the Gūḍhārtha-Prakāsaka edited by FitzEdward Hall (Bibliotheca Indica, published by the Asiatic society of Bengal, Nos. 79, 105, 115, 146, Calcutta, 1859). New edition, together with a commentary called Sudhavarsini, by Mahamahopadhyaya Sudhakara Dvivedi (*idem*, new series, Nos. 1187, 1296, Fasc. I–II, Calcutta, 1909–1911). English translation with elaborate notes by Ebenezer Burgess (Journal American Oriental Society, vol. 6, 141–498, New Haven, 1859–1860. Many of the notes were contributed by Professor Whitney and Hubert A. Newton).

The Sūrya Siddhānta is divided into 14 chapters, as follows: (1) Mean motions of the planets; (2) True places of the planets; (3) Direction, place and time; (4) Eclipses, especially lunar; (5) Parallax in a solar eclipse; (6) Projection of eclipses; (7) Planetary conjunctions; (8) Asterisms; (9) Heliacal risings and settings; (10) Moon's rising and setting; elevation of her cusps; (11) Certain malignant aspects of the sun and moon; (12) Cosmogony, geography, dimensions of the creation; (13) Armillary sphere and other instruments; (14) Different modes of reckoning time.

Criticism—Burgess's translation and commentary (1860). G. Thibaut: Astronomie, Astrologie, und Mathematik (Grundriss der indo-arischen Philologie, III, 9, Strassburg, 1899). A. von Braunmühl: Geschichte der Trigonometrie (I, 34–35, 1900. Containing the table of sines and comparisons with modern values). G. R. Kaye: Indian Mathematics (Isis, II, 326–356, 1919). M. Winternitz: Geschichte der indischen Litteratur (3, 557–561, 1920).

CH'IEN LO-CHIH

Ch'ien[2] Lo[4]*-chih[1] (1736, 7331, 1787). Flourished under the Liu[2] Sung[4] (7276, 10462), c. 436. Chinese astronomer. He constructed in 436 the earliest uranorama, a celestial sphere which was moved one degree each day.

L. Wieger: La Chine (161, 448, 1920).

HO CH'ÊNG-T'IEN

Ho[2] Ch'êng[2]-t'ien[1] (3941, 761, 11208). Flourished under the Liu Sung, c. 443. Chinese astronomer. He claimed that the solstices ought to be determined by direct observation.

L. Wieger: La Chine (306, 1920).

V. HELLENISTIC AND CHINESE ALCHEMY, PHYSICS, AND TECHNOLOGY

SYNESIOS

Συνέσιος. Born in Cyrene c. 370 to 375, died probably before Hypatia. Neoplatonic philosopher, later Christian. Pupil of Hypatia. Bishop of Ptolemaïs in Cyrenaica, after 410. In a letter to Hypatia (Ed. Hercher, Ep. 15, p. 172) he mentions a *βαρύλλιον*, that is, a kind of hydrometer. He composed one of the most important of the early alchemic writings (letter to Dioscoros), a commentary on (pseudo) Democritos.

Text and Translations—Opera omnia graece et latine, edited by Dionysius Petavius (Paris, 1612); improved edition appended to the works of Cyrillos of Jerusalem (Paris, 1640). French translation with introduction by H. Druon (632 p., Paris, 1878).

Edition of the Epistolae, Rudolf Hercher: Epistolographi Graeci (Greek and Latin, Paris, 1873). Edition of the alchemic writings by M. Berthelot: Collection des anciens alchimistes grecs (Vol. I, Paris, 1887. Greek text, French translation and commentary).

Criticism—Henri Druon: Étude sur la vie et les oeuvres de Synésius (306 p., Paris, 1859). Richard Volkmann: Synesius von Cyrene (268 p., Berlin, 1869). Eugen Gaiser: Des Synesius ägyptische Erzählungen oder über die Vorsehung (Diss., Erlangen, 40 p., Wolfenbüttel, 1886). Wilhelm Fritz: Die Briefe des Synesius. Ein Beitrag zur Geschichte des Attizismus im IV. and V. Jahrhundert (236 p., Leipzig, 1898). R. T. Glover: Life and Letters in the Fourth Century (320 356, 1901). A. Ludwig: Die Schrift περὶ ἐνυπνίων des Synesios (Theologie und Glaube, 7 Jahrg., Paderborn, 1905. A book on dreams of c. 403, interesting for the study of Neoplatonic superstition, and also for the history of psychology).

Scientific Criticism—John Ferguson: On the First Editions of the Chemical Writings of Democritus and Synesius (Proc. Philosoph. Soc. Glasgow, 11 p., 1884); Bibliotheca Chemica (t. 2, 421–422, Glasgow, 1906). Ed. O. von Lippmann: Entstehung und Ausbreitung der Alchemie (p. 96–98, Berlin, 1919).

Synesios was supposed to have mentioned the astrolabe in a letter to Peonios. This was a mistake (see P. Tannery, Mémoires, IV, 243).

OLYMPIODOROS

Ὀλυμπιόδωρος. Born in Thebes, Egypt, flourished under Honorius, 395 to 423, and a little later. Greek historian and alchemist (*ποιητής*). Member of an embassy sent by Honorius to Attila in 412. Author of a history of the Western Empire from 407 to 425, and of a considerable work on alchemy in which Greek philosophy is amalgamated with Egyptian speculation.

Text and Translation—The History is known only through Photios's summary of it (second half of the ninth century); it is published in Dindorf, Historici graeci minores (t. I). The alchemic text has been published and translated into French by M. Berthelot. Collection des anciens alchemistes grecs (t. I, (2) p. 69–106, (3) p. 75–115, Paris, 1887).

Criticism—Edmund O. von Lippmann: Alchemie (98–102, 1919). Mrs. Ingeborg Hammer-Jensen: Die älteste Alchemie (Danish Academy of Sciences, Copenhagen, 1921, Isis, IV, 523–530).

Note on Glass Manufacture in China

I have not spoken of glass-making in the ancient world because it is impossible to date its discovery. There is in the Berlin Museum a piece of glass bearing the name of Amenemhet III, a king of the Twelfth Dynasty, who ruled throughout the second half of the nineteenth century B. C. The manufacture of glass beads was already known in Egypt under Thutmose III, a king of the Eighteenth Dynasty, who ruled throughout the first half of the fifteenth century B. C. Glass beads were made in Babylonia even earlier. Some beads of glazed frit have been found to be "common" in a cemetery of the Third Dynasty of Ur (c. 2450 B. C.), near Ur. The earliest dated Assyrian glass is a glass vessel of Sargon's reign (end of eighth century B. C.). See R. Campbell Thompson: Chemistry of the ancient Assyrians (p. 12, London, 1925; Isis, IX). There are of course innumerable examples of Roman glass. (F. M. Feldhaus: Die Technik, 449, 1914.)

According to Strabon and Pliny, the greatest center of glass-making in the Roman world was Alexandria, and it was probably thence that various objects of glass were imported into China, both by land and by sea; we know this through the annals of the Han Dynasty. According to later annals, those of the Three Kingdoms (221–264), ten kinds of colored glasses, liu²-li² (7244, 6899)[a] were then

[a] As opposed to white, transparent, glass, rock crystal, po¹li² (9333, 6899).

imported from Ta[4] Ch'in[2] (10470, 2093) (the Roman Empire). Thus the Chinese had had some familiarity with glass, probably since the beginning of our era, but it does not follow that they were aware of its artificial nature; it would seem, on the contrary, that for a considerable time they considered glass as a natural substance, comparable to rock crystal or precious stones. At any rate, they were not able to manufacture glass before the fifth century. It is interesting to note that this process was introduced at about the same time and independently both in North and in South China (which were then separated). With regard to the Northern Kingdom: During the reign of T'ai Wu (424–52) of the Northern Wei Dynasty, glass manufacture was introduced by artisans coming from Indo-Scythia (probably Khotan). They found all the necessary material near the capital, the modern Ta[4] t'ung[2] fu[3] (10470, 12269, 3682), in Shensi, and made glass superior (?) to the Western glass. With regard to the Southern Kingdom: During the reign of Wên Ti (424–54) of the Liu Sung Dynasty, glass-making was introduced into his capital (the modern Nanking) by sea. The Roman emperor sent to Wên Ti a number of glass objects, and a few years later a skilled artisan who was able "to change stone into crystal" (Stephen W. Bushell: L'art chinois, annoté par H. d'Ardenne de Tizac. 243–246, Paris, 1910).

VI. Chinese and Armenian Geography

FA-HSIEN

Fa[2*]-hsien[3] (3366, 4523). This was his religious name; his family name was Kung[1] (6579). Born in Shensi; flourished c. 399 to 414. Chinese Buddhist who made a very long journey to India in order to obtain Buddhist books and images. This journey being one of the most remarkable which was ever accomplished (it would be a considerable feat today), it is worth while to give some idea of its itinerary. Being distressed at the imperfect state of the Buddhist "Disciplines," and determined to obtain new and better copies in India, Fa-hsien left Ch'ang-an in 399 with a few brethren. He traveled westward to Chang[1]-yeh[4*] (416, 12972) (in Kansuh), Tun[4]-huang[2] (12208, 5115) (at the end of the Great Wall), crossed the Gobi desert (17 days), passed south of the Lop-Nor, then to Kara-shahr, Khotan, Karghalik, Kāshgar; then southward to Peshāwur, Mount Safed Koh; then in a southeastern direction along the Jumna and Ganges valleys, but with various excursions to the holy places attracting Buddhist pilgrims. This journey was interrupted by many long stays in monasteries for the purpose of edification, study, and rest. In one of the Hindu monasteries Fa-hsien remained three years to learn Sanskrit and copy the "Disciplines." He finally reached the mouth of the Hoogly. He remained in a monastery of that neighborhood two more years, copying out sūtras and drawing sacred pictures. He then took passage on a merchant vessel and proceeded to Ceylon, where he stayed two years and obtained more books of the Buddhist Canon. He then sailed back to his country via Java, finally landing in the Shantung promontory near Chiao[1]-chou[1] (1346, 2444), in 414. To use his own words:[l] "Fa-hsien spent six years in traveling from Ch'ang-an to Central India;[m] he stayed there six years and it took him three more to

[l] Almost at the end of his book.

[m] What we would call Northern India, he called repeatedly Central India. He did not travel south of the Lower Ganges, but his book contains some hearsay account of the Deccan (including a reference to an immense monolith monastery).

reach Ch'ing[1]-chou[1] (2184, 2444). The countries he passed through amounted to rather fewer than thirty." Fa-hsien wrote at least one account of his journey. We have a short one entitled Fo[2*] kuo[2*] chi[4] (3589, 6609, 923), "Records of the Buddhist Kingdoms," this being the earliest Chinese account of India; there seems to have been a longer one, which is lost. The account which has come down to us contains many marvelous stories, which had been told him for his edification and which he transmits in the same spirit, but aside from that, it has considerable value because of many topographical and ethnographical notes which seem quite trustworthy. He gives also some information on plants, on chandālas (lepers?), and on free hospitals. The chief interest of these Records lies in their testimony with regard to the enormous spread of Buddhism, both Hīnayāna and Mahāyāna, in the India and Central Asia of those days. There are many allusions to the "Precious Trinity."

Text and Translations—First Western edition, French translation by Rémusat completed by Klaproth and Landresse (424 p., Paris, 1836, with abundant notes), The pilgrimage of Fa Hian from the French edition of the Foe Koue Ki of Rémusat, Klaproth, and Landresse (380 p., Calcutta, 1848, with abundant notes). S. Beal: The Travels of Fah Hian and Sung Yun (London, 1869; revised edition in 1884 in Beal: Buddhist Records of the Western World). James Legge: A Record of Buddhistic Kingdoms, being an Account by the Chinese Monk Fā-Hien of his Travels in India and Ceylon in Search of the Buddhist Books of Discipline. Translated and annotated, with a Corean recension of the Chinese text (Oxford, 1886). New English translation by H. A. Giles (112 p., Cambridge, 1923. The author has been able to avail himself of geographical identifications of Chavannes, Kurita, and Stein).

Criticism—T. Watters: Fa-hsien and his English Translators (China Review (1879–80). Herbert Henry Gowen: The Travels of a Buddhist Pilgrim (American Antiquarian, vol. 21, 3–13, Chicago, 1899).

For Armenian geography, see my note on Moses of Chorene in Section VIII.

VII. ROMAN, HELLENISTIC, HINDU, AND KOREAN MEDICINE (INCLUDING BOTANY AND BIOLOGY)

MARCELLUS EMPIRICUS

Born in Bordeaux, flourished at the end of the fourth century and the beginning of the fifth. Gallo-Roman physician. Magister officiorum under Theodosius I (379–95). Wrote, c. 410, a book of medicaments, "De medicamentis," an extraordinary mixture of traditional knowledge, popular (Celtic) medicine, and rank superstition. Interesting also for the historian of botany, because of the great number of plants mentioned.

Text and Translations—Edition by Georg Helmreich (1889). By M. Niedermann: Corpus medicorum latinorum, V (394 p., Leipzig, 1916; Isis, III, 321; Antoine Thomas, Journal des Savants, 15–21, 1920). Latin text with French translation by Louis Baudet, appended to Serenus Samonicus: Préceptes médicaux (265–279, Paris, 1845).

Criticism—Jacob Grimm: Über Marcellus Burdigalensis (Akad. d. Wissensch., 32 p., Berlin, 1849). E. H. F. Meyer: Geschichte der Botanik (vol. 2, 299–315, 1855, with list of plants). Georges Touflet de Mesnil: Epigraphie de la Gaule sceltane (175 p., Rouen, 1883. Contains a chapter on the Gallic forms in Marcellus). Rich. Heim: De rebus magicis Marcelli Medici, in Schedae Philologicae Hermanno Usener oblatae (119–137, Bonn, 1891). Samuel Chabert: De latinitate

Marcelli (Thesis, 137 p., Paris, 1897); Marcellus et la syntaxe française (107 p., Paris, 1901). Max Niedermann: Sprachliche Bemerkungen zu Marcellus (H. Blümner Festgabe (328–339, Zürich, 1914). Eduard Liechtenhan: Sprachliche Bemerkungen zu Marcellus (Diss., 126 p., Basel, 1917, with long bibliography).

CASSIUS FELIX

Born in Cirta, Numidia; flourished in Carthage? about and before 447. Roman physician; Christian. Wrote about the end of his life, in 447, a medical compilation entitled "De medicina ex graecis logicae sectae auctoribus liber translatus." It deals chiefly with pathology and therapeutics and is mainly derived from Galen.

Text and Translations—Text edited by Val. Rose (Leipzig, 1879).

Criticism—E. Gurlt: Geschichte der Chirurgie (vol. 1, 501–505, 1898). Otto Probst: Biographisches zu Cassius Felix (Philologus, t. 67, 319–320, 1908); Glossen aus Cassius (*ibid.*, t. 68, 550–559, 1909).

For St. Augustine's theory of potential creation, see my note in Section II.

CAELIUS AURELIANUS

Of Sicca, Numidia; he was probably a contemporary of Cassius Felix. Roman physician. The greatest Latin medical writer after Celsus. Famous for his translations of Soranos (q. v., first half of second century), chiefly of the "De morbis acutis et chronicis,"[n] a compendium of medicine.

Text and Translations—Partial editions: Tardarum passionum libri quinque, by J. Sichard (Basel, 1529); Celerum passionum libri tres, by J. Guinter of Andernach (Paris, 1533). First complete edition, Lyon, 1566. Edition by J. C. Amman (Amsterdam, 1709; reprinted in 1755). By Albrecht von Haller (2 vols., Lausanne, 1774). A new edition was being prepared by Friedel in 1892(?).

Criticism—V. H. Friedel: De scriptis Caelii Aureliani (Diss., 50 p., Bonn, 1892). M. Wellmann, in Pauly-Wissowa (vol. 5, 1256–1258, 1897). E. Gurlt: Geschichte der Chirurgie (vol. 1, 493–498, 1898). G. Helmreich: Zu Caelii acutarum passionum libri III (Archiv für lateinische Lexicographie, vol. 12, 309–331, 1901). Wilh. Streve: Die Pathologie und Therapie der Phthisis bei Caelius (Diss., 31 p., Jena, 1910). L. Meunier: Maladies aigües et maladies chroniques. Le méthodisme. (Janus, vol. 11, 128–138, 208–217, Leyde, 1906.) G. Helmreich: Zum sogenannten Aurelius de acutis passionibus (Rheinisches Museum für Philologie, vol. 73, 46–58, 1921. This is an extract from the work of Caelius Aurelianus by an unidentified author).

PSEUDO-APULEIUS

Herbarium or De herbarum virtutibus (or medicaminibus). This botanic writing has been ascribed to Apuleius (q. v., second half of second century), it dates probably from the end of the fourth or the beginning of the fifth century, and is largely derived from Greek models.

PALLADIOS THE IATROSOPHIST[o]

Παλλάδιος. Flourished in Alexandria, probably in the fourth or fifth century. Greek physician. He wrote commentaries on Hippocrates (on the sixth book

---

[n] This great treatise, indeed, is largely based upon a lost work of Soranos περὶ ὀξέων καὶ χρονίων παθῶν.

[o] Such is his title, ἰατροσοφιστής, meaning originally a teacher of medicine, but used later, and until modern times, to designate any learned physician.

of Epidemics; on the treatise on fractures) and a treatise on fevers, containing interesting explanations of them.

Text—Εἰς ἕκτον τῶν ἐπιδημιῶν ὑπόμνημα. First edition in Julius Paulus Crassus: Medici antiqui graeci (Basel, 1581). Apollonii Citiensis, etc., scholia in Hippocratem et Galenum (vol. 2, 1–204, Königsberg, 1834).

Σχόλια εἰς τὸ περὶ ἀγμῶν Ἱπποκράτους. Palladii scholia in librum Hippocratis de fracturis, edited by Jac. Santalbinus, in Anutius Foesius: Hippocrates (Francfort, 1595. Greek and Latin). Also in Chartier's works of Hippocrates and Galen (Paris, 1679).

Περὶ πυρετῶν σύντομος σύνοψις, edited by Jo. Steph. Bernard (Leiden, 1745. Greek and Latin). Also in J. L. Ideler: Physici et medici graeci minores (t. 1, 107–121, 1840). Demetrius Sicurus: Theophili et Stephani Atheniensis de febrium differentia (46 p., Florence, 1862).

Criticism—Iwan Bloch, in Puschmann: Geschichte der Medizin (vol. 1, 526–527, 1902).

Hindu Medicine

The Bower manuscript (discovered by Lieutenant Bower in 1890) contains two old medical tracts. It is a Sanskrit text dating from c. 450, and is, because of its date, of immense importance. Suśruta is explicitly quoted.

A. F. H. Hoernlé: The Bower Manuscript. Facsimile Leaves. Nāgarī Transcript, Romanized Transliteration and English Translation with Notes (Archaeological Survey of India, Reports, vol. 22, Calcutta, 1893–1912).

Korean Influence in Japan in the Fifth Century

Upon request of the Emperor Ingyō (ruling from 412 to 453), the king of Silla sent a physician to him, named Kon-Bu. Kon-Bu arrived in Yamato in 414 and cured the Emperor. Another Korean physician, named Tokurai, came to Japan at the beginning of the reign of Yūryaku, who ruled from 457 to 479. Tokurai settled in Naniwa, and his descendants continued the practice of medicine.

Y. Fujikawa: Geschichte der Medizin in Japan (5, Tokyo, 1911).

VIII. HELLENISTIC, ROMAN, ARMENIAN, AND CHINESE HISTORIOGRAPHY

EUNAPIOS

Εὐνάπιος, born at Sardis in Lydia, c. 347, flourished in Athens, died after 414. Greek historian (pagan). He wrote a history of his time (in 14 books; Μετὰ Δέξιππον χρονικὴ ἱστορία, from 270 to 404;[p] it is lost) and, about the beginning of the fifth century, biographies of 23 Neoplatonic philosophers (βίοι φιλοσόφων καὶ σοφιστῶν).

Text—De vitis philosophorum et sophistarum, nunc primum Graece et Latine editus, interprete Hadriano Junio Hornano (Antwerp, 1568). Edition by J. F. Boissonade (664 p., Amsterdam, 1822).

English translation by E. Smith, appended to Diogenes Laertius (vol. 2, 297–460, London, 1696).

Philostratus and Eunapius; the Lives of the Sophists, with an English translation by Wilmer Cave Wright (Loeb Library, London, 1922).

---

[p] The period from 270 to c. 355 is dealt with in the first book. Eunapios's main object was to eulogize Julian the Apostate (q. v., in previous chapter).

Criticism—Vilhelm Lundström: Prolegomena in Eunapii vitas (35 p., Upsala, 1897).

ZOSIMOS

Ζώσιμος. Flourished at Constantinople about the middle of the fifth century. Greek historian (pagan). He wrote a history of the Roman Empire, in 6 books, dealing chiefly with the events of the fourth century and of his own time.[a] (Our texts of it stop at the year 410, when Rome was sacked by Alaric.) He was inspired by Polybios and by his older contemporary Eunapios.

Text—First Latin edition by Johann Loewenklau (Bale, 1576); first Greek edition by H. Stephanus in 1611 (in Herodianos, Hist. lib. VIII, p. 322–470). Edition by I. Bekker, in Corpus scriptorum historiae byzantinae (t. 29, Bonn, 1837, with Latin translation). Edition by Ludwig Mendelssohn (Leipzig, 1887).
English translation, London, 1684. French translation by Louis Cousin (Paris, 1686). German translation by Seybold and Heyler (2 vols., Frankfurt, 1802–04).
Criticism—M. Croiset: Histoire de la littérature grecque (t. 5, 1014–1016, 1899).

For Olympiodoros, see Section V.

SOCRATES OF CONSTANTINOPLE

Σωκράτης, born at Constantinople c. 379; advocate in Constantinople, hence his surname Scholasticos (σχολαστικός). Greek church historian. He completed Eusebios's work, writing an "Ecclesiastical History" (in 7 books) from the reign of Constantine the Great, 305, to that of the younger Theodosius, 439.

Text—See collected editions of Greek church historians by Henri de Valois (Paris, 1659–1673, 1677). Also Migne's Greek Patrology (vol. 67). Edition by R. Hussey with Latin translation (3 vols., Oxford, 1853).
English translation, together with that of Eusebios, by Meredith Hanmer (London, 1607, and later ones in the Greek ecclesiastical historians, vol. 3, London, 1844, and in Bohn's ecclesiastical library, London, 1874).
Armenian versions have also been published.

SOZOMEN

Σωζόμενος, advocate in Constantinople, c. 439. Greek church historian. His "Ecclesiastical History" (in 9 books), from 324 to 425, is largely based upon that of Socrates, yet valuable.

Text—This history has been generally published together with that of Socrates.
Criticism—Joseph Bidez: La traduction manuscrite de Sozomène et la Tripartite de Théodore le Lecteur (100 p., Leipzig, 1908).

THEODORETOS

Θεοδώρητος. Born c. 386 at Antioch, died c. 458, probably at Cyrus. Greek theologian and church historian. Bishop of Cyrus (or Cyrrhus) in Syria from 423. Friend of Nestorios, whom he did not condemn until 451. He wrote, c. 450, an Ecclesiastical History (in 5 books) from 322 to 427, which seems independent from that of Socrates, and is important.

Text—Opera omnia (vols. 1 to 4 edited by Jacobus Sirmondus, vol. 5 by Joannes Garnerius. With Latin translation, Paris, 1642–1684).
For the Ecclesiastical History, see Henri de Valois: Historiae ecclesiasticae scriptores graeci, III. Scientific edition by Léon Parmentier in the collection of

---

[a] It is called Ἱστορία νέα.

Early Greek Fathers edited by the Prussian Academy (vol. 19, 535 p., Leipzig, 1911). English translation in Bohn's ecclesiastical library (494 p., London, 1854).

Criticism—Max Neuburger: Die Medizin in Macrobius und Theodoretus (Janus 28, 155–172, 1925; Isis, VIII, 534).

OROSIUS

Paul Orosius. Born in Spain, probably at Tarragona; c. 414 he went to Hippo, attracted by his admiration for St. Augustine; a little later the latter sent him to Bethlehem to warn St. Jerome against Pelagian errors; he returned to Hippo c. 416. Roman historian and theologian. His universal history ("Historiarum adversum paganos libri VII"), extends from the creation down to 417; its purpose was theological, and it was dedicated to St. Augustine.[r] It contains an outline of universal geography, which, imperfect as it is, was held in high esteem during the Middle Ages (e. g., by Bede, Alfred the Great, Dante).

Text and Translations—Editio princeps (Augsburg, 1471). Edition by C. Zangemeister (Leipzig, 1889).

Anglo-Saxon version by Alfred the Great (King of the West Saxons, 849 to 901) edited with an English translation by Daines Barrington (London, 1773); by B. Thorpe (London, 1853, appended to Reinhold Pauli: Life of Aelfred); by Joseph Bosworth (London, 1858; also 1859); by Henry Sweet (London, 1883, Early English Text Soc., 79; with Latin text). It is also included in Alfred the Great's Whole Works (II, 10–198, 1858).

Criticism—H. Sauvage: De Orosio (Thesis, Paris, 1874). Hugo Schilling: König Aelfred's Bearbeitung (Diss., 61 p., Halle, 1886). Paget Toynbee: Dante's Obligations to Orosius. (Romania, vol. 24, 385–398, 1895). Pierre de Labriolle: Littérature latine chrétienne (579–586, Paris, 1920).

MOSES OF CHORENE[s]

Born at Khor'ni in Tarōn, Turuberan, Armenia; educated in Alexandria, visited Rome and Athens and arrived at Constantinople in 440 on his way home. Armenian historian and geographer. Author of a history of his country ("Genealogical Account of Great Armenia") in three books, down to the death of his teacher Mesrop in 440. It is based largely on Armenian sources, also on Eusebios. It is valuable though not very trustworthy, and the text, if really written by him, has been considerably interpolated by later editors. The Geography ascribed to him is based mainly on Pappos and has also been much interpolated, especially by an editor working c. 657. It contains valuable information on Armenia and neighboring countries.

Text—Historiae armeniacae libri III. Accedit Epitome geographiae. Armenian and Latin edition by William Whiston (London, 1736). Edited and translated into French by P. E. Le Vaillant de Florival (2 vols., Paris, 1841). New French translation in Victor Langlois: Collection des historiens de l'Arménie (t. 2, 45–175, 1869). Italian version by Giuseppe Cappelletti (Venezia, 1841); German version by M. Lauer (Regensburg, 1869).

Geography edited and translated into Latin by Whiston (London, 1736). Saint Martin: Mémoires historiques et géographiques sur l'Arménie (vol. 2, 310, Paris, 1819). More critical edition by K. P. Patkanov (St. Petersburg, 1877). Josef

---

[r] It was a sort of supplement to the "City of God" and was, in fact, the earliest Christian universal history.

[s] Once called the Herodotos of Armenia, he is now very much discussed, and has lost much of his prestige.

Marquart: Ērānšahr nach der Geographie des ps. Moses Xorenac'i. Mit histor.-krit. Kommentar (358 p., Abhdl. d. Ges. d. Wiss., Göttingen, Phil. kl., Bd. 3, 1901).

Criticism—E. H. F. Meyer: Geschichte der Botanik (vol. 3, 331–338, 1856). Auguste Carrière: Moïse de Khoren et les généalogies patriarcales (46 p., Paris, 1891); Nouvelles sources de Moïse (111 p., Vienne, Impr. des Mechitharistes, 1893–94). Article in Enc. Brit. (vol. 18, 897–898, 1911) by Alfred von Gutschmid and F. C. Conybeare. Jos. Fischer: Pappus und die Ptolemaeus Karten (Z. der Ges. für Erdkunde, 336–358, Berlin, 1919; Isis, IV, 131).

FAN YEH

Fan[4] Yeh[4]* (3426, 13021). Governor of Hsüan[1]-ch'êng[2] (4805, 763) in Anhui; executed in 445. Chinese historian. Author of the History of the Eastern Han dynasty[t] (25 to 220), called Hou[4] Han[4] shu[1] (4025, 3836, 10024), the third of the Twenty-four Histories. It would seem that the "treatises" of that history (that is, memoirs on harmony, chronology, rites, sacrifices, astronomy, elemental influences, geography, offices, and sumptuary regulations which form a standard part of each dynastic history) are not Fan's own work, but were taken from an earlier work, the supplementary history of the Eastern Han written by Ssŭ[1]-ma[3] Piao[1] (10250, 7576, 9112) (b. 240, d. 305) which became a part of the Hou Han shu only about the beginning of the eleventh century.

Text—Chinese edition (Nanking, 1869; 120 chüan in 14 vols.).

Criticism—Wylie: Notes on Chinese Literature (p. 17, 1902). Giles: Biographical Dictionary (219, 671, 1898).

IX. ROMAN AND BARBARIAN LAW

Roman Law

The "Valentinian Law of Citations" issued from Ravenna in 426 by Theodosius II, acting as tutor of Valentinian III (then only 7 years old), sanctioned the authority, the canonicity, of the legal writings of Papinian, Paul, Gaius, Ulpian, and Modestine. In case of conflict, Papinian's authority was to be preponderant.

Codex Theodosianus

The "Codex Theodosianus" was elaborated by order of Theodosius II, Emperor of the East from 408 to 450. The work was ordered in 429, earnestly begun in 435, and published at Constantinople in 438. This code superseded all previous ones. It came into force in the East on January 1, 439, and in the West on January 12, 439. It is divided into 16 books and is very comprehensive. Collections of statutes of the Western Empire were added to this code from time to time between 444 and 469; they are called "Novellae Post-Theodosianae." The Theodosian Code exerted a tremendous influence upon all barbarian law elaborated after the fall of the Western Empire (476), and of course Justinian's code drew heavily upon it.

Text—Monumental edition of the Theodosianus by J. Gothofredus (Lyon, 1665). Re-edited with additions by J. D. Ritter (7 vols., Leipzig, 1736–1741). New edition by Th. Mommsen and Paul M. Meyer: Theodosiani libri XVI cum constitutionibus Sirmondianis[u] et leges novellae ad Theodosianum pertinentes (Berlin, 1905). Henri Omont: Code théodosien, livres 6–8. Reproduction réduite du MS. Latin

[t] Capital, Lo[4]*-Yang[2] (7328, 12883).

[u] So called after their first editor, J. Sirmondus, 1631. It is a collection of constitutions dating from 331 to 425 and dealing mainly with church matters.

9643 (Paris, Bibliothèque Nationale, 1909). New critical edition by Paul Krüger (Berlin, 1923 sq).

Codex Arcerianus

The "Codex Arcerianus," one of the oldest great manuscripts extant, dating probably of the sixth century and certainly not later than the seventh, was so called in 1607 because it had been the property of Joannes Arcerius of Groningen from 1566 to 1604. The collection of administrative documents which it contains was made probably about the middle of the fifth century for the use of Roman officials. It deals with surveying, land division, agrarian law, and kindred subjects. It contains the Archimedian theorem giving the sum of the first *n* square numbers. The compiler was hardly able to understand surveying, yet his work is valuable for the history of the Roman agrimensores. The following are quoted by him: Frontinus (second half of the first century); Hyginus[v] (first half of the second century); Balbus (first half of the second century); Marcus Junius Nipsus (second century?); Epaphroditus, Vitruvius Rufus. It is generally impossible to determine the exact dates of these agrimensores. Some at least had probably derived their mathematical knowledge (very rudimentary) from Heron's writings. It is expedient to consider them all together. However, see my notes on Frontinus, Hyginus, and Balbus.

Texts—F. Blume, Karl Lachmann, und A. A. F. Rudorff: Die Schriften der römischen Feldmesser (2 vols., Berlin, 1848–1852). Charles Thulin: Corpus agrimensorum romanorum (vol. 1, fasc. 1, Leipzig, 1913, with 144 technical illustrations from manuscripts).

Criticism—M. Cantor: Die römischen Agrimensoren und ihre Stellung in der Geschichte der Feldmesskunst (Leipzig, 1875; Vorlesungen, Bd. 1^3, 551–561, 1907).

Irish Law

The largest and most important document of Irish law is the "Great Old Law Book" (Senchus Mór), which "was purified and written" in 438. The text of it was published and Englished in the first three of the six volumes edited by the Brehon Law Commission, "Ancient Laws of Ireland," 1865 to 1901.

Criticism—Laurence Ginnell: Brehon Laws (1894; and his article bearing the same title in the Enc. Brit. 1911, 8 cols.). Henry d'Arbois de Jubainville et Paul Collinet: Etudes sur le droit celtique (2 vols., Paris, 1895).

X. ARMENIAN AND GREEK PHILOLOGY

For the Translations of the Bible, other than the Armenian, and for St. Patrick's introduction of Latin into Ireland, see Section II.

St. Mesrop[w]

Flourished in Armenia, died in 440. Armenian bishop and vartabed (doctor), who invented the first (successful) Armenian alphabet,[x] at the request of Sahak

[v] Not to be mistaken for C. Julius Hyginus, second prefect of the Palatine Library (q. v., second half of the first century B. C.).

[w] Or Mesrōb, Maschthotz.

[x] It is based mainly on the Greek, but also on Oriental alphabets. Mesrop knew Greek, Zend, Pahlawī, Syriac, and various Armenian dialects. He chose among the latter as standard the Ararat dialect. Mesrop's alphabet included 36 letters (2 more were added about the end of the twelfth century). The fifteenth centenary of the Armenian alphabet was celebrated in 1913, together with the fourth centenary of Armenian printing (first printed book, Venice, 1513).

the Great.[y] He may thus be called the father of Armenian literature. He translated into Armenian the New Testament and part of the Old Testament, causing the rest to be translated by others under his direction.[z] The invention of the older Georgian alphabet is also ascribed to him; it is different from the Armenian alphabet, but similar to it.

Criticism—A life of Mesrop was written in the fifth century in Armenian by Goriun (surnamed Skantcheli, the Admirable). French translation, Biographie du bienheureux et saint docteur Mesrob, by Jean Raphael Emine, in Langlois: Collection des historiens de l'Arménie (t. 2, 3–16, 1869).

Article on Armenian language by F. C. Conybeare (Encyc. Brit., vol. 2, 571–574, 1911). Jacques de Morgan: Histoire du peuple arménien (110, 301–305, 312, 1919).

ORION[a]

Ὠρίων. Born in Thebes, Egypt; flourished in Alexandria, then in Constantinople, c. 421. Greek lexicographer. Teacher of Proclos and of Eudocia, consort of Theodosios II. (She married the emperor in 421 and died in 460.) He compiled an etymological lexicon much used by Byzantine scholars.

Text—Orion Thebanus. Etymologicon, first edited by F. G. Sturzius (Leipzig, 1820).

Criticism—Sandys: History of Classical Scholarship (t. 1^3, 377, 1921).

HESYCHIOS OF ALEXANDRIA

Ἡσύχιος. Flourished at a very uncertain time, probably in the fifth century. Greek lexicographer. He compiled the most extensive Greek lexicon of antiquity. In its original form it seems to have included the names of the authorities for each statement.

Text—First edition. Dictionarium (Aldine of Marcus Musurus, Venice, 1514); Florence, 1520; Hagenau, 1521. Edition by Ioannes Albertus (2 vols., Leyde, 1746–1766). Lexicon post Ioannem Albertum recensuit Mauricius Schmidt (5 vols., Jena, 1858–1868). Smaller edition by same (Jena, 1867).

Criticism—Pauly-Wissowa (vol. 16, 1317–1322, 1913). Sandys: History of Classical Scholarship (vol. 1^3, 378, 1921).

---

[y] Sahak I (St. Sahak, Catholicos of Armenia 387–428, 432–439); he died in 439.

[z] Mesrop's translation was made from the Greek. Another was made by Sahak from the Syriac. After 430 Mesrop compared his translation with Sahak's and revised it. A number of works (chiefly religious and theological) were translated into Armenian from the Greek and the Syriac, during the fifth century. For a brief list of the works of that golden age see Conybeare's article quoted below; see also Victor Langlois: Collection des historiens de l'Arménie (2 vols., Paris, 1867–1869. Vol. 1 contains translations from the Greek and Syriac into Armenian; vol. 2, Armenian chronicles of the fifth century). The Armenian translation of the Bible may be called the foundation-stone of Armenian literature.

[a] Often confounded with another grammarian, probably his contemporary, named Oros, Ὦρος.

CHAPTER XXII

THE TIME OF PROCLOS

(Second Half of Fifth Century)

I. Survey of Science in Second Half of Fifth Century. II. Religious Background. III. Hellenistic, Syriac, and Latin Philosophy. IV. Latin, Hellenistic, and Hindu Mathematics. V. Latin, Hellenistic, Chinese, and Hindu Astronomy. VI. Chinese Geography. VII. Latin and Singhalese Historiography. VIII. Roman and Barbarian Law. IX. Chinese Philology.

I. SURVEY OF SCIENCE IN SECOND HALF OF FIFTH CENTURY

1. This age was on the whole one of inferior activity; the contrast with the preceding one is striking. Yet this is only like another phasis in the movement of a pendulum. If one does not restrict one's horizon, there is always some activity which lends part of its glamour to its surroundings. For example, this was a golden age of Neoplatonism, and, therefore, we are right in calling it the Age of Proclos.

2. *Religious Background*—The main event was the completion of the Babylonian Talmud toward the end of the century. The Talmud is an encyclopaedic work of enormous proportions, which constitutes, together with the Old Testament, the religious and intellectual foundation of Jewish life. It is thus impossible to understand fully Jewish thought and to appreciate correctly Jewish contributions to the intellectual development of the Middle Ages—contributions which were at once manifold and considerable—without a sufficient knowledge of that sacred book.

The only Christian theologian worth mentioning was Prosper of Aquitania, who took considerable pains fighting Pelagianism, but he interests us more as a historian and will be dealt with in Section VII below.

3. *Hellenistic, Syriac, and Latin Philosophy*—The outstanding figure of this period is that of Proclos, who was the head of the Academy until 485 and the greatest representative of Neoplatonism in its latest stage. Under the influence of oriental mysteries and religions, Neoplatonism had become more and more imbued with mysticism, yet it had retained some interest in science, especially in mathematics and astronomy. Thus Proclos was not only a philosopher and a saint, but a mathematician. The pseudo-Aristotelian treatise on causes ("Liber de causis"), one of the main channels through which Neoplatonic thought was transmitted to the Muslims and the Jews, is in part a summary of a work of Proclos and in part a commentary upon it. Two direct disciples of Proclos must be named: Asclepiodotos of Alexandria, who composed a commentary on the Timaeos, and Marinos of Sichem, who wrote an enthusiastic biography of his master.

Joannes Stobaeos compiled an anthology which is one of our main sources for the history of ancient philosophy. The mysterious "Dionysios the Areopagite" flourished probably at about the same time; he influenced considerably Greek and Latin mediaeval philosophy. Another work, the so-called "Theology of Aristotle," extant only in an Arabic version, exerted also a deep influence upon Muslim and

Christian scholasticism. It is a Neoplatonic work probably posterior to Proclos. The fact that it was ascribed to Aristotle caused the early Muslim philosophers to have an entirely wrong idea of Peripateticism.

The Nestorian Probos, who flourished about the middle of the century in Antioch, wrote Syriac commentaries on Aristotle and Porphyry; the earliest Syriac translation of the Isagoge was composed about this time or a little earlier; it has been ascribed to Ibas, who died in 457.

Latin thought was represented by the encyclopaedic treatise of Martianus Capella, which gives us a fair idea of the scientific knowledge of an educated man of this time.

4. *Latin, Hellenistic, and Hindu Mathematics*—The astronomer Victorius wrote an arithmetical treatise including tables of multiplication.

The philosopher Proclos wrote an important commentary on the first book of Euclid; he attempted to prove the parallel postulate. Domninos of Larissa, a classmate of Proclos, wrote treatises on the theory of numbers. Metrodoros was the editor of the arithmetical epigrams of the Greek Anthology.

Āryabhaṭa wrote in 499 an important mathematical treatise, containing in a more systematic form the trigonometry of the Siddhāntas and various new results.

5. *Latin, Hellenistic, Chinese, and Hindu Astronomy*—Victorius of Aquitania composed in 457 a treatise on the calendar which was the first step toward the introduction of the Christian era. Capella's encyclopaedia is especially interesting from the astronomical point of view; it contains an explanation of the ancient hemi-heliocentrical system. Proclos wrote an introduction to Ptolemaic astronomy. Julianos composed an astronomical treatise c. 497.

The Chinese mathematician and astronomer Tsu Ch'ung-chih devised the calendar of 463. He knew the value of π accurately down to the sixth decimal place included.

The Hindu mathematician Āryabhaṭa developed the astronomy of the Siddhāntas, adding the theory of the daily rotation of the earth around its axis.

6. *Chinese Geography*—The only event which I have to record is not even a real, but a fanciful one. The monk Hui-shên was said to have returned in 499 from a long voyage to the East; one even spoke of his having discovered America, or rediscovered it, for his account implies that other monks had preceded him in 458, more than a millennium before Columbus! However, there is nothing to substantiate that account.

7. *Latin and Singhalese Historiography*—Prosper of Aquitania continued St. Jerome's chronicle down to 445–455. The most important historical work of the time is a chronicle of the history of Ceylon from the middle of the fifth century B. C. to about the middle of the fifth century after Christ. It was written in Pāli by Mahānāma.

8. *Roman and Barbarian Law*—Three legal monuments deserve mention: The "Syro-Roman Law Book," written in Greek some time between Theodosius and Justinian and very popular in the Near East; the so-called "Consultatio," a book written in Gaul about the end of the fifth or the beginning of the sixth century; and the earliest Visigothic code, dating from the time of King Euric (466 to 485).

9. *Chinese Philology*—Shên Yo was first to distinguish the four tones. This was a considerable progress as well from the lexicographical as from the purely phonetical point of view. Shên Yo's discovery was probably made under Hindu influence. The advance of Buddhism obliged some Chinese scholars to study

Sanskrit, and in its turn this study improved their technical understanding of their own language.

This is not the first time that I point out a connection between language and religion; in fact, the connections are numerous and unusually strong. Nothing has a stronger hold on men than the faith of their fathers and the language of their mothers.

10. *Final Remarks*—To consider the West first, while the preceding period had been one of Christian triumph, this was one of Neoplatonic supremacy. In the Near East we witnessed the completion of the Talmud, which symbolizes a golden age of Jewish scholasticism. We witnessed also the beginning of Syriac literature outside of the Biblical translations; this is important, for that literature was one of the bridges through which Greek knowledge ultimately reached Europe. In India, Ceylon, and China the most interesting events were, respectively, the systematization of Siddhānta knowledge by Āryabhaṭa, the historical activity of Mahānāma, and the conscious discrimination between tones by Shên Yo.

II. RELIGIOUS BACKGROUND

The Talmud

During the first five centuries of our era a great body of rabbinical law and tradition grew up in the Jewish schools of Palestine and Babylonia. That body, of which it is well-nigh impossible to date the various elements, was largely constituted in the fifth century. It is called the Talmud (meaning in Hebrew, teaching, learning).

In fact, there were not one but two Talmuds, the one in Palestine, the other in Babylonia. The Palestinian Talmud[a] was the first to be completed, c. 425. The Babylonian Talmud[b] was substantially complete by the end of the fifth century. It was more elaborate and more scientific than the former Talmud[c] and displaced it gradually during the Middle Ages. When one speaks of the Talmud, it is always the Babylonian Talmud that is meant, unless the other is specifically mentioned.

Each Talmud was developed in two stages. The first stage was the elaboration of the Mishnāh[d] (Hebrew, repetition, teaching), a collection of law developing the Tōrāh. The second stage was the Gemārā, a compilation of supplementary material of the same kind. The Mishnāh, however, is essentially halākā, while the Gemārā is partly halakik and partly haggadic. It is noteworthy that the Mishnāh was written in Hebrew and the Gemārā in Aramaic.

The Talmud is subdivided into six orders (sedarīm), each of which contains a certain number of tractates (massektōth).[e] The orders are: (1) Seeds (agriculture); (2) Festivals; (3) Women (marriage laws, etc.); (4) Damages (civil and criminal law, etc.); (5) Holy things (sacrifices, etc.); (6) Purifications (causes of pollution, etc.). The Mishnāh contains from 60 to 70 tractates. Besides, the

---

[a] Also called the Talmud of the Land of Israel, the Talmud of the West, or (incorrectly) the Jerusalem Talmud.

[b] Or Talmud Babli. See my note on Ashi in the previous chapter.

[c] There is more haggādah (narrative, homily, popular exposition) in the Palestinian, and more halākā (legal, ritual, scientific material) in the Babylonian Talmud.

[d] See my note on Judah ha-Nasi, second half of the second century.

[e] Literally, weavings; cfr. our word text.

Palestinian Talmud contains the Gemārā relative to 39 tractates, and the Babylonian that relative to 36½ tractates.[f]

The Talmud might be considered a code of laws, but it is a very ill-digested one, full of irregularities, incongruities, and discontinuities of all kinds,[g] and it contains much material which has nothing to do with law. Its contents are truly encyclopaedic. Hence its tremendous importance for the student of Hebrew civilization. It is a mirror of early Judaism. For the Jews themselves it has become a sacred book, forming, together with the Old Testament, the equivalent of the Christian Bible.

The completion of the Tōrāh in the fifth century B. C., that of the Mishnāh in the second half of the second century of our era, and that of the whole Talmud in the second half of the fifth century are three successive steps in the codification of Hebrew thought.[h] For an exhaustive study of early Judaism it would not suffice to consider the Tōrāh and the Talmud, however. It would be necessary to examine also the complementary materials collected in the Midrāshīm and the Targūmīm.[i]

The princeps edition of the Talmud appeared in Vienna, 1520–1523. A second edition, less intolerant of other faiths, appeared in Bâle, 1578–1581. A very large literature has been devoted to the Talmud in general and to sundry topics, some of which are of special interest to us (such as mathematics or medicine); but as this enormous body of Hebrew law and lore is not the fruit of one but of five centuries, it has seemed more appropriate to speak of Talmudic literature in the chapter on Israel.

For Prosper of Aquitania and his writings against Pelagianism see Section VII.

III. HELLENISTIC, SYRIAC, AND LATIN PHILOSOPHY

PROCLOS

Proclos the Successor[j] (Πρόκλος ὁ Διάδοχος). Born at Byzantium in 410, but brought up at Xanthos in Lydia, where his parents resided; studied at Alexandria and Athens; died on April 17, 485. Neoplatonic philosopher and saint, mathematician, astronomer. Head of the Academy until 485 and chief representative of the later Neoplatonists ("the Hegel of Neoplatonism," said J. B. Bury). He wrote extensive commentaries on Hesiod, Plato, Aristotle, on Euclid's "Elements," on

---

[f] However, the Babylonian Talmud is about three times fuller than the other.

[g] The most shocking feature to the modern mind is perhaps the frequent juxtaposition and confusion of ethics and rite. But we find the same sort of thing in the Old Testament, in the early works of many nations (in the Confucian writings, for example), and, we may add, in the mentality of the average man of to-day.

[h] The first three steps, the only ones which were of a collective nature. Later syntheses were due to individuals, chiefly Isaac Alfasi in the second half of the eleventh century, Maimonides in the second half of the twelfth century, Joseph Qaro in the second half of the sixteenth century.

[i] The Midrāsh (Hebrew from dārash, to enquire) is a body of tradition (both halakik and haggadic) auxiliary to the Talmud and partly contemporary to it. For the Targūm, see my note on Old Testament translations in my chapter on the first half of the third century B. C.

[j] The meaning of this surname is not quite clear. Whose successor? I would take it to mean Plato's genuine successor and thus to be a witness of Proclos's fame, but it may refer to Syrianos. See F. Überweg: Grundriss der Geschichte der Philosophie des Altertums (11. Aufl., 651, footnote. 1920).

Ptolemy's "Quadripartitum." It is possible that his commentary on Euclid extended to many books of the "Elements," but this can not be proved and only the commentary on Book I is extant.[k] This is of considerable value for the study of ancient Greek geometry because of the historical information which it contains, derived from the lost works of Eudemos (q. v., second half of the fourth century B. C.) and Geminos (first half of the first century B. C.). The most interesting part of this commentary from the mathematical point of view is the discussion of Euclid's parallel-postulate and of Ptolemy's attempt to prove it, together with a new attempt of the same kind. His commentary on Plato's "Republic" proves that the Egyptian fractions continued to be used until that time.[l] He seems to have studied some higher curves, e.g., the hippopede. Cinematical construction of curves, e. g., ellipse considered as the locus of a point marked on a ruler the extremities of which glide along the two sides of a right angle.

He wrote an introduction to the astronomy of Hipparchos and Ptolemy (Hypotyposis) which contains some very remarkable items: (1) Description of the method of measuring the apparent diameter of the sun by means of Heron's water-clock (derived from Pappos); (2) proof of the geometrical equivalence of the epicycles and eccentrics; (3) mention (with reference to Sosigenes the Peripatetician) of an annular eclipse of the sun; (4) mention of the precession of the equinoxes, the existence of which is denied![m] (5) suggestion that the greatest distance of a planet is equal to the smallest distance of the planet immediately above it and thus that there is no vacant space between the spheres (an idea which was very popular during the Middle Ages).

Text and Translations—The commentary on Euclid was first published in Grynaeus's Greek edition of Euclid (Basel, 1533). Latin translation by Barocius (1560). Also in Commandino's edition of Euclid (Pisauri, 1572). In primum Euclidis elementorum librum commentarii, ed. Gottfried Friedlein (515 p., Leipzig, 1873). Translation by Thomas Taylor, together with Proclos's life by Marinos (his pupil and successor) (2 vols., London, 1788–89; new edition, 1792).

Edition of various philosophical treatises with Latin translation by Victor Cousin (6 vols., Paris, 1820–1827); Opera inedita, ed. by the same (Paris, 1864).

Of the Platonic commentaries I quote only the latest editions: In Cratylum comm., ed. Georg Pasquali (162 p., Leipzig, 1908). In Rem Publicam, ed. Wilh. Kroll (2 vols., Leipzig 1899–1901). In Timaeum, ed. C. E. Chr. Schneider and Ernst Diez (3 vols., 1903–1906). Initia philosophiae ac theologiae ex Platonicis fontibus ducta sive Procli et Olympiodori in Platonis Alcibiadem comm. (4 parts, Francfurt, 1820–1825). Some of these commentaries and of Proclos's philosophical writings have been Englished by Thomas Taylor. Commentaire sur le Parménide, suivi du commentaire anonyme sur les sept dernières hypothèses, trad. franç. de A. E. Chaignet (3 vols., Paris, 1900–1903). Metaphysical elements translated by Thos. M. Johnson (218 p., Oscola, Mo., 1909).

Istitutio physica (στοιχείωσις φυσική) sive de motu (περὶ κινήσεως), commentary on the Aristotelian theory of motion, edited in Greek with German translation by Alb. Ritzenfeld (75 p., Leipzig, 1911; 2d ed., 94 p., Leipzig, 1912).

Hypotyposis astronomicarum positionum (ὑποτύπωσις τῶν ἀστρονομικῶν ὑποθέσεων), edited by Karl Manitius, with German translation and comment (423 p., Leipzig,

---

[k] At any rate, it is not probable that the commentaries upon the other books were completed.

[l] For example, Proclos writes $\frac{1}{2}\ \frac{1}{3}\ \frac{1}{15}\ \frac{1}{50}$ for 23/25.

[m] About this see my note on Theon of Alexandria in the second half of the fourth century.

1909). Greek text with French translation, in Halma's edition of Ptolemy (Paris, 1820).

Libellus de circulis spherae (περὶ σφαίρας), astronomiam discere incipientibus utilissimus (38 p., Ex Libera Argentina, 1539. Chiefly based on Geminos). De sphaera liber, edited with other writings by Marcus Hopper (Basel, 1547; again 1561). Italian translation by Ignazio Dante (Florence, 1573).

Paraphrasis in Ptolemaei Libros IV de siderum effectionibus (παράφρασις εἰς τὴν Πτολεμαίου τετράβιβλον), edited with Latin translation by Leo Allatius (300 p., Leyde, 1635). Ptolemy's tetrabiblos, newly translated from the Greek paraphrase by Proclus, by J. M. Ashmand (London, 1822).

Divine arithmetic, a subject long since forgotten. Translation by A. C. Ionides (138 p., London, 1917).

General Criticism—Adolphe Berger: Proclus. Exposition de sa doctrine (128 p., Paris, 1840). Martin Altenburg: Die Methode der Hypothesis bei Platon, Aristoteles und Proklus. (Diss., 240 p., Marburg, 1905). Ulrich von Wilamowitz-Moellendorff: Die Hymnen des Proklos und Synesios (Sitzungsber. d. preuss. Akad. d. Wiss., 272–295, 1907). H. F. Müller: Dionysios, Proklos, Plotinos; ein historischer Beitrag zur neuplatonischen Philosophie (110 p., Beitr. zur Philos. des Mittelalters, vol. 20, Münster i. W., 1918). Th. Whittaker: The Neo-Platonists. Second edition, with a supplement on the commentaries of Proclus (p. 229–314, Cambridge, 1918). James Lindsay: Le système de Proclus (Revue de métaphysique et de morale, t. 28, 497–523, 1921).

Mathematics—B. Boncompagni: Intorno al commento di Proclo (Boncompagni's Bull., t. 7, 152–165, 1874). L. Maier: Proklos über die Petita und Axiomata bei Euklid (Progr., 35 p., Tübingen, 1875). Paul Tannery: Le vrai problème de l'histoire des mathématiques anciennes (Bull. des sci. math., t. 9, 104–120, 209–220, 1885); Le résumé historique de Proclus (*ibidem*, t. 10, 49–64, 1886). J. G. van Pesch: De Procli fontibus (Diss., 168 p., Leiden, 1900. See Biblioth. Mathem., t. 2, 160–161). W. B. Frankland: The First Book of Euclid's Elements, with a Commentary Based Principally upon that of Proclus (155 p., Cambridge, 1905). M. Cantor: Geschichte der Mathematik (vol. 1^3, 497–500, 1907). Nicolai Hartmann: Des Proclus philosophische Anfangsgründe der Mathematik nach den ersten zwei Büchern des Euklidkommentars dargestellt (Philosophische Arbeiten, vol. 4, 57 p., Giessen, 1909). T. L. Heath: Greek Mathematics, vol. 2, 529–537, 1921).

Astronomy—J. L. E. Dreyer: Planetary Systems (1906). P. Duhem: Système du Monde (t. 2, p. 324, 1914. On his astrological views: the stars are the secondary causes of sublunary events).

Liber de causis—This pseudo-Aristotelian work, which was very popular in mediaeval times, is considered here because it is based upon the Theological Institution of Proclos[a] (στοιχείωσις θεολογική). More exactly, it contains two parts, of which the first is an abstract of Proclos's work and the second a short commentary on it. It was one of the best vehicles by means of which late Neoplatonic thought was transmitted to the Muslims and Jews and then to the schoolmen of Western Europe. Albert the Great ascribed this compilation (which is certainly of Muslim or Jewish origin) to the Jew Avendeut (see Joannes Hispalensis, first half of the twelfth century), but it is undoubtedly of an earlier date, probably earlier even than the time of al-Fārābī (first half of the tenth century), to whom it has also been credited. It was known to Alain de Lille (Alanus ab Insulis), the "Universal Doctor" (died Clairvaux c. 1203), author of the didactic poem "Anticlaudianus"; the school of Chartres was acquainted with it in the twelfth century; Gilbert de la Porrée (q. v., first half of the twelfth century) commented upon it; Gherardo Cremonese trans-

[a] Itself translated into Latin by William of Moerbeke at Viterbo, 1268.

lated it into Latin. This book was called "On Pure Goodness" by al-Fārābī, the "Light of Lights" by Avicenna, "The Flower of Divine Things" by al-Ghazzālī, "Metaphysics" and "Liber de Causis" by Gilbert de la Porrée and the schoolmen; Albert the Great's commentary was called "Liber de causis et processu universitatis a causa prima."

O. Bardenhewer: Die pseudo-aristotelische Schrift über das reine Gute bekannt unter dem Namen liber de causis (Freiburg i. Br., 1882). P. Duhem: Système du monde (t. 4, 329–347, 1916. On the sources of Muslim Neoplatonism). Sandys: History of Classical Scholarship (vol. 1^3, 1921, by index).

ASCLEPIODOTOS OF ALEXANDRIA

Ἀσκληπιόδοτος. Flourished probably in the second half of the fifth century. Neoplatonic philosopher; pupil of Proclos; called "the great" and famous in his day for his knowledge of mathematics, natural history, and medicine, but nothing of his has remained. He wrote a commentary on the Timaeos.

Criticism—E. H. F. Meyer: Geschichte der Botanik (vol. 2, 370–373, 1855). Freudenthal, in Pauly-Wissowa (vol. 4, 1641, 1896). Rudolf Asmus: Der Neuplatoniker Asklepiodotos der Grosse (Arch. f. Gesch. d. Med., vol. 7, 26–42, 1913).

MARINOS OF SICHEM

Marinos of Sichem, i. e., Flavia Neapolis in Palestine. *Μαρῖνος*. Possibly a Jew; flourished about the end of the fifth century. Neoplatonic philosopher. Pupil of Proclos, whom he succeeded as head of the Academy in 485. Wrote a life of Proclos, a preface to Euclid's "Data" and possibly commentaries on Plato and Aristotle.

Vita Procli, ed. Jo. Fr. Boissonade (Leipzig, 1814. Greek and Latin). For the preface to the Data see H. Menge's edition of the Data (Euclidis Opera Omnia, Vol. VI, ed. H. Menge, 1896).

STOBAEOS

Joannes Stobaeos. Ἰωάννης ὁ Στοβαῖος, of Stobi in Macedonia; flourished probably in the second half of the fifth century. Greek writer. Compiler of an anthology, containing extracts from more than 500 Greek authors of all ages, some of which are not found elsewhere. Stobaeos's Florilegium (Ἀνθολόγιον) deserves to be quoted here because it is one of our main sources for the history of ancient Greek philosophy. The anthology was divided into four books dealing respectively with: (1) Philosophy; theology; natural science; (2) Theory of knowledge, dialectic, rhetoric, poetry, ethics; (3) Virtues and vices; (4) Domestic and public economy, politics, arts.[o]

Text—The earlier editions—Conrad Gesner (Antwerp, 1545), etc.—reproduced the text as garbled by mediaeval copyists. Augustus Meineke's edition (4 vols., Leipzig, 1855–1857) was based on a revision of the manuscripts. The first edition, wherein the original order was restored, was that of Curtius Wachsmuth and Otto Hense (5 vols., Berlin, 1884–1912).

Criticism—M. Croiset: Littérature grecque (t. 5, 979–980, 1899). John Burnet: Early Greek Philosophy (3d edition, 34, 1920).

---

[o] Mediaeval copyists broke the work into two distinct parts, the one (Books 1 and 2), entitled "Eclogae physicae et ethicae" (Ἐκλογαὶ φυσικαὶ διαλεκτικαὶ καὶ ἠθικαί); the other (Books 3 and 4), entitled "Florilegium" or "Sermones" (Ἀνθολόγιον). Besides, they altered the original order of the fragments.

"DIONYSIOS THE AREOPAGITE"

Dionysios Areopagita, Διονύσιος 'Αρεοπαγίτης. Christian Neo-Platonist. His real name is unknown, but he was active most probably about the end of the fifth century and the beginning of the sixth century. His mystical theology exerted a deep influence on mediaeval thought,[p] especially on the Syrian, John of Damascus (q. v., first half of the eighth century), on Erigena (second half of the ninth century),[q] on Aquinas, etc. He has sometimes been called the father of scholasticism.

Text—Opera Dionysii (in Latin) by Marsilio Ficino (Strasbourg, 1503); in Latin by Joachimus Perionius (Cologne, 1557). Edition by Balthazar Corder (2 vols., Paris, 1644).

Criticism—Georgius Pachymeres: Paraphrasis in omnia Dionysii Aeropagitae opera (456 p., Paris, 1561). Jean Daillé: De scriptis quae sub Dionysii Aeropagitae et Ignatii Antiocheni nominibus circumferuntur (545 p., Genevae, 1666).

H. F. Müller: Dionysios, Proklos, Plotinos (Beitr. zur Gesch. der Philos. des Mittelalters, vol. 20, 3, 110 p., Münster i. W., 1918). Ferdinand Morel: Essai sur l'introversion mystique (Genève, 1918). J. Durantel: St. Thomas et le pseudo-Denis (Thèse, 278 p., Paris, 1919).

The "Theology of Aristotle"

It is very difficult, if not impossible, to date this famous pseudo-Aristotelian work with any accuracy. Friedrich Dieterici had concluded that it was posterior to Plotinos (second half of third century), from whose "Enneads" many extracts are included or paraphrased, and anterior to Iamblichos (first half of the fourth century), and he had not hesitated to ascribe it to Porphyry, a pupil of Plotinos. Duhem showed that the latter ascription was unwarranted and that the Theology was of a later date, probably posterior to Proclos. We might thus say that the "Theology of Aristotle" is a late Neoplatonic compilation dating from the fourth, the fifth, or the sixth century; and we will not be far wrong if we place it tentatively at the end of the fifth century, keeping in mind the previous qualification.

The Muslims became acquainted with Aristotle through Persian and even more through Syriac channels. At first they knew him primarily as a logician; later they became familiar with the rest of his writings, but they remained to a large extent unable to distinguish between the genuine and the apocryphal. The "Theology of Aristotle" in particular was taken by such men as al-Kindī (first half of the ninth century) and al-Fārābī (first half of the tenth century) to be genuine, and as they attached an immense value to it, the consequences of their mistake were far-reaching. Muslim philosophy was thus entirely dominated by Neoplatonic mysticism and it took a very long time for the purer Peripateticism to come to the surface. These misunderstandings were transmitted by them to the Jews and the Christians, entailing everywhere similar results.

The Greek text is lost, but we learn from the preface to the Arabic translation that the latter had been made c. 835 by a Christian, 'Abd al-Masīḥ Nā'ima of Ḥimṣ (Emessa) at the request of the caliph al-Mu'taṣim (833–842) and im-

---

[p] Not simply Christian (in the East and in the West), but also Jewish (Kabbala), and even Muslim (Ṣūfīsm).

[q] Erigena was the first translator of his works into Latin; he was followed by many others, the sixth being Marsilio Ficino. A copy of the Greek text was presented by the Byzantine emperor, Michael II Balbos, in 827, to Louis the Pious.

proved a little later by al-Kindī. The Arabic text (discovered in Damascus, 1516, by Francesco Roseo) was translated literally into Italian by a Jew of Cyprus, Moses Rova, and this Italian text was turned into Latin in 1519 by Pietro Niccolò de Castellani of Faenza. Jacques Charpentier published in 1572 a Latin paraphrase of Castellani's translation.

Text and Translations—Castellani's text appeared in Rome, 1519, being entitled "Aristotelis Theologia sive mistica phylosophia secundum Aegyptios noviter reperta." . . . . The Arabic text was edited by Fr. Dieterici (Leipzig, 1882): Die sogenannte Theologie des Aristoteles aus arabischen Handschriften hrg., and translated by him into German in 1883, both works forming volumes 12 and 13 of "Die Philosophie der Araber."

Criticism—Duncan B. Macdonald: Development of Muslim Theology (163 sq., New York, 1903). P. Duhem: Système du monde (t. 1, 271–275, 1913, discussing the idea of time; t. 2, 335–341, 1914, the theory of tides and astrology; t. 4, 364–376, 398–401, 1916, metaphysics and theory of human intelligence).

PROBOS[r]

Πρόβος. Flourished about the middle of the fifth century, at Antioch. Syrian Nestorian. Commentator on Aristotle and Porphyry.[s] He wrote commentaries on (1) the Isagoge, (2) the περὶ ἑρμηνείας, (3) the Prior Analytics. He composed a treatise on the representation of numerals by means of letters of the Syriac alphabet.

Texts—A. Baumstark: Aristoteles bei den Syrern vom V.–VIII. Jahrhundert (Leipzig, 1900. Syriac and German).

G. Hoffmann: De hermeneuticis apud Syros Aristoteleis (Syriac, Arabic, Latin, Leipzig, 1869; 1873).

A. van Hoonacker: Le traité de Probus sur les Premiers analytiques (Journal asiatique, juillet-août 1900. Syriac and French).

Criticism—R. Duval: Littérature syriaque (247, 1907). A. Baumstark: Geschichte der syrischen Literatur (101–102, 1922).

CAPELLA

Martianus Mineus Felix Capella. Born in Madaura, Africa, flourished in Carthage c. 470. Roman writer. Author of an encyclopaedic composition, completed about 470 and entitled "Satyricon" or "De nuptiis Philologiae et Mercurii et de septem artibus liberalibus libri novem," in prose and verse. Books I and II deal with the introductory allegory; Books III to IX, with each of the seven arts in the following order: grammar, dialectics, rhetoric, geometry (strangely mixed with geography), arithmetic, astronomy, music including poetry; Book VIII, dealing with astronomy, contains an explanation of the hemi-heliocentric system.

Text and Translations—Editio princeps (Vicenza, 1499. See D. E. Smith, Rara Arithmetica, p. 66–67, 1908). Scientific edition by Franz Eyssenhardt (556 p., Leipzig, 1866).

Criticism—Joh. Juergensen: De tertio Martiani Capellae libro (Commentationes philologicae, p. 57–96, 1874). E. Narducci: Intorno ad un commento inedito di

---

[r] In Syriac, Prōbhos, Prōbhā, or Prōbhē.

[s] The oldest Syriac translation of the Isagoge has been ascribed to his contemporary Ibas (Hībhā) who died in 457. But though Ibas was called "the translator" (methargemana), no certain proof of his activity can be given.

Remigio d'Auxerre al Satyricon, e ad altri commenti (Bull. di bibliografia d. sci. matem., t. 15, p. 505–580, Roma, 1882. With the text of the commentary by Remigius of Auxerre, who died in 908). Carl Thulin: Die Götter des Martianus Capella und der Bronzeleber von Piacenza. (Religionsgeschichtliche Versuche, Vol. III, 1, 92 p., Giessen, 1906. Important contribution to the history of Roman and Etruscan astrology, and incidentally to the solution of the Etruscan enigma). Perc. Rich. Cole: Later Roman Education in Ausonius, Capella, and the Theodosian Code, with Translation and Commentary (39 p., New York, 1909). Assunto Mori: La misurazione eratostenica del grado ed altre notizie geografiche della geometria di Marciano Capella (Riv. geogr. italiana, t. 18, 177–191, 1911). P. Duhem: Système du Monde, t. 3, 47–52, 1915. On the motions of Venus and Mercury).

IV. LATIN, HELLENISTIC, AND HINDU MATHEMATICS

For Victorius, see Section V, and for Proclos, Section III.

DOMNINOS

Domninos of Larissa, Syria (Δομνῖνος). Mathematician and philosopher; condisciple of Proclos under Syrianos. He was the head of the Academy after Syrianos and before Proclos, but probably only for a short time. Author of a summary of the theory of numbers (Ἐγχειρίδιον ἀριθμητικῆς εἰσαγωγῆς), which marks a reaction against Nicomachos, a return to the Euclidean tradition. He wrote also (or planned to write?) a more elaborate treatise on the same subject (Ἀριθμητικὴ στοιχείωσις; lost).

Text and Translations—The Ἐγχειρίδιον has been published by J. Fr. Boissonade in his Anecdota graeca (Vol. IV, p. 413–429, Paris, 1832). A fragment entitled πῶς ἔστι λόγον ἐκ λόγου ἀφελεῖν was edited by Ch. Em. Ruelle (Revue de philologie, t. 7, 82–93, 1883). French translation of the Manual with introduction, by Paul Tannery (Revue des Etudes grecques, t. 19, 359–382, 1906; Mémoires, III, 255–281).

Criticism—Paul Tannery: Domninos (Bull. des sci. math., t. 8, 288–296, 1884; Mémoires, II, 105–117); Notes critiques sur Domninos (Revue de philologie, t. 9, 129–137, 1885; Mémoires, II, 211–222). Fr. Hultsch, in Pauly-Wissowa (t. 9, 1521–1525, 1903. Containing a summary of the Manual). Paul Tannery: Introduction to the translation quoted above (1906).

METRODOROS

Μητρόδωρος. Flourished about the end of the fifth or the beginning of the sixth century. Editor of the 46 arithmetical epigrams of the Greek Anthology. Whichever be his own date, the epigrams are probably of the end of the third century or the fourth (one refers to Diophantos); some can be traced back to Plato and even to the fifth century B. C. These epigrams leading to simple systems of equations are interesting for the historian of arithmetic.

Text and Translation—The best edition of the Greek anthology is by Hugo Stadtmueller (Leipzig, 1894–1896). Handy edition in three volumes with English translation by W. R. Paton (Loeb Library, 1916–1917).

Criticism—T. L. Heath: Diophantus (Cambridge, 1910). Robert King Atwell: The Number Rhymes of Metrodorus (Teachers' College Record, Vol. XIII, 63–67, New York, 1912). T. L. Heath: Greek Mathematics (vol. 2, 442, 1921). D. E. Smith: History of Mathematics (vol. 2, 532 sq., 1925).

ĀRYABHAṬA

Born at Kusumapura near Pāṭaliputra (Patna); he was 23 years old in 499. Hindu mathematician and astronomer. He wrote in the year 3600 of Kaliyuga (i. e., A. D. 499) a treatise called Āryabhaṭīya (or Laghv-Āryabhaṭīya),[t] which is essentially a systematization of the results contained in the Siddhāntas (q. v., first half of the fifth century). It is written in verse and divided into four parts, as follows: (1) Daśagītikāsūtra, a system of number writing; (2) Gaṇitapāda, a mathematical treatise in 33 stanzas; (3) Kālakriyāpāda, elements of astronomical chronology; (4) Golapāda, on celestial spheres. Part 2 to 4 are often considered as a whole, entitled Āryāshṭaśata.

General solution of indeterminate equations of the first degree by a method essentially identical to the continued fraction process. Solution of quadratic equation implied in the rule for finding the number of terms of an arithmetic series when the sum, difference, and first term are given.

$$n = \frac{1}{2}\left(1 + \frac{-2a \pm \sqrt{[(d-2a)^2 + 8sd]}}{d}\right)$$

Rules for summing an arithmetic series after the pth term, which we would express by the formula

$$s = n\left[a + \left(\frac{n-1}{2} + p\right)\right]$$

Extremely accurate value of π, viz., $3\frac{177}{1250} = 3.1416$. Tables of sines and versed sines (as in the Pauliśa-Siddhānta).

The astronomy is almost identical to that of the Sūrya-Siddhānta, except in one important respect. Āryabhaṭa taught that the daily rotation of the heavens is only apparent, being due to the rotation of the earth around its axis. This was a very daring hypothesis which was not accepted by later Hindu astronomers, Varāhamihira and Brahmagupta.

Text and Translations—Āryabhaṭīya, edited with commentary by H. Kern (Leyden, 1874). L. Rodet: Leçons de calcul d'Aryabhata (Journal Asiatique, t. 13, 393–434, Paris, 1879). Mahāsiddhānta, a treatise on Astronomy, edited with his own commentary by Sudhākara Dvivedi. Benares Sanskrit series (Nos. 148–150, 1910).

Criticism—A. von Braunmühl: Geschichte der Trigonometrie (vol. 1, 1900). G. R. Kaye: Notes on Indian Mathematics (Journal Asiatic Society, vol. 4, 111–141, Calcutta, 1908); The two Āryabhaṭas (Bibliotheca Mathematica, t. 10, 289–292); Indian Mathematics (Isis, II, 333–335, 1919). J. F. Fleet: Āryabhaṭa's System of Expressing Numbers (Journal Asiatic Society, 109–126, 1911). M. Winternitz: Indische Litteratur (3, 561–563, 1922). D. E. Smith: History of Mathematics (2 vols., 1923–1925).

V. LATIN, HELLENISTIC, CHINESE, AND HINDU ASTRONOMY

VICTORIUS

Victorius of Aquitania. Astronomer. Composed in 457 the Canon paschalis, to determine the date of Easter. Combining the Metonic cycle of 19 years with a cycle of 7 × 4 = 28 years,[u] he formed a new period of 19 × 28 = 532 years,

---

[t] Also Ārya-Siddhānta, but this is misleading, for a treatise of the same name is ascribed to another Āryabhaṭa who lived much later, possibly as late as the middle of the tenth century.

[u] The numbers 4 and 7 derive respectively from the Julian periodicity (one leap year in four) and from the number of days in the week (Easter must fall on a Sunday). 532 is the least common multiple of 4, 7, and 19.

at the end of which Easter days would reappear in the same succession (the so-called Dionysian period, see my note on Dionysius in the first half of the sixth century). Victorius also wrote a calculus (a series of arithmetical tables with short preface), interesting for the history of computation.

Text and Translation—Victorii calculus ex codice Vaticano editus a God. Friedlein (Bull. di bibliogr. e di storia d. sci. mat., t. 4, 443–463, Roma, 1871).
Criticism—G. Friedlein: Der Calculus des Victorius (Z. f. Math. u. Physik, vol. 16, 42–79, 253–254, 1871). M. Cantor: Geschichte der Mathematik (vol. 1^{3}, 531, 1907). F. K. Ginzel: Handbuch der mathematischen Chronologie (vol. 3, 245–247, 1914).

For Capella and Proclos, see my notes in Section III.

JULIANOS

Julianos of Laodicea (which?) (Ἰουλιανός). Flourished at the end of the fifth century. Astronomer and astrologer. His Ἐπίσκεψις ἀστρονομική (astronomical examination) is chiefly astronomical; the constellations described in it correspond to the date October 28, 497, the coördinates of the stars to c. 500.

F. Boll: Catal. cod. astrol. (IV, 100 sq.) Franz Cumont et Paul Stroobant: La date où vivait l'astrologue Julien de Laodicée (Bull. Ac. royale de Belgique, classe des lettres, p. 554–574, 1903). Boll, in Pauly-Wissowa (vol. 19, 13–15, 1917).

Ch. E. Ruelle published in the Catalogus codicum astrologorum graecorum (t. 8, 126–154, Brussels, 1911), an anonymous fragment entitled De revolutionibus lunae. This fragment has been discussed by Paul Tannery (*ibidem*, p. 125) according to whom it must date of the fifth or sixth century (see his Mémoires, III, 310–311; Isis, IV, 340).

TSU CH'UNG-CHIH

Tsu^{3} Ch'ung^{1}-chih^{1} (11826, 2909, 1787). Born in Fan^{4}-yang^{2} (3426, 12883) 430, died in 501. Chinese mathematician, astronomer, mechanician. Author of a mathematical work called Chui^{4}-shu^{4*} (2814, 10053); this work being lost, it is not possible to translate its title exactly (method of circle measurement?, treatise on calendar?). It contained two fractional values of π; the so-called inaccurate value, $\frac{22}{7}$ (that is, the Archimedian estimate) and the so-called accurate value, $\frac{355}{113}$ (it is accurate to the sixth decimal place included). Tsu devised a new calendar (463), which was not adopted; he invented a new kind of "south-pointing vehicle" and an automobile vessel (?).

Criticism—Yoshio Mikami: The Development of Mathematics in China and Japan (p. 50–53, Leipzig, 1912). Louis van Hée: The Ch'ou-Jen Chuan of Yüan Yüan (Isis, VIII, 109, 1926).

For Hindu astronomy, see my note on Āryabhaṭa in the previous section.

VI. CHINESE GEOGRAPHY

A Geographical Legend of End of the Fifth Century

The "History of the Liang Dynasty" (502–557), contains (chapter 54) a very curious account according to which a Buddhist monk named Hui^{4}-shên^{1} (5193,

9823) came back in 499 after a long journey to the East.[v] He reached a country called Fu[2] sang[1] (3613, 9566), about which he tells marvelous stories. At the end of his account Hui-shên says that the people of that country were unacquainted with Buddhism until the year 458, when five monks came from Chi[4]-pin[1] (978, 9233) (Kabul) and evangelized them.

This mysterious country, Fu sang, thus named after a tree, has been identified by various writers not only with Japan and other Pacific islands, but also with America, more specifically with California, Mexico, Peru. The tree fu sang has been identified with a Chinese tree of the malvaceous family, or, by the defenders of the American theory, with a kind of cactus or aloe.

One can imagine how alluring this account must be to the many people who are as inordinately fond of marvelous stories as children: America discovered by Buddhist monks more than a thousand years before Columbus! Unfortunately there is nothing at all to substantiate it. Either Hui-shên was "a consummate humbug," or if he did actually travel to the East it was perhaps to some island of the Western Pacific.

Western literature on the subject began with Joseph de Guignes's paper in the Mémoires de l'Académie des Inscriptions (vol. 28, 1761). Karl Friedrich Neumann wrote an elaborate memoir in 1841, containing the original narrative with commentary. I know this only through the English translation, which forms the main part of Charles Godfrey Leland: Fusang or the Discovery of America by Chinese Buddhist Priests in the Fifth Century (231 p., London, 1875). This book is a summary of the whole argument; it includes various other documents on the subject, notably the article of Emil Bretschneider, first published in the Chinese Recorder (vol. 3, 114–120, 1870). This article and a later one, which I have not seen (Über das Land Fu-sang, 1876), proved the absurdity of the American theory. Yet we must expect it to reappear periodically, as all freakish conceptions do.

Léon de Rosny: Les peuples orientaux connus des Chinois (2 éd., Paris, 1886). Article Fu-sang, in Encyclopaedia Sinica (199, 1917). Henri Cordier: Histoire de la Chine (t. 1, 558, 1920). Panduranga S. S. Pissurlancar: Recherches sur la découverte de l'Amérique par les anciens hommes de l'Inde (22 p., Sanquelim-Goa, 1920; Isis, V, 271).

VII. LATIN AND SINGHALESE HISTORIOGRAPHY

PROSPER OF AQUITANIA

Tiro Prosper, born c. 390, died c. 463. Christian theologian and historian. He wrote a chronicle ("Chronicon consulare") extending that of St. Jerome down to 445, and later to 455.[w] Most of his time and energy, however, were devoted to theological propaganda (against Pelagianism and Semi-Pelagianism.)[x]

Text—Chronicon (Venice, 1482). Complete works in Migne's Latin Patrology (vol. 51). Edition of the Chronica in the Monumenta Germaniae historica, by Mommsen (1892).

---

[v] The account was repeated by Ma Tuan-lin (second half of the thirteenth century) and other historians, and embellished by Chinese poets.

[w] For the last 30 years it is our unique or main source of information.

[x] His main work of that kind is a poem (1002 hexameters), called περὶ ἀχαρίστων, Hoc est de ingratis, which Guizot considered one of the best Christian philosophical poems. See my note on Pelagianism in the previous chapter.

French translation of the De ingratis by Lemaistre de Sacy (Paris, 1646, 1650), and of the whole works by C. Lequeux (Paris, 1762).

Criticism—P. de Labriolle: Littérature latine chrétienne (574–578, 1920).

MAHĀNĀMA

Flourished at the Dīghasanda Hermitage and at Anurādhapura in the second half of the fifth century. Singhalese historian. Author of a history of Ceylon from the fifth century B. C. to about the middle of the fifth century of our era, written in Pāli verse and called the "Great Chronicle" (Mahāvaṃsa). It is based on earlier native works and is of great historical value.

Text—Editio princeps, with English translation, by George Turnour (Colombo, 1837; first Pāli text made known in Europe; only one volume published). New edition by Wilhelm Geiger (Pali Text Society, 422 p., London, 1908). English translation by the same, assisted by Mabel Haynes Bode (*ibidem*, 363 p., London, 1912).

Criticism—W. Geiger: Dīpavaṃsa and Mahāvaṃsa (Leipzig, 1905. Englished by Ethel M. Coomaraswamy, Colombo, 1908). Article by T. W. R. Davids, in Encyl. Britannica (1911), containing a brief analysis of the work.

VIII. ROMAN AND BARBARIAN LAW

The Syro-Roman Law Book

Manual of law written in Greek some time between Theodosius and Justinian. We have translations of it into Syriac, Arabic, and Armenian. It was apparently very popular in the Near East.

Text—K. G. Bruns and Ed. Sachau: Syrisch-Römisches Rechtsbuch aus dem 5. Jahrhundert (Leipzig, 1880). Complete collection of the versions and German translation by Sachau (vol. 1, Berlin, 1907. Leges Constantini Theodosii Leonis).

Paul Collinet: Les travaux des professeurs de l'Ecole de droit de Beyrouth au Ve siècle (Congrès international d'histoire de Bruxelles, 1923).

Consultatio

The Consultatio (published in 1577 by Cujas under the title "Veteris cujusdam jurisconsulti consultatio") is a book of law probably written in Gaul about the end of the fifth or the beginning of the following century. It is valuable because of older materials kept in it.

Text—Collectio Juris Antejustiniani (t. 3, 203–220, Berlin, 1895). Girard: Textes de droit romain (3e éd., 510–606).

Barbarian Law

Laws of the Visigoths (Leges Wisigothorum). Their earliest code dates back to King Euric (466 to 485). It applied to all cases concerning only Goths or Goths and Romans. In 506 a special code of Roman law was prepared, to be used in cases concerning exclusively Romans (see first half of the sixth century, Breviarium Alarici).

Text—Legis romanae Wisigothorum fragmenta ex codice palimpsesto Sanctae Legionensis ecclesiae. Madrid, 1906 (with facsimile reproduction of the codex; publication of the Spanish Academy of History). Edited by Karl Zeumer in the Monumenta Germ. Hist. (Leges, I, 606 p., Hanover, 1902. Legum codicis euriciani fragmenta. Liber judiciorum sive Lex Visigothorum edita ab Recessuindo rege a. 654, renovata ab Ervigio rege a. 681; accedunt leges novellae extravagantes).

Criticism—Felix Dahn: Westgothische Studien. Entstehungsgeschichte, Privatrecht, Strafrecht, Civil- und Straf-process und Gesammtkritik der Lex Visigothorum (334 p., Würzburg, 1874). Rafael de Ureña y Smenjaud: Una edición inédita de las Leges Gothorum Regum preparada por Diego y Antonio de Covarruvias en la segunda mitad del siglo XVI (Madrid, 1909).

IX. CHINESE PHILOLOGY

SHÊN YO

Shên[3] Yo[1]* (9849, 13349). Native of Wu[3]-k'ang[1] (12744, 5908) in Chehkiang, in 441; he was a high official under the Ch'i and Liang dynasties, and died in 513. Chinese civil servant, lexicographer, and historian. The four tones were differentiated and explained for the first time in his lost work called Ssŭ[4] shêng[1] (10291, 9883).[v] He seems to have had some knowledge of Sanskrit, which stimulated his study of Chinese philology. He wrote histories of the Chin, Liu Sung, and Ch'i dynasties (see p. 437).

H. A. Giles: Biographical Dictionary (648, 167, 1898); Encyclopaedia sinica (1917), articles Lexicography and Tones.

---

[v] Meaning Four tones. From the lexicographical or grammatical point of view, this discovery was of very great importance, as important as that of the fan ch'ieh by Sun Yen (q. v., second half of the third century). Indeed, these two discoveries made accurate lexicography possible. The first conscious distinction of the tones is sometimes ascribed to Chou[1] Yung[2] (2450, 13501), a native of An[1]-ch'êng[2] (44, 762), Honan, who flourished also in the fifth century and wrote a treatise on that subject and another discussing the three main schools of Buddhism.

CHAPTER XXIII

THE TIME OF PHILOPONOS

(First Half of Sixth Century)

I. Survey of Science in First Half of Sixth Century. II. Religious Background. III. Byzantine, Syriac, and Latin Philosophy. IV. Byzantine, Latin, and Hindu Mathematics. V. Hindu, Chinese, Byzantine, and Latin Astronomy. VI. Byzantine Physics and Technology. VII. Byzantine and Latin Botany. Chinese Husbandry. VIII. Chinese and Byzantine Geography. IX. Latin, Byzantine, Syriac, Persian, and Chinese Medicine. X. Byzantine, Latin, Syriac, and Chinese Historiography. XI. Roman and Barbarian Law. XII. Byzantine, Latin, and Chinese Philology and Pedagogy.

I. SURVEY OF SCIENCE IN FIRST HALF OF SIXTH CENTURY

1. The period which we are now going to consider is generally supposed to be one of the darkest of the Dark Ages. We shall see presently that it was a period of remarkable complexity and activity—an activity which was not restricted to a single intellectual field or to a single country, but which affected every department of science and did honor to many nations. It is true, the political conditions were in general unfavorable to the development of civilization, yet it is a fact that civilization continued and even progressed. The darkness, of which historians complain, is essentially the darkness of their own ignorance.

2. *Religious Background*—The famous Academy of Athens was closed in 529 by order of Justinian (the Lyceum had long ceased to exist), but this had its compensations. For one thing, the importance of the Academy was now largely of a historical and sentimental nature; its supremacy had ended together with the supremacy of Greece; when Athens had become a provincial city, less active and prosperous than a good many others, its Academy had become a provincial school. Moreover, the year which saw the death of the Academy witnessed the birth of Monte Cassino. I have already explained the immense cultural value of Christian monasticism. A great step forward was made by St. Benedict, who was the real organizer of monasticism in Western Europe and indirectly the greatest defender of civilization in those days. The Benedictine rule was one of great moderation; it encouraged not only devotion but as well useful work. During this and the three following centuries, western civilization developed mainly under the protection of St. Benedict's habit. The real signification of these two great events of 529 is the triumph of Christianity: if this meant to some extent an intellectual regression, it meant also a moral advance, and these two facts must be considered together. In the last analysis morality is an essential factor of intellectual progress.

While Christianity was nursing human virtues in the West and defending struggling men against themselves, a similar function was accomplished in the East by Buddhism. Bodhidharma, the first eastern patriarch, founded, c. 520, near Lo-yang, the Ch'an or contemplative school of Buddhism which has remained to this day, under many forms, the most popular. The Chinese monk Sung Yün traveled from China to India and back (518 to 522) to obtain Buddhist writings, thus repeating the admirable feat performed by Fa-hsien a century before.

Another Chinese monk, Sêng-yu, wrote various Buddhist works, including a catalogue of the Buddhist books which were already available in Chinese. The fact that such a catalogue had become necessary is an eloquent proof of the enormous growth of Chinese Buddhism.

The Persian Mazdak created a new religious sect, distinguished by ascetic and communistic tendencies. This sect was promptly and completely destroyed by Kawādh in 528–529, but its spirit survived (it is easy enough to kill people, but somehow their influence continues) and has reappeared, and will reappear, under many semblances.

3. *Byzantine,*[a] *Syriac, and Latin Philosophy*—Greek philosophy ended nobly. We can still name a number of distinguished successors of Proclos, who cultivated philosophy and mathematics in a very creditable way. Ammonios, son of Hermias, wrote commentaries on Aristotle and Porphyry. Damascios, the last head of the Academy, wrote commentaries on Plato. Philoponos, a Christian, wrote commentaries on Aristotle; in spite of his scholastic tendencies he was undoubtedly the most original thinker of that time, as will be indicated below. Simplicios was also a learned and wise commentator of Aristotle. Priscianos of Lydia and Asclepios of Tralles were lesser personalities. It is interesting to note that after the closure of the Academy, seven philosophers, including Damascios, Simplicios, and Priscianos, took refuge at the court of the Persian king Chosroës (Nūshīrwān). This migration, unfortunately of short duration (they returned to Europe c. 533) was one of the channels through which Greek wisdom penetrated Asia.

Another channel was the activity of Syrian translators. The most famous of these was Sergios of Resaina, who translated a great number of philosophic, scientific, and medical works from Greek into Syriac and wrote some original works inspired by Greek examples. But the greatest center of intellectual exchange and syncretism was the Persian school of Jundīshāpūr, with which I shall deal presently in the medical section.

In the meanwhile, Greek thought was carried westward by Boetius and Cassiodorus, both exerting a deep influence upon the development of Western learning. The most popular of Boetius's writings was his "Consolation of Philosophy," which helped many good men to preserve their equanimity in days of trial. Cassiodorus completed the work of St. Benedict and bequeathed the Western monks an encyclopaedia of the seven liberal arts, which remained for centuries one of the mainsprings of their worldly knowledge.

4. *Byzantine, Latin, and Hindu Mathematics*—In 532, Justinian having ordered the reconstruction of Hagia Sophia, put in charge of this work two mathematicians, Anthemios of Tralles and Isidoros of Miletos. The latter became the center of a school of mathematicians who were especially interested in Archimedian and Apollonian geometry, that is, the most advanced mathematics of ancient times. Anthemios, who had made a special study of parabolic mirrors, was familiar with the main properties of the parabola, and knew how to construct it by means of its focus and directrix. (The focus of the parabola is not even mentioned in Apollonios's Conics.) Eutocios wrote commentaries on Archimedes and Apollonios; it is probably due to him that the Greek text of Books I to IV of the Conics is still extant. Another work of the same school was the so-called Book XV of Euclid, which deals with the regular solids.

---

[a] Henceforth I shall use the word Byzantine instead of Hellenistic, to designate works written in Greek or their authors.

The Neoplatonic philosophers, of whom I spoke in the previous section, were all mathematicians. The division of mathematics into the four branches of the mediaeval quadrivium seems to have been introduced by Ammonios. The ascription of Book XV of Euclid to Damascios is unwarranted but typical. Philoponos and Asclepios of Tralles wrote commentaries on Nicomachos's arithmetic. Simplicios wrote a commentary on Euclid. Two long fragments of his writings are of considerable importance for the history of mathematics and astronomy.

The Roman philosopher Boetius was also a distinguished mathematician. He wrote treatises on each branch of the quadrivium, a classification which was introduced by him in the Latin West, and obtained considerable success. Some mathematics will be found also, of course, in Cassiodorus's encyclopaedia.

The astronomical treatise of Varāhamihira contains an elaboration of Hindu trigonometry.

5. *Hindu, Chinese, Byzantine, and Latin Astronomy*—The Pañcasiddhāntikā of Varāhamihira, written in 505, is one of the outstanding scientific works of the age. It is largely based upon Greek knowledge, but offers certain Hindu peculiarities, the most valuable of which is the introduction of Hindu trigonometry. It deals also with astrology.

The Chinese calendar seems to have been improved at the beginning of the century; it remained very rudimentary.

Heliodoros, younger brother of Ammonios, made astronomical observations c. 498 to 509, and wrote an astronomical text-book. To Philoponos is due the earliest treatise on the astrolabe which has come down to us in its original form. Simplicios tried to explain the stability of celestial bodies.

The Christian era was introduced c. 525 by Dionysius Exiguus. Its adoption was extremely slow; it was a matter of many centuries.

6. *Byzantine Physics and Technology*—Two anonymous Byzantine treatises dealing with the art of war may belong to this period. The "Anonymus Byzantinus" flourished probably in the time of Justinian; the date of the "Anonymus de rebus bellicis" is more uncertain, but it is expedient to consider these two treatises together. The second contains a description of a ship equipped with paddle-wheels, but this may be a later interpolation.

The greatest physicist of the age was Philoponos. He refused to accept the Aristotelian theories on motion and on the impossibility of vacuum. He had some vague notion of what we call inertia. These ideas, when placed in their proper background, are so strikingly original, so daring, and yet so prophetic of modern mechanics, that Philoponos has been called a "forerunner of Galileo." This may seem an exaggeration; yet he was the greatest mechanician within the very long period which extended from Archimedes to Buridan (first half of the fourteenth century). Simplicios also did some original thinking on the nature of motion. Anthemios studied parabolic mirrors and burning-glasses.

7. *Byzantine and Latin Botany; Chinese Husbandry*—The famous manuscript of Dioscorides of St. Mark's Library in Venice was written before 512. It contains many admirable illustrations of plants and is one of the greatest monuments in the history of botanical iconography.

The pseudo Dioscoridean treatise "De herbis femininis" is probably an Italian work of the sixth century.

Chia Ssŭ-hsieh wrote the earliest Chinese treatise on husbandry.

8. *Chinese and Byzantine Geography*—The Chinese monk Sung Yün left China

(presumably Lo-yang) in 518 and traveled to India, returning home in 522. A record of his journey, written in 547, is of great geographical interest.

The Egyptian Christian Cosmas Indicopleustes, who traveled extensively, going as far as Ceylon and Ethiopia, wrote a geographical treatise, a "Christian Topography," the main purpose of which was to refute the theory of the sphericity of the earth. Cosmas knew the sources of the Blue Nile. Byzantine geography of that time is represented also by the map of Mādabā, which is the oldest true geographical map extant (a map of Palestine), and by the geographical dictionary of Stephanos of Byzantium.

9. *Latin, Byzantine, Syriac, Persian, and Chinese Medicine*—The Byzantine physician Anthimus wrote a Latin letter on diet to Theodoric, King of the Franks. Moschion composed a little book on women's diseases and midwifery, which is essentially derived from Soranos. Moschion's treatise was exceedingly popular during the Middle Ages, being finally retranslated into Greek. Its manuscripts are very important for the study of anatomical and gynaecological iconography. Two other Latin treatises, the so-called "Aurelius" and "Aesculapius," are possibly contemporary.

Aëtios of Amida, physician to Justinian, compiled a medical encyclopaedia in 16 books, which contains much material of scientific or historical interest. The book devoted to eye diseases was the best of its kind up to that date.

The Syrian philosopher Sergios translated various medical works from Greek into Syriac. A medical center had been gradually built up at Jundīshāpūr under the protection of the Sassanidae. It became especially important after the expulsion of the Nestorians from Edessa in 489 and even more after the banishment of the Neoplatonists from Athens in 529. It reached its greatest prosperity during the rule of Nūshīrwān the Just (531–79). Jundīshāpūr became then one of the greatest clearing-houses of philosophic and scientific ideas—Greek, Jewish, Christian, Syrian, Hindu, and Persian ideas being constantly compared and exchanged in its cosmopolitan environment.

The Taoist T'ao Hung-ching composed a great treatise on materia medica, and other medical, alchemical, and archeological writings. Chia Ssŭ-hsieh wrote a treatise on diet.

10. *Byzantine, Latin, Syriac, and Chinese Historiography*—Hesychios of Miletos wrote a world history down to 518 and a Byzantine history from 518 to c. 530.

Cassiodorus wrote a history of the Goths which we know only through Jordanes's abridgment.

The earliest Syriac chronicles date from the same time; the chronicle formerly ascribed to Joshua the Stylite was composed in 507; another chronicle, c. 540. Both were written in Edessa, probably by orthodox authors, though the second reveals some Nestorian tendencies.

Shên-yo wrote the official history of the Liu Sung dynasty and Hsiao Tzŭ-hsien that of the Nan Ch'i dynasty.

11. *Roman and Barbarian Law*—The best proof that the Barbarians, who accelerated the decomposition of the Western Empire, were not simply destructive, is afforded to us by their legal monuments. Three of these are pre-Justinian: Theodoric's "Edict," a compilation of Roman and Gothic law, made c. 500 to 515; Alaric's "Breviary," another compilation, promulgated in 506, and of enormous importance for the history of mediaeval law; finally, a compilation of Roman and Burgundian law promulgated in 517. These three codes show very clearly that the

purpose of the Barbarians was not to destroy, but on the contrary to assimilate Roman institutions as well as they could and to adapt them to their special needs. This impression is not modified by the study of the Barbarian codes proper which were published at about the same time. The Burgundian Law (after 500) and the Salic Law (c. 510) show that the Barbarians were anxious to preserve their own traditions. That was natural enough. It does not follow that they wanted to destroy Roman traditions. As a matter of fact, it was probably the very prestige of everything Roman which obliged them to preserve their own traditions with greater care and to codify them in the Roman manner. On the other hand, it can not be denied that their original traditions contained much that was crude and irrational.

The most important juridical work of that time, and indeed one of the most important of all times, was accomplished by order of the Emperor Justinian, who has been correctly named Justinian the Great. It is hardly necessary to dwell upon this. The consolidation of Roman law which bears his name has remained a model and an inspiration for the jurists of all nations and ages. The greatest part of the "Corpus juris" was completed before the middle of the century, the "Constitution" being promulgated in 529, the "Institutes" shortly before 533, and the "Digest" in 533. It is noteworthy that this Byzantine code was largely in Latin, but Greek translations and paraphrases were promptly made.

12. *Byzantine, Latin, and Chinese Philology and Pedagogy*—It is not improper to deal in this section with some pedagogical works which are not concerned with the study of language, because pedagogy was essentially centered upon that study, even when its subject-matter was different. It is difficult even now to dissociate these ideas, and when we think of a pedagogue we usually see a grammarian.

The African Priscian wrote a Latin grammar which was almost as famous as that of Donatus. He wrote also a treatise on numerals, weights, and measures. I have already indicated the immense educational work accomplished or inspired by St. Benedict and Cassiodorus. In ancient and mediaeval times every philosopher and, we might almost say, every man of science, was an educator; outside of the regular schools, which were not very numerous, the disciples flocking around each man of wisdom and learning would naturally form as many extraordinary schools of more or less duration.

The historian Hesychios compiled a Greek lexicon which included a biographical summary of Greek literature.

Chou Hsing-ssŭ wrote the famous "Thousand Character Essay," which has remained to this day one of the fundamental books of Chinese education. Chia Ssŭ-hsieh wrote a treatise on husbandry and alimentation. Ku Yeh-wang compiled a new dictionary, the Yü p'ien, wherein the characters are classified under 542 radicals.

13. *Final Remarks*—I believe that the statement which I made at the beginning of this chapter has been sufficiently substantiated by this rapid survey. The end of the school of Athens was a very honorable one. Men like Ammonios, Damascios, and Simplicios would have done credit to any school. Philoponos was one of those very rare men of genius who represented the Archimedian spirit before the seventeenth century. The new schools created in the West under St. Benedict's inspiration, which used the treatises compiled by Boetius and Cassiodorus, were of course much humbler in their intellectual aims than the Pagan schools, yet they rendered wonderful services. Their task was no longer one of intellectual pio-

neering, but rather one of reclamation and education. The Persian school of Jundīshāpūr was apparently more ambitious, yet its main purpose was one of transmission rather than of creation. Many fragments of Greek knowledge were translated or paraphrased in Latin and Syriac works. Nor was the source of Greek knowledge entirely dried up. The mathematical school of Constantinople did not hesitate to tackle the most difficult problems; Aëtios of Amida was not a mere compiler, he added many original observations to those of the ancient physicians which he helped to transmit.

In the meanwhile, Varāhamihira continued the elaboration of trigonometry on the basis of Greek and Hindu wisdom. More links between East and West were forged by Cosmas, who traveled from Egypt to Ceylon, and by Sung Yün, who traveled from China to India. Historians were at work everywhere trying to determine accurate knowledge of the past, their own past. Philologists were carrying on their ungrateful but indispensable task, in the West, in the Near East, and in the Far East.

But, taken all in all, the greatest achievement of that age was the publication of the Justinian Code, which, imperfect as it was, remained an indestructible symbol of order and justice. The Barbarians who conquered the Western Empire were not sufficiently educated to understand Greek knowledge, even in its Roman garb, but their pride was humbled by the powerful combination of Roman law and Christian morality.

II. RELIGIOUS BACKGROUND

ST. BENEDICT

Benedictus Cassinensis, born at Nursia, near Spoleto, in Umbria, c. 480, died c. 544. Patriarch of Western monasticism.[b] He founded, in 529, the monastery of Monte Cassino and set forth the Benedictine rule which rapidly superseded all other monastic rules in Western Europe (save Ireland), and remained there until the tenth century, the only form of monasticism. It is "conspicuous for its discretion." Excessive austerity was discouraged, useful work encouraged, law and order firmly established.

His disciple St. Maur (c. 510 to 584) founded before 542 the first Benedictine monastery in France, at St. Maur-sur-Loire. During the sixth, seventh, eighth, and ninth centuries the Benedictine monasteries were the chief civilizing agencies in western Europe.

Text—Sancti Benedicti Regula monachorum, edited by Edward Cuthbert Butler (235 p., Freiburg i. B., 1912). Edition by Benno Linderbauer (Metten, 1922).

The rule of St. Benet. Latin and Anglo-Saxon interlinear version edited by H. Logeman (Early English Text Soc., 90, 188 p., London, 1888). Three Middle English versions, edited by Ernst A. Koch (*Idem*, 120, 272 p., London, 1902). English translation by Abbot F. A. Gasquet (158 p., London, 1909). Old Portuguese version edited by John M. Burnam (78 p., Cincinnati, 1911; Alcobaça manuscript No. 300, Lisbon)

Criticism—Heribert Plenkers: Untersuchungen zur Überlieferungsgeschichte der ältesten lateinischen Mönchsregeln (München, 1906). Ludwig Traube: Textgeschichte der Regula S. Benedicti (2. Aufl. hrg. von H. Plenkers., 127 p., Bayer. Ak. der Wiss., Abhdl., phil. Cl., t. 25, 1910). Cuthbert Butler: Benedictine

---

[b] For a qualification of this statement see my note on Christian monasticism in the first half of the fourth century.

monachism (395 p., London, 1919). Sandys: History of Classical Scholarship (t. 1[3], 270–272, 1921). Ildephonsus Herwegen: St. Benedict, a Character Study. Translated by Dom Peter Nugent (184 p., London, 1924. German edition, Düsseldorf, 1919).

BODHIDHARMA

In Chinese, P'u[2]-t'i[2]-ta[2]*-mo[2] (9511, 11003, 10473, 7974), usually shortened to Ta-mo. In Japanese, Daruma. Born in Southern India, arrived in India c. 520 and settled at the monastery of Shao[3]-lin[2] (9746, 7157) at the base of the Shao[3]-shih[4]* (9746, 9974) Mountain near Lo[4]*-yang[2] (7328, 12883), Honan; he died c. 528.[c] Twenty-eighth and last Western (or Hindu) and first Eastern (or Chinese) patriarch of Buddhism. He founded the Ch'an[d] or Contemplative School of Buddhism. His teaching was impregnated with Vedāntism.

H. A. Giles: Biographical Dictionary (6, 1898); R. F. Johnston: Buddhist China (London, 1913). L. Wieger: Histoire des croyances en Chine (523–532, 1922. Maintaining that Bodhidharma's teaching was Vedāntic rather than Buddhist; this account does not strike me as very impartial).

Bodhidharma was one of many Hindu refugees in China. According to an account quoted by A. K. Reischauer (Japanese Buddhism, 74, 1917), there were more than 6,000 Hindu refugees in China at the beginning of the sixth century. The number of Buddhist temples was already upward of 13,000.

For Sung Yün, see my note in the geographical section below.

SÊNG-YU

Sêng[1]-yu[4] (9617, 13438). Flourished under the Liang dynasty c. 520. Chinese Buddhist. Author of three important Buddhist works. Ch'u[1]* san[1]-ts'ang[4] chi[4]-chi[2]* (2620, 9552, 11681, 923, 906), a catalogue of Buddhist works translated into Chinese from 67 to 520; Hung[2]-ming[2]-chi[2]* (5282, 7946, 906), Buddhist history and apologetics in 14 books;[e] Shih[4]*-ch'ieh[2]-p'u[3] (9983, 1558, 9515), a history of Buddha and of the origins of Buddhism.

L. Wieger: La Chine (384, 487, 496, 530, 1920).

MAZDAK

Flourished at Persepolis or at Nishapur, assassinated by order of Kawādh I in 528–529. Founder of a Persian religious sect,[f] ascetic and communistic. The Mazdakites were entrapped and massacred by Kawādh in 528–529, but their views have been periodically revived since, for example, by the Ismā'īlīs and more recently by the early Bābīs.

The Fars-nāma is the main source for the story of Mazdak. Th. Nöldeke: Über Mazdak und die Mazdakiten. (Appendix to his Geschichte der Perser und Araber

---

[c] The dates relative to Bodhidharma are the earliest in the long succession of patriarchs to be well established.

[d] The Ch'an[2] tsung[1] (348, 11976) is by far the most popular in China, but it is subdivided into many branches. It was introduced into Japan in 1191 and 1227 and is better known in the West under its Japanese name, Zen. The Sanskrit name is Dhyāna, meaning meditation. The mystical tendencies of that school were as favorable to the development of art as they were unfavorable to the increase of positive knowledge. Bodhidharma discouraged the use of books.

[e] Continued by Tao-hsüan, q. v., second half of seventh century.

[f] A sort of Manichaeism.

zur Zeit der Sasaniden, 1879. Being a translation of the relevant part of Ṭabarī's history.) E. G. Browne: Literary History of Persia (I, 166–172, 1908). Arthur Christensen: Le règne du roi Kawādh I et le communisme mazdakite (Danske Vidensk. Selskab, hist. Meddelelser, IX, 6. 127 p., Copenhagen, 1925. Completing Nöldeke's study by the use of new sources).

III. BYZANTINE, SYRIAC, AND LATIN PHILOSOPHY

AMMONIOS, SON OF HERMIAS

Ἀμμώνιος. Flourished at Alexandria at the end of the fifth and the beginning of the sixth century. Greek philosopher and commentator of Aristotle and Porphyry.[g] Pupil of Proclos at Athens and, as leader of the school of Alexandria, teacher of Damascios, Philoponos, Simplicios. He divided mathematics[h] into four branches: arithmetic, geometry, astronomy, music, a classification which came down almost to modern times (see my notes on Martianus Capella, second half of fifth century, and on Boetius, below).

Text—The following commentaries have appeared in the Berlin edition of Commentaria in Aristotelem graeca: (1) In Porphyrii Isagogen (1891); (2) In Categorias (1895); (3) In De interpretatione (1897). (1, 2, 3 edited by Ad. Busse); (4) In Analyticorum priorum librum I, edited by Max. Wallies (1899).

Criticism—Freudenthal, in Pauly-Wissowa (t. 1, 1863–1865, 1894). P. Tannery: Mémoires (VII, 223, 1925).

DAMASCIOS

Δαμάσκιος. Born in Damascus c. 458, died after 533. Neoplatonic philosopher, head of the Academy from c. 510 until its closure by Justinian in 529. From 531 to 533 a refugee of the court of Chosroës I, King of Persia. Disciple of Proclos, even more mystical than he. Wrote commentaries on Plato, a life of his master Isidoros, and a hair-splitting book on the doubts and solutions concerning the first principles (ἀπορίαι καὶ λύσεις περὶ τῶν πρώτων ἀρχῶν).

The so-called "Fifteenth Book of Euclid" has been ascribed to him, but without serious foundation.

Text and Translations—Excerpta ex Damascii libro ms. περὶ ἀρχῶν, edited by Joh. Christ. Wolf, in his Anecdota graeca (t. 3, 195–262, Hamburg, 1722). Complete edition of the same work by Jos. Kopp (424 p., Francfurt, 1826). French translation of Isidoros's Life by A. Ed. Chaignet: Proclus le Philosophe (t. 3, p. 241–371, Paris, 1903). Rudolf Asmus: Das Leben des Philosophen Isidoros von Damaskios, wiederhergestellt, übersetzt, und erklärt (240 p., Leipzig, 1911).

Criticism—Emil Heitz: Der Philosoph Damascius (Strassburger Abhdl. zur Philosophie, E. Zeller's Festschrift, Freiburg i. B., p. 1–24, 1884). Kroll, in Pauly-Wissowa (t. 8, 2039–2042, 1901). Th. L. Heath: The Thirteen Books of Euclid's Elements (Vol. III, Cambridge, 1908).

PHILOPONOS

Joannes Philoponos, John the Grammarian (Φιλόπονος), flourished in Alexandria in the first half of the sixth century. Christian philosopher. Pupil of Ammonios, son of Hermias. He wrote extensive commentaries on Aristotle's writings and contributed much to the amalgamation of the Peripatetic and Chris-

[g] His commentary on the "Isagoge" is the earliest Greek extant.
[h] According to Aristotle's classification (q. v.).

tian doctrines. He wrote also a commentary on Porphyry's "Isagoge," a commentary on the arithmetic of Nicomachos and the earliest treatise on the astrolabe (the only one that has come down to us from ancient times). He showed remarkable freedom of thought and some of his views on physics and mechanics were amazingly original. He contested the Aristotelian ideas on motion and anticipated vaguely the concept of inertia. He denied that bodies of greater weight fall more quickly, referring to experiment. Neither did he accept the Aristotelian doctrine about the impossibility of vacuum. It is through his commentary on the "Isagoge" that the Aristotelian classification of science was transmitted to the Arabic, and later to the Jewish, philosophers.

Text and Translations—Philoponos's commentaries to Aristotle have been published in the Berlin edition of Greek commentaries as follows: Categories, ed. Adolf Busse (XIII, 1, 1898); Prior and posterior Analytics, by Maxim. Wallies (XIII, 2 and 3, 1905–1909); Meteorology, by Mich. Hayduck (XIV, 1, 1901); de Generatione et Corruptione, by Hier. Vitelli (XIV, 2, 1897); de Generatione Animalium by Mich. Hayduck (XIV, 2, 288 p., 1903; this commentary is ascribed to Philoponos, but appears to be the work of one of Psellos's pupils, Michael of Ephesus, who flourished in the second half of the eleventh century); de Anima, by Mich. Hayduck (XV, 690 p., 1897); Physics, by Hier. Vitelli (XVI, XVII, 1020 p., 1887–88; this commentary was written in 517).

De aeternitate mundi contra Proclum, ed. Hugo Rabe (713 p., Leipzig, 1899; written a little after 529). De opificio mundi libri VII, rec. Walt. Reichardt (Leipzig, 1897).

In Nichomachi introductionem arithm., ed. Rich. Hoche (1864–1867). De usu astrolabi eiusque constructione libellus ed. by H. Hase (47 p., Bonn, 1839; also Rheinishes Museum, p. 127–171, 1839).

Criticism—A general study of Philoponos is badly needed, the more so in that his writings are repellingly prolix; it would be worth while to extract from them the original ideas and to discuss their origin and fortune. Moritz Steinschneider: Johannes Philoponus bei den Arabern (Mém. de l'acad. des sciences de Saint Pétersbourg, t. 13, 152–176, 1869. An appendix to Steinschneider's great memoir on al-Fārābī). P. Tannery: Notes critiques sur le traité de l'astrolabe de Philopon (Revue de philologie, t. 12, p. 60–73, 1888; Mémoires, IV, 241–260; Isis, IV, 342); short article in Grande Encyclopédie (vol. 26, 707). Arthur E. Haas: Ueber die Originalität der physikalischen Lehren des Philoponus (Bibliotheca mathematica, t. 6, 337–342, 1906). Em. Wohlwill: Ein Vorgänger Galileis im VI. Jahrhundert (Physikalische Zeitschrift, t. 7, 23–32, 1906). P. Duhem: Le système du monde (t. 1, p. 313–320, 1913, on place and vacuum; t. 2, p. 108, 1914, on the value of astronomical hypotheses; p. 494, earliest criticism of Genesis from the physical point of view). E. Mach: The Science of Mechanics (Supplement to third English ed., p. 17–18, Chicago, 1915).

Among P. Tannery's unpublished manuscripts there is a translation of Philoponos's treatise on the astrolabe and also an article dealing with that treatise.

SIMPLICIOS

Σιμπλίκιος. Born in Cilicia, disciple of Ammonios and Damascios, flourished in Athens until 529, then until 533 at the court of Chosroës, King of Persia. Greek philosopher. One of the last Neoplatonists. He wrote a commentary on the Enchiridion of Epictetos and on many works of Aristotle (probably after 533). The Aristotelian commentaries are of great value to the history of philosophy, mathematics, and astronomy. Simplicios wrote a commentary on Book I of

Euclid. He explained the stability of the celestial bodies by the excess of their impetus over their gravity.

Text and Translations—The Berlin edition of Greek commentaries of Aristotle include the following by Simplicios: In vol. 2, de anima, ed. Mich. Hayduck (375 pp., 1882); vol. 7, de coelo, ed. J. L. Heiberg (796 p., 1894); vol. 8, categoriae, ed. Carl Kalbfleisch (1907); vols. 9–10, physicorum libri, ed. Hermann Diels (2 vols., 1,500 p., 1882–1895).

Ferdinand Rudio: Der Bericht des Simplicius über die Quadraturen des Antiphon und des Hippokrates. Griechisch und Deutsch (194 p., Leipzig, 1907).

Criticism—Moritz Steinschneider: Simplicius der Mathematiker (Bibliotheca mathematica, p. 7–8, 1892). R. O. Besthorn: Über den Commentar des Simplicius zu den Elementa (*ibidem*, 65–66). Paul Tannery: Simplicius et la quadrature du cercle (Bibliotheca mathematica, t. 3, 342–349, 1902; Mémoires, III, 119). Wil. Schmidt: Zu dem Berichte des Simplicius über die Möndchen des Hippokrates (Bibliotheca mathematica, t. 4, 118–126, 1903). P. Duhem: Etudes sur Léonard de Vinci (t. 2, p. 64, 1909, on gravity); Système du Monde (t. 2, p. 108, 1914, on the value of astronomical hypotheses). Ferdinand Rudio has written various papers on Simplicios; they are summarized in the introduction to his edition of Simplicios above mentioned.

PRISCIANOS

Πρισκιανὸς ὁ Λυδός. Priscian the Lydian. Flourished in the time of Justinian. One of the seven philosophers who took refuge at the court of the Persian King Chosroës after the closure of the Academy; they remained there until c. 533, when the treaties of peace between Chosroës and Justinian enabled them to return to their own country. Priscianos wrote a commentary on Theophrastos's treatise on the senses and a collection of answers to Chosroës's questions.

Text—Μεταφράσις τῶν Θεοφράστου περὶ αἰσθήσεως (Basel, 1541). Also in Wimmer's edition of Theophrastos (vol. 3, Leipzig, 232–282, 1862).

The Greek text of the Answers is lost, but we have a ninth century Latin translation (Quicherat ascribed it to John Scotus Erigena, q. v., second half of ninth century): Solutiones eorum de quibus dubitavit Chosroës Persarum rex. Fragments published by Fr. Dübner in the edition of Plotinos by Fr. Creuzer and G. H. Moser (p. 545–579, Paris, 1855).

Complete edition, together with the Metaphrasis. Prisciani Lydi quae extant, edited by I. Bywater, in the Supplementum Aristotelicum (Vol. I, part II, Berlin, 1886).

ASCLEPIOS OF TRALLES

Ἀσκληπιός; pupil of Ammonios; he outlived Simplicios, who died c. 560 to 570. Greek philosopher and mathematician. Author of commentaries on Nicomachos's arithmetic and on Aristotle's metaphysics.

Text—In Aristotelis Metaphysicorum libros α–ξ commentaria, ed. Michael Hayduck (Comm. in Aristotelem graeca, VI, 2, Berlin, 1888).

Criticism—Gercke, in Pauly-Wissowa (t. 2, 1697, 1896, 14 l).

SERGIOS

Sergios of Resaina, studied at Alexandria, flourished at Ra's al-'ain in Mesopotamia: died at Constantinople in 536. Syriac Monophysite.[i] Physician and

[i] His religion was a little unstable, for he showed leanings toward Orthodoxy and toward Nestorianism.

philosopher. Chief physician at Ra's al-'ain. He was one of the greatest translators from Greek into Syriac.[i] In this respect he was to the Monophysites what Probos had been to the Nestorians a little before (second half of fifth century.) He introduced them to many new treasures of Greek philosophy and medicine. His most important translations are those of Plato (?), Aristotle, Porphyry, of Hippocrates (?) and Galen (26 books), of the Peripatetic treatise περὶ κόσμου. He was possibly the translator or the editor of the Syriac Geoponica. He translated also some of the works of "Dionysios the Areopagite" (second half of the fifth century) and possibly the "Ars Grammatica" of Dionysios Thrax (second half of second century B. C.). He wrote also original works in Syriac, notably a treatise on logic (in seven books; lost). His tract on the action and influence of the moon is an elaboration of a work of Galen's.[k] Some of his translations were revised in the ninth century by Hunain ibn Isḥāq.

Texts—Salomon Schueler: Die Uebersetzung der Categorien des Aristoteles von Jacob von Edessa (Berlin, 1897. Schueler ascribed this version to Jacob of Edessa). Richard J. H. Gottheil: The Syriac Version of the Categories (Hebraica, t. 9; 166–215, 1893).

The version of the περὶ κόσμου was edited by Paul de Lagarde in his Analecta syriaca (p. 134, London, 1855).

H. Pognon: Une version syriaque des Aphorismes d'Hippocrate (Leipzig, 1903).

Extracts from some of the translations of Galen were edited by Adalbert Merx (Z. der deutschen morgenl. Ges., t. 39, 237, 1885) and by Ed. Sachau: Inedita syriaca (88–97, Wien, 1870).

Paul de Lagarde: Geoponicon in sermonem syriacum versorum quae supersunt (Leipzig, 1860). Fragment in J. P. N. Land: Anecdota syriaca (IV, 60). See also my note on Cassianos Bassos in next chapter.

Tract on the influence of the moon, followed by an appendix on the movement of the sun, edited by Sachau: Inedita syriaca (101–126).

See also my note on Syrian anatomy in the second half of the second century for a Syriac text edited by E. Wallis Budge in 1913.

Criticism—E. Renan: De philosophia peripatetica apud Syros (Paris, 1852). P. de Lagarde: De Geoponicon versione syriaca (Berlin, 1855; reprinted in his Gesam. Abh., Leipzig, 1866). Victor Ryssel: Über den textkritischen Wert der syrischer Übersetzungen griechischen Klassiker (Leipzig, 1880–81). A. Baumstark: Lucubrationes syro-graecae; Aristoteles bei den Syrern vom V.–VIII. Jahrhundert (Leipzig, 1900). R. Duval: Littérature syriaque (3ᵉ éd., 1907). A. Baumstark: Syrische Literatur (167–169, 1922). M. Meyerhof: New Light on Hunain ibn Isḥāq (Isis, VIII, 703, 1926).

For the last days of the school of Athens and its closure in 529 by order of Justinian, see P. Tannery: Sur la période finale de la philosophie grecque (Revue philosophique, vol. 42, 266–287, 1896; Mémoires, vol. 7, 211–241). For the Persian school of Jundīshāpūr, see my note in the medical section below.

BOETIUS

Anicius Manilius Severinus Boetius (or Boethius). Born at Rome?, c. 480, executed in Pavia, 524. Roman philosopher and statesman; friend of Theodoric

[i] The value of Syriac translations has been much discussed. H. Pognon (1903) judges them very severely; on the other hand, V. Ryssel considers Sergios's version of the περὶ κόσμου a masterpiece far superior to Apuleius's version (second half of second century).

[k] The περὶ κρισίμων ἡμερῶν, Book III.

the Great. He might be called the last Roman philosopher and writer or the first of the scholastics. He used the word "quadruvium" to designate the four mathematical disciplines, arithmetic, music, geometry, and astronomy, and wrote manuals for each of them. Those on arithmetic and music are extant; the authenticity of the geometry is uncertain. He gave the rule for finding the number of combinations of n things taken two at a time.[l] Boetius wrote many translations of Greek authors, chiefly Aristotle,[m] and commented upon them. He also wrote a commentary upon the Topica of Cicero. At the end of his life, while in prison, he composed his "golden book," de consolatione philosophiae, which was translated into many early vernaculars. Boetius's influence during the Middle Ages was immense; his manuals remained long in favor as school-books; it was from him that most mediaeval people derived their knowledge of Aristotle.

Text and Translations—Ed. princeps of the collected works (Venice, 1491–92.) Collected works in Migne's Patrology (2 vols., Paris, 1847).

De consolatione philosophiae, ed. Theod. Oblatius (Jena, 1843, with extensive prolegomena). Philosophiae consolationis libri V. Accedunt ejusdem atque incertorum opuscula sacra, rec. Rud. Peiper (Leipzig, 1871). Latin text with French translation of de consolatione, by Louis Judicis de Mirandol (Paris, 1861). The Theological Tractates, with English translation by H. F. Stewart and E. K. Rand. The Consolation of Philosophy with the English Translation by "I. T." (1609) revised by H. F. Stewart (Loeb Classical Library, 434 p., London, 1918).

Commentarii in librum Aristotelis περὶ ἑρμηνείας, rec. Carl Meiser (2 pts., Leipzig, 1877–1880). Commentariorum in Topica Ciceronis denuo edendorum specimen, ed. F. N. Klein (Progr., Confluentibus, 1829). In Isagogen Porphyrii commenta, rec. Samuel Brandt (Corpus script. ecclesiast. latin., 48, 509 p., Vienna, 1906).

Arithmetica. Ed. princeps, Augsburg, 1488. (See D. E. Smith: Rara arithmetica, p. 25–28, 1908). Boetius's arithmetic is an adaptation of Nicomachos; it is purely theoretical. Fragmentum de arithmetica et epigramma Gerberti, ed. C. F. Weber (16 p., Cassel, 1847). De institutione arithmetica libri II, de institutione musica libri V. Accedit geometria quae fertur Boetii, ed. God. Friedlein (Leipzig, 1867).

Boetius und die griechische Harmonik. Des Boetius fünf Bücher über die Musik, German translation, with commentary, by Oscar Paul (435 p., Leipzig, 1872).

General Criticism—Hugh Fraser Stewart: Boethius (289 p., Edinburgh, 1891. The most comprehensive study of Boetius, though his scientific work is not considered. One will find in it a general account of all the ancient translations of the Consolation: Beowulf, Alfred, the Provençal translation, etc. Many special studies have been devoted to these early translations, but I do not quote them, for they are of greater interest to modern philologists than to us). Arthur Patch McKinlay: Stylistic Tests and the Chronology of the Works of Boethius (Harvard Studies in Classical Philology, vol. 18, 123–156, 1907). Gregor Anton Müller: Die Trostschrift des Boethius. Eine literarhistorische Quellenuntersuchung (Diss., 57 p., Berlin, 1912).

There is also an abundant literature on Boetius's religion. He was certainly influenced by Christianity, yet there is no reference to it in the Consolation. He was probably an Orthodox Christian, but deeply imbued with Pagan philosophy; on the other hand, Theodoric was an Arian. This religious difference may have been one of the causes of Boetius's execution.

---

[l] Modern equivalent, $\frac{1}{2}n(n-1)$.

[m] For his translation of Aristotle's "Logic" see my note on Direct Translations from the Greek in the twelth century.

Mathematics—G. Friedlein: Gerbert, die Geometrie des Boethius und die indischen Ziffern (60 p., 6 pl., Erlangen, 1861). F. Gustaffson: De codicibus Boetii de institutione arithmetica librorum Bernensibus (Act. soc. scient. Fenn., t. XI, 341–344, Helsingfors, 1879). J. Paulson: De fragmento Lundensi de institutione arithmetica librorum (Arsskrift 21, 30 p., University of Lund, 1885). Fr. Th. Köppen: Notiz über die Zahlwörter im Abacus des Boethius (Ac. des sciences de St. Pétersbourg, Bull., vol. 35, 31–48, 1892). Paul Tannery: Notes sur la pseudo-géometrie de Boèce (Bibliotheca mathematica, p. 39–50, 524, 1900; Mémoires, t. 5, 211–228; Isis, VI, 431); Grande Encyclopédie (t. 7, 28); Une correspondance d'écolâtres au XIe Siècle (Notices et extraits 1901, t. 36 (2), 487–543; Mémoires, t. 5, 229–303; Isis, VI, 432). Georg Ernst: De geometricis illis, quae sub Boëthii nomine nobis tradita sunt, questiones (Progr., 32 p., Bayreuth, 1903). D. E. Smith and L. C. Karpinski: The Hindu-Arabic Numerals (Boston, 1911. Chapter V, p. 63–90, deals with the question of the introduction of the numerals into Europe by Boetius, the authors concluding that Boetius may very easily have known these numerals without the zero, though no proof of it can be given).

Music—Boetius's manual of music is based chiefly upon the Pythagorean tradition, as opposed to the Aristoxenian; it is an important source for the history of ancient music. Wal. Miekley: De Boethii libri de musica primi fontibus (Diss., 30 p., Jena, 1898).

Logic—Will. L. Davidson: The Logic of Definition (London, 1885. An appendix, p. 319–330, deals with Boetius).

CASSIODORUS

Flavius Magnus Aurelius Cassiodorus Senator. Born c. 490 at Scylacium, in Bruttium, died c. 580. Ostrogothic statesman and scholar. He founded a monastery near Scylacium (Squillace) in part for the preservation of learning, and composed an encyclopaedia of the seven liberal arts, with various other instructions (Institutiones divinarum et humanarum litterarum). His most important work is the Variarum (epistolarum) libri XII published c. 537; he wrote a "Historia Gothorum," which is known only through the abridgment made by his contemporary Jordanes (or Jornandes, q. v., next chapter). He collected and emended ancient manuscripts, and caused his monks to copy them.

Text and Translations—The first edition of the collected works was published in Paris, 1579; many have followed, chiefly Migne's in the Patrologia latina (vols. 69–70), but there is no modern edition. The first edition of the Variae appeared in Ausgburg, 1533. Variae rec. Theod. Mommsen; accedunt Epistulae Theodericianae variae, etc. (779 p., Berlin, 1894; Monumenta Germaniae historica, auctorum antiquissimorum, XII; with important prolegomena). Condensed English translation of the Variae epistolae, with an introduction by Thomas Hodgkin (588 p., London, 1886).

General Criticism—Alex. Olleris: Cassiodore conservateur des livres de l'antiquité classique (Thèse, 72 p., Paris, 1841). Adolph Franz: Cassiodorus. Ein Beitrag zur Geschichte der theologischen Literatur (137 p., Breslau, 1872). Hermann Usener: Anecdoton Holderi. Ein Beitrag zur Geschichte Roms in orthogothischer Zeit (79 p., Bonn, 1877. Text of a fragment relating to Symmachus, Boetius, and Cassiodorus with commentary). Ludwig Schaedel: Plinius der Jüngere und Cassiodorus (Progr., 36 p., Darmstadt, 1887). Hartmann, in Pauly-Wissowa (t. 6, 1672–1676, 1899).

Scientific Criticism—Karl Schmidt: Quaestiones de musicis scriptoribus romanis imprimis de Cassiodoro et Isidoro (Diss., Giessen, 62 p., Darmstadt, 1899). Victor Mortet: Notes sur le texte des Institutiones de Cassiodore; notes et corrections relatives au de geometria; observations sur le caractère de la géométrie dans l'oeuvre de Cassiodore etc.; observations sur la géométrie de Cassiodore (Revue de philologie, t. 24, 103–118, 272–281, Paris, 1900; t. 27, 65–78, 139–150, 1903). Camille Vieillard: La Médecine néolatine d'après Cassiodore (Bull. soc. franç. hist. méd., t. 2, 516–527, 1903).

IV. BYZANTINE, LATIN, AND HINDU MATHEMATICS

ANTHEMIOS

Ἀνθέμιος. Born in Tralles, flourished in Constantinople, died c. 534. Byzantine mathematician, mechanician, and architect. Eldest brother of Alexander of Tralles (q. v., next chapter). He and Isidoros of Miletus were intrusted, in 532, with the reconstruction of St. Sophia. Author of a treatise on burning-glasses, interesting for the history of conic sections. He speaks of mirrors constructed by the juxtaposition of a great number of small plane mirrors, and by means of which the ancient burned hostile ships. Construction of a parabola by means of its directrix and focus.

Text and Translations—L. Dupuy: περὶ παραδόξων μηχανημάτων. Fragment d'un ouvrage grec d'Anthémius sur des paradoxes de mécanique (Paris, 1777; reprinted in Hist. de l'acad. des inscriptions, t. 42, 392–427, 1786). New edition by A. Westermann in his παραδοξογράφοι, scriptores rerum mirabilium graeci (Braunschweig, 1839).

Criticism—Hultsch, in Pauly-Wissowa (t. 2, 2368–2369, 1894). Sir T. L. Heath: The Fragment of Anthemius on Burning Mirrors and the "Fragmentum mathematicum Bobiense." (Bibliotheca mathematica, t. 7, 225–233, 1907).

EUTOCIOS

Εὐτόκιος. Born c. 480 at Ascalon, on the coast of Palestine, elder contemporary of Anthemios. Byzantine mathematician. Wrote commentaries on three works of Archimedes (περὶ σφαίρας καὶ κυλίνδρου, κύκλου μέτρησις, περὶ ἐπιπέδων ἰσορροπιῶν) and on the first four books of Apollonios's Conics.

Text and Translations—Most editions of Archimedes's and Apollonios's works contain Eutocios's commentaries. The best texts will be found in Heiberg's edition of Archimedes, volume 3, 1915, and in his edition of Apollonios, volume 2, 1893.

Criticism—Paul Tannery: Eutocius et ses contemporains (Bull. des sci. mathém., t. 8, 315–329, 1884; Mémoires, t. 2, 118–136). Hultsch, in Pauly-Wissowa (t. 11, 1518, 1907).

THE SO-CALLED BOOK XV OF EUCLID

This book deals with the geometry of the regular solids; how to inscribe certain of them in certain others; how to calculate the number of edges and the number of solid angles; how to determine the angle of inclination between faces meeting in an edge. The author was a pupil of Isidoros of Miletus, architect of St. Sophia (c. 532).

The text has been published by Heiberg in Vol. V of his edition of Euclid (p. 39–67, 1888), with Latin translation.

For criticism, see Kluge: De Euclidis elementorum libris qui feruntur XIV et XV (Leipzig, 1891. He suggests that Book XV may be the work of different authors). T. L. Heath: Euclid's Elements (Vol. III, p. 519–520, 1908).

For other mathematical works of this period see my notes on the Neoplatonic philosophers, on Boetius and Cassiodorus in Section III, and on Varāhamihira in Section V.

V. HINDU, CHINESE, BYZANTINE, AND LATIN ASTRONOMY

VARĀHAMIHIRA

Born near Ujjain, flourished c. 505. Hindu astronomer and poet. His main work is the Pañcasiddhāntikā, which is a summary of astronomy and astrology. It is of great historical value because it contains a summary of the five Siddhāntas, in karaṇa form. That is, the Siddhāntas are purely theoretical, while Varāhamihira's work is practical. The calculations of the Pañcasiddhāntikā refer to the year 427 of the Saka era (= A. D. 505). Hence we must admit that Varāhamihira flourished at about that time.[n] Varāhamihira quotes various other astronomers, including Āryabhaṭa (q. v., second half of fifth century), but apparently the Pañcasiddhāntikā superseded all previous works dealing with astronomy and astrology. According to Varāhamihira, jyotihśāstra (that is, a combination of astronomy and astrology) is divided into three branches: (1) tantra, mathematical astronomy; (2) horā, making of horoscopes; (3) śākhā or saṃhitā, natural astrology, prognostications. He wrote a treatise on pure astrology, in verse, called Bṛihatsaṃhitā. This treatise contains some information on precious stones (ch. 80–83), on the geography of India (ch. 14), and on many other subjects, always from the astrological point of view. Varāhamihira wrote various other works dealing with natural astrology and with horoscopes (horā). The latter subject is clearly of Greek origin, the Hindu developments being comparable to those found in the treatise of Firmicus Maternus (q. v., first half of the fourth century).

Varāhamihira's astronomy seems also to be largely derived from Greek sources.[o] He also says that the earth is spherical. Two of his works were translated into Arabic by al-Bīrūnī (q. v., first half of the eleventh century).

The Pañcasiddhāntikā contains rules equivalent to our formulas

$$\sin^2 a + \operatorname{versin}^2 a = 4 \sin^2 \frac{a}{2}$$

$$\sin \frac{a}{2} = \sqrt{\frac{1 - \cos a}{2}}$$

Text—Pañcasiddhāntikā, edited and largely translated by G. Thibaut and Sudhākara Dvivedī (Benares, 1889).

Bṛhatsaṃhitā, edited by H. Kern in the Bibliotheca Indica (Calcutta, 1865). Edition with commentary by Bhaṭṭotpala, edited by S. Dvivedī in the Vizianagram Sanskrit Series (Benares, 1895–1897). Partial translation by H. Kern (Journal

[n] Though he is said to have died in 587. Kern (in his preface to the Bṛhatsaṃhitā) suggests that 505 may be his birthyear. However, our best basis for dating Varāhamihira's activity is the astronomical date of his work, and it is wiser to adhere to that.

[o] The only one of the earlier astronomical treatises quoted by Varāhamihira, which is extant, the Vṛiddha-garga-saṃhitā (or Vṛiddha-gārgīya)—a work of unknown date, which Kern has placed tentatively in the first century B. C.—acknowledges the Greek origin in the following way: "To be sure, the Greeks are barbarians, but they have a good knowledge of this science (astronomy) and because of that even they are honored like Ṛṣis; how much more would a Brahman be honored if he knew astronomy" (Winternitz. op. cit., III, 566).

Roy. As. Soc., 1870–1875). Complete translation by Chidambaram Iyer (Madura, 1884).

The chapters on precious stones are edited and translated in Louis Finot: Les lapidaires indiens (Paris, 1896).

There are many native editions of the smaller astrological treatises.

Criticism—H. Jacobi: De astrologiae indiae Horā appellatae originibus, accedunt Laghujātaki capita inedita III–XII (Diss., Bonn, 1872. Varāhamihira devoted two special treatises to horā, the Bṛihajjātaka and the Laghujātaka). M. Cantor: Geschichte der Mathematik (vol. 1³, 600, 1907). M. Winternitz: Geschichte der indischen Litteratur (vol. 3, 1922).

Chinese Chronology

In ancient times the Chinese divided the day into 100 k'o⁴* (6099). At the winter solstice there were officially 40 day k'o and 60 night k'o; at the summer solstice, 60 day k'o and 40 night k'o; at the equinox, an equal number of each. The k'o were counted by means of clepsydras.

In 507 this old system was replaced by the institution of the shih² ch'ên² (9921, 652), the twelve divisions of the day. The k'o were then reduced in number to 96 ($= 8 \times 12$). The winter and summer solstices counted respectively 45 and 65 day k'o. The number of day k'o was changed progressively every ninth day. It increased or decreased each time by one k'o.[p] Midday was determined by means of a gnomon. This system remained in usage until the twentieth century.

L. Wieger: La Chine (161, 1920). L. de Saussure remarks in T'oung Pao (t. 15, 463), that the Chinese did not discover the inequality of the seasons until 550, and even then they continued to divide the year into four equal parts until the arrival of the Jesuits.

HELIODOROS

Ἡλιόδωρος. Younger brother of Ammonios, son of Hermias, flourished in Alexandria c. 498 to 509. Neoplatonic philosopher and astronomer. He studied under Proclos at Athens. He made astronomical observations c. 498 to 509. He wrote an astronomical text-book (Ἀστρονομικὴ διδασκαλία) and a commentary on the astrological introduction of Paul of Alexandria (q. v., second half of fourth century). He may be the author of an introduction to the "Almagest."

Text—Fragments of his works are quoted in the Catal. cod. astrol. (IV, 81–83, 136–138, 152–154; VII, 101, 113).

The introduction to the Almagest is often quoted in manuscripts under the title *Θέωνος καὶ ἑτέρων σοφῶν καὶ μαθηματικῶν ἀνδρῶν προλεγόμενα εἰς τὴν σύνταξιν τοῦ Πτολεμαίου*

Criticism—Boll, in Pauly-Wissowa (t. 15, p. 18, 1912).

For Philoponos and Simplicios, see my notes in Section III.

DIONYSIUS EXIGUUS

Born in Scythia, came to Rome c. 497, died c. 540. Chronologist. He introduced, c. 525, the method of reckoning years with reference to the Christian era which is now in use in the greatest part of the civilized world (see Victorius of Aquitania, second half of the fifth century); the year 1 extending from January 1 to December 31, 754 U. C.

---

[p] From one solstice to another there are about 180 days $= 9 \times 20$, and $65 - 45 = 20$.

The era most commonly used in Dionysius's day was the Diocletian era, which the Christians called the "era of the martyrs." It began on August 29, 284.[q] Dates were often established with reference to the Roman consuls.[r] It should not be supposed that the Christian era was adopted at once. Even the Roman Curia did not use it currently until the tenth century. In the Byzantine Empire, Dionysius's reform was not accepted at all. Byzantines numbered their years with reference to the 15 years indiction cycles and to the creation of the world. The Christian era was introduced in Russia only in the time of Peter the Great. The habit of counting pre-Christian years with reference to the Christian era (of saying, for example, 148 B. C.) is a very recent innovation.

Text—Migne: Patrologia latina (vol. 67).
Criticism—Jülicher, in Pauly-Wissowa (t. 9, 998–999, 1903). F. K. Ginzel: Handbuch der mathematischen Chronologie (vol. 3, 247–251, 1914). Brief account in E. Cavaignac: Chronologie (15–16, 1925).

VI. BYZANTINE PHYSICS AND TECHNOLOGY

The greatest physicist of the age was Philoponos, who has been dealt with in Section III. For Simplicios, see also Section III and for Anthemios and Isidoros, Section IV.

Military Science

Two Byzantine writings on the art of war should be considered. The authors are unknown and have been called respectively the Anonymus Byzantinus and the Anonymus de rebus bellicis.

The first text, περὶ στρατηγικῆς, has been published with a German translation and notes by H. Köchly and W. Rüstow: Griechische Kriegsschriftsteller (II, 2, 358 p., Leipzig, 1855). See Max Jähns: Geschichte der Kriegswissenschaften (t. I, 146–151, München, 1889). It dates from the time of Justinian.

The second text, entitled de rebus bellicis, is more difficult to date with certainty. According to the latest scholar, R. Neher, the most probable date is 527, but Schneider considers it as a fourteenth century forgery. Chapter 8 of this work contains the description of a ship equipped with paddle-wheels moved by oxen.

This text was published for the first time by Sigmund Gelenius in 1552. Latest edition by R. Schneider in Berlin 1908. Richard Neher announced in 1911 that he was preparing a new critical edition, illustrated.

For criticism, see Max Jähns (op. cit.). M. Berthelot: Le livre d'un ingénieur militaire à la fin du XIVe siècle (Journal des savants (1–15, 85–94, 1900); Sur le traité de rebus bellicis qui accompagne la Notitia dignitatum dans les manuscrits (*ibidem*, 171–177). Richard Neher: Der Anonymus de rebus bellicis (Diss., 86 p., Tübingen, 1911. An exhaustive study with complete bibliography). F. M. Feldhaus: Die Technik (25, 936, Leipzig, 1914).

Alia.—H. Diels: Über die von Prokop beschriebene Kunstuhr von Gaza. Mit einem Anhang enthaltend Text und Übersetzung der ἔκφρασις ὡρολόγιου des Prokopios von Gaza (Abh. d. preuss. Ak. d. Wiss., philos. Kl., 39 p., 2 pl., 1917; Isis, IV, 133).

---

[q] It was especially popular with the Copts and was used by the Muslim astronomers.

[r] The last Western consul was Decius Paulinus Iunior in 534; the last Eastern consul, Flavius Basilius Iunior in 541. Later years were fixed by saying "so many years after the consulate."

VII. BYZANTINE AND LATIN BOTANY; CHINESE HUSBANDRY

The famous Codex Aniciae Julianae, dating from about 512, is of immense importance for the history of plant illustration. See under Dioscorides, second half of first century.

Anton von Premerstein: Anicia Juliana in Wiener Dioscorides Kodex (Jahrb. der kunsthistor. Samml. des Kaiserhauses, t. 24, 105–124, Wien, 1903).

The de herbis femininis ascribed to Dioscorides is a compilation drawn from Dioscorides, pseudo-Apuleius (first half of fifth century), and Pliny. It contains the description of 71 herbs and their properties. It is probably an Italian work of the sixth century.

This text has been published by H. F. Kästner (Hermes, t. 31, 578–636, 1896). See C. Singer: Studies (t. II, 68, 1921).

For Chinese husbandry, see my note on Chia Ssŭ-hsieh, in Section XII.

VIII. CHINESE AND BYZANTINE GEOGRAPHY

SUNG YÜN

Sung⁴ Yün² (10462, 13812). Born in Tun⁴-huang² (12208, 5115), flourished c. 520. Chinese Buddhist traveler. He was sent to India in 518, with the priest Hui⁴ Shêng¹ (5199, 9865) by the Empress Dowager Hu² (4930) of the Northern-Wei dynasty (capital Lo-yang), to study Buddhism. They went as far as Gandhāra and Udyāna, and stayed two years in those countries. They returned to China in 522, bringing back 170 Buddhist works. The original records of their travels are lost, but the substance of them has been kept in a work on the monasteries of Lo-yang entitled Lo⁴*-yang² Ch'ieh² lan² chi⁴ (7328, 12883, 1558, 6732, 923), written in 547 by Yang² Hsüan⁴-chih¹ (12878, 4797, 1787).

Text and Criticism—This text has been translated into German by C. F. Neumann: Pilgerfahrten buddhististischer Priester von China nach Indien (Leipzig, 1833). Translation into English by Samuel Beal: Travels of Fah-Hian and Sung-Yun from China to India (283 p., with map, London, 1869). A more accurate and elaborate translation (into French) is due to E. Chavannes: Voyage de Song Yun dans l'Udyāna et le Gandhāra (518–522): Bulletin de l'école française d'Extrême Orient (t. 3, 379–441, Hanoi, 1903. With a long introduction and extensive notes; followed by an appendix, p. 430–441, on the various works on India published in China before the T'ang).

H. A. Giles: Biographical Dictionary (341, 703, 1898).

COSMAS INDICOPLEUSTES

Κοσμᾶς ὁ Ἰνδικοπλεύστης. Born in Egypt, probably in Alexandria, flourished in the second quarter of the sixth century. Traveler. Christian (possibly, Nestorian). He visited Ceylon, the Sinaitic peninsula, Ethiopia. He knew the sources of the Blue Nile. He was at Adulis, Ethiopia, c. 525, and copied the famous Adulitic inscriptions (referring to Ptolemaeos Euergetes's expedition into Asia, 247 B. C.). He wrote a book on geography c. 534 to 547, entitled "Christian Topography" (τοπογραφία χριστιανική), which is of great interest, though the author's aim was chiefly to refute the theory that the earth was round and to prove that Moses's tabernacle was a model of the universe. He also wrote a more extensive work on geography, which is lost, but from which the so-called eleventh book of the Topography (on Ceylon), *Καταγραφὴ περὶ ζῴων Ἰνδικῶν καὶ περὶ δένδρων Ἰνδικῶν καὶ περὶ τῆς Ταπροβάνης νήσου*, may be an extract. Cosmas's work is probably the source of the earliest Christian maps. Cosmas is the first Western writer who speaks of China (Tzinitza) in a matter-of-fact way.

Text and Translations—The Topography was discovered by Emeric Bigot in the latter half of the seventeenth century, and extracts from it were published in Thévenot's Relation de divers voyages, c. 1686, with a French translation. The first complete edition appeared in 1706 in the Nova collectio patrum et scriptorum graecorum, ed. by Father Bernard de Montfaucon (Vol. II, 113–345, with Latin translation and introduction). This text was reprinted in vol. 88 of Migne: Patrologia graeca (Paris, 1864). John W. McCrindle has used Montfaucon's text to prepare an English translation published with notes, introduction, and illustrations by the Hakluyt Society, London, 1897 (vol. 98 of their collection; 412 p., 37 fig.). A better Greek text has been edited by E. O. Winstedt, with geographical notes (386 p., 14 pl., Cambridge, 1909). Cosimo Stornajolo: Le miniature della Topografia di Cosmas, codice vaticano greco 699 (52 p., 64 pl., fol. Milano, 1908. A very fine uncial manuscript of the eighth or ninth century containing copies of sketches drawn by Cosmas himself). Extracts relative to China in Sir Henry Yule: Cathay (vol. 1, new ed., 212–232, 1915, with abundant notes). A Slavonic translation of the sixteenth century was published by the Society of Russian bibliophiles (publ. No. 86), St. Petersburg, in 1886 (see brief note in Archiv für slavische Philologie, t. XI, 1888, 155).

Criticism—E. H. F. Meyer: Geschichte der Botanik (t. 2, 381–389, 1855). Josef Strzygowski: Der Bilderkreis des griechischen Physiologus, des Kosmas Indikopleustes und Oktateuch nach Hdsch. der Bibliothek zu Smyrna (Leipzig, 1899). Josef Wittmann: Sprachliche Untersuchungen zu Cosmas (Diss., München, 73 p., Borna, 1913). Article by Wecker, in Pauly-Wissowa (t. 22, 1487–1490, 1922).

The Map of Mādabā

In 1896 a mosaic map of Palestine was discovered in Mādabā, Moab, Palestine, but only when part of it had been irreparably destroyed. This map dates from c. 520 to 550. It is the oldest true geographical map extant, for the Tabula Peutingeriana (q. v., first half of the third century) is of another kind, a map of the world, a sort of pictorial itinerary, and the map of Cosmas (q. v.) is a cosmographic map. Besides, the map of Mādabā alone represents a Byzantine tradition; the other maps I have named and the itineraries are Occidental works. The names of the map of Mādabā agree with those of Eusebios's Onomasticon (*περὶ τῶν τοπικῶν ὀνομάτων τῶν ἐν τῇ θείᾳ γραφῇ*) a minor work of Eusebios of Caesarea, q. v., first half of the fourth century.

The earliest study devoted to it is Ὁ *ἐν Μαδηβᾷ μωσαικὸς καὶ γεωγραφικὸς περὶ Συρίας Παλαιστίνης καὶ Αἰγύπτου χάρτης ὑπὸ Κλεόπα* M. *Κοικυλίδου* (Jerusalem, 1897). Eugène Germer-Durand: La carte mosaīque de Madaba (4 p., 12 pl., Paris, 1897. Photographs of the map with a short introductory text). Adolf Schulten: Die Mosaikkarte von Madaba und ihr Verhältnis zu den ältesten Karten und Beschreibungen des heiligen Landes (Abhdl. d. Ges. d. Wiss. zu Göttingen, philol.-histor. Klasse, Bd. IV, 121 p., 4 pl., 1900). Adolf Jacoby: Das geographische Mosaik von Madaba (Stüdien über christliche Denkmäler, 3, 120 p., 1 pl., Leipzig, 1905). O. M. Dalton: Byzantine Art (p. 423, Oxford, 1911). A large colored drawing of this map is on exhibition in the National Museum, Washington.

STEPHANOS OF BYZANTIUM

Στέφανος. Flourished at an uncertain period, possibly under Justinian. Byzantine lexicographer and geographer. Author of a very extensive geographical dictionary (ἐθνικά), almost entirely lost, but known through an epitome compiled by a certain Hermolaos (Ἑρμόλαος), in the sixth century.[s]

Text and Translations—Hermolaos's Epitome was first published under the title περὶ πόλεων (de urbibus). The best editions are by Wilh. Dindorf, with the notes of L. Holsten, A. Berkel, and Th. de Pinedo (4 enormous vols., Leipzig, 1825); by Ant. Westermann (Leipzig, 1839), by August Meineke (Berlin, 1849, incomplete.)

Criticism—Wilh. Knauss: De Stephani Byzantii ethnicorum exemplo Eustathiano (Diss., 114 p., Bonn, 1910).

IX. LATIN, BYZANTINE, SYRIAC, PERSIAN, AND CHINESE MEDICINE

ANTHIMUS

Banished from Byzantium. Flourished at the court of Theodoric the Great, first King of the Ostrogoths, 493 to 526. Ambassador of Theodoric to the court of Theodoric, King of the Franks, 511 to 534. He addressed to the latter a memoir on the dietetic and therapeutic value of various victuals and beverages.

Text—Die Diätetik des Anthimus (Epistula Anthimi viri inlustris comitis et legatarii ad gloriosissimum Theudericum regem Francorum de observatione ciborum), published with notes, introduction, and glossary by Valentin Rose in his Anecdota graeca et graecolatina (2. Heft, p. 41–102, Berlin, 1870). New edition with commentary and glossary by Shirley Howard Weber (160 p., Princeton thesis, Leiden, 1924).

Criticism—Max Neuburger: Geschichte der Medizin (t. 2, 248–9, 1911).

MOSCHION[t]

Flourished in Northern Africa in the fifth or sixth century; more probably in the sixth. Latin gynaecologist. Unknown author of a popular catechism on women's diseases and midwifery (Gynaecia; De mulieribus passionibus), which is largely based upon Soranos (q. v., first half of second century) and upon a similar treatise, called Γενέσια, ascribed to one Cleopatra (fourth or fifth century?).[u]

Text—Greek text edited by Wolphius; Μοσχίωνος περὶ τῶν γυναικείων παθῶν (Bale, 1566).[v] Greek-Latin edition by F. O. Dewez (Vienna, 1793. Based upon the Greek text referred to in the footnote).

Sorani gynaeciorum vetus translatio latina, appended by Val. Rose to his edition of Soranos (Leipzig, 1882). German translation of Soranos by H. Lüneburg, with notes by J. Chr. Huber (München, 1894).

Cleopatra's work is included in the ancient collections of gynaecological writings edited by Casp. Wolphius (Bale, 1566) and Israel Spach (Strassburg, 1597).

Criticism—Robert Fuchs, in Puschmann: Geschichte der Medizin (t. 1, 321, 347, 1902). M. Neuburger: Geschichte der Medizin (t. 2, 72, 1911). Joh. Medert:

---

[s] See also Eustathios (second half of twelfth century).

[t] Moschio, Muscio, Mustio. Not to be mistaken for an earlier physician bearing the same name, quoted by Galen and Soranos.

[u] Moschion's book was given more importance because Soranos's own work was lost and forgotten. So much so, that some time in the fifteenth century Moschion's book was translated into Greek. Later this new Greek text was retranslated into Latin!

[v] Note that the original text of Soranos was not published until 1838.

Quaestiones criticae et grammaticae ad Gynoecia Mustionis pertinentes (Diss., Giessen, 1911).

Iconographic Traditions—A manuscript of Moschion's work, in the Royal Library, Brussels, and dating from about the middle of the ninth century; contains illustrations of uterus, ovaries, and oviducts. There is good reason to believe that these illustrations represent ancient traditions going back to Soranos or even to an earlier time. It is said that Soranos prepared figures explaining the anatomy of pregnancy. The many medieval illustrations of female viscera *in situ* and of foetus *in utero* may be descendants and representatives of Soranos's schema. See on this subject, F. Weindler: Geschichte der gynaekologisch-anatomischen Abbildung (Dresden, 1908); L. Choulant: History of Anatomic Illustration (Chicago, 1920; Isis, IV, 357); K. Sudhoff: Drei noch unveröffentliche Kindeslagenserien des Soranos-Muscio aus Oxford und London (Archiv für Geschichte der Medizin, t. 4, 109–128, 2 pl., 1910). K. Sudhoff and C. Singer: Fasciculus medicinae of Johannes of Ketham (Milano, 1924; Isis, VI, 547). K. Sudhoff: Neue Uteruszeichnungen in einer bisher unbekannt gebliebenen Mustio-Handschrift zu Vicenza (Archiv für Geschichte der Medizin, t. 17, 1–11, 1 pl., 1925. Manuscript of the first half of the thirteenth century).

"AURELIUS" AND "AESCULAPIUS"

Two Latin medical works, the so-called Aurelius and Aesculapius, date from a period which is not easy to determine exactly, but which is not earlier than the sixth century. (The Medicina Plinii, for which see my note on Pliny, second half of first century, is probably an earlier production.)

The "Aurelius" is a treatise dealing with acute diseases, while the "Aesculapius" deals with chronic ones. Both are derived from Caelius Aurelianus (q. v., first half of fifth century). The latter was published in Strassburg 1533 and 1544; the former in Paris only in 1857 (also in Henschel's Janus, vol. 2).

Translations of Greek medical works into Latin were made at about the same time (say, some time between the fifth and eighth centuries): fragments of Hippocrates, Dioscorides, Rufus, Galen, Oribasios, Alexander of Tralles.

M. Neuburger: Geschichte der Medizin (t. 2, 256, 1911).

AËTIOS

Aëtios of Amida (Ἀέτιος Ἀμιδηνός). Born in Amida, Mesopotamia. Flourished under Justinian I, Emperor of the East, 527 to 565. Physician to the Byzantine court. Author of a medical encyclopaedia in 16 books (βιβλία ἰατρικὰ ἑκκαίδεκα), an eclectic compilation chiefly based upon Galen and Archigenes. It is of considerable historical value because of the many extracts from ancient medical writings which it contains. Special importance is given to the materia medica, but the encyclopaedia is very extensive and includes internal medicine, surgery, obstetrics, gynaecology, ophthalmology. Description of diphtheria. Aëtios's ophthalmology (Book VII of the encyclopaedia) is the best and most complete of ancient times. Introduction of cloves for medical purposes.

Text and Translations—There is no complete edition of the Greek text of the encyclopaedia or Tetrabiblon (so-called because in certain manuscripts the text is divided into four sections τετράβιβλοι of four λόγοι each). Ed. princeps of Books I to VIII (Venice, 1534). Latin translation of the whole work by Cornarius and Montanus (Bale, 1533–1535), and a much better one by Janus Cornarius (Bale,

1542). Book VII (ophthalmology) has been edited in Greek and German by Julius Hirschberg (Leipzig, 1899). Book IX edited by Skevos Zervos (Athens, 1912. Diseases of the digestive organs, worms). Book XII edited by George A. Costomiris (Paris, 1892. Sciatica, rheumatism, arthritis). Book XIII edited by Sk. Zervos (Syros, 1908. Wounds caused by poisonous animals; counterpoisons; various skin diseases). Book XV edited by same (Athens, 1909. Swellings, aneurisms, favus, pharmacy). Book XVI by same (Athens, 1901); partial German translations by Max Wegscheider (160 p., Berlin, 1901. Gynecology, obstetrics cosmetics, embalming).

Criticism—E. Gurlt: Geschichte der Chirurgie (t. 1, 544–555, 1898). Max Wegscheider: Einiges aus der Geburtshilfe und Gynäkologie des Aëtios (Archiv f. Gynäkologie, t. 66, 3–16, 1902). Ch. Em. Ruelle: Quelques mots sur Aëtius (Bull. soc. franç hist. méd., t. 2, 112–123, Paris, 1903). A. Olivieri: Gli ἰατρικὰ di Aetios nel codice messinese No. 84 (Studii di filologia classica, t. 9, 294–347, Firenze, 1904. This manuscript contains Books I and II and part of Book III with scholia). Max Neuburger: Geschichte der Medizin (t. 2, 104–109, 1911). Alfred Lehmann: Die zahnärztliche Lehre des Aëtios (Diss., 48 p., Halle a. S., 1921; Isis, IV, 578).

For Syriac medicine see my note on Sergios of Resaina in Section III.

Persian School of Medicine

It is difficult to say when the school (or university) of Jundīshāpūr[w] was founded. It may date back to the fifth or even to the fourth century (see my note on Theodoros or Theodosios, second half of the fourth century). It became a refuge for the Nestorians driven from Edessa in 489, and later for the Neoplatonists banished from Athens in 529. The Nestorians brought with them Syriac translations of Greek medical works (see Sergios of Resaina); the Neoplatonists, their philosophic ideas, the influence of which is easily traceable in the later Persian mysticism. The school was at the height of its glory in the reign of Nūshīrwān the Just,[x] the greatest Sassanian king, who ruled from 531 to his death in 579. It became then the greatest intellectual center of the time; there Greek, Jewish, Christian, Syrian, Hindu, and Persian ideas could be compared, exchanged, and eventually syncretized. Persian translations of Aristotle and Plato were made by order of Nūshīrwān. Jundīshāpūr was especially important as a medical center; the medical teaching was essentially Greek, but with Hindu, Syrian, and Persian accretions. This medical school flourished until at least the end of the tenth century; it was little affected by the Arab conquest in the seventh century, but it was not until the latter half of the eighth century that its influence began to be widely exerted upon the Muslims (E. G. Browne: Arabian medicine, p. 23, 1921).

The reign of Nūshīrwān was the golden age of Pahlawī literature[y] (see Burzūya, infra). It was then that the historical annals were compiled upon which Firdawsī's epic was based at the end of the tenth century. Nūshīrwān consolidated

[w] City founded by the Sassanian king Shāpūr I (241–272), near Kazerun, between Susa and Ecbatana. Also spelled Gandisapora and Gondi Sapor (Gibbon, c. 42; Bury's edition, IV, 361). E. B. Browne (Arabian medicine, p. 19 sq.), who discusses the etymology of this name, spells it Jundī Shāpūr. It is well-nigh impossible to obtain a complete agreement on this spelling, for it is the problem of a Persian name, passing through Arabic and Syriac script and expressed in Low Latin.

[x] Or Anūshīrwān. He was called Chosroës by the Greeks and Kisrā by the Arabs.

[y] The Pahlawī language was used from the fourth to the ninth century on; but in the seventh century the period of original use was already over.

Persian law; he improved the system of taxation, the organization of the army, the communications and the irrigation of his country. He is one of the greatest among kings.

A comprehensive study of Sassanian civilization, and especially of the school of Jundīshāpūr, is badly needed. The chronicle of Ṭabarī (q. v., first half of tenth century) deals chiefly with political and theological matters. There is a French translation of it in 4 volumes by Hermann Zotenberg (Paris, 1867–1874). The part devoted to the Sassanian period has been translated into German by Theodor Nöldeke, with an elaborate commentary: Geschichte der Perser und Araber zur Zeit der Sasaniden. Aus der arabischen Chronik des Ṭabarī (531 p., Leyden, 1879). One may find some information also in the histories of Persia, M. Sykes: History of Persia (Vol. I, 1915, c. 40 and 41) and in the histories of Persian literature, Edw. G. Browne: A Literary History of Persia (Vol. I, 1909, c. 4), but I know no general account from our point of view.

T'AO HUNG-CHING

T'ao² Hung²-ching³ (10831, 5282, 2143). His style name was T'ung¹-ming² (12294, 7946); he was also called T'ao² yin³ chü¹ (10831, 13276, 2987), meaning T'ao the hermit, and Hua²-yang² chên¹jên² (5005, 12883, 589, 5624), meaning the saint of Hua-yang. Born at Mo⁴*-ling² (8005, 7235), Kiangsu, near Nanking, in 451; flourished at the court of the Ch'i² (1074) emperor Kao¹ Ti⁴ (5927, 10942); in 492 he retired to the mountains, in Hua-yang; he died in 536. Chinese Taoist, physician, and alchemist. He wrote, or edited, one of the most important ancient treatises on materia medica, the Ming²-i¹-pieh²*-lu⁴* (7940, 5380, 9155, 7386).[a] To the 365 drugs mentioned in the Shên-nung Pên-ts'ao (q. v., first half of the fourth century B. C.), he added 365 new ones, recommended by famous physicians of the Han and Wei dynasties. The Pieh-lu was presented to the Liang² (7021) emperor Wu³ Ti⁴ (12744, 10942) who reigned from 502 to 549. He wrote another treatise on materia medica entitled Pên³-ts'ao³ ching¹-chu⁴ (8846, 11634, 2122, 2537)[b] and other medical works.

He edited, in or after 489, the main work devoted to the most mystical and fantastic aspects of Taoism, the so-called Declaration of the Genii, Chên¹-kao⁴ (589, 5953). Finally he wrote a treatise on the manufacture of famous swords, Tao¹-chien⁴-lu⁴* (10783, 1659, 7386).

Text—A chapter of the Pieh-hu was translated into French by Visdelou Du Halde: Description de la Chine (t. 3, 453–459, 1735).

Criticism—E. Bretschneider: Botanicon sinicum (part 1, 42–43, 1882; part 3, 1896, passim). A. Wylie: Chinese Literature (143, 219, 1902). H. A. Giles: Biographical Dictionary (718, 1898). L. Wieger: Taoisme (t. 1, 1911, passim); La Chine (402, 528, 1920); Histoire des croyances (lecon 61, 1922). F. Huebotter: Guide (25, Kumamoto, 1924).

For Chia Ssŭ-hsieh's treatise on alimentation, see my note in Section XII.

X. BYZANTINE, LATIN, SYRIAC, AND CHINESE HISTORIOGRAPHY

HESYCHIOS OF MILETUS

Ἡσύχιος Μιλήσιος, also called Illustris, Ἰλλούστριος. Flourished under Justinian. Byzantine historian and lexicographer. Author of a world history in

---

[a] Meaning special records by famous physicians. Usually shortened to Pieh-lu, special records.

[b] It is possible that this is only another title of his first work.

six books (called Ἱστορία Ῥωμαϊκή τε καὶ παντοδαπή by Photios, and Χρονικὴ ἱστορία by Suidas) from the time of the Assyrian King Belos to 518; of a Byzantine history from 518 to c. 530, and of a Greek lexicon which contained also biographies of the most prominent Greek writers (Ὀνοματολόγος ἢ πίναξ τῶν ἐν παιδείᾳ ὀνομαστῶν). (Only extracts from these works remain.)

Text—Opuscula duo quae supersunt, edited by Jo. Conr. Orelli (Leipzig, 1820). Better edition by C. Müller in his Fragmenta historicorum graecorum (t. 4, 143–177).

Onomatologi quae supersunt cum prolegomenis, edited by Jo. Flach (334 p., Leipzig, 1882).

Criticism—K. Krumbacher: Byzantinische Litteraturgeschichte (2. Aufl., 323–325, 1897).

For Cassiodorus's historical activity, see my note in Section III.

Syriac Chronicles

Syriac literature reached its climax in the sixth century; the earliest historical works extant in that language date from that time. A chronicle covering the period 495 to 506 was composed in 507 at Edessa by an unknown author (probably Orthodox). It was formerly ascribed to Joshua (Yēshū') the Stylite, and is generally called by his name. It has been transmitted to us by Dionysios of Tell-Maḥrē (q. v., first half of the ninth century), who incorporated it in his own history. It is the best account of the war between the Persian and Byzantine empires during the reigns of Kawādh and Anastasios (502–506).

Text—Editio princeps by the abbé Paulin Martin. Chronique de Josué le Stylite (Abhdl. für die Kunde des Morgenlandes, t. 6, 1876. Syriac and French). Wm. Wright: The Chronicle of Joshua the Stylite (186 p., Cambridge, 1882. Syriac and English).

Criticism—Abbé Nau: Analyse des parties inédites de la chronique attribuée à Denys de Telmahré (Suppt. de l'Orient chrétien, 1897, Paris, 1898).

Another anonymous chronicle deals with the history of Edessa during the period extending from 132 B. C. to 540. The beginning of it is too concise, but from the third century on it is a very valuable document for the history of the Near East and even of western Europe. The author was Orthodox, but with a leaning toward Nestorianism.

Text—Editio princeps by G. S. Assemani in his Bibliotheca Orientalis (t. 1, 388–417, 1719). Ludwig Hallier: Untersuchungen über die Edessenische Chronik mit dem syrischen Texte und einer Übersetzung (176 p., Leipzig, 1892). New edition by Ignazio Guidi, with Latin translation in the Corpus scriptorum christianorum orientalium (Paris, 1903).

Criticism—R. Duval: Littérature syriaque (3e ed., 178–180, Paris, 1907).

SHÊN-YO

Shên3-yo1* (9849, 13349). Flourished under the Liang2 (7021) dynasty, which lasted from 502 to 557. Chinese historian. Author of the official history of the Liu2 Sung4 (7270, 10462) dynasty (420–78).[b] His work, called Sung4-shu1 (10462, 10024) is the sixth of the Twenty-four Histories (see p. 413).

Text—Chinese edition (Nanking, 1874. 100 chüan in 16 vols.).

Criticism—Wylie: Notes on Chinese Literature (18, 1902).

---

[b] Capital, Nanking.

HSIAO TZŬ-HSIEN

Hsiao[1] Tzŭ[3]-hsien[3] (4324, 12317, 4523) 487–537. Flourished under the Liang dynasty. Chinese historian. Author of the official history of the southern Ch'i dynasty (479–501).[c]

This work, called Nan[2] Ch'i[2] shu[1] (8128, 1074, 10024) (History of the southern Ch'i), is the seventh of the Twenty-four Histories.

Text—Chinese edition (Nanking, 1874. 59 chüan, in 6 vols.).

Criticism—Wylie: Chinese Literature (18, 1902). H. A. Giles: Biographical Dictionary (284, 1898).

XI. ROMAN AND BARBARIAN LAW

Roman Law Adapted to Barbarian Needs

Some of the Barbarians who disrupted the Roman Empire tried to assimilate its civilization, and especially to adapt its jurisprudence to their own needs. Three of these adaptations are especially important. All three are pre-Justinian.

Edictum Theoderici—A compilation of Roman, and subsidiarily of Gothic, law made at Rome between 500 and 515 by Theodoric, King of the Ostrogoths from 475 to 526. It is divided into 155 chapters.

Text—Edited by Friedrich Bluhme in the Monumenta Germaniae hist. (Leges, t. 5, 145 sq.).

Breviarium Alarici[d] (*Alaric's "Breviary"*)—This compilation is far more important than the previous one; in fact, it is the most important codification of Roman law made by order of a Barbarian king. It was promulgated by Alaric II, King of the Visigoths, at Ayre in Gascony, in 506. It includes 16 books of the Theodosian Code; various post-Theodosian novels down to 465; parts of the Institutes of Gaius;[e] 5 books of the "Sententiae Receptae" of Julius Paulus; parts of the Gregorian and Hermogenian codes and of the first book of Papinian's "Responsa." Our knowledge of the first 5 books of the Theodosian code and of the 5 books of Paulus's "Sententiae Receptae" is derived exclusively from it. If one realize that before the eleventh century, the people in the West who knew the "Digest" at all were exceedingly few, the importance of Alaric's "Breviary" increases considerably. Indeed, until the rise of the law school of Bologna (twelfth century) it was, in western Europe, the main source of Roman law.

Text—Edited in the Jus Civile Ante-Justinianum (Berlin, 1815). Also by G. Hänel: Lex Romana Visigothorum (Berlin, 1847–1849), and Max Conrat (Cohn): Breviarium Alaricianum; römisches Recht im fränkischen Reich in systematischer Darstellung (832 p., Leipzig, 1903).

Lex Romana Burgundionum—Compilation of Roman law made by order of King Gundobad (who died in 516) for his Roman subjects. It was published in

---

[c] Capital, Nanking.

[d] Or Alaricianum. Also called Lex Romana Wisigothorum The Visigoths called it probably Lex Romana or Lex Theodosii. The names Liber (or Breviarium) Aniani are also common, authentic copies of the code being signed by one Anian, the king's referendary. The word Breviarium seems to date only from the sixteenth century.

[e] It was our only source for the latter until the discovery of the Verona manuscript in 1816 (see Gaius, second half of second century).

517 by King Sigismund. A codification of Burgundian law had been made before (Lex Gundobada).

Text—Edited by Bluhme in the Mon. Ger. hist., Leges (t. 3, 505 sq.).

Barbarian Law

The Burgundian Law (*Lex Burgundionum*)[f] is a code compiled by order of King Gundobad (475–516), probably after 500. It was applicable to cases between Burgundians and between Burgundians and Romans. (A special code of Roman law applied to the cases between Romans; see Lex Romana Burgundionum.) It was still in force at least as late as the ninth century.

Text—Edited by F. Bluhme, in Mon. Germ. hist., Leges (t. 3). J. E. Valentin-Smith: La loi gombette. Reproduction intégrale de tous les MSS. connus. Traduction de Gaupp et de Bluhme (2e éd., Lyon, 1889).

The Salic Law (*Lex Salica*) is a small collection of the customs of the Salians, the chief of the peoples collectively known as the Franks. The first compilation of it dates back to the last years of Clovis, who died in 511. The last revision of it was made by order of Charlemagne. The earliest text (in 65 chapters) is singularly free from Christian and Roman influences. Later versions contain Christian interpolations. To show the barbarity of the Salic law it will suffice to say that, according to it, evidence was almost wholly that of ordeal and compurgation.

Text—There are many editions. J. M. Pardessus (820 p., Paris, 1843); Joh. Merkel (Berlin, 1850); J. F. Behrend (Berlin, 1874); Alfred Holder (Leipzig, 1879, etc.); J. H. Hessels (synoptic ed., London, 1880); Heinrich Geffcken (Leipzig, 1898).
Criticism—Victor Gantier: La langue, les noms, et le droit des anciens Germains (282 p., Paris, 1901).

Justinian

Justinian I, the Great. Flavius Anicius Justinianus. Born near Tauresium, Illyria, 483; died 565. The greatest Emperor of the East (527 to 565). Immortalized by the codification or rather the consolidation of Roman law which was accomplished by his order. The Corpus juris which bears his name comprises four parts: (1) The "Codex constitutionum" promulgated in 529 (revised edition called "Codex repetitae praelectionis" in 534; the first edition is lost), a collection of imperial ordinances from the time of Hadrian on; (2) the Digest or Pandects ("Digesta," πάνδεκται), a collection of 9,123 extracts from 39 jurists promulgated in 533; about one-third of it is quoted from Ulpian (q. v., first half of the third century); (3) an elementary manual, the Institutes ("Institutiones"), promulgated a little before the Digest; (4) The "Novellae constitutiones post codicem" (νεαραὶ διατάξεις), an unauthorized collection of ordinances subsequent to the revised codex; this fourth part is mostly in Greek.

Justinian ordered the closure of the Academy of Athens in 529 and the reconstruction of the Hagia Sophia in 532.

He made efforts to reopen the silk trade route to the Far East which had been blocked by the New Persian Empire of the Sassanidae. He endeavored also to introduce the silk manufacture into Greece. Sericulture had been introduced from China into Khotan by a Chinese princess in 419. Eggs of silkworms were brought from Khotan to Constantinople in 552, probably by Nestorian monks.

---

[f] Also called Liber Constitutionum or Lex Gundobada, Lex Gombata.

It is said that all European true silkworms originate from these eggs (for further information, see my note on Chinese technology and on Zemarchos in the following chapter).

Text and Translations—Corpus juris civilis. Editio stereotypa altera (3 vols., Berlin, 1877 sq., t. I: Institutiones, rec. Paul Krüger (1867); Digesta rec. Theod. Mommsen (1870); t. II: Codex Justinianus, rec. Paul Krüger (1877); t. III: Novellae, rec. Rud. Schoell et Wilh. Kroll, Greek and Latin). English translation of the Digest by Charles Henry Monro (2 vols., Cambridge, 1904–1909). English translation of the Institutes by Thomas Collett Sandars (London, 1853); by J. T. Abdy and Bryan Walker (Cambridge, 1876); by J. B. Moyle (2 vols., Oxford, 1883). These translations have often been reprinted; the latter two also contain the Latin text. Digestorum codex Florentinus olim Pisanus phototypice expressus (Roma, 1902–1910).

Criticism—James Bryce: Article, Justinian (Smith and Wace's Dictionary of Christian Biography, Vol. III, 538–559, 1882). Charles Diehl: Justinien et la civilisation byzantine au VIe siècle (735 p., Paris, 1901). Will. Gordon Holmes: The Age of Justinian and Theodora (2 vols., 780 p., London, 1905–1907).

I read in the Comptes rendus de l'Académie des Sciences (t. 145, p. 1956, Paris, 1907) that the Prix Binoux has been awarded to Dr. F. Brunet, médecin de 1re classe de la Marine, for his "Histoire des sciences médicales à Byzance au temps de Justinien." I have not been able to find this book and wonder whether it has been published.

For the silk trade see C. R. Beazley: Dawn of Modern Geography (vol. 1, 186–191, 1897). T. F. Carter: Invention of Printing in China (ch. 12, 1925; Isis, VIII, 368).

Roman Law in the East

A Greek paraphrase of the "Institutes" was made in Constantinople in the time of Justinian, possibly by Theophilos Antecessor. According to Ferrini, this Greek code was essentially based on Gaius; was, in fact, a translation of Gaius's own text, made at Beirut and later adapted to the "Institutes." Other Greek translations of Roman law or commentaries date from about the same time.

Text—Editions by G. O. Reitz (2 vols., The Hague, 1751) and by E. C. Ferrini (2 vols., Berlin, 1884–1897, with Latin translation). French translation by J. C. Frégier (Paris, 1847).

Criticism—C. Krumbacher: Byzantinische Litteratur (605, 609, 1897).

XII. BYZANTINE, LATIN, AND CHINESE PHILOLOGY AND PEDAGOGY

PRISCIAN

Priscianus; born at Caesarea in Mauretania; flourished at Constantinople, c. 512. Roman grammarian. His Latin grammar in 18 books,[g] "Commentariorum grammaticorum libri XVIII," based chiefly on Apollonios Dyscolos (first half of second century), was one of the most popular text-books of the Middle Ages, and he shared the fame of Donatus. He wrote also a treatise on numerals, weights, and measures (using Greek sources), and a free translation of Dionysios's Periegesis (q. v., second half of the first century).

Text—Opera (Venice, 1476, etc.). Opera minora, edited by Friedrich Lindemann (Leyden, 1818). Opera, edited by August Krehl (2 vols., Leipzig, 1819)

[g] Books 1 to 16 on Accidence; books 17 and 18 on Syntax. A copy of it was made, at Constantinople, in 526–27, by his disciple Theodorus.

De laude imperatoris Anastasii et de ponderibus et mensuris carmina, edited by S. L. Endlicher (Vienna, 1828). Edition by M. Hertz and H. Keil, 1855–1859.

Criticism—Otto Wischnewski: De Prisciani institutionum grammaticarum compositione (Diss., 101 p., Königsberg, 1909). Ernest Mueller: De auctoritate et origine exemplorum orationis solutae Graecorum quae Priscianus contulit (Diss., 52 p., 1911, Königsberg). Alfred Luscher: De Prisciani studiis graecis (Breslauer phil. Abhdl., 44, 1912). Sandys: History of Classical Scholarship (t. 1^3, 272–275, 1921).

For the Western monastic schools of that time, see my notes on St. Benedict in Section II and on Boetius and Cassiodorus in Section III.

See also my note on Hesychios of Miletus in Section X.

CHOU HSING-SSŬ

Chou^1 Hsing^1-ssŭ^4 (2450, 4611, 10258). Flourished as subprefect, at Kuei^4 yang^2 (6435, 12883), Honan; died in 521. Chinese educator. Author of the "Thousand Character Essay," Ch'ien^1 tzŭ^4 wên^2 (1725, 12324, 12633),[h] a collection of 1,000 different characters, which is the second book learned by every Chinese school-boy.[i] The characters are arranged in such a manner that each series of eight forms a sentence. The Japanese also use the Ch'ien tzŭ wên, but they read these three characters Senjimon. According to a self-refuting tradition, the Senjimon was brought to Japan at the same time as the Rongo, by the Korean Ajiki (for whom see my note on Confucius), in 284!

Text—Stanislas Julien: Le livre des mille mots. Texte chinois avec double traduction (Paris, 1864).

Criticism—H. A. Giles: Biographical Dictionary (161, 1898). Encyclopaedia sinica (554, 1917).

CHIA SSŬ-HSIEH

Chia^3 Ssŭ^1-hsieh^2* (1182, 10271, 4393). Flourished under the Northern Wei (Pei^3 Wei^4, 8771, 12567) dynasty, c. 540. Chinese educator. He wrote, c. 540, the Ch'i^2-min^2 yao^4-shu^4* (1074, 7908, 12889, 10053), a treatise on rural economy and alimentation, the first of its kind and one of the best. This treatise contains, among other things, the earliest recipe for the preparation of ink.

G. Vacca: Una leggenda sul baco de seta (Note cinesi, 1) (Rivista degli studi orientali, t. 6, 131–133). L. Wieger: La Chine (163, 324, 537, 1920). Frank B. Wiborg: Printing ink (16, New York, 1926; Isis, IX).

KU YEH-WANG

Ku^4 Yeh^3-wang^2 (6254, 12989, 12493). Native of K'un^1-shan^1 (6537, 9663) Kiangsu, in 519; died in 581. Chinese lexicographer. In 543 he completed the Yü^4* p'ien^1 (13630, 9220), a graphic dictionary based on the Shuo wên;[j] the earliest

---

[h] Also called the White head essay, Pai^2 shou^3 wên^2 (8556, 10014, 12633), because the author's hair turned white in the effort to compose it in a single night! This work is possibly of a much later date.

[i] The first being the San^1 tzŭ^4 ching^1 (9552, 12324, 2122), for which see Wang^2 Ying^4-lin^2 (12493, 13294, 7186) (second half of thirteenth century).

[j] For which see Hsü Shên, first half of second century.

one wherein the fan ch'ieh and the ssŭ shêng are systematically applied.[k] The characters are arranged in the Yü p'ien under 542 radicals.[l]

H. A. Giles: Biographical Dictionary (381, 1898). Encyclopaedia sinica (299, 1917, P. Pelliot).

---

[k] For these two great discoveries see respectively Sun Yen (second half of third century) and Shên Yo (second half of fifth century).

[l] We know the Yü p'ien only through later editions, although fragmentary T'ang manuscripts of it were recovered some years ago. The Yü p'ien was revised in 674 by Sun[1] Ch'iang[2] (10431, 1292) and in 1013 by Ch'ên P'êng-nien (q. v., first half of the eleventh century).

CHAPTER XXIV

THE TIME OF ALEXANDER OF TRALLES

(Second Half of Sixth Century)

I. Survey of Science in Second Half of Sixth Century. II. Religious Background. III. Persian Philosophy. IV. Byzantine and Chinese Mathematics. V. Chinese Technology. Its Diffusion, West and East. VI. Byzantine Husbandry. VII. Byzantine Geography. VIII. Byzantine, Korean, and Japanese Medicine. IX. Byzantine, Latin, Syriac, Persian, and Chinese Historiography. X. Sanskrit and Chinese Lexicography. Chinese Education.

I. SURVEY OF SCIENCE IN SECOND HALF OF SIXTH CENTURY

1. As far as the West was concerned, this was a period of temporary retrogression, but we shall witness considerable activity in the East. Students, who do not deem any civilization worth considering but the Western, reach the conclusion that this was a very dark age. But that conclusion is obviously wrong. It would be wrong even from their own (Western) point of view, for Alexander of Tralles was a very distinguished physician and Gregory one of the greatest popes. Moreover, they have the right to stand in the shade, but not to deny that the sun is shining elsewhere. While Western Europe was shivering in the cold, China was basking in the morning sun. A little later these conditions would again be reversed. During the course of my studies of human progress, I have often had the impression that everything happens as if mankind was working in shifts. The accomplishment of its essential task is so hard that periods of creation are often followed by periods of fallowness.

2. *Religious Background*—The outstanding figure in the West was Gregory the Great, who may be called the father of mediaeval papacy. He was a great administrator and completed the organization of the Christian church and of its educational activities, which had been so well begun by Benedict and Cassiodorus.

The Hindu Buddhist Paramārtha went to China about the middle of the century and spent there the rest of his life translating many writings (not simply Buddhist) from Sanskrit into Chinese. A little later, in 560, another Hindu Buddhist, Jinagupta, went to China for the same purpose and resided ten years at a Turkish court, thus promoting the diffusion of Buddhism among the Turkish peoples. Chih-i founded a new school of Buddhism, the T'ien-t'ai school, which is less mystical than the Ch'an; its main book is the Lotus sūtra. Fa-ching compiled a new catalogue of Chinese Buddhist works, not less than 2,257 works being quoted.

In 552, Buddhism was finally introduced into Japan from Korea. This is an extremely important date; it marks the beginning of Japanese civilization. That beginning was naturally slow and obscure, and we know little about it, but however small our knowledge, it is of considerable significance.

3. *Persian Philosophy*—The only philosopher worth mentioning was Paul the Persian, who flourished under Nūshīrwān. He wrote commentaries on Aristotle in Syriac and Pahlawī. Another Persian must be named, Nūshīrwān's physician, Burzūya, who brought back from India the game of chess and the fables of Pil-

pay, which he translated from Sanskrit into Pahlawī. Thus was built a new channel through which Hindu wisdom reached Iran and later, by means of Islām, the whole world.

4. *Byzantine and Chinese Mathematics*—We shall not be far wrong if we consider the Akhmīm papyrus as a product of this period; however, the date matters very little, for this papyrus would have been written in essentially the same way many centuries before. It is a Greek manual of calculation which reproduces to a large extent the very ancient Egyptian methods.

Hsia-hou Yang wrote an elementary arithmetical treatise largely based upon earlier Chinese works. Chên-luan wrote commentaries on the ancient mathematical works and on the points of mathematical interest in the Classics. Chang Ch'iu-chien composed an arithmetical text-book wherein special attention was paid to fractions. It would seem that Hindu mathematics penetrated China about this time, for many books devoted to the explanation of Hindu mathematics and astronomy are mentioned in the catalogue of the Sui dynasty (589 to 618). Of course, this is just what we would expect; Hindu knowledge must needs enter China in the wake of Buddhism.

Some modicum of Chinese mathematics (and possibly of Hindu mathematics) may have reached Japan, via Korea, before the end of the century.

It is noteworthy that outside of the Akhmîm papyrus, whose presence here is purely accidental, we have nothing to report about Byzantine or Latin mathematics (or astronomy); all the names mentioned in this section are Chinese.

5. *Chinese Technology; its Diffusion West and East*—It is possible that block printing was already practiced in China toward the end of the sixth century, if not before, but it is more probable that the invention was not completed long before the middle of the eighth century.

Sericulture was introduced from Khotan into the Byzantine Empire in 552, probably by Nestorian monks, and developed rapidly in the Peloponnesos. At the same time, Chinese civilization was slowly penetrating into Japan. Scales or balances and tiles are said to have been imported during the rule of Sushun-tennō (588 to 592).

6. *Byzantine Husbandry*—Cassianos Bassos, who flourished probably in the sixth century, compiled a collection of Greek writings on husbandry, which would be, in its turn, the basis of the imperial edition of the tenth century.

7. *Byzantine Geography*—The only remarkable event of the period was the journey accomplished by Zemarchos in 568 from Constantinople to Samarkand, via Crimea and Southern Russia. This established a new contact between the Byzantine and the Turkish peoples.

8. *Byzantine, Korean, and Japanese Medicine*—The Byzantine physician, Alexander of Tralles, who finally established himself in Rome, was not a mere compiler. His works contain many original observations (e. g., on the subject of medical helminthology). In part because of his contemporary fame, his works were soon translated into various oriental languages. He is thus doubly important—intrinsically, because of the value of his writings; extrinsically, because of the influence which he wielded. Taken all in all he was the greatest scientist of that age.

Korean physicians introduced Chinese medicine into Japan in 554. Twenty-nine Chinese medical books are said to have been brought to Japan in 562. It is probable that these facts are not absolutely correct; but it is undoubtedly true that Chinese medicine began to be known in Japan through Korean intermediaries at about this time.

9. *Byzantine, Latin, Syriac, Persian, and Chinese Historiography*—Procopios wrote historical accounts of Justinian's time. Malalas compiled a world chronicle, centered upon Antioch, down to 563–573. This was the earliest Byzantine monastic chronicle; it became a very popular model for many other mediaeval chronicles. Evagrios's ecclesiastical history, down to 593, is the most important continuation of Eusebios.

Three distinguished historians wrote in Latin: Jordanes in the Balkans, the Englishman Gildas in Britanny, Gregory in Tours. The last named was by far the greatest.

Syriac historiography is represented by an anonymous chronicle of c. 569, which includes a translation of the lost chronicle of Zaccharias Rhetor, and by the ecclesiastical history of John of Asia. Both John and the anonymous author were Monophysites.

The Kārnāmak is the oldest version of the Persian epic which blossomed out finally into Firdawsī's "Shāhnāma." It is written in Pahlawī and dates from the end of the sixth century.

The only Chinese historian of the period was Wei Shou, who compiled the official chronicle of the Northern Wei dynasty.

10. *Sanskrit and Chinese Lexicography. Chinese Education*—Amara, whose date is unfortunately very uncertain, wrote a dictionary of Sanskrit synonyms, the "Amarakośa," which is of considerable importance and had enormous influence, if one may judge from the great number of commentaries devoted to it.

Lu Tê-ming compiled a glossary of the Classics, the characters being explained in the order in which they appear.

Yen Chih-t'ui wrote a treatise on familial education wherein he insists upon mental culture.

11. *Final Remarks*—The scientific achievements of this age are not great, but the slow work of education is progressing steadily, this time perhaps more actively in the East under the inspiration of Mahāyāna Buddhism. There were a number of distinguished historians, representing and developing the national consciousness of many nations. At the same time, the knitting together of the nations is proceeding; they become progressively aware of each other's existence, their borrowings and exchanges increase, yet many barriers continue to separate them, and new ones are built which it will take centuries to destroy. This is unavoidable. Education must do its work first and bring them all up to a tolerable level of charity and understanding before they can be made to realize their common purpose and their intrinsic solidarity.

We witnessed the appearance upon the intellectual scene of two new provinces of mankind, the Turkish peoples, reclaimed by Buddhism, as much as they could be reclaimed in those days, and the Japanese, who would soon develop one of the greatest civilizations of the world.

II. RELIGIOUS BACKGROUND

GREGORY THE GREAT

St. Gregory; Gregory I. Born in Rome c. 540; prefect of the city in 573; c. 574 he founded six monasteries in Sicily and one (St. Andrew) in Rome, becoming himself a monk in the last one; from 578 to c. 586 papal ambassador in Constantinople; in 586 abbot of St. Andrew's; pope[a] from September 3, 590, to his death on March 12, 604. Fourth (and last) doctor of the Latin Church, he marked the transition between the ancient and the mediaeval types of Christianity and may be considered the father of the mediaeval papacy. He wrote (probably during his abbacy) many theological works and biblical commentaries, and a biography of St. Benedict. He was a great administrator and completed the organization of monasticism, missionary activity,[b] liturgy, and church music.

Text—Migne: Latin Patrology (vol. 77). Critical Edition of the Letters by P. Ewald and L. M. Hartmann in the Monumenta Germaniae historica (Berlin, 1887–1899).

Henry Sweet: King Alfred's West Saxon version of Gregory's Pastoral Care. With an English Translation, the Latin Text, and Notes (550 p., Early English Text Society, London, 1871–72).

Criticism. Biography and Generalities—Vita beatissimi papae Gregorii Magni antiquissima, a life written by a monk of the monastery of Whitby (probably c. 713), now for the first time fully printed from manuscript Gallen 567, by F. A. Gasquet (56 p., Westminster, 1904). Georg Johann Lau: Gregor I (568 p., Leipzig, 1845). Frederick Homes Dudden: Gregory the Great (2 vols., London, 1905). Max Manitius: Lateinische Litteratur des Mittelalters (t. 1, 92–106, 1911). Walter Stuhlfath: Gregor I, sein Leben bis zu seiner Wahl zum Papste nebst einer Untersuchung der ältesten Viten (122 p., Heidelberg, 1913).

Gregorian Music—Wilhelm Brambach: Gregorianisch. Bibliographische Lösung der Streitfrage über den Ursprung des gregorianischen Gesanges (32 p., Leipzig, 1895). E. G. P. Wyatt: St. Gregory and the Gregorian Music (40 p., Plainsong and Mediaeval Music Society, London, 1904). Amédée Gastoué: L'art grégorien (Les maitres de la musique) (Paris, 1911). Coelestin Vivell: Von Musik-Traktate Gregors des Grossen (161 p., Leipzig, 1911).

Anglo-Saxon Translation of the Cura Pastoralis—Theses by Gustav Wack (60 p., Greifswald, 1889) and Albert Dewitz (64 p., Breslau, 1889). J. H. Kern: Zur Cura pastoralis (Anglia, vol. 33, 270–276, 1910). Karl Jost: Zu den Handschriften der Cura pastoralis (Anglia, vol. 63–68, 1913).

PARAMĀRTHA

His name is transcribed by the Chinese as Po^1-lo^2-mo^{4*} T'o^2 (9336, 7291, 7999, 11358) and they translate it Chen^1 Ti^4 (589, 10947). According to the Hsü kao sêng ch'uan, written by the T'ang scholar Tao-hsüan (q. v., second half of the seventh century), chüan 1, chapter 1, he was also named Chü^1-na^2-lo^2 T'o^2 (2948, 8090, 7291, 11358).

Hindu Buddhist monk born in 499; died in 569. He went from Magadha to China in 546 (or 539?) and remained there until the end of his life, translating books from Sanskrit into Chinese. After 557, he translated works of Īśvarakṛishṇa and Vasubandhu; and he wrote a biography of the latter.

For the dates of these translations and biographical information see my notes on Īśvarakṛishṇa and Vasubandhu (first half of the fourth century). See also M. Winternitz: Geschichte der indischen Litteratur (t. 2, 257–259, t. 3, 451–452, 1920–22).

---

[a] He was the first monk to become pope.

[b] It is during his pontificate that St. Augustine went to Britain (596); he directed missionary activities in many other countries.

JINAGUPTA

We know only his Chinese name Shê^{2}-na^{3}-chüeh^{2*}-to^{1} (9783, 8090, 3230, 11302), which was a transcript of the Sanskrit original.[c] Hindu Buddhist who lived from 528 to 605. One of the main translators of Buddhist texts into Chinese. Among his many translations I shall quote only those of the Buddhacarita and of the Saddharmapuṇḍarīka sūtra. When he went to China in 559–60, he followed a road which was very similar to that followed, in the opposite direction, by Sung Yün in 518 (see previous chapter). From 575 to 585 he resided at the court of the Turkish chieftain T'o^{1*}-po^{4*} (11400, 9386) and of the latter's successor. He met there a number of Chinese monks coming back from India with sacred books which he helped to catalogue. This long residence of a learned Hindu at a Turkish court is of great cultural interest, as it enables us to understand the spread of Buddhism among Turkish peoples. In 575 the Chinese emperor had ordered the translation of the Mahāparinirvāṇasūtra into Turkish for this same T'o-po.

A list of Jinagupta's translations will be found in Bunyiu Nanjio's Catalogue of the Chinese Tripiṭaka. A biography of Jinagupta was included by Tao-hsüan (q. v., second half of the seventh century) in his Hsü kao sêng ch'uan. French translation with abundant notes by Ed. Chavannes: T'oung Pao (vol. 6, 332–356, 1905). For additional information on contemporary translations from Chinese into Turkish (Uighūr), see Chavannes (*ibidem*, vol. 10, 100, 1909).

CHIH-I

Chih^{4}-i^{3} (1784, 5472). That was his religious name. His own name was Ch'ên Tê^{2*}-an^{1} (658, 10845, 44). He is also called Chih^{4} K'ai^{3} (1784, 5472). Born at Ying^{3}-ch'uan^{1} (13337, 2728), Anhui, in 538. From 575 on, his home was in the T'ien^{1}-t'ai^{2} (11208, 10583) Mountains in Northeastern Chehkiang; he died in 597. Founder of the T'ien-t'ai school of Buddhism, which is partly a reaction against the extreme mysticism of the Ch'an[d] and partly an attempt to harmonize various Buddhist divergencies. His favorite sūtra was the so-called "Lotus sūtra" or "Lotus of the True Law." He wrote two commentaries upon it. The most important of his own works is the Mo^{1}-ho^{1}-chih^{3}-kuan^{1} (7969, 3940, 1837, 6363), in which he explains the T'ien-t'ai philosophy.

Text of the Lotus Sūtra—This sūtra, which is often called Pure Land sūtra, is the translation of Saddharmapuṇḍarīka. The Sanskrit text was edited by H. Kern and B. Nanjio (St. Petersburg, 1908–9). French translation by Eugène Burnouf (Paris, 1852). English translation by H. Kern: Sacred Books of the East (vol. 21, Oxford, 1884).

Many translations had soon been made from Sanskrit into Chinese, the earliest (lost) in 255; the most popular was that by Kumārajīva (q. v., first half of the fifth century). The Chinese title is Chêng^{4} Fa^{2*}-hua^{2}-ching^{1} (687, 3366, 5005, 2122), also Miao^{4} Fa^{2*} Lien^{2}-hua^{1} ching^{1} (7857, 3366, 7115, 5002, 2122).

Criticism—A. Wylie: Chinese Literature (209, 1902). H. A. Giles: Biographical Dictionary (147, 1898). R. F. Johnston: Buddhist China London, 1913). L. Wieger: La Chine (181, 427, 510, etc., 1920).

Introduction of the T'ien-t'ai tsung into Japan—It was introduced into Japan in 806 by Dengyō-daishi (q. v., first half of the ninth century). The Japanese call

[c] Bunyiu Nanjio would reconstruct it Jñānagupta. I adopt Chavannes's and Sylvain Lévi's reconstruction, which seems more plausible. See their argument in T'oung Pao (vol. 6, 332, 1905).

[d] For example, it allowed the use of books.

it Tendai-shū or Tendai. They often call Chih-i, Shintan no Shaka, meaning the Buddha of China. They call the Lotus sūtra, Hokké-kyo.

FA-CHING

Fa[2]*-ching[1] (3366, 2122). Flourished under the Sui[2] (10394), c. 594. Chinese Buddhist. He completed in 594 a catalogue of Chinese Buddhist books; 2,257 works are quoted, among which more than 400 were then already lost.

L. Wieger: La Chine (182, 297, 521, 1920).

Introduction of Buddhism into Japan

Buddhism was introduced into Japan in 552, when king Seimei of Kudara[e] sent a message and Buddhist books to the emperor of Japan Kimmei (who ruled from 540 to 571). It is probable that other missionaries had come from Korea before[f] but this was the first introduction of which we have a definite record. It was not very successful.

We have other proofs of the growing relations between Japan, Korea, and indirectly, China. Under the same Emperor Kimmei, a group of 35 literati was brought from Kudara. The emperor gave them the family name Metsura-Omi. They settled in the provinces of Yamato and Ōmi and acted as osa, that is, interpreters of the Korean and Chinese languages.

In 553 or 554, Wang[2] Tao[4]-liang[2] (12493, 10780, 7017), a Korean doctor of i (that is, the doctrine of changes in the I[4]-ching[1], 5497, 2122), and Wang[2] Pao[3]-sun[1] (12493, 8711, 10431), a doctor of chronology, came from Korea to Japan and introduced Chinese mathematics. These facts mark the beginning of Japanese science and civilization, but they are very bare, and the history of Japanese civilization before the seventh century is very uncertain.

It may be useful to know that the Japanese call the Buddha, Shaka; Buddhism, Bukkyō, Butsudō, or Buppō; Hīnayāna, Shō-jō; Mahāyāna, Dai-jō. The names of various sects will be given when I come to them.

E. Papinot: Historical Dictionary (article Mononobe Okoshi, on p. 401, and osa on p. 492, 1909). Y. Mikami: Development of Mathematics in China and Japan (p. 179, Leipzig, 1912. Speaks of the Korean doctor Wang Liang-tung, whom I have not been able to identify, unless it be the same personality as Wang Tao-liang named in the Japanese work of T. Endō quoted below). M. Anesaki: Buddhist Art (19, Boston, 1915. Says that Buddhism was brought to Japan from Kudara in 538). A. K. Reischauer: Studies in Japanese Buddhism (80, New York, 1917). T. Endō: History of Japanese Mathematics (in Japanese, p. 6, Tokyo, 1918; Isis, IV, 70).

III. PERSIAN PHILOSOPHY

PAUL THE PERSIAN

Born in Dērshar?, flourished under Nūshīrwān, King of Persia from 531 to 579. Syrian philosopher.[g] Author of a (Syriac) "Treatise on the logic of Aris-

[e] For the evangelization of Kudara see previous note (second half of fourth century).

[f] For example, one Ssŭ[1]-ma[3] ta[2]* (10250, 7576, 10473) is said to have come some 30 years before, but he remained almost unnoticed.

[g] Christian or Zoroastrian?

totle addressed to King Chosroës." He clearly distinguished between scientific knowledge and faith. A Persian commentary on the περὶ ἑρμηνείας is also ascribed to him.[h]

Text—J. P. N. Land: Anecdota syriaca (t. 4, 1875. With translation). E. Renan: Journal asiatique (t. 19, 312–319, 1852. Edition and translation of the introduction).

Criticism—Wm. Wright: Syriac Literature (122, 1894). Jerôme Labourt: Le christianisme dans l'empire perse sous la dynastie sassanide (2e éd., Paris, 1904). R. Duval: Littérature syriaque (250, 1907).

BURZŪYA

Or Burzōe (Περζωέ). Physician to Nūshīrwān. He was sent by him to India, whence he brought back works on medicine, and also the game of chess and the fables of Pilpay (or Bidpai), that is, the fables of the Five Books (Pañcatantra), called in Arabic the fables of Kalīla and Dimna. He translated these fables from Sanskrit into Pahlawī.

Th. Nöldeke: Burzôes Einleitung zu dem Buche Kalīla wa-Dimna (Schriften d. wissensch. Gesell., 12 Heft, 27 p., Strassburg, 1912).

IV. BYZANTINE AND CHINESE MATHEMATICS

THE AKHMÎM PAPYRUS

This Greek papyrus is interesting because it gives us, so to say, a last glimpse of Egyptian mathematics. Strangely enough, it is also the earliest document on Greek practical arithmetic. (However, see my note on Michigan mathematical papyrus No. 621, first half of fourth century.) The author was a Christian. The papyrus is Byzantine and anterior to the Arabic invasion, 640–641. It dates probably from the sixth or seventh century.

The text has been published by J. Baillet: Le papyrus mathématique d'Akhmîm (Mémoires publiés par les membres de la mission archéologique française au Caire, t. 9, 91 p., 8 pl., Paris, 1892). See M. Cantor: Ein historischer Papyrus in griechischer Sprache (Z. f. Mathematik, t. 38, hist. Abt., 81–87, 1893); Geschichte d. Mathematik (Vol. I, third ed., p. 504, 1907. As to the date of the papyrus, Cantor has misunderstood Baillet).

HSIA-HOU YANG

Hsia[4]-hou[2] Yang[2] (4227, 4006, 12883). Flourished probably in the middle or in the second half of the sixth century. Chinese mathematician. The "arithmetical classic of Hsia-hou Yang," Hsia-hou Yang Suan[4]-ching[1] (10378, 2122) is an elementary text-book of arithmetic based partly upon the Nine Sections (see Chang Ts'ang, first half of second century B. C.), partly upon Sun-Tzŭ (q. v., first half of third century), partly upon the Wu[3]-ts'ao[2] (12698, 11636) Suan-ching, an arithmetical classic dating probably from the Han dynasty.

Text—The text is preserved in the encyclopaedia Yung-lo, but cut into parts. These parts were put together and thus the text reconstructed in its integrity by Tai[4] Chên[4] (10567, 642) in 1776. (M. Courant: Catalogue des livres chinois, No. 4844).

Criticism—Yoshio Mikami: Development of Mathematics in China and Japan (p. 39, Leipzig, 1912). D. E. Smith and Y. Mikami: History of Japanese Mathe-

---

[h] This was translated into Syriac by Severus Sēbōkht (q. v., second half of seventh century). See Journal asiatique (t. 16, 73, 1900).

matics (p. 21, Chicago, 1914. Apropos of the use of rods). Louis Van Hée: The Arithmetic Classic of Hsia-hou Yang (American Mathematical Monthly, vol. 31, 235–237, 1924; Isis, VII, 182; facsimile of the title page of the princeps of 1776 in Isis, VII, pl. 5, facing p. 170).

CHÊN-LUAN

Chên[1]-luan[2] (618, 7457). Flourished under the Pei (Northern) Chou dynasty c. 566. Chinese mathematician. He wrote commentaries on the ancient mathematical treatises and thus saved them from destruction. His main work is the Wu[3]-ching[1] suan[4]-shu[4]* (12698, 2122, 10378, 10053), wherein every question of mathematical interest in the Classics is discussed. He arranged the calendar of 566.

Text—His main works are collected in the Tai[4]-chiao[4] suan[4]-ching[1] shih[2]*-shu[1] (10569, 1302, 10378, 2122, 9959, 10024), 1773.
Criticism—L. Wieger: La Chine (162, 422, 513, 525, 1920).

CHANG CH'IU-CHIEN

Chang[1] Ch'iu[1]-chien[4] (416, 2313, 1592). Flourished probably in the latter part of the sixth century. Chinese mathematician. The "arithmetical classic of Chang Ch'iu-chien" (Chang Ch'iu-chien suan-ching) is a text-book of arithmetic of greater importance than that of Hsia-hou Yang. Special attention is paid to the treatment of fractions. Division by a fraction is equivalent to multiplication by the reversed fraction (this is not explicitly stated). Problems in percentage partition, surplus, and deficiency; simultaneous equations. Sum of arithmetical progressions. Area of a circular segment. Indeterminate equations.

Yoshio Mikami: The Development of Mathematics in China and Japan (p. 39–43, Leipzig, 1912). This classic has been partly preserved through a Sung edition of 1084, with commentaries by Liu[2] Hsiao[4]-sun[1] (7270, 4334, 10431) and by Li Shun-fêng (q. v., second half of the seventh century).

Chinese Knowledge of Hindu Mathematics and Astronomy During the Sui Dynasty (589 to 618)

The Chinese must already have had some good knowledge of Hindu science toward the end of the sixth century, or at least before 610, because many works explaining Hindu mathematics and astronomy are mentioned in the catalogue of the Sui dynasty. This catalogue, completed c. 610, forms chapters 32 to 35 of the Sui shu, for which see my note on Wei Chêng (first half of seventh century). It is the earliest Chinese catalogue extant, save that of the Han completed in 6 B. C.

Brahmanical astronomy, P'o[2]-lo[2]-mên[2] t'ien[1]-wen[2]-ching[1] (9412, 7291, 7751; 11208, 12633, 2122), by the Brahman Shê, Shê[3] hsien[1]-jên[2] (9790, 4449, 5624), in 21 books.

Astronomical dissertations by the Brahman Chieh-ch'ieh: P'o-lo-mên (Brahmanical) Chieh[2]*-ch'ieh[2] (1459, 1558) hsien[1]-jên[2] (immortal man) t'ien[1]-wen[2]-shuo[1]* (11208, 12633, 10164, astronomical dissertations) in 30 books.

Brahmanical astronomy. P'o-lo-mên t'ien-wen, in one book.

Brahmanical methods of calculation. P'o-lo-mên suan[4]-fa[2]* (10378, 3366), in three books.

Brahmanical method of calculating time. P'o-lo-mên yin[1] yang[2] suan[4] ching[1] (13224, 12883, 10378, 2122), in one book.

Treatise on Brahmanical mathematics. P'o-lo-mên suan ching, in three books.

All these works are apparently lost. L. Wieger: La Chine (182, 1920).

For the introduction of Chinese mathematics into Japan, see my note on Japanese Buddhism in Section II.

V. CHINESE TECHNOLOGY. ITS DIFFUSION WEST AND EAST

Invention of Block Printing

It is often stated that block printing was invented in China at some time in the sixth century and that the earliest authenticated account dates from 593, in which year the Sui emperor Wên-ti ordered all worn out images to be recarved and the classics to be collected. This text occurs in Lu⁴* Shên¹'s (7432, 9823) Ko²* chih⁴ ching⁴ yüan² (6029, 1832, 2170, 13700) and the first to draw attention to it was Stanislas Julien in L'imprimerie en Chine au VIe siècle (1850). But does this text actually refer to block printing? Is Julien's interpretation not forced? Note also that Lu Shên's text is at least nine centuries later than the event reported![i]

It is not impossible that block printing was practiced in China as early as the sixth or seventh century. The use of seals goes back (in China) at least to the third century B. C. (they are first mentioned c. 255 B. C.).[j] The seal impressions of the Han dynasty were made, like those of Europe, in a soft substance (clay in China, wax in Europe), but some time about the fifth or sixth century, as the use of paper increased,[k] sealing with clay was gradually replaced by sealing with ink, the seal being used as we use a rubber stamp. Now, the stamping of a seal with ink is not very far removed from block printing. That the seal is the ancestor of the printing block is proved by the fact that the same word yin⁴ (13282) denotes both print and seal even to this day. The transition from seal to block-print was probably caused by the great demand for charms, Taoist and Buddhist. The seal was used for authentication purposes, but its convenience was obvious, and as the demand for charms increased it was natural to produce them by the expeditious seal technique. As the charms increased in size the seal technique was replaced by the printing-block technique. On the other hand, the Confucian Classics, had been cut in stone as early as the year 175 A. D., and very soon afterward the practice of making inked rubbings from these inscriptions developed. This practice, too, led to block-printing, though in the latter case the inscriptions or images had to be cut in reverse.

It is thus possible that some crude form of block-printing was already practiced in the sixth or seventh century, but it is more probable that the discovery of block-printing was not completed until a little later, say until the first half of the eighth century.[l] As a matter of fact, the earliest printed document is a Buddhist charm printed, not in China but in Japan, by order of the empress Shōtoku (q. v.), c. 770.

Arthur Waley: Note on the Invention of Wood-Cuts (New China Review, vol. 1, 412–415, 1919). T. F. Carter: Invention of Printing in China (New York, 1925, wherein the main documents are fully quoted; Isis, VIII, 365).

---

[i] Lu Shên was born in Shanghai in 1477, died in 1544. (Giles's Biographical Dictionary, 548, 1898). The Ko chih ching yüan contains also a mention of chess, that is, real chess, hsiang⁴ ch'i² (4287, 1031); this is the earliest mention of Chinese chess, if the Ko chih is as early as we suppose it to be. See Encyclopaedia Sinica (92, 631, 1917).

[j] See my note on Mêng T'ien (second half of third century B. C.).

[k] For the invention of paper, c. 105, see my note on Ts'ai Lun (first half of second century).

[l] See my note on Ming Huang (first half of eighth century.)

Diffusion of Chinese Technology, West and East

The first Chinese silkworms were introduced into the West during the reign of Justinian, c. 552 (q. v., in previous chapter). This introduction was probably made by Nestorian monks. It is probable that the mulberry tree (*Morus alba*) was introduced at the same time. Sericulture developed rapidly in the Peloponnesos, so many mulberry trees (μορέα) being planted that the country was named Morea (Procopios: De bello gothico, 4, 17).

It would be wrong to conclude that no silk was made in the ancient classical world. Some was spun out of the cocoons of wild silkworms living on oaks, ashes, and cypresses. Aristotle speaks of this in the Historia animalium (V, 19) adding that a Coan woman named Pamphilia, daughter of Plateus, was said to be the first to weave that silk. A fuller account is given in Pliny (XI, 22, 23), who mentions the Coan dresses (vestae Coae, bombycinae, sericae), light transparent dresses made in Cos. Were these really made in Cos? At any rate, the true mulberry silkworm was unknown in the West until its introduction from Khotan in 552. But before that time increasing amounts of Chinese silk (νῆμα σηρικόν, μέταξα) had been brought by caravans into the Roman Empire, silk being the staple importation from China.

To complete this story, I may add that the European silk industry was for many centuries restricted to Greece. After the war of Roger II of Sicily against Manuel Comnenos, it was introduced into Sicily (1147). For a sketch of further developments see F. M. Feldhaus: Die Technik (1016, 1914).

So much for the West. At about the same time, Chinese civilization was beginning to percolate into Japan in the wake of Buddhism. We hear that under the reign of Sushun-tennō, thirty-second emperor of Japan (588–592), scales or balances were introduced from China and tiles were used for the first time for roofing (in the Hōkō-ji, a famous temple in Kyōto). E. Papinot: Historical Dictionary (610, 1909).

VI. BYZANTINE HUSBANDRY

CASSIANOS BASSOS

He was called σχολαστικός, that is, the legal adviser; this title shows that he flourished in the sixth century or possibly at the beginning of the seventh. Byzantine compiler of writings on husbandry (γεωπονικά). His compilation is based on two earlier ones, by Vindonius Anatolius and by Didymos (q. v., second half of fourth century); it became in its turn the basis of the compilation made c. 950 by order of the Emperor Constantine VII (q. v.)

Texts and Translations—The oldest edition I know is "Constantini Caesaris selectarum praeceptionum, de agricultura libri viginti, Iano Cornario medico physico interprete, recens in lucem emissi" (Venice, 1538). First complete edition by Peter Needham (Cambridge, 1704). Improved edition in four volumes by Jo. N. Niclas (Leipzig, 1781). Critical edition, Geoponica sive de re rustica eclogae, by H. Beckh (Leipzig, 1895).

Geoponicon in sermonem Syriacum versorum quae supersunt, edited by P. de Lagarde (126 p., Leipzig, 1860). For other translations (Armenian, French, German), see Krumbacher.

Criticism—E. H. F. Meyer: Geschichte der Botanik (t. 3, 344–349, 1856). K. Krumbacher: Geschichte der byzantinischen Litteratur (2 Aufl., 261–263, München, 1897, with full bibliography). M. Wellmann, in Pauly-Wissowa (vol. 6, 1667, 1899).

VII. BYZANTINE GEOGRAPHY

ZEMARCHOS

Zemarchos the Cilician. Greek traveler to Central Asia. He was sent in August 568 by Justin II (Justinian's successor) as his ambassador to Dizabul, the Turkish Khan. He went from Constantinople to Samarkand by way of Kerch and the plains of Astrakhan. The purpose of that embassy was, in part at least, to form an alliance with the Turkish khan and oblige Persia to resume the silk trade (see my note on Justinian in the previous chapter).

C. R. Beazley: Dawn of Modern Geography (t. 1, 186–188, 1897).

VIII. BYZANTINE, KOREAN, AND JAPANESE MEDICINE

ALEXANDER OF TRALLES[m]

'Αλέξανδρος. Born c. 525; traveled extensively, finally settling down in Rome; died in 605. Byzantine physician; the first original physician since Galen. Youngest brother of Anthemios (q. v., previous chapter). His main work is a general treatise on pathology and therapeutics (θεραπευτικά) in 11 books. He also wrote on fevers (περὶ πυρετῶν, sometimes considered as the twelfth book of the previous work), on intestinal worms (περὶ ἑλμίνθων), on eye diseases (περὶ ὀφθαλμῶν). His works were very influential and not simply in the Greek-speaking world, for they were soon translated into Syriac, Arabic, Hebrew, and Latin. Introduction of rhubarb (as drug).

Text and Translations—Latin edition (Lyon, 1504, often reprinted). First Greek edition (Paris, 1548). Greek and Latin edition (Basel, 1556). French translation (Poitiers, 1556). Greek text, edited by Theod. Puschmann, with German transl. and introduction (2 vols., Vienna, 1878–79). Ophthalmological fragments of great interest were published by the same editor in his Nachträge (quoted below), and it was suggested that these fragments were part of Alexander's work; it seems more probable that they are of a later date. Bernhard Nosske: Alexandri (Tralliani?) liber de agnoscendis febribus ex pulsibus et urinis (Diss., 39 p., Borna-Leipzig, 1919; Isis, IV, 578).

Criticism—Edward Milward: Trallianus Reviviscens, or an account of Alexander Trallian, one of the Greek writers that flourished after Galen . . . . being a supplement to Dr. Freind's History of Physic (230 p., London, 1734). Theodor Puschmann: Nachträge zu Alexander Trallianus. Fragmente aus Philumenos und Philagrios nebst einer bisher noch ungedruckten Abhandlung über Augenkrankheiten (with German transl. 189 p., Berliner Studien für classische Philologie, t. 5, Berlin, 1887). Max Wellmann, in Pauly-Wissowa (t. 1, 1460, 1894); Eine neue Schrift des Alexander von Tralles (Hermes, t. 42, 533–541, 1907). Hans Pohl: Ein Pseudo-Galen Text aus den frühen Mittelalter betitelt "de pulsis et urinis omnium causarum" aus der Handschrift Nr. 44 der Stiftsbibliothek zu St. Gallen (Diss., 20 p., Leipzig, 1922. For comparison; see Isis, V, 493).

Maurice Villaret and Joseph Hariz: Contribution à l'étude de la médecine avant l'Islam (Bull. soc. franç. hist. méd., t. 16, 223–229, 1922).

---

[m] Tralles in Lydia.

Korean Influence on Japanese Medicine

During the reign of the Emperor Kimmei (540–571), in 554, the physician Ōyu-Ryōda and the pharmacists Han-Ryoho and Tei-Yuda[n] came from Kudara to Japan. They brought with them various Korean drugs. This marked the beginning of a period during which Japanese medicine was increasingly influenced by Korean models.

An epidemic (of measles?) raged throughout Japan in 552.

The earliest Chinese books on medicine, 29 in number, are said to have been introduced into Japan in 562.

Y. Fujikawa: Geschichte der Medizin in Japan (5, 96, 1911).

IX. BYZANTINE, LATIN, SYRIAC, PERSIAN, AND CHINESE HISTORIOGRAPHY

PROCOPIOS

Προκόπιος. Born about the end of the fifth century at Caesarea in Palestine; flourished at Constantinople when not abroad with Belisarios; died after 562. Byzantine historian. Secretary and legal adviser to Belisarios, Justinian's greatest general. His earliest and most important work (550 to 554) is his "History" (in eight books Ἱστορικόν) describing the wars against the Persians (two books), against the Vandals (two books), and against the Goths (three books) (Book 8 is a summary of events down to 554). It is essentially a history of Justinian's time. His other works are the Anecdota (Ἀνέκδοτα, or "Historia arcana," 550), and a study on Justinian's monuments (περὶ κτισμάτων, de aedificiis, after 558).

Texts—Opera omnia, edited by G. Dindorf (3 vols., Corpus scriptorum historiae byzantinae, Bonn, 1833–1838). By Jakob Haury (3 vols., Leipzig, 1905–1913. Greek text with English translation by H. B. Dewing (6 vols., Loeb Library, London, 1914).

Of the buildings of Justinian, translated by Aubrey Stewart (Palestine Pilgrims' Text Soc., 3, London, 1886).

Criticism—Krumbacher: Geschichte der Byzantinischen Litteratur (2. Aufl., 230–237, 1897). M. Croiset: Littérature grecque (t. 5, 1018–1020, 1899). H. Schröder: Das klinische Bild der Pest bei Procopius (Wien. klin. Wchschr., 581–582, 1913. Apropos of the plague of 542 in Constantinople).

MALALAS

John Malalas (Ἰωάννης Μαλάλας).[o] From Antioch. Flourished under the Emperors Anastasios I and Justinos II, hence at least from 518 to 565. Syrian-Byzantine historian. Author of a world chronicle (Χρονογραφία), centered upon Antioch, from the legendary times of Egypt to 563.[p] This is the earliest specimen of a Byzantine monastic chronicle. It is distinctly of a popular type, and because of that it exerted a deep influence upon later mediaeval chronicles (Byzantine, Syriac, Ethiopian, Georgian, Slavonic, Latin).

---

[n] The names of these three men would read, in Chinese as follows: Wang[2]-yu[3] Ling[2]-t'o[2] (12493, 13376, 7235, 11358); Fan[1] Liang[2]-fêng[1] (3388, 7015, 3578); Ting[1] Yu[3]-t'o[2] (11253, 13376, 11358).

[o] Greek form of the Syriac word malāl, meaning rhetor. This explains the accentuation. Malalas is sometimes called John of Antioch (Joannes Antiochenus); this is not incorrect, but misleading and should be avoided (see first half of seventh century).

[p] Probably to 565, possibly to 573, but the end of the work is lost.

Text—Edited by Edm. Chilmeadus (Oxford, 1691, with Latin translation; also Venice, 1733). By L. Dindorf: Corpus script. hist. byz., 14, 874 p., Greek and Latin, Bonn, 1831). Migne's Patrologia graeca (t. 97, 9–790).

Criticism—Heinrich Gelzer: Sextus Julius Africanus (vol. 2, 129–138, 1885). K. Krumbacher: Byzantinische Litteratur (2. Ausg., 325–334, 1897).

EVAGRIOS

Evagrios Scholasticos (Εὐάγριος). Born at Epiphania, Syria, c. 536; flourished in Antioch, and lived until the end of the sixth century. Byzantine church historian. The most important continuer of Eusebios. His Ecclesiastical History (dealing with the period 431 to 593) is the best source for the history of the Christian dogmas in the fifth and sixth centuries; it contains valuable information on profane history.

Text—Ecclesiasticae historiae libri VI, edited by Henri de Valois with Latin translation in 1679 (with Theodoretos's Historia), and again, in 1695, in his Hist. eccles. script. graeci (III, 251–464). English translation, together with that of Theodoretos, in Bohn's Library (London, 1854).

Criticism—Krumbacher: Byzantinische Litteraturgeschichte (2. Aufl., 245–247, 1897).

JORDANES[q]

Born in Moesia, region situated south of the Danube and north of Greece;[r] flourished there about the middle of the sixth century. Historian of the Goths. He wrote, in 551, two works: (1) A Roman history (Romana; de summa temporum vel origine actibusque gentis Romanorum) from the creation to 550 (of hardly any value, except with regard to the period 450 to 550); (2) a history of the Goths (Getica; de rebus geticis; de origine actibus Getarum), which is essentially a summary of the lost work written by Cassiodorus in 526 to 533. It tells the history of the Goths from their origins to 539.

Text—Romana et Getica, edited by Theod. Mommsen (Monum. Germ. hist., Berlin, 1882).

The Origin and Deeds of the Goths, Englished by Charles C. Mierow (109 p., Thesis, Princeton, 1908). German translation of the Getica with extracts translated from the Romana, by Wilhelm Martens (Leipzig, 1884). Latin text of both works with French translation by Auguste Savagner (Pancoucke Collection, Paris, 1842).

Criticism—Johann Friedrich: Über die kontroversen Fragen im Leben Jordanes (Bayer. Ak. der Wiss., Sitzungsber. phil. Cl., 379–442, 1907). Fritz Werner: Die Latinität der Getica (Diss., 163 p., 1908, Halle). Article by Thomas Hodgkin and Ernest Barker (Encycl. Brit., 11th ed., 1911, 3 col.).

GILDAS

Born c. 516; died c. 570. British historian. He probably moved to Brittany c. 550, founded a monastery at Ruys near Vannes, and wrote, c. 560, a history called "liber querulus de excidio Britannae." This history is valuable chiefly because of the lack of anything better.

Text—Princeps edition by Polydore Vergil: De calamitate, excidio et conquestu Britanniae, quam Angliam nunc vocant (88 p., London, 1525). Modern edition

[q] Not Jornandes.

[r] Jordanes was not a Goth, and he had ceased to be an Arian. He was friendly both to the Goths and to the Byzantine Empire. He was interested chiefly in Danubian affairs, his own world being limited by the triangle Sirmium, Larissa, Constantinople (Mommsen).

by Joseph Stevenson (163 p., English Historical Society, London, 1838); edition in Monum. germ. hist. (1848, again in 1894). De excidio Britanniae, de paenitentia et Lorica edited by Hugh Williams (Society of Cymmrodorion, 2 parts, London, 1899–1901).

First English translation called The Epistle of Gildas, by Thomas Habington (London, 1638). Other translation in Bohn's collection called Six Old English Chronicles, edited by J. A. Giles (p. 295–380, London, 1848).

Criticism—Article by T. F. Tout (Dictionary of National Biography, t. 21, 1890, or t. 7, 1223–1225, 1908), Günther Leonhardi: Die Lorica des Gildas (Diss., 49 p., Leipzig, 1905). Joseph Fonssagrive: St. Gildas de Ruis et la société bretonne au VIe siècle (Paris, 1908). M. Manitius: Lateinische Literatur des Mittelalters (t. 1, 208–210, 1911; t. 2, 798).

Charles Singer: The Lorica of Gildas the Briton (? 547). A magico-medical text containing an anatomical vocabulary (Proc. R. Soc. Med., Hist. section, t. 12, 124–144, 1920. Whether this Gildas is the same as the historian is doubtful).

GREGORY OF TOURS[a]

Born at Clermont-Ferrand in 538; bishop of Tours since 573; died in 593 or 594. Historian of the Franks. His main work is the "Historia Francorum" in 10 books, down to 591. Book I is a historical summary from the creation to 397; Books 2 to 4 deal with the period 397 to 575; Books 5 to 10 with the period 575 to 591. The last five books are personal memoirs of great value. Because of the great attraction exerted by St. Martin's shrine, Tours was then an excellent center of information. Between 575 and 582 he wrote the De cursibus ecclesiasticis, from which some idea may be obtained of Gregory's very limited scientific knowledge.

Text—Complete works, edited by Theod. Ruinart (1 vol., fol., Paris, 1699). Modern edition, by W. Arndt and Br. Krusch (972 p., in 2 vols., Hanover, 1884–1885).

Histoire ecclésiastique des Francs. Latin and French texts by J. Guadet and N. R. Taranne (Soc. de l'histoire de France, 2 vols., Paris, 1836–1838). Histoire des Francs. Grégoire de Tours et Frédégaire, traduction de Guizot (1823) revue et augmentée de la géographie de Grégoire et Frédégaire par A. Jacobs (2 vols., Paris, 1862). Reproduction réduite du MS. de Beauvais en onciale, Bibliothèque nationale, Latin 17654 (Paris, Bibliothèque nationale,190?). Histoire des Francs, texte des MSS. de Corbie et de Bruxelles publié par Henri Omont et Gaston Collon (531 p., Paris, 1913). History of the Franks. Selections in English, with Notes by Ernest Brehaut (309 p., New York, 1916).

Le livre des miracles et autres opuscules. Latin and French texts by H. L. Bordier (4 vols., Paris, 1857–1864).

Criticism—Johann Wilhelm Loebell: Gregor und seine Zeit (2. Aufl., 471 p., Leipzig, 1869). G. Monod: Études critiques sur les sources de l'histoire mérovingienne (Paris, 1872). Max Bonnet: Le latin de Grégoire (791 p., Paris, 1890). Georg Osterhage: Bemerkungen zu Gregors kleineren Schriften (Progr., 28 p., Berlin, 1895). Charles Galy: La famille à l'époque mérovingienne (432 p., Paris, 1901). Godefroid Kurth: Études franques (2 vols., Paris, 1919). P. de Labriolle: Littérature latine chrétienne (678–684, 1920).

---

[a] His original name was Georgius Florentinus. He later received (deservedly) the following surnames: "the Herodotos of the Barbarians;" "le Père de notre histoire" (Claude Fauchet, sixteenth century).

Syriac Chronicle of 569

This anonymous chronicle, dealing with the fifth and the sixth centuries and dating from the end of the sixth century (569 or later), includes a Syriac translation of the Ecclesiastical History of Zaccharias the Rhetor[t] (the Greek original dating from the end of the fifth or beginning of the sixth century, is lost). The author was a Monophysite. His compilation is based on many other Syriac and Greek writings. It is divided into 12 books. The most interesting parts are a description of the city of Rome and its buildings after the conquest of Rome by the Ostrogoths under Totila in 547 (chapter 16 of Book 10), and the description of the universe by Ptolemy (chapter 7 of Book 12) which contains information on the progress of Christianity in the East and the kind of writing which the Huns had then but recently introduced.

Text—J. P. N. Land: Anecdota syriaca (t. 3, 1870). K. Ahrens and G. Krueger: Die sogenannte Kirchengeschichte des Zacharias Rhetor (502 p., Leipzig, 1899. German translation). F. J. Hamilton and E. W. Brooks: The Syriac Chronicle known as that of Zachariah of Mytilene (London, 1899. English translation).

Criticism—R. Duval: Littérature syriaque (184–187, 1907).

JOHN OF ASIA

Also called John of Ephesus. Born at Āmid on the Tigris, c. 505; flourished at Āmid and Constantinople; bishop of Ephesus; died in 585 or soon after. Syriac Monophysitic chronicler. Author of an ecclesiastical history which is very important for the history of the Monophysitic church in the sixth century. It is divided into three parts containing six books each. Parts 1 and 2 deal with the period extending from the time of Julius Caesar to 572; part 3 with the period 571 to 585.[u] He wrote also (c. 566) a collection of "Lives of the Eastern (meaning Monophysitic) Saints.

Text—Lives of Saints and Fragments of part 2, edited by J. P. N. Land in his Anecdota Syriaca (t. 2). Wm. Cureton: The Third Part of the Ecclesiastical History of John, Bishop of Ephesus (Oxford, 1853). Jessie Payne Margoliouth: Extracts from the Ecclesiastical History (116 p., in Syriac, with notes; Leiden, 1909). Lives of the Saints, edited and Englished by E. W. Brooks (Paris, 1923).

English translation by Payne Smith (1860). German translation by Schoenfelder (1862).

Criticism—R. Duval: Littérature syriaque (150, 181-184, 1907). Jean Maspéro (1885–1915): Histoire des patriarches d'Alexandrie depuis la mort de l'empereur Anastase jusqu'à la réconciliation des églises Jacobites (518 to 616). (446 p., Paris, 1923. Frequent references to John of Asia.) Edouard Jeanselme: Une observation d'ulcère phagédénique des organes génitaux (Bull. soc. franç. hist. méd., t. 18, 23–28, 1924; Isis, VII, 182).

Iranian History

The Kārnāmak. The oldest version of the Persian epic, which found its ultimate development in Firdawsī's Shāhnāma (first half of eleventh century), is a Pahlawī text entitled the Book of the Deeds of Ardashīr, the son of Pāpak (Kārnāmak-i-Artakshatr-i-Pāpakān), composed about the very end of the sixth century.

[t] About whom see K. Krumbacher: Byzantinische Litteratur (403, 1897). According to R. Duval, this Zaccharias Rhetor is different from Zaccharias Scholasticos, bishop of Mytilene.

[u] Part 1 is lost; only fragments of part 2 remain; part 3 is almost complete.

A comparison of this text with the corresponding sections of the Shāhnāma proves Firdawsī's fidelity to his sources.

Text—Pahlawī edition by Kayqubad Ādharbād Dastūr Nūshīrwān (Bombay, 1896). German translation, with important introduction and notes by Nöldeke (Göttingen, 1878).

Criticism—Theodor Nöldeke: Das Iranische Nationalepos (Strassburg, 1896; new edition 126 p., 1920). E. G. Browne: Literary History of Persia (vol. 1, 1908, by index; p. 137–151 contain a very interesting comparison with Firdawsī's Shāhnāma).

WEI SHOU

Wei[4] Shou[1] (12567, 10009). Canonized as Wên[2] Chên[1] (12633, 607). Author of the official history of the Northern Wei dynasty (386 to 556).[v] That history, called Wei[4] shu[1] (12567, 10024), has become the tenth of the Twenty-four Histories.

Text—Chinese edition. Nanking 1872 (114 chüan in 20 vols.).

Criticism—Wylie: Chinese Literature (19, 1902). Giles: Chinese Biographical Dictionary (867, 1898).

X. SANSKRIT AND CHINESE LEXICOGRAPHY; CHINESE EDUCATION

AMARA

Or Amarasiṃha. Flourished probably about the middle of the sixth century? Hindu Buddhist. Sanskrit lexicographer. His dictionary called Amarakośa[w] superseded all previous works of the same kind; it is as fundamental in the field of Sanskrit lexicography as Pāṇini's work in that of grammar. It is essentially a dictionary of synonyms, the words being arranged according to subject-matter. It contains 1,500 verses.

Text—The earliest good edition is that by H. T. Colebrooke (Calcutta, 1808; republished in 1825). Better edition by Cintāmaṇi Sāstrī Thatte and F. Kielhorn, together with Maheśvara's commentary (Bombay, 1877). There are many other commentaries.

Criticism—Theodor Zachariae: Die indischen Wörterbücher (kośa). (Grundriss der indo-arischen Philologie, I, 3 B., Strassburg, 1897, chiefly p. 18–20.) M. Winternitz: Geschichte der indischen Litteratur (vol. 3, 411, 1922. Insisting upon the great uncertainty of Amara's date; he flourished at some time between the sixth century and the eighth century, which marks the end of Hindu Buddhism).

LU TÊ-MING

Lu[4]* Tê[2]*-ming[2] (7432, 10845, 7946). Flourished at the end of the sixth century. Chinese lexicographer. He compiled, c. 583, a glossary of the Classics called Ching[1] tien[3] shih[4]* wên[2] (2122, 11177, 9983, 12633) (Etymological Explanations of the Classics), which is the most famous work of that kind. The char-

[v] A Tartar dynasty, the capital of which was at the modern Ta[4]-t'ung[2] fu[3] (10470, 12269, 3682) in Northern Shansi.

[w] Meaning Amara's dictionary. Its real title was Nāmaliṅgānuśāsana, that is, treatise on the words and genders, the gender of the words being indicated. It was also called Trikāṇḍa or Trikāṇḍī, because it is divided into three parts. The claim that it was translated into Chinese c. 550 is unsubstantiated.

acters are not classified, but dealt with in the order of their appearance in the Classics.[x]

Encyclopaedia Sinica (301, 1917, P. Pelliot).

YEN CHIH-T'UI

Yen[2] Chih[1]-t'ui[1] (13110, 1787, 12185). Born at Lin[2]-i[2] (7165, 5438), Shantung, 531; flourished under the Northern Ch'i and the Sui dynasties; died in 595. Chinese philologist and educator. He wrote a treatise on education within the family, called Yen[2]-shih[4] chia[1]-hsün[4] (13110, 9978, 1139, 4881), wherein he insists on mental culture. It is largely Confucian, but contains some Buddhist points of view. He helped Lu Fa-yen (q. v., first half of seventh century) to compile his phonetic dictionary.

A. Wylie: Chinese Literature (158, 1902). H. A. Giles: Biographical Dictionary (936, 1898). L. Wieger: La Chine (480, 541, 1920).

---

[x] The original text of this glossary is lost but for fragments found at Tun-huang (Bibl. nationale, Paris). It was revised in 972 and later, and has come down to us in the garb of those successive recensions.

CHAPTER XXV

THE TIME OF HSÜAN TSANG

(First Half of Seventh Century)

I. Survey of Science in First Half of Seventh Century. II. Religious Background. III. Philosophers and Patrons of Learning in Latin and Byzantine Worlds, in India, Japan, and China. IV. Chinese and Hindu Mathematics. V. Byzantine, Muslim, Chinese, and Japanese Astronomy. VI. Chinese Geography. VII. Byzantine, Hindu, Chinese, and Japanese Medicine. VIII. Byzantine, Persian, Chinese, and Japanese Historiography. IX. Barbarian and Japanese Law. X. Arabic, Tibetan, and Chinese Philology.

I. SURVEY OF SCIENCE IN FIRST HALF OF SEVENTH CENTURY

1. The seventh century has been spoken of as the nadir of the human mind (Henry Hallam). The following pages will show the lopsidedness of that judgment. It is true, as we shall see later, that the second half of the century was a period of momentary depression and exhaustion, but this may have been partly caused by the extreme activity of the first half. The first half of the seventh century was a golden age in at least four countries—Arabia, Tibet, China, and Japan—chiefly in China, and if we cared to name our chapters after great rulers, the present chapter might very properly have been entitled: The Time of T'ai Tsung.

2. *Religious Background*—The most astounding event was, of course, the birth and explosive development of Islām. The Hegira, which marks its true beginning, occurred in 622. The Prophet died ten years later. Zaid ibn Thābit edited the Qur'ān a first time soon after 633 and a second time c. 650; this second edition was final. By this time the Arabs had conquered not only Arabia and Syria, but also Egypt and Persia—all in a period of only twenty years—thus the seats of two of the most ancient and advanced civilizations had become a part of the Muslim world, and they have remained so until our days. Other conquerors had appeared before, whose achievements had been equally gigantic and rapid, but their empires had not lasted much longer than their own lives. The remarkable feature of the Muslim conquests, these early conquests, is that they were apparently final. It was the first time, indeed, that a religion—and one of a relatively high order—had been the true motive power of imperialism; the secular rulers might change, the religion would endure.

In the meanwhile, Buddhism continued in a quieter and gentler way its conquest of central and eastern Asia. Under the rule of the great king Song-tsen Gam-po, Buddhism and civilization were introduced into Tibet. Shan-tao completed the development of the Pure Land school begun in the second half of the fourth century. A new school of Chinese Buddhism, the Lü tsung, was founded by Tao Hsüan; this was a new reaction against excessive mysticism. The Hōryū-ji, the earliest Japanese temple, was founded in 607, near Nara, by prince Shōtoku; the two earliest Japanese sects, the Sanron and the Jōjitsu, were founded in 625, both by Ekwan, who had introduced them from Korea. By the middle of the century Buddhism had become an integral part of Japanese life.

The civilizing power of Buddhism manifested itself also by the movements of pilgrims who came from many countries to visit the holy places of their faith and who carried back, incidentally, Hindu knowledge and Hindu customs. The most famous of these pilgrims was Hsüan Tsang; but he was not the only one. Some came even from far distant Korea.

The main centers of Jewish teaching were the Babylonian academies of Sura and Pumbedita. The heads of these academies, the geonim, continued the interpretation of the Talmud and the definition of Jewish orthodoxy.

The only Christian theologian of interest to us is Maximos Confessor. He it is who introduced the ideas of Dionysios the Areopagite into the Eastern Church and thus influenced the mystical development not only of Greek Christianity but also, indirectly, of Israel and Islām.

3. *Philosophers and Patrons of Learning in the Latin and Byzantine Worlds, in India, Japan, and China*—The main representative of higher culture in the West was the Spaniard Isidore. The scientific level of his writings was certainly not very high, as must necessarily happen, when there is no real creation and the original (Greek) sources become more and more distant and less and less distinct.

Stephanos of Alexandria wrote commentaries on Aristotle and possibly on Galen and Hippocrates. Alchemical treatises are ascribed to him.

Dharmakīrti continued the elaboration of Buddhist logic, which K'uei-chi introduced into China.

Prince Shōtoku (d. 621) may be considered the father of Japanese civilization. Thanks to his enlightened patronage, the acceptance of Buddhist worship and philosophy made considerable progress, and Chinese thoughts, crafts, and manners were gradually assimilated.

The second T'ang Emperor, T'ai Tsung, consolidated and reorganized China and patronized art and learning. He established at his capital, Si-an-fu, an immense library, and gave many proofs of intelligence and tolerance. The golden age of China began under his influence.

4. *Chinese and Hindu Mathematics*—Wang Hsiao-t'ung composed an arithmetical treatise which contains the earliest Chinese examples of cubic equations.

The greatest mathematician of the period, and one of the greatest of mediaeval times, Brahmagupta, solved determinate and indeterminate equations of the first and second degree, and made an elaborate study of combinatorial analysis and of cyclic quadrilaterals.

5. *Byzantine, Muslim, Chinese, and Japanese Astronomy*—The astronomical activity of this period was almost entirely restricted to the practical problems connected with the calendar. The only exceptions are the astronomical treatise composed by Stephanos of Alexandria and Fu Jên-chün's compilation.

The main principles of the lunar calendar of the Muslims were laid down in the Qur'ān. The Muslim era began on July 15, 622.

The records of the T'ang dynasty give the names of the scholars to whom the determination of the Chinese calendar was intrusted (e. g., calendar of 618). It is very significant that these names are Hindu. In 626 the Chinese astronomer Fu Jên-chün collected the astronomical observations of the ancients.

The Chinese calendar was introduced into Japan by the Korean bonze Kwanroku, in 604, under Shōtoku's patronage. The Chinese custom of counting years with reference to regnal periods (one or more for each reign) was introduced in 645, the first "nengō" being the Taikwa, which lasted from 645 to 650.

6. *Chinese Geography*—P'ei-chü wrote a geography of the Tarim region, and

later, a "Record of Western Countries," based upon diplomatic and commercial reports and illustrated with maps. Prince Li-t'ai ordered the compilation of a geography called Kua-ti-chih.

The outstanding scientific event of the period was the journey of Hsüan Tsang to India, his long stay there, and the publication of his records in 648. These records have a very great geographical value and they give us a splendid picture of the Hindu civilization of those days. Hsüan Tsang spent the rest of his life translating sacred books from Sanskrit into Chinese and apparently also from Chinese into Sanskrit.

7. *Byzantine, Hindu, Chinese, and Japanese Medicine*—A number of distinguished physicians gave luster to this age. Theophilos Protospatharios wrote many treatises, which were largely derived from Galen. The most important were one on physiology and another on urine, which considerably influenced later works on the subject. Stephanos of Alexandria and Stephanos of Athens wrote commentaries on Hippocrates and Galen. Aaron of Alexandria compiled a medical encyclopaedia divided into 30 sections; it included a description of smallpox. Another encyclopaedia of greater importance was written by Paulos Aegineta. Finally, the Jacobite bishop John the Grammarian prepared an epitome of the "sixteen books" of Galen. The three last-named physicians were flourishing in Alexandria about the time of the Muslim conquest of Egypt; their writings were thus among the first Greek medical writings to come to the knowledge of Muslim physicians and their influence upon Arabic literature was very great.

Vāgbhaṭa the Elder, the last of the great Hindu physicians, wrote a general treatise on medicine.

Ch'ao Yüan-fang composed, c. 607, a treatise which contains the description of a great many diseases of all kinds.

The Korean Kwanroku, already mentioned with reference to the calendar, introduced Chinese medicine into Japan. Soon afterward (608) Japanese students were sent to China to obtain more medical knowledge.

8. *Byzantine, Persian, Chinese, and Japanese Historiography*—Many historical writings were composed during the reign of Heraclios (610 to 645), namely, those of Simocattes, of John of Antioch, and the anonymous Easter Chronicle.

Another version of the Persian Epic was composed during the reign of the last Sassanian king (634 to 642) by Dānishwar.

The emperor T'ai Tsung was apparently deeply impressed with the necessity and the duty of editing accurate annals of the past and determined to do his full share of this meritorious work, for a good number of the dynastic histories were compiled during his reign: Fang Hsüan-ling wrote (or edited) the history of the Chin dynasty (265–419); Yao Chien, those of the Liang and Ch'ên dynasties (502 to 580); Li Po-yao, that of the Northern Ch'i (550 to 577); Ling-hu Tê-fên, that of the Northern Chou (557 to 581); Wei Chêng, that of the Sui (581 to 618), and Li Yen-shou, two broader compilations called respectively the Southern and the Northern Annals. Still another historian must be named, Ching Po, who wrote a biography of the great emperor and collaborated in various other works.

Shōtoku taishi wrote (or edited), in 612, a collection of imperial biographies and, in 620, the first history of Japan. These works were written in Chinese.

9. *Barbarian and Japanese Law*—A number of Barbarian codes date from this time: the "Lex Ripuaria," the "Pactus Alamannorum," the "Edictus Langobardorum."

Shōtoku compiled in 604 the "Seventeen-Article Constitution," which is often called the earliest written law of Japan. However, it is less a code of laws than a collection of moral maxims summarizing Buddhist and Confucian wisdom. The Emperor Kōtoku initiated the so-called reform of the Taikwa era (645–650), which involved a reorganization of Japanese government upon the Chinese pattern.

10. *Arabic, Tibetan, and Chinese Philology*—The publication of the Qur'ān introduced into the literary world a new language, which was destined to remain for half a millennium at least one of the main vehicles of knowledge and culture. The very sacredness and infallibility of the Qur'ān established the Arabic language in a permanent form. It is not possible to write better Arabic, because the language of God is, by definition, perfect. The religious interdiction against translating the Qur'ān favored the ecumenical use of Arabic, which has remained to this day one of the international languages of the world.

Tibetan became a literary language at about the same time as Arabic. As the Tibetans were intermediaries between the Hindus on one side and the Chinese and Mongolians on the other, their language became one of the learned languages of Asia. It is still one of the most important languages for the student of Buddhism.

In 601, Lu Fa-yen compiled the earliest phonetic dictionary of the Chinese language, the words being classified under 204 rhymes. In 649, Hsüan Ying compiled a Buddhist glossary wherein he explains the pronunciation of Sanskrit terms; this is of considerable value for the study of Chinese phonetics.

11. *Final Remarks*—The events of this age, which were at once the most striking and the most pregnant, were the apparition of two new civilizations, the Muslim and the Tibetan; we might almost say three, for though we have already had some glimpses of Japanese history, what occurred before the seventh century is a matter of conjecture rather than knowledge. And though it be true that two of these civilizations have long ceased to make any important contributions to humanity, the third has remained fertile to this day.

Another striking fact is the almost complete absence of Latin writings. Outside of a few Barbarian codes, I had nothing to mention except Isidore's "Etymologies," and that was not very much.

But if we look toward the east, what a contrast! To begin with the Byzantine world, we witnessed the activity of Maximos Confessor, Stephanos of Alexandria, and Stephanos of Athens, Theophilos Protospatharios, Aaron of Alexandria, Paulos Aegineta, John the Grammarian, Simocattes, and John of Antioch. The intellectual life of Islām has not yet begun; but its eclosion is being slowly prepared. In the meanwhile, the last Pahlawī chronicle appears. For India, I named only three men, but two of these were very great: Dharmakīrti, Brahmagupta, Vāgbhaṭa. In Tibet, the great king Song-tsen Gam-po and his collaborator Saṃbhoṭa. In China, a tremendous array: Shan tao, Tao Hsüan, K'uei-chi, T'ai Tsung, Wang Hsiao T'ung, Ch'ü-t'an, Fu Jên-chün, P'ei-chü, Li-t'ai, Hsüan Tsang, Ch'ao Yüan-fang, Fang Hsüan-ling, Yao Chien, Li Po-yao, Ling-hu Tê-fên, Wei Chêng, Li Yen-shou, Ching Po, Lu Fa-yen, Hsüan Ying. In Korea, Ekwan and Kwanroku. Finally, in Japan, Shōtoku and Minabuchi Shōan.

If we consider separately the main branches of science, we find that important additions to knowledge were made in mathematics by Brahmagupta; in geography, by Hsüan Tsang; and finally in medicine, by Paulos Aegineta and Vāgbhaṭa. Of the outstanding names, one is Greek, one is Chinese, and two are Hindu. It is clear that the main cultural progress is now being made in the East.

II. RELIGIOUS BACKGROUND

The Beginning of Islām

Mohammedanism, or better, Islām[a] is the third and last master branch of the monotheistic religion of which we found the earliest viable shoot in the eighth century B. C.[b] Judaism developed first, then, some eight centuries later, Christianity, and finally, in the first half of the seventh century, Islām. These three branches are flourishing to-day, but each, and more especially the last two, has given birth to a great number of smaller branches and twigs, forming a tree of bewildering complexity.

The extraordinary beginning of Islām is so trite a subject that, in spite of its tremendous importance (also for the history of thought), the briefest account of it will be sufficient. Abū-l-Qāsim Muḥammad of the tribe of Quraysh was born at Mecca c. 570. He felt a call to prophesy c. 610, and began to do so about three years later. The critical time of his life came in September 622, when he migrated with his followers from his indifferent native place to Yathrib.[c] This time of crisis was called al-Hijra,[d] meaning the withdrawal. Its decisive importance was quickly appreciated, and not long after the Prophet's death, which occurred in 632, this momentous withdrawal to Medīna was chosen as the origin of a new era, the Muslim era.[e] This chronology was fixed probably by the caliph 'Umar about 638–639.

Nothing speaks more for the explosive growth of Islām than the successful establishment of this new era only 17 years after the initial event. It took from five to ten centuries to establish the Christian era (see my note on Dionysius Exiguus, first half of sixth century). It should be noted that the Muslim era does not begin with the day of the Ḥijra (c. September 20), but with the first day of the moon of Muḥarram of the Ḥijra year (July 15, 622). This was due to the fact that the Muslim calendar was introduced (by the Qur'ān) before the determination of the era.

The revelations and utterances made by Muḥammad, in the name of God, are collected in the Qur'ān,[f] edited in its present form soon after the Prophet's death, by Zaid ibn Thābit (q. v.). It contains 114 chapters or sūras, varying considerably in size, form, and content. The whole is smaller than the New Testament.

The Qur'ān is the sacred book of Islām. It is considered by the greatest number of Muslims, to this day, as the Word of God. However, there have been endless controversies among them as to the real nature of its authority and finality, not to speak of more radical ones started by rationalists. For example, was the Qur'ān created or uncreated? These controversies have exerted a very deep influence upon the development of a large province of mankind, even as similar ones relative to the Jewish and Christian Scriptures have strongly affected, for good or evil, other provinces of it.

---

[a] Islām means (in Arabic) obedience, submission (to God).

[b] See my note on Amos (eighth century B. C.).

[c] Later named al-Medīna, the City (of the Prophet).

[d] Anglicized Hegira. The common translation, flight, is misleading. The verb hajara means to break off relations, to abandon one's tribe, to emigrate.

[e] The period preceding it was called the time of ignorance or paganism (al-Jāhiliyya).

[f] Alias Koran, Alcoran. Qur'ān means reading (cfr. our words Scriptures, Bible); from qara'a, to read.

Jean Gagnier: La vie de Mahomet (2 vols., Amsterdam, 1732. Of historical interest). Gustav Weil: Muhammed (Stuttgart, 1843. Unbiased but partly superseded). Aloys Sprenger: Das Leben und die Lehre des Mohammads (3 vols., Berlin, 1861–1865). Sir William Muir: Life of Mahomet (4 vols., London, 1858–1861; 2d ed., 1876; 3d ed., 1894. Revised edition in one vol., by T. H. Weir, Edinburgh, 1912). Syed Ameer Ali: The Life and Teachings of Mohammed and the Spirit of Islam (693 p., London, 1891. Apologetic). E. Lamairesse et G. Dujaric: Vie de Mahomet (Paris, 1897. Also from the Muslim point of view). D. S. Margoliouth: Mohammed (508 p., New York, 1905; also his article in vol. 17 of Enc. Brit., 1911, 399–410). Paul Casanova: Mohammed et la fin du monde (Paris, 1911; Isis, IV, 618). Tor Andrae: Die Person Muhammeds in Lehre und Glaube seiner Gemeinde (Archives d'études orientales, 16, 407 p., Stockholm, 1918; see Der Islam, t. XI, 277–283; Thesis, Upsala, 1917). H. Lammens: La Mecque à la veille de l'Hégire (Mélanges de l'Université Saint Joseph, t. 9, fasc. 3, 340 p., Beyrouth, 1924; Journal des Savants, 23, 140–142, 1925).

For the native sources on Muḥammad's life see my notes on Ibn Isḥāq and al-Wāqidī (second half of eighth century), on Ibn Hishām and al-Bukhārī (first half of ninth century).

ZAID IBN THĀBIT

Abū Sa'd Zaid ibn Thābit Ibn al-Ḍaḥḥāk al-Anṣārī[g] belonged to the tribe of the Khazraj; native of Medina, where he died in 673–674. One of Muḥammad's amanuenses, and later amanuensis to the caliphs Abū Bakr and 'Umar, and guardian of the public treasury under 'Uthmān. He was the first editor of the Qur'ān. He edited it twice—the first time after 633 at Abū Bakr's request; the second time in 650–51 by order of 'Uthmān. The latter edition was final; it has remained the standard edition ever since.

Text of the Qur'ān—Alessandro de Paginini of Brescia, who printed in Venice between 1485 and 1499, published an edition of the Qur'ān, the earliest Arabic printing in Europe. Another edition of the Qur'ān was printed in Italy in 1518 (T. F. Carter: Invention of Printing, 233, 1925). Corani textus arabicus, edited by Gustav Flügel (3d ed., Leipzig, 1869). English translation by G. Sale (London, 1734; often reprinted). Also by E. H. Palmer: Sacred Books of the East (t. 6 and 9, Oxford, 1880).

Criticism—Ibn Khallikān (De Slane) (t. 1, 372, 1842). C. Brockelmann: Arabische Litteratur (t. 1, 35, 1898). Victor Chauvin: Bibliographie des ouvrages arabes (fasc. X, Le Coran et la Tradition, Liège, 1907). Theodor Nöldeke: Geschichte des Qorans (Göttingen, 1860; new edition by Friedrich Schwally, 3 vols., Leipzig, 1909–1926. See DLZ, 32–35, 1921). Also article Koran by these two scholars in Encyclopaedia Britannica (vol. 15, 898–906, 1911).

EARLY MUSLIM CONQUESTS

It is not part of my plan to tell the extraordinary story of the Muslim conquest. This may be found in treatises dealing with general history, or, for example, in that excellent compendium of Muslim annals, Sir William Muir's "The Caliphate" (first ed. 1883; 3d ed., 1899; new and revised ed. by T. H. Weir, Edinburgh, 1915). It will suffice to recall some of the main dates relative to this period. I quote the dates also in Muslim style, to evidence the swiftness of these developments.

Damascus fell in the year 14 (March 635). In the same year (November 635)

[g] Meaning one of Muḥammad's allies.

the victory of Qādisīya put an end to the Persian Empire, and marked a new beginning in the intellectual history of Persia. Jerusalem capitulated in 15 (January 637). In 16, the capital of Persia, al-Madāin (near Baghdad) was captured (March 637), Mesopotamia was reduced, and the rival cities al-Baṣra and al-Kūfa were founded (638). In 19–20 (640–41), Egypt was conquered. The conquest of Persia was completed in 21–22 (642–643), the decisive battle of Nihāvend occurring in 21 (642).

The great significance of the conquest of Persia will appear so often in the following pages that it is not necessary to insist upon it now. It will suffice to remark that Muslim civilization, at its best, was essentially a grafting of a new and vigorous scion (Arabic) upon the old Persian tree. That Persian tree itself had derived its main nourishment and strength from a Greek soil.

The conquest of Egypt was equally important. It opened an entirely new period in the intellectual life of that old country. I am concerned here especially with an episode of that conquest, the alleged destruction of the famous library of Alexandria (q. v., first half of third century B. C.). To begin with, Alexandria was invested twice by the Arabs, the first time in 20, when the city capitulated, but soon after having obtained Byzantine aid it revolted and was reinvested in 25 (646). This second time Alexandria was taken by storm and given up to plunder. If the library was destroyed it was then more probably after the second siege. However, this story is entirely unproved. The first mention of it occurs only after an interval of six centuries in the account of Egypt written by 'Abd al-Laṭīf (q. v., first half of thirteenth century). Moreover, to prove that the Muslim destroyed that famous library, it would be necessary first to prove that it still existed in the seventh century, and this is really very doubtful. It is very probable that a good part of it had been destroyed by the Christians many centuries before. That treasure-house of pagan knowledge had been, at best, so much neglected that what remained of it in the seventh century was only a shadow of its former self.

L. Krehl: Über die Sage von der Verbrennung der alexandrinischen Bibliothek durch die Araber (Acts of the Fourth International Congress of Orientalists, Florence, 1880). P. Casanova: L'incendie de la bibliothèque d'Alexandrie (C. R. de l'Acad. des Inscriptions, 163–171, 1923).

Development of Buddhism

During the seventh century the Mahāyāna Canon was essentially completed. The earliest Mahāyāna scriptures date back to the time of Aśvaghosha (first half of second century); the latest, that is, the latest true ones (e. g., the Mantrasūtras) date from the seventh century. A good summary of this difficult question will be found in A. K. Reischauer: Studies in Japanese Buddhism (158–182, 1917).

In the following notes I shall deal with the introduction of Buddhism into Tibet and more briefly with its growth in China and Japan.

Tibetan Buddhism

Buddhism was introduced into Tibet by Song-tsen Gam-po,[h] King of Tibet from c. 623 to his death c. 650. This king had two wives, one Chinese and the other Nepalese, both Buddhists, and they converted him. This story ascribes a

[h] Whom the Chinese call Ch'i[4] tsung[1] lung[4] tsan[4] (1116, 11976, 7507, 11521), which may be shortened to Lung tsan, or Ch'i[4]-su[1]-nung[2] (1116, 10320, 8408).

dual (Chinese-Hindu) origin to Tibetan Buddhism; it would seem, however, that the Hindu influences were predominant at least in the beginning. Song-tsen's armies captured Upper Burma and Western China, but his main title to fame is to be virtually the founder of Tibetan civilization. In 632 he sent Tụn-mi[i] to India to investigate Buddhism, to obtain copies of the Scriptures, and to study the adaptation of the Sanskrit alphabets to the Tibetan language. An alphabet was thus introduced into Tibet and the Tibetan language was then for the first time reduced to writing. Because of its Hindu origin, that alphabet was very convenient for the transliteration of Sanskrit words, a matter of special importance, inasmuch as Tibetan literature was largely composed of translations from the Sanskrit. It is said that the king retired into seclusion for four years in order to learn reading and writing. He established laws, encouraged Buddhist worship and learning, and the missionaries who came to his court from Nepal, Kashmir, and the East, introduced the arts and customs of India and China.[j] He founded Lhasa in 639 and built a palace for himself on the Red Hill (near that city).[k]

Tibetan civilization received its first impulse from India, and subsidiarily from China, but the Chinese influences became gradually more important, especially after the fall of Buddhism in its native land. The common kinship of Tibetans, Chinese, and Mongolians asserted itself against the Hindu leadership. It should be noted also that the first Hindu teachings reached Tibet through Nepal, the population of which is essentially Mongolian. Thus even the Hindu influences were not purely Hindu, but already colored by Mongolian conceptions. This may help to explain the strange development of Tibetan Buddhism.

Song-tsen's grandson introduced tea from China.

Alexander Csoma de Körös: Enumeration of historical and grammatical Works to be met in Tibet (J. As. Soc. of Bengal, vol. 7, part 2, 147 sq., 1838; reprinted in J. and Proc. As. Soc. of Bengal, vol. 7, extra No. (1911), p. 81–87, 1912). The first of the Annals (lo-gyus) mentioned by Csoma is the Māni-kābum composed by Song-tsen Gam-po and containing his laws.[l] A little further on he says: "The most ancient grammatical work" extant for the Tibetan language is that made by "Sambota" in the seventh century. Its Tibetan name is "Lung-du-ston-pa-sum-chu-pa" and "r, Tags-kyi-P, jug-pa," or grammatical introduction in thirty slókas and the adding of the characteristic letters (for the formation of several cases of nouns, etc.)."

Berthold Laufer: Origin of Tibetan Writing (Journal Am. Or. Sec., vol. 38, 34–116, 1918; Isis, III, 322). Sir Charles Bell: Tibet (Oxford, 1924).

Kanjur and Tanjur

This may be the best place to make a few elementary remarks with regard to the Tibetan scriptures—the Tibetan equivalent of the Tripiṭaka—though in so doing I anticipate to some extent further developments.

The Kanjur (Kang-gyur; Bkah-hgyur; meaning Translation of the Word) is

---

[i] Tun[4]-mi[3] (12221, 7802) or T'ung[1]mi[4]* (12294, 7835). That was his Chinese clan name. His individual name was Sa[1]*-ha[1]*-pa[1] (9530, 3754, 8510) or San[3]-p'u[2]-la[3]* (9561, 9511, 6654), a transcription of the Sanskrit Saṃbhoṭa.

[j] They brought from China butter and cheese, barley-beer, ceramics, and water-mills.

[k] This palace no longer exists, but the present palace of the Dalai Lama, the famous Potala, completed c. 1680, was built at the same place.

[l] There is a magnificent copy of it in the Newberry Library, Chicago, No. 826, written in silver on black.

a collection of 108 (or 100, 105) volumes containing 1,083 distinct works, the whole forming the Buddhist Canon of the Tibetans. These works were translated from the Sanskrit, and subsidiarily from the Chinese and Uighur languages, between the seventh and the thirteenth centuries. The translations dating back to the reign of Song-tsen Gam-po are probably but a very small proportion of the whole; yet the most certain date of the Kanjur is that of its beginnings in that reign, and this justifies our speaking of it at this moment. A great part of the Canon was probably translated in the second half of the ninth century (see my note on Ral-pa-chan). This immense collection is of considerable value, because most of the Sanskrit originals are lost, and the very literality of the Tibetan translations enables one almost to reconstruct the Sanskrit texts.

There are at least two distinct editions of the Kanjur: the older edition is printed at Narthang in Western Tibet (100 volumes of c. 1,000 pages each); the other and later edition is printed at Der-ge in Eastern Tibet (108 volumes). It would seem that both editions contain the same number of writings, but that the distribution is different; the Eastern edition was made to fill 108 volumes instead of 100 because of the mystical properties of the number 108. Other editions were and are printed in Bhōtan, in Mongolia, and in Peking (e. g., imperial edition printed in red). A Mongolian translation was completed in c. 1310 (see my note in first half of fourteenth century).

The Kanjur is essentially equivalent to the Chinese Tripiṭaka. It is thus divided into three main sections (vessels or baskets): (1) Dulva (Sanskrit, Vinaya) or Discipline; (2) Dô (Sanskrit, Sūtra), Sermons of the Buddha; (3) Ch'os-non-pa (Sanskrit, Abhidharma), Metaphysics. In the western edition of the Tibetan Canon these three sections occupy respectively 13, 66, and 21 volumes.

This enormous canon was soon supplemented by a commentary more than twice as large, the so-called Tanjur (Tan-gyur; Bstan-hgyur), which fills generally 225 large volumes. Some parts of this commentary date back also to the first half of the seventh century, though the main bulk was composed later. The Tanjur is divided into two main classes, the Rgyud and Mdo (Dô), corresponding to the Sanskrit Tantra (ritual, ceremonies) and Sūtra (science, literature). The sūtra class is of special interest to us, as it contains a number of works which are neither specifically Buddhist nor even religious, even as the Christian Bible does not contain only religious texts, but many others of secular interest. The early sacred writings of each people are the true equivalents of our modern encyclopaedias; they are meant to include the whole of knowledge. Some five volumes of the Tanjur are devoted to medicine, others deal with astronomy or astrology; another is an index to the whole, and still another contains a Tibeto-Sanskrit dictionary of Buddhist terms.

The pioneer work on the study of both Kanjur and Tanjur was made by the great Hungarian scholar Alexander Csoma de Körös (1784?–1842), who published analyses of them in Asiatic Research (vol. 20, 4 memoirs, 279 p. in all, Asiatic Society of Bengal, Calcutta, 1836). These fundamental papers were translated into French by Léon Feer: Annales du Musée Guimet (vol. 2, 1884, with alphabetical tables of the Sanskrit titles of the Kanjur, and index of proper names). A biography of this hero of learning was written by Theodore Duka (London, 1885, with analyses of his published and unpublished works). See also Alexander Csoma Memorial Volume (Journal and Proc. As. Soc. of Bengal, Vol. VII, extra No., 1911,

Calcutta, 1912, containing reprints of 14 papers by Csoma on Tibetan subjects). Csoma's work is not yet superseded, though many publications have appeared since. I quote only the most important.

W. W. Rockhill: The Life of the Buddha, and the Early History of his Order. From Tibetan Works in the Bkah-hgyur and Bstan-hgyur. With notices on the early History of Tibet and Khotan (284 p., London, 1884); The Land of the Lāmas (400 p., London, 1891). L. Austine Waddell: The Buddhism of Tibet (618 p., illustr., London, 1895, with bibliography).

Kanjur—According to B. Laufer (Descriptive Account of the Collection of (Oriental) Books in the Newberry Library, Chicago, 1913), the best edition of the Kanjur is that of which the blocks were completed at Narthang in 1742.[m] Lalitavistara. Traduction par Philippe Edouard Foucaux (Paris, 1848). Léon Feer: Textes tirés du Kandjour et du Tripiṭaka (11 parts in 1 vol., lithographed, Paris, 1864–1871); Fragments extraits du Kandjour, traduction française (Annales du Musée Guimet, t. 5, 590 p., Paris, 1883). W. W. Rockhill: Udānavarga (252 p., London, 1883). Berthold Laufer: Die Kanjur-Ausgabe des Kaisers K'ang-hsi (Bull. de l'Acad. de St. Pétersbourg, vol. 3, 567–574, 1909).

Tanjur—On Csoma's Tibetan-Sanskrit dictionary based upon the Tanjur, see Duka's biography (p. 207–217). On Tibetan numerals and calendar (*ibidem*, 286–289). F. A. Schiefner: Buddhistische Triglotte, d. h. Sanskrit-Tibetisch-Mongolisches Wörterverzeichniss (73 p., St. Petersbourg, 1859. Largely based upon the Buddhist dictionary above mentioned). H. Laufer: Beiträge zur Kenntnis der tibetischen Medizin (2 parts, 90 p. in all, Berlin and Leipzig, 1900, Berlin, 1900. For more information on Tibetan medicine, see my note on the subject, second half of the eighth century). Palmyr Cordier: Index du Bstan-hgyur. Catalogue du fonds tibétain de la Bibliothèque Nationale (Paris, 1909–1915. Left incomplete; Cordier died in 1914). Berthold Laufer: Das citralakshaṇa, nach dem tibetischen Tanjur, hrg. und übersetzt. Documente der indischen Kunst (203 p., Leipzig, 1913). P. Cordier had been preparing an elaborate Tibetan-French dictionary which may still be published. Ed. Chavannes: T'oung Pao (t. 15, 551–553, 1914).

A complete concordance between the Chinese Tripiṭaka and the two editions of the Kanjur is badly needed. Indeed, it would seem that the Chinese and Tibetan canons influenced one another, some Tibetan writings being translations from the Chinese, while some parts of the Tripiṭaka contain traces of a Tibetan origin. An enormous amount of research remains to be done before a complete analysis of Buddhist literature and a reconstruction of the development of Buddhist knowledge becomes possible.

Chinese Buddhism

The greatest teacher of the Pure Land school (for which see Hui Yüan, second half of fourth century) was Shan^{4} Tao^{3} (9710, 10781) (in Japanese, Zendō or Zendō daishi), who flourished at Ch'ang^{2}-an^{1} (450, 44) in the first half of the seventh century. A Nestorian mission was established at that time in the same city. Whether the Ching-t'u was then influenced by Christianity or not is and will ever be a moot question.

A new school of Buddhism called Lü tsung[n] was founded by Tao^{4} Hsüan^{1} (10780, 4805) (595–667), who insisted on morality and discipline, and encouraged

[m] Copies of Tibetan books are printed in certain monasteries at a special time of each year, according to the orders received.

[n] Lü^{4*} tsung^{1} (7548, 11976). Lü means law and is here the equivalent of the Sanskrit vinaya, designating the Books of Discipline, a part of the Tripiṭaka. That school is also called the Nan^{2} Shan^{1} tsung^{1} (8128, 9663, 11976) (Southern Hill school).

practical rather than mystical activities. He himself carried on some historical investigations (for which see my notes in next chapter).[o]

Japanese Buddhism

By the middle of the century Buddhism had already progressed considerably. The earliest temple and monastery had been founded in 607, near Nara, by prince Shōtoku (q. v.); this was the famous Hōryū-ji (also called Ikaruga-dera). By the end of empress Suiko's reign (628), there were already 46 temples in existence, and 816 priests and 569 nuns had been consecrated.

The four earliest sects of Japan date from the seventh century, and the two earliest, from the first half of that century, namely:

Sanron-shū[p] (625)—This earliest of all Japanese sects was introduced from Korea, in 625, by Ekwan, who established himself at the Hōryū-ji. It is now extinct. It was a highly metaphysical school, belonging to the Provisional Mahāyāna, a development of the Mādhyamaka school founded by Nāgārjuna (q. v., first half of third century). It corresponded to the Chinese San[1]-lun[4] tsung[1] (9552, 7475, 11976).

Jōjitsu-shū (625)—This sect was also introduced by the Korean bonze Ekwan, presumably at the same time. In fact, it remained subordinated to the Sanron. It corresponds to the Hindu Satyasiddhi-śāstra, belonging to the Hīnayāna, and to the Chinese Ch'êng[2] Shih[2]* tsung[1] (762, 9947, 11976). It is also extinct.

Buddhist Pilgrims

See in Section VI my note on the famous pilgrim Hsüan Tsang. Hsüan was not the only Chinese Buddhist who went to India, but he was by far the most representative member of a relatively large group. Some pilgrims came over from Korea in 638 and 650. For a list of them, see Frederick Starr: Korean Buddhism (99–100, Boston, 1918); see also A. K. Reischauer: Studies in Japanese Buddhism (New York, 1917). The travels of these men contributed to a considerable degree to spread and advance civilization, but it would take me too far off my main track to speak of them individually. Nor did I mention, and for the same reason, the many missionaries who brought civilization together with Christianity to the barbarians of Europe. Of these holy men—to whom our debt is so great—I can only speak if they left important writings or contributed in some other way to the progress of knowledge.

The main point to emphasize is that the diffusion of Buddhism had for central and eastern Asia the same tremendous significance as the diffusion of Christianity for Europe. In both cases religion was the vehicle of a higher civilization; and, however much these two religions may have opposed or impeded the progress of science at later periods, we must not forget that it is they who made its birth possible and stimulated its first efforts in many and vast regions of the world. It is literally true that Christianity and Buddhism brought light and science with them, whenever they penetrated uncivilized countries.

The number of sects developing at almost the same time proves at once the interest of the people and the increasing complexity of their religious needs.

---

[o] The center of the school to-day is at Pao[3]-hua[2] Shan[1] (8720, 5005, 9663), near Nanking.

[p] Shū means religion, sect, cfr. tsung in Chinese; this word must not necessarily be attached to the name of the sect. This sect was called Sanron because it was based upon three (san) sūtras: Chū-ron, Hyaku-ron, and Jū-ni-mon-ron. It was also called Ichi-dai-kyō-shū.

Development of Judaism

After the completion of the Talmud, in the second half of the fifth century, Babylonia remained for many centuries the predominant center of Jewish thought. The heads of the two Babylonian academies (at Sura and Pumbedita) received the honorary title of Gaon (Excellence). It is not possible to say exactly when this title was introduced; the first geonim of Sura and Pumbedita entered upon office respectively in 609 and 589;[a] the two last geonim of both academies died respectively in 1034 and 1038. Thus the Babylonian gaonate lasted some four centuries. Its importance was very great. Not only were the geonim the recognized authorities of Judaism; they influenced indirectly Muslim and Christian thought. Many of the geonim and of their adversaries, the Qaraites, will be mentioned in the following pages. Their official language was Aramaic, and, of course, they also used Hebrew, but Arabic became gradually the foremost tongue of the Jews.

See article Gaon (with chronological list of geonim) in Jewish Encyclopaedia (t. 5, 567–572, 1903), by A. Eckstein and W. Bacher.

MAXIMOS CONFESSOR

Μάξιμος ὁ Ὁμολογητής, born c. 580 at Constantinople; died in exile at Lazika in 662. The greatest Christian theologian of his time. He it is who introduced the teachings of "Dionysios the Areopagite" (second half of fifth century) into the Eastern Church and thus to a considerable extent influenced Christian, Jewish, and Muslim mysticism.

For editions of his works and general information about him see Karl Krumbacher: Byzantinische Litteratur (61–64, 600, 1897).

III. PHILOSOPHERS AND PATRONS OF LEARNING IN THE LATIN AND BYZANTINE WORLDS, IN INDIA, JAPAN, AND CHINA

ISIDORE OF SEVILLE

Isidorus Hispalensis; St. Isidore; born in Cartagena or Seville c. 560; died, Seville 636. Encyclopaedist. Bishop of Seville from c. 600 to his death. His main work is the "Etymologiarum sive Originum libri XX," written probably between 622 and 633; an encyclopaedia based upon classical authors, chiefly grammarians, and even more upon patristic literature. It served as a model for later encyclopaedias and its influence upon mediaeval thought was very great. Poor as the Origines are, they reveal a genuine interest in science, independently from theology. Of Isidore's many writings (chiefly historical, philological, religious), we must quote his "De natura rerum" dedicated to Sisebut, King of the Visigoths (612 to 621), a compendium of cosmography, astronomy, and meteorology.

Text—Of the complete editions, the best is that prepared by F. Arevalo (7 vols., Rome, 1797–1803), reprinted in Migne: Patrologia Latina (vols. 81 to 84).

The earliest edition of the Etymologiae I know of is that of Augsburg, 1472. Another appeared in Strasbourg c. 1473. The latest was edited by Wallace Martin Lindsay (2 vols., Oxford, 1911). A manuscript has been reproduced in facsimile: Etymologiae. Codex Toletanus (nunc Matritensis) 15, 8 phototypice editus.

[a] That is, according to Sherira's account (as quoted in the Jewish Encyclopaedia, t. 5, 571); these dates are not certain. Sherira was the last gaon, but one, of Pumbedita (see the note devoted to him in second half of tenth century).

Praefatus est Rud. Beer (Leyden, 1909; Codices graeci et latini photographice depicti, t. 13).

De natura rerum liber rec. Gust. Becker (Berlin, 1857. This treatise, which was very popular in mediaeval times, bears also other titles—de astris caeli, de astronomia seu natura rerum, liber astronomicus, rotarum liber).

General Studies—Carlos Cañal: San Isidoro. Exposición de sus obras é indicaciones acerca de la influencia que han ejereido en la civilización Española (179 p., Sevilla, 1897). Ernest Brehaut: An Encyclopedist of the Dark Ages. Isidore (Columbia Studies in History, vol. 48, 274 p., New York, 1912. Mainly an analysis of the Etymologies with extracts). Charles Henry Beeson: Isidor-Studien (Quellen und Untersuchungen zur lateinischen Philologie des Mittelalters, t. 4, 174 p., München, 1913. Part of it was a doctor's thesis; it is chiefly devoted to the study of Isidorean tradition outside of Spain to the middle of the ninth century; also to Isidore's poems). A. Schmekel: Isidorus. Sein System und seine Quellen (301 p., Berlin, 1914. According to Wellmann, worthless).

Special Studies—P. Duhem: Système du Monde (t. 3, p. 1–12, p. 14, 1915. The de ordine creaturarum is apocryphal).

Antonio Blázquez: San Isidoro. Mapa-mundi. Primera publicación en castellano de un libro de geografia del sabio arzobispo español (121 p., Madrid, 1908) Hans Philipp: Die historisch-geographischen Quellen in den etymologiae des Isidorus (Diss., Teil I, 1911; Teil II, Berlin, 1913. Quellen und Forschungen zur alten Geschichte und Geographie, 25 und 26).

Karl Schmidt: Quaestiones de musicis scriptoribus romanis imprimis de Cassiodoro et Isidoro (Diss., Giessen, 62 p., Darmstadt, 1899).

Otto Probst: Isidors Schrift de medicina (Archiv für Gesch. d. Med., t. 8, 22–38, 1914; Isis, III, 321). Karl Sudhoff: Die Verse Isidors auf dem Schrank der medizinischen Werke seiner Bibliothek (Mit. zur Gesch. d. Medizin, t. 15, 200–204, 1916). G. R. J. Fletcher: Isidore and his Book on Medicine (Proc. R. soc. of Med., Histor. Section, 1919). Gerhard Ritter: Zahnärztliches aus den encyclopädischen Werken Isidors und Bartholomaeus Anglicus (Diss., Sudhoffs Institut, 25 p., Leipzig, 1922).

Ludwig Traube: Die Geschichte der tironischen Noten bei Suetonius und Isidorus (20 p., Berlin, 1901). Auraicept na n-éces. The scholars' primer, edited by George Calder (Edinburgh, 1917. Interesting because the reputed author of this work, Cennfaeladh, wrote it under Isidore's influence).

Arno Schenk: De Isidori de natura rerum libelli fontibus (Diss., 73 p., Jena, 1909). E. H. F. Meyer: Geschichte der Botanik (t. 2, 389–397, 1855, with list of plants).

STEPHANOS OF ALEXANDRIA

Στέφανος, flourished at Constantinople at the court of Heraclios, emperor from 610 to 641. Philosopher, mathematician, astronomer; physician?, alchemist?. He wrote commentaries on Aristotle (and on Galen and Hippocrates?), and a treatise on astronomy. Alchemical and prophetical writings are ascribed to him.

Stephanos of Alexandria has sometimes been identified with Stephanos of Athens. Both flourished at the same time and probably in the same place, Constantinople; commentaries on Galen and Hippocrates have been ascribed to both. The identification is plausible, but can not be accepted as proved until a deeper study and comparison of their writings has been made.

Texts—In librum Aristotelis de interpretatione comm., edited by Mich. Hayduck (Comm. in Aristotelem graeca, XVIII, 3, Berlin, 1885).

The astronomical work entitled *Διασάφησις ἐξ οἰκείων ὑποδειγμάτων τῆς τῶν προχείρων κανόνων ἐφόδου τοῦ Θέωνος*, is still unpublished.

Apocryphal Works—Alchemical work, περὶ χρυσοποιΐας, edited by J. Lud. Ideler: Physici et medici graeci minores (vol. 2, 199–253, 1842). Partly reprinted in Berthelot et Ruelle. Collection des anciens alchimistes grecs (3e livraison, 289, Paris, 1888. Seven lessons on alchemy, more mystical than practical).

Ἀποτελεσματικὴ πραγματεία. Opusculum apotelesmaticum, edited by Hermann Usener (Bonn, 1879. Dating probably of c. 775; it contains prophecies on the Prophet and the future of Islam).

Criticism—L. Leclerc: Médecine arabe (t. 1, 64–69, 1876). Hermann Usener: De Stephano Alexandrino (58 p., Bonn, 1880). M. Berthelot: Introduction à l'étude de la chimie des anciens et du moyen âge (287–301, Paris, 1889). K. Krumbacher: Byzantinische Litteratur (1897, by index). Ed. O. v. Lippmann: Entstehung und Ausbreitung der Alchemie (103–105, Berlin, 1919).

DHARMAKĪRTI

Ācārya Dharmakīrti, the excellent Dharmakīrti. Tibetan name: Chos-grags. Chinese name Fa2*-shang4 (3366, 9733) or Fa-yang2 (12876). Born in a Brāhmin family in Trimalaya; assumed the Buddhist habit in Magadha; died in the land of Kalinga. He was a contemporary of king Song-tsen Gam-po. We may say that he flourished toward the end of the first half of the seventh century. Hindu, Buddhist logician. He wrote many treatises on logic, criticizing and completing Dignāga's work. They are extant in the Tibetan Tanjur, and the original Sanskrit of one of them (the Nyāyabindu) has been discovered. His influence can not easily be dissociated from Dignāga's, which was immense.

Same sources as those quoted in my note on Dignāga (second half of the fourth century), mainly S. C. Vidyabhusana: Mediaeval School of Indian Logic (103–118, 1909). A. B. Keith: Buddhist Philosophy (308–313, Oxford, 1923).

K'UEI-CHI

K'uei1-chi1 (6493, 850). Disciple of Hsüan Tsang; flourished about the middle of the seventh century. Chinese Buddhist. The main introducer of formal logic, that is, Dignāga's logic (q. v., second half of fourth century), into China.

Sadajiro Sugiura: Hindu logic as preserved in China and Japan (38–41, Philadelphia, 1900. The historical part of the account is very unsatisfactory). L. Wieger: La Chine (329, 1920).

SHŌTOKU TAISHI

Or Prince Shōtoku (taishi means prince, heir apparent). Surnamed Umayado and also Yatsu-mimi nō Ōji (the prince with eight ears). Eldest son of the Emperor Yōmei. Born in 572, died in 621. Regent of Japan under the Empress Suiko (593 to 628). He has been called the father of his country's civilization and the "Constantine of Japanese Buddhism." It is true that the introduction of Buddhism and, together with it, of Chinese civilization, into Japan, is largely due to him. Many special innovations are traditionally ascribed to him: calendar (604, see below, my note on Kwanroku), abacus, and arithmetic. With the assistance of Suiko's chief minister, Soga no Umako, he compiled, in 604, a collection of Buddhist and Confucian maxims, the so-called Seventeen Article Constitution (Jūshichi kempō); in 612, a series of imperial biographies, the Tennō-ki (lost); in 620, the first history of Japan. This history, written in Chinese, was later called Kujihongi, or Kujiki; parts of it may have survived in the Kojiki (q. v., first half of the eighth century). Shōtoku it was who sent the first embassy to China, in 607.

A good account of Shōtoku's work, together with a translation of his Seventeen Articles, will be found in F. Brinkley: History of the Japanese people (London, 1915). Cl. E. Maitre: La littérature historique du Japon des origines aux Ashikaga (Bull. Ecol. franç d'extrême orient, t. 3, 564–596, 1903; t. 4, 580–616, 1904; for a critical study of the Kujiki, see t. 4, 586–98, concluding that it is an apocryphal work, containing, however, some seventh century fragments).

T'AI TSUNG

T'ai[4] Tsung[1] (10573, 11976). This is his dynastic title, his imperial name. His own name was Li[3] Shih[4]-min[2] (6884, 9969, 7908). Born in 597, in 618 he placed his father upon the throne as first emperor of the T'ang dynasty, he himself being called Prince of Ch'in[2] (2093); he succeeded his father in 627; he died in 649. Second T'ang emperor and real founder of the T'ang dynasty. He consolidated the new empire, crushing its internal and external enemies; reorganized the civil and military services, and fostered art and learning. He erected at his capital (Si-an-fû) a library which contained 200,000 volumes. He gave a magnificent example of religious toleration; himself a Taoist,[r] he patronized Confucianism and Buddhism, received the first Nestorian missionaries (636), Byzantine ambassadors (643), the deposed king of Persia and his Mazdean priests. The reign of T'ai Tsung may be considered the beginning of the Augustan age of China, which lasted a little more than a century,[s] and placed China for that time at the head of the world's civilization.

IV. CHINESE AND HINDU MATHEMATICS

WANG HSIAO-T'UNG

Wang[2] Hsiao[4]-t'ung[1] (12493, 4334, 12294). Flourished c. 625. T'ang mathematician. Author of the Ch'i[4]*-ku[3] suan[4]-ching[1] (1091, 6188, 10378, 2122), the Ch'i-ku arithmetical classic, which in its present form (for the end of it is lost) contains 20 problems, some of which involve cubic equations, the earliest cubic equations in Chinese literature. These equations are solved by a method similar to the extraction of a cubic root. The problems deal with the measurement of solids.

Text—The complete text has come down to us in the Tai[4]-chiao[4] suan[4]-ching[1] shih[2]*-shu[1] (10569, 1302, 10378, 2122, 9959, 10024). Various commentaries have been devoted to it by modern Chinese scholars, namely by Chang[1]-tun[1]-jên[2] (416, 12203, 5627) in 1801; Li[3] huang[2] (6884, 5125) in 1820; Ch'ên[2]-chieh[2]* (658, 1500), c. 1843.

Criticism—A. Wylie: Chinese Literature (115, (1867) 1902). Y. Mikami: Mathematics in China and Japan (53–56, Leipzig, 1912. Some of the problems are reproduced). L. Wieger: La Chine (457, 494, 536, 1920).

BRAHMAGUPTA

Born in 598, flourished in Ujjain. Hindu mathematician. One of the greatest scientists of his race and the greatest of his time. Author, c. 628, of the Brāhma-

---

[r] See my note on Hsüan Tsang, below.

[s] See my note on Ming Huang (first half of eighth century).

sphuṭa-siddhānta. the revised system of Brahma, which is largely based upon the Sūrya-siddhānta and Āryabhaṭa but contains original developments. Chapter 11 is devoted to the criticism of earlier writers, chiefly Āryabhaṭa; chapters 12 and 18 deal with mathematics. Solution of determinate and indeterminate equations of the first and second degree ($nx^2 + 1 = y^2$, incompletely; $ax^2 + bx = c$). Fairly complete study of cyclic quadrilaterals. If a, b, c, d, x, y represent the sides and diagonals of such a quadrilateral, s the half of its perimeter, S its surface,

$$(1) \qquad S = \sqrt{(s-a)(s-b)(s-c)(s-d)}$$

$$(2) \qquad \begin{cases} x^2 = (ad + bc)(ac + bd)/(ab + cd) \\ y^2 = (ab + cd)(ac + bd)/(ad + bc) \end{cases}$$

If $a^2 + b^2 = c^2$ and $\alpha^2 + \beta^2 = \gamma^2$, then (3) the quadrilateral ($a\gamma, c\beta, b\gamma, c\alpha$) is cyclic and has its diagonals at right angles. Proposition (2) is sometimes called "Brahmagupta's theorem," and proposition (3) "Brahmagupta's trapezium." Value of $\pi, \sqrt{10}$. Volume of the frustum of a pyramid with square bases of sides s_1 and s_2, given as equal to $\frac{1}{3}h\,(s_1^2 + s_2^2 + s_1s_2)$. Rules to find the number of permutations of n things taken r at a time, with and without repetition, and the number of combinations of n things taken r at a time without repetition.

Text and Translation—Algebra with arithmetic and mensuration from the Sanskrit of Brahmegupta and Bhascara. Translated by Henry Thomas Colebrooke (462 p., London, 1817).

Criticism—M. Simon: Zu Brahmaguptas diophantischen Gleichungen zweiten Grades (Archiv d. Mathematik, vol. 20, 280–281, 1913). G. R. Kaye: Indian Mathematics (Calcutta, 1915, passim; also in Isis, II, 326–356).

V. BYZANTINE, MUSLIM, CHINESE, AND JAPANESE ASTRONOMY

For Byzantine astronomy, refer to my note on Stephanos of Alexandria in Section III.

For the Muslim calendar, see my note on the beginning of Islam, in Section II. Remarks on the calendar will be found in the Qur'ān, sūra II, 214; IX, 36, 37; X, 5. A full discussion will be found in F. K. Ginzel: Handbuch der matematischen Chronologie (Vol. I, 238–309, 1906. This also contains an account of the Arabic pre-Islamic calendar).

CH'Ü-T'AN

Ch'ü[4]-t'an[2] (3081, 10700). Four astronomers bearing this name are mentioned in the Records of the T'ang dynasty (T'ang shu). They were attached to the Astronomical Board. Their names prove their Hindu origin (Ch'ü-t'an is a transcription of Gautama).

Ch'ü-t'an Chuan[4] (2717). Flourished c. 618. Composed a calendar system in 618, for Kao Tsu, the first T'ang emperor (618 to 627).

Ch'ü-t'an Lo[2] (7291). President of the Astronomical Board. Composed the calendar called Kuang[1]-chai[2]*. (6389, 240.)

Y. Mikami: Development of Mathematics in China and Japan (p. 58–59, Leipzig, 1912).

FU JÊN-CHÜN

Fu[4] Jên[2]-chün[1] (3632, 5627, 3294). Flourished under the T'ang, c. 626. Chinese

Taoist astronomer. In 626, he collected the astronomical observations of the ancients.

L. Wieger: La Chine (195, 301, 1920).

KWANROKU

Also named Sōzu. Born in the kingdom of Kudara. Flourished c. 602. Korean bonze who came to Japan in 602 and taught the Japanese how to make a calendar in the Chinese way. The luni-solar calendar (Genka-reki)[f] introduced by him with the assistance of a Japanese, Yakoshiso Tamafuru, remained in use from 604 to 680.

The calendar previously used in Japan was called Hi-oki. It was, apparently, very imperfect, being based only upon the moon and the seasons. A first attempt to introduce the Chinese calendar had been made vainly in 552, also from Kudara; the king of Kudara having sent then some astronomers (reki-hakase) to Japan.

In 680 or 690, the Genka-reki was improved and became known as Gihō-reki. Later calendars, each of which included some improvement or modification, were introduced as follows: Taien-reki in 763; Goki-reki in 856; Semmei-reki in 861. The latter remained in use 823 years until 1684, when an entirely new departure was made with the Tenkyō-reki.

For the introduction of Chinese reign titles, which the Japanese call nengō, see my note on Japanese law in Section IX.

E. Papinot: Historical Dictionary (116, 157, 316, 1909. Brief history of the Japanese calendar; 340, 836–840. Explanation of Japanese calendar).

VI. CHINESE GEOGRAPHY

P'EI-CHÜ

P'ei[2]-chü[3] (8831, 3009). Also called Hung[2]-ta[4] (5282, 10470). Born at Wên[2]-hsi[3] hsien[4] (12651, 4073, 4545), Shansi; flourished under the Northern Ch'i, Sui, and T'ang dynasties; died c. 630, an octogenarian. He wrote a geography of the Tarim region c. 606. The emperor T'ai Tsung having ordered him to study the trade relations with Central Asia, he used the reports sent by envoys and traders to compile a "Record of Western Countries," Hsi[1] yü[4]* t'u[2] chi[4] (4031, 13662, 12128, 923), illustrated with maps.

H. A. Giles: Biographical Dictionary (620, 1898). L. Wieger: La Chine (381, 1920). Fritz Jäger: Leben und Werk P'ei kü. Ein Kapitel aus der chinesischen Kolonialgeschichte (Ostasiatische Z., vol. 9, 81–115, 216–231, 1921–1922. Containing translations of the few fragments of P'ei chü's work which are extant; Isis, VI, 144).

LI-T'AI

Li[3]-t'ai[4] (6884, 10596). Imperial prince of the T'ang dynasty, died in 652. Chinese geographer. He ordered the compilation of a geography Kua[4]*-ti[4]-chih[4] (6288, 10956, 1918) after 636.

Text—Only fragments of the text exist. It was saved from destruction by Chang[1] Shou[3]-chieh[2]* (416, 10012, 1477) in 737 and reconstructed by Sun[1] Hsing[1]-yen[3] (10431, 4602, 13113), (1752–1818) in 1797.

Criticism—L. Wieger: La Chine (345, 393, 403, 505, 1920).

---

[f] Reki is the Japanese reading of the Chinese character meaning calendar, li[4]* (6923 or 6924). The Japanese call it koyomi.

HSÜAN TSANG

Hsüan[2] Tsang[4] (4790,[u] 2758). This was his religious name; his original name was Ch'ên[2] I[1] (658, 5542). Born in Honan, 602, died in 664. Chinese Buddhist who spent 16 years in India. He returned to China in 645, carrying with him 657 Buddhist books and 150 relics. The rest of his life was devoted to the translating of these books and the writing of an account of his travels, the Hsi[1]-yü[4*] chi[4] (4031, 13662, 923), Record of Western Countries, completed in 648.[v] This famous book is also called the Deva of the Greater Development or Mokshadeva. It contains an admirable account of Hindu civilization, the scientific value of which is very great.[w] In 647, the emperor T'ai tsung ordered Hsüan Tsang to prepare (with the collaboration of Taoïst doctors) a Sanskrit translation of the Tao tê ching for the king of Kumāra (this translation is lost). A copy of Hsüan's translation of the Diamond sūtra is the earliest Chinese book printed in Japan.

Text—A facsimile edition of the Chinese text has been published by the Book Publishing Co. (Tokyo, 1911). Mémoires sur les contrées occidentales traduits du sanscrit en chinois en l'an 648 par Hiouen-Thsang et du chinois en français par Stanislas Julien (2 vols., Paris, 1857–1858. With elaborate commentary). Si-yu-ki: Buddhist Records of the Western World, translated from the Chinese by Samuel Beal (2 vols., London, 1884). Thomas Watters (1840–1901): On Yuan Chwang's Travels in India (edited by T. W. Rhys-Davids and S. W. Bushell, 2 vols., London, 1904–1905. Better translation than Beal's).

Life of Hsüan Tsang—Histoire de la vie de Hiouen-Thsang et de ses voyages dans l'Inde par Hoeï-Li et Yen-Thsong, traduite du chinois par Stanislas Julien (556 p., Paris, 1853). The Life of Hiuen-Tsiang by the Shamans Hwui Li and Yen-Tsung, with a preface containing an account of the work of I-Tsing, by Samuel Beal (255 p., London, 1888. New edition with preface by L. Cranmer-Byng, 265 p., 1911). This life written by one of Hsüan Tsang's disciples, then enlarged and completed by another, must be read together with the Hsi-yü chi, which it often elucidates; both the French and the English translations are abbreviated.

Criticism—Max Müller: Buddhism and Buddhist pilgrims. A review of Stanislas Julien's "Voyages . . . . " (Reprinted from the Times of April 17 and 20, 54 p., London, 1857). Alexander Cunningham: The Ancient Geography of India (1871). James Ferguson: On Hiouen-Thsang's Journey from Patna to Ballabhi (Journal of the Royal Asiatic Society, vol. 6, 213–274, 1873). H. A. Giles: Chinese Biographical Dictionary (p. 313, 1898). A. Foucher: Notes sur la géographie ancienne du Gandhāra (Bull. de l'école française d'Extrême Orient, 322 sq., 1901). Paul Pelliot: Autour d'une traduction sanscrite du Tao tö king (T'oung Pao, vol. 13, 351–430, 1912); Trois manuscrits de l'époque des T'ang récemment publiés au Japon par Naitō Torajirō (T'oung Pao, vol. 13, 482–507, Leide, 1912. The manuscript of special interest to us is entitled (I quote Pelliot's translation) "Mémoriaux et rapports du Maître de la Loi, Hiuan-tsang, [docteur] du Tripiṭaka, sous les grands T'ang." It contains new documents. Pelliot states that the time has come to publish a new edition of Hsüan Tsang's work comparable to Yule's edition of Marco Polo, for all other editions, even Watters's, are now antiquated). William Boulting: Four Pilgrims (p. 1–64, n. d., London, 1921?. Popular publication; Hsüan

---

[u] 4790 is a tabooed character which is generally written, even in combination, as 4791 or 4792 (altered forms of 4790) or is replaced by 13744, Yüan[2]. 2758 is often written homophonously 11583.

[v] Not to be mistaken for two other well-known Chinese books bearing a similar title: Hsi[1]-yu[2] chi[4] (4031, 13423, 923). See Couling: Encyclopaedia Sinica (p. 241, 1917).

[w] Sir Aurel Stein has proved the correctness of Hsüan Tsang's topographical indications. See his Sand-buried Ruins of Khotan (London, 1903, passim).

Tsang is the first pilgrim). Louis Finot: Hiuan-tsang and the Far East (Journal Roy. Asiatic Soc., 447–452, 1920). Sir Aurel Stein: The Desert Crossing of Hsüan-tsang, 630 A. D. (Indian antiquary, vol. 50, 15–24, 1921). A. von Staël-Holstein: Hsüan-tsang and Modern Research (Journal Northern China Branch of R. A. S., vol. 54, 16–24, 1923).

VII. BYZANTINE, HINDU, CHINESE, AND JAPANESE MEDICINE

THEOPHILOS PROTOSPATHARIOS

Θεόφιλος ὁ Πρωτοσπαθάριος, meaning head of the imperial body-guard. Flourished in Constantinople, under Heraclios, emperor from 610 to 641. Author of various medical and physiological writings.[x] His work on the constitution of the human body (περὶ τῆς τοῦ ἀνθρώπου κατασκευῆς) is a treatise on Galenic physiology, combined with theology. He remarks that the shapes of the skull and spine are determined by the development of the brain and the spinal cord. His works on defecation (περὶ διαχωρημάτων), on the pulse (περὶ σφυγμῶν), and on urine (περὶ οὔρων) are also largely based on Galen; the last named was the most influential writing of its kind in mediaeval times.[y]

Texts and Translations—περὶ τῆς τοῦ ἀνθρώπου κατασκευῆς (First edition, Paris, 1540). New edition by A. Mustoxydes and D. Schinas (Venice, 1816). Edition with Latin translation and notes, Theophili de corporis humani fabrica libri V, by William Alexander Greenhill (441 p., Oxford, 1842).

Περὶ διαχωρημάτων by Mustoxydes and Schinas (Venice, 1816); by Jul. Ludw. Ideler: Physici et medici graeci minores (vol. 1, 397–408, Berlin 1841).

Περὶ οὔρων. Greek text with Latin translation by F. Morel (Paris, 1608). Ideler (op. cit., vol. 1, 261–283). Bussemaker, Revue de philologie 1845. A Latin translation is included in all the editions of the Articella or Thesaurus operum medicorum antiquorum (Venice, 1483 sq.).

Περὶ σφυγμῶν. Greek and Latin texts, in Ermerins: Anecdota medica graeca (1–77, Leyden, 1840). Latin translation in the Articella.

Theophili et Damascii commentarii in Hippocratis aphorismos cum fragmentis et longioribus et brevioribus e Stephani, Atheniensis philosophi, sive Meletii, commentario in eundem librum. F. R. Dietz: Scholia in Hippocratem et Galenum, t. 2, 1834, 236–544 (Greek text with notes).

Criticism—K. Krumbacher: Geschichte der byzantinischen Litteratur (2 ed., 614, 616, 1897). Puschmann: Handbuch der Geschichte der Medizin (vol. 1, 545–547, 1902. Iwan Bloch). Max Neuburger: Geschichte der Medizin (vol. 2, 120, 1911).

STEPHANOS OF ATHENS

Στέφανος. Pupil of Theophilos Protospatharios. Byzantine physician. He wrote commentaries on Hippocrates and Galen, and treatises on fever and on urine.

Texts—(1) Scholia in Hippocratis Prognosticon; comm. in priorem Galeni librum therapeuticum ad Glauconem. Greek text edited by Fr. Reinh. Dietz, in Scholia in Hippocratem et Galenum (t. 1, 51–361; t. 2, 238 sq., Königsberg, 1834). (2) Στεφάνου φιλοσόφου[z] ἐξήγησις εἰς τὸ προγνωστικὸν τοῦ Ἱπποκράτους, edited by A. Mai. Spicilegium romanum (t. 5, 2, 1–160, 1841). (3) Dem. Sicurus: Theophili Protosphatharii et Stephani Atheniensis de febrium differentia (Florence, 1862). (4)

[x] Some of the writings enumerated by me are possibly apocryphal.

[y] E. g., see Maurus (second half of twelfth century).

[z] Observe the epithet philosopher commonly given to Stephanos of Alexandria (q. v.).

On Urine, edited by Bussemaker (Revue de philologie, vol. 1, 415–438, 543–560, 1845).

Criticism—K. Krumbacher: Byzantinische Litteratur (614, 616, 1887). See my note on Stephanos of Alexandria in Section III.

AARON OF ALEXANDRIA

'Ααρών; Heb., Aharōn; Ar., Hārūn. Flourished probably at the time of Heraclios, emperor from 610 to 641. Unknown Jewish (?) author of a Greek medical encyclopaedia (Pandectae medicinae), divided into 30 sections. It contained a description of smallpox. It was translated into Syriac and Arabic.[a]

F. Wüstenfeld: Arabische Aerzte (p. 7, 9, 1840). L. Leclerc: Médecine arabe (t. 1, 77–81, 1876. Disquisition on the names of the Syriac and Arabic translators; the Arabic translator was probably one Masarjawai). Iwan Bloch, in Puschmann: Geschichte der Medizin (t. 1, 557, 1902).

PAULOS AEGINETA

Παῦλος Αἰγινήτης. Born on the island of Aegina, Saronic Gulf; flourished in Alexandria c. 640. Latest representative of Greek medicine before the Muslim supremacy. Remained in Alexandria after the Arabic invasion (640). Wrote a medical encyclopaedia in seven books, largely based upon Galen and Oribasios (called ὑπόμνημα or, by Suidas, ἐπιτομῆς ἰατρικῆς βιβλία ἑπτά). Muslim tradition ascribes to him other books on gynaecology and toxicology which are lost. His influence upon Muslim medicine was very great.

Text and Translation—Editio princeps, Aldine (Venice, 1528). Later edition (Bale, 1538).

This medical encyclopaedia was soon translated into Arabic (by Ḥunain ibn Isḥāq or Johannitius, second half of ninth century) but relatively late into Latin, except Book III (dealing with topical affections a capite ad calcem) which was translated in South Italy as early as the ninth (or eighth ?) century. This text is very important for the history of Salernitan medicine. It has been edited by Joh. L. Heiberg: Pauli Aeginetae libri tertii interpretatio antiqua (256 p., Leipzig, 1912). The Latin translation by Joh. Guinterius (Opus de re medica nunc primum latinitate donatum) was the first to be published (Paris, 1532).

An English translation of the seven books by Francis Adams, with introduction, commentary, index, was published by the Sydenham Society (3 vols., London, 1844–1847). Adams had already published, in 1834, the translation of Books I to III. His translation is based upon the old Greek text and the Latin versions, chiefly that of Cornarius published by Henri Estienne in his Medicae artis principes (Paris, 1567). A new Greek text of Book VI (dealing with surgery) has been edited by René Briau, with French translation and introduction: La chirurgie de Paul d'Egine (Paris, 1855). A German translation by J. Berendes has appeared in Janus (Vol. XIII, 1908, to Vol. XVII, 1912; also in book form, Leiden, 1914).

Critical edition by J. L. Heiberg in the new Corpus med. graec. Pars prior (Libri I–IV, 397 p., Leipzig, 1921); Pars altera (Libri V–VII, 420 p., 1924).

Criticism—E. H. F. Meyer: Geschichte der Botanik (vol. 2, 412–421, 1855). E. Gurlt: Geschichte der Chirurgie (t. 1, 558–590, 1898). Iwan Bloch: Schiffsärzte in byzantinischer Zeit (Janus, t. 7, p. 15–16, 1902). A. P. Kouzis: L'oeuvre médicale de Paul de Nicée (Janus, vol. 16, 738–755, 1911. That work is entirely derived from Paulos Aegineta). J. L. Heiberg: De codicibus Pauli Aeginetae ob-

[a] This work seems lost but for an Arabic fragment. It is often quoted by Rhazes.

servationes (Revue des études grecques, t. 32, 268–277, 1919). Konrad Straubel: Zahn- und Mundleiden und deren Behandlung bei Paulos von Aigina (Diss., 24 p., Leipzig, 1922).

JOHN THE GRAMMARIAN

John of Alexandria—Joannes Alexandrinus grammaticus s. medicus. Yaḥyā al-Naḥwī. Flourished in Alexandria c. 627 to 640. Jacobite bishop who endeared himself to the Arabs (for example to the conqueror of Egypt, 'Amr ibn al-'Āṣ) by his repudiation of trinitarianism. He wrote commentaries on Hippocrates and Galen.[b] An epitome of the "sixteen books" of Galen is ascribed to him.[c]

The "Sixteen Books of Galen" is the name given to the Byzantine canon of Galenic writings, divided into 16 parts, edited at about the beginning of the seventh century. This canon was arranged as follows: (I) de sectis; (II) ars medica; (III) de pulsibus ad tirones; (IV) ad Glauconem de medendi methodo; (V) de elementis secundum Hippocratem; (VI) de temperamentis; (VII) de facultatibus naturalibus; (VIII) five books on anatomy; (IX) six books on the causes and symptoms of diseases; (X) de locis affectis; (XI) four books on the pulse; (XII) de differentiis febrium; (XIII) de crisibus; (XIV) de diebus criticis; (XV) methodi medendi libri XIV; (XVI) de sanitate tuenda. There was also a Byzantine canon of Hippocratic writings divided into 12 parts. These Galenic and Hippocratic canons formed the core of Syro-Arabic medicine. On the Muslim tradition of the sixteen books of Galen see L. Leclerc: Médecine arabe (vol. 1, 38–55, 1876).

Text—Fragment of commentary on Hippocrates's De natura pueri in Dietz's Scholia in Hippocratem. . . . . Königsberg 1834. Explanation of Galen's commentary on the sixth book of the Epidemics (Latin translation of thirteenth century) in Articella.

Criticism—Fihrist (passim, especially p. 254 sq.). V. Rose: Ions Reisebilder und Joannes Alexandrinus der Arzt (Hermes, vol. 5, 205–215, 1871). L. Leclerc: Histoire de la médecine arabe (vol. 1, 56–60, 1876. Wrongly identifies him with John Philoponos, q. v., first half of sixth century). Iwan Bloch, in Puschmann: Geschichte der Medizin (vol. 1, 556, 1902). Edward G. Browne: Arabian Medicine (p. 17, 26, Cambridge, 1921).

VĀGBHAṬA

Vāgbhaṭa the Elder. The date of his activity is uncertain, but may be placed tentatively in the seventh century, c. 625, for I-ching (q. v. in next chapter) seems to refer to his Saṃgraha. One of the three greatest Hindu physicians (the two others being Caraka and Suśruta, q. v.). Author of a medical treatise called Ashṭāṅgasaṃgraha, which may be translated Sum or Compendium of the eight parts (of medicine).

Another treatise called Ashṭāṅgahṛidayasaṃhitā (Compendium of the quintessence of the eight parts) is obviously a later work derived from the former. It is written entirely in verse, while the earlier work is written partly in prose and partly in verse. It is assumed that the second treatise was written by another author, Vāgbhaṭa the Younger. The elder Vāgbhaṭa was certainly, and the younger probably, a Buddhist. Later Hindu physicians call the earlier work

---

[b] Note that commentaries on Galen are ascribed also, though wrongly, to Philoponos.

[c] Arabic translation in British Museum, MS. Arundel Or. 17.

Vṛiddha-Vāgbhaṭa, the later one Vāgbhaṭa. It is interesting to note that the later treatise was translated into Tibetan.

Text—The Ashṭāṅgasaṃgraha was published in Bombay in 1888.

The Ashṭāṅgahṛidayasaṃhitā, together with Aruṇadatta's commentary, was edited by A. M. Kunte (Bombay, 1880; again, 1891).

Criticism—Palmyr Cordier: Vāgbhaṭa et l'Ashṭāngahridayasaṃhitā (Besançon, 1896). J. Jolly: Zur Quellenkunde der indischen Medizin (1. Vāgbhaṭa) (Zeit. d. deut. morg. Ges., t. 54, 260–274, 1900). J. Jolly: Indische Medizin (Strasburg, 1901). Iwan Bloch: Indische Medizin, in Neuburger und Pagel (Handbuch der Geschichte der Medizin, vol. 1, p. 119–52, 1902, with bibliography). Max Neuburger: Geschichte der Medizin (Vol. I, p. 66–91, 1906). A. F. Rudolf Hoernlé: Studies in the Medicine of Ancient India. Part I. Osteology (Oxford, 1907, passim). M. Winternitz: Geschichte der indischen Litteratur (vol. 3, 549, 1922).

CH'AO YÜAN-FANG

Ch'ao[2] Yüan[2]-fang[1] (520, 13744, 3435). Flourished c. 605 to 609. Chinese physician. Author of a treatise on theoretical medicine, the Ping[4]-yüan[2]-hou[4]-lun[4] (9300, 13704, 4021, 7475), written between 605 to 609, in 50 parts. It contains descriptions of seven kinds of genito-urinary troubles, of impetigo contagiosa, "sandlice," scabies. Part 27 deals with hair diseases; part 28, with eye diseases; part 31, with tooth complaints; parts 39 to 42, with women's complaints; parts 43 to 44 with midwifery; parts 45 to 50, with children's diseases. Little reference to pulse.

F. Huebotter: Guide (26–28, Kumamoto, 1924)

JAPANESE MEDICINE

During the reign of the Empress Suiko (593 to 628), in 602, a Buddhist physician named Kwanroku (q. v., *supra*) came from Kudara to Japan, and taught medicine to a few Japanese students. Later, in 608, the Empress sent a number of young Japanese physicians to China. The direct influence of Chinese upon Japanese medicine may be dated from that time.

Y. Fujikawa: Geschichte der Medizin in Japan (6, 97, Tokyo, 1911).

VIII. BYZANTINE, PERSIAN, CHINESE AND JAPANESE HISTORIOGRAPHY

SIMOCATTES

Theophylactos Simocattes or Simocatta (Θεοφύλακτος Σιμοκάττης or Σιμόκατος). Born in Egypt; flourished in Constantinople under Heraclios, emperor from 610 to 641. Byzantine historian. Imperial secretary and prefect. Author of a book on natural curiosities and wonders (Quaestiones physicae; περὶ διαφόρων φυσικῶν ἀπορημάτων καὶ ἐπιλύσεως αὐτῶν), and of a history of the reign of Emperor Mauricios (582 to 602) in eight books (Ἱστορίαι). This contains a curious account of China (Ταυγάς).

Texts—Physical questions edited by B. Vulcanius (Leyden, 1596 or 1597); by J. Fr. Boissonade (Paris, 1835. Greek and Latin); by J. Ideler: Scriptores physici et medici (vol. 1, 168–183, 1841).

French translation by F. Morel (Paris, 1603).

History, edited by Jacob Pontanus (Ingolstadt, 1604. With Latin translation). First critical edition by Carl de Boor (Leipzig, 1887. Greek text only).

Criticism—Karl Krumbacher: Byzantinische Litteratur (2. Ausg., 247–251, 1897). H. Yule: Cathay (new ed., vols. 1 and 4, 1915–1916).

JOHN OF ANTIOCH

Ἰωάννης Ἀντιοχεύς, flourished probably under Heraclios. Byzantine historian Author of a chronicle of the world from Adam to 610 (Ἱστορία χρονική or Ἔκθεσις περὶ χρόνων καὶ κτίσεως κόσμου)

Text—Fragments edited by C. Müller: Fragmenta historicorum graecorum (vol. 4, 535–622; vol. 5, 27–28).

Criticism—Karl Krumbacher: Byzantinische Litteratur (2. Aufl., 334–337, 1897).

THE EASTER CHRONICLE

The "Chronicon Paschale" or "Easter Chronicle"; also called "Chronicon Alexandrinum," "Chronicon Constantinopolitanum," "Fasti Siculi." The Greek title, very long, begins thus: Ἐπιτομὴ χρόνων τῶν ἀπὸ Ἀδάμ. This chronicle of the world from the creation of Adam to 629 was composed c. 629 to 641. It is, together with the works of Eusebios and Syncellos, the most important monument of Greek and Christian chronography; it represents, however, a much more popular type of work than theirs. It derives its name from an introduction dealing with the computation of Easter dates.

Text—Ed. princeps. Chronicon Alexandrinum idemque astronomicum et ecclesiasticum (vulgo Siculum seu Fasti Siculi) studio Matthaei Raderi (München, 1615. With Latin translation). Better edition by C. du Cange (Greek and Latin, 666 p., Paris, 1688). Edition by L. Dindorf (2 vols., Corpus script. hist. byz., 15–16, Bonn, 1832). Reproduced in Migne's Greek patrology (vol. 92, 1–1158).

Criticism —Heinrich Gelzer: Sextus Julius Africanus (vol. 2, 138–176, 1885). Karl Krumbacher: Byzantinische Litteratur (2. Aufl., 337–339, 1897).

IRANIAN HISTORY

The Khudhāy-nāmak. A revision of the Pahlawī text of the whole Persian epic,[d] from Gayūmarth (the Zoroastrian Adam) to Khusraw Parwīz (627), was composed by the dihqān (squire) Dānishwar during the reign (634 to 642) of the last Sassanian king Yazdigird III. This Khudhāy-nāmak was translated into Arabic by Ibn al-Muqaffaʿ (q. v., second half of eighth century) and was largely used by Muslim historians. Unfortunately, both the Pahlawī and the Arabic versions are lost.

E. G. Browne: Literary History of Persia (vol. 1, 122, 1908).

FANG HSÜAN-LING

Fang[2] Hsüan[2]-ling[2] (3440, 4790, 7218). Also named Fang[2] Ch'iao[2] (3440, 1395); ennobled as duke and canonized as Wên[2] Chao[1] (12633, 473). Born at Lin[2]-tzŭ[1] (7165, 12371), Shantung, in 578; died in T'ai Tsung's palace in 648. He was appointed in 630 by the T'ang emperor T'ai Tsung to edit the official history of the Chin dynasty.[e] This history, Chin[4] shu[1] (2069, 10024), dealing with the period 265 to 419, is the fifth of the Twenty-four Histories. It was compiled under Fang's direction from the writings of 18 preceding historians (644 to 646).

---

[d] See my note on Iranian history in the second half of the sixth century.

[e] This work is sometimes ascribed to T'ai Tsung himself. The capital of the Chin dynasty was at Lo[4*]-yang[2] (7328, 12883) until 317, then at Nanking.

Text—Chinese edition (130 chüan in 20 volumes, Nanking, 1871).
Criticism—Wylie: Notes on Chinese Literature (18, 1902). Giles: Biographical Dictionary (221, 1898).

YAO CHIEN

Yao² Chien³ (12935, 1604) or Yao² Ssŭ¹-lien² (12935, 10271, 7128); canonized as K'ang¹ (5908). Born in Wan⁴-nien² (12486, 8301), Shensi; died in 643. He was ordered in 629 by the emperor T'ai Tsung to complete the official histories of the Liang dynasty (502 to 557) and of the Ch'ên dynasty (557 to 589) both begun by his father Yao² Ch'a²* (12935, 200) (533 to 606). These works, called respectively Liang² shu¹ (7021, 10024) and Ch'ên² shu¹ (658, 10024), form the eighth and ninth of the Twenty-four Histories.

Text—Chinese edition of the Liang shu (Nanking, 1874, 56 chüan in 6 volumes); of the Ch'ên shu (*ibidem*, 1873, 36 chüan in 4 volumes).
Criticism—Wylie: Chinese Literature (18, 1902). Giles: Biographical Dictionary (921, 923, 1898).

LI PO-YAO

Li³ Po⁴*-yao⁴ (6884, 9340, 12958)[f] (565 to 648). Born in 565, died in 648. Chinese historian. He completed, after 618 (i. e., under the T'ang) the officia history of the Northern Ch'i dynasty (550 to 577) begun by his father Li³ Tê²*-lin² (6884, 10845, 7157) (530–90). His work, called the Pei³ Ch'i² shu¹ (8771 1074, 10024) is the eleventh of the Twenty-four Histories.

Text—Chinese edition (Nanking, 1874, 15 chüan in 4 vols.).
Criticism—Wylie: Chinese Literature (19, 1902). Giles: Biographical Dictionary (456, 466, 1898).

LING-HU TÊ-FÊN

Ling⁴-hu² Tê²*-fên¹ (7199, 4956, 10845, 3529). Canonized as Hsien⁴ (4547). Born at Hua²-yüan² (5005, 13700), Shensi, in 583; died in 666. Chinese historian. During the reign of T'ai Tsung, he was ordered to collect the records of previous dynasties, to write the history of the Northern Chou dynasty (557–581), and to revise the history of the Wei dynasty.[g] His history of the Northern or Later Chou, Hou⁴ Chou¹ shu¹ (4025, 2450, 10024), is the twelfth of the Twenty-four Histories.[h] Its style is an imitation of that of the Shu ching (q. v., note on Confucius).

Text—Chinese edition (Nanking, 1874, 50 chüan in 4 vols.).
Criticism—Wylie: Chinese Literature (20, 1902). Giles: Biographical Dictionary (487, 1898).

WEI CHÊNG

Wei⁴ Chêng¹ (12567, 720). Canonized as Wên² Chên¹ (12633, 607). Born at Ch'ü³-ch'êng² (3062, 763), Chihli, in 581, flourished at the T'ang court; died in 643. Chinese historian. He wrote the official history of the Sui dynasty (581 to 618)[i] by order of T'ai Tsung. His work called the Sui² shu¹ (10394. 10024), is the thirteenth of the Twenty-four Histories. Chapters 81 to 84

---

[f] Character 12958 is also read yo⁴* and yüeh⁴*.
[g] For which see Wei Shou (second half of sixth century).
[h] The text of Ling-hu's and of Li Po-yao's histories are the most mutilated of the whole collection.
[i] Capital first at Ch'ang²-an¹ (450, 44) and after 605, at Lo⁴*-yang² (7328, 12883).

contain valuable information on the neighboring peoples, especially those of Central Asia (Tarim).

Text—Chinese edition (Huai-nan, 1871, 85 chüan in 12 vols.).
Criticism—Wylie: Chinese Literature (20, 1902). Giles: Biographical Dictionary (856, 1898).

LI YEN-SHOU

Li[3] Yen[2]-shou[4] (6884, 13080, 10019). Born at Hsiang[1]-chou[1] (4249, 2444), Honan; flourished under T'ai Tsung. Chinese historian. He wrote two great historical compilations: one, called the "Southern Annals," Nan[2] shih[3] (8128, 9893), is a summary of the annals of the Liu Sung, Southern Ch'i, Liang, and Ch'ên dynasties (420 to 589); the other called the "Northern Annals," Pei[3] shih[3] (8771, 9893), is a summary of the annals of the Northern Wei, Northern Ch'i, Chou, and Sui dynasties (386 to 581). The author being a northerner, his second compilation is distinctly better. Both works are useful in that they supply information not contained in the original annals. They form respectively the fourteenth and fifteenth of the Twenty-four Histories.

Text—Chinese edition of the Nan shih (Nanking, 1873, 80 chüan in 12 vols.); of the Pei shih (Nanking, 1873, 100 chüan in 20 vols.).
Criticism—Wylie: Chinese Literature (21, 1902). Giles: Biographical Dictionary (474, 1898).

CHING PO

Ching[4] Po[4] (2144, 9369). Graduated in 627; flourished at the court of T'ai Tsung; died in 649. Chinese historian. He collaborated in the compilation of the annals of the Chin dynasty[j] and wrote, with Hsü Ching-tsung,[k] the History of the Rise of the T'ang Dynasty. He wrote also a biography of T'ai Tsung and a preface to Hsüan Tsang's Record (q. v.).

H. A. Giles: Biographical Dictionary (157, 1898).

For the beginnings of Japanese historiography, see my note on Shōtoku taishi in Section III.

IX. BARBARIAN AND JAPANESE LAW

Barbarian Law

The so-called Ripuarian Law (Lex Ripuaria) probably dates back to the reign of Dagobert I, who died in 638. It was the law of the Ripuarian Franks, whose territory extended between the Meuse and the Rhine, with Cologne as center.

Text—Edited by R. Sohm in the Mon. Germ. hist. (Leges, 1883).

The earliest code of the Alamanni,[l] called Pactus Alamannorum, dates from the same period.

Text—Edited by Karl Lehmann in the Mon. Germ. hist. (Leges).

The earliest code of the Lombards (Edictus Langobardorum) was promulgated by King Rothar at Pavia in 643. The method of presentation, but not the sub-

---

[j] For which see Fang Hsüan-ling, above.
[k] Hsü[3] Ching[4]-tsung[1] (4761, 2144, 11976). Born at Hangchow 592, died in 672 (Giles, p. 302).
[l] They dwelt between the Rhine and the Lech.

stance, shows Roman influence. It consists of 388 chapters. Many additions were made from time to time, the latest versions dating from the tenth century (Capitulari Langobardorum) and of the eleventh (q. v.).

Text—Edited by Friedrich Bluhme in the Mon. Germ. hist. Edictus ceteraeque Langobardorum leges cum constitutionibus et pactis principum Beneventanorum (Fontes juris germanici antiqui). New edition by the same (Hannover, 1869).

Japanese Law

For the so-called Seventeen Article Constitution, which is rather a collection of moral precepts than a code of laws, see my note on Shōtoku taishi in Section III.

However, under the stimulation of Chinese examples, the Japanese gradually felt the need of an improved kind of administration and of a definite codification. The infiltration of Chinese ideas and manners was taking place slowly but continually. One of the latest instances had been the teaching of Minabuchi Shōan, one of the eight students who had accompanied the Sui ambassador returning to China in 608. After his return home, Shōan taught Confucianism and Chinese methods (F. Brinkley: History of the Japanese People, 148, 1914).

The reign of Kōtoku-tennō, thirty-sixth Emperor of Japan (645 to 654), introduced a new form of administration largely based upon the Chinese pattern. This reform is called Taikwa (or Daika) no kaishin, the reform of the Taikwa era; it remained in vigor until the promulgation of the Daihō code (q. v., first half of the eighth century), thus from 645 to 701.

Incidentally, the Taikwa era (645 to 650) was the first Japanese nengō; that is, the first Japanese application of the Chinese chronological method, the dating of events with reference to reign titles, nien²-hao⁴ (8301, 3884). These nien-hao or nengō[m] recalled the accession of a new emperor or some other important landmark. There was at least one for each reign, but there might be more; e. g., 11 for the reigns of the Han emperor Wu Ti and the Western Chin emperor Hui Ti, 14 for the T'ang emperor Kao Tsung, etc. In Japan, two reigns counted as many as 8 nengō, this being the maximum number.

Before the introduction of the nien hao, the Japanese dated events with reference to the beginning of their history (660 B. C.), or to the commencement of each reign, or again by means of the sexagesimal cycle. From the Taikwa (645) to the Meiji (1868), there have been 229 nengō divided among 87 reigns. At the time of the Meiji restoration, it was decided that each future reign should have only one nengō.

F. K. Ginzel: Handbuch der mathematischen Chronologie (Bd. 1, 480–483, 522–528, 1906). E. Papinot: Historical Dictionary (437, 823–824, Tōkyo, 1909). A list of nengō will be found in each of these works.

X. ARABIC, TIBETAN, AND CHINESE PHILOLOGY

The Qur'ān established Arabic as a literary language and stabilized it as much as any language can be stabilized. The text of the Qur'ān is, by definition, perfect. There is an essential difference in this respect between the Qur'ān and the Old Testament. Few Christians read the latter in the original Hebrew text; they must be content to use translations which are more or less removed from

[m] Nengō is simply the Japanese reading of the characters read nien-hao by the Chinese.

the original. However perfect the original may have been, the translations must necessarily participate in many human imperfections. The Muslims avoided this by forbidding the translation of their Sacred Book. An important consequence of that interdiction was to create, between all the Muslim peoples, scattered all over the world, not only a religious bond, but also a linguistic one, hardly less holy and less solid.

Arabic was thus, at once, a sacred and an indispensable language. During a great part of the Middle Ages it remained one of the main languages of the world; in fact, from the eighth to the eleventh century inclusive it was by far the most important vehicle of civilization.

It should not be concluded from what I have just said that Arabic literature only began with the preaching of the Muslim faith. On the contrary, the Arabic-speaking tribes had already developed in their days of ignorance (al-jāhiliyya) a very remarkable literature, chiefly in the form of poetry. Yet Islām it was which stabilized that language and gave it an international significance. If it had not been the sacred organ of Islām, it would have remained a tribal dialect instead of becoming, as it did, one of the few world languages. For information on pre-Islamic Arabic literature, see histories of Arabic literature, e. g., C. Brockelmann: Geschichte der arabischen Litteratur (vol. 1, 11–32, Weimar, 1898).

The policy of the Roman Catholic Church may be compared to that of the Muslim community and has been as beneficent for the Latin language as the Muslim policy has been for the Arabic. The Roman Church has never encouraged the reading of the Bible in the vernacular. On the other hand, St. Jerome's Latin version (q. v., second half of fourth century), the so-called Vulgate, was fully sanctioned and obtained a canonical value; priests were obliged and laymen were allowed to read it. Moreover, Latin was and has remained the liturgical and official language of that church. Whatever vitality Latin still possesses today it owes essentially to the Roman Catholic Church.

The Tibetan language was crystallized at the same time as the Arabic. It has played an important part in the conservation and transmission of Buddhist doctrine. See my note on Tibetan Buddhism in Section II.

LU FA-YEN

Lu[4]* Fa[2]*-yen[2] (7432, 3366, 13025). Flourished at the end of the sixth and the beginning of the seventh century. He compiled with the assistance of Yen Chih-t'ui (q. v., second half of sixth century) the earliest extant (Chinese) phonetic dictionary. This work, called Ch'ieh[4]* yün[4] (1552, 13843), was completed in 601. The words are classified under 204 rhymes, the tones being taken into account.[a]

The Ch'ieh-yün was revised in 677 by Ch'ang[2]-sun[1] No[4]*-yen[2] (450, 10431, 8373, 13025); then again, in 751, by Sun[1] Mien[3] (10431, 7889). A third revision, upon which all modern editions are based, was made in 1011 by Ch'ên P'êng-nien (q. v., first half of eleventh century).

H. A. Giles: Biographical Dictionary (543, 1898). Encyclopaedia sinica (300, 1917. P. Pelliot). . Bernhard Karlgren: Etudes sur la phonologie chinoise (700 p., 1915); Analytic Dictionary of Chinese (Paris, 1923; Isis, VII, 567).

---

[a] Yün means rhyme; for ch'ieh refer to fan ch'ieh under Sun Yen (second half of third century).

HSÜAN YING

Hsüan^{2} Ying^{4} (4790, 13294). Flourished c. 649. Chinese lexicographer. He compiled, c. 649, the earliest Buddhist glossary. It is called I^{1*} ch'ieh^{4*} ching^{1} yin^{1} i^{4} (5342, 1552, 2122, 13209, 5454), that is, the sounds and meanings of terms used in the Buddhist canon. It explains the meaning and gives the correct pronunciation of the many terms translated or transcribed from the Sanskrit.

A. Wylie: Chinese Literature (211, 1902). H. A. Giles: Catalogue of the Wade Collection in Cambridge (25, 1898); Biographical Dictionary (314, 1898).

CHAPTER XXVI

THE TIME OF I-CHING

(Second Half of Seventh Century)

I. Survey of Science in Second Half of Seventh Century. II. Religious Background. III Latin, Syriac, and Muslim Philosophy. IV. Syriac and Chinese Mathematics and Astronomy. V. Byzantine and Muslim Alchemy. VI. Byzantine, Latin, Syriac, and Chinese Geography. VII. Byzantine, Latin, and Chinese Medicine. VIII. Latin and Syriac Historiography. IX. Barbarian, Muslim, and Japanese Law. X. Latin, Syriac, Arabic, and Japanese Philology.

I. SURVEY OF SCIENCE IN SECOND HALF OF SEVENTH CENTURY

1. As I announced at the beginning of the previous chapter, this is a period of comparative retrogression. The great activity of the preceding period is followed by relative calm and rest; this is especially true of China. Yet it is proper to call this time the time of I-ching. Indeed, the main purpose of these titles is mnemotechnic. The names of Hsüan Tsang and I-ching will cling easily together in our memory. The symmetry of these two Chinese titles will help us to recall that the seventh century was the time of two great pilgrims, who were separated by almost half a century, but whose activities and purposes were the same.

2. *Religious Background*—Buddhism continued to progress in China, in Japan, and even in India. The Hindu development, if our tentative dating is correct, was represented by the works of the great poet Śāntideva, but, alas! these were almost the last fruits of Buddhism in its native country.

The vitality of Chinese Buddhism was attested by the literary labor of Tao-hsüan and Tao-shih and by I-ching's famous pilgrimage.

Two new sects were established in Japan, the Hossō-shū in 654 and the Kusha-shū in 658. Soon after that, the infiltration of Buddhism and Chinese culture was much accelerated by the immigration of many Korean refugees driven from Kudara and Koma by the Shiragian conquest.

The earliest Muslim sect, one that represents unto this day the simplicity of primitive Islam, but is not considered orthodox, was founded by Ibn Ibāḍ, at Baṣra, c. 680.

3. *Latin, Syriac, and Muslim Philosophy*—To call St. Aldhelm, Abbot of Malmesbury, a philosopher may seem a gross exaggeration; yet he was the foremost thinker of the Latin world of those days.

The highest thought of the period was expressed in Syriac. Severus Sēbōkht was not only a very distinguished student of Aristotelian philosophy, he was steeped in geographical and astronomical knowledge. Under his leadership the monastery of Qen-neshrē became one of the main centers of Greek learning. Much of Greek and perhaps of Hindu knowledge was transmitted to the Arabic-speaking peoples, thanks to his efforts. He was aware that scientific progress is essentially an international activity. While Sēbōkht was teaching in Upper Mesopotamia, another remarkable man, George, Bishop of the Arabs, was flourishing in Babylonia. He translated the Organon into Syriac and wrote a valuable commentary upon it.

The Umayyad prince Khālid ibn Yazīd, who was living in Egypt, was interested in Greek science and philosophy and caused the first translations to be made from Greek into Arabic.

4. *Syriac and Chinese Mathematics and Astronomy*—Severus Sēbōkht wrote a treatise on the astrolabe and dealt with other astronomical subjects; he was the first writer, outside of India, to mention the nine Hindu numerals, which were the ancestors of our own numerals. George, Bishop of the Arabs, composed a poem on the calendar.

Li Shun-fêng wrote commentaries on the ancient mathematical treatises, and explained a method of solving indeterminate equations; he wrote a history of Chinese astronomy down to the T'ang dynasty.

5. *Byzantine and Muslim Alchemy*—The architect Callinicos is said to have invented the so-called Greek fire, which was used for the first time when a Muslim fleet besieged Constantinople in 673.

Various alchemical writings are traditionally ascribed to Khālid ibn Yazīd; however, it is not possible to substantiate these attributions.

6. *Byzantine, Latin, Syriac, and Chinese Geography*—Two curious geographical texts date probably from this time, the Cosmography of Aethicus, a Greek text which we know only through a Latin translation, and the anonymous cosmography of Ravenna. The latter is by far the most important work, in fact, the most valuable work of its kind in the early Middle Ages in the West.

Severus Sebōkht was interested in geography, and even more so, his disciple, the grammarian Jacob of Edessa, who wrote an Hexaëmeron, the third part of which is largely geographical.

The Chinese diplomat Wang Hsüan-ts'ê went four times to India; his records are lost, but parts of them have come down to us through other Chinese publications. The monk I-ching, following the noble examples of Fa Hsien and Hsüan Tsang, went to India to obtain a deeper knowledge of Buddhism; he left Canton in 671 and reached the mouth of the Hooghly by sea; he returned to Lo-yang, in 695, with some 400 Buddhist works, and spent the rest of his life translating them.

7. *Byzantine, Latin, and Chinese Medicine*—The monk Meletios wrote a theological treatise on the constitution of the human body.

Benedictus Crispus composed a medical poem dealing with the treatment of 26 diseases, arranged from head to foot.

Two new revised editions of the Chinese materia medica (pên ts'ao) were compiled during the rule of the third T'ang emperor, Kao Tsung. The first revision was directed by Li Chi, the second by Su Kung. The Taoist physician Sun Ssŭ-mo compiled an immense collection of medical recipes and wrote a treatise on eye diseases.

8. *Latin and Syriac Historiography*—It is remarkable that no Byzantine or Chinese annals of any importance have come down to us from that period. On the other hand, the most important Latin annals of the whole century, a chronicle of Frankish events from 584 to 642 (664), was compiled by the Burgundian (?) Fredegarius Scholasticus.

Syriac historiography is represented by a small Nestorian chronicle dealing with the last half century of Sassanian rule, and by the revision and extension of Eusebios's chronicle, which was carried out c. 692, by Jacob of Edessa.

9. *Barbarian, Muslim, and Japanese Law*—The earliest Visigothic code had been promulgated in the second half of the fifth century, the latest date from the second

half of the seventh century, but the influence of Visigothic law was felt until a much later time, e. g., in Spain until at least the thirteenth century.

I have already referred (in section 2) to the earliest Muslim sect, the Ibāḍite. This was also the earliest school of Muslim law, for in Islām it is impossible to dissociate law from theology.

The earliest Japanese code of law, as distinguished from Shōtoku's ethical summary, was the Ōmi ritsu-ryō, completed about the year 667. Census taking was introduced into Japan at about the same time.

10. *Latin, Syriac, Arabic, and Japanese Philology*—St. Aldhelm wrote a long dialogue on Latin prosody, which was apparently the only philological contribution of the West in those days.

Jacob of Edessa composed the earliest systematic treatise on Syriac grammar; he introduced seven vowel signs, diacritical marks, and accents.

Muslim tradition ascribes the discovery of Arabic grammar to Abū-l-Aswad of Baṣra. However, the school of Baṣra, the earliest school of Arabic grammar, did not fully develop until about a century later.

After his return from China in 653, Sakaibe Iwazumi compiled a large dictionary of new Japanese words written by means of Chinese characters.

11. *Final Remarks*—The most valuable work of this period was accomplished by Syrians: Severus Sēbōkht, George of the Arabs, and Jacob of Edessa.

Important contributions to geographical knowledge were made by the Chinese Wang Hsüan-ts'ê and I-ching. Four other Chinese seem to have been very distinguished men: the mathematician Li Shun-fêng, the physician Sun Ssŭ-mo, and the Buddhist scholars Tao-hsüan and Tao-shih. Hindu genius was represented by another Buddhist, the very lovable Śāntideva. The new Muslim civilization is beginning to give some intellectual fruits; witness the activities of Ibn Ibāḍ, Khālid ibn Yazīd, Abū-l-Aswad.

Though our interest in philology is only secondary, the awakening of grammatical consciousness is too precious an index of the development of new civilizations to be neglected. From that special point of view, the second half of the seventh century was a privileged period, for it saw the beginning of Syriac grammar and the first dawn of Arabic and Japanese philology.

II. RELIGIOUS BACKGROUND

ŚĀNTIDEVA

Born of a royal family in Saurāshṭra (modern Gujarak, 71 miles from Lahore, on the road from Lahore to Peshawar). Flourished at an uncertain time, probably about the middle of the seventh century. The greatest of the later Hindu teachers of Mahāyāna doctrine, and one of the greatest Sanskrit poets. He wrote two very important works. The "Śikshāsamuccaya" ("The Sum of Doctrine") is a treatise on Mahāyāna ethics, containing a great number of extracts from earlier writings, most of which are lost; the author insists upon the value of bodhicittam, that is, thinking which aims at perfect knowledge or wisdom (bodhi). The "Bodhicaryāvatāra" ("Entrance into the Life of Bodhi; Introduction to Perfection") is a famous poem devoted to the same subject.

Text—The Śikshāsamuccaya was translated into Tibetan between 816 and 838. Sanskrit text edited by Cecil Bendall in the Bibliotheca Indica (St. Petersburg, 1897–1902).

English translation by Cecil Bendall and W. H. D. Rouse (335 p., London, 1922).

Bodhicaryāvatāra. Text edited by I. P. Minayeff, in Zapiski (IV, 1889); again in Journal of the Buddhist Text Soc. (1894). New edition with Prajñākaramati's commentary, by L. de la Vallée Poussin, in Bibliotheca Indica (Calcutta, 1901, etc.).

French translation by L. de la Vallée-Poussin, in Revue d'histoire et de littérature religieuse (Paris, 1905–1907); French translation, Marche à la Lumière, by Louis Finot (Paris, 1920; Isis, VII, 184).

Partial English translation by L. D. Barnett: The Path of Light (107 p., Wisdom of the East, London, 1913 ?; Isis, I, 515).

Criticism—M. Winternitz: Geschichte der indischen Litteratur (vol. 2, 259–266, 379, 1920).

TAO-HSÜAN

Tao[4]-hsüan[1] (10780, 4805). Born in 595, died in 667. Founder of the Lü tsung.[a] He compiled in 667 a collection of biographies of famous Buddhist monks who lived from 519 to 665, in 30 books, entitled Hsü[4]* kao[1] sêng[1] ch'uan[2] (4773, 5927, 9617, 2740).[b] He had prepared in 664 a new edition of the Hung ming chi,[c] called Kuang[3] (6397) hung ming chi, in 30 books.

Text—The Hsü kao sêng ch'uan is included in the Chinese Tripiṭaka (Tokyo edition, vol. 35).

Criticism—A. Wylie: Chinese Literature (208, (1867) 1902). L. Wieger: La Chine (402, 499, 503, 521, 522, 1920).

TAO-SHIH

Tao[4]-shih[4] (10780, 10007). Chinese Buddhist who flourished c. 656 to 668. He compiled c. 656 to 660 a good summary of Buddhist ethics in 20 books, called Chu[1]-ching[1] yao[4]-chi[2]* (2571, 2122, 12889, 906). In 668 he completed a Buddhist encyclopaedia, in 120 books, called Fa[2]*-yuan[3]-chu[1]-lin[2] (3366, 13720, 2549, 7157).

A. Wylie: Chinese Literature (207 (1867), 1902). Alluded to by S. Levi, in Les Missions de Wang Hiuen-ts'e dans l'Inde (Journal asiatique, vol. 15, 297–341, 401–468, 1900. Containing translations of fragments). Wieger: La Chine (402, 492, 530, 1920).

JAPANESE BUDDHISM

I have spoken in the last chapter of the two earliest Buddhist sects founded by Ekwan. Two more sects were established before the end of the century, the Hossō-shū in 654 and the Kusha-shū in 658.

The Hossō-shū (654), also called Yuishiki, was introduced from China by the Japanese bonze Dōshō. This Dōshō, who died in 700, was one of the creators of Japanese civilization. He was not concerned exclusively with religious matters; he is said to have built bridges, to have made rivers navigable, etc. The introduction of Hindu logic into Japan, c. 658, is also ascribed to him.[d] The Hossō-shū corresponds to the Hindu Dharmalakshaṇa (or Vijñānavāda), belonging to the Pro-

---

[a] For which see my note on Chinese Buddhism in the first half of the seventh century. I speak of him here because as far as we can judge from the dates of his works, his literary activity occurred only toward the end of his life.

[b] This was a continuation of the Kao sêng ch'uan, a similar collection for the period 67 to 519 compiled by Hui[4]-chiao[3] (5193, 1305) in 519. A further continuation, called Sung[4] (10462) kao sêng ch'uan, down to the year 988, was written by Tsan-ning (q. v., second half of tenth century).

[c] For which see my note on Sêng-yu, first half of the sixth century.

[d] See my notes on Dignāga (second half of the fourth century) and on K'uei-chi (first half of the seventh century).

visional Mahāyāna. It is still represented in Japan to-day, but only by 41 temples (c. 1917).

The Kusha-shū (658) was introduced from China by two Japanese bonzes, Chitsū and Chitatsu. It corresponds to the Hindu Abhidharmakośa and to the Chinese Chü[1] shê[4] tsung[1] (3019, 9789, 11976) and is regarded as the best representative of Hīnayāna Buddhism. It is now extinct.

It is interesting to note that the two earliest sects had been introduced from Korea, while the two of which I have just spoken were brought in directly from China. This does not mean that relations with Korea were interrupted, but that a more direct contact had been established with China.

The infiltration of Chinese civilization into Japan was greatly accelerated, a little later, by the fact that two of the three Korean kingdoms were conquered by the third one, Shiragi, Kudara being invaded in 660 and Koma in 668. Many refugees emigrated from the subdued countries and settled in Japan. There are still many traces of the emigration from Kudara in the province of Settsu.

IBN IBĀḌ

'Abdallāh ibn Ibāḍ, flourished at Baṣra c. 680. Muslim theologian. He was the leader of the more moderate section of the Khārijites, and the founder of the sect of the Ibāḍites, which represents to this day[e] the simplicity of primitive Islām in theology, law, and politics. Their code of law antedates those of the four orthodox schools; it is based on the Qur'ān, prophetic usage, and (Ibāḍite) agreement.

D. B. Macdonald: Development of Muslim Theology (25, 26, 116, 1903).

III. LATIN, SYRIAC, AND MUSLIM PHILOSOPHY

ST. ALDHELM

Born c. 640; flourished at Malmesbury; died in 709 at Doulting, near Wells, buried at Malmesbury. English humanist.[f] He knew Greek and possibly Hebrew. Educated at Malmesbury and at Canterbury.[g] Abbot of Malmesbury (675). He visited Rome in 692 and was Bishop of Sherborne from 705 to his death. He wrote a Latin prosody (Liber de Septenario) containing "aenigmata" in verse, interesting because of the natural lore implied.

Text—Collected works in Migne's Patrologia (vol. 89) and in the Patres Ecclesiae Anglicanae edited by J. A. Giles (Oxford, 1844, containing various hitherto unpublished works). New edition by Rud. Ehwald (Berlin, 1913-1914. Monumenta Germaniae historica).

Criticism—Article by the Rev. William Hunt, in Dictionary of National Biography (vol. 1, 245–246, 1885). Leo Bönhoff: Aldhelm, ein Beitrag zur angelsächsischen Kirchengeschichte (Diss., Leipzig, 126 p., Dresden, 1894). G. F. Browne: St. Aldhelm, his Life and Times (366 p., London, 1903). M. Manitius: Lateinische Literatur des Mittelalters (vol. 1, 134–141, 1911; vol. 2, 797). J. E. Sandys:

[e] The Ibāḍites hold their own against other Muslims (who consider them heretics) in 'Umān (Southeastern Arabia), in Zanzibar, and along the coast of East Africa generally. Their main home, however, is in the Mzab (Southern Algeria).

[f] "The first Englishman who cultivated classical learning with success, and the first of whom any literary remains are preserved." (Stubbs in Dictionary of Christian Biography.)

[g] Under Theodore, sent to England in 668 by Pope Vitalian to be archbishop and under Hadrian, an African, who had come from a convent near Monte Cassino. This was the beginning of an English Renaissance in which Aldhelm was foremost.

History of Classical Scholarship (vol. 1[3], 465–467, 1921). Lynn Thorndike: History of magic (Vol. I, 636, 1923).

SEVERUS SĒBŌKHT[h]

Born in Nisibis. Flourished in Qen-neshrē about the middle of the seventh century. Philosopher, scientist. He wrote commentaries on Aristotle ("Prior Analytics; De interpretatione"). Bishop of the convent of Qen-neshrē (or Kennesré on the Upper Euphrates), which under his leadership became the main center of Greek learning in Western Syria at that time. He wrote on geographical and astronomical subjects (zodiac, eclipses). His treatise on the plane astrolabe (composed before 660) is based exclusively upon Greek sources. In another writing (in 662) he alludes to the nine [Hindu] numerals, the value of which he fully appreciated. This is the first mention of them outside of India. He may have been one of the agencies by means of which the knowledge of the astrolabe was transmitted from the Greeks, and that of the numerals from the Hindus, to the Arabs. He claimed that science can not be the monopoly of any nation, but is international.

Text—Abbé F. Nau: Le traité de l'astrolabe plan de Sévère Sébokt, publié pour la première fois d'aprés un MS. de Berlin (Journal Asiatique, vol. 13, p. 56–101, 238–303, 1899. Syriac text with French translation). For the text on the Figures of the Zodiac see Ed. Sachau: Inedita syriaca (127–134, Wien, 1870).

Criticism—William Wright: Short History of Syriac literature (p. 137–139, London, 1894). F. Nau: Notes d'astronomie syrienne (Journal Asiatique, vol. 16, 219–28, 1910. (II) Ataliā, ou le dragon céleste, cause des éclipses de lune d'après Sévère Sébokt; (III) La plus ancienne mention orientale des chiffres indiens; (IV) La date du traité de Sévère Sébokt sur l'astrolabe plan). Eugen Loeffler: Zur Geschichte der indischen Ziffern (Archiv der Mathematik und Physik, vol. 19, 174–178, 1912. Review of Nau's work). Jekuthial Ginsburg: New Light on our Numerals (Bulletin American Mathematical Society, vol. 23, 366–369, New York, 1917).

GEORGE, BISHOP OF THE ARABS

He was ordained in 686, bishop of the Monophysitic Arab tribes of Mesopotamia, his residence being in 'Aqōlā;[i] he died in 724. Syriac philosopher and theologian. His main work is a version of the Organon of Aristotle with commentary.[j] He also wrote a poem on the calendar, commentaries on the Bible, and completed the Hexaëmeron of Jacobus of Edessa.

Text—V. Ryssel: Georgs des Araberbischofs Gedichte und Briefe (Leipzig, 1891). Extracts from the Organon in J. Georg E. Hoffmann: De hermeneuticis apud Syros aristoteleis (Leipzig, 1869).

Dom R. H. Connolly and H. W. Codrington: Two commentaries on the Jacobite liturgy by George, bishop of the Arab tribes, and Moses bār Kēphā, together with the Syriac Anaphora of St. James and the Book of Life (267 p., London, 1913. Syriac and English).

Criticism—E. Renan: De philosophia peripatetica apud Syros (Paris, 1852). Wm. Wright: Syriac Literature (156–159, 1894). R. Duval: Littérature syriaque (253, 377, 1907).

---

[h] This name, be it noted, is Persian.

[i] al-Kūfa in 'Irāq. It is south of Bagdad and a little west of the Euphrates.

[j] Renan considered it the most important Syriac commentary. Only the following parts are extant: Categories, De interpretatione, first book of the Analytics.

For Muslim philosophy see my note on Ibn Ibāḍ in Section II and on Khālid ibn Yazīd in Section V.

IV. SYRIAC AND CHINESE MATHEMATICS AND ASTRONOMY

For Syriac mathematics and astronomy see my notes on Severus Sēbōkht, and on George, Bishop of the Arabs, in Section III.

LI SHUN-FÊNG

Li[3] Shun[2]-fêng[1] (6884, 10139, 3554). T'ang mathematician and astronomer who flourished about the middle of the century. He composed the Lin[2]-tê[2]* (7186, 10845) calendar in 664. Method of two differences, p'ing[2] and ting[4] (9318, 11248) to determine A and B from $Ax + Bx^2 = C$. He used for π the value $\frac{22}{7}$, that is the "inaccurate" value of Tsu Ch'ung-chih (q. v., second half of fifth century). He wrote commentaries on the Chou[1] pi[3] suan[4] ching[1] (2450, 8989, 10378, 2122), one of the oldest Chinese treatises on mathematics;[k] on the Arithmetic in Nine Sections and the Sea Island Arithmetic;[l] and finally on a treatise of uncertain date called the Arithmetic classic of Chang Ch'iu-chien, Chang[1] Ch'iu[1]-chien[4] suan[4]-ching[1] (416, 2313, 1592, 10378, 2122). He was one of the authors of the chih of the Sui shu,[m] which include a history of Chinese astronomy down to the T'ang. He realized that the movements of celestial bodies are not independent.

Text—The text of his commentaries on Chang Ts'ang and Liu Hui's arithmetical treatises have been extracted piecemeal from the Yung-Lo Ta-tien (q. v., first half of the fifteenth century).

The text of the Chang Ch'iu-chien suan-ching has come down to us directly from a Sung edition.

Criticism—A. Wylie: Chinese Literature (20, 106, 107, 113–115 (1867), 1902). Yoshio Mikami: Development of Mathematics in China and Japan (Leipzig, 1912).

V. BYZANTINE AND MUSLIM ALCHEMY

CALLINICOS

Καλλίνικος, of Heliopolis, Syria, flourished c. 673. Architect to whom Byzantine chroniclers ascribe the invention of the so-called "Greek fire" (πῦρ ὑγρόν, feu grégeois),[n] which is said to have been used for the first time at the siege of Constantinople by the Arabs in 673, the Muslim fleet being fired by its means. It was probably a mixture of quicklime, naphtha, pitch, and sulphur and could spread fire under water. Whether it contained saltpeter or not is a moot question.

---

[k] It is ascribed to the Chou dynasty (1122–249 B. C.). Its text is included in the Tai[4]-chiao[4] suan[4]-ching[1] shih[2]*-shu[1] (10569, 1302, 10378, 2122, 9959, 10024), a collection of the ten oldest mathematical treatises edited in 1773 by Tai[4]-chên[4] (10569, 642).

[l] For these two classics, see my notes on Chang Ts'ang (first half of second century B. C.) and on Liu Hui (second half of third century).

[m] The Sui shu is the thirteenth of the Twenty-Four Dynastic Histories (see my note on Wei Chêng, first half of the seventh century). The chih[4] (1918) or memoirs, is the part of such histories dealing with more technical subjects, such as astronomy, geography, chronology, jurisprudence, etc. The chih of the Sui shu deal not simply with the Sui dynasty (589 to 620) but with some others of the six dynasties which preceded the T'ang.

[n] Byzantine writers call it also πῦρ θαλάσσιον, σκευαστόν, ῥωμαϊκόν, μηδικόν, ἐνεργόν, μαλθακόν. I have used the name which is most common.

Ludovic Lalanne: Recherches sur le feu grégeois et sur l'introduction de la poudre à canon en Europe (2de édition, 96 p., Paris, 1845). E. M. Quatremère: Observations sur le feu grégeois (Journal Asiatique, 62 p., 1850). M. Berthelot: Feu grégeois. Grande Encyclopédie (3 col., c. 1893). F. M. Feldhaus: Die Technik (302, Leipzig, 1914). See also the publications relative to the invention of gunpowder (thirteenth century).

KHĀLID IBN YAZĪD

Khālid ibn Yazīd ibn Mu'āwiya, called the Ḥakīm—the philosopher—of the family of Marwān, flourished in Egypt, died in 704 or 708. Umayyad prince who was supposed (according to Muslim tradition) to have encouraged Greek philosophers in Egypt to translate Greek scientific works into Arabic: "These were the first translations made in Islām from one language into another" (Fihrist). He was himself deeply interested in medicine, astrology, and alchemy.

He was said to have studied alchemy under an Alexandrian scholar called Marianos (Morienus Romanus, Morienes, etc.). All this is pure legend. The "Book of Morienus" is an alchemical treatise of a later time known only through Robert of Chester's Latin text (see my note on Robert of Chester, first half of twelfth century). As shown by Ruska (1924) we have no positive knowledge of any kind upon Khālid's scientific activity; as is usually the case, the legend relative to Khālid's alchemical studies became more definite as the centuries elapsed; Ḥājjī Khalīfa knew much more about it than al-Mas'ūdī or Ibn al-Nadīm!

Many alchemical writings are ascribed to him, but it is impossible to confirm any attribution. Even the "Book of Crates," the only Arabic witness, dating *apparently* from Khālid's time, can not be ascribed to him. This Arabic adaptation of a Greek work dates probably from the end of the eighth century, if not from a later time.

Fihrist (passim, especially p. 354). al-Mas'ūdī. Prairies d'Or (vol. 8, 176, and by index). C. Brockelmann: Arabische Litteratur (vol. 1, 67, 1898). John Ferguson: Bibliotheca chemica (Vol. I, p. 449, Glasgow, 1906, under the heading Kalid ben Jesid; read also preceding notice devoted to Kalid ben Jazichi, with full bibliography). Lippmann: Entstehung und Ausbreitung der Alchemie (357–359, Berlin, 1919). Ed. G. Browne: Arabian Medicine (p. 15, 19, Cambridge, 1921). Richard Reitzenstein: Alchemistische Lehrschriften und Märchen bei den Arabern (Religions-geschichtliche Versuche und Vorarbeiten, Bd. 19, H. 2, 61–86, Giessen, 1923). Julius Ruska: Arabische Alchemisten. 1. Chālid ibn Jazīd (56 p., Heidelberg, 1924. The first scientific study of the sources, very important; Isis, VII, 183). E. O. von Lippmann: Ruska's neue Untersuchungen über die Anfänge der arabischen Alchemie (Chemiker Z., Nr. 1 u. 7, 1925; reprint, 7 p.).

VI. BYZANTINE, LATIN, SYRIAC, AND CHINESE GEOGRAPHY

Cosmography of Aethicus

The Cosmography of Aethicus is a collection of marvels ascribed to one Aethicus[a] Ister, or Istriacus, a Greek of Istria or a "Scythian," who is supposed to have traveled very extensively. The Greek text is lost and we know it only through an abbreviated Latin translation by one Presbyter Hieronymus, who flourished

[a] Or Ethicus, meaning philosopher?

probably in the seventh century.[p] Isidore of Seville is quoted in the Latin text.[q] It is a good specimen of the debased geographical knowledge of that time.

Text—Armand d'Avezac: Ethicus et les ouvrages cosmographiques intitulés de ce nom (Mémoires, Académie des inscriptions, vol. 2, 230–552, Paris, 1852). Heinrich Wuttke: Cosmographia Aethici Istriaci ab Hieronymo ex Graeco in latinum breviarium redacta (Leipzig, 1853).

Criticism—K. A. F. Pertz: De Cosmographia Ethici (Berlin, 1853). Berger, in Pauly-Wissowa (vol. 1, 697–699, 1894). M. Manitius: Lateinische Literatur des Mittelalters (vol. 1, 229–234, 1911). Lynn Thorndike: History of Magic (vol. 1, 600–604, 1923).

Anonymous Geographer of Ravenna

A description of the world (Cosmographia) in five books was compiled about the middle of the seventh century by an unknown cleric. It is based on the Bible, Ptolemy, the Tabula Peutingeriana (?), Orosius, Jordanes, Isidore, etc. It is in many respects the most elaborate work of its kind produced in the early Middle Ages in the West. See my note on Guido (first half of twelfth century).

Text—M. Pinder and G. Parthey: Ravennatis anonymi Cosmographia et Guidonis Geographica (p. 1–445, Berlin, 1860).

Criticism—J. K. Wright: Geographical Lore (49, and by index, 1925).

For the geographical writings in Syriac see my notes on Severus Sēbōkht in Section III, and on Jacob of Edessa in Section X.

WANG HSÜAN-TS'Ê

Wang[2] Hsüan[2]-ts'ê[4]* (12493, 4790, 11691). Flourished c. 643 to 664. Chinese diplomat and traveler who went four times to India (Magadha), the first time in 643 to 646 when he crossed Nepal; the second time in 646 to 648, when he brought back to China with him as prisoner the usurper of the throne of Magadha; a third time in 657 to 661; a fourth time in 663–64. He wrote, before 666, a book entitled "Relation of Travel in Central India," Chung[1]-t'ien[1]-chu[2]*-kuo[2]* hsing[2] chi[4] (2875, 11208, 2574, 6609, 4624, 923) in 10 chapters. This work is lost, but fragments of it are included in Tao-shih's Buddhist encyclopaedia (668). An official compilation on Western Kingdoms (i. e., here India), made in 666, the Hsi[1] yu[2] chi[4] (4031, 13423, 923),[r] was based on the accounts of Wang Hsüan-ts'ê and Hsüan Tsang.

H. A. Giles: Chinese Biographical Dictionary (824, 1898). Sylvain Lévi: Les missions de Wang Hiuen-ts'e dans l'Inde (Journal asiatique, vol. 15, 297–341, 401–468, 1900. Containing translations of the fragments relative to Wang Hsüan-ts'ê; also translations of the latter's inscriptions by Chavannes). L. A. Waddell: Tibetan Invasion of Mid India (Imperial Asiatic Quarterly, 37–65, 1911). S. Lévi: Wang Hiuan-ts'ö et Kaniṣka (T'oung Pao, vol. 13, 306–309). Paul Pelliot: Autour d'une traduction sanscrite du Tao Tö king (*ibidem*, 351–430).

---

[p] He was previously identified with St. Jerome.

[q] This text should not be mistaken for another, bearing the same name, and published by Alex. Riese in his Geographi lat. min. (71–103, Heilbronn, 1878). Riese's text has been identified with other writings of Julius Honorius (Orator) and Orosius (first half of fifth century).

[r] Or Hsi[1] kuo[2]* chi[4] (6609). It contains 100 chapters (60 for the text and 40 for the maps and drawings).

I CHING

I^4 Ching^4 (5454, 2177). This was his religious name, by which he is generally called. His personal name was Chang^1 Wên^2-ming^2 (416, 12633, 7946). Born in Fan^4-yang^2 (3426, 12883), Chihli, in 634; died in 713. Buddhist pilgrim to India. He left Canton in 671 on a Persian ship and went to Palembang in Sumatra, later to Tamralipti at the mouth of the Hooghly; he stayed ten years in Nālanda (the greatest center of learning of the time). He returned to Lo-yang in 695, carrying back with him some 400 Buddhist works, many of which he translated, and 300 relics. He wrote an account of his travels entitled Ta^4-t'ang^2 hsi^1-yü^{4*} ch'iu^2-fa^{2*} kao^1-sêng^1-ch'uan^2 (10470, 10767, 4031, 13662, 2315, 3366, 5927, 9617, 2740). The geographical value of this account is smaller than that of Hsüan Tsang's account, for I Ching was more interested in the pilgrims than in the places which they visited. He speaks of 60 Chinese pilgrims who went to India in his time. His book is a part of the Chinese Tripiṭaka (No. 1491 of Bunyiu Nanjio's Catalogue).

Text—Edouard Chavannes: Mémoire composé à l'époque de la grande dynastie T'ang sur les Religieux Eminents qui allèrent chercher la Loi dans les pays d'occident par I-Tsing, traduit en français (240 p., Paris, 1894. With introduction and elaborate commentary). I-Tsing: A Record of the Buddhist Religion as Practiced in India and the Malay Archipelago (671 to 695), translated by J. Takakusu (Oxford, 1896).

Criticism—See Hsüan Tsang. Jyun Takakusu: An introduction to I-tsing's Record of the Buddhist Religion as Practiced in India and the Malay Archipelago (671 to 695) (Diss., Leipzig, 64 p., Oxford, 1896). H. A. Giles: Biographical Dictionary (348, 1898). Liétard: Le pélerin bouddhiste chinois I-tsing et la médecine de l'Inde au VIIe siècle (Bulletin de la soc. d'hist. de la médicine, vol. 1, 472–487, 1902). Julius Jolly: I-tsing and Vāgbhaṭa. (Journal R. Asiatic Society, 1907, 172–175.)

VII. BYZANTINE, LATIN, AND CHINESE MEDICINE

MELETIOS

Meletios the Monk (Μελέτιος μοναχός). Flourished in the seventh or eighth century. Phrygian monk. Author of a treatise on the constitution of man's body (περὶ τῆς τοῦ ἀνθρώπου κατασκευῆς), the aim of which is theological rather than scientific.

Text—Greek text edited by J. A. Cramer in his Anecdota graeca (vol. 3, p. 1–15, Oxford, 1836). Partial edition of same text by Fr. Ritschl (32 p., Breslau, 1837. From a Cracovian MS.). Latin translation by N. P. Corcyraeus: Meletii de natura structuraque hominis (Venice, 1552).

Criticism—Neuburger und Pagel: Handbuch der Geschichte der Medizin (Vol. I, p. 558–559, 1902). G. Helmreich: Handschriftliche Studien zu Meletius (Abhdl. d. Preuss. Ak. d. Wiss., philos. hist. Kl., 62 p., Berlin, 1918; Isis, IV, 134).

CRISPUS

St. Benedictus Crispus, Benedetto Crespo, of Amitermum (Aquila or S. Vittorino); archbishop of Milano since 681; died in 725 or 735. He wrote a medical poem (241 hexameters) entitled "Commentarium medicinale," with an introduction in prose. It deals with the treatment, by means of herbs, of 26 diseases arranged a capite ad calcem.

Text—First edition by Angelo Mai (Roma, 1828). Later edition by Joannes Val. Ullrich (Kitzingae, 1835). Also in Migne's Latin Patrology (vol. 89, 361–376, 1844).

Criticism—E. H. F. Meyer: Geschichte der Botanik (vol. 2, 421–423, 1855.) Puschmann: Handbuch (vol. 1, 629, 1902). Max Neuburger: Geschichte der Medizin (vol. 2, 253, 1911).

Ç. Carbonelli: Frammento medico del secolo VII (Cod. Vat. Urb. Lat., 293, 20 p., fol., Roma, 1921). Facsimile reproduction and transcription correcting Cardinal Mai's previous edition. It is a fragment from medical excerpta made in one of the Italian monasteries; it deals with diseases affecting the head.

J. L. Heiberg: Glossae medicinales (Det Kgl. Danske Videnskabernes Selskab, hist. Medd., IX, 1, 96 p., Copenhagen, 1924). Glossæ extracted from the Liber glossarum, an encyclopaedia compiled c. 700 in Spain, or rather in southern Gaul (W. M. Lindsay is preparing an edition of it).

Chinese Materia Medica

The T'ang emperor Kao[1] Tsung[1] (5927, 11976), soon after his accession in 650, ordered the revision and completion of the materia medica, pên ts'ao,[s] then in use, which was the one edited at the beginning of the sixth century by T'ao Hung-ching (q .v.) on the basis of earlier works. This revision was directed by a high official, Li[3]-chi[1]* (6884, 829), also styled Ying[1] Kung[1] (13308, 6568). Thus originated the T'ang Pên ts'ao of Ying Kung. A few years later a new revision was edited by another high official, Su[1] Kung[1] (10320, 6574).[t] This was the New pên ts'ao of the T'ang, T'ang hsin[1] (4574) pên ts'ao.

The substance of this pên ts'ao was classified under the following headings: minerals, man, quadrupeds, birds, insects, fishes, cereals, vegetables, fruits, trees, herbs and natural objects not employed in medicine. It was contained in 20 books, with one for the index, plus 25 books of illustrations and 7 books explaining the illustrations.

E. Bretschneider: Botanicon sinicum (part 1, 44–45, Shanghai, 1881).

SUN SSŬ-MO

Sun[1] Ssŭ[1]-mo[4]* (10431, 10271, 7998). Born in Hua[2]-yüan[2] (5005, 13700), Shensi, died at a very old age in 682. Author of many Taoist medical works, the most important perhaps being the Sun[1]-chên[1]-jên[2] ch'ien[1]-chin[1]-fang[1] (10431, 589, 5624, 1725, 2032, 3435), an immense collection of recipes and the Yin[2]-hai[3] ching[1]-wei[1] (13253, 3767, 2138, 12586), a treatise on eye diseases (however, this seems a much later production?).

The Ch'ien-chin-fang is divided as follows: (1–4) Women's diseases; (5) children's diseases; (6–21) special pathology and therapeutics; (22, 23) swellings, ulcers, hemorrhoids, etc.; (24) antidotes; (25) emergency cases; (26, 27) dietetics;

---

[s] Pên[3] ts'ao[3] (8846, 11634). Sometimes incorrectly translated by the word herbal. It is better to use the Chinese term pên ts'ao which is more comprehensive.

[t] This Su kung does not appear in the biographies or in the official catalogues of the Old T'ang, New T'ang, and Sung Annals. Su-ching, on the other hand (q. v., my note on Wake Hiroyo, second half of eighth century) was a T'ang official, who is credited in the Annals with two editions of the Pên ts'ao. The later edition is often referred to simply as T'ang Pên-ts'ao. I surmise that Su Kung is simply another name of Su[1]-ching[4] (10320, 2144); these two words kung[1] and ching[4] being equivalent.

(28) pulse; (29, 30) acupuncture, and moxibustion. Sun describes the ulcer of jealousy (soft chancre?).

Text—A medical work of Sun ssŭ-mo was printed under the Mongol dynasty c. 1300. A copy of that early edition was found by P. K. Kozlov at Kara-Khoto Mongolia.

Criticism—H. A. Giles: Biographical Dictionary (695, 1898). L. Wieger: Taoïsme (vol. 1, 1911, by index); La Chine (393, 521, 542, 1920). F. Huebotter: Guide (28–30, Kumamoto, 1924).

VIII. LATIN AND SYRIAC HISTORIOGRAPHY

FREDEGARIUS

Fredegarius Scholasticus. Flourished c. 663 to 666, probably in the St. Marcel monastery near Chalon, Burgundy. Author of a compilation containing, together with older works, a new chronicle of Frankish events from 584 to 642 (with some allusions to the years 652–664).[u] This is the only larger historical work of the seventh century (in the West). Fredegarius was chiefly interested in Burgundy and Austrasia and was ill-disposed toward the Neustrians.

Text—Oldest edition by Flacius Illyricus, appended to his edition of Gregory of Tours, Bale, 1586, together with a part of the continuation. Edition by Gabriel Monod, in his Études critiques (vol. 2, 1885). Bruno Krusch: Chronicarum quae dicuntur Fredegarii Scholastici libri IV cum continuationibus (Monum. Germ. hist., 193 p., 1888).

French translations by Claude Bonnet in 1610 and by Guizot, Collection de mémoires (vol. 2, 153–265, 1823). German translation by Otto Abel: Geschichtschreiber der deutschen Vorzeit (3, Berlin, 1849).

Criticism—G. Monod, in Grande Encyclopédie (c. 1892). Oskar Haag: Die Latinität Fredegars (Diss., Freiburg i. B, 1898). Gustav Schnürer: Die Verfasser der sogenannten Fredegar-Chronik (266 p., Freiburg, 1900). M. Manitius: Lateinische Literatur des Mittelalters (vol. 1, 223–227, 1911; vol. 2, 799). Ferdinand Lot: Encore la chronique du Pseudo-Frédégaire (Revue historique, vol. 115, 305–337, Paris, 1914).

There has been considerable discussion in regard to the identity of the author or authors of this important chronicle. For a summary of it, see Manitius or even Potthast (vol. 1, 468–469).

SYRIAC CHRONICLE

A small Nestorian chronicle completed c. 670 to 680 is of special importance. It deals with the later times of the Sassanian rule (from the death of Hormizd IV, 589, to the Battle of Nevahend, 641) in 'Irāq and Khūzistān.

Text—Ignazio Guidi: Un nuovo testo siriaco degli ultimi Sassanidi (Leyden, 1891. Also in Actes du 8e Congrès des orientalistes, vol. 2, 1–36). New edition by Guidi with Latin translation in the Corpus scriptorum christianorum orientalium (Paris, 1903). German translation with commentary by Th. Noeldeke in the Sitzber. of the Vienna Academy (1893).

Criticism—R. Duval: Littérature syriaque (193, 1907).

See my note on Jacob of Edessa, in Section X.

---

[u] This chronicle was continued by three other men down to 768.

IX. BARBARIAN, MUSLIM, AND JAPANESE LAW

Last Visigothic Codes

The last Visigothic codes date from the second half of the seventh century (for the earliest, see second half of fifth century). The "Liber judiciorum" or "Forum judicum," issued by Recceswinth (649–672) was applicable to Visigoths and Romans alike; that is, it was not personal, but territorial. A recension of it made in 681 by King Erwig is called "Lex Wisigothorum renovata." A still later edition dates from the end of the century. A Castilian version was made by order of Ferdinand III, King of Castile and Leon, after his conquest of Cordova in 1236.

Text—Edited by Karl Zeumer in the Monum. Germ. hist. (Leges, 1, 606 p., Hannover, 1902. See second half of fifth century). S. P. Scott: The Visigothic code (Forum judicum) (493 p., Boston, 1910. English translation and index; Scott calls it "the most remarkable monument of legislation which ever emanated from a semibarbarian people, and the only substantial memorial of greatness or erudition bequeathed by the Goths to posterity.")

For early Muslim law, see my note on Ibn Ibād in Section II.

Japanese Law

Shōtoku's Jūshichi Kempō,[v] completed in 604, was not a code of law but an ethical code. The earliest code proper is the code and penal law of Ōmi (Ōmi ritsu-ryō),[w] so-called because Shiga, in Ōmi, on the shore of Lake Biwa, was then the seat of the imperial court. It was compiled during the reign of the Empress Saimei (655 to 661) or of the Emperor Tenchi (662 to 671). The date given by Kamatari is 667. At any rate, the census register was introduced during Tenchi's reign. Kamatari (614 to 669)[x] probably took a prominent part in the compilation of the Ōmi ryō. This early code is lost. A revision of it was begun in 681 and promulgated under the reign of the Empress Jitō in 692. This revised code is also lost.

Brinkley: History of Japan (1915). E. Papinot: Historical Dictionary (88, 314 437, 616, 1909).

X. LATIN, SYRIAC, ARABIC, AND JAPANESE PHILOLOGY

For Latin philology see my note on St. Aldhelm in Section III.

JACOB OF EDESSA

Born c. 633 in 'Ēn-dēbhā, province of Antioch; bishop of Edessa, probably from 684 to 688; died at the convent of Tell-'Addā in 708. Syriac Monophysitic (Jacobite) grammarian, historian, philosopher, theologian, commentator on the Bible. He studied under Severus Sēbōkht at the famous convent of Qen-neshrē.

---

[v] For which, see my note on Shōtoku-taishi, in previous chapter.

[w] Ritsu means penal law; ryō, code. These two characters are read by the Chinese, respectively lü[4*] (7548) and ling[4] (7199); but the distinction between lü and ling is not as sharp as that between ritsu and ryō.

[x] Originally named Nakatomi no Kamako. He later changed his family (uji) name Nakatomi to Fujiwara. He was the founder of the most famous family of Japan. It is interesting to note that every later revision of Japanese law was presided over by a Fujiwara.

He composed the first systematic treatise on Syriac grammar, chiefly for the purpose of introducing vowel sounds, seven in number, diacritical marks, and accents (36 in number!). Judging from Jacob's grammar, it would seem that the Syrians were acquainted with a more advanced stage of Greek grammar than were the contemporary Arabs (see following note). He revised Eusebios's chronicle (first half of fourth century) and continued it to 692.[y] He also revised the Pěshīṭtā[z] of the Old Testament. He wrote a Hexaëmeron[a] in seven parts, the third part of which is devoted to geography.

Text—S. Schüler: Die Übersetzung der Kategorien des Aristotles von Jacob von Edessa nach einer Hdsch. d. Bibliothèque Nationale zur Paris und einer der K. Bibliothek zu Berlin (Diss., Erlangen; Berlin, 1897). Wm. Wright: Fragments of the Syriac Grammar of Jacob of Edessa (London, 1871). Arthur Hjelt: Etude sur l'Hexaméron de Jacques d'Edesse, notamment sur les notions géographiques contenues dans le 3e traité (Texte syriaque publié et traduit, Helsingfors, 1892).

Criticism—Isidoro Carini. Miscellanie paleografiche ed archeologiche (Siena, 1889. Un carme di Giacomo Edessano). Adalbert Merx: Historia artis grammaticae apud Syros (Leipzig, 1889). Arthur Hjelt: Pflanzennamen aus dem Hexaëmeron Jacobs von Edessa (Orientalische Studien Th. Nöldeke gewidmet, Giessen, 571–579, 1906). William Wright: Syriac literature (chiefly p. 141–154, London, 1894). R. Duval: Littérature syriaque (3e ed., 1907). Hans von Mžik: Afrika nach der arabischen Bearbeitung der Γεωγραφικὴ ὑφήγησις des Ptolemaeus von al-Khwārizmī (Ak. der Wiss. in Wien, phil. Kl., Denkschriften, vol. 59, 1916; Isis, V, 208). A. Baumstark: Geschichte der syrischen Literatur (248–256, 1922).

ABŪ-L-ASWAD

Abū-l-Aswad al-Du'alī (meaning, from the tribe of Du'il). Flourished at Baṣra, where he died probably in 688/9, aged 85 Muslim years. The discovery of Arabic grammar is traditionally ascribed to him. According to the legend, he had received a hint from 'Alī ibn Abī Ṭālib, son-in-law of the Prophet, fourth and last orthodox caliph (656–661). Says Ibn Khallikān (vol. 1, p. 663) "'Alī laid down for him this principle: the parts of speech are three, the noun, the verb, and the particle, telling him to found a complete treatise upon it." Now this reminds one of Aristotelian grammar, for Aristotle too recognized only three parts of speech: ὄνομα, ῥῆμα, σύνδεσμος. It is certain that the Arabs were acquainted with Greek logic and that their grammatical efforts were influenced by it; it is probable that they were not acquainted with Greek grammar proper.[b] However, even if they had some knowledge of Greek grammar, that could not help them in the same way as it helped the Latin grammarians, for the genius of their own language was essentially different.[c]

---

[y] The translation into Syriac of Aristotle's "Categories" and "De interpretatione," formerly ascribed to him, are not his. The translation of the "Categories" was made by Sergios of Resaina (q. v., first half of the sixth century).

[z] The "simple" or "plain version," the Syriac vulgate, produced probably at Edessa (see my note, second half of second century).

[a] Completed by his friend George, Bishop of the Arabs.

[b] For which see, e. g., my note on Dionysios Thrax (second half of second century B. C.).

[c] In other words, Arabic grammar is essentially different from the Greek, because of its own nature and not because the Arabs did not know the works of the Greek grammarians. Grammar exists before the grammarians; these do not invent it, they simply discover it. Of course later elaborations may be artificial, but the essence of grammar is a natural and spontaneous creation.

It is interesting to note that the earliest schools of Arabic grammar originated, not in Arabia, but in the rival cities of Baṣra and Kūfa in 'Irāq. This is what we would expect. Even as Greek grammar was born, not in Athens, but in Alexandria, because of the practical needs of its mixed population, even so Arabic grammar, which the Bedouin did not need, became a real necessity for the people of 'Irāq, who spoke Persian and Syriac as much as Arabic. The school of Baṣra, which is traced back to Abū-l-Aswad, was the earliest; however, it did not really develop until about a century later; the school of Kūfa began about the end of the eighth century.

Ibn Khallikān (De Slane) (vol. 1, 662–667, 1842). G. Flügel: Die grammatischen Schulen der Araber (Abhdl. für die Kunde des Morgenlandes, II, 4, Leipzig, 1862). C. Brockelmann: Arabische Litteratur (vol. 1, 42, 96–98, 1898). R. A. Nicholson: Literary History of the Arabs (342–343, 1907). J. E. Sandys: History of Classical Scholarship (vol. 1^3, 97, 1921).

SAKAIBE IWAZUMI

Flourished c. 653 to 683. Japanese lexicographer. He went to China in 653. After his return, he published a collection of new words written in Chinese characters, in 44 vols. (683). That collection is lost

E. Papinot: Historical Dictionary (532, 1909).

CHAPTER XXVII

THE TIME OF BEDE

(First Half of Eighth Century)

I. Survey of Science in First Half of Eighth Century. II. Religious Background. III. Philosophical Background and General Advance of Civilization. IV. Latin and Chinese Mathematics and Astronomy. V. Byzantine and Muslim Alchemy; Japanese Technology. VI. Japanese, Chinese, and Latin Geography. VII. Japanese and Latin Historiography. VIII. Barbarian, Byzantine, Muslim, Chinese, and Japanese Law. IX. Arabic and Japanese Philology.

I. SURVEY OF SCIENCE IN FIRST HALF OF EIGHTH CENTURY

1. It is a little misleading to call this age the Time of Bede. To be sure, Bede was a great personality, one which commands our full respect and affection, but it is a lonely one; it represents the monastic learning of Christian Europe, but it does not represent any original and progressive movement. However, I chose Bede as the standard-bearer of this time, because he was, all considered, the most prominent writer on scientific subjects. And then this was my last chance, in this volume, of giving a Christian title to a chapter. The time of Bede is one of intellectual stagnation. The relaxation which set in in the second half of the seventh century continued until about the middle of the eighth century. Latin science is at a low ebb; Muslim science has not yet begun. But from the middle of the eighth century until the twelfth century, Latin culture will be almost entirely overshadowed by Muslim culture.

2. *Religious Background*—Christian endeavor was represented at its best by Willibrord and Bede in the West and by John of Damascus in the Near East. Willibrord evangelized the country north of the Lower Rhine, and Denmark. John of Damascus wrote the "Fountain of Knowledge" and other theological works which exerted a deep influence not only upon the Greek church, but as well upon Muslim and Jewish theology.

The earliest orthodox school of Muslim law, the Ḥanīfite, was founded, probably in the second quarter of the eighth century, by Abū Ḥanīfa. It may seem strange to speak of law in this section, but Muslim law is inseparable from religion, and in fact is more of the nature of theology than of law as we understand it now. Muslim law was derived to some extent from Roman law, but it was so deeply permeated with religion as to become something essentially different. Now that we have entered the realm of Islām, our religious introductions to each chapter become more necessary than ever, for religious faith dominated Muslim life to an unprecedented extent. No people ever took their religion as seriously as the Muslims, and this was undoubtedly the main cause of their cohesion and of their strength against enemies who were divided and whose faith was weak and tepid. Yet it should not be supposed that the whole of Islām was united; schisms had already appeared between them even in those days. For example, Ja'far al Ṣādiq, to whom various alchemical and magical treatises are traditionally ascribed, already represented an entirely different type of devotion.

By 714, Buddhism had developed to such an extent in China as to be considered by a large number of people as a nuisance, and, from now on, monks and nuns were periodically persecuted and their numbers forcibly reduced. The last school of Chinese Buddhism, the True Word (or Secret Teaching) school, essentially devoted to Tantrism and magic, was introduced from Ceylon by Pu K'ung. It is interesting to note this direct relation between Ceylon and China, but it was unfortunately one of ill omen, for Pu K'ung's teachings increased the superstitious tendencies of the Chinese and thus lessened their scientific aptitudes. In 730, Chih Shêng compiled a catalogue of Buddhist writings with biographical notices.

This epoch marked the beginning of one of the golden ages of Japan, the so-called Nara period (710 to 794). Much progress was due to the stimulation of the Korean bonze Gyōgi. He it was who first thought of amalgamating Buddhism with the native Shintō: thus was Buddhism actually grafted upon the Japanese tree and its existence insured forever. Two more sects were founded in 736 and 754, both of them by Chinese bonzes: the Kegon-shū, a Mahāyāna sect, by Dōsen, and the Ritsu-shū, a Hīnayāna sect, by Kanshin.

3. *Philosophical Background and General Advance of Civilization*—I preferred to speak of Bede in this section rather than in the previous one, because Bede influenced his contemporaries and a few of the following generations not so much in his priestly capacity as by virtue of the lay knowledge which he managed to assimilate and to publish. He was the most synthetic mind of that time, and his acquaintance with Pliny enabled him to go far beyond Isidore of Seville. The "Fountain of Knowledge" of John of Damascus contains a philosophical introduction, the substance of which is derived indirectly from Aristotle.

Kumārila, who flourished in Southern India, wrote a great treatise on Mīmāṃsā philosophy, violently anti-Buddhist. The historian of science has nothing to find in that but he must take Kumārila's activity into account.

The rule of the sixth T'ang emperor, Ming Huang, marked the climax of the Augustan age of China. He founded the Imperial Academy (Han-lin Yüan), which remained for centuries the national agency for the promotion of historical research and the maintenance of literary standards. It was probably about this time that the invention of block printing was completed.

A great number of facts prove that the penetration of Chinese culture into Japan was especially active during this period.

4. *Latin and Chinese Mathematics and Astronomy*—It is typical that, with the solitary exception of Bede, the only work of this period worth recording was done in China.[a]

To speak of Bede first, he wrote various treatises on arithmetic and chronology and we owe him a curious account of finger reckoning or symbolism.

The Chinese treatises of Ch'ü-t'an Hsi-ta and I-hsing are of special value as witnesses of the penetration of Hindu mathematics into China. It is possible that the Hindu numerals were introduced into China at this time, though we have no positive evidence of it. I-hsing solved problems of indeterminate analysis. Both Ch'ü-t'an and I-hsing were Tantrists.

A Chinese catalogue of stars, the Hsing-ching, which is supposed to date from the Earlier Han, has come down to us in the form given to it by an unknown T'ang editor.

[a] We shall see that during the following period all of the mathematical and astronomical work was done by Muslims.

5. *Byzantine and Muslim Alchemy; Japanese Technology*—Heliodoros the Alchemist, who flourished probably under Theodosios III, wrote obscure poems dealing with alchemy. I have already referred to the alchemical writings ascribed to Ja'far al-Ṣādiq; these ascriptions have not yet been substantiated.

The awakening of Japan under Buddhist and Chinese stimulation did not affect simply the religious and political aspects of its life; it touched and transformed every side of it. It is hardly necessary to recall the artistic glory of the Nara period, one of the greatest in the whole gamut of artistic endeavor; it has been given to but a few nations to reach such a height of beauty even for a short time. Japanese activity was not less remarkable on humbler planes; roads and bridges were built and the ceramic art began to be cultivated. The holy man Gyōgi proved himself a great leader in these practical matters. The construction of a gigantic statue of the Buddha was completed at Nara in 750; this was a wonderful technical achievement.

6. *Japanese, Chinese, and Latin Geography*—What might be called the earliest monuments of Japanese geography, the Fūdoki, were compiled by order of the empress Gemmei in 713. The Fūdoki were gazetteers describing the natural features, the traditions, and the remarkable objects and events of each province. Four of them are still extant.

A Chinese expedition crossed the Pamirs and Hindu Kush in 747, following the glacier pass of the Darkot (15,400 feet).

Bede published a remarkable theory of tides which contains the first reference to what is called the establishment of a port. Fergil, Bishop of Salzburg, expressed his belief in the existence of the antipodes.

6 bis. *Medicine*—It is very remarkable that this chapter contains no medical section, this being the first occurrence of the kind. Of course, medical work is never interrupted, but this does not imply a continuance of medical research. Nothing illustrates more clearly the intellectual stagnation of this age than the fact that even medical research was apparently brought to a temporary standstill.

Some information of medical interest may be found in the Daihō-ryō, the earliest Japanese code (see Section VIII). It must be pointed out also that Mādhavakara, with whom I shall deal in the next chapter, may already have been active in the present period.

7. *Japanese and Latin Historiography*—The earliest Japanese chronicle is the Kojiki, edited by Ōno Yasumaro in 711–12. The second chronicle, the Nihongi, was compiled in 714 by various scholars; a new edition, called Nihon shoki, was completed in 720 by the same Ōno and Prince Toneri. These two chronicles were essentially different, the former being purely Japanese, while the latter was more closely modeled upon the Chinese histories.

Bede completed his ecclesiastical history of England in 731. He was one of the best historians of mediaeval Europe.

8. *Barbarian, Byzantine, Muslim, Chinese, and Japanese Law*—Two Barbarian codes, the Alamannic and the Bavarian, date from this time.

Summaries of Justinianian jurisprudence and various special codes, dealing with agriculture, navigation, and military matters, were compiled by order of Leon the Isaurian, Emperor of the East from 717 to 741.

Muslim law has been dealt with in Section II. This will be my constant practice, for Muslim law is more closely connected with theology and religion than with jurisprudence as lawyers understand it.

Wu Ching wrote a treatise on the principles of government.

The earliest Japanese code extant is the Daihō-ryōritsu, completed in 701. It was revised in 718 and was then called Yōrō-ryōritsu. These first two editions, as also later ones, represent different stages in the adaptation of Chinese law to Japanese circumstances and traditions.

9. *Arabic and Japanese Philology*—The ferocious al-Ḥajjāj encouraged the development of the school of Baṣra. He himself is credited with the "invention" of vowel marks and consonantal points. It is very probable that he did not invent these marks, but that he simply applied a Syriac invention to the needs of Arabic.

Kibi Makibi, who was one of the main promoters of Chinese culture in Japan, is said to have invented the kata-kana, the earliest syllabary, derived from a small number of Chinese ideographs, to reproduce the sounds of Japanese syllables. This ascription can not be proved, but the interesting fact to remember is that by this time the Japanese had apparently reached sufficient linguistic consciousness to develop an original system of writing.

10. *Final Remarks*—This was a golden age in China and even more distinctly so in Japan, but the Chinese had no scientific curiosity and the Japanese were still too undeveloped to have a genuine interest in knowledge. Yet the Japanese activity of those days was wonderful; never before had one witnessed such a deliberate and powerful effort to assimilate an alien culture. Buddhism was on the point of disappearing in its native land; however, a last wave of Buddhist influence rolled on from India to China in the form of Tantrism. This was a very unfortunate event; Tantric magic combined with Taoist superstitions debased the Chinese mind and disqualified it almost entirely for scientific work of the highest order. Yet it is possible that Hindu numerals reached Japan in the wake of Tantrism. It is also possible that the invention of block printing was completed about this time; the enormous popular demand for Taoist and Buddhist charms was probably the main social cause of the invention.

The Muslims were not yet entirely ready to do their share of the intellectual advance of mankind, but their time had almost come.

In Europe very little was done. I could but mention three names: Bede, Willibrord, and John of Damascus. These were undoubtedly great names, but the last two were of religious rather than of scientific importance. The case of Bede was different. He was a great scholar; his merits and influence were considerable, but he was like a lonely star in a darkening night.

II. RELIGIOUS BACKGROUND

WILLIBRORD

St. Willibrord or Wilbrord. Born in Northumbria, c. 657; educated in Ireland from 679 to 690; died c. 739, on November 6; buried at Echternach, near Treves. English Benedictine monk. "Apostle of the Frisians." He went to the country of the Frisians (north of the lower Rhine) c. 690 and spent there the greater part of his life, his seat being in Utrecht. He also did some evangelical work in Denmark.

Text—The calendar of St. Willibrord from manuscript Paris Lat., 10837. Facsimile with transcription, introduction and notes, edited by H. A. Wilson. (Henry Bradshaw Society, vol. 55, London, 1918.)

Criticism—The main sources of his life are Alcuin's Vita Willibrordi and Bede's Historia ecclesiastica.

Alexander Grieve: Willibrord, Missionary in the Netherlands (including a translation of Alcuin's Vita, 139 p., London, 1923).

JOHN OF DAMASCUS

Joannes Damascenus[b] (Ἰωάννης ὁ Δαμασκηνός), born in Damascus toward the end of the seventh century; retired before 736 to the St. Sabbas monastery in Palestine; died before 754, probably in that monastery. Syrian theologian. The greatest theologian of the Greek church. His influence upon the theology of that church and indirectly upon Muslim theology was considerable. His main work is the "Fountain of Knowledge" (Πηγὴ γνώσεως, Fons Scientiae) divided into three parts: (1) Philosophical introduction, indirectly based on Aristotle (Κεφάλαια φιλοσοφικά); (2) study of about 100 heresies, including Islām[c] (Περὶ αἱρέσεων); (3) doctrinal theology (Κεφάλαια δογματικά or Ἔκδοσις ἀκριβὴς τῆς ὀρθοδόξου πίστεως), this being by far the largest part. The "Fountain of Knowledge" was the essential text-book of the Greek Middle Ages. Through a Latin translation by Burgundio da Pisa (second half of twelfth century) it exerted some influence upon Western scholasticism (especially upon Petrus Lombardus and Aquinas).

Text—Complete edition by Michel Lequien (Greek and Latin, 2 vols., Paris, 1712. Reproduced in Migne's Greek Patrology, vols. 94–96).

Burgundio's Latin translation is still unpublished.

Criticism—K. Krumbacher: Byzantinische Litteratur (2. Aufl., 68–71, 674–676, 679, etc., 1897). P. Duhem: Système du monde (vol. 3, 35–37, 1915).

Barlaam and Ioasaph—The story of the monk Barlaam and the Hindu prince Ioasaph, perhaps the most famous religious romance of the Middle Ages, was traditionally ascribed to John of Damascus until recently. It is of considerable interest, because it is a syncretism of Christian and Buddhist elements; the latter having reached the west probably through a Manichee channel. The Greek text, which seems to be the original version of the story, dates back probably to the first half of the seventh century (it contains earlier elements; for example a long fragment of Aristides's Apology, second half of second century). The author was probably one John, monk in the St. Sabbas monastery. The extraordinarily wide dissemination of the story began in the eleventh century; versions of it exist in most Western and Eastern languages. Ioasaph (or Josaphat) is a Christian avatar of the Buddha. He was canonized both by the Latin and the Greek churches. Thus has the Buddha become twice a Christian saint!

(*a*) *Text*—Editio princeps of the Greek text by Fr. Boissonade (Anecdota graeca, 4, 1832. Reprinted in Migne's Greek Patrology, vol. 96, 857–1250). Edition by K. S. Macdonald, with notes by John Morrison (Calcutta, 1895). Greek and English texts by G. R. Woodward and H. Mattingly (Loeb Library, London, 1914).

(*b*) *Criticism*—E. Kuhn: Barlaam (Abhdl. bayer. Ak., vol. 20, 88 p., 1894, with a biographical survey of all versions). Karl Krumbacher: Byzantinische Litteratur (2. Aufl., 886–891, 1897). Paul Peeters: S. Barlaam du Mont Casius (Mélanges de l'Université St. Joseph, vol. 3, 805–813, 1909).

ABŪ ḤANĪFA

Abū Ḥanīfa al-Nu'mān ibn Thābit. Born at Kūfa in 699–700 or 680–81, the grandchild of a Persian slave, died at Medīna c. 768. Muslim jurist. Founder

---

[b] Not to be mistaken for Janus Damascenus, Serapion the Elder (second half of ninth century).

[c] No Christian refuted Islām with as much impartiality until almost modern times. Unfortunately, John's work never had enough influence in the West to modify public opinion on the subject. That (mediaeval western) opinion was based largely upon absurd legends.

of one of the four orthodox schools of law, the Ḥanīfite school.[d] This was the earliest school to take a definite form.[e] The main characteristic of it is the deductive extension of jurisprudence by means of analogy (qiyās).[f] He insisted upon the right of preference (istiḥsān) of a ruling suited to local needs. Abū Ḥanīfa's efforts tended to humanize Muslim law. It should here be observed that Muslim law contained to some extent the traditions of Roman law, not simply in its particular regulations, but also what is far more important, with regard to questions of principle in methodology.[g]

Text—No legal writings of his are extant, but we have a book on the revenues of the state (Kitāb al-kharāj) by his disciple Abū Yūsuf Ya'qūb (q. v., second half of eighth century).

Criticism—C. Brockelmann: Arabische Litteratur (vol. 1, 169–171, 1898). D. B. Macdonald: Development of Muslim Theology (1903).

JA'FAR AL-ṢĀDIQ

Abū 'Abdallāh Ja'far al-Ṣādiq[h] ibn Muḥammad al-Bāqir ibn 'Alī Zain al-'Ābidīn ibn al-Ḥusain ibn 'Alī ibn Abī Ṭālib.[i] Born in 699–700, died in 765, buried at Medina. One of the twelve imāms of the Imāmīya sect (the sixth). According to the Shī'ites, says the Fihrist, he was the teacher of Jābir ibn Ḥaiyān. Various astrological, alchemical, and magical treatises are traditionally ascribed to him. These ascriptions, as well as his alleged relation with Jābir, are unwarranted.

Text—One text ascribed to Ja'far has been published by Ruska with a German translation, the Kitāb risāla Ja' far al-Ṣādiq fī 'ilm al-ṣanā'a wal-ḥajar al-mukarram (Book of the Epistle of Ja'far on the Science of the Art and the Noble Stone) (Heidelberg, 1924; Isis, VII, 119–121); this text is not earlier than the eleventh century and not later than the thirteenth. See also H. E. Stapleton and R. F. Azo: An Alchemical Compilation of the Thirteenth Century (Memoirs of the Asiatic Society Bengal, vol. 3, 57–94, Calcutta, 1910).

Criticism—See Ruska's Introduction. C. Brockelmann: Arabische Litteratur (vol. 1, 220, 1898). E. O. von Lippmann: Ruska's neue Untersuchungen über die Anfänge der arabischen Alchemie (Chemiker Z., 1925; reprint, 7 p.).

CHINESE BUDDHISM

The progress of Buddhism had been so great that a reaction set in and, by 714, 12,000 monks and nuns were compelled by Hsüan Tsung (emperor from 713 to 756) to return to secular life. The same emperor, however, caused an edition of the Buddhist canon (Tripiṭaka) to be published.

The last school of Chinese Buddhism dates from the first half of the eighth century. It was introduced from Ceylon by Pu K'ung (q. v., below). Its principal scripture was the sūtra of the Sun Buddha, Vairocana—Ta^{4}-jih^{4*} ching^{1} (10470, 5642, 2122). It was called the Mi^{4*} tsung^{1} (7835, 11976), meaning Secret Teaching or Chên^{1} Yen^{2} tsung^{1} (589, 13025, 11976), meaning True Word school.

---

[d] Still authoritative in Central Asia, Northern India, and among the Turks.

[e] That is, if one does not take the Ibāḍite school into account.

[f] Leading to what we call legal fiction.

[g] Ignaz Goldziher: Progress of Islamic Science (St. Louis Congress of 1904, vol. 2, 505, 1906).

[h] The trustworthy.

[i] Ja'far was thus an 'Alid, that is a descendant of 'Alī ibn Abī Ṭālib, son-in-law of the Prophet.

The teaching of that school was distinctly Tantric, a sort of magical pantheism of which the higher thoughts were never appreciated by the Chinese, while the lower aspects appealed to their love of mystery. In 806 it was introduced into Japan, where, under the name of Shingon, it was immensely successful. The original school is extinct in China, but a large residue of Tantric superstitions has combined with Taoist delusions of the same kind and has become an essential part of Chinese thought.

Tantric speculations easily took the form of astrology. It is thus not surprising that some of the Tantrists were astrologers and mathematicians. I shall deal with two of them, Ch'ü-t'an Hsi-ta and I-hsing, in Section IV below.

PU K'UNG

Pu[1]* K'ung[1] (9456, 6595). His Hindu name was Amōghavajra or Amōgha. Singhalese Buddhist of Brahmanic lineage who came to China from Ceylon in 733 or before. He flourished at the court of three T'ang emperors in Ch'ang[2]-an[1] (450, 44) and died in 774. He wrote various Tantric treatises and exerted a great influence—on the whole an evil one—as Tantrism, Pi[4]-mi[4]*-chiao[4] (8932, 7835, 1352) became very popular, thanks to him. He taught the use of a great many magical formulas.

H. A. Giles: Biographical Dictionary (634, 1898). L. Wieger: Histoire des croyances en Chine (535–539, 1922).

CHIH SHÊNG

Chih[4] Shêng[1] (1784, 9880). Flourished c. 730. Chinese Buddhist. Author of a bibliography of 1,142[j] Buddhist works published, in Chinese, between 67 and 730, K'ai[1] yüan[2] shih[4]* chiao[4] lu[4]* (5794, 13744, 9983, 1352, 7386),[k] in 20 books. It is very comprehensive and contains biographical notices of each author (i. e., translator) and a list of 41 Buddhist catalogues previously published. I spoke of two of these in my notes on Sêng-yu (first half of sixth century) and Tao-hsüan (second half of the seventh century).

A. Wylie: Chinese Literature (207, (1867) 1902). H. A. Giles: Catalogue of Wade Collection (A, 413–415, Cambridge, 1898). L. Wieger: La Chine (427, 499, 1920).

JAPANESE BUDDHISM

The Nara period[l] (710 to 784) was in many respects the golden age of Japan. This felicity was largely due to the more complete assimilation of Chinese culture and to the progress of Buddhism, which stimulated advances in every direction. An epidemic of smallpox (mogasa), introduced from Korea into Kyūshū, in 735, spread to the other islands, and caused some panic and a renewed religious fervor. The gigantic Nara Daibutsu was cast in 749; an enormous bell dates from the same time. Both are in the Tō-dai-ji at Nara. See my note on Japanese technology in Section V below.

---

[j] Wylie says 2,278; Giles, 1,142 ?

[k] Often called K'ai-yüan-lu.

[l] Thus called because the capital was then at Nara, the earliest real city of Japan. In 784 the Emperor Kwammu built a new capital in Yamashiro and called it Heian-kyō (the capital of peace). This remained the capital (Kyōto) until 1868.

GYŌGI

Often called Gyōgi-Bosatsu.[m] Born in Korea in 670; died in 749. Bonze of the Hossō-shū. He is one of the founders of Japanese civilization. Not only did he preach Buddhism, but he caused the people to build bridges, dikes, and roads. The invention of the potter's wheel is traditionally ascribed to him.[n] He was the first to attempt a reconciliation of Buddhism with the native Shintō,[o] a pregnant endeavor which was fully developed in the following century.[p]

E. Papinot: Dictionary of Japan (134, 1909). F. Brinkley: History of the Japanese People (195, 228, 1915).

KEGON AND RITSU

Two more Buddhist sects were founded in 736 and 754 and these, together with the four sects introduced the previous century, are commonly called the Six Sects of Nara. These two sects are the Kegon and the Ritsu.

The Kegon-shū was introduced by the Chinese bonze Dōsen in 736. Its favorite scripture is the Avataṃsakasūtra (Kegonkyō), one of the main Mahāyāna writings. The Kegon sect was the earliest representative of the true Mahāyāna; that is, it was the earliest interpreter of the form of Buddhism which finally triumphed in Japan. This particular sect is represented only by 32 temples (c. 1917), of which the Tō-dai-ji, at Nara, is the earliest and the chief.

The Ritsu-shū[q] was introduced, in 754, by the Chinese bonze Kanshin[r] (three previous attempts at introduction had failed). Its scriptures were the Hīnayāna vinaya. It is now extinct, like the other Hīnayāna sects.[s] Its principal seat was at the Tōshō-daiji (Yamato).

III. PHILOSOPHICAL BACKGROUND AND GENERAL ADVANCE OF CIVILIZATION

BEDE

Baeda Venerabilis. Born c. 673, in or near Jarrow, Durham. He spent most of his life in Jarrow and died there on May 26, 735. Benedictine. English historian, scientist, theologian. The father of English history and one of the best mediaeval historians; the greatest master of chronology in the Middle Ages (R. L. Poole). He understood Greek and had some acquaintance with Hebrew. His main work is the "Historiae ecclesiasticae gentis Anglorum libri quinque" (completed in 731). His "De natura rerum" is based chiefly on Pliny and Isidore of Seville (deals with various phenomena, which are referred to natural causes; the earth is a sphere surrounded by a watery heaven). The "De loquela per gestum digitorum" (or de indigitatione) is our main (almost our only) source for

---

[m] The Emperor Shōmu (749–58) bestowed upon him the honorary titles of Dai-Sōjō (great hierarch) and Dai-Bosatsu (great Bodhisattva).

[n] It was used to make an unglazed, gray-colored porcelain called gyōgi-yaki. Of course, the potter's wheel had been invented ages before in prehistoric Egypt; the earliest literary mention occurs in Homer (q. v.).

[o] Under his influence the emperor dreamed that the Sun goddess at Ise was identical with Birushana (i. e., the Hindu Vairocana) or Dainichi (great sun)-Nyorai (another Japanese rendering of Vairocana Tathāgata).

[p] The Ryōbu-Shintō, for which see my notes on Dengyō and Kōbō daishi (first half of ninth century).

[q] Or Risshū, Kairitsu. As the introduction of the Ritsu occurred in 754, it really belongs to the following period. I speak of it here in order not to interrupt my narrative too often

[r] Or Ganjin (687 to 763). In 758 he received the name of Taishin-oshō.

[s] It has been extinct since the thirteenth century.

the study of mediaeval finger reckoning or symbolism. Bede also wrote various works on arithmetic and chronology. The De temporum ratione is particularly important. It contains a remarkable theory of tides based upon Pliny, but also upon personal observation; first mention of the establishment of a port (i. e., the mean interval between the moon's meridian passage and high water following; this interval is different in different ports). Bede's scientific knowledge is superior to that of Isidore, this superiority being due chiefly to his knowledge of Pliny.

Text and Translations—Opera omnia (6 vols., fol., 1544–1545, Paris; again 1554, 8 vols., fol., by F. Hervagius, Basel, 1563). Basel edition, reprinted at Cologne 1612, again 1688. The best edition of the complete works was given by John Allen Giles (12 vols., London, 1843–1844. It contains an English translation of the historical work and a life of Bede; the scientific tracts are in Volume VI, 1843). The edition included in Migne's Patrologia (1844) contains many spurious works.

Historia ecclesiastica: A ninth century manuscript (codex Bernensis 363), containing also other writings, has been reproduced in facsimile by Herm. Hagen: Codices graeci et latini photographice depicti, II (Leiden, 1897). Editio princeps (Strassburg, c. 1473). Many fifteenth and sixteenth century editions. The first edition of the Latin text, together with the Anglo-Saxon version by King Alfred, was edited by Abraham Wheelock (Cambridge, 1643–1644). A monumental edition was given by John Smith (Cambridge, 1722). The latest edition (a revision of Smith's) is due to Charles Plummer (2 vols., Oxford, 1896. Together with other historical writings of Bede's).

Modern editions of the Old English version have been published by Thomas Miller: Early English Texts Society (2 vols., London, 1890–1898) and by J. Schipper (790 p., Leipzig, 1897–1899). Modern English translation by L. Gidley (1870). English translations have been published in Bohn's Library and in Everyman's Library.

De natura rerum, together with two works on chronology (Basle, 1529).

General Criticism—Hendrik Gehle: De Bedae vita et scriptis (Leiden, 1838). Karl Werner: Beda der Ehrwürdige und seine Zeit (Wien, 1875, 2d ed. 1881. Important). William Hunt, in Dictionary of National Biography (vol. 4, 98–105, 1885). Charles Plummer's introduction to his edition of the Historia ecclesiastica (Oxford, 1896). William Bright: Chapters of Early English Church History (3d ed., Oxford, 1897). Sir Henry H. Howorth: The Golden Days of the Early English Church. From the Arrival of Theodore (669) to the Death of Bede (3 vols., London, 1917). Bishop George Forrest Browne: The Venerable Bede. His Life and Writings (340 p., London, 1919. First ed., 1879).

Special Criticism—Georg Wetzel: Die Chronicen des Baeda (Diss., 62 p., Halle, 1878). Karl Welzhofer: Beda's Citate aus der naturalis historia des Plinius (Abhdl. Wilhelm von Christ dargebracht, 25–41, München, 1891). Thomas Miller: Place Names in the English Bede and the Localization of the Manuscripts (Quellen und Forschungen zur Sprach- und Culturgeschichte der germanischen Völker, 78, 82 p., Strassburg, 1896). P. Duhem: Système du Monde (vol. 3, 16–20, 1915). Paul Lehmann: Wert und Echtheit einer Beda abgesprochenen Schrift (Sitzungsber. der Bayer. Ak. der Wiss., philos. Kl., 21 p., 1919. Liber quaestionum, partly genuine; Isis, VII, 184).

Apocryphal—Friedrich Albrecht Reum: De temporibus, ein echtes Werk des Abtes Aelfric (Diss., Leipzig, 48 p., Halle a. S., 1887. This is an abridgement of Bede's De natura rerum; it was included by Thomas Wright, in his Popular Treatises on Science, 1841; Aelfric wrote it probably in 991). For the Pseudo-Bede, author of De mundi caelestis terrestrisque constitutione liber, see first half of ninth century.

For Byzantine philosophy, see my note on John of Damascus in Section II.

KUMĀRILA

Also: Kumārilasvāmin, Kumārilabhaṭṭa, Tutāta. Flourished in southern India[t] about the end of the seventh century and in the first half of the eighth century. Mīmāṃsist philosopher. He wrote a great commentary on the Bhāshya, divided into three parts (the Ślokavārttika, the Tantravārttika, and the Tupṭīkā). It is very erudite and ingenious, but a great part of it is devoted to hair-splitting and sterile arguments; it is violently anti-Buddhist. Naturally enough, for Buddhists denied the sacredness and infallibility of the Veda.

The founder of the Mīmāṃsā system of philosophy was Jaimini, of whom we know nothing. According to that system, the Veda is uncreated and eternal. It is essentially a collection of rules for the interpretation of the Veda and the accomplishment of rites. Mīmāmsā literalism led naturally to elaborate philological investigations. The Pūrvamīmāṃsāsūtra ascribed to Jaimini is certainly a very ancient work, pre-Christian. The earliest extant commentary on Jaimini is the Bhāshya by Śabarasvāmin, dating probably from the fifth century (Englished by G. Jhā, in Indian Thought, vol. 2, 1911). Two ulterior commentaries based upon Śabarasvāmin's commentary caused the fission of the Mīmāṃsā into two schools; they were (in chronological order) the Brihatī (the great commentary) made by Prabhākara (Englished by G. Jhā, in Indian Thought, vols. 2 and 3, 1911), and Kumārila's commentary.

Texts—The Ślokavārttika was edited in the Benares Sanskrit Series (1898–99). Englished by Gañgānātha Jhā, together with extracts from other commentaries (Bibliotheca Indica, Calcutta, 1907, 1900–1908).

The Tantravārttika, edited in the Benares Sanskrit Series, in many parts, by Gañgādhara Śāstrī (1,184 p., 1903). Englished by Gañgānātha Jhā (Bibliotheca Indica, many parts, Calcutta, 1903–1924).

The Ṭupṭīkā, edited in the Benares Sanskrit Series by Gañgādhara Śāstrī (Benares, 1904).

Criticism—M. Winternitz: Geschichte der Indischen Litteratur (Bd. 3, Leipzig, mainly p. 425–428, 1922).

MING HUANG

Ming[2] Huang[2] (7946, 5106). His personal name was Li[3] Lung[2]-chi[1] (6884, 7504, 850). Born in 685; emperor from 712 to 756; he died in 762. Sixth emperor of the T'ang dynasty. His rule marks the climax and the end of the Augustan age of China. He was a patron of literature and founded the Imperial Academy, called Han-lin Yüan,[u] which had charge of the historical and scientific undertakings of the empire. It is possibly under Ming Huang's reign that the invention of block printing was completed;[v] this date is consistent with the fact that the earliest printed documents in existence are the charms printed c. 770 by order of the empress Shōtoku (q. v., next chapter)—it would have taken so much time and not more for the art to reach Japan. The earliest printed documents of China were lost because of the revolutions and persecutions which followed Ming Huang's reign.[w]

---

[t] Kumārila apparently had some knowledge of Dravidian languages.

[u] Han[4]-lin[2] (3828, 7157) means forest of pencils; yüan[4] (13752), college or academy.

[v] For which see my note on Chinese technology in the second half of the sixth century. Rubbings, printed silks, stencils, seals, stamps introduced the invention gradually. Ample archaeological evidence for every one of these steps was found at Tun-huang and at Turfan.

[w] It is the Buddhists who were persecuted, and the earliest printed documents were in all probability Buddhist texts. The earliest printed book extant is a copy of the "Diamond sūtra" of 868, in Chinese (see my note on technology in the second half of the ninth century).

Further Penetration of Chinese Culture into Japan

During the eighth and ninth centuries Japan made gigantic efforts to assimilate Chinese culture and to imitate it as closely as possible. Especially during the Nara period (710 to 784), every effort was made to follow the lead given by the Chinese capital, Si-an-fu. As instances of the penetration of Chinese ideas and customs, I shall briefly mention the following facts:

In 701, the annual celebration in honor of Confucius began.

In 708, the first mint was established.

I do not know when the University (Daigaku or Daigaku-ryō) of Nara was established, but it existed already in 733.[x] Indeed, in early days rice-fields were granted, whose revenues served to support the students. These rice-fields were called kwangaku-den. Shōmu-tennō, forty-fifth emperor (724 to 748) was the first to make such a grant to the University in 733.[y] Another grant was made by Kwammu-tennō, fiftieth emperor (782 to 805) in 785. University teaching of those days was largely restricted to myōhōdō (or myōhō), i. e., Chinese law.

In 735, a Chinese scholar became the head of the University of Nara.

In the same year, Kibi Makibi (q. v., Section IX) returned from China, full of learning and prestige. In the same year also, or in 736, the bonze Gembō returned, bringing with him 5,000 Buddhist books. He died in 746.

E. Papinot: Historical Dictionary (63, 338, 588, 1909). F. Brinkley: History of the Japanese People (1914). T. F. Carter: Invention of Printing in China (33, 1925).

Many further evidences of Chinese influence will be found in the following sections; it is not too much to say that every new departure was made under Chinese stimulation, but further developments very quickly assumed a Japanese flavor.

IV. LATIN AND CHINESE MATHEMATICS AND ASTRONOMY

Latin mathematics—we might almost say Latin learning—was represented almost exclusively by the Englishman Bede, dealt with in the previous section.

Eastward Transmission of Hindu Mathematics in the Wake of Tantrism

CH'Ü-T'AN HSI-TA

Ch'ü[2]-t'an[2] Hsi[2]*-ta[2]* (3081, 10700, 4138, 10473). This name is a transcription of the Sanskrit Gotama Siddha (Gautama Siddharta).[z] Hindu-Chinese astrologer, who flourished at the T'ang court in the first quarter of the eighth century. He wrote a great treatise on Tantric divination and astrology, in 110 books, called the Ta[4] T'ang[2] K'ai[1]-yüan[2] chan[1] ching[1] (10470, 10767, 5744, 13744, 267, 2122)—astrological treatise relative to the K'ai-yüan era, 713–742, which is valuable because it contains (Books 103 to 105) a detailed account of several ancient systems of chronology, notably the Hindu system, chiu[3]-chih[2]*-li[4]* (2263, 1795, 6924) as translated by the author from the Sanskrit. This Hindu system is specially important, because it implied the Hindu decimal notation and rules, which were thus introduced—or reintroduced[a]—into China. The circle was

---

[x] It dates back probably to the very beginning of the century.

[y] During the reign of the same emperor a public drug-store (shiyaku-in) was established.

[z] For other astronomers named Chü-t'an, see first half of seventh century.

[a] For a possible introduction at an earlier date, see my notes on Chinese mathematics in the second half of the sixth century. On the other hand, the earliest trace of the use of zero in China dates only from the middle of the thirteenth century.

divided into 360 degrees, each degree into 60 minutes. Arithmetical computations were done in writing.

Text—The Chiu-chih-li was reedited in 1617 by Chang[1] I[1]*-hsi[1] (416, 5342, 4115) and has often been reprinted since.

Criticism—A. Wylie: Chinese Literature (131, (1867) 1902). Y. Mikami: Development of Mathematics in China and Japan (58–60, Leipzig, 1912). L. Wieger: La Chine (502, 524, 1920).

I-HSING

I[1]*-hsing[2] (5342, 4624). This being the religious name of Chang[1] Sui[4] (416, 10402). Born in 683, died in 727. Buddhist (Tantric) bonze. Astronomer and magician. His Ta[4]-yen[3] li[4]* (10470, 13113, 6924), a calendar begun in 721 and completed in 727, was a great improvement upon previous ones, including the Chiu-chih. It involved problems of indeterminate analysis which I-hsing solved by the method called ta[4]-yen[3] shu[4]* (10470, 13113, 10053). He constructed a new uranorama, wherein the movements of the celestial bodies were indicated relatively to the ecliptic, instead of the equator; it was moved by water power (?). He was ordered by the emperor to investigate the chronological and arithmetical notions which Ch'ü-t'an Hsi-ta had introduced from India, but died before the completion of his work.

H. A. Giles: Chinese Biographical Dictionary (p. 349, 1898. The dates of birth and death according to Giles are 672 and 717). Y. Mikami: Development of Mathematics in China and Japan (p. 60, 61, 63, 65, 1912). According to Alex. Wylie (Chinese Researches, Part III, 155, Shanghai, 1897), I-hsing would have noticed an Eastern magnetic declination (?).

The earliest Chinese catalogue of stars, the Hsing[1]-ching[1], (4602, 2122), is supposed to date from the Earlier Han, or even from an earlier time. The text that has come down to us is an undated T'ang elaboration.

L. Wieger: La Chine (195, 519, 1920).

V. BYZANTINE AND MUSLIM ALCHEMY; JAPANESE TECHNOLOGY

HELIODOROS THE ALCHEMIST

Ἡλιόδωρος. Flourished under the Emperor Theodosios, probably Theodosios III, who reigned from 716 to 717.[b] Christian alchemist. He dedicated to Theodosios a very obscure alchemical poem on the mystic art of the philosophers (περὶ τῆς τῶν φιλοσόφων μυστικῆς τέχνης; 268 lines). He is probably the author of three other poems of about the same length and style and dealing with the same subject.

Text—Günther Goldschmidt: Heliodori carmina quattuor ad fidem codicis Casselani. Religionsgeschichtliche Versuche und Vorarbeiten, Bd. 19, H. 2, 60 p. Giessen, 1923. (Text of four Greek poems, with Latin introduction. The four poems are ascribed in the text respectively to Heliodoros, Theophrastos, Ierotheus, Archelaos, but Goldschmidt claims they all are of the same eighth century author, Heliodoros).

Criticism—E. C. von Lippmann: Alchemie (95, 1919).

For Muslim alchemy, see my note on Ja'far al-Ṣādiq, in Section II.

---

[b] E. O. v. Lippmann (Alchemie, 95, 1919) assumes that Theodosios I is meant, who ruled from 379 to 395; Boll (Pauly-Wissowa, vol. 15, p. 19, 1912) assumes that it is Theodosios II, who ruled from 408 to 450. I follow the latest editor of the text, Günther Goldschmidt, whose opinion is based on stylistic grounds.

Japanese Technology

In my note on Gyōgi, in Section II, I have referred to the beginning of Japanese ceramics and to the construction of bridges and roads which was encouraged by him. The most famous of these early Japanese roads was the Nakasendō (also called Kiso-kaidō, because it follows the (river) Kiso-gawa for a long distance), constructed in 702 to connect Kyōto and Edo; it counted 69 relays (eki).

When I spoke of the progress of Buddhism during the first half of the Nara period, I alluded to the gigantic statue of the Buddha which was built at Nara, within the precincts of the Tō-dai-ji, a temple of the Kegon-shū. The construction of the Tō-dai-ji Daibutsu was not simply a great event from the artistic and religious point of view; it had also some interesting technological aspects.

The erection of the Daibutsu was ordered by the Emperor Shōmu in 743. The image was built up with bronze plates soldered together. The sitting Buddha was more than 16 meters high, the face alone being almost 5 meters long; attendant bosatsu on either side were above 9 meters high. The casting was done by a Korean who had established himself in Kuninaka (Yamato) and was named Kuninaka Kimimaro. The actual work of casting was begun in 747 and was completed in three years, after seven failures. The construction of the image required the use of 986,030,000 pounds of copper, and 870 pounds of refined gold were needed for the gilding of its surface. Not enough gold could be imported from China for this purpose; happily in 749 some native gold was discovered in Mutsu. The ceremony of unveiling ("opening the eyes," kaigen) took place in 752.

E. Papinot: Historical Dictionary (318, 325, 429, 1909). F. Brinkley: History of the Japanese People (193, 1915).

VI. JAPANESE, CHINESE, AND LATIN GEOGRAPHY

The Fūdoki

In 713, the Empress Gemmei (708–714) ordered every province of Japan to submit to her the so-called fūdoki (Records of natural features). These were gazetteers describing or enumerating towns, villages, rivers, mountains, productions, traditions, and remarkable occurrences of every kind. Only four of these records are extant; they are those dealing with Hitachi, Harima, Izumo, and Bungo. That of Izumo is the only complete one.

Papinot's Dictionary (85, 1909). Brinkley: History of Japan (3, 1915)

The Chinese Expedition of 747

A Chinese army crossed the Hindu Kush in 747, following the glacier pass of the Darkot (15,400 feet), and thus penetrated the valleys which lead into Kashmir. The passages in the Chinese annals, relative to that expedition, have been published by Edouard Chavannes in his "Documents sur les Tou-kiue (Turcs) occidentaux" (St. Pétersbourg, 1903).

Sir Aurel Stein: A Chinese Expedition across the Pamirs and Hindu Kush (Indian Antiquary, vol. 52, 1923. Of special interest, because Sir Aurel has personal experience of that region; Isis, VII, 184).

For Bede's theory of tides, see my note on Bede in Section III.

FERGIL

Virgilius of Salzburg, St. Fergil. Born in Ireland c. 710, died in Salzburg 784. Irish monk; Bishop of Salzburg; apostle of Carinthia; canonized in 1233. He got into trouble with the Roman church c. 748 because of his belief in the existence of the antipodes.[c]

Vergilius is the first name quoted in Gustav Hellmann's chronology of German meteorology because of his "Decalogium de metheorologicis impressionibus." (Repertorium der deutschen Meteorologie, p. 965, Leipzig, 1883). Herman vander Linden: Virgile de Salzbourg et les théories cosmographiques au VIIIe siècle (Bull. de l'Acad. royale de Belgique (lettres), 163–187, 1914; Isis, II, 437).

VII. JAPANESE AND LATIN HISTORIOGRAPHY

Japanese Historiography

If one except the apocryphal Kujiki, ascribed to prince Shōtoku (q. v., first half of seventh century), the earliest Japanese history is the Kojiki, or Furu-koto-bumi ("Records of Ancient things") which was edited in 711–712 by Ōno Yasumaro (d. 723). It retraces the history of Japan from the creation to the death of the empress Suiko in 628 (3 vols.).

The second history, in point of date, is the Nihongi, or Yamato-bumi, Nihonki ("Chronicle of Japan"), which was compiled in 714 by various scholars, using the materials collected by other scholars in the second half of the seventh century. It was written for the most part in the Manyō syllabary.[d] Hence it is sometimes called Kana Nihongi (Syllabic chronicle). A revision was completed in 720 by Ōno Yasumaro and Prince Toneri;[e] this is called the Nihon shoki (Written Chronicle of Japan). The Nihon shoki deals with the period extending from the creation to the abdication of the Empress Jitō in 696 (in 31 volumes, of which one is lost).

These two works are not very critical, yet they are extremely important, because there is no other authority for all that concerns the ancient history of Japan, and also because practically the whole of Shintō mythology is contained in them. These works are very different. The Kojiki is essentially based on native traditions as remembered by one Hieda no Are, it is thus purely Japanese; the Nihon shoki, on the contrary, is the result of long literary labor inspired by the historical Classics of China, and is thus essentially Chinese.

The "Nihon shoki" was the first of the Six National Histories (Riku-kokushi), the five others being modeled upon it. They are:

"Zoku Nihongi," or "Shoku-Nihon-ki" ("Supplementary Chronicles of Japan"), from 697 to 791, in 40 volumes, completed in 798 by Fujiwara Tsuginawa (727–796) and others.

"Nihon kōki" ("Later Chronicles of Japan") from 792 to 833, in 40 volumes (only 10 extant), completed in 840 by Fujiwara Otsugu (773–843).

"Zoku (or Shoku) Nihon kōki" ("Supplementary Later Chronicles"), from 834 to 850, in 20 volumes, completed in 869 by Fujiwara Yoshifusa (804–872).

---

[c] "Quod alius mundus et alii homines sub terra sint seu sol et luna" (Monumenta Germaniae historica, Epistolae, III, 360, No. 80; letter from Pope Zachary to St. Boniface in 748). The last four words may be a later interpolation.

[d] For which see my note on Kibi Makibi in Section IX.

[e] Toneri-shinnō (676–735), son of the emperor Temmu.

"Montoku jitsu-roku" ("True Annals of Montoku"), from 851 to 858, in 10 volumes, completed in 879 by Fujiwara Mototsune (836–891).

"Sandai jitsu-roku" ("True Annals of Three Reigns), from 859 to 887, in 50 volumes, completed in 901 by Fujiwara Tòkihira (871–909).

Text—English translation of the Kojiki, by Basil Hall Chamberlain (Trans. Asiatic Soc. Japan, Supp. to vol. 10, 490 p., Yokohama, 1882, 1883).

The Nihongi was the first Japanese history to be published (1589–1610). Until that time only Sūtras and Chinese classics had been printed in Japan. There are many editions of this fundamental text. Japanese text, with French translation by Léon de Rosny (vol. 1, Paris, 1887). German translation of books 22 to 30, by Karl Florenz (Mitt. Deuts. Ges., Supp., 5 parts, Tokyo, 1892–1897), and of books 1 and 2 by the same (*ibidem*, Supp., 350 p., Tokyo, 1901). English translation by W. G. Aston (Trans. and Proc. Japan Society, 2 vols., London, 1896).

Criticism—Cl. E. Maistre: La littérature historique du Japon des origines aux Ashikaga (Bull. de l'école française d'Extrême orient, vol. 3, 564–596, 1903; vol. 4, 580–616, 1904. Very learned work, with abundant Japanese and Western bibliography). E. Papinot: Historical Dictionary of Japan (Tokyo, 1909). F. Brinkley: History of the Japanese People (London, 1915).

For the contemporary Latin historiography, see my note on Bede in Section III.

VIII. BARBARIAN, BYZANTINE, MUSLIM, CHINESE, AND JAPANESE LAW

Barbarian Law

The later code of the Alamanni,[f] called "Lex Alamannorum," dates from the period 709 to 730.

Text—Edited by K. Lehmann (Mon. Germ. hist., Leges).

The Bavarian law (Lex Baiuwariorum) is partly based upon the Alamannic. It probably dates from the period 743 to 749.

Text—Edited by Joh. Merkel (*ibidem*).

Bibliography with regard to both codes in August Potthast (Bibliotheca, 723, 724, 1896).

Byzantine Law

A revised abstract of Justinianian law was made by order of Leon the Isaurian (Emperor of the East from 717 to 741), in 740. It was called Ἐκλογὴ *τῶν νόμων ἐν συντόμῳ γενομένη ἀπὸ τῶν ἰνστιτούτων, τῶν διγέστων, τοῦ κώδικος, τῶν νεαρῶν τοῦ μεγάλου Ἰουστινιανοῦ διατάξεων καὶ ἐπιδιόρθωσις εἰς τὸ φιλανθρωπότερον*. Other codes, of a more special kind, were compiled under his direction: the agricultural law (Νόμος *γεωργικός*),[g] the Rhodian navigation law (Νόμος Ῥοδίων *ναυτικός*), and the military law (Νόμος *στρατιωτικός*).

Text—Edited by K. E. Zachariae von Lingenthal, in Collectio librorum iuris Graeco-Romani ineditorum (Vol. I, 1–52, Leipzig, 1852). New edition by Ant. G. Monferratus (Athens, 1889).

Criticism—C. Krumbacher: Byzantinische Litteratur (605, 609, 1897).

For Muslim law, see my note on Abū Ḥanīfa in Section II.

---

[f] For the earlier, see first half of seventh century.

[g] Of special interest, because it shows the great influence gradually exerted by Slavs upon Byzantine institutions.

WU CHING

Wu[2] Ching[1] (12748, 2173). Born at Pien[4]-chou[1] (9205, 2444), Honan; died in 742. Chinese student of government. He wrote a treatise on the principles of government in 10 books and 40 chapters, Chên[1]-kuan[1] chêng[4]-yao[4] (607, 6363, 692, 12889), in the form of conversations between the emperor T'ai Tsung (q. v., previous chapter) and his ministers.

A. Wylie: Chinese Literature (32, (1867) 1902). H. A. Giles: Biographical Dictionary, 1898, 881.

Japanese Law

The Ōmi ryō (q. v., second half of seventh century) is lost. The earliest code of law is the so-called Daihō[h] -ryōritsu (in 11 volumes), a revision of the former and a continuation of the reforms begun in the Taikwa era, promulgated in 701 by order of the emperor Mommu,[i] under the direction of Fujiwara Fuhito (659–720). It is hardly necessary to add that it was largely based upon Chinese law.

The Daihō laws were revised in 718 by order of the Empress Genshō, again under the direction of Fuhito, and were then called the Yōrō laws.[j] To the laws were added bodies of official rules (kyaku) and of rites and customs (shiki).

These rules and customs were redrafted three times in the ninth century and in the beginning of the tenth century, each time under the supervision of a Fujiwara. These three versions were later named Rules and Regulations of the Three Generations (San-dai-kyaku-shiki). All these editions of the Daihō laws were but successive stages in the assimilation of Japanese to Chinese tradition.

A brief analysis of these laws may be found in Brinkley: History of the Japanese people (176–184, 1915). See also in Papinot's Dictionary (1909), the articles Ritsu-ryō-kyaku-shiki, Taihō-ryōritsu, Shimotsukenu Komaro.

The Daihō-ryō gives us valuable information on education and on medicine. See Y. Fujikawa: Geschichte der Medizin in Japan (7–9, Tokyo, 1911. Contains a list of the Chinese medical works then used in Japan).

IX. ARABIC AND JAPANESE PHILOLOGY

AL-ḤAJJĀJ IBN YŪSUF

Abū Muḥammad al-Ḥajjāj ibn Yūsuf. Died at Wāsiṭ,[k] in 714, aged 53 Muslim years. Arabic soldier[l] and grammarian. Governor of 'Irāq under 'Abd al-Malik. He deserves to be quoted here because the birth of the grammatical school of Baṣra was largely due to his interest and influence.[m] Besides, an invention of tremendous importance is ascribed to him, namely, the use of the

[h] Or Taihō (Great treasure), nengō corresponding to the period of 701 to 704.

[i] Mommu-tennō, forty-second emperor, 697 to 707.

[j] Yōrō being the nengō corresponding to the years 717 to 724.

[k] City founded by himself in 703. It was named Wāsiṭ (intermediate) because of its location between the two capitals Baṣra and Kūfa.

[l] Sadly famous for his ferocity.

[m] Two schools of Arabic grammar and humanism developed during the eighth century, one at Baṣra, the other at Kūfa; the first being the earliest and most famous. Before the foundation of Bagdad, Baṣra and Kūfa were the main centers of Arabic culture outside of Arabia. See my note on Abū-l-Aswad (second half of seventh century).

vowel marks (ḥarakāt) and of diacritical points (nuqaṭ) placed above or below similar consonants.[n]

Ibn Khallikān: De Slane (vol. 1, 356–365, 1842). Jean Périer: Vie d'al-Hadjdjādj ibn Yousof d'après les sources arabes (Bibl. de l'école des hautes études, 385 p., Paris, 1904). E. G. Browne: Literary History of Persia (vol. 1, 230, 1908).

KIBI MAKIBI

Also Makibi alone, or Kibi no Mabi. Kibi is the name of a Japanese region where he lived. His original name was Shimotsumichi Asomi. Born in 693; he went to China in 716, returning home in 735. In 752 he went again to China as an ambassador. He died in 775. Japanese statesman and Confucianist; one of the main artisans of the reorganization of his country upon Chinese patterns. He obtained in China a profound knowledge of "history, the five classics, jurisprudence, mathematics, philosophy, calendar-making, and other sciences." After his return in 735, he enjoyed considerable prestige and influence. He is said to have introduced into Japan the game of go, the biwa (a four-stringed lute), and the art of embroidery. He was the tutor of the empress Shōtoku (q. v., next chapter).

In my note on the Nihongi (in Section VII), I observed that the greatest part of these annals were written by means of the Manyō-gana (or Manyō syllabary), that is to say, they were written in Japanese language, using Chinese characters phonetically. The Chinese characters were written in full. Now, the idea must have occurred to many intelligent men that, inasmuch as the same characters were continually repeated, it would be simpler to abbreviate them; in fact, common practice must have led to such abbreviations long before the thought originated of standardizing them. The invention of the earliest Japanese syllabary (kana), namely the kata-kana, is traditionally ascribed to Makibi. This kana was simply a table of 47 symbols derived from abbreviated Chinese ideographs, which made possible a swift phonetic reproduction of the Japanese language, syllable by syllable. A second syllabary, the hiragana, is said to have been invented by Kōbō daishi (q. v., first half of the ninth century). It is certain that both kana were known and used before the end of the ninth century, but their ascription to Makibi and Kōbō can not be checked. These syllables (or variants of them) are used unto this day to write Japanese, together with Chinese characters.

E. Papinot: Historical Dictionary (274, 1909). F. Brinkley: History of the Japanese People (1915).

For information on the kana see, for example, the introduction to F. Brinkley's Unabridged Japanese-English Dictionary (Tōkyō, 1896), or Japanese grammars.

---

[n] This was probably borrowed from the (then) new form of Syriac writing, itself influenced by Greek usage. See my note on Jacob of Edessa (second half of seventh century).

CHAPTER XXVIII

THE TIME OF JĀBIR IBN ḤAIYĀN

(Second Half of Eighth Century)

I. Survey of Science in Second Half of Eighth Century. II. Religious Background. III. Cultural Background, East and West. IV. Muslim and Latin Mathematics and Astronomy. V. Muslim and Latin Alchemy; Japanese Technology. VI. Muslim, Chinese, and Japanese Natural History. VII. Latin and Chinese Geography. VIII. Latin, Syriac, Muslim, Hindu, Tibetan, Chinese, and Japanese Medicine. IX. Latin, Muslim, and Japanese Historiography. X. Muslim Philology.

I. SURVEY OF SCIENCE IN SECOND HALF OF EIGHTH CENTURY

1. The intellectual relaxation which characterized the second half of the seventh century and the first half of the eighth, at least as far as Europe and the Near East were concerned, was followed by a period of renewed activity. This was almost entirely due to Muslim initiative, for the Carolingian renaissance did not really begin until the end of the century. It is thus entirely proper to give to this period, which marks the beginning of Muslim science, an Arabic name. Yet to call it the time of Jābir is somewhat of a challenge. Let it be so! An elaborate study of all the Jābir texts, whether Arabic or Latin, is one of the most urgent and promising tasks of scholarship. And even if that study did not substantiate the hopes of some Arabists, Jābir would still remain a very impressive personality, at once because of his own achievements and because of the glamour traditionally attached to him.

2. *Religious Background*—An anti-Talmudic movement, the so-called Qaraism, initiated by Anan ben David, is of importance because it considerably influenced Jewish thought for some four centuries. Qaraism did to some extent for Israel what the Protestant Reformation did for Christianity.

The greatest disciple of Abū Ḥanīfa, the Qāḍī Abū Yūsuf, wrote a legal treatise on taxation which is still authoritative among the Ḥanīfites to-day. The second of the four orthodox schools of Islam, the Mālikite, was founded by Mālik ibn Anas. This same Mālik compiled the earliest collection of traditions.

A Buddhist renaissance was initiated in Tibet by King Ti-song De-tsen, with the assistance of the Hindu guru Padma-sambhava. The specific form of Tibetan Buddhism, Lamaism, may be dated back to this time: it was a mixture of Tantrism with various Himālayan superstitions.

Wu K'ung, following the memorable examples of Fa Hsien, Hsüan Tsang, and I-ching, sojourned a long time in India in order to collect books and relics and to obtain a deeper knowledge of Buddhism. The earliest Christian monument of China, a Nestorian stela, was erected at Ch'ang-an in 781. Its existence is of considerable archaeological interest; it gives some color of plausibility to the theories according to which Nestorianism influenced some of the Mahāyāna doctrines. However, this matter is still under dispute; this much is certain: if Chinese Buddhism was at all influenced by Christianity, the influence either was very slight or it was soon smothered by more powerful ones.

3. *Cultural Background, East and West*—Many rulers used their authority to promote the intellectual welfare and progress of the peoples which Fate had intrusted to them. I have already spoken of the efforts made by the Tibetan king Ti-song De-tsen. Two of the 'Abbāsid caliphs distinguished themselves greatly in this respect: the second, al-Manṣūr, who founded Bagdad, and, even more so, the fifth, Hārūn-al-Rashīd, whose fame has been immortalized by many legends. Both encouraged the work of the translators who were busily unlocking the treasures of Greek knowledge.

While Hārūn was ruling Islām, Charlemagne was leading the Christian West. At the very end of the century, on Christmas 800, he revived the imperial dignity, being crowned by the Pope, in Rome, Emperor of the West (Holy Roman Empire). With the help of an English monk, Alcuin, Charlemagne undertook a number of educational reforms. Alcuin took pains to transmit to the Franks the learning and culture accumulated by Bede. He was by far the noblest figure of that time in the West, but even like Bede in the previous period, he was almost entirely alone.

Japanese civilization was fostered by the energetic solicitude of the empress Shōtoku, who ruled twice, from 749 to 758 and from 765 to 770. It was during her first reign that the Daibutsu of Nara was completed.

4. *Muslim and Latin Mathematics and Astronomy*—With the sole exception mentioned at the end of this section, all of the mathematical and astronomical work of this period was done by Muslims. It is interesting to recall that the mathematical work of the previous period had been done almost exclusively by Chinese. In both cases some amount of stimulation had come from India, and even as we witnessed in the previous chapter the eastward transmission of Hindu mathematics, we shall now find evidences of their westward transmission. But in the case of Muslim mathematics, the Hindu stimulation was accompanied and completed by a much more powerful one, which failed to reach the Far East until many centuries later—the Greek one.

Ibrāhīm al-Fazārī is said to have been the first Muslim to construct astrolabes. Ya'qūb ibn Ṭāriq and Muhammad, son of Ibrāhīm al-Fazārī, are the first to be mentioned in connection with Hindu mathematics: Ya'qūb met at the court of al-Manṣūr, a Hindu astronomer called Kankah (?), who acquainted him with the Siddhānta, and Muḥammad was ordered to translate it. The physician al-Baṭrīq translated Ptolemy's Quadripartitum. Two astrologers, one of them a Jew named Māshāllāh, the other a Persian called al-Naubakht, worked together to make the measurements necessary for the building of Bagdad. Al-Naubakht's son, al-Faḍl, wrote astrological treatises and translations from the Persian into Arabic.

The only mathematical writer in Europe was Alcuin, who composed some very elementary texts for teaching purposes. One of them is interesting because it contains the earliest examples of arithmetical problems which remained for many centuries a permanent feature of school-books (problems of pursuit).

5. *Muslim and Latin Alchemy, Japanese technology*—It is noteworthy that the earliest alchemical texts in Arabic and Latin are contemporaneous, that is, if our dating of them is correct. The most famous alchemist of Islām, Jābir ibn Ḥaiyān, seems to have had a good experimental knowledge of a number of chemical facts; he was also an able theoretician, but it is impossible to appreciate his scientific merit with any finality until a comparative study of all the writings ascribed to him and to Geber has been completed.

The Compositiones ad tingenda date probably from the time of Charlemagne, but they represent in the main a much older—an Hellenistic—tradition. The recipes are technical or practical rather than alchemical or speculative. The Mappae clavicula is another collection of the same kind, representing the same tradition and having the same practical purposes, but probably of a somewhat later period.

During her second reign, the empress Shōtoku ordered the *printing* of a great number of charms. Some of these charms are still extant, being the earliest printed documents of any country. In all probability, printing had been practiced in China before and imported thence into Japan, together with a great many other elements of Chinese culture. If similar charms had been printed in China, the exportation of the printed leaves, or of the blocks, or of the invention itself would naturally follow the transmission of religious ideas. During the rule of the emperor Kwammu, at the end of the century, the cotton industry was introduced into Japan (?).

6. *Muslim, Chinese, and Japanese Natural History*—The Arab al-Aṣma'ī composed various books on the horse, on the camel, on wild animals, on the making of man, which offer some scientific interest, though their purpose was rather anecdotic and philological.

Lu Yü wrote the earliest book on tea; it is a very comprehensive treatise.

The cultivation of cotton is said to have been introduced into Japan from India at the end of the century.

7. *Latin and Chinese Geography*—The historian Paulus Diaconus suggested a novel theory of tides; that theory is wrong but curious. The Spanish monk Beatus drew a map of the world which is one of the earliest Christian maps extant.

Chia Tan completed in 801 a map of China and of the barbaric countries surrounding it. This was, as far as I am aware, the earliest map of a large part of the world on a large scale (20 miles to an inch). The same Chia Tan compiled a series of itineraries from China to Tongking, Korea, Central Asia, India, and Mesopotamia.

8. *Latin, Syriac, Muslim, Hindu, Tibetan, Chinese, and Japanese Medicine*—There was no eminent physician in the Latin West, but of course medicine continued to be practiced and ancient traditions were kept alive in the Benedictine monasteries.

Theophilos of Edessa, a Maronite father, prepared some translations from Greek into Syriac, including one of Galen.

The first member of an illustrious Nestorian family of physicians, the Bakhtyashū', appeared at this time. This was George son of Gabriel. He is said to have been the first to translate medical works into Arabic. Other medical translations were made by Ibn al-Muqaffa' and by al-Baṭrīq.

Two Sanskrit treatises, one dealing with pathology and the other with therapeutics, date probably from this time. The former is ascribed to Mādhavakara, the latter to Vṛinda, but it is probable that these two names cover the same personality.

The best-known Tibetan treatise on medicine, called the Four Tantras, is said to have been published during the rule of Ti-song De-tsen. That treatise is still the basis of the native medical teaching.

Wang Tao published in 752 a very elaborate medical treatise entitled "Important Secrets of the Outer Terrace." In 761, Wang Ping compiled the earliest commentary on Huang Ti's "Simple Questions."

The Chinese physician Kanjin came to Japan in 755. Toward the end of the century, the Japanese physician and educator, Wake Hiroyo, compiled a treatise on materia medica, upon the model of the Chinese pên-ts'ao.

9. *Latin, Muslim, and Japanese Historiography*—Paulus Diaconus wrote a history of the Lombards and another of the diocese of Metz.

Ibn al-Muqaffa' translated various books from Pahlawī into Arabic, mainly the Persian annals and the tales of Kalīla wa-Dimna. The earliest biography of Muḥammad was written by Ibn Isḥāq, but we know it only through a later recension. Various other works dealing with Arabian history and antiquities were compiled by Abū 'Ubaida, al-Aṣma'ī, Hishām ibn Muḥammad, and al-Wāqidī.

The second of the Six National Histories of Japan, the Zoku Nihongi, was completed in 798.

9 bis. *Muslim and Latin Law*—I have already dealt with Muslim law, inseparable from theology, in Section II. The only important juridical publications of the West were those ordered by Charlemagne; but they do not really belong to this period, because they date from the beginning of the ninth century only.

10. *Muslim Philology*—Arabic grammar finally took shape within this period. Khalīl ibn Aḥmad, of the school of Baṣra, was especially active in this field. He systematized Arabic prosody, developed the notion of mensural music, and began the compilation of the first Arabic lexicon. The first Arabic grammar, called "The Book," was written by his disciple, the Persian Sībawaihi.

11. *Final Remarks*—In spite of the contributions which were possibly made by the alchemist Jābir and of some Chinese geographical work, this period can hardly be called one of creation. But its cultural importance is very great. The transmission of knowledge and its reassimilation by new peoples went on briskly in many places. Chinese culture continued to pour into Japan and to begin there a new development. However, it is in Lower Mesopotamia, the Arabian 'Irāq, that the greatest intellectual activity could be observed. A new concentration of culture was being accomplished with youthful energy in the newly founded cities of Bagdad, Baṣra, and Kūfa—comparable in many respects to that which had taken place centuries before in Alexandria. Streams of knowledge were converging in the Caliphate from the Byzantine Empire, from Persia, and from India. But this new concentration was not by any means as easy as the old Alexandrian one; that had been mainly a prolongation of the Greek culture, with a few foreign additions of minor importance. On the contrary, the vehicle of the new Muslim civilization was a language which had never been used before for any scientific purpose. Almost every bit of knowledge had to be translated either from Greek, or from Sanskrit, or from Pahlawī before it could be assimilated. And not only that, but these interpretations necessitated the creation of a philosophic and scientific terminology which did not exist. When one takes all this into consideration, instead of being surprised at the relative smallness of the first harvest, one can not help admiring the immensity of the effort. This effort was of such a nature that no people could have endured it for a long time, but only during a period of exaltation and youthful optimism. It must be added that the early Muslim men of science were apparently bewildered by the amount of knowledge pouring in upon them from East and West and do not seem to have realized at once the overwhelming superiority of the western source. Indeed, how could they realize it? For at the beginning, Greek knowledge reached them only in a very impure state, after having filtered through Byzantine and Syrian minds.

The great racial and cultural complexity of Islām, even in those early days, is a very curious spectacle. How strong must the religious bond have been to keep together such disparate elements! To begin with, the 'Abbāsid court was entirely permeated with foreign influences—Persian, Jewish, and Nestorian. The Persian influence was predominant; one might say that the Persians conquered their Arab victors even as the Greeks conquered the Romans. The consequences were curiously similar in both cases. The Persians introduced into the Caliphate a greater love of beauty, urbanity, intellectual curiosity, and much fondness for discussion. These conditions were favorable for the progress of science, but unfortunately free thought was often followed by libertinage and immorality. No wonder that the genuine Arabs looked down upon the Persian intruders even as the old Romans looked down upon the Greeks. The fact is that every civilization acts as a poison upon those who have not been properly inoculated; it would act that way even were it perfectly pure and did not contain (as it always does) evil elements. The Arabic strength and virtue were gradually undermined by Persian urbanity.

To come back to the Muslim scholars: al-Aṣma'ī, Qāḍī Abū Yūsuf, Mālik ibn Anas, Ibn Isḥāq, Hishām ibn Muḥammad, Khalīl ibn Aḥmad, were real Arabs, Arabs of the Arabs, but they were, all of them, historians and theologians, not scientists. Those who might more properly be called scientists were either Persians, or Jews, or Christians. Ibrāhīm al Fazārī and his son Muḥammad, Ya'qūb ibn Ṭāriq, al-Naubakht and his son al-Faḍl, Ibn al-Muqaffa', Sībawaihi, were Persians. Māshāllāh was an Egyptian Jew and Abū 'Ubaida a Persian one. Al-Baṭrīq was probably a Christian of some sort. The powerful Bakhtyashū' family were Nestorians. Jābir ibn Ḥaiyān was either a Sabian or a Mazdean. The linguistic complexity was not less bewildering. To be sure, all of them understood Arabic, but some also spoke or read Persian, Syriac, Sanskrit, Hebrew, or Greek. I repeat it, the confusion was much greater than it had been at Alexandria, where the majority of the élite used its own native language. In 'Irāq the intellectual élite was obliged to use a foreign language and to adapt it gradually to the expression of new ideas. Under these circumstances it is not at all surprising that the first Arabic grammar was composed by a Persian. The remarks which I made in Chapter IX (p. 179) on Hellenistic philology might be repeated here, mutatis mutandis, with reference to Arabic.

II. RELIGIOUS BACKGROUND

Birth of Qaraism

ANAN BEN DAVID

Flourished in the second half of the eighth century in Babylonia; he failed to become exilarch[a] c. 760; was imprisoned in 767 and thus met Abū Ḥanīfa, a fellow prisoner, by whom he was clearly influenced. Died about the end of the century. Jewish theologian. Founder of the Qaraite[b] sect, a powerful anti-Talmudic movement, a sort of Jewish Reformation, which has great importance

[a] That is, the civil head of the Babylonian Jews. Anan had some hereditary qualifications for that office. The Gaon was the religious head.

[b] From qara, to read. Qera or miqra is the equivalent of our word Bible. Jews and Muslims call their sacred books readings (Miqra, Qur'ān), not writings as we do. The Qaraites were followers of the Bible (to the exclusion of rabbinical traditions).

because it stimulated considerably the development of Jewish thought, either directly or by way of reaction against it, for some four centuries. He completed c. 770 the "Book of Precepts" ("Sefer ha-mizwot").[c]

Qaraism throve best in Palestine and Egypt, but it had exhausted its strength by the end of the twelfth century. It has now vanished entirely, but for a few remnants in Turkey and Southern Russia.

Articles "Anan ben David" by A. Harkavy (Jewish Encyclopaedia, vol. 1, 553–556, 1901) and "Karaites and Karaism" (*ibidem*, vol. 7, 438–447, 1904), by the same, with a corrective note by Rabbi Kaufmann Kohler.

Muslim Theology

ABŪ YŪSUF

Abū Yūsuf Ya'qub ibn Ibrāhīm ibn Ḥabīb al-Kūfī al-Anṣārī. Born of old Arabian stock at Kūfa in 731/2; he lived in Bagdad, being appointed qāḍī in 782/3;[d] he died in 798/9. Ḥanīfite jurist; the greatest disciple of Abū Ḥanīfa. Upon the request of Hārūn al-Rashīd, he wrote a legal treatise on revenue (taxes), called Kitāb al-kharāj, which is still in use to-day in the Ḥanīfite communities.

Text—Arabic edition (Būlāq, 1302). French translation with notes by E. Fagnan: Le Livre de l'impôt foncier (368 p., Paris, 1921. The contents of this treatise are far more varied than the title suggests; Isis, IV, 579).

Criticism—C. Brockelmann: Arabische Litteratur (vol. 1, 171, 1898). Eilhard Wiedemann: Über Wasseranlagen nach dem Werk von Abū Jūsuf über die Grundsteuern (Beitr. 10, Sitzungsber. d. phys. med. Soz. in Erlangen, Vol. 38, 313–315, 1906). Carra de Vaux: Les penseurs de l'Islam (vol. 3, 340–349, 1923).

MĀLIK IBN ANAS

Abū 'Abdallāh Mālik ibn Anas al-Aṣbaḥī. Born at Medina in 715/6, died there in 795/6. Muslim jurist. Founder of the Mālikite school, one of the four orthodox schools of law.[e] His main work, called "Kitāb al-muwaṭṭa'" ("The Book of the Beaten Road"), contains about 1,700 juridical traditions arranged by subjects, with remarks on the ijmā' of Medina.[f] He insisted upon the principle of public advantage (istiṣlāḥ): justice must not be sacrificed to theory. The Muwaṭṭa' was the earliest publication of traditions (but it was restricted to legal traditions).

C. Brockelmann: Arabische Litteratur (Vol. I, 175, 1898). D. B. Macdonald: Development of Muslim Theology (1903). F. H. Ruxton: Māliki Law (435 p., London, 1916).

Tibetan Buddhism

It would seem that the efforts made by Song-tsen Gam-po (q. v., first half of the seventh century) to introduce Buddhism into his country, did not bear permanent fruits and that after his death Tibet relapsed into barbarism. At any rate,

---

[c] A book bearing the same title is ascribed to the cofounder of Qaraism, Benjamin Nahawendi (q. v., first half of ninth century).

[d] He was the first to receive the dignity of supreme judge (qāḍī-l-quḍā). He is often called Qāḍī Abū Yūsuf.

[e] It is still in force in Upper Egypt and in Northern Africa, west of Egypt. It was authoritative in the Western Caliphate.

[f] The agreement, the sanctioned usage of Medina.

his work had to be done anew by one of his successors, the great king Ti-song De-tsen.

Ti-song De-tsen (Thi-sroṅ Detsan) was the son of a Chinese princess, which helps to explain his Buddhist fervor. During his reign, Tibet became one of the great military powers of Asia; he extended his rule over the greater part of Yünnan and Ssŭch'uan and even conquered Chang-an, the Chinese capital. He established codes of civil and penal law, founded monasteries, and procured the services of a number of Hindu and Kashmīri scholars to translate the Buddhist canon and commentaries into Tibetan.[g] In 747 (or according to Chinese sources, in 755), he invited Padma-sambhava to come to Tibet; this was probably his most pregnant initiative.

Guru Padma-sambhava,[h] born in Udyāna (northwest of Kashmir), was a representative of the Tantric Yogācāra school; at the time of the king's invitation he was residing at the great college of Nālanda. He came to Tibet, founded the earliest monastery at Sam-yé (50 miles southeast of Lhasa) and was the real originator of the special form of Tibetan Buddhism (Lamaism), of which many sects survive unto this day.[i] This was a mixture of Tantric Buddhism with the original Bön superstitions and probably also with Udyāna superstitions. Padma-sambhava, whom the Tibetans call Guru Rim-po-ch'e (the precious teacher) or simply Lô-pön (teacher), is regarded by them with unbounded veneration; they place him on the same level as the Buddha. Padma had 25 disciples, each of whom is credited with some special magical power. In 802, he felt obliged to leave Tibet to preach the gospel of Buddhism in other lands; his departure took the form of a transfiguration and ascension, in the presence of the king, priests, and a multitude of the people.

Lawrence Austin Waddell: Buddhism of Tibet (London, 1895); Lhasa and its Mysteries (2d ed., London, 1905). Article by Mrs. S. Couling, in Encyclopaedia Sinica (284, 1917). Sir Charles Ball: Tibet (Oxford, 1924).

Chinese Buddhism—Wu K'ung

Wu[4] K'ung[1] (12704, 6595). This is his religious name; his own name was Ch'ê[1] Fêng[4]-ch'ao[1] (574, 3574, 518). Born at Hsiang[4]-i[4] (4265, 5454), Shensi, in 730; died after 791. Chinese Buddhist who was a member of a mission to Gandhāra in 751. After this he spent forty years in India and Central Asia, studying Sanskrit and collecting books and relics. After his return to China, he devoted himself to the translation of sūtras into Chinese.

H. A. Giles: Biographical Dictionary (885, 1898). L. Wieger: La Chine (375, 1920).

Nestorian Monument of 781

This monument, bearing an inscription in Chinese and another in Syriac (estrangelo characters written vertically), was discovered in 1625 in or near the Ch'ung[2] shêng[4] ssŭ[4] (2930, 9892, 10295), outside the western gate of Ch'ang[2]-an[1] (450, 44), i. e., Hsi[1]-an[1] (4031, 44); that was probably the place of its first erection

[g] A number of these translators are quoted by Waddell: Buddhism of Tibet (30).

[h] Guru means teacher in Sanskrit; Padma-sambhava, the "lotus-born one."

[i] The Red Hat sect represents more especially the primitive Tibetan Buddhism of Padma-sambhava.

in 781. The Chinese call it Ching[3] chiao[4] pei[1] (2143, 1352, 8764). It is of great importance as being the earliest Christian monument in China. A limestone replica of this great tablet was brought to the United States as a result of an expedition undertaken by Fritz V. Holm, of Copenhagen. This replica is in the Metropolitan Museum, New York.

Henri Havret (S. J.): La stèle chrétienne de Si-ngan-fou. Chang-hai, 1895–1902. (Variétés sinologiques No. 7, 1895, Facsimilé de l'inscription; No. 12, 1897, Histoire du monument; No. 20, Commentaire partiel et pièces justificatives avec la collaboration du P. Louis Cheikho). Alexander Wylie: The Nestorian Tablet in Si-ngan Foo (Chinese Researches, Part II, 24–77, Shanghai, 1897). The Nestorian tablet, with special reference to the expedition of Frits V. Holm and with Wylie's translation and notes (The Open Court, January 1909). P. Yoshio Saeki: The Nestorian Monument (352 p., London, 1916. Discussing Christian Influences on China and Japan). Article Nestorian Christians, in Encyclopaedia Sinica (394–396, 1917). Article Adam (*ibidem*, 7). Adam is the Persian missionary who wrote the inscription; his Chinese name is Ching[3] Ching[4] (2143, 2177).

III. CULTURAL BACKGROUND, EAST AND WEST

AL-MANṢŪR

Abū Ja'far 'Abdallāh al-Manṣūr, i. e., the victorious. Died in 775 at Bīr Maimūn, near Mecca, at the age of 63 to 68 Muslim years, i. e., 61 to 66 Christian years. Second 'Abbāsid caliph from 754 to his death. A great statesman and the founder of Bagdad. Memorable because of the many translations from the Syriac, Persian, Greek, and Hindu languages into the Arabic which were accomplished in his reign.

Theodor Nöldeke: Orientalische Skizzen (Berlin, 1892); English translation revised (Edinburgh, 1892. Chapter IV, p. 107–145, is devoted to al-Manṣūr, but little is said of the translations). Guy Le Strange: Baghdad During the 'Abbāsid Caliphate from Contemporary Sources (Oxford, 1900; reprinted 1924).

HĀRŪN AL-RASHĪD

Born in 763 or 766 at al-Ray; died at Ṭūs in 809. Caliph from 786 to his death; the fifth and one of the greatest 'Abbāsid monarchs. Magnificent patron of science, art, and literature. Many more Greek works were translated by his order. In 807 he presented a very remarkable water-clock to Charlemagne (Einhard).

E. H. Palmer: Haroun Alraschid (228 p., London, 1881). Article by K. V. Zetterstéen, in the Encyclopaedia of Islam (Vol. II, 271, 1916. Very little on the intellectual side).

Like his contemporary Charlemagne, Hārūn soon became a legendary figure (See the Alf laila wa-laila (the Thousand and One Nights). For example, Payne's edition, vol. 9, p. 318 ff., Burton's 12-vol. ed., vol. 8, p. 121 ff.).

CHARLEMAGNE

Charles the Great. Born c. 742; died in 814. King of the Franks since 768; crowned Emperor of the West on Christmas 800 by Leo III in Rome. He caused Alcuin to organize schools and promote the education of his people. He ordered the execution of great public works, introduced a new system of weights and measures, a new calendar, reformed the coinage, and issued ordinances (capitularies) to advance commerce, agriculture, and civilization. His favorite residence was Aachen (Aix-la-Chapelle).

One of his capitularies, dated Thionville 805, deals with medical education; a later one (813) condemns medical superstitions. He began a grammar of his native language and gave Germanic names to the months and to the points of the wind-rose (Einhard, sec. 29). The names of the months failed to be adopted (instead of the Latin names), but the names of the winds are those in use to-day (east, south, west, north, and their combinations).

Texts—The text of the Capitularia regum Francorum will be found in the Monumenta Germaniae historica, Leges, edited by Alfred Boretius (Hannover, 1883). Selections have been edited by Dana Carleton Munro: Translations and Reprints from the Original Sources of European History (VI, 5, 33 p., Philadelphia, 1900. Contains extracts relating to education). Karl Gareis: Die Landgüterordnung Kaiser Karl des Grossen (capitulare de villis vel curtis imperii). Text with notes and Introduction (68 p., Berlin, 1895. This capitulary dates probably from 812; it is very important for the history of agriculture). New German translation, with notes by Wilhelm Fleishmann (76 p., Berlin, 1919).

Biographies and General Studies—The early biographies and annals have been published in the Monumenta Germaniae historica (Scriptores, Vols. I and II). A. J. Grant: Early Lives of Charlemagne by Eginhard and the Monk of St. Gall (210 p., London, 1905). Einhard's (d. 840) Life of Charlemagne, Latin text, edited, with notes and introduction, by H. W. Garrod and R. B. Mowat (140 p., Oxford, 1915). Heinrich Hoffmann: Karl der Grosse im Bilde der Geschichtschreibung des frühen Mittelalters, 800 to 1250 (180 p., Berlin, 1919).

H. W. Carless Davis: Charlemagne, the Hero of Two Nations (New York, 1899). Hans Pruts: The Age of Charlemagne (translated by J. H. Wright, 332 p., Philadelphia, 1905). Franz Kampers: Die Grundlegung der mittelalterlichen Kultur und Weltanschauung (Mainz, 1910). Louis Halphen: Etudes critiques sur l'histoire de Charlemagne (314 p., Paris, 1921).

Charlemagne soon became a legendary figure. For a summary of the Charlemagne legends, see Margaret Bryant's article in the Encyclopaedia Britannica, 11th ed., under Charlemagne (p. 894–897, 1911).

Special Studies—E. H. F. Meyer: Geschichte der Botanik (vol. 3, 396–415, 1856). Henry Card: The Reign of Charlemagne considered Chiefly with Reference to Religion, Law, Literature, and Manners (208 p., London, 1807). F. Piper: Karl der Grosse, Kalendarium und Ostertafel (Berlin, 1858). F. von Wyss: Karl der Grosse als Gesetzgeber (Zürich, 1869). J. B. Mullinger: The Schools of Charles the Great and the Restoration of Education in the Ninth Century (London, 1877. See also under Alcuin). Friedrich Beck: Der Karlsgraben (92 p., Nürnberg, 1911. Also published as a Munich Gymn. Progr.; deals with the Fossa Carolina, a canal built by Charlemagne in 793 between the Rednitz and the Altmühl. Remains of it are still extant). Karl Manitius: Naturwissenschaftliches in der Geschichtschreibung der Karolingerzeit (Archiv für Geschichte der Medizin, 15, 68–77, 1923); Naturwissenschaft im beginnenden Mittelalter (41 p., Crimmitschau, 1924). Georg Sticker: Die gebräuchlichen Heilkräuter in Deutschland zur Zeit Karls des Grossen (Janus, 28, 21–41, 1924; Isis, VIII, 535).

ALCUIN

Or Albinus. His original English name was Ealwhine, Alchvine. Born in York, c. 735. He was educated there and became eventually, in 778, the master of the York school. He went to Rome in 780 and, on his way back, met Charlemagne at Parma in 781. Charlemagne intrusted to him the educational reorganization of the empire. He retired in 796 as abbot of St. Martin in Tours and died there on May 19, 804. English theologian and educator. The greatest representative of learning and culture in the West in those days; the most prominent figure of the Carolingian revival. He organized a sort of academy at the imperial palace, a library, and school. It was under his inspiration that Charlemagne published the famous manifesto "De litteris colendis." The value of Alcuin's services can hardly be exaggerated; he was the main instrument in the transmission to the ignorant Franks of the relatively high culture which had been attained in English monasteries under Bede's guidance. He wrote theological and philosophical works, a life of Willibrord, and various school-books (on grammar and arithmetic). One of them, the "Propositiones ad acuendos iuvenes" deserves separate mention, because it contains a collection of puzzle problems which has influenced text-book writers for a thousand years.

Text and Translation—Complete works edited by And. Quercetanus (Paris, 1617). New edition by Frobenius (2 vols., Ratisbon, 1777). Epistolae, edited by Ernest Duemmler, in the Monumenta Alcuiniana quoted below (p. 132–912, 1873). Alcuins pädagogische Schriften. Übers., bearb. und mit einer Einleitung versehen von Joseph Freundgen (180 p., Paderborn, 1889).

Biographies and Criticism—Monumenta Alcuiniana a Philippo Iaffeo praeparata ediderunt Wilhelm Wattenbach et Ernst Duemmler (Bibliotheca rerum germanicarum, ed. Philippus Iaffé, vol. 6, 920 p., Berlin, 1873. Fundamental). Frederick Lorenz: The Life of Alcuin, translated by Jane Mary Slee (290 p., London, 1837). Karl Werner: Alcuin und sein Jahrhundert (Neue Ausgabe, 428 p., Wien, 1881). Andrew Fleming West: Alcuin and the Rise of the Christian Schools (205 p., New York, 1892. With many extracts from Alcuin's writings). C. J. B. Gaskoin: Alcuin, his Life and his Work (297 p., Cambridge, 1904). Rolph Barlow Page: The Letters of Alcuin (Thesis, Columbia, 103 p., New York, 1909). M. Manitius: Lateinische Literatur des Mittelalters (vol. 1, 273–288, 1911; vol. 2, 800–801). H. Bastgen: Alkuin und Karl der Grosse in ihren wissenschaftlichen und kirchenpolitischen Anschauungen (Historisches Jahrbuch, Bd. 32, 809–825, 1911). Don F. Cabrol: Les écrits liturgiques d'Alcuin (Congrès international d'histoire de Bruxelles, 1923). D. E. Smith: History of Mathematics (vol. 1, 186, 1923, apropos of the puzzle-problems), vol. 2, 546, 1925 (problem of the hound pursuing a hare, earliest European form of the traditional problems of pursuit).

SHŌTOKU-TENNŌ

Empress of Japan from 749 to 758, under the name of Kōken, then again from 765 until her death in 770, under the name of Shōtoku.[i] She was then at once the forty-sixth and the forty-eighth emperor of Japan. Her own name was Abe Nai-shinnō; she was the daughter of Shōmu-tennō, whom she succeeded in 749. Ardent Buddhist. The Daibutsu of Nara was cast during her first reign, c. 750.[k] The first temple of Nikkō was built during her second reign (767).[l] She ordered the printing of one million charms which were distributed c. 770 among ten temples. Some of these charms are still extant; they are of considerable interest, being the earliest printed documents of any country (two pieces

[i] Not to be confused with Shōtoku-taishi, q. v., first half of the seventh century. Taishi means prince; tennō, emperor.

[k] For which see my note on Japanese technology in the first half of the eighth century.

[l] By Shōdō-shōnin (735–817) it was called Shihonryū-ji; rebuilt in 808, it was then called Honryū-ji.

of printed silk in the treasure of Nara are dated 734 and 740, but that is another matter). The art of printing had certainly come from China[m] together with many other features of Chinese civilization, which the Japanese of that time were assimilating as fast as they could. Six different charms were printed on two different kinds of paper; they are extracts from the "Vimala nirbhasa sūtra"[n] in Sanskrit, transliterated by means of Chinese characters.

For a description and a photograph of the charms, and an account of their printing derived from the Shoku Nihongi, see Thomas Francis Carter: Invention of Printing in China (1925; Isis, VIII, 365).

IV. MUSLIM AND LATIN MATHEMATICS AND ASTRONOMY

IBRĀHĪM AL-FAZĀRĪ

Abū Isḥāq Ibrāhīm ibn Ḥabīb ibn Sulaimān ibn Samura ibn Jundab. Died c. 777. Muslim astronomer. The first to construct astrolabes. Author of a poem (qaṣīda) on astrology and of various astronomical writings (on the astroabe, on the armillary spheres, on the calendar).

H. Suter: Die Mathematiker und Astronomen der Araber (3, 208, 1900).

YA'QŪB IBN ṬĀRIQ

Probably of Persian origin, flourished in Bagdad, c. 767–778, died c. 796. One of the greatest astronomers of his time. He probably met, c. 767, at the court of al-Manṣūr, the Hindu Kankah (or Mankah?), who had brought there the Siddhānta. He wrote memoirs on the sphere (c. 777); on the division of the kardaja;[o] on the tables derived from the Siddhānta.

H. Suter: Die Mathematiker und Astronomen der Araber (p. 4, 1900).

MUḤAMMAD IBN IBRĀHĪM AL-FAZĀRĪ

Abū 'Abdallāh Muḥammad ibn Ibrāhīm al-Fazārī. Son of the astronomer Ibrāhīm dealt with above, for whom he is sometimes mistaken (he may be the author of the astrological poem ascribed to his father). Died c. 796 to 806. Muslim scientist and astronomer. He was ordered by the Caliph al-Manṣūr in 772/3 to translate the Sanskrit astronomical work Siddhānta.[p] This translation was possibly the vehicle by means of which the Hindu numerals were transmitted from India to Islām.

H. Suter: Die Mathematiker und Astronomen der Araber (p. 4, 1900). Cantor: Geschichte der Mathematik (I, 3d ed., 698, 1907). D. E. Smith and L. C. Karpinski: The Hindu-Arabic Numerals (p. 92, Boston, 1911). Carra de Vaux: Penseurs de l'Islam (vol. 2, 197–201, 1921).

For al-Baṭrīq, see my note in Section VIII, below.

---

[m] See my note on Ming Huang (first half of eighth century).

[n] In Japanese, Mu-ku Jō-kō kyō.

[o] The Hindu and Muslims divided the circle into 96 parts (that was an Archimedian tradition). The arc (225') or the sine of each of these parts was called kardaja, possibly a corruption of a Sanskrit term, for which see my note on the Siddhāntas (first half of the fifth century).

[p] Al-Bīrūnī says that the translation of the Siddhānta was already completed in 770–71. Does he refer to the same work?

MĀSHĀLLĀH

His real name was probably Manasseh (in Arabic, Mīshā). Latin translators named him Messahala (with many variants, as Macellama, Macelarama). Māshāllāh is a contraction of mā shā' Allāh meaning "What wonders Allāh has willed." (What hath God wrought.) Flourished under al-Manṣūr, died c. 815 or 820. One of the earliest astronomers and astrologers in Islām, himself an Egyptian (?) Jew. Only one of his writings is extant in Arabic, but there are many mediaeval Latin and Hebrew translations. The Arabic text extant deals with the prices of wares and is the earliest book of its kind in that language. He took part with the Persian astrologer al-Naubakht in the surveying preliminary to the foundation of Bagdad in 762–63. His most popular book in the Middle Ages was the "De scientia motus orbis," translated by Gherardo Cremonese.

Text and Translation—The De scientia motus orbis is probably the treatise called in Arabic "the twenty-seventh;" printed in Nuremberg 1504, 1549. The second edition is entitled: De elementis et orbibus coelestibus, and contains 27 chapters. The De compositione et utilitate astrolabii was included in Greg. Reisch: Margarita phylosophica (ed. pr., Freiburg, 1503; Suter says the text is included in the Basel edition of 1583). Other astronomical and astrological writings are quoted by Suter and Steinschneider.

An Irish astronomical tract based in part on a mediaeval Latin version of a work by Messahalah. Edited, with preface, translation, and glossary, by Maura Power (Irish Texts Society, vol. 14, 194 p., 1914. A relatively modern translation of the De scientia motus orbis; the preface is uncritical).

Criticism—Fihrist (273–274. Also in commentary, p. 129, note 10). H. Suter: Die Mathematiker und Astronomen der Araber (5–6, 1900; Nachträge, 158, 1902). M. Steinschneider: Die arabische Literatur der Juden (15–23, Frankfurt, 1902). P. Duhem: Système du Monde (vol. 2, 204–206, 1914. On the precession of the equinoxes).

AL-NAUBAKHT[q]

Astrologer to al-Manṣūr; he died c. 776–77. Persian astronomer and engineer. Together with Māshāllāh he made the measurements preliminary to the construction of Bagdad[r] (762–63). A book on astrological judgments (Kitāb al-aḥkām) is ascribed to him.

H. Suter: Mathematiker und Astronomen (3, 1900; 158, 1902).

AL-FAḌL IBN NAUBAKHT

Abū Sahl al-Faḍl ibn Naubakht. Son of the preceding, thus of Persian origin. Chief librarian to Hārūn al-Rashīd; died c. 815–6. Muslim astronomer. He made translations from Persian into Arabic for the caliph. He wrote various astrological treatises.[s]

Two other astrologers of the same family, presumably grandsons or nephews of al-Faḍl, flourished a little later (first half of ninth century): Al-Ḥasan ibn Sahl ibn Naubakht (who was also a translator from Persian into Arabic) and (his brother?) 'Abdallāh ibn Sahl ibn Naubakht.

---

[q] Better than Nūbakht. Naubakht means, in Persian, new luck.

[r] This construction took place under the direction of Khālid ibn Barmak.

[s] The "Liber alfadhol i. est arab de bachi" (?) quoted among the writings of Gherardo Cremonese may be the translation of one of these treatises?

Fihrist, in Suter's translation (p. 28). H. Suter: Mathematiker und Astronomen (5, 16, 1900; 158, 1902).

For Latin mathematics and astronomy, see my notes on Charlemagne and Alcuin, above.

V. MUSLIM AND LATIN ALCHEMY, JAPANESE TECHNOLOGY

JĀBIR IBN ḤAIYĀN

Abū Mūsā Jābir ibn Ḥaiyān al-Azdī (al-Ṭūsī, al-Ṭarṭūsī; al-Ḥarrānī meaning that he was a Sabian?; al-Ṣūfī). Flourished mostly in Kūfa, c. 776. The most famous Arabic[t] alchemist; the alchemist Geber[u] of the Middle Ages. He may be the author of a book on the astrolabe, but his fame rests on his alchemical writings preserved in Arabic: the "Book of the Kingdom," the "Little Book of the Balances," the "Book of Mercy," the "Book of Concentration," the "Book of Eastern Mercury," and others. According to the treatises already translated (by Berthelot), his alchemical doctrines were very anthropomorphic and animistic. But other treatises (not yet available in translation) show him in a better light. We find in them remarkably sound views on methods of chemical research; a theory on the geologic formation of metals; the so-called sulphur-mercury theory of metals (the six metals differ essentially because of different proportions of sulphur and mercury in them); preparation of various substances (e. g., basic lead carbonate; arsenic and antimony from their sulphides). Jābir deals also with various applications, e. g., refinement of metals, preparation of steel, dyeing of cloth and leather, varnishes to water-proof cloth and protect iron, use of manganese dioxide in glass-making, use of iron pyrites for writing in gold, distillation of vinegar to concentrate acetic acid. He observed the imponderability of magnetic force.

It is possible that some of the facts mentioned in the Latin works, ascribed to Geber and dating from the twelfth century and later, must also be placed to Jābir's credit. It is impossible to reach definite conclusions until all the Arabic writings ascribed to Jābir have been properly edited and discussed. It is only then that we shall be able to measure the full extent of his contributions, but even on the slender basis of our present knowledge, Jābir appears already as a very great personality, one of the greatest in mediaeval science.

Text and Translations—M. Berthelot: La chimie au moyen âge (vol. 3, L'alchimie arabe, Paris, 1893. The Arabic text of a few of Jābir's writings is edited by Octave Houdas. French translation, p. 126–224. See E. J. Holmyard's criticism in Isis, VI, 479–499, 1924). Ernst Darmstaedter: Die Alchemie des Geber (212 p., 10 pl., Berlin, 1922. German translation of the Latin treatises ascribed to Geber; reviewed by J. Ruska in Isis, V, 451–455, concluding that these Latin treatises are apocryphal); Liber misericordiae Geber. Eine lateinische Übersetzung des grösseren Kitāb al-raḥma (Archiv für Geschichte der Medizin, vol. 17, 181-197, 1925; Isis, VIII, 737).

Criticism—M. Berthelot: Article Géber in Grande Encyclopédie (3 cols., c. 1892); article in the Revue des Deux Mondes (Sept. 15, Oct. 1, 1893). H. Suter: Die Mathematiker und Astronomen der Araber (p. 3, 208, 1900). E. Wiedemann: Über Magnetismus (Beiträge, 2, Sitzungsber der phys. med. Gesellschaft, Erlangen, vol. 36, 322–331, 1904). John Ferguson: Bibliotheca chemica (p. 299–304, Glas-

---

[t] I say Arabic and not Muslim, for he was possibly a Sabian.

[u] I do not use this name, because it is a source of confusion. Jābir means literally one who sets bones, and by extension a restorer, reorganizer.

gow, 1906). Baron Carra de Vaux: Article Djābir ibn Ḥaiyān, in Encyclopaedia of Islam (vol. 1, 997, 1912, with bibliography); Les Penseurs de l'Islam (vol. 2, 369, 375, 382, 1921). E. J. Holmyard: Arabic Chemistry (Nature, vol. 110, 573, 1922. Believes that Berthelot's opinion needs revision; Jābir and Geber might after all be one and the same?). E. O. von Lippmann: Über den Dschābir des 8. und den sog. Geber des 13. Jahrhundert (Chemiker. Z., 321, 1923, against Holmyard; Isis, V, 494). E. J. Holmyard. Jābir ibn Ḥayyān (Proc. Roy. Soc. Medicine, vol. 16, histor. section, p. 46–57, 1923. Elaborate study with catalogue raisonné of Jābir's works); The Identity of Geber (Nature, vol. 111, 191–193, 219, 1923; Isis, VI, 144); The Emerald Table (Nature 112, 525–526, 1923; Isis, VI, 215); Accuracy of Weighing in the Eighth Century (Nature, 115, 963, 1925; Isis, VIII, 535); Chemistry to the Time of Dalton (16–20, 43–44, London, 1925); Science Progress (January 1925. Considering the identity of Geber and Jābir as definitely established). Julius Ruska: Über das Schriftenverzeichnis des Jābir und die Unechtheit einiger ihm zugeschriebenen Abhandlungen (Archiv für Geschichte der Medizin, vol. 15, 53–67, 1923. Ruska shows that the Jābir question can not be solved until we have critical editions of the Arabic texts ascribed to him); Arabischen Alchemisten II. Ja'far al-Ṣādiq (Heidelberg, 1924; Isis, VII, 119–121). Ernst Darmstaedter: Geber-Handschriften (Chemiker-Z., 48, 441, 1924); Die Geber Inkunabel Hain 7504 (Archiv für Geschichte der Medizin, vol. 16, 214–217, 1925. Analysis of this incunable, Flos naturarum, s. 1., 1473, which has nothing to do with Geber; it is an account of organotherapeutic superstitions).

Compositiones ad Tingenda

Collection of technical recipes dating from the time of Charlemagne. These recipes were probably collected by a master craftsman; they deal with decorative arts of various kinds: preparation of pigments (e. g., cinnabar from mercury and sulphur), gilding of metals, dyeing of skins, coloring of glass used in mosaics, writing in gold, etc. First use of the names vitriol (vitriolum) to designate an (impure) sulphate of iron, and bronze (brandisium), to designate an alloy of copper, tin, and lead.

These recipes are clearly of Hellenistic origin. One of the recipes (Berthelot, p. 10) is almost literally identical with one in the Leiden papyrus (q. v., second half of third century). It is probable that some of the recipes represent even older traditions, the technical traditions of ancient Egypt which had become an integral part of Hellenistic knowledge. The collection is purely technical and entirely free from superstition.

The text was first published from a Lucca manuscript by Ludovico Antonio Muratori in his Antiquitates italicae medii aevi (vol. 2, 365–392, Milan, 1739), under the following descriptive title: Compositiones ad tingenda musiva, pelles et alia, ad deaurandum ferrum, ad mineralia, ad chrysographiam, ad glutina quaedam conficienda, aliaque artium documenta, ante annos nongentos scripta.

Mappae Clavicula

This work, very similar to the "Compositiones" but more extensive and of a later date, exists in two manuscripts, the earlier dating from the tenth century is in the library of Schlettstadt, Alsace, the later is probably of the first half of the twelfth century. Its text is more elaborate than that of the earlier manuscript and contains many interpolations, e. g., Arabic names and two English words which suggest that it was edited by an Englishman. This second edition of the

"Mappae Clavicula" has been ascribed to Adelard of Bath (q. v., first half of twelfth century).

We are concerned here only with the earlier text, which, like the "Compositiones," shows no trace of Muslim influence. Yet the Clavicula is a later work than the "Compositiones" and is largely based upon it or upon identical sources. The "Clavicula" contains most of the recipes of the "Compositiones" plus many more, and also a number of magical and mystical formulas. It deals with transmutation, a subject hardly touched upon in the "Compositiones." It includes the so-called "Cardan's suspension," for which see my note on Philon of Byzantium (second half of second century B. C.). It is possible that the "Clavicula" dates only from the ninth century, but it was better to consider it together with the earlier work.

The earlier text of the "Little Key to Painting" has not been published, but the later one was edited by Sir Thomas Phillipps: "Mappae clavicula," a manuscript treatise on the preparation of pigments and on various processes of the decorative arts practiced during the Middle Ages (Archaeologia, vol. 32, 183–244, London, 1847).

The later edition of the Clavicula contains a recipe for the preparation of alcohol, this being the earliest known (first half of twelfth century). I would not mention this at this place, but for the fact that there has been much discussion as to the possible discovery of alcohol at an earlier time. H. Diels would have traced it back to antiquity (Die Entdeckung des Alkohols, Abhd. der Preuss. Ak., phil. Kl., Nr. 3, 1913); Hermann Degering claimed to have found an eighth century recipe (Sitzungsber. der Preuss. Ak., vol. 36, 503–515, 1917); the recipe of the Clavicula was considered as a link connecting the later mediaeval recipes with Hellenistic alchemy. I can not go into that at present, but the following references will enable the reader to begin his study: Isis, I, 760; III, 322, 323, 324; V, 544.

For both treatises, Compositiones and Clavicula, see M. Berthelot. Chimie au Moyen-âge (vol. 1, 1893). Ed. O. von Lippmann: Alchemie (467–472, 1919) J. M. Stillmann: The Story of Early Chemistry (185–189, New York, 1924).

For contemporary Japanese technology, see my notes on Shōtoku-tennō in Section III, and on the introduction of cotton in Section VI.

VI. MUSLIM, CHINESE, AND JAPANESE NATURAL HISTORY

AL-AṢMA'Ī

'Abd al-Malik ibn Quraib al-Aṣma'ī. A true Arab born at Baṣra in 739–40; he flourished at Bagdad and Baṣra, and died at Baṣra c. 831. Arab scholar; one of the greatest of his time; the rival of Abū 'Ubaida. Being an Arab of the Arabs,[v] he execrated the Shu'ūbite tendencies of the latter and was very pious. He wrote many works, chiefly on the horse (Kitāb al-khail), on the camel (Kitāb al-ibil), on wild animals (Kitāb al-wuḥūsh), on the sheep (Kitāb al-sha'), on the making of man (Kitāb khalq al-insān). The latter shows that the Arabs already had a considerable knowledge of human anatomy. His studies on Arabic poetry were fundamental.

---

[v] Or to use an American vulgarism, a 100 per cent Arab!

Text—The book of distinction (Kitāb al-farq) was edited by D. H. Müller (Vienna, 1876); the book of the wild animals by R. Geyer (Vienna, 1887); the book of the horse by A. Haffner (Vienna, 1895); the book of the sheep by the same (Vienna, 1896).

Criticism—Ibn Khallikān (De Slane) (vol. 2, 123–127, 1843). C. Brockelmann: Arabische Litteratur (vol. 1, 104, 1898).

LU YÜ

Lu[4*] Yü[3] (7432, 13617). Born and educated in Ching[4]-ling[2] (2166, 7235), Hupeh, hence he is often called Ching-ling tzŭ. Became a hermit c. 775; died in 804. Chinese writer. Author of the Ch'a[2] ching[1] (208, 2122), the earliest work on tea, divided into 10 sections, as follows: Origin of the plant, utensils for gathering, manufacture of the leaf, implements for the preparation, infusion, drinking, history, producing districts, summary, explanation of plates.

Text—Original text and additions published by Lu[4*] T'ing[1]-ts'an[4] (7432, 11284, 11568) in 1735 under the title Hsü[4*] Ch'a[2]-ching[1] (4773).

Criticism—A. Wylie: Chinese Literature (148, (1867) 1902.) H. A. Giles: Biographical Dictionary (552, 1898).

JAPANESE COTTON

The cultivation and technical use of cotton originated in India or in Egypt or independently in both countries, at a very remote but unknown time. The earliest literary references to cotton are found in Herodotos, Book III, chapters 47 and 106; the first (*εἴρια ἀπὸ ξύλου*) is only incidental, the second is more specific: "There too (i. e., in India) grows on wild trees wool more beautiful and excellent than the wool of sheep; these trees supply the Indians with clothing." The Asiatic wars acquainted the Romans with the use of cotton. The earliest specimens of cotton fabric were found in a tomb at Akhmīm in Upper Egypt. A summary of the history of cotton will be found in F. M. Feldhaus: Die Technik (73–75, 1914).

In 799, during the reign of Kwammu-tennō, fiftieth emperor of Japan (782 to 805), cotton grains were introduced from India into Japan. According to tradition, these grains were brought in a junk which drifted to the coast of Mikawa. They were planted in Nankaidō and Saikadō. This marks the beginning of cotton culture in Japan and of the making of cotton fabrics (momen).

That account needs further evidence to be accepted. An astonishing feature of it is that the introduction of cotton is reported as having been made directly from India by sea. This is not impossible, but it is not convincing. As a matter of fact, the earliest record of cotton culture and industry in China is of a much later date (Marco Polo).

E. Papinot: Historical Dictionary (337, 1909). F. Brinkley: History of the Japanese People (280, 1915). Encyclopaedia Sinica (134, 1917). B. Laufer: Sino-Iranica (1919).

VII. LATIN AND CHINESE GEOGRAPHY

For the curious theory of tides of Paulus Diaconus, see the note relative to him in Section IX, below.

BEATUS

Beatus Libaniensis or Livaniensis, from the place, Liebana, Asturias de Santillana, where St. Beatus flourished. Born c. 730; died in 798 in the abbey of Vallecava (Valcavado), near Saldaña. The map of the world (Mappa Mundi, 776) illustrating his Commentaria in Apolypsin is one of the earliest Christian maps Many (10) later maps were derived from it.

Konrad Miller: Die Weltkarte des Beatus (776 n. Chr., 70 p., illustr. and facsimile, Mappae mundi, 1, Stuttgart, 1895). The second number of the same collection, also 1895, contains reproductions of later Beatus maps. J. K. Wright: Geographical lore (68–69, 1924).

CHIA TAN

Chia[3] Tan[1] (1181, 10615). Born in 730, died in 805. Chinese geographer. The most famous cartographer of the T'ang dynasty. He was ordered in 785 by the emperor to draw up a map of China. His work, entitled "Map of China and of the barbaric countries within the seas" Hai[3]-nei[4] hua[2]-i[2] t'u[2] (3767, 8177, 5005, 5397, 12128), was completed in 801. It was 30 feet long and 33 feet high, on the scale of one inch to one hundred li.[w] Another work of Chia Tan is preserved, in an abbreviated form, in the "New T'ang History" (chüan 43).[x] That work, compiled during the period 785 to 805, contains a series of itineraries from various parts of China (including Tongking) to Korea, Central Asia, India and Bagdad. It is of great value for the historical geography of Asia.

See Chiu T'ang shu, chapter 138 and T'ang shu, chapter 166, quoted by Ed. Chavannes: Les deux plus anciens spécimens de la cartographie chinoise (Bulletin de l'Ecole française d'Extrême Orient, vol. 3, 214–247, 244, Hanoï, 1903). Paul Pelliot: Deux itinéraires de Chine en Inde à la fin du VIIIe siècle (*ibidem*, vol. 4, 131–413, 1904). Very elaborate memoir dealing with two of the itineraries above mentioned. It is derived from the Hsin T'ang shu and subsidiarily from the Man[2] shu[1] (7644, 10024) of Fan[2]-ch'o[4]* (3408, 2439) composed c. 860.[y] A French translation of the two itineraries is given on p. 364–373. That translation is preceded by an abundant commentary and followed by a number of complementary notes.

VIII. LATIN, SYRIAC, MUSLIM, HINDU, TIBETAN, CHINESE, AND JAPANESE MEDICINE

Latin Medicine

We have only glimpses of the medical practice and thinking in the West. It was largely restricted to Benedictine monasteries. One of these glimpses is afforded to us by the Bamberger Codex L, iii, 8, written in Germany in the ninth century. The main text of this manuscript is the "Libri V curationum," essentially derived from the "Medicina Plinii," as it appears in the Roman edition of 1509. But this text is preceded by a defense of medicine written in a German Benedictine monastery, c. 750–850. This defense was edited by Karl Sudhoff: Eine Verteidigung der Heilkunde aus den Zeiten der Mönchsmedizin (Archiv für Geschichte der Medizin, vol. 7, 223–237, 1913).

[w] Five li approximate one mile.

[x] Hsin T'ang shu, for which see my note on Ou-yang Hsiu, in the second half of the eleventh century.

[y] For information on the Man shu and on Fan ch'o, see P. Pelliot's memoir, p. 132.

THEOPHILOS OF EDESSA

Theophilos son of Thomas. Thīyūfīl ibn Thūmā. Died in 785, nearly ninety years old. Maronite. Chief astrologer to the third 'Abbāsid caliph, al-Mahdī (775–785). Translator from Greek into Syriac. He composed a poor translation of Galen's "De tuenda sanitate" (revised later by Hunain ibn Ishāq), a chronology of the world's history, and at least a partial translation of Homer.

H. Suter: Die Mathematiker der Araber (223, 1900). Anton Baumstark: Syrische Litteratur (341, 1922). Max Meyerhof: New Light on Ḥunain (Isis, VIII, 704, 1926).

IBN BAKHTYASHŪ'

Jirjīs ibn Jibrīl ibn Bakhtyashū'.[z] In charge of the hospital of Jundī-shāpūr until 765/6, when he was called to Bagdad by al-Manṣūr; he returned to Jundī-shāpūr in 769/70 and died in 771. Christian (Nestorian) Persian physician; the earliest known to us of a great medical family (the Bakhtyashū'), which was attached to a long series of 'Abbāsid caliphs and exerted a deep influence upon Muslim medicine in the eighth and ninth centuries. His arrival at Bagdad, with two pupils, marked the beginning of a great scientific activity. He is said to have been the first, upon the caliph's request, to translate medical works into Arabic.[a] See my note on his grandson Jibrīl (first half of ninth century).

F. Wüstenfeld: Arabische Aerzte (14, 1840). L. Leclerc: Médecine arabe (vol. 1, 96–98, 1876).

AL-BAṬRĪQ

Abū Yaḥyā al-Baṭrīq, died c. 796–806. One of the translators employed by al-Mansūr. He translated into Arabic some of the works of Hippocrates and Galen and, for 'Umar ibn al-Farrukhān, Ptolemy's Quadripartitum.

L. Lerclerc: Médecine arabe (vol. 1, 178, 1876). Suter: Die Mathematiker und Astronomen der Araber (p. 4, 1900).

Other medical translations were made by Ibn al-Muqaffa', q. v., in Section IX below.

MĀDHAVAKARA

Son of Indukara. Flourished at an unknown time in the eighth or ninth century. Hindu physician. Author of treatise called "Rugviniścaya" ("Study of the Diseases) or "Mādhavanidāna" (Nidāna for short.) It deals mainly with pathology and, judging by the number of commentaries, is very popular.

Text—Many Hindu popular editions, but no critical edition.

Extracts translated by M. Vallauri in Giornale della Soc. Asiat. Ital., vol. 26, 253 sq., 1914.

Criticism—Mario Vallauri: Un testo medioevale indiano di medicina (Riv. di storia della scienza, vol. 3, 6–10, 1916. Contains a table of contents of the treatise).

VRINDA

Hindu physician who flourished not long after Mādhavakara, if not at about the same time. It is even probable that Vṛinda and Mādhavakara are but two names of the same person. Author of a medical treatise entitled "Vṛindamā-

---

[z] George son of Gabriel. Bakhtyasū' would mean Jesus's happiness.

[a] However, these works are not named and his stay in Bagdad was very short.

dhava" or "Siddhiyoga" ("Perfect Cure"), wherein prescriptions are given for a number of diseases arranged in the same order as in the Rugviniścaya.

Text—Published in Ānandāśrama's Sanskrit series (No. 27, Poona, 1894) together with a commentary by Śrīkaṇṭhadatta.

Criticism—A. F. R. Hoernlé: Studies in ancient Indian medicine (Journal R. As. Soc., 283–302, 288, 1906. Hoernlé and Vallauri maintain that Mādhavakara = Vṛinda). M. Winternitz: Geschichte der indischen Literatur (vol. 3, 550, 1922).

Tibetan Medicine

In my note on Tibetan Buddhism in the first half of the seventh century, I gave a brief account of the Kanjur and the Tanjur. I mentioned that the latter collection includes five volumes on medicine. Some medical information may also be gleaned in the Kanjur. But outside of these two collections, there is an independent medical treatise entitled "rGyud-bṣi" ("The Four Tantras"). According to native traditions, a Tibetan interpreter, Bairotsana (Vairocana), translated it in Kashmir with the assistance of a physician-pandit and presented it to King Ti-song De-tsen (q. v., *supra*). We may assume that it dates back to that time, at least in its original (Tibetan) form. It is divided (as the title indicates) into four parts, as follows: (1) Arteries, veins, nerves, and pulses; (2) "explanation" of the body and causes of diseases; (3) "instruction" as to the treatment of diseases; (4) "external" treatment, manual operation, etc.

Alexander Csoma de Körös published an English analysis of it on the basis of the Tibetan summary prepared for him by his Lama instructor (Journal Asiatic Society of Bengal, vol. 4, 1835; reprinted in the Tibetan Studies, Journal Asiatic Soc. of Bengal, vol. 7, 1911, extra No., 47–65). See also Heinrich Laufer: Beiträge zur Kenntnis der tibetischen Medizin (2 parts, 90 p., Berlin, and Leipzig, 1900. Elaborate study of Tibetan medicine arranged in systematic order, all the facts relative to each medical subject, say physiology, special pathology, diagnostic or balneology being put together; this very important investigation was carried out with the philological assistance of the author's brother, Berthold. Unfortunately, only 200 copies were printed). E. H. C. Walsh: The Tibetan Anatomical System (Journal R. As. Soc., 1215–1245, 1910, 1 large plate. This deals mainly with an anatomical chart kept in the Temple of Medicine at Lhasa, which, together with its connected monastery, forms the medical college of Tibet. Every Tibetan doctor is taught his anatomy from it. It is called Pyang-khok las-thig, i. e., the chart divided by lines; it is divided into a number of squares to identify the locations of particular organs. A facsimile of the chart is attached to this memoir). K. Sudhoff: Die anatomischen Ganzfiguren in tibetanischer Überlieferung (Archiv für Geschichte der Medizin, vol. 8, 143–145, 2 fig., 1915).

WANG TAO

Wang² Tao⁴ (12493, 10798). Flourished under the T'ang, c. 752. Chinese physician. Author of a very comprehensive medical treatise, published in 752, entitled "Important Secrets of the Outer Terrace" Wai⁴-t'ai²-pi⁴*-yao⁴ (12442, 10577, 8922, 12889), in 40 parts. It includes every branch of medicine and therapeutics, and even a brief summary of veterinary art (diseases of mules, horses, cows, and dogs).

Text—The text at present available is very doubtful.

Criticism—F. Huebotter: Guide (31, Kumamoto, 1924).

WANG PING

Wang[2] Ping[1] (12493, 9277). Flourished c. 761. Chinese physician. He wrote in 761 the earliest commentary (in 24 books) on the "Huang-ti Nei-ching su-wên," traditionally considered the oldest Chinese treatise on medicine.[b]

A. Wylie: Chinese Literature (96, (1867) 1902). L. Wieger: La Chine (462, 495, 1920); Histoire des croyances (305–309, 1922. Analysis of the Su-wên). F. Huebotter: Guide (6–9, 30, Kumamoto, 1924).

KANJIN

His name reads in Chinese Chien[4]-chên[1] (1644, 589). He died in 763 at the age of 77. Chinese physician who came to Japan in 755 and seems to have been the most important physician of that time in Japan.

The earliest (Japanese) hospital of any importance was founded at Nara, in 758, by order of the empress Kōmyō, who had become a nun at the time of the abdication of her husband, Shōmu, in 749. This foundation may thus be ascribed to Buddhist influence.

Y. Fujikawa: Geschichte der Medizin in Japan (10, 97, Tokyo, 1911).

WAKE HIROYO

Flourished toward the end of the eighth century. Japanese educator and physician. He wrote an important treatise on materia medica, called "Yakkeitaiso," in two volumes. It is derived from the Chinese work, Hsin[1]-hsiu[1] pên[3]-ts'ao[3] (4574, 4661, 8846, 11634) by Su[1]-ching[4] (10320, 2144). (See my note on Chinese materia medica in second half of seventh century.) It deals with 254 drugs, borrowed from the three kingdoms of nature, explaining their preparation, preservation, use, and effects. He was the chief of the medical department (ten-yaku-ryō) of the imperial court. He was also the head of the university (Daigaku-bettō) and endowed it. Toward the year 800 he founded a private school, with a large library. This school, Kōbun-in, was the first free school in Japan.

E. Papinot: Historical Dictionary (293, 734, 1909). Y. Fujikawa: Geschichte der Medizin in Japan (20, 1911).

IX. LATIN, MUSLIM, AND JAPANESE HISTORIOGRAPHY

PAULUS DIACONUS

Paulus Casinensis (Paul Warnefrid). Born in Istria, near Cividale del Friùli, between 720 and 725, died at Monte Cassino c. 797. Benedictine monk. Historian. His "History of the Lombards" (to 744) was widely read in the Middle Ages. He also wrote a history of the diocese of Metz (to 766).

He explained the tides by assuming the existence of abysses (sea-navels), wherein the waters were absorbed, and wherefrom they were rejected, twice a day. He assumed the existence of such an abyss (the main of them) off the Norwegian coast. He had probably heard of the Maelstrom whirlpool in the Lofot islands, which was so famous that its name became a common name ("a maelstrom of vice").

---

[b] See my note on Chinese medicine in the first half of the fourth century B. C.

Text—The Historia Langobardum was first edited by Guillaume Petit (Paris, 1514). Edition by Hugo Grotius, appended to his Historia Gotthorum (Amsterdam, 1655). By Bianchi, in Muratori's Rerum italicarum scriptores; reprinted in Migne's Latin patrology (vol. 95). By Georg Waitz, in Mon. Germ. hist. (1878).

History of the Langobards, translated by William Dudley Foulke (479 p., New York, 1907). Paulus Diaconus und die übrigen Geschichtschreiber der Langobarden übersetzt von Otto Abel (Berlin, 1849; Leipzig, 1888).

The Gesta episcoporum mettensium are also edited in the Mon. Germ. Hist.

Sexti Pompei Festi de verborum significatu cum Pauli epitome, edited by Wallace M. Lindsay (Leipzig, 1913).

Die Gedichte des Paulus Diaconus ed. by Karl Neff (251 p., München, 1908).

Criticism—Article by C. Couderc (2 cols. in Grande Encyclopédie, vol. 14, c. 1892). Roberto Almagià: La dottrina della marea nell' antichità classica e nel medio evo (Lincei, Memorie, serie 5, vol. 5, 425, 1905). M. Manitius: Lateinische Literatur des Mittelalters (vol. 1, 257–272, 1911; vol. 2, 800). P. Duhem: Système du monde (vol. 3, 112–125, 1915).

IBN AL-MUQAFFA'

'Abdallāh ibn al-Muqaffa'. Of Persian origin;[c] flourished at Baṣra, where he was executed in 757–58. Translator from Pahlawī into Arabic. He translated works on logic and medicine, but is chiefly known (1) for his translation of the "Book of Kings" (Khudhāy-nāmak, q. v., first half of seventh century; entitled, in Arabic, the "History of the Kings of Persia," Siyar mulūk al-'ajam);[d] (2) for the "Kalīla wa-Dimna," an Arabic translation of the Pahlawī version of the "Fables of Bidpai."[e] The "Kalīla wa-Dimna" is one of the earliest Arabic classics in prose.

Text—The Kalīla wa-Dimna was edited by Silvestre de Sacy (Paris, 1816). English translation of the Arabic text by the Rev. Wyndham Knatchbull (378 p., Oxford, 1819). German translation of the Arabic text by Philipp Wolff (Stuttgart, 1837; 2. ed. in 1839).

Criticism—Keith-Falconer: Kalilah and Dimnah, or the Fables of Bidpai (Cambridge, 1885. With a table showing the relationships of the different versions and their dates). Victor Chauvin: Bibliographie des ouvrages arabes (fasc. 2. Kalīlah. Liége, 1897). C. Brockelmann: Arabische Litteratur (vol. 1, 151, 1898). J. H. Breasted: The tales of Kalila and Dimna (Oriental Institute Communications, vol. 1, 82–87, 1922; **Isis**, V, 264). C. Brockelmann: Encyclopaedia of Islam (vol. 2, 694–698, 1924) (oriental versions of the tales).

IBN ISḤĀQ

Abū 'Abdallāh Muḥammad ibn Isḥāq. Flourished at Medina until 733/4; he spent the last years of his life in Bagdad under al-Manṣūr and died there in 768/9. Arabic historian. The first biographer of Muḥammad. He completed his biography at Bagdad. The original (Kitāb sīrat rasūl allāh, the life of the apostle of God) is lost and known only through Ibn Hishām's recension (q. v., first half of ninth century).

C. Brockelmann: Arabische Litteratur (vol. 1, 134).

---

[c] His Persian name was Rūzbih. He professed Islām, but seems to have remained at heart a Zoroastrian.

[d] This translation is lost.

[e] Or Pilpay. The original Sanskrit text dates from c. 300; the Pahlawī version from c. 570. See my note on Burzūya, second half of sixth century. See also Sprengling (Isis, V, 264). Innumerable versions of this text (or its prototypes) exist in almost every language.

ABŪ 'UBAIDA

Abū 'Ubaida Ma'mar ibn al-Muthannā. Born as a slave of Jewish-Persian parents at Baṣra in 728; he flourished at Baṣra and died there c. 825. One of the greatest Muslim scholars of his time. His abundant works on historical and philological subjects are lost, but have been extensively used[f] by Abū-l-Faraj al-Iṣfahānī (q. v., first half of tenth century) and by Ibn al-Athīr (q. v., first half of thirteenth century). He was an ardent Shu'ūbite[g] and rendered himself odious to the people of Baṣra.

Criticism—Ibn Khallikān (De Slane) (vol. 3, 368–98, 1868. Including a list of his writings; there is also a very long list in the Fihrist). I. Goldziher: Muhammedanische Studien (vol. 1, 194–206, Halle, 1888). C. Brockelmann: Arabische Litteratur (vol. 1, 103, 1898).

See the note devoted to Abū 'Ubaida's main opponent, al-Aṣma'ī, in Section VI.

HISHĀM IBN MUḤAMMAD

Abū-l-Mundhir Hishām ibn Muhammad ibn al-Sā'ib al-Kalbī. Born at Kūfa, flourished at Bagdad; died c. 820. Arab historian and archaeologist. He completed the studies of his father[h] on Arabian antiquity and became the leading authority of his time on the subject. His main work deals with the genealogy of the Arabs (Kitāb al-nasab al-kabīr or al-jamhara fī-l-nasab).

C. Brockelmann: Arabische litteratur (vol. 1, 138–140, 1898).

AL-WĀQIDĪ

Abū 'Abdallāh Muhammad ibn 'Umar al-Wāqidī. Born at Medina in 747/8; flourished at Medina and later at Bagdad, where he died in 823. Arab historian. He wrote a history of Muḥammad's campaigns (History of the wars, Kitāb al-maghāzī).

Text—The first third of this work has been edited by A. von Kremer (Calcutta, 1856). Abridged German translation by J. Wellhausen: Muhammed in Medina (Berlin, 1882).
Criticism—C. Brockelmann: Arabische Litteratur (vol. 1, 135, 1898).

The second of the Six National Histories of Japan, the Zoku Nihongi, dealing with the period 697 to 791, was completed in 798 by Fujiwara Tsuginawa and others (see my note on historiography in the first half of the eighth century).

X. MUSLIM PHILOLOGY

KHALĪL IBN AḤMAD

Born in 'Omān, Arabia; flourished at Baṣra; died in 791/2, aged 74 years. Arab grammarian and lexicographer. The discovery of (Arabic) prosody is unanimously ascribed to him. He contributed much to the systematization of Arabic grammar and was the first to attempt the compilation of an Arabic lexicon

[f] Especially the Kitāb aiyām al'arab (Book of the days of battle of the Arabs).
[g] The Shu'ūbites were Muslims refusing to acknowledge the superiority of the Arab race. On the contrary, they insisted on the superior qualities of other races, chiefly the Persian. Abū 'Ubaida's main work on this subject was the Kitāb al-mathālib (the vices of the Arabs reprehended).
[h] Muḥammad ibn al-Sā'ib, who died in 763/4.

(the Kitāb al-'ain).[i] His Book of Rhythm (Kitāb al-īqā'), unfortunately lost, contained already some notion of mensural music.

C. Brockelmann: Arabische Litteratur (vol. 1, 100, 1898). H. G. Farmer: Clues for the Arabian Influence on European Musical Theory (Jour. As. Soc., 72, 1925; Isis, VIII, 508-511).

SĪBAWAIHI

His original name was Sībuya. Abū Bishr (or Abū-l-Ḥasan) 'Amr ibn 'Uthmān ibn Qanbar. A Persian who came to Baṣra, at the age of 32; later he went to Bagdad and, finally, returned to his own country; he died near Shīrāz, at the age of 40, c. 795. Pupil of Khalīl ibn Aḥmad. He wrote an Arabic grammar, called simply "The Book" (al-Kitāb), which is the earliest systematic presentation of the subject. It is essentially complete, and further improvements and changes in the terminology have hardly altered its substance.

Text—Le livre de Sibawaihi. Texte arabe publié par Hartwig Derenbourg (2 vols., Paris, 1881–1889). German translation based upon Derenbourg's text, with extracts from the commentaries of Sīrāfī (d. 978/9) and others by G. Jahn (2 vols. in 3, Berlin, (1895) 1894–1900).
Criticism—C. Brockelmann: Arabische Litteratur (vol. 1, 101, 1898).

[i] He did not live to complete it.

CHAPTER XXIX

THE TIME OF AL-KHWĀRIZMĪ

(First Half of Ninth Century)

I. Survey of Science in First Half of Ninth Century. II. Religious Background. III. Cultural Background. Byzantine, Latin, Muslim, and Hindu Philosophy. IV. Muslim, Latin, Byzantine, and Hindu Mathematics and Astronomy. V. Muslim and Latin Natural History. VI. Latin, Muslim, and Chinese Geography and Geology. VII. Byzantine, Arabic, and Japanese Medicine. VIII. Latin, Byzantine, Syrian, Muslim and Japanese Historiography. IX. Barbarian, Chinese, and Japanese Law. X. Latin, Semitic, and Japanese Philology and Education.

I. SURVEY OF SCIENCE IN FIRST HALF OF NINTH CENTURY

1. The ninth century was essentially a Muslim century. To be sure, intellectual work did not cease in other countries; far from it; but the activity of the Muslim scholars and men of science was overwhelmingly superior. They were the real standard-bearers of civilization in those days. Their activity was superior in almost every respect. To consider only the first half of the century, the leading men of science, al-Kindī, the Sons of Mūsā, al-Khwārizmī, al-Farghānī, were all Muslims; Ibn Māsawaih, it is true, was a Christian, but he wrote in Arabic.

Throughout the century, the Japanese continued their gigantic effort to assimilate Chinese culture; but, strangely enough, while that culture was thriving in an alien soil, it had come to a temporary standstill in its native country.

2. *Religious Background*—Benjamin Nahawendi completed the foundation of Qaraism, and thus rendered a considerable service to Jewish thought.

Al-Shāfi'ī founded the Shāfi'ite school and Ibn Ḥanbal the Ḥanbalite school. These were the last two of the four orthodox schools of Sunnite Islām. The importance of these schools can hardly be exaggerated; not only did they mold the theological and juridical views of the great majority of Muslims, but they influenced to a considerable extent their world conceptions. The founders of the four orthodox schools (the four imāms) and the first caliphs are considered by the Muslims as the holiest men of their faith. Ibn Ḥanbal compiled a vast collection of traditions, called the Musnad. Another collection of the same kind, but classified in a different way, according to legal topics, was edited by the Shāfi'ite doctor al-Bukhārī. This second collection, named al-Ṣaḥīḥ, is one of the most important theological or juridical books of Islām.

The decadence of Chinese Buddhism continued during the ninth century. The evil tendencies which had begun to permeate Chinese Buddhism in the first half of the eighth century had developed to such an extent that the intellectual well-being of the country was jeopardized. The persecutions of which the Buddhists were the victims during the rule of Wu Tsung (841 to 846) were thus on the whole beneficent, even if Wu's intentions were not.

Two new sects were founded in Japan at the beginning of the century and were so well adapted to the religious needs of the people that they soon eclipsed the earliest sects and have been thriving unto this day. These two sects were founded by truly great men, the Tendai in 805 by Dengyō and the Shingon, a year later, by Kōbō. Both sects were introduced from China, and both were characterized by broad syncretism; they had something to offer to every mind, to the humblest as well as to the highest. Their success was partly due to the inclusion of the national Shintō religion within the fold of Buddhism (Ryōbu-Shintō). Kōbō was one of the founders of Japanese civilization; he is one of the most lovable personalities in the whole history of Japan. One of Dengyō's successors, Jikaku, spent nine years in China studying Buddhist literature; upon his return he published very elaborate accounts of his investigations.

3. *Cultural Background. Byzantine, Latin, Muslim, and Hindu philosophy*—Leon of Thessalonica, who flourished about the middle of the century, was an encyclopaedic writer who will be many times mentioned below. He was the initiator of the Byzantine renaissance of the ninth and tenth centuries, to which we owe some of the best Greek manuscripts.

The most singular and one of the greatest figures of the Carolingian renaissance was St. Agobard, who was almost alone in denouncing a number of popular and official superstitions. It is easy enough to scorn the prejudices of foreign peoples or remote times; this requires neither intelligence nor courage; but nothing calls for a clearer vision and a higher moral valor than to fight the superstitions of one's own environment. In that respect, men like St. Agobard are rare in any time and they can not be honored too much. Another great Carolingian was Alcuin's pupil, Hrabanus Maurus, who was the first teacher of Germany; and still another was Einhard, of whom I shall speak in the historical section below.

Yaḥyā ibn Baṭrīq translated various books of Plato and Aristotle into Arabic. The text of the Arabic version of the "Secretum secretorum" is also ascribed to him. This gives us the opportunity of dealing with that curious work, by far the most popular of pseudo-Aristotelian writings. It is highly probable that the original text was either Syriac or Arabic. It is a brief encyclopaedia of popular lore and superstition on a great many subjects. The seventh 'Abbāsid caliph, al-Ma'mūn (813 to 833), was even a greater patron of letters and science than Hārūn al-Rashīd. He founded a scientific academy in Bagdad, tried to collect as many Greek manuscripts as possible, and ordered their translation; he encouraged scholars of all kinds, and an enormous amount of scientific work was done under his patronage. Aḥmad ibn Sirin wrote an Arabic treatise on the interpretation of dreams, derived from Egyptian, Hindu, and Persian sources. The Mu'tazilite philosopher al-Naẓẓām expounded a curious theory of evolution. The greatest philosopher of the time was al-Kindī, who was steeped in Greek learning and wrote a large number of scientific treatises. His influence upon mediaeval thought was considerable. The assimilation of Greek knowledge was accelerated by the generous efforts of three brothers, the sons of Mūsā ibn Shākir, who took abundant pains to obtain Greek manuscripts and have them properly translated. They themselves were deeply interested in science and wrote many treatises.

The greatest exponent of Vedantic philosophy, Śaṅkara, lived probably about the beginning of the ninth century.

4. *Muslim, Latin, Byzantine, and Hindu Mathematics and Astronomy*—A very large amount of mathematical and astronomical work was done during this period, chiefly by Muslims. It is practically impossible to separate mathematics from astronomy, for almost every mathematician was an astronomer or an astrologer, or both. Some of the most important steps forward were made in the field of trigonometry in the course of computing astronomical tables. Thus it

is better to consider mathematicians and astronomers at one and the same time, but they are so numerous that I have divided them into five groups, as follows: the geometers, the arithmeticians and algebraists, the translators of the "Almagest," the astronomers and trigonometricians, the astrologers. It is hardly necessary to say that these groups are not exclusive, but overlap in various ways.

Geometers—Al-Ḥajjāj ibn Yūsuf was the first translator of Euclid's "Elements" into Arabic. Al-'Abbās wrote commentaries upon them. Abū Sa'īd al-Ḍarīr wrote a treatise on geometrical problems. Two of the Banū Mūsā, Muḥammad and Ḥasan, were especially interested in geometry; the third, Aḥmad, was a student of mechanics. Books on the measurement of the sphere, the trisection of the angle, and the determination of two mean proportionals between two given quantities are ascribed to them. They discovered kinematical methods of trisecting angles and of drawing ellipses.

Arithmeticians and Algebraists—The Jewish astrologer Sahl ibn Bishr wrote a treatise on algebra. The greatest mathematician of the time, and, if one takes all circumstances into account, one of the greatest of all times was al-Khwārizmī. He combined the results obtained by the Greeks and the Hindus and thus transmitted a body of arithmetical and algebraic knowledge which exerted a deep influence upon mediaeval mathematics. His works were perhaps the main channel through which the Hindu numerals became known in the West. The philosopher al-Kindī wrote various mathematical treatises, including four books on the use of Hindu numerals. This may have been another source of Western knowledge on the subject. In any case, the Arabic transmission eclipsed the Hindu origin, and these numerals were finally known in the West as Arabic numerals.[a]

Translators of the "Almagest"—The earliest translator of the "Almagest" into Arabic was the Jew Sahl al-Ṭabarī. Another translation was made a little later (in 829), on the basis of a Syriac version, by al-Ḥajjāj ibn Yūsuf.

Astronomers and Trigonometricians—Aḥmad al-Nahāwandī made astronomical observations at Jundīshāpūr and compiled tables. The caliph al-Ma'mūn built an observatory in Bagdad and another in the plain of Tadmor. His patronage stimulated astronomical observations of every kind. Tables of planetary motions were compiled, the obliquity of the ecliptic determined, and geodetic measurements carefully made. Al-Khwārizmī was one of the first to compute astronomical and trigonometrical tables. Ḥabash al-Ḥāsib seems to have been one of the greatest astronomers working for al-Ma'mūn. He edited three astronomical tables, seems to have been the first to determine the time by an altitude, and introduced the notion of shadow (umbra versa) corresponding to our tangent. He compiled a table of tangents, probably the earliest of its kind. Sanad ibn 'Alī was the chief of al-Ma'mūn's astronomers. Astronomical tables were compiled by him and by Yaḥyā ibn abī Manṣūr; it is probable that those tables (and those of Ḥabash already quoted) were due to the cooperative efforts of many astronomers. Observations were made by the geometers al-'Abbās, 'Alī ibn 'Īsā al-Aṣṭurlābī, Yaḥyā ibn abī Manṣūr, al-Marwarrūdhī, and al-Khwārizmī; I might mention here also the observations made by al-Dīnawarī[b] in 849–50 in Iṣpahān.

The geometer Abū Sa'īd al Ḍarīr wrote a treatise on the drawing of the meridian. 'Alī ibn 'Īsā al-Aṣṭurlabī was a famous maker of instruments; he wrote a treatise

---

[a] However, this wrong appellation was not given until the first half of the thirteenth century. (See my note on Sacrobosco.)

[b] I shall deal with him in the historical section of next chapter.

on the astrolabe. But by far the most notable of that distinguished company was al-Farghānī (Alfraganus). He was apparently the first Muslim to write a comprehensive treatise on astronomy. That treatise was very popular until the fifteenth century; it influenced not only the Muslim, but also, through Latin and Hebrew translations, the Christian and Jewish astronomers.

Astrologers—It is safe to assume that every astronomer was also, incidentally, an astrologer. However, I must still mention a few men who were chiefly if not exclusively concerned with astrology. They added nothing to astronomical knowledge; on the contrary, they contributed powerfully to its debasement, for some of their works were exceedingly popular throughout the Middle Ages. It is necessary to mention them, because of their very popularity, however harmful it was. Though the historian of science is mainly interested in the progress of science, he must take retrogressive movements into account. The main astrologers of this period were 'Umar ibn al-Farrukhān and his son Muḥammad, Abū Ma'shar (Albumasar), Sahl ibn Bishr, and Abū 'Alī al-Khaiyāṭ.

There is very little to say about mathematical and astronomical work in the non-Muslim world. Latin science is represented by some of the many writings of Hrabanus Maurus and by various anonymous treatises (if our dating of them is correct), for example, the "De mundi caelestis terrestrisque constitutione," formerly ascribed to Bede; the "De forma celi," introducing "Nimrod the Astronomer," and possibly also the pseudo-geometry ascribed to Boetius.

The only Byzantine contributions are those of Leon of Thessalonica. These contributions are unimportant, but mathematicians owe Leon some gratitude for initiating the Byzantine renaissance which gave us some excellent Greek manuscripts, notably one of Archimedes.

The Jaina mathematician Mahāvīra, who flourished in Mysore, wrote c. 830 a very interesting arithmetical treatise.

4 bis. *Byzantine and Muslim Alchemy, Physics, and Technology*—Leon of Thessalonica invented various mechanical contrivances for the Magnaura palace, where a sort of university had been organized. The arrangement of the optical telegraph used in the Byzantine Empire was also ascribed to him.

The astronomer Sanad ibn 'Alī is said to have made investigations on specific gravity. Al-Kindī wrote a treatise on geometrical and physiological optics; he criticized alchemy. His writings on music are the earliest of their kind extant in Arabic; they contain a notation for the determination of pitch. Among the works ascribed to the Banū Mūsā, is one on the balance.

5. *Muslim and Latin Natural History*—The theologian al-Naẓẓām developed a curious theory of evolution: Adam and his descendants appear in succession, but they were all created at the same time. The physician 'Alī al-Ṭabarī wrote an encyclopaedic treatise, the "Paradise of Wisdom," which contains abundant information on natural history.

Walafrid Strabo composed a Latin poem, Hortulus, containing a description of the herbs of his monastic garden.

6. *Latin, Muslim, and Chinese Geography, and Geology*—The Irish monk Dicuil compiled a geographical treatise which contains the earliest account of Iceland and a reference to the ancient canal connecting the Nile and the Red Sea.

Al-Ma'mūn ordered geodetic measurements, to determine the size of the earth, and the drawing of a large map of the world. The mathematician al-Khwārizmī wrote a geographical treatise, entitled the Face of the Earth, which was essentially a revised edition of Ptolemy's geography; it included maps. Sulaimān the Merchant traveled to the coast-lands of the Indian Ocean and to China; an account of his journeys was published in 851..

Some idea of Muslim views on minerals may be obtained in the so-called "Lapidary" of Aristotle. That compilation is probably of Syriac and Persian origin, and one may tentatively place the Arabic version in the first half of the ninth century. 'Uṭārid's lapidary, the earliest work of its kind in Arabic, dates probably from the same time.

Tu Yu's administrative encyclopaedia, the T'ung tien, contains a summary of Chinese geographical knowledge with regard to China and to the barbarian countries surrounding it. Li Chi-fu wrote a geographical description of China and drew various maps.

7. *Byzantine, Arabic, and Japanese Medicine*—It is noteworthy that I have nothing to report in this chapter on either Latin or Chinese medicine, and that my account of Byzantine medicine is restricted to a reference to Leon of Thessalonica. Leon compiled a medical encyclopaedia, in which much attention was paid to surgery. Practically all the medical work of this period was due either to Japanese or to Arabic-speaking physicians.

To consider the latter first, I said advisedly "Arabic speaking" and not "Muslim," because out of the eight physicians whom I have selected as the most important, six were Christians, most probably Nestorians. Of the two remaining, one was a true Arab, the other a Persian. A great part of the activity of these men was devoted to translating Greek medical texts, especially those of Hippocrates and Galen, into Syriac and into Arabic. All of these translators were Christians, the most prominent being Yaḥyā ibn Baṭrīq, Ibn Sahdā, Salmawaih ibn Bunān, Ibn Māsawaih, and Ayyūb al-Ruhāwī.

Jibrīl ibn Bakhtyashū' collected Greek manuscripts and patronized the translators, but he also wrote some medical works. Salmawaih ibn Bunān showed that the use of aphrodisiacs, always so popular in the East, was dangerous. The greatest of all these physicians was the Christian Ibn Māsawaih (Mesuë Major). He dissected apes and composed various anatomical and medical writings, notably the earliest ophthalmological treatise extant in Arabic and a collection of aphorisms. The philosopher al-Kindī wrote medical works also, the most important being one wherein he tried to establish posology on a mathematical basis. The Persian 'Alī al-Ṭabarī completed, in 850, a medical encyclopaedia entitled Paradise of Wisdom.

Even as some Romans, like Cato the Censor, attempted to resist the incoming tide of Greek medicine, some Japanese apparently resented the introduction of new medical methods from China and tried to restore their own native medicine. Such an attempt was made about the year 808 by order of the Emperor Heijō. Roman and Japanese medicine were inferior respectively to Greek and Chinese medicine, and hence the efforts made to restore them were bound to fail. Indeed, in a civilized society, unsound scientific ideas can not hold the ground against sounder ones, and must sooner or later be superseded by them. Nevertheless, the triumph of Greek medicine in Rome and of Chinese medicine in Japan was amazingly rapid. The earliest Japanese treatises on hygiene and on surgery were written respectively by Hiroizumi Monobe and by Fukuyoshi Ōmura; both were derived from Chinese models.

8. *Latin, Byzantine, Syrian, Muslim, and Japanese Historiography*—The activity of Chinese annalists has been so continuous during the whole past that the ab-

sence of Chinese historical works is again somewhat surprising.[c] It enables us to appreciate the depth of Chinese decadence in those days.

Before speaking of the Latin writings, it is well to recall that the present period marks the beginning of the so-called Age of the Vikings. Archaeological remains of that age, notably the Viking ships of Oseberg, are of value for the history of technology.

The greatest Latin historian was Einhard, who wrote a biography of Charlemagne, often considered the best mediaeval biography. Frechulph of Lisieux wrote a history of the world down to his own days.

Many historical works of that time were written in Greek. Georgios Syncellos wrote a chronicle from the creation to 284, which is of special value for chronological purposes. Theophanes Confessor continued Syncellos's work down to 813. Theophanes's work is important for the study not simply of Byzantine but also of Muslim events. Other histories were composed by Nicephoros Patriarches and Georgios Monachos. The influence of these writings was considerable. Latin translations popularized their use in the West. The chronicle of Georgios Monachos became one of the main historical sources of Slavonic writers; it was also translated into Georgian.

Dionysios of Tell-Maḥrē wrote annals of the world, from the creation to his own time, in Syriac.

The earliest biography of the Prophet extant was written by Ibn Hishām, on the basis of Ibn Isḥāq's lost work. Ibn Sa'd wrote a collection of biographies of the Prophet and of his companions, helpers, and followers.

Imube Hironari wrote, in 808, a work on Japanese archaeology. The Shōjiroku was compiled about 815. It contains the genealogy of a number of noble Japanese families, about one-third of them claiming a Chinese or Korean ancestry. Yoshimine Yasuyo wrote various historical works and contributed to the third of the National Histories, the Nihon-kōki, which was published after his death, in 840, by Fujiwara Otsugu.

9. *Barbarian, Chinese, and Japanese Law*—Three important Barbarian codes date from the beginning of the ninth century—the Saxon law, the Frisian law, and the Thuringian law.

Tu Yu compiled an administrative encyclopaedia, which contains, among many other things, a history of Chinese jurisprudence.

A large collection of Japanese law, the Kōnin-kyakushiki, was published in 811. Kiyowara Natsuno wrote a commentary on Chinese law in ten volumes.

10. *Latin, Semitic, and Japanese Philology and Education*—The greatest educator of the West was Hrabanus Maurus, who composed a very important treatise on the education of the clergy, a Latin grammar derived from that of Priscian, and a Latin-German glossary.

An Arabic letter addressed to the Jewish community of Fez by Jehuda ben Quraish is the earliest contribution to comparative Semitic philology.

Kōbō-daishi invented a new syllabary (the hiragana) and established one of the earliest public schools of Japan. Sugawara Kiyogimi reformed the imperial university and introduced Chinese methods in its administration; this task was continued by his son Sugawara Koreyoshi.

11. *Final Remarks*—This period marked the beginning of a new renaissance, which brings back to mind the memory of Alexandria, but the main intellectual center

---

[c] However, Tu Yu's encyclopaedia, mentioned in the following section, is to some extent a historical work.

this time was in Bagdad. The renaissance which was then heralded with so much vigor would be a Muslim renaissance, but a great deal of the preparatory work was done by non-Muslims, chiefly Nestorian Christians.

The Carolingian renaissance was in full swing at the same time, but does not bear comparison with the Muslim revival. To be sure, it produced some great men, like Hrbanus Maurus, St. Agobard, and Einhard. These men continued in a worthy manner the glorious tradition of Bede and Alcuin, but, however great, they were no longer in the vanguard, but distinctly behind the times. The reason of this is simple. The West had gradually lost touch with the Greek springs of knowledge; thus they were condemned to rediscover very slowly most of the results which had been previously obtained in the Greek world, before being able to go forward. As a whole, they had much less genius than the Greeks, and hence their rediscovery was bound to be slower than the original discovery. The latter, be it noted, had not been as rapid as one often imagines; the development of Greek science had been a matter of many centuries, and we have no idea of how many centuries of anonymous preparation had been needed to make this development possible. Keeping that restriction in mind, the Carolingian renaissance was a noble movement which lifted Western Europe up to a much higher level than it had ever reached before.

But that was not all. A third renaissance was initiated in the Byzantine Empire by Leon of Thessalonica; a fourth was apparently awakening Southern India (Saṅkara came from Malabar and Mahāvīra from Mysore); and still a fifth was continuing with unabated energy in Japan. Thus it would seem that the whole civilized world was reviving. Few periods in the past could ever muster such an array of men (I quote them approximately in chronological order): Śaṅkara, Kōbō-daishi, Mahāvīra, al-Khwārizmī, al-Farghānī, Ibn Māsawaih, St. Agobard, Hrbanus Maurus, Leon of Thessalonica, al-Kindī, the Banū Mūsā. . . .

To come back to the Muslim renaissance, which was by far the most important, its success was essentially due to the wave of enthusiasm and energy which lifted these peoples up for a time almost above themselves. Any renaissance is essentially due to internal causes; but such causes, however necessary, are never sufficient. The Muslim revival would probably have remained on the same level as the Carolingian if the treasures of Greek knowledge had been as little available to the Arabic-speaking people as they were to the people of Western Europe. But, on the contrary, the Muslims were brought into a relatively intimate contact with Greek knowledge by the activity of Jewish and even more of Syrian interpreters. Thus it came to pass that the intellectual weapons of Islām were actually forged by Christians. And it so happened that after a while those Christians disappeared and the inestimable treasures of Greek knowledge remained almost exclusively in the keeping of Muslims. Many centuries were to elapse before Islām would return them to Christendom.

One of the best ways of characterizing this early period of the Muslim revival is to show how the protagonists were divided with regard to religion and race. To speak of the non-Muslims first, the following were Christians: Yaḥyā ibn Baṭrīq, Yaḥyā ibn abī Manṣūr, Jibrīl ibn Bakhtyashū', Salmawaih ibn Bunān, Ibn Māsawaih, Ayyūb al-Ruhāwī. The following were Jews (or of Jewish origin): Benjamin Nahawendi, Sahl al-Ṭabarī, and his son 'Alī, Sanad ibn 'Alī, Sahl ibn Bishr, Jehuda ben Quraish. All of them but the last hailed from Persia or Khurāsān. Jehuda came from North Africa, and he brings to our notice, for the first time, the people of Fez, in Morocco.

With regard to the Muslims, the first question which occurs to our mind is, How many of them were Arabs? Very few: al-Shāfi'ī, Ibn Ḥanbal, al-Kindī, Ibn Hishām, Ibn Sa'd. With the exception of al-Kindī, these men were not men of science, but theologians and historians. Al-Kindī was the only philosopher and scientist, and he was a great one, but his Arabian origin was deemed so remarkable that he was called "the philosopher of the Arabs." In fact, he was the only great philosopher of his race.

With the exception of al-Kindī, all of the Muslim scientists of this time came from Persia or from further east. 'Umar ibn al-Farrukhān and his son Muḥammad came from Ṭabaristān; Abū Sa'īd al-Ḍarīr, from Jurjān, just east of the Caspian; al Khwārizmī, from Khwārizm, south of the Aral Sea; Mūsā ibn Shākir and his three sons, Ḥabash al-Ḥāsib, al-Marwarrūdhī, Abū Ma'shar, from Khurāsān;[d] al-Bukhārī and al-Farghānī from Transoxiana. It is interesting to notice how many of the best men came from the easternmost parts of Islām.

The Carolingian, Byzantine, and Japanese revivals were essentially national movements. On the contrary, the Muslim renaissance was, almost from the beginning, an international awakening. During the period which we have just considered, it had already influenced the whole of the Near East and had reached the doors of Central Asia. This is another reason why the historian of civilization must make a close study[e] of Islām if he would really understand mediaeval progress.

II. RELIGIOUS BACKGROUND

Development of Qaraism

BENJAMIN NAHAWENDI

Benjamin ben Moses Nahawendi. Flourished at Nahawend, Persia, at the end of the eighth and the beginning of the ninth century. Jewish theologian. He completed the foundation of Qaraism begun by Anan ben David (second half of eighth century),[f] insisting upon the value of free thought. Inquiry is a duty, and errors occasioned by inquiry do not constitute sins. He wrote commentaries on the Bible, mostly in Arabic; he also wrote in Hebrew.

Article in Jewish Encyclopaedia (vol. 3, 32, 1902) by I. Broydé.

Muslim Theology

AL-SHĀFI'Ī

Muḥammad ibn Idrīs al-Shāfi'ī. Born in Gaza (?) in 767/68 of a Quraishitic family; died at Fusṭāṭ in 820. Muslim jurist. One of the greatest jurists of all times. Pupil of Mālik ibn Anas at Medina. Founder of the Shāfi'īte school of law, one of the four orthodox schools. Shāfi'īte law is based on (1) the Qur'ān, (2) the ḥadīth, (3) the use of analogy (qiyās; legal fiction), (4) the agreement of the people (ijmā').

The Shāfi'īte school is still authoritative in Lower Egypt, Syria, southern India, and the Malay archipelago.

---

[d] Ibn Ḥanbal too. I counted him among the Arabs, because he was of the Arabian race, but he was born in Bagdad of a Merwian family.

[e] A much closer one than most of them have made heretofore.

[f] He was clearly influenced by Philon (first half of first century) and by the Mu'tazilites.

F. Wüstenfeld: Der Imām el Schāfi'ī, seine Schüler und Anhänger bis zum J. 300 (Abhdl. der Ges. der Wiss., vol. 36, Göttingen, 1890); Die gelehrten Schafi'iten des IV. Jahrhundert (*ibidem*, vol. 37, 1891). C. Brockelmann: Arabische Litteratur (vol. 1, 178–180, 1898). D. B. Macdonald: Development of Muslim Theology (1903).

IBN ḤANBAL

Abū 'Abdallāh Aḥmad ibn Muḥammad ibn Ḥanbal. Born in Bagdad in 780, of Arab parents residing at Merw; traveled extensively; flourished at Bagdad, where he died in 855. Muslim theologian and jurist. Disciple of al-Shāfi'ī. The Ḥanbalite school of law, the last of the four orthodox schools, was founded by his disciples after his death. It was a reactionary movement, insisting on a more literal interpretation of the Qur'ān and of the traditions, minimizing the value of analogy and agreement. Aḥmad ibn Ḥanbal compiled the Musnad, a collection of some 30,000 traditions arranged, not according to subjects, but according to the Companions of the Prophet, who vouched for them. It is the best and largest compilation of its kind.

The founders of the four orthodox Sunnite schools—Abū Ḥanīfa, Mālik ibn Anas, al-Shāfi'ī, Aḥmad ibn Ḥanbal—are called "the four Imāms." The Ḥanbalite school was by far the least successful of those four schools, except in raising trouble. Its law has no force to-day except among the Wahhābīs in Central Arabia.

Ibn Khallikān (De Slane) (vol. 1, 44–46, 1842). C. Brockelmann: Arabische Litteratur (vol. 1, 181–183). D. B. Macdonald: Development of Muslim Theology (1903). W. M. Patten: Aḥmed ibn Ḥanbal and the Miḥna (211 p., Leiden, 1897).

AL-BUKHĀRĪ

Abū 'Abdallāh Muḥammad ibn Ismā'īl al-Bukhārī al-Ju'fī, born at Bukhārā of an Iranian family in 810; he traveled for 16 years collecting traditions, and then returned to Bukhārā, being about 32 years old. He died in exile at Khartank, in the district of Samarkand, in 870. Muslim traditionalist. Anti-rationalistic and, in law, Shāfi'ite. Author of the most famous muṣannaf (classified) collection of traditions (ḥadīth). This work, called Kitāb al-jāmi' al-ṣaḥīḥ,[g] has become almost sacred, enjoying a reverence second only to that of the Qur'ān. It contains 7,275 traditions selected by Bukhārī out of some 600,000. They are classified according to the chapters of common law,[h] forming a complete system of concrete jurisprudence. It may here be remarked that the criticism of their religious traditions by the Muslims, which goes back even to the eighth century, was the earliest example of such critical activity in the world. This criticism was not unbiased, but remarkably accurate.[i]

Text—Arabic text of the Ṣaḥīḥ, edited by L. Krehl and T. W. Juynboll (Leyden, 1862–1868). French translation, Les traditions islamiques, by O. Houdas and W. Marçais (4 vols., Paris, 1903–1914). Oscar Rescher: Sachindex zu Bokhārī nach der Ausgabe von Krehl und Juynboll und der Uebersetzung von Houdas und

---

[g] Or in brief, al-Ṣaḥīḥ, the Genuine.

[h] Indeed, books on the law (al-fiqh) were written before traditions (ḥadīth) were collected and published. See D. B. Macdonald: Development of Muslim Theology (77, 1903).

[i] Ignaz Goldziher: Progress of Islamic Science (St. Louis Congress of Arts and Sciences, vol. 2, 497 sq., 502, 1906).

Marçais (52 p., Stuttgart, 1923). Le livre des testaments traduit avec éclaircissements par Frédéric Peltier (Alger, 1909).

Criticism—Ibn Khallikān (De Slane) (vol. 2, 594–597, 1843). C. Brockelmann: Arabische Litteratur (vol. 1, 157–160, 1898). D. B. Macdonald: Development of Muslim Theology, 1903; also 11. ed. of the Enc. Brit. (article Bukhārī).

Chinese Buddhism

The decadence of Chinese Buddhism begun in the eighth century continued during the ninth. It was caused chiefly by the growing superstition of all classes of people and the gradual corruption of doctrine and ritual. Yet Buddhism was more popular than ever and the number of monks increased incessantly. Thus did reaction and persecution become almost inevitable. Under the rule of the Taoist emperor Wu[3] Tsung[1] (12744, 11976), (841 to 846), Buddhism was prohibited, 4,600 large temples and 40,000 smaller establishments were ordered demolished, and their lands and property confiscated; 260,500 monks were forcibly returned to secular life. These numbers are probably exaggerated. Yet the persecution was thorough and Chinese Buddhism never did fully recover from it. It should be noted that Wu Tsung's edicts embraced not only Buddhists but the Ta[4]-ch'in[2] (10470, 2093) (Nestorians), the Mu[4*]-hu[4] (8082, 4979) (Zoroastrians) and the Mo[1]-ni[2] (7969, 8194) (Manichaeans?).[j] The history of Chinese Buddhism ends here, as far as we are concerned. No new activities are worth recording, indeed, in a history of thought, except perhaps the publication of various editions of the Buddhist Canon. (The first printed edition appeared under the auspices of the first Sung emperor, T'ai[4] Tsu[3] (10573, 11826), who ruled from 960 to 976.)

Japanese Buddhism

The six Nara sects originated in the seventh and eighth centuries (see my notes on Buddhism during these centuries). Two new sects, the first two Kyōto sects, appeared almost simultaneously at the beginning of the ninth century, and then no more sects were introduced for more than three centuries.

These two sects are the Tendai and the Shingon. The Tendai was founded, in 805, by Dengyō daishi, and the Shingon, in 806, by Kōbō daishi. They soon eclipsed the older sects. They have been flourishing ever since and are still very important to-day.

A branch of the Tendai-shū, the Jimon, was founded in 858 by Enchin,[k] who had been in China in 853.

An attempt to introduce the Zen-shū was apparently made as early as about 815 by a Chinese bonze, Gikū, who returned to China to die. The real introduction of that sect did not occur until 1202. See my notes on Eisai (second half of twelfth century) and on religion in the thirteenth century. Brief note on Gikū, in E. Papinot, Historical Dictionary (118, 1909).

DENGYŌ DAISHI

His family name was Miura; his religious name, Saichō. Shortly before his death he received the title Dengyō-hōshi (reverend), changed posthumously in 866 to Dengyō-daishi. He is best known under the last name. Born in Ōmi in 767; traveled in China from 802 to 805; died in 822. Japanese Buddhist. He brought back from the Buddhist monastery in the T'ien-t'ai Mountains the

---

[j] G. F. Moore: History of Religions (vol. 1[2], 85).

[k] Enchin (814 to 891); posthumous title (927), Chishō-daishi.

T'ien t'ai tsung, called in Japan Tendai-shū.[l] This was the earliest of the so-called Kyōto sects.[m] Its seat was established at the Enryaku-ji on the Hiei-zan, a mountain near Kyōto. It was a syncretism of Hīnayāna and Mahāyāna tendencies, of the highest metaphysics and the humblest Amidaism. It included all previous aspirations of Buddhism; no wonder, then, that it became in its time the parent of nearly all the great sects subsequently founded in Japan. This syncretism was so broad that it embraced Shintō as well. Dengyō is indeed one of the originators of the honchi-suijaku,[n] the central doctrine of the Ryōbu-Shintō.[o]

The Tendai sect is now (c. 1917) represented in Japan by 4,711 temples (out of a total of 72,191).

E. Papinot: Dictionary of Japan (1909). F. Brinkley: History of the Japanese People (227, 367, 1915). A. K. Reischauer: Japanese Buddhism (91–94, 1917)

KŌBŌ DAISHI

Kōbō daishi is his posthumous name, granted in 921, under which he is best known. Daishi is an honorific title which might be translated Great Master. His family name was Saiki; at the age of 19 he assumed the religious name Kūkai. Born in 774 at Byōbu-ga-ura, Sanuki; he traveled in China from 804 to 806; he retired in 816 to Mount Kōya,[p] where he died in 835. Japanese Buddhist. Grammarian, theologian, artist, saint. One of the founders of Japanese civilization. He brought back from China hundreds of paintings and the ideals of the Chên Yen tsung (True Word School).[q] He thus founded the Shingon-shū, one of the most popular Buddhist sects of Japan. The Shingon sect is extremely comprehensive and syncretic; it might be compared with Christian Gnosticism. It combined the highest speculations with the crudest magic and the most literal mysticism. Its very name suggests this superstitious literalism for the "True Word" is the word which is magically efficacious (the Hindu mantra). It is now (c. 1917) the third largest sect of Japan, being represented by 12,717 temples (out of 72,191).

Kōbō is also considered one of the founders of the Ryōbu-Shintō or two-sided Shintō, a doctrine holding that the Shintō gods are avatars of the Buddhist ones and hence that Shintoism and Buddhism are but two aspects of one single religion. This doctrine prevailed until the eighteenth century, when archaeologists began to prepare a revival of pure Shintō. Since 1868, Shintoism is the only state religion of Japan.

He is said to have invented a new syllabary, the hiragana. I explained the meaning of that invention when I spoke of the katakana in my note on Kibi Makibi (first half of eighth century). The katakana was a square style of writing derived from the Chinese square characters; the hiragana is a cursive and easier

---

[l] See my note on Chih-i (second half of sixth century).

[m] As opposed to the Nara sects, for which see my notes on Japanese Buddhism in the seventh and eighth centuries.

[n] Honchi means native place; suijaku, passage. India is the native land of the Shintō gods, Japan a land of passage.

[o] See my notes on Gyōgi (first half of eighth century) and Kōbō, below.

[p] Kōya-san in Kii. The earliest and main temple of that mountain, the Kongō-bu-ji was founded by Kōbō in 816.

[q] That is, the Hindu Mantra introduced into China in the eighth century. It is now extinct in China. (See my note on Chinese Buddhism in the first half of the eighth century.)

form of the same 47 syllables. These syllables are named iroha, after the first three (even as we call the alphabet, ABC; the word iroha has also the same derivative meaning as ABC, rudiments). A charming little poem wherein these 47 syllables are used without repetition (the iroha-uta, or iroha) is traditionally ascribed to Kōbō; every Japanese child knows it by heart.

As Kōbō was a great artist, it is not surprising that he was also a great calligraphist; he could trace Chinese characters most beautifully. The Japanese call him one of the Three Calligraphists (Sampitsu).

He established the earliest public school in Japan (or one of the earliest). He promoted sericulture.

Text—Léon de Rosny: Zitu-go-kyau. Do-zi-kyau. L'enseignement de la vérité, ouvrage du philosophe Kobaudaïsi, et l'enseignement de la jeunesse. Publiés avec une transcription européenne du texte original et traduits pour la première fois du japonais. (Thus quoted without place or date by H. Cordier. Bibliotheca Japonica, 537, 1912). Text and French translation of the Iroha-uta in Michel Revon: Anthologie de la littérature japonaise (137, 1910).

Criticism—Tomeri Tanimoto: Kobo Daishi. His Position in the History of Japanese Civilization (published by the Japan Chronicle in 1907, not seen). Papinot's Dictionary (Tokyo, 1909). F. Brinkley: History of the Japanese People (1915). A. K. Reischauer: Japanese Buddhism (94–99, 1917).

JIKAKU DAISHI

His own name was Ennin. Jikaku daishi is a posthumous title. Born in the province of Shimotsuke in 794; Tendai-zasu (i. e., head of Tendai-shū) in 854; died at Kyōto in 864. Japanese Tendai Buddhist. He resided in China from 838 to 847, visiting many Buddhist temples and copying books. After his return to Japan, he published the results of his investigations in 21 works, forming 559 volumes.

E. Papinot: Historical Dictionary (226, 1909).

III. CULTURAL BACKGROUND—BYZANTINE, LATIN, MUSLIM, AND HINDU PHILOSOPHY

Byzantine Philosophy

LEON OF THESSALONICA

Λέων. Leon the Iatrosophist, or Leon the Philosopher.[r] Flourished under the emperors Theophile, 829 to 842, and Michael III, 842 to 867. Byzantine encyclopaedist. Archbishop of Thessalonica, professor at the University of the Magnaura palace (ἡ Μαγναύρα) in Constantinople. The invention of the mechanical contrivances (automata, etc.) of the Magnaura and of the optical telegraph used in the Byzantine Empire was ascribed to him. He wrote on mathematics, astrology, medicine. His medical encyclopaedia (Σύνοψις ἰατρική), compiled during the reign of Theophile, is a remarkable treatise in seven books; surgery is given much attention in his therapeutics. He initiated the Byzantine renaissance of the ninth and tenth centuries, to which we owe the best manuscripts of the Greek classics, notably one of Archimedes.

---

[r] This last name ought to be avoided because it is confusing. The Byzantine Emperor Leon VI (886 to 911) was also called Leon the Philosopher or the Wise.

Text and Translations—The Σύνοψις ἰατρική has been edited in F. Z. Ermerins: Anecdota medica graeca (p. 79–221, Leiden, 1840). Another medical or physiological writing (Σύνοψις εἰς τὴν φύσιν τοῦ ἀνθρώπου) is still unpublished.

Criticism—J. L. Heiberg: Der Byzantinische Mathematiker Leon. Bibliotheca Mathematica (p. 33–36, 1887). E. Gurlt: Geschichte der Chirurgie (vol. 1, 590, 1898). Neuburger und Pagel: Handbuch der Geschichte der Medizin (vol. 1, 559, Jena, 1902).

Latin Philosophy

ST. AGOBARD

Born c. 779, died 840. Archbishop of Lyon. Defender of reason against superstition, "the clearest head of his time." He denounced the fallacies involved in witchcraft persecution, trial by ordeal, judicial duel, image-worship, and the magical explanation of storms.

Text and Translations—The editio princeps was published in Paris, 1605, by Papyre Masson, the discoverer of his works. More complete edition by Etienne Baluze (2 vols., 1666). Migne's Patrologia (vol. 104, 29–307, 319–351). The De grandine et tonitruis was published, with a French translation and notes by Antoine Péricaud l'aîné (55 p., Lyon, 1841).

Criticism—Acta Sanctorum Bolland. (June 2, 748). Histoire littéraire de la France (vol. 4, 567–583, 1738). P. Chevallard. L'église et l'état au IXe siècle. Saint Agobard, sa vie et ses écrits (Lyon, 1869). A. Ebert: Gesch. d. Litteratur des Mittelalters (Vol. II, 1880). A. D. White. History of the Warfare of Science with Theology (Vol. I, 301, 351, 1896).

HRABANUS MAURUS

Also Rabanus, Rhabanus. Born in Mayence c. 776, died in Winkel on the Rhine in 856. Carolingian educator. "Primus Germaniae praeceptor." Pupil of Alcuin in Tours. Abbot of Fulda, later archbishop of Mayence. He organized the school of Fulda, which, thanks to his efforts, obtained considerable prestige. His most important works are the "De universo libri XXII, sive etymologiarum opus," a sort of Biblical dictionary or encyclopaedia, compiled c. 844, and the "De institutione clericorum" in three books, wherein the methods of educating clerks are explained; it is a complete treatise on education, dealing with the seven liberal arts. Among his voluminous writings I must still mention an "Excerptio" from Priscian's grammar (q. v., first half of sixth century), which was exceedingly popular; also a computus and a Latin-German glossary ("Glossaria latina-theodisca"). His knowledge was still on the patristic level, but he was one of the last prominent men of whom this can be said. He had some slight understanding of Greek and even of Hebrew.

Text—Opera omnia in Migne's Patrology (vols. 107 to 112). Critical edition of the De institutione clericorum libri tres, by Aloisius Knoepfler (Münich, 1900). Paedagogische Schriften, übersetzt, bearbeitet und mit einer Einleitung versehen v. Joseph Freundgen (Paderborn, 1890).

Criticism—E. H. F. Meyer: Geschichte der Botanik (vol. 3, 415–421, 1856). Stefan Fellner: Compendium der Naturwissenschaften an der Schule zu Fulda im IX. Jahrhundert (247 p., Berlin, 1879. Analysis of the De universo; important). F. Picavet: Les discussions sur la liberté au temps de Gottschalk (c. 808 to c. 867), de Raban Maur, d'Hincmar et de Jean Scot (Comptes rendus de l'ac. des sci. morales, Paris, 1896). Dietrich Türnau: Rabanus Maurus, der praeceptor Germaniae (72 p., München, 1900). J. B. Hablitzel: Hrabanus. Ein Beitrag zur Geschichte der mittelalterlichen Exegese (Diss., 105 p., München, 1906). G. L. Bertolini: I quattro angoli del mondo e la forma della terra nel passo di Rabano Mauro (Boll. d. soc. geograf. italiana, Vol. XI, 1433–1441, 1910). M. Manitius: Lateinische Literatur des Mittelalters (vol. 1, 288–302, 1911; vol. 2, 802). P. Duhem: Le système du monde (Vol. II, 20 sq., 1915).

The house in which Hrabanus died in Winkel is still supposed to exist. This matter has been investigated by P. Eichholz, see Geschichtsblätter für Technik (vol. 3, 265, 1916).

Muslim Philosophy

YAḤYĀ IBN BAṬRĪQ

Abū Zakarīyā Yaḥyā[s] ibn Baṭrīq. Son of the physician al-Baṭrīq dealt with in the previous chapter. Flourished at the beginning of the ninth century. Translator from Greek or Rūmī into Arabic. He translated Plato's Timaeos, Hippocrates's book on the signs of death, various works of Aristotle,[t] and Galen's De theriaca ad Pisonem. The Arabic text of the Secretum secretorum (Sirr al-asrār) is also ascribed to him. According to Ḥunain ibn Isḥāq, he knew Latin even better than Greek.

L. Leclerc: Médecine arabe (vol. 1, 181, 1876). C. Brockelmann: Arabische Litteratur (vol. 1, 203, 1898). H. Suter: Mathematiker und Astronomen (16, 1900; 160, 1902). Max Meyerhof: New Light on Ḥunain (Isis, VIII, 705, 1926).

Secretum Secretorum

None of the many writings which were attributed in mediaeval times to Aristotle has enjoyed a wider popularity than the so-called "Secretum (secreta) secretorum." It was translated into many European vernaculars and influenced to a degree every important literature. It is a confused compilation of folk-lore and superstition with regard to physiognomy, dietetics, etc., the value of which has not yet been properly investigated. It is now generally admitted that the original work, though based on Greek sources, was not Greek, but Arabic or Syriac. That is, the text which was given out as a translation from the Greek is either the original compilation or a later recension of it. It may have originated in the interaction between Persian and Syriac ideas which took place in the seventh to ninth centuries.[u] The original would then probably be Syriac, but no copy of it has thus far been found. The earliest Arabic text dates probably from the beginning of the ninth century, for the introduction of the Arabic secretum (called Sirr al-asrār) ascribes it to Yaḥyā ibn Baṭrīq, who was supposed to have translated it from Greek into Rūmī (Syriac? or Byzantine Greek?) and from Rūmī into Arabic. This text was soon known in the Western Caliphate; a reference to it is found in the anthology[v] of Ibn 'Abdi Rabbihi of Cordova, who died in 939–40. Joannes Hispalensis (q. v., first half of the twelfth century), made a Latin version of it and a little later it was translated into Hebrew by Judah al-Harizi (fl. in Spain 1190 to 1218).[w] A Castilian translation, Poridad de la poridades, belongs

---

[s] Or Yūḥannā, Christian (Syriac) equivalent of Yaḥyā. Cfr. Joannes, John, etc.

[t] He translated the De coelo et mundo, De anima, and the Meteorology into Arabic; the History of animals and the Politics into Syriac (?)

[u] As suggested by Robert Steele in his edition of Bacon's version, 1920.

[v] The so-called "Unique necklace," Al-'iqd al-farīd.

[w] Edited by Moses Gaster, with English translation (Journal Royal Asiatic Society, 879–912, 1907; 111–162, 1065–1084, 1908).

to the same—Western—tradition. Joannes's version was translated into many other vernaculars.

In the meanwhile, the Arabic text received various accretions and a new form of it, which Steele calls the "Eastern form," was fully developed c. 1220. One Philip of Tripoli found a copy of it in Antioch and translated it into Latin some time during the second quarter of the thirteenth century (c. 1243?). This Latin translation after extensive revision became the vulgate text, two editions of which appeared before 1500. In 1501 Alessandro Achillini of Bologna published a new Latin text which has been followed in all subsequent editions.

Of the many translations in vernaculars, the most interesting are perhaps the Castilian already quoted, the Anglo-Norman by the Irish Dominican Geoffrey of Waterford (d. 1300), and the Flemish by Jacob van Maerlant (1235–c. 1291).

Of the Latin versions, the most interesting is certainly that by Roger Bacon, completed c. 1257, with an introduction dating from c. 1270 (see my note on Bacon).

Text—There are many incunabula editions: De secretis secretorum vel liber de regimine principum. Cologne 1480 (that is, Philip's translation). Le gouvernement des princes (Paris, 1497, etc.). See Förster's paper quoted below.

The part of the work dealing with physiognomy has been carefully edited by Richard Förster: Physiognomoniae secreti secretorum pseudoaristotelici versiones latinae, in his Scriptores physiognomonici graeci et latini (vol. 2, 181–222, Leipzig, 1893. See also the Prolegomena in vol. 1, p. CLXXVIII–CLXXXI).

Secretum secretorum cum glossis et notulis. . . . . Fratris Rogeri. Nunc primum edidit Robert Steele. Accedunt versio anglicana ex arabico edita per A. S. Fulton, versio vetusta anglo-normanica nunc primum edita (382 p., Oxford, 1920).

Of the many editions of this work in modern languages, I will only quote the following: Lydgate and Burgh: Secrees of old philosoffres. Edited by Robert Steele (Early English Texts Society, extra series, 66, 156 p., London, 1894). Translation in rime royal begun by John Lydgate (1370?–1451?), continued by Benedict Burgh (fl. 1472). Three prose versions of the Secretum secretorum edited by Robert Steele, with a glossary by T. Henderson (vol. 1, 1898. Same collection, 74).

Criticism—Richard Förster: De Aristotelis quae feruntur secretis secretorum (41 p., Kiel, 1888). Richard Förster: Handschriften und Ausgaben des Secretum Secretorum (Centralblatt für Bibliothekswesen, vol. 6, 1889, 1–22, 57–76, 218–219). Carl Brockelmann: Geschichte der arabischen Litteratur (vol. 1, 203, 1898). C. H. Haskins: Studies in Mediaeval Science (137–140, 1924). The best general study will be found in R. Steele's introduction to his edition of 1920.

I do not know any elaborate study of the scientific ideas contained in this family of texts.

AL-MA'MŪN

'Abdallāh al-Ma'mūn. Born in Bagdad in 786, died near Tarsus in 833. The seventh and greatest 'Abbāsid caliph (813–833). His mother and wife were Persians, which explains his Persian and 'Alid proclivities. He was an ardent Mu'tazil,[1] and tried to enforce his views by means of violence. He wrote four long letters to explain that the Qur'ān was created, and he cruelly punished those who dared entertain different views (e. g., Ibn Ḥanbal). He thus combined in a remarkable way free

---

[1] Literally: a seceder. In opposition to the Orthodox, the Mu'tazila believed in relative freedom of the will, that the Qur'ān is not "uncreated and eternal," that God will not be visible on the Day of Resurrection, etc.

thought and intolerance.[y] While persecuting those who objected to Mu'tazilism, Jews and Christians were very welcome at his court. He was even a greater patron of letters and science than Hārūn al-Rashīd. He took considerable pains to obtain Greek manuscripts and even sent a mission to the Byzantine Emperor Leon the Armenian (813 to 820) for that purpose. He ordered the translation of these manuscripts. He organized at Bagdad a sort of scientific academy called the House of Wisdom (Bayt al-ḥikma), which included a library and an observatory. This was the most ambitious undertaking of its kind since the foundation of the Alexandrian Museum (q. v., first half of third century B. C.). He built another observatory on the plain of Tadmor (Palmyra). The inclination of the ecliptic was found by his astronomers to equal 23° 33′ and tables of the planetary motions were constructed. He ordered two degree-measurements to be made to determine the size of the earth, one of them near Tadmor (a degree = 56⅔ miles, hence circumference of the earth = 20,400 miles; diameter = 6,500 miles). A large map of the world was drawn for him.[z] He encouraged philosophers, philologists, traditionalists, and other jurists, mathematicians, physicians, astrologers, and alchemists.

Fihrist (116, 243 and passim). Gustav Weil: Geschichte der Chalifen (vol. 2, 198–294). J. T. Reinaud: Géographie d'Aboulféda (vol. 1, 269 sq., 1848). J. L. E. Dreyer: History of the Planetary System from Thales to Kepler (p. 245, 249, 278, Cambridge, 1906). R. A. Nicholson: Literary History of the Arabs (359, 1907).

AḤMAD IBN SIRIN

Interpreter of dreams of al Ma'mūn, caliph from 813 to 833. Muslim author of a treatise on oneirology, in 304 chapters, based upon Egyptian, Hindu, and Persian sources. This treatise is apparently lost in Arabic, but it is available in Greek. The Greek text was translated into Latin by Leo Tuscus in 1176.[a]

Aḥmad ibn Sirin is possibly identical with Abū Ma'shar (q. v., in Section IV). About the middle of al-Ma'mūn's reign, Abū Ma'shar was already 40 years old. An Arabic edition of Aḥmad's work (Bulaq, 1868), calls him Muḥammad. The Latin edition of Aḥmad's work, Francfort, 1577, calls the author Apomasar; now Apomasar (*'Απομιαξάρ*) is very probably a corruption of Abū Ma'shar. The matter needs further investigation.

Text—*Βιβλίον ὀνειροκριτικὸν, ὅπερ συνῆξεν καὶ συνέταξεν 'Αχμὲτ υἱὸς Σηρεὶμ ὁ ὀνειροκρίτης τοῦ πρώτου συμβούλου Μαμοῦν*. Text edited by Nicolas Rigault in his edition of Artemidoros (q. v., second half of second century) (Paris, 1603). A Latin translation by Leunclavius (different from Tuscus's translation) was published in Francfort 1577 (under the name of Apomasaris; see my note on Abū Ma'shar). French translation (Paris, 1581).

A Greek treatise on astrology by one Aḥmad (*'Αχμάτης*) mentioned in the Cat. Cod. Astrol. Graec. (II, 122), may be a work by the same author. See Thorndike: History of Magic (vol. 2, 292).

---

[y] That combination is inconsistent but quite common. It characterized also the rule of the following caliph, al-Mu'taṣim (833 to 842).

[z] According to Mas'ūdī (q. v., first half of the tenth century), who saw it. Livre de l'avertissement, 53. For the geodesic measurements, see *ibidem*, 44.

[a] Leo's translation represents a tradition older than the extant Greek manuscripts. The date which I quote is that given by C. H. Haskins. (The date previously accepted was 1160). Leo Tuscus was secretary to Manuel I Comnenos, emperor from 1143 to 1180; he flourished c. 1166 to 1176.

Criticism—Moritz Steinschneider: Ibn Shabin und Ibn Sirin (Z. D. Deuts. morgenl. Ges., vol. 17, 227–244, 1863); Die hebräischen Übersetzungen des Mittelalters, (566–570, 1893); Die europäischen Übersetzungen (p. 2, 38, 1905).

R. Hercher: Zu Achmets 'Ονειροκριτικόν· (Philologus, 10, 346, 1855). Ch. E. Ruelle: La clef des songes d'Achmet Abou-Mazar. Fragment inédit et nouvelles variantes. Revue des études grecques (vol. 7, 305–312, 1894). C. Krumbacher: Byzantinische Literatur (630, 1898). F. X. Drexl: Achmets Traumbuch; Einleitung und Probe eines kritischen Textes (Diss., München, 1909). Lynn Thorndike: History of Magic (vol. 2, 291, 1923). C. H. Haskins: Mediaeval Science (216–218, 1924).

AL-NAẒẒĀM

Died in 845. One of the leading Mu'tazilite philosophers. Master of al-Jāḥiẓ. I quote him chiefly because of his theory of creation: Adam and the sons of Adam were all created at the same time, though they can appear only in succession. A part only of creation is apparent, the rest is hidden (kumūn). Compare with St. Augustine's theory of potential creation (first half of fifth century).[b]

Criticism—T. J. de Boer: Geschichte der Philosophie im Islam (51–53, Stuttgart, 1901). D. B. Macdonald: Development of Muslim Theology (140, 143, 152, New York, 1903). M. Horten: Die Lehre von Kumūn bei Naẓẓam (Z. d. deutschen morgenl. Ges., vol. 63, 774–792, 1909. Important).

AL-KINDĪ

Abū Yūsuf Ya'qūb ibn Isḥāq ibn al-Ṣabbāḥ al-Kindī (i. e., of the tribe of Kinda). Latin name, Alkindus. Born in Baṣra at the beginning of the ninth century, flourished in Bagdad under al-Ma'mūn and al-Mu'taṣim (813 to 842), persecuted during the orthodox reaction led by al-Mutawakkil (847 to 861); died c. 873. "The philosopher of the Arabs;" so-called probably because he was the first and only great philosopher of the Arab race. His knowledge of Greek science and philosophy was considerable. He made a deep study of Aristotle from the Neoplatonic point of view. Encyclopaedic scientist. Relatively few of his numerous works (270?) are extant. They deal with mathematics, astrology, physics, music, medicine, pharmacy, and geography. He wrote four books on the use of the Hindu numerals. Many translations from the Greek into Arabic were made or revised by him or under his direction. He considered alchemy as an imposture. Two of his writings are especially important: "De aspectibus," a treatise on geometrical and physiological optics (largely based on Euclid, Heron, Ptolemy; no dioptrics), which influenced Roger Bacon, Witelo, etc.; "De medicinarum compositarum gradibus," an extraordinary attempt to establish posology on a mathematical basis. He is the earliest Muslim writer on music whose works have come down to us; they contain a notation for the determination of pitch. Many writings of his were translated into Latin by Gherardo da Cremona. His influence was long felt and Cardano considered him as one of the twelve greatest minds.

Text and Translation—The De medicinarum compositarum gradibus investigandis libellus was published in Strassburg (1531). Die philosophischen Abhandlungen des al-Kindī. Zum ersten Male hrg. von Albino Nagy (Beitr. zur Gesch. d. Philos. des Mittelalters, II, 5, 118 p., Münster, 1897. This contains the following

[b] I am not writing a history of philosophy, even less of theology. Hence I can not follow the development of such theories in detail, but it is well to quote a few typical examples to serve as hints to the student of the general concept of evolution.

mediaeval translations (some at least by Gherardo Cremonese): De intellectu; De somno et uisione; De quinque essentiis; Liber introductorius in artem logicae demonstrationis; and also a study of the original texts and the translations and elaborate notes). Alkindi, Tideus, and Pseudo-Euklid. Drei optische Werke. Herausgegeben und erklärt von A. A. Björnbo und Seb. Vogl (Leipzig, 1912). Containing the Liber Jacob Alkindi de causis diuersitatum aspectus et dandis demonstrationibus geometricis super eas (or De aspectibus); the text of this translation by Gherardo Cremonese was very carefully established by the late Björnbo; free translation and commentary by Vogl (70 p.). Otto Loth: Al-Kindī als Astrolog (Morgenländische Forschungen). Festschrift H. L. Fleischer gewidmet (261–310, Leipzig, 1875). Contains the text of an astrological treatise entitled "Sendschreiben des al-Kindī über das Reich der Araber und wie lange es dauern wird" (this treatise was plagiarized by Abū Ma'shar). De pluviis, imbribus et ventis ac aeris mutatione (Venice, 1507). Eilhard Wiedemann: al-Kindī's Schrift über Ebbe und Flut (Annalen der Physik, vol. 67, 374–387, 1922. German translation of al-Kindī's treatise on tides, hitherto unpublished).

Criticism—Fihrist (p. 255–261). G. Flügel: Al-Kindī genannt "der Philosoph der Araber." Ein Vorbild seiner Zeit und seines Volkes (Abhdl. f. die Kunde des Morgenlandes, I, 2, 54 p., Leipzig, 1857. Containing a list of his writings, 265 in number). A. Nagy: Sulle opere dell' al-Kindī. Rendiconti d. Acc. dei Lincei, cl. d. sci. morali (vol. 4, 157–170, Roma, 1895). Does al-Kindi's writing "sur les lignes et la multiplication avec le nombre des grains" refer to the use of the abacus? Eneström in Bibliotheca Mathematica (1897, p. 120). C. Brockelmann: Arabische Litteratur (vol. 1, 209, 1898). H. Suter: Die Mathematiker und Astronomen der Araber (23–26, 1900; Nachträge, 161, 1902). Rudolf Haubold: Ein Münchener handschriftlicher Text angeblich des Alkindi: de signis astronomiae applicatis ad medicinam (Diss., 7 p., Leipzig, 1921; Munich MS., Latin, 267). Curt Lantzsch: Alkindi und seine Schrift de medicinarum compositarum gradibus (Diss., Leipzig, Auszug, 8 p., n. d., 1921?). H. G. Farmer: Clues for the Arabian Influence on European Musical Theory (Jour. R. As. Soc., 61–80, 1925; Isis, VIII, 508–511).

Eilhard Wiedemann: Besprechung eines Stückes aus der Beschreibung Ägyptens von el-Kindī und der darin erwähnten Gelehrten (Beiträge III, 221–236, 1905. That text had been edited, together with a Danish translation by J. Oestrup, Copenhagen Academy, 1896); Aus al Kindīs Optik (Beiträge XIII, 245–248, 1907); Über eine astronomische Schrift von al-Kindī (Beiträge XXI, 294–302, 1910. Apropos of the instrument called dhāt al-shu'batain[c] used for astronomic and geodetic measurements); Über einen astrologischen Traktat von al-Kindī (Archiv f. Gesch. d. Naturw., vol. 3, 224–226, 1911); Über Stahl und Eisen bei den muslimischen Völkern (Beiträge XXV, 114–30, 1911); Über die Grösse der Meere nach al-Kindī (Beiträge XXVII, 35–37, 1912. Apropos of the treatise on flood and ebb, fī-l-madd wal-jazr, of which Wiedemann has given us since the German translation above mentioned). (All of Wiedemann's "Beiträge" have been published in the Sitzungsber. der physikalisch-medizinischen Societät in Erlangen).

THE BANŪ MŪSĀ

That is, the sons of Mūsā ibn Shākir, who died in the reign of al-Ma'mūn; also called the Three Brothers. Mathematicians, astronomers, patrons of science. They devoted the greater part of their wealth to the acquisition and translation of Greek manuscripts. Among the translators employed by them were Ḥunain ibn Isḥāq and Thābit ibn Qurra (q. v., next chapter). Many mathematical, mechanical, and astronomical writings are ascribed to them, the most important

[c] Literally, the feminine thing with the two branches.

being the Book on the Balance (farasṭūn or qarasṭūn)[d] and the Book on the measurement of the sphere, the trisection of the angle, and the determination of two mean proportionals between two given quantities (translated into Latin by Gherardo da Cremona under the title Liber trium fratrum de geometria). Kinematical trisection of the angle. So-called gardener's construction of the ellipse (by means of a string attached to the foci).

It is difficult to distinguish the part played by each brother; the most important seems to have been Abū Ja'far Muhammad ibn Mūsā (died in 872/3) a student of Euclid and the "Almagest," a logician; Aḥmad was especially interested in mechanics and Ḥasan in geometry.

Text and Translations—Verba filiorum Moysi, filii Sekir, id est Maumeti, Hameti et Hasen. Der Liber trium fratrum de geometria. Nach der Lesart des Codex Basiliensis F. II, 33 mit Einleitung und Commentar herausgegeben von Maximilian Curtze (Nova Acta acad. germ. naturae curiosorum, vol. 49, 105–167, Halle, 1885. That is, Gherardo's translation quoted above).

Criticism—Fihrist (271, commentary; Suter's translation, 24). M. Steinschneider: Die Söhne des Musa ben Schakir (Bibliotheca Mathematica, 44–48, 71–75, 1887). Carra de Vaux: Une proposition du Livre des Fils de Mousa sur les calculs approchés (Bibliotheca Mathematica, p. 1, 1898. Apropos of the last proposition of Curtze's text). H. Suter: Die Mathematiker und Astronomen der Araber (20–21, 1900); Nachträge (160, 1902); Über die Geometrie der Söhne des Mūsā. (Bibliotheca Mathematica, vol. 3, 259–272, 1902. Criticism of Curtze's text and translation of a few fragments from better manuscripts). Eilhard Wiedemann: Bemerkungen zum Werk fī-l-ḥijal (Beiträge VI, 6, 55, 1906, deals with pneumatic tricks, ḥiyal; Beiträge X, 341–8, 1906, extracts from same treatise; Beiträge XII, 200–205, 1907; *idem*, lamps). E. Wiedemann und F. Hauser: Über Trinkgefässe und Tafelaufsätze nach al-Jazarī und den Benū Mūsā (Der Islam, vol. 8, 55–93, 268–291, 1918; Isis, III, 478). Friedrich Hauser: Über das Kitāb al-ḥijal, das Werk über die sinnreichen Anordnungen, der Benū Mūsā (Abhdl. zur Gesch. der Naturwis. und der Medizin, Heft 1. 188 p., 22 pl., Erlangen, 1922; Isis, V, 208).

Hindu Philosophy

Śaṅkara

Śaṅkarācārya (Master Saṅkara). Born in the territory of Kerala, modern Malabar, probably c. 788, traveled as far as Kashmir; died in Kāñci, Koñjivaram, at the age of 32? (These dates are far from certain, but it is very probable that Śaṅkara was flourishing about the end of the eighth and the beginning of the ninth century). Hindu philosopher. The greatest exponent of Vedantic philosophy.[e] He wrote many commentaries on the Brahmasūtra of Bādarāyaṇa, on the ten principal Upanishads, on the Bhagavadgītā, his main purpose being to emphasize the absolute monism of these works.[f] He also wrote many independent Vedantic treatises.

Text—The Sanskrit editions of his commentaries are too numerous to be quoted. Das Palladium der Weisheit (Viveka chudamani) übersetzt von Mohini Chatterji (Leipzig, 1898). Vedānta-sūtras with Śaṅkara's commentary, translated by

[d] On these variant forms see long note in commentary on Fihrist (Vol. II, p. 127, note 8). The note throws grave doubt on the existence of qarasṭūn. It is said by some to be Rūmī, i. e., Greek (D. B. M.).

[e] So much so that by the name of Vedānta his own doctrine is generally understood.

[f] His doctrine is called Kevalādvaita, meaning absolute non-duality.

George Thibaut (3 vols., Sacred Books of the East, vols. 34, 38, 48, Oxford, 1890–1894).

Criticism—C. N. Krishnasami Aiyar: Sri Sankaracharya. His Life and Times. His Philosophy by Sitanath Tattvabhushan (Madras, 1903). Barend Faddegon: Çaṃkara's Gītābhasya toegelicht en beoordeeld (Diss., 126 p., Amsterdam, 1906). Paul Deussen: The Philosophy of the Upanishads (Edinburgh, 1906); Outline of the Vedanta System according to Shankara, translated by J. H. Woods and C. B. Runkle (51 p., New York, 1906); Complete translation of the same work by Charles Johnston (530 p., Chicago, 1912; Isis, II, 407–408). M. Winternitz: Indische Litteratur (vol. 3, 432–436, 1920). Magandal A. Buch: The Philosophy of Shankara (Baroda, 1921). V. S. Ghate: Dictionary of Religion and Ethics (Vol. XI, 185–189, 1921).

IV. MUSLIM, LATIN, BYZANTINE, AND HINDU MATHEMATICS AND ASTRONOMY

Muslim Mathematics and Astronomy

AL-ḤAJJĀJ IBN YŪSUF

al-Ḥajjāj ibn Yūsuf ibn Maṭar. Flourished some time between 786 and 833, probably in Bagdad. The first translator of Euclid's "Elements" into Arabic and one of the first translators of the "Almagest." (Kitāb al-mijisṭi, hence our word almagest).[g] Al-Ḥajjāj's translation of the Almagest was made in 829–830 on the basis of a Syriac version (by Sergios of Resaina? q. v., first half of sixth century). A later adaptation of the Almagest was made by Abū-l-Wafā' (q. v., second half of tenth century).

He twice translated the "Elements" of Euclid, first under Hārūn al-Rashīd, then again under al-Ma'mūn.

Text and Translation—al-Ḥajjāj's second translation of the Elements has been edited by R. O. Besthorn and J. L. Heiberg, with a Latin translation: Codex Leidensis 399, 1. Euclidis Elementa ex interpretatione al-Hadschdschadschii cum commentariis al-Nazirii (Copenhagen, 1893, etc. The title of this manuscript ascribes the translation to Isḥāq ibn Ḥunain, the Arabic preface to al-Ḥajjāj).

Criticism—Fihrist (252, 265, 268). H. Suter: Die Mathematiker und Astronomen der Araber (p. 9, 208, 1900).

AL-'ABBĀS

al-'Abbās ibn Sa'īd al-Jauharī. Flourished under al-Ma'mūn. Muslim mathematician and astronomer. He took part in the astronomical observations organized at Bagdad in 829–30[h] and at Damascus in 832–833.[i] He wrote commentaries on Euclid's Elements.

H. Suter: Mathematiker (12, 1900).

ABŪ SA'ĪD AL-ḌARĪR

Abū Sa'īd al-Ḍarīr al-Jurjānī.[j] Pupil of Ibn al-A'rābī, who died in 845/6; thus he flourished in the first half of the ninth century. Muslim astronomer

---

[g] The word mijisṭi is probably not derived from μεγίστη as is generally believed; it is more probably an artificial contraction of the two words μεγάλη σύνταξις (see Brockelmann: Arabische Literatur, vol. 1, 203, 1898).

[h] Other observers being Yaḥyā ibn abī Manṣūr; Sanad ibn 'Alī etc.

[i] Together with Sanad ibn 'Alī; 'Alī ibn 'Īsā; al-Marwarrūdhī, etc.

[j] Of Jurjān (East of the Caspian). Al-Darīr means the blind.

and mathematician. He wrote a treatise on geometrical problems and another on the drawing of the meridian (apparently unique in Arabic literature, though the subject is dealt with more or less fully in every zij.)

Text—Carl Schoy: Abhandlung über die Ziehung der Mittagslinie dem Buche über das Analemma entnommen, samt dem Beweis dazu von Abū Sa'īd ad-Ḍarīr (Ann. d. Hydr. usw., 265–271, 4 figs., 1922; Isis, V, 495).

Criticism—H. Suter: Die Mathematiker und Astronomen der Araber (27, 1900).

BANŪ MŪSĀ

See my note in Section III.

AL-KHWĀRIZMĪ

Abū 'Abdallāh Muḥammad ibn Mūsā al-Khwārizmī.[k] The last-mentioned name (his nisba) refers to his birthplace, Khwārizm, modern Khiva, south of the Aral Sea. It is under that name that he was best known, as is witnessed by the words algorism and augrim (Chaucer) derived from it. Flourished under al-Ma'mūn, caliph from 813 to 833, died c. 850. Muslim mathematician, astronomer, geographer. One of the greatest scientists of his race and the greatest of his time. He syncretized Greek and Hindu knowledge. He influenced mathematical thought to a greater extent than any other mediaeval writer. His arithmetic (lost in Arabic; Latin translation of the twelfth century extant) made known to the Arabs and Europeans the Hindu system of numeration. His algebra, Ḥisāb al-jabr[l] wal-muqābala, is equally important. It contains analytical solutions of linear and quadratic equations and its author may be called one of the founders of analysis or algebra as distinct from geometry. He also gives geometrical solutions (with figures) of quadratic equations, for ex., $x^2 + 10x = 39$, an equation often repeated by later writers. The "Liber ysagogarum Alchorismi in artem astronomicam a magistro A. [Adelard of Bath?] compositus" deals with arithmetic, geometry, music, and astronomy; it is possibly a summary of al-Khwārizmī's teachings rather than an original work. His astronomical and trigonometric tables, revised by Maslama al-Majrīṭī (q. v., second half of tenth century), were translated into Latin as early as 1126 by Adelard of Bath. They were the first Muslim tables and contained not simply the sine function but also the tangent (Maslama's interpolation?). Al-Khwārizmī probably collaborated in the degree measurements ordered by al-Ma'mūn (q. v.). He improved Ptolemy's geography, both the text and the maps (Ṣūrat al-arḍ, "The Face of the Earth").

General Studies—Fihrist (p. 274 and comm.). H. Suter: Die Mathematiker und Astronomen der Araber (10, 1900); Nachträge (158–160, 1902). L. C. Karpinski's edition of the Algebra (1915), quoted below, contains a general summary of al-Khwārizmī's life and works.

Mathematics (*text*)—The Arithmetic has been published by Baldassare Boncompagni: Trattati d'aritmetica (Roma, 1857. Algoritmi de numero Indorum; Joannis Hispalensis liber algorismi de pratica arismetrice—a development of the first work). The Algebra of Muhammad ben Musa, edited and translated by Frederic Rosen (London, 1831. Ruska has shown that this translation is inferior to

---

[k] Khwārazmī. As the vowels are generally not indicated in Arabic texts, there is often some indecision with regard to the vocalization of proper names. It is better not to worry too much about that, but to focus one's attention upon the consonants.

[l] Hence the word algebra.

that of Gerard of Cremona, published by Libri). Guil. Libri: Histoire des Sciences mathématiques en Italie (vol. 1, 253–297, Paris, 1838). Aristide Marre: Le Messāhat[m] de Mohammed ben Moussa, extrait de son Algèbre, trad. et ann. (Nouvelles Annales de Mathématiques, vol. 5, 1846; new revised ed., Roma, 1866). Louis Charles Karpinski: Robert of Chester's Latin translation of the Algebra of al-Khowarizmi. With an introduction, critical notes, and an English version (164 p., New York, 1915; Isis, IV, 504). For the Liber Ysagogarum, see Alfred Nagl (Z. f. Math. u. Physik, hist. Abt., vol. 34, 129–146, 161–170, 1889); Max Curtze: Über eine Algorismus-Schrift des XII. Jahrhundert (Abhdl. z. Gesch. d. Math., 8. Heft, p. 1–27, 1898).

For trigonometry, see Astronomy.

Mathematics (*criticism*)—H. Suter: Über die im "Liber augmenti et diminutionis" vorkommenden Autoren (Bibliotheca Mathematica, vol. 3, 350–354, 1902, cfr. Cantor's Vorlesungen, vol. 1, 3d ed., 730). Max Simon: Zu Hwarizmi's hisāb al gabr wal muqābala (Archiv d. Math., vol. 18, 202–203, 1911). L. C. Karpinski: Robert of Chester's Translation of al-Khowarizmi (Bibliotheca Mathematica, vol. 11, 125–131. Preliminary note concerning the author's translation, 1915). Julius Ruska: Zur ältesten arabischen Algebra und Rechenkunst (Sitzungsberichte der Heidelberger Ak. d. Wiss., philos. Klasse, 1–125, 1917. Capital, see Isis, III, 477; IV, 67–70, Karpinski). H. Wieleitner: Die Erbteilungsaufgaben bei Alchwarazmi (Z. f. math. und naturwiss. Unterricht, vol. 53, 57–67; Isis, V, 210).

Astronomy and Trigonometry (*text*)—Die astronomischen Tafeln des Muḥammed ibn Mūsā in der Bearbeitung des Maslama ibn Ahmed al-Madjriti und der latein. Übersetzung des Athelard von Bath auf Grund der Vorarbeiten von A. Björnbo und R. Besthorn, hrg. und kommentiert von H. Suter (Mémoires de l'Ac. des sciences de Danemark, section des lettres, vol. 3, 280 p., Copenhague 1914. Capital; Isis, IV, 502).

Astronomy and Trigonometry (*criticism*)—H. Suter: Der Verfasser des Buches "Gründe der Tafeln des Chowārezmī (Bibliotheca Mathematica, vol. 4, 127–129, 1903. The author of this commentary on al-Khwārizmī's tables is al-Bīrūnī, q. v., first half of eleventh century). A. A. Björnbo: Al-Chwārizmī's trigonometriske Tavler (Festskrift til H. G. Zeuthen, 1–17, Köbenhavn, 1909). J. Frank: Die Verwendung des Astrolabs nach al-Chwārizmī (Abhdl. zur Gesch. der Naturw. und der Med., 3, 32 p., Erlangen, 1922. Including a translation of the relevant text; Isis, V, 208). E. Wiedemann und Josef Frank: Zirkel zur Bestimmung der Gebetszeiten (Sitzungsber. der phys. mediz. Sozietät in Erlangen, vol. 52, 122–125, 1922; Isis, V, 495).

Geography—Spitta bey. Huwarazmi's Auszug aus der Geographie des Ptolemaeus (Z. d. deutsch. morgenl. Ges., vol. 33, 294–297, 1879). C. A. Nallino: Al-Huwārizmī e il suo rifacimento della geografia di Tolomeo (Atti d. Acc. d. Lincei, cl. d. sci. mor., vol. 2, 53 p., Roma (1894) 1896). Hans von Mžik: Ptolemaeus und die Karten der arabischen Geographen (Mitt. d. geogr. Ges. in Wien, vol. 58, p. 152–176, 7 pl., 1915). Afrika nach der arabischen Bearbeitung der γεωγραφικὴ ὑφήγησις des Ptolemaeus von Muḥ. ibn Mūsā (Denkschriften d. Ak. d. Wiss., phil. Kl., vol. 59, 105 p., Wien, 1916, with a map of the Nile a reconstruction of al-Khwārizmī's map of northern Africa down to latitude 15° south, and comparisons with the geographical knowledge of Ptolemy, Jacobus of Edessa, and al-Battānī; see Isis, V, 208). J. Ruska: Neue Bausteine zur Gesch. d. arabischen Geographie (Geograph. Z., vol. 24, 77–81, 1918). The text of the Ṣūrat al-arḍ, as contained in the unique manuscript of the University of Strassburg, has been published in the "Bibliothek arabischer Historiker und Geographen" edited by Hans v. Mžik (180 p., 5 pl., Leipzig, 1926). A German translation will appear in the same collection.

---

[m] masāḥa = measuring, surveying.

AL-KINDĪ

See my note in Section III.

SAHL AL-ṬABARĪ

Also called Rabbān al-Ṭabarī, meaning the Rabbi of Ṭabaristān. Flourished about the beginning of the ninth century.[n] Jewish astronomer and physician. The first translator of the Almagest into Arabic.

H. Suter: Die Mathematiker und Astronomen der Araber (14, 1900). M. Steinschneider: Die arabische Literatur der Juden (23–34, Frankfurt, 1902).

AḤMAD AL-NAHĀWANDĪ

Aḥmad ibn Muḥammad al-Nahāwandī. Flourished at Jundīshāpūr at the time of Yaḥyā ibn Khālid ibn Barmak, who died in 802–3; he himself died c. 835 to 845. Muslim astronomer. He made astronomical observations at Jundīshāpūr and compiled tables called the comprehensive (Mushtamil).

H. Suter: Mathematiker und Astronomen (10, 1900).

AL-MA'MŪN

See my note in Section III.

ḤABASH AL-ḤĀSIB

Aḥmad ibn 'Abdallāh al-Marwazī (i. e., from Merv) Ḥabash[o] al-Ḥāsib (the calculator). Flourished in Bagdad; died a centenarian between 864 and 874. Astronomer under al-Ma'mūn and al-Mu'taṣim. (He observed from 825 to 835.) He compiled three astronomical tables: the first were still in the Hindu manner; the second, called the "tested" tables,[p] were the most important; they are likely identical with the "Ma'mūnic" or "Arabic" tables and may be a collective work of al-Ma'mūn's astronomers; the third, called tables of the Shāh, were smaller. Apropos of the solar eclipse of 829, Ḥabash gives us the first instance of a determination of time by an altitude (in this case, of the sun); a method which was generally adopted by Muslim astronomers. He seems to have introduced the notion of "shadow," umbra (versa), equivalent to our tangent, and he compiled a table of such shadows which seems to be the earliest of its kind.

A son of Ḥabash called Abū Ja'far ibn Ḥabash was also a distinguished astronomer and instrument maker.

Criticism—Caussin: Le livre de la grande table Hakémite d'Ibn Younis. Notices et extraits des manuscrits (vol. 7, an XII, p. 100). H. Suter: Die Mathematiker und Astronomer der Araber (12, 27, 1900). Dreyer: Planetary systems (250, 1906). Fihrist (p. 275 and comm.); Mas'ūdī. Livre de l'avertissement (295). C. Schoy: Beiträge zur arabischen Trigonometrie (Isis, V, 392, 1923. On his tables of sines and versed sines); Über den Gnomonschatten und die Schattentafel (29 p., Hanover, 1923; Isis, VII, 573. Important).

---

[n] The date is determined from the fact that his son 'Alī (q. v., below), a prominent physician, was the teacher of al-Rāzī and embraced Islām c. 835.

[o] Ḥabash is a nickname, but what it means here I do not know. Al-Ḥabash would mean "the Abyssinian." Habisha in Syriac would mean "monk."

[p] Tabulae probatae (Bagdad, 832–33).

SANAD IBN 'ALĪ

Abū-l-Ṭaiyib Sanad[q] ibn 'Alī. Flourished under al-Ma'mūn, died after 864. Muslim[r] astronomer and mathematician. Chief of the astronomers who made observations under al-Ma'mūn. He constructed the Kanīsa (an observatory; that Persian-Arabic word really means church, synagogue, temple) at Bagdad. He compiled astronomical tables and wrote on astronomical (or mathematical) subjects. Investigations on specific gravity.

H. Suter: Mathematiker (13, 226, 1900; 160, 1902).

'ALĪ IBN 'ĪSĀ AL-AṢṬURLĀBĪ

Flourished at Bagdad and Damascus c. 830 to 832. Muslim astronomer. Famous maker of astronomical instruments.[s] He took part in the degree measurement ordered by al-Ma'mūn and made astronomical observations at Bagdad and Damascus in 829–30 and 832–33. He wrote one of the earliest Arabic treatises on the astrolabe.

Text—Louis Scheicho: L'astrolabe et la manière de s'en servir. Traité inédit de 'Alī ibn 'Īsā (20 p., Beyrouth, 1913; Isis, V, 211).
Criticism—H. Suter: Die Mathematiker der Araber (13, 209, 1900. Important note on the Muslim degree measurement).

YAḤYĀ IBN ABĪ MANṢŪR

Abū 'Alī Yaḥyā ibn abī Manṣūr. Of Persian origin,[t] in the service of al-Ma'mūn; he died c. 831 and was buried at Ḥaleb. Persian astronomer, writing in Arabic. He made astronomical observations[u] at Bagdad in 829–30 and wrote various books on astronomy. He compiled astronomical tables, the so-called Tested Ma'mūnic Tables.

A grandson of Yaḥyā's, Hārūn ibn 'Alī, who died at Bagdad in 900–1, also compiled astronomical tables which were much used, and constructed astronomical instruments.

Fihrist, in Suter's translation (p. 29). H. Suter: Mathematiker und Astronomen (8, 34, 1900; 158, 1902).

AL-MARWARRŪDHĪ

Khālid ibn 'Abd al-Malik al-Marwarrūdhī.[v] Flourished under al-Ma'mūn. Muslim astronomer. One of those who took part in the solar observations made at Damascus in 832–33.

His son Muḥammad and his grandson 'Umar were also astronomers. The latter compiled astronomical tables and wrote a book on the astrolabe (al-musaṭṭaḥ, meaning flattened).

H. Suter: Mathematiker und Astronomen (11, 26, 38, 1900).

---

[q] Better than Sind.
[r] Of Jewish birth.
[s] Hence his surname. See also my note on Ḥāmid ibn 'Alī (next chapter).
[t] He became a Muslim only after having been taken into the caliph's service.
[u] On some of his instruments, each degree was divided into six parts.
[v] Meaning of Marw al-Rūdh (or Marrūd, Little Marw) in Khurāsān not to be mistaken for another Marw (the present Merv) in the same province. (A native or inhabitant of Great Marw would be called al-Marwazī.)

AL-DĪNAWARĪ

See Section VIII in next chapter.

AL-FARGHĀNĪ

In Latin: Alfraganus. Abū-l-'Abbās Aḥmad ibn Muḥammad ibn Kathīr al-Farghānī. Born in Farghānā, Transoxiana, flourished under al-Ma'mūn, was still living in 861. One of the greatest astronomers employed by al-Ma'mūn and his successors. He wrote "Elements of Astronomy" ("Kitāb fī ḥarakāt al-samāwīya wa jawāmi' 'ilm al-nujūm", book on celestial motions and the complete science of the stars), which were translated into Latin in the twelfth century and exerted a great influence upon European astronomy before Regiomontanus. He accepted Ptolemy's theory and value of the precession, but thought that it affected not simply the stars, but also the planets. Diameter of the earth: 6,500 miles. Determination of the greatest distances and of the diameters of the planets. In 861 he superintended the erection of a nilometer[w] in Fusṭāṭ.

Text and Translations—The Elements of Astronomy (this book bears various other titles) was translated into Latin by John Hispalensis and Gherardo Cremonese and into Hebrew by Jacob Anatoli. Hispalensis's translation, Compilatio astronomica, was first printed in Ferrara (1493). Then again edited by Melanchthon from Regiomontanus's papers in Nürnberg, 1537, and again in Paris (1546). Anatoli's version was translated into Latin by Jacob Christmann (Frankfurt, 1590).

Editio princeps of the Arabic text (with Latin translation) by Jacob Golius: Muhammedis fil. Ketiri Ferganensis qui vulgo Alfraganus dicitur Elementa Astronomica, arabice et latine (Amsterdam, 1669).

Two works on the astrolabe are still unpublished.

Criticism—Fihrist (I, 279, commentary, p. 132). H. Suter: Die Mathematiker und Astronomen der Araber (p. 18, 1900; Nachträge, p. 160, 1902); Encyclopaedia of Islam (vol. 2, 66, 1914). P. Duhem: Système du Monde (vol. 2, 204–214, 1914. Discussing Alfraganus's views on precession). E. Wiedemann: Einleitungen zu arabischen astronomischen Werken (Das Weltall, 20. J., 21–26, 1919. The first chapter of this series, for which see Isis, IV, 432, contains an annotated translation of Alfraganus's introduction to a book on the astrolabe; Berlin MS.). E. Wiedemann und Josef Frank: Zirkel zur Bestimmung der Gebetszeiten (Sitzungsber. der physik. mediz. Sozietät in Erlangen, vol. 52, 122–125, 1922; Isis, V, 495). Gaston Wiet: Une restauration du nilomètre de l'ile de Rawda sous Mutawakkil (247/861) (C. R. d l'Acad. des Inscriptions, 202–206, 1924).

Influence of al-Farghānī—Paget Toynbee: Dante's obligations to Alfraganus in the Vita nuova and Convivio (Romania, 413–432, 1895). Romeo Campani: Alfragano. Il "Libro dell' aggregazione delle stelle" (Dante, Convivio, II, VI–134, secondo il codice Mediceo-Laurenziano pl. 29, cod. 9). (Collezione di opuscoli danteschi, vol. 87–90, 175 p., Firenze, 1910).

'UMAR IBN AL-FARRUKHĀN

Abū Ḥafṣ 'Umar ibn al-Farrukhān al-Ṭabarī. From Ṭabaristān, flourished in Bagdad, died c. 815. Muslim astronomer and architect. He translated various books from Persian into Arabic, some of them by order of al-Ma'mūn, and wrote on astrological and astronomical subjects (e. g., a commentary on the Quadripartitum translated by al-Baṭrīq).

---

[w] The Fihrist ascribes to him a book on the construction of rukhāmāt, which, I imagine, means sundials. Also an abstract of the "Almagest." (D. B. M.)

One of these writings, on the principles of astrology (Kitāb al-uṣūl bi-l-nujūm), may be the work of his son Muḥammad?

H. Suter: Die Mathematiker und Astronomen der Araber (p. 7, 1900; p. 158, 1902).

MUḤAMMAD IBN 'UMAR

Abū Bakr Muḥammad ibn 'Umar ibn al-Farrukhān al Ṭabarī. Of Persian origin; son of the preceding; flourished at the beginning of the ninth century. Muslim astronomer. Author of various astrological treatises.

Text—His treatise on nativities was translated into Latin by Joannes Hispalensis (twelfth century). Omar Tiberiadis de navitatibus et interrogationibus (Venice, 1503).
Criticism—H. Suter: Mathematiker und Astronomen (17, 1900).

ABŪ MA'SHAR

Abū Ma'shar Ja'far ibn Muḥammad ibn 'Umar al-Balkhī. Latin name: Albumasar. Born in Balkh, Khurāsān; flourished in Bagdad; died in Wāsiṭ, a centenarian, in 886. Astrologer more frequently quoted in the West than any other. Many astrological writings are ascribed to him and were soon translated into Latin. The most important is The Great Book of Introduction (Kitāb al-mudkhal ilā 'ilm aḥkam al-nujūm), which contains an astrological theory of tides, which was very popular during the Middle Ages.

Text and Translations—(*a*) The "Great Book of Introduction:" translated into Latin by Joan. Hispalensis and by Hermannus Secundus (or Dalmata). The latter translation was printed in Augsburg, 1489, under the title: "Introductorium in astronomiam Albumasaris abalachii . . . ;" also Venice 1495, 1506.
(*b*) "Book of the Revolution of the Birth Years:" translated by Joan. Hispalensis. Albumasar de magnis conjunctionibus et annorum revolutionibus ac eorum profectionibus (Augsburg, 1489; Venice, 1515). This book is a plagiarism of al-Kindī (see, in my note on al-Kindī, the reference to Otto Loth. Al-Kindī als Astrolog, 1875).
(*c*) "Albumasaris flores astrologiae:" translated by Joan. Hispalensis. Probably an extract from (*b*).
(*d*) "Apomasaris Apotelesmata, sive de significatis et eventis insomniorum ex Indorum, Persarum, Aegyptiorumque disciplina" (Francfurt, 1577). See my note on Aḥmad ibn Sirin, in Section III.
Other Latin editions, which I have not seen, are quoted in Houzeau and Lancaster: Bibliographie de l'astronomie (vol. 1, 702–705, 1887). For the Arabic texts and unpublished mediaeval translations, see the Fihrist (or Suter's translation of it) and Suter's articles quoted below.
Criticism—Fihrist (I, 277, Commentary, p. 131). J. Lippert: Abū Ma'shars Kitāb al-ulūf (that is, "the book of the thousands," over the houses of worship) (Wiener Zeitschrift f. d. Kunde d. Morgenlandes, IX, 351–358, 1895. Deals with the temples and other monumental buildings which have been erected in each millennium over the whole world). See Comm., in Fihrist (p. 131, note 6), and reference there to Mas'ūdī (Les Prairies d'Or, Vol. IV, pp. 91, 92). H. Suter: Die Mathematiker und Astronomen der Araber (28–30, 1900; Nachträge, 162, 1902; article Abū Ma'shar in Encycl. of Islam (I, 99, 1908). Moritz Steinschneider: Die europäischen Übersetzungen (p. 35–38, Wien, 1906). P. Duhem: Système du monde (II, 369–386, 1914, la théorie des marées selon les Arabes; 503–504, le mouvement d'accès et de recès). Gustav Hellmann: Die Wetterhervorsage im ausgehenden Mittelalter (200–201, 1917; Isis, IV, 185. Apropos of a treatise de

pluviis (imbribus) or de mutatione temporis which is possibly the work of Abū Ma'shar). Lynn Thorndike: History of Magic (vol. 1, 649–652, 1923. Including a note on the memorabilia ascribed to a pupil of Abū Ma'shar's, called Abū Sa'īd Shādsān).

SAHL IBN BISHR

Abū 'Uthmān Sahl ibn Bishr ibn Ḥabīb ibn Hānī (or Hāyā). Flourished in Khurāsān in the first half of the ninth century. Jewish astrologer who wrote many treatises on astrology in Arabic, also a book on algebra (lost?). One of his treatises (Fatidica) was translated into Latin in 1138 by Hermann of Dalmatia.

Text—His Introductorium de principiis judiciorum was printed already in 1493, in Venice, at the end of Ptolemy's Quadripartitum. Another Venetian edition of the same year contains other treatises of his: De interrogationibus; De electionibus; De temporum significationibus in judiciis.
Criticism—H. Suter: Die Mathematiker und Astronomen der Araber (15, 1900; 160, 1902). Lynn Thorndike: History of Magic (vol. 2, 389–390, 1923. Apropos of a treatise on seals by Thetel or Zehel, Zahel the Israelite, of which a Latin translation appears in Thomas of Cantimpré).

ABŪ 'ALĪ AL-KHAIYĀṬ

Abū 'Alī al-Khaiyāṭ (the tailor) Yaḥyā ibn Ghālib.[a] Disciple of Māshāllāh; died c. 835. Muslim astronomer. He wrote many astrological treatises.

Text—I have included this Abū 'Alī mainly, because one of his treatises—de judiciis nativitatum—seems to have attracted much attention. It was translated into Latin by Plato of Tivoli in 1136 and again by Joannes Hispalensis in 1153. The latter translation was edited by Johann Schöner (Nürnberg, 1546, 1549): Albohali de judiciis nativitatum liber etc.
Criticism—H. Suter: Mathematiker und Astronomen (9, 1900).

LATIN MATHEMATICS AND ASTRONOMY—ANONYMOUS TREATISES

The "De mundi caelestis terrestrisque constitutione liber" was formerly ascribed to Bede and is included in Bede's works as edited in Migne's "Patrologia" (vol. 90, col. 881–910). It is now proved to be of a later date, probably of the ninth century.

P. Duhem: Un disciple de Macrobe. Le pseudo-Bède et son traité De mundi constitutione (Le système du monde, vol. 3, 76–87, 1915). Duhem's views are criticized by J. L. E. Dreyer in Studies in the History and Method of Science (Vol. II, p. 106, 1921).

An astronomical treatise composed at the beginning of the ninth century, probably in Gaul, is entitled De forma celi et quomodo decurrit inclinatum (or Sphera celi). It introduces the legendary figure of Nimrod the Astronomer, who was later quoted by Philip of Thaon (q. v., first half of twelfth century) as an authority on chronology on the same level as Bede, Helperic, and Gerland. See C. H. Haskins: Studies in Mediaeval Science (336–345, 1924).

For the Pseudo-Geometry ascribed to Boetius, and which is probably also a production of this period—a wretched one—see P. Tannery, in Bibliotheca Mathe-

[a] Also Ismā'īl ibn Muhammad (Fihrist)?

matica (vol. 1, 39–50, 1900; reprinted in the Mémoires, vol. 5, 211–228, Isis, VI, 431).

For Hrabanus Maurus, see Section III.

Byzantine Mathematics and Astronomy

See my note on Leon of Thessalonica in Section III.

Hindu Mathematics and Astronomy

MAHĀVĪRA

Often called Mahāvīrācārya (Master Mahāvīra). Flourished in Mysore, southern India, in the ninth century? Hindu, Jaina, mathematician. Author of the "Gaṇitasārasaṃgraha," c. 830 (brief explanation of the compendium of calculation). Mahāvīra's treatment is fuller but more elementary than Brahmagupta's (first half of seventh century). His is the only Hindu work dealing with ellipses (inaccurately). Geometric progressions. The sides of a rational right-angled triangle are $2mn$, $m^2 - n^2$, $m^2 + n^2$; m and n are the "elements" of this triangle. Solution of the three types of quadratic equations (Mahāvīra's equations contain the unknown quantity and its square root; imaginary roots are excluded). To divide by a fraction it suffices to multiply by the inverse of that fraction.

Text and Translations—M. Raṅgācārya: The Gaṇita-Sāra-Sangraha of Mahāvīrācārya. With English Translation and Notes (352 p., Madras, 1912).
Criticism—D. E. Smith: The Gaṇita-Sāra-Sangraha (Bibliotheca Mathematica, vol. 9, 106–110, 1908). G. R. Kaye: Indian Mathematics (Isis, II, 326–356, 1919). D. E. Smith: History of Mathematics (vol. 1, 161, 1923; vol. 2, 1925).

V. MUSLIM AND LATIN NATURAL HISTORY

Muslim Natural History

See my notes on al-Naẓẓām, in Section III, and on 'Alī al-Ṭabarī, in Section VII.

Latin Natural History

WALAFRID STRABO

Walafrid or Walahfrid. Strabo (Strabus) means the squint-eyed. Born in 808 or 809 in Swabia, died in France in 849. Carolingian educator; botanist. Pupil of Hrabanus Maurus in Fulda. Abbot of Reichenau. His "glosa ordinaria" (or glosa), a Biblical encyclopaedia, remained very popular throughout the Middle Ages, even until the seventeenth century. His poem "Hortulus" is a description of the various herbs of his monastic garden, with references to their properties.

Text—Opera omnia, in Migne's Latin Patrology (vol. 113, 114). Carmina, edited by Ernest Dümmler: Monumenta Germaniae historica (Poëtae latini aevi Carolini, II, 259–472, Berlin, 1884). Ad Grimaldum coenobii S. Galli abbatem Hortulus, edited by Joach. v. Watt (Vadianus) (Wien, 1510). German translation of the Hortulus by J. Berendes (reprint from Pharm. Post, 48 p., 1908). English translation by R. S. Lambert (39 p., Wembley Hill, 1924; Isis, VII, 535).
Criticism—Leopold Eigl: Walahfrid Strabo. Ein Mönchs- und Dichterleben (67 p., Wien, 1908). M. Manitius: Lateinische Literatur des Mittelalters (vol. 1, 302–314, 1911; vol. 2, 802).

VI. LATIN, MUSLIM, AND CHINESE GEOGRAPHY AND GEOLOGY

DICUIL

Flourished c. 816 to 825. Irish astronomer and geographer. He completed some time between 814 and 816 a treatise on astronomy and on the computus (without title) in four books. He completed in 825 the "De mensura orbis terrae," based not simply on older writings, but also upon the reports of recent travelers. It contains the earliest definite account of Iceland (Irish voyage of 795) and a reference to the ancient canal connecting the Nile and the Red Sea (which had finally been blocked up in 767).

Text and Translations—Edition by C. A. Walckenaer (93 p., Paris, 1807). By Antoine Letronne, with long commentary (Paris, 1814). By Gustav Parthey (112 p., Berlin, 1870).
Criticism—C. Raymond Beazley: The Dawn of Modern Geography (vol. 1, p. 317–327 and passim, London, 1897). M. Manitius: Lateinische Literatur des Mittelalters (vol. 1, 647–653, 1911; vol. 2, 813). Fridtjof Nansen: In Northern Mists (vol. 1, 162–167, and by index, 1911).

Muslim Geography

See my notes on al-Ma'mūn in Section III and on al-Khwārizmī in Section IV.

SULAIMĀN THE MERCHANT

Flourished probably in the first half of the ninth century. Muslim traveler, the account of whose journeys in the Far East was written in 851 by an anonymous author. This is the first Arabic account of China and of many of the coast-lands of the Indian Ocean. It will interest the historian of civilization, and the more so that commercial relations between China and Islām had then reached their highest point (before being brutally interrupted by the sack of Canton in 878), but its geographical importance is small. Sulaimān records the use of finger-prints as signature by the Chinese.[y]

Another Muslim, named Ibn Wahb, traveled to China in 870, and an account of his journey was written by Abū Zaid (q. v., first half of tenth century). From such voyages, strangely confirming earlier traditions,[z] gradually developed the series of narratives which have crystallized around the name of Sindbad the Sailor (see the Alf laila wa-laila).

Text and Translations—Abbé Eusèbe Renaudot: Anciennes relations des Indes et de la Chine de deux voyageurs mahométans qui y allèrent dans le IXe siècle (Paris, 1718; English transl., London, 1733). The Arabic text was edited by Langlès and printed in 1811, but remained unpublished until 1845, when J. T. Reinaud published it with a French translation under the title: Relation des voyages faits par les Arabes et les Persans dans le IXe siècle (2 small vols., Paris, 1845; for

---

[y] The Chinese had been using finger impressions for the purpose of identification at least since the beginning of the T'ang dynasty. See B. Laufer: History of the Finger Print System (Annual Report Smithsonian Inst., p. 631–652, 1912. An early T'ang writer, Chia^3 Kung^1-yen^4 (1181, 6568, 13106), author of a commentary on the I-li, the I^2-li^3 chu^4-shih^{4*} (5455, 6949, 2542, 9983) makes a distinct allusion to that practice); see also Science (vol. 45, 504–505, 1917). M. A. Stein has published three Chinese documents bearing finger-print signatures and dated 782, 786. Ancient Khotan (Vol. I, 525–529, 1907).

[z] Probably Hindu. For the Byzantine versions see the article Syntipas, in Krumbacher: Geschichte der byzant. Litt. (891–895, 1897).

the finger prints see Vol. I, p. 42). Voyage de Sulaymān suivi de remarques par Abū Zayd Ḥasan; Traduction française par Gabriel Ferrand (157 p., Paris, 1922; Isis, VI, 146).

Criticism—Guignes: Chaîne historique des contrées, des mers et des poissons, avec un traité sur la science de la sphère. Recueil de divers voyages et particulièrement de deux voyages aux Indes et à la Chine, dans les IXe et Xe siècles (MS. arabe 597) (Notices et extraits des manuscrits, Vol. I, 156–164, 1787). J. T. Reinaud: Fragments arabes et persans relatifs à l'Inde. Note préliminaire (Journal asiatique, vol. 4, 114 sq., 1844); Géographie d'Aboulféda (Vol. I, p. LIII, 1848); Mémoire sur l'Inde antérieurement au milieu du XIe siècle d'après les écrivains arabes, persans et chinois (Mém. de l'Acad. des Inscriptions, vol. 18 (2), 1–399, 1849). Ed. Dulaurier: Etude sur la Relation des voyages . . . . de Reinaud (Journal Asiatique, 96 p., 1846). M. J. de Goeje: De reizen van Sindebaad, in De Gids (No. 8, 1889). C. R. Beazley: Dawn of Modern Geography (vol. I, 1897); article Sindbad, in Enc. Brit. (11th ed., 1911). Victor Chauvin: Bibliographie des ouvrages arabes (Fasc. VII, 1–93, Liège, 1903, full bibliography). Miguel Asín Palacios: Escatologia musulmana en la Divina Comedia (pp. 262–276, Madrid, 1919).

Muslim Mineralogy

The so-called "Lapidary of Aristotle" is very likely a compilation of Syriac and Persian origin (many stone names are Iranian) of no later date than the ninth century. Julius Ruska has published the Arabic text (supposed to be a translation by Lūqā ben Serapion),[a] the Latin version of a Liège manuscript, and a translation of the Arabic text with notes. There is another Latin version of the same text in Montpellier and one in Hebrew in Munich. This lapidary is extremely different from Theophrastos's mineralogy. It will interest the student of superstitions as well as the student of Oriental science.

Julius Ruska: Das Steinbuch des Aristoteles mit literargeschichtlichen Untersuchungen nach der arabischen Handschrift der Bibl. nationale (214 p., Heidelberg, 1912. 92 p. of it published the previous year as Diss.). For further references see Isis, I, 266, 341–350.

The Syriac tradition of that work may be traced back to the second half of the sixth century. A Syriac text was published by Karl Ahrens: Das Buch der Naturgegenstände (with German translation, Kiel, 1892). Further discussion by Max Wellmann: Aristoteles de lapidibus (Sitzungsber. der Preuss. Ak., philol. Kl., 79–82, 1924; Isis, IX).

'UṬĀRID

'Uṭārid ibn Muḥammad al-Ḥāsib (or al-Kātib) ('Uṭārid is the Arabic name of the planet Mercury; al-ḥāsib means the computer, the accountant; al-kātib, the scribe). Flourished in the ninth century. Author of the oldest Muslim lapidary extant. It deals with the properties of precious stones. 'Uṭārid is quoted in Rhazes's Continens.

Text—Kitāb manāfi' al-aḥjār or Kitāb al-jawāhir wal-aḥjār (unpublished).

Criticism—M. Steinschneider: Intorno ad alcuni passi relativi alla calamita (Boncompagni's Bullettino, 28, 43, 44, 1871); Arabische Lapidarien (Z. der Deutschen Morgenländischen Gesellschaft, vol. 49, 249, 1895). C. Brockelmann: Arabische Litteratur (vol. 1, 243, 1898).

---

[a] Syriac name. The Arabic equivalent would be Lūqā ibn Sarāfyūn. Brief reference to him in Leclerc: Médecine arabe (Vol. I, 175, 1876).

Chinese Geography

For Tu Yu's encyclopaedia, see Section IX.

LI CHI-FU

Li^{3} Chi^{2*}-fu^{3} (6884, 909, 3624). Born 758, died 814. Chinese geographer of the T'ang dynasty. He executed for Hsien^{4} Tsung^{1} (4547, 11976) (emperor from 806 to 821) a military map of the country north of the Yellow River. He wrote a treatise in 54 scrolls, containing a geographical and historical study of every fortified town of the empire and a map of every district. This treatise was called: "Map of the commands and kingdoms composed during the period yüan-ho" (806–821), Yüan^{2}-ho^{2} chün^{4} hsien^{4} chih^{4} (13744, 3945, 3273, 4545, 1918).

Chiu T'ang shu (chapter 148) and T'ang shu (chapter 146) quoted by E. Chavannes: Les deux plus anciens spécimens de la cartographie chinoise (Bulletin de l'Ecole française d'Extrême Orient, vol. 3, 214–247, 245, 1903); see also P. Pelliot (*ibidem*, vol. 3, 716–718, vol. 4, 131).

VII. BYZANTINE, ARABIC, AND JAPANESE MEDICINE

Byzantine Medicine

See my note on Leon of Thessalonica, in Section III.

Arabic Medicine

YAḤYĀ IBN BAṬRĪQ

See my note in Section III.

IBN SAHDĀ

Flourished at al-Karkh (a suburb of Bagdad), probably about the beginning of the ninth century. Translator of medical works from Greek into Syriac and Arabic. According to the Fihrist he translated some works of Hippocrates into Arabic. According to Ḥunain ibn Isḥāq, he translated the "De sectis" and the "De pulsibus ad tirones" of Galen into Syriac.

Max Meyerhof: New Light on Ḥunain ibn Isḥāq (Isis, VIII, 704, 1926).

JIBRĪL IBN BAKHTYASHŪ'

Grandson of Jirjīs ibn Jibrīl, q. v., second half of eighth century; physician to Ja'far the Barmakide, then in 805–6 to Hārūn al-Rashīd and later to al-Ma'mūn; died in 828–29; buried in the monastery of St. Sergios in Madāin (Ctesiphon). Christian (Nestorian) physician, who wrote various medical works and exerted much influence upon the progress of science in Bagdad. He was the most prominent member of the famous Bakhtyashū' family. He took pains to obtain Greek medical manuscripts and patronized the translators.

F. Wüstenfeld: Arabische Aerzte (15–16, 1840). L. Leclerc: Médecine arabe (vol. 1, 99–102, 1876). M. Meyerhof: New Light on Ḥunain (Isis, VIII, 717, 1926).

SALMAWAIH IBN BUNĀN

Christian (Nestorian) physician, who flourished under al-Ma'mūn and al-Mu'taṣim and became physician in ordinary to the latter. He died at the end of 839 or the beginning of 840. He helped Ḥunain to translate Galen's Methodus medendi and later he patronized Ḥunain's activity. He and Ibn Māsawaih were scientific rivals. Salmawaih realized the perniciousness of aphrodisiacs.

L. Leclerc: Médecine arabe (vol. 1, 118, 1876). M. Meyerhof: New Light on Ḥunain (Isis, VIII, 718, 1926).

IBN MĀSAWAIH

Latin name: Mesuë, or, more specifically, Mesuë Major; Mesüe the Elder. Abū Zakarīyā Yūḥannā[b] ibn Māsawaih (or Māsūya). Son of a pharmacist in Jundishāpūr; came to Bagdad and studied under Jibrīl ibn Bakhtyashū'; died in Sāmarrā in 857. Christian physician writing in Syriac and Arabic. Teacher of Ḥunain ibn Isḥāq. His own medical writings were in Arabic, but he translated various Greek medical works into Syriac. Apes were supplied to him for dissection by the caliph al-Mu'taṣim c. 836. Many anatomical and medical writings are credited to him, notably the "Disorder of the Eye" ("Daghal al-'ain"), which is the earliest systematic treatise on ophthalmology extant in Arabic, and the Aphorisms, the Latin translation of which was very popular in the Middle Ages.

Text and Translations—Aphorismi Johannis Damasceni (Bologna, 1489. Translation of the al-nawādir al-ṭibbīya). Many other editions. In the early editions of this and other works, Joannes [Janus] Damascenus is named as the author. (See my note on Serapion the Elder, second half of the ninth century).

Criticism—Fihrist (295). Wüstenfeld: Geschichte der arabischen Aerzte (23, 1840). Leclerc: Médecine arabe (Vol. I, 105–111, 1876). C. Pruefer and M. Meyerhof: Die Augenheilkunde des Juhanna ibn Māsawaih (Der Islam, vol. 6, 217–268, 1916; vol. 7, 108. Important; contains a complete analysis of the "Disorder of the Eye" and of a smaller book, a regular cram-book of ophthalmology; also a study of early Syriac and Arabic ophthalmology). E. G. Browne: Arabian Medicine (37, Cambridge, 1921). M. Meyerhof: New Light on Ḥunain (Isis, VIII, 717, 1926).

AL-KINDĪ

See my note in Section III.

AYYŪB AL-RUHĀWĪ

Ayyūb al-Ruhāwī al-Abrash. Job of Edessa, the Spotted. Job Lentiginosus. The dates of his birth and death are unknown, but his son is mentioned by Ibn abī Uṣaibi'a as a contemporary of the 'Abbāsid caliphs al-Mutawakkil and al-Mu'tazz (d. 869). One of the main translators of medical works from Greek into Syriac. Ḥunain ibn Isḥāq ascribed to him the translation of 35 Galenic works.

Max Meyerhof: New Light on Ḥunain ibn Isḥāq (Isis, VIII, 703, 1926).

'ALĪ AL-ṬABARĪ

Abū-l-Ḥasan 'Alī ibn Sahl (ibn) Rabbān al-Ṭabarī. Flourished under the caliphate of al-Mutawakkil (847 to 861). Muslim physician, son of a Persian Jew, Sahl al Ṭabarī, q. v., above. Teacher of Rhazes. His main work, completed in 850, is the "Paradise of Wisdom" ("Firdaus al-ḥikma") dealing chiefly with medicine, but also with philosophy, meteorology, zoology, embryology, psychology, astronomy. It is based on Greek and Hindu sources (it ends with a

[b] Or Yaḥyā, the Arabic equivalent of the Syriac Yūḥannā (cfr. Joannes, John, etc).

summary of Hindu medicine). He also wrote a defense of Islām entitled "The Book of Religion and Empire."

Text and Translation—E. G. Browne "hopes to edit and perhaps translate" the Paradise of Wisdom, hitherto unpublished. (Browne died in 1926.)

The Book of Religion and Empire was Englished by A. Mingana (193 p., Manchester, 1922; Isis, VIII, 536).

Criticism—Fihrist (p. 296 and commentary, pp. 141 f.). Wüstenfeld: Geschichte der Arabischen Aerzte (21, 1840). Leclerc: Médecine arabe (Vol. I, 292–293, 1876. See on p. 290, a notice on 'Alī's father). C. Brockelmann: Arabische Litteratur (1, 231, 1898). E. G. Browne: Arabian Medicine (37–44, 1921. With a short analysis of the Paradise of Wisdom).

Japanese Medicine

By the beginning of the ninth century, if not earlier, Chinese medicine had completely superseded the old medical lore of Japan.[e] An attempt to restore the latter was made during the Daidō era (806 to 810) by order of the Emperor Heijō. A collection of ancient recipes was compiled by Hirosada Idzumo and Manao Abe; it is called the Daidō-rui-shiu-hō ("The Classified Collection of Recipes of the Daidō Era). This attempt proved unsuccessful and was soon forgotten. A manuscript of the work was discovered in 1827 in the Bungo province; it has been published many times. The work is divided into 100 chapters, of which the first thirteen deal with various drugs (most of them vegetal) and the others with 122 diseases or symptoms. The authenticity of that work (that is, in its present state) is very doubtful. For example, it contains an elaborate description of syphilis, which, it is claimed, was not introduced into Japan until 1569. This may be an interpolation, however. The subject requires further study.

Another similar work was compiled by order of the Emperor Seiwa (ruling from 859 to 876) during the Jōkwan era (859 to 877). It is called Kiran-hō and is divided into 50 volumes. The main editor was Minetsugu Sugawara. It is also lost and the modern edition, bearing its name, is of very doubtful authenticity.

B. Scheube, in Puschmann: Geschichte der Medizin (vol. 1, 39, 1902). Y. Fujikawa: Geschichte der Medizin in Japan (13, 1911).

HIROIZUMI MONOBE

Born in 785, died in 860. Japanese physician. Author of the earliest Japanese treatise on hygiene, the Setsuyō-yōketsu, which is said to have been a work in 20 volumes, but is lost.

Y. Fujikawa: Geschichte der Medizin in Japan (21, 1911).

FUKUYOSHI ŌMURA

Flourished in the Shōwa era, 834 to 848. Japanese surgeon He wrote, c. 834 to 848, the earliest Japanese treatise on surgery. It is entitled Chi-sō-ki and is of pure Chinese derivation.

Y. Fujikawa: Geschichte der Medizin in Japan (19, 1911).

---

[e] Some information on this native lore may be found in the Nihongi, for which see my note on Japanese historiography in the first half of the eighth century.

VIII. LATIN, BYZANTINE, SYRIAN, MUSLIM, AND JAPANESE HISTORIOGRAPHY

Age of the Vikings

The age of the Vikings begins (as far as historical records are concerned[d]) at the end of the eighth century and extends to the tenth and eleventh. According to O. Montelius (Les temps préhistoriques en Suède, Paris, 1895) this period extends from c. 800 to c. 1050. The historian of technology will be particularly interested in the early Viking ships.

A brief account of them will be found in Feldhaus: Die Technik (920, 1914). The first was discovered in 1863 in Schleswig; Feldhaus places the construction of these ships between 300 and 1000 A. D.? See also Karl Radunz: Wikingerschiffe (Prometheus, p. 649–653, 1905). The publication of an extensive description of the Oseberg ship (dating from the middle of the ninth century) and of the archaeological treasure buried with it was announced in 1916 by the University Museum of Christiania.

Paul B. Du Chaillu: The Viking Age: The Early History, Manners, and Customs (2 vols., New York, 1889). Mary W. Williams: Social Scandinavia in the Viking age (465 p., New York, 1920. A very comprehensive and accurate survey, with illustrations and bibliography, but no chronological attempt). Publications of the Viking (club or) Society for Northern Research, organized in London (1892). T. J. Arne: La Suède et l'Orient. Etudes archéologiques sur les relations de la Suède et de l'Orient pendant l'âge des Vikings (244 p., Upsal, 1914; Isis, III, 96). Johannes Steenstrup: Etude sur les temps des Vikings (Academy of Sciences, Copenhagen, 1923).

EINHARD

Also Eginhard. Born near the River Main c. 770, educated at the Fulda monastery c. 788 to 791; flourished at the court of Charlemagne in Aachen; died at Seligenstadt in 840. Carolingian historian and educator. Possibly the architect of the Aachen cathedral. His main work is a "Life of Charlemagne" ("Vita Karoli Magni") modeled upon Suetonius's "Life of Augustus." This is the noblest fruit of the Carolingian revival; it is also the best contemporary account of the age, the best mediaeval biography.

Text—Opera omnia. Edition by G. H. Pertz in the Mon. Germ. hist. (2 vols., Hanover, 1826–1829). Latin and French edition by Alexandre Theulet (Paris, 1840–1843).

Vita Karoli: First edition (Cologne, 1521). Edition by G. H. Pertz reprinted from the Mon. Germ. hist., 4th ed. revised by G. Waitz (Hannover, 1880; 5th ed., 78 p., 1905). Edition by H. W. Garrod and R. B. Mowat (Oxford, 1915).

Translations of the Life: In French, by Helies Vinet. Poitiers, 1546; by Louis Halphen, with Latin text (150 p., Paris, 1923). In German, by Otto Abel (67 p., Leipzig, 1850; 3d ed., 1888). In English, by Wm. Glaister (London, 1877).

Criticism—Hans Wibel: Kritik der Annales regni Francorum und der Annales q. d. Einhardi (I. Handschriftliche Überlieferung. 125 p.; Diss., Strassburg, 1902). Marguerite Bondois: La translation des saints Marcellin et Pierre; étude sur Einhard et sa vie politique de 827 à 834 (Bibl. école hautes ét., 132 p., Paris, 1907).

---

[d] The first recorded attack of the Vikings on western Europe occurred in 779 near Bordeaux, but their raids increased in number and violence in the ninth century, reaching their climax in the second half of that century. The first country which they tried to conquer for settlement was Ireland, c. 840. They reached Iceland c. 860, and their permanent settlement there began in 874. (See note on the discovery of Iceland in next chapter.)

M. Manitius: Lateinische Literatur des Mittelalters (vol. 1, 639–646, 1911; vol. 2, 813). Maximilian Buchner: Einhard als Künstler (Studien zur deutschen Kunstgeschichte, 210, 157 p., 2 pl., Strassburg, 1919). Sandys: History of Classical Scholarship (vol. 1^3, 480–482, 1921).

FRECHULPH

Frechulph[e] of Lisieux. Probably educated at Tours together with Hrabanus, under Alcuin; Bishop of Lisieux since c. 825; died in 852 or 853. Carolingian historian. He wrote a history of the world, in five books, from the beginning down to his own days; the last book is naturally the most important. It is essentially a mosaic derived from a good many sources. This was the first attempt, in France, to tell a history of the world, which was more than a chronology. Frechulph dedicated to the Emperor Charles the Bald an edition of Vegetius's work on the military art (q. v., second half of fourth century), corrected by him.

Text—Chronicorum tomi II (Cologne, 1539). Various other editions, including one in Migne's Patrology (vol. 106).

Criticism—M. Manitius: Lateinische Literatur des Mittelalters (vol. 1, 663–668, 1911, vol. 2, 814).

Byzantine Historiography

SYNCELLOS

Georgios Syncellos (Γεώργιος ὁ Σύγκελλος);[f] flourished in Constantinople about the end of the eighth century; still living in 810. Byzantine historian. He wrote, after 806, a chronicle (Ἐκλογὴ χρονογραφίας), from the creation to 284, which is, together with the history by Eusebios, the most important work for the study of Christian chronology.

Text—Editio princeps by Jacques Goar, Greek and Latin (Paris, 1652). Edition by Wilhelm Dindorf (2 vols., Corp. script. hist. byz., vols. 11–12, Bonn, 1829).

Criticism—Heinrich Gelzer: Sextus Julius Africanus (vol. 2, 176–249, 1885). K. Krumbacher: Byzantinische Litteratur (2 Aufl., 339–342, 1897).

THEOPHANES CONFESSOR

Θεοφάνης Ὁμολογητής,[g] founded a monastery near Sigriane on the Sea of Marmora, died in banishment on the island of Samothrace, c. 817. Byzantine annalist. After the death of his friend Syncellos, he continued the latter's work[h] (c. 811 to 814), carrying his "Chronicle" (Χρονογραφία) from 284 to 813. It contains a summary of Byzantine, and accessorily of Muslim, chronology. It is one of the best Byzantine chronicles.

A continuation of Theophanes's chronicle (the so-called Theophanes continuatus, Οἱ μετὰ Θεοφάνην) carries the story down to 961.[i]

---

[e] Freculf, Freculph, Frechulf.

[f] Meaning the private secretary of the Patriarch. He was secretary to Patriarch Tarasios (784 to 806).

[g] Canonized under that surname by the Greek church.

[h] At Syncellos's own request, using probably the materials accumulated by him.

[i] It is divided into six books, of which Books 1 to 5 deal with the period 813 to 886 and Book 6 with a longer period, 886 to 961. This last book (composed c. 961 to 963) has been ascribed to Theodoros Daphnopates (Θεόδωρος ὁ Δαφνοπάτης, also Μάγιστρος) who flourished about the middle of the tenth century.

Text—Theophanes's Chronicle. First edition by Jac. Goar (posthumously) and Leo Grammaticus (Greek and Latin, 676 p., Paris, 1655). Edition in Corpus script. byz. hist. (in 2 vols., Bonn, 1839–1841. Volume 1, edited by Joh. Classen, contains Theophanes's chronicle; vol. 2, by Im. Bekker, Anastasius's historia tripertita). The Bonn edition was reprinted in Migne's Greek Patrology (vol. 108). Critical edition by Carl de Boor (2 vols., Leipzig, 1883–1885. Vol. 1, Theophanes; vol. 2, Anastasius, excellent index).

Anastasius's translation. Theophanes's Chronicle was translated into Latin by the papal librarian Anastasius between 873 and 875. Anastasius's Historia tripertita, indeed, was compiled from the chronicles of Nicephoros, Syncellos, and Theophanes. This translation was as important in the West as the original text in the East. It was edited by A. Fabrotus (Paris, 1649). Later editions have been mentioned above.

Theophanes continuatus. Edited by F. Combefis: Scriptores post Theophanem (Paris, 1685). Edition by Im. Bekker in Corpus script. byz. hist. (Bonn, 1838) and in Migne's Patrology (vol. 109, 1–500).

Criticism—K. Krumbacher: Byzantinische Litteratur (2. Aufl., 342–349, 1897)

NICEPHOROS PATRIARCHES

Νικηφόρος πατριάρχης (Saint Nicephoros). Patriarch of Constantinople from 806 to his banishment in 815; died in 829. Byzantine theologian and annalist. Chiefly famous for his fight against the iconoclast emperor Leon V the Armenian (813–820). He wrote two historical works: the "Short History" (Ἱστορία σύντομος, Breviarium Nicephori), dealing with the period 602 to 769, is very important (it contains, among other things, a digression on the origin and wanderings of the Bulgarians); the "Short Chronography" (Χρονογραφικὸν σύντομον) from Adam to 829, though far less valuable, was far more popular.[i]

Text—Breviarium. First edition by Dionysius Petavius (Paris, 1616). Edition by Im. Bekker (with Latin translation) in the Bonn Byzantine corpus (1837). Critical edition by Carl de Boor (Leipzig, 1880).

Chronography—First edition by Jos. Justus Scaliger (Leyde, 1606). By Jacob Goar, together with the text of Syncellos, Greek and Latin (Paris, 1652). By L. Dindorf (Bonn, 1829); reproduced in Migne's Greek patrology (vol. 100, 995–1060). New edition by Karl Aug. Credner: Nicephori chronologia brevis (Progr., Giessen, 1832–1838). By Carl de Boor (1880. With the Breviarium).

Criticism—Heinrich Gelzer: Sextus Julius Africanus (vol. 2, 384–388, 1885). K. Krumbacher: Byzantinische Litteratur (2. Aufl., 349–352, 71–73, 1897).

GEORGIOS MONACHOS

Γεώργιος μοναχός,[k] flourished about 842. Byzantine monk and annalist. Author of a world chronicle (Χρονικὸν σύντομον) in four books, from Adam to 842. The latest part of it (813 to 842) is particularly important. It is a typically monkish chronicle. Its popularity was immense and its influence upon Byzantine and Slavonic thought incalculable. Because of its very popularity, many editions and elaborations were soon made of that work, rendering the establishment of its text extremely difficult. For the Slavs it became the main historical source

---

[i] We know it only through an elaboration of it dated 850. It was translated into Latin c. 870 by Anastasius, and included in his "Historia tripertita" (see Theophanes). It has been continued in various manuscripts down to 886, 944, 976.

[k] Meaning the solitary, the monk. He was also called ἁμαρτωλός, the sinner, and ῥακενδύτης, clothed in rags.

for all but their own history. It was translated also into Georgian. A continuation of Georgios's chronicle down to 948 was made by Symeon the Logothete. Some manuscripts carry the story down to 1071, 1081, 1143. See my note on Symeon Metaphrastes (second half of tenth century).

Text—First complete edition (with the continuations down to 1143) by Edouard de Muralt (1068 p., St. Petersburg, 1859), reproduced in Migne's Patrology (vol. 110, with a Latin translation. This edition is altogether insufficient).

Criticism—K. Krumbacher: Byzantinische Litteratur (2. Aufl., 352–361, 1897). J. B. Bury: History of the Eastern Roman Empire from the Fall of Irene to the Accession of Basil I (802 to 867) (545 p., London, 1912. Ch. 14, 434–450. Art, Learning and Education).

Syrian Historiography

DIONYSIOS OF TELL-MAḤRĒ

Or Dionysios Tell-Maḥrāyā. Tell-Maḥrē is a village situated between al-Raqqah and Ḥiṣn Maslamah, near the river Balīkh. Studied in the convents of Qenneshrē and Kaisūm; appointed (monophysitic) patriarch in 818 until his death in 845, August 22; buried at Qenneshrē. Syriac historian. He wrote important Annals of world history, from the creation down to his own time. They existed in two recensions, a longer and a shorter; the longer extended at least to the year 837; the shorter ended with the year 776.

Texts—Eusebii Canonum epitome ex Dionysii Telmaharensis Chronico petita, edited by Carl Siegfried and Heinrich Gelzer (100 p., Leipzig, 1884).

C. A. Hedenskog: Berättelse om Alexander den Store, etc. (78 p., Lund, 1868. Syriac and Swedish).

Jean Baptiste Chabot: Chronique de Denis de Tell-Maḥré, quatrième partie (2 vols., Paris, 1895. Syriac and French).

Criticism—Heinrich Gelzer: Sextus Julius Africanus (vol. 2, 396–401, 1885). William Wright: Syriac Literature (196–203, 1894). Anton Baumstark: Syrische Litteratur (275, 1922).

Muslim Historiography

IBN HISHĀM

Abū Muḥammad 'Abd al-Malik ibn Hishām ibn Aiyūb al-Ḥimyarī al-Baṣrī. He spent the end of his life at Fusṭāṭ, where he died in 833. Arabic historian. Author of the earliest biography of the Prophet (Sīrat al-rasūl) which has come down to us, a recension of Ibn Isḥāq's work (q. v., second half of eighth century).

Text—The Arabic text has been edited by F. Wüstenfeld (Göttingen, 1858–1860). Abridged German translation by Gustav Weil (2 vols., Stuttgart, 1864).

Criticism—Paul Brönnle: Die Commentatoren des Ibn Isḥāq und ihre Scholien (Diss., 87 p., Halle, 1895). C. Brockelmann: Arabische Litteratur (vol. 1, 135, 1898). Henri Lammens: Fāṭima et les filles de Mahomet (Rome, 1912).

IBN SA'D

Abū 'Abdallāh Muḥammad ibn Sa'd ibn Manī' al-Zuhrī, generally called Kātib al-Wāqidī;[1] died at Bagdad in 845. Muslim historian. His main work is the "Kitāb al-ṭabaqāt al-kabīr" (the great book of the classes), which contains an extensive biography of the Prophet and shorter notices on his companions, helpers, and followers, arranged in classes (ṭabaqāt).

[1] Wāqidī's secretary. See my note on al-Wāqidī, second half of eighth century.

Text—Julius Wellhausen: Die Schreiben Muhammads und die Gesandschaften an ihn in Skizzen und Vorarbeiten (vol. 4, 85–194, 1–78, 1889. Arabic and German). Arabic text, edited under the direction of E. Sachau (Leiden, 1904).

Criticism—O. Loth: Das Klassenbuch des Ibn Sa'd (Leipzig, 1869). C. Brockelmann: Arabische Litteratur (vol. 1, 136, 1898).

Japanese Historiography

IMUBE HIRONARI

Flourished c. 808. Japanese archaeologist. He wrote, in 808, the Kogo-shūi, a work dealing with the customs, language, etc., of old Japan.

Text—Kogoshūi or Gleanings from ancient stories. Translated with an introduction and notes by Genchi Kato and Hikoshiro Hoskins. With a facsimile of the Yoshida Manuscript of the Kogoshūi, the oldest manuscript now extant (114 p., 4 pl., Dresden, 1924).

Criticism—The Kogo-shūi is often quoted by F. Brinkley in his History of the Japanese People (1914). See E. Papinot: Historical Dictionary (204, 1909).

The Shōjiroku

The Shōjiroku was compiled about 815, in Chinese. It contains the genealogy of 1,182 noble families of Japan, about one-third of them claiming a Chinese or Korean ancestry.

W. G. Aston: Japanese Literature (126, 1899).

YOSHIMINE YASUYO

Son of Kwammu-tennō, emperor from 782 to 805, born in 785; died in 830. Japanese scholar. He was one of the editors of the Nihon-kōki and of other similar compilations. The introduction of water-wheels (noria), for the irrigation of rice fields, is ascribed to him.

E. Papinot: Historical Dictionary (757, 1909).

The Nihon-kōki

The third of the "Six National Histories" (Riku-kokushi), the Nihon-kōki, dealing with the period 792 to 833, was edited in 840 by Fujiwara Otsugu and others. Only 10 volumes of it are still extant.

IX. BARBARIAN, CHINESE, AND JAPANESE LAW

Barbarian Laws

Three important codes of laws date from the beginning of the ninth century. They have been edited by Karl von Richthofen in the Mon. Germ. hist. (Leges).

(1) The Saxon Law (Lex Saxonum) dates from 803. It is entirely Christianized.

Ernst Theodor Gaupp: Recht und Verfassung der alten Sachsen, in Verbindung mit einer kritischen Ausgabe der Lex Saxonum (244 p., Breslau, 1837).

(2) The Frisian Law (Lex Frisionum) is far more heterogeneous and contains non-Christian elements side by side with the Christian, and many other contradictions. It dates probably from the end of Charlemagne's reign.

Edition by E. T. Gaupp (Breslau, 1832).

(3) The Thuringian Law (Lex Angliorum et Werinorum, hoc est, Thuringorum) dates also from c. 803.

Edition by E. T. Gaupp: Das alte Gesetz der Thüringer in ihrer Verwandschaft mit der Lex Salica und Lex Ripuaria herausgegeben (434 p., Breslau, 1834).

Chinese Law

TU YU

Tu^{4} Yu^{4} (12043, 13437). Native of Wan^{4}-nien^{2} (12486, 8301), Shensi; died in 812. Chinese writer on government and economics. He wrote an encyclopaedic treatise on those subjects, called T'ung^{1} tien^{3} (12294, 11177) and divided into nine sections: food and goods, examinations and degrees, government offices, ceremonies, music, army, punishments, geography, national defence. It might be called an administrative encyclopaedia. Chapters 163 to 170 contain an account of Chinese jurisprudence, with a summary of its evolution. Chapters 171 to 200 contain a summary of geographical knowledge with regard to China and neighboring countries.

Text—This work has often been revised. The Wade Library in Cambridge contains an edition issued in 1747 by order of the Emperor Ch'ien Lung (Giles's Catalogue, B. 476–488).
Criticism—A. Wylie: Chinese Literature (68 (1867), 1902). H. A. Giles: Biographical Dictionary (785, 1898). Encyclopaedia sinica (296, 1917).

Japanese Law—Official Codes

The earliest Japanese code, Ōmi-ryō, was promulgated in the second half of the seventh century (q. v.). That code is lost. The second code, the earliest extant, Daihō-ryō, was promulgated in 701 (q. v., first half of the eighth century). A third code was published in 811, during the Kōnin nengō (810–824) containing all the ordinances enacted since 701. It is called Kōnin-kyaku-shiki: the kyaku fill ten volumes and the shiki, forty.

E. Papinot: Historical Dictionary (514, 1909).

KIYOWARA NATSUNO

Also called Narabi-no-oka no Otodo. Born in 782, died in 837. Japanese philosopher and educator. He wrote, in 833, the Ryō no gige, a commentary on Chinese law in ten volumes, forming a sort of complement to the Daihō code of 701. Chinese law (myōhō) formed the core of Japanese higher education in those days.

E. Papinot: Historical Dictionary (289, 520, 1909).

X. LATIN, SEMITIC, AND JAPANESE PHILOLOGY AND EDUCATION

The greatest grammarian and educator in the West was Hrabanus Maurus q. v., in Section III.

JEHUDA BEN QURAISH

Judah ibn Qarīsh. Born at Tahort, northern Africa; flourished in the eighth and ninth centuries. Jewish philologist (Qaraite?). He wrote a letter (Risāla) in Arabic to the Jewish community at Fez, which is the earliest contribution to comparative Semitic philology. He recognized the affinity of Semitic languages, that is, their subjection to the same linguistic laws. He also wrote a dictionary (lost).

Text—Epistola de studii Targum utilitate et de linguae chaldaicae, misnicae, talmudicae, arabicae, vocabulorum item nonnullorum barbaricorum convenientia cum hebraea. Textum arabicum litteris hebraicis exaratum ex unico Bibliothecae Bodleianae cod. ms. descriptum nunc primum ed. J. J. J. Bergès et B. Goldberg (Paris, 1857).

Criticism—Short article by Rabbi J. Z. Lauterbach in Jewish Encyclopaedia (vol. 7, 345, 1904).

For Japanese philology, the invention of the hiragana, see my note on Kōbō-daishi, see Section II.

SUGAWARA KIYOGIMI

Born in 770; died in 842. Japanese scholar. One time rector of the Imperial University (Daigaku no kami). He reformed the university and introduced Chinese methods in the administration. His son—

SUGAWARA KOREYOSHI

Born in 812, died 880. Professor of Literature (bunshō-hakase) at the University; later he became its rector.

E. Papinot: Historical Dictionary (604, 1909).

CHAPTER XXX

THE TIME OF AL-RĀZĪ

(Second Half of Ninth Century)

I. Survey of Science in Second Half of Ninth Century. II. Religious Background. III. Philosophical Background. Greek, Latin, English, Syriac, and Arabic Writings. IV. Arabic and Latin Mathematics and Astronomy. V. Muslim Alchemy and Physics; Chinese Technology. VI. French and Scandinavian Travel and Exploration. English and Muslim Geography. VII. Latin, Byzantine, Muslim (or Arabic), Jewish, and Coptic Medicine. VIII. Latin, English, Byzantine, Syrian, Muslim, and Japanese Historiography. IX. Byzantine and Japanese Law. X. Latin, English, Byzantine, Slavonic, Syriac, and Arabic Philology.

I. SURVEY OF SCIENCE IN SECOND HALF OF NINTH CENTURY

1. The remark which I made at the beginning of the previous chapter applied to the whole of the ninth century. I said that that century was essentially a Muslim century. This is more true of the second half than of the first, for with the exception of King Alfred, practically all the scientific leaders were Muslims, or at any rate were working with and for Muslims and wrote in Arabic.

2. *Religious Background*—The main event in Christendom was the evangelization of the Khazars and of the Moravians and Pannonians by St. Cyril and St. Methodios.

The islamization of Iran did not by any means destroy Zoroastrianism. As a matter of fact, two of the most important Zoroastrian texts date from the second half of the ninth century. The "Dīnkart," which formed a sort of Zoroastrian encyclopaedia, was begun under the rule of al-Ma'mūn and completed by Ātūrpāt c. 881. A shorter text, composed by Martān-farukh, the "Shikand-gūmānīg vījār," is practically the only philosophical treatise written in Pahlawī; it is a defense of Zoroastrianism against other religions, chiefly against the Jews, Christians, Muslims, and Manichees.

The great toleration shown to non-Muslims by the early 'Abbāsid caliphs, and especially by al-Ma'mūn and al-Mu'taṣim, came to a sudden end under al-Mutawakkil (847–861), who approved himself a fanatical champion of Sunnite orthodoxy and persecuted with equal cruelty the people of other faiths and the Mu'tazila, that is, the liberals, of his own faith. Yet al-Mutawakkil continued to protect men of science, chiefly the physicians, and he encouraged the school of translators headed by Ḥunain ibn Isḥāq.

Dā'ūd al-Ẓāhirī founded a new school of theology, based upon a more literal interpretation of the Qur'ān; that school, however, did not survive very long. Muslim published a new collection of traditions, arranged according to legal topics, like Bukhārī's, but more theoretical. The Egyptian Dhū-l-Nūn is generally considered the founder of Ṣūfīsm, that is, of Muslim mysticism. We must take the development of Ṣūfīsm into account, though its influence upon the progress of science was, on the whole, a negative one; that is, it obstructed that progress. Like any other kind of mysticism, Ṣūfīsm is not a definite doctrine, but a mental attitude, largely an attitude of revolt against the scientific methods; it draws its elements capriciously from everywhere. It is thus not surprising that there are many points of contact and comparison between Ṣūfism and various other forms of mysticism. About the year 864, under the influence of 'Abdallāh ibn Maymūn al-Qaddāḥ, a new mystical movement took definite shape, this time among the Shī'a—the Ismā'īlī movement. In this case, mystic ideas were combined with social and political theories and thus the movement obtained a greater cohesion and a strength which was still increased by a secret organization. The influence of the Ismā'īlī, not simply upon the political, but also upon the scientific life of Islām, was considerable. This is especially true of a subsect called the Qarmaṭians after their leader Ḥamdān Qarmaṭ ibn al-Ash'ath. That influence was largely, but not always, occult; we shall have occasions of detecting it in the following chapters.[a]

The organization of Tibetan Buddhism and the composition of the Kanjur and Tanjur were continued by King Ral-pa-chan, the third and last of the "Three Religious Kings" of Tibet.

3. *Philosophical Background. Greek, Latin, English, Syriac, and Arabic writings*—Photios, Patriarch of Constantinople, composed a collection of erudite "reviews" of earlier writings, chiefly, but not exclusively, historical and theological writings.

Erigena, head of the court school of Charles the Bald, King of the Franks, wrote in 867 a very original philosophical treatise entitled "The Division of Nature." About the end of the century a pupil of Hrabanus, Remi of Auxerre, was teaching in Paris. That teaching was far less original than Erigena's, but far more popular. It continued the tradition of Bede, Alcuin, and Hrabanus, and may be considered the first germ of that University of Paris which would remain for so many centuries the main stronghold of mediaeval conservatism against every innovation. Erigena represented a relative freedom of thought, a creative thought, which could not be understood except by very few and would become by and by a spring of heresies; on the contrary, Remi was the champion of tradition. And still a third intellectual movement was initiated in the Christian West by Alfred the Great. King Alfred was not a deep philosopher like Erigena, whom he patronized, but he was at least as original and his activity had far-reaching consequences in the right direction. Of these three men, indeed, King Alfred is the one who came nearest to the scientific ideal. His aims were more modest, his curiosity more concrete, he was more matter of fact. He was one of the first teachers in the West to realize—or rather to divine—the importance of vernaculars, and this was in itself sufficient evidence of his profound originality.

Syrian thought was represented by the theologian and commentator Moses bar Kēphā.

The two main Muslim philosophers were al-Jāḥiẓ, who wrote various treatises based partly upon Greek knowledge, partly upon Muslim folk-lore, and al-Sarakhsī, al-Kindī's main disciple.

4. *Arabic and Latin Mathematics and Astronomy*—I am again obliged to say "Arabic" instead of "Muslim," because some of the most important work accomplished under Muslim tutelage was actually done by non-Muslims. There were so many mathematicians and astronomers in Islām that it is necessary to divide them into four groups: geometers; arithmeticians; astronomers and trigonometricians; astrologers.

---

[a] For example, see my note on the Brethren of Purity (second half of tenth century).

Geometers: Al-Māhānī wrote commentaries on Euclid and Archimedes, and tried in vain to divide a sphere into two segments, being in a given ratio. That Archimedian problem became a classical Muslim problem; it led to a cubic equation which was called al-Māhānī's equation. Hilāl al-Ḥimṣi translated the first four books of Apollonios into Arabic. Aḥmad ibn Yūsuf wrote a book on proportions which is of special importance, because through it Western mathematicians became acquainted with the theorem of Menelaos. Al-Nairīzī wrote commentaries on Ptolemy and Euclid. Thābit ibn Qurra made very remarkable measurements of parabolas and paraboloids, but is best known as the leader of a school of translators which produced Arabic versions of some of the main mathematical classics: Euclid, Archimedes, Apollonios, Theodosios, Ptolemy. Thābit himself was the foremost translator and revised some of the translations made by others. The two most important translators of his school, outside of himself, were Yūsuf al-Khūrī and Isḥāq ibn Ḥunain. A comparison of this brief account with the similar section in the previous chapter will show that much progress had already been made in geometry since the beginning of the century. To be sure, that activity was entirely derived from Greek sources, but it was, nevertheless, considerable.

Arithmeticians: I mentioned in the previous chapter that the writings of al-Kindī and al-Khwārizmī were in all probability the main channels through which the Hindu numerals became known in Islām and later in the West. The earliest Muslim documents bearing such numerals date from 874 and 888. The propagation of these numerals may have been accelerated by the fact that the Muslim trade was exceedingly active in those very days and reached every part of the world.

Thābit ibn Qurra developed the theory of amicable numbers. Qusṭā ibn Lūqā translated Diophantos.

Astronomers and trigonometricians: Al-Māhānī made a series of astronomical observations from 855 to 866. Al-Nairīzī compiled astronomical tables and wrote an elaborate treatise on the spherical astrolabe; he made systematic use of the tangent. Ḥāmid ibn 'Alī became famous as a constructor of astrolabes. Thābit ibn Qurra published solar observations; he tried to improve the Ptolemaic theory of planetary motions by the addition of a ninth sphere to account for the (imaginary) trepidation of the equinoxes. Qusṭā ibn Lūqā wrote a treatise on the spherical astrolabe. Jābir ibn Sinān, of whom we know nothing, but who may have been al-Battānī's father, constructed astronomical instruments, notably a spherical astrolabe.

The greatest astronomer of the age and one of the greatest of Islām was al-Battānī (Albategnius). He made a number of observations from 877 on, compiled a catalogue of stars for the year 880, determined various astronomical coefficients with great accuracy, discovered the motion of the solar apsides, and wrote an elaborate astronomical treatise which remained authoritative until the sixteenth century. That treatise included naturally a trigonometrical summary wherein not only sines, but tangents and cotangents, are regularly used. It contains a table of cotangents by degrees and a theorem equivalent to our formula giving the cosine of a side of a spherical triangle in function of the cosine of the opposite angle and of the sines and cosines of the other sides.

Astrologers: The most famous astrologers were Abū Bakr (Albubather), Aḥmad ibn Yūsuf, and Ibn Qutaiba.

The whole mathematical and astronomical work of the period showed a distinct improvement upon that of the previous one. There were fewer astrologers and more geometers; the astronomical work was far more original than in the first half of the century and on a relatively high level. It is true, Thābit ibn Qurra introduced an unfortunate error of which a great many later astronomers (including Copernicus!) remained prisoners, but original research always implies the possibility of error. Thābit's error was not discreditable. The elaboration of trigonometry was continued with great skill and originality. Much attention was paid to astronomical instruments and especially to a new one, the spherical astrolabe. Al-Battānī's masterly work was a fitting climax to this wonderful activity.

So much for Islām. What was being done at the same time in the rest of the world? Nothing. The only interesting item in the West was Erigena's extension of the geoheliocentrical system of Heraclides to two more planets, but that was hardly more than an accidental conceit of a daring philosopher, and can not be counted an astronomical discovery.

5. *Muslim Alchemy and Physics; Chinese Technology*—According to Muslim tradition, Dhū-l-nūn was an alchemist, but in all probability that Ṣūfī alchemy was very much like the Taoist alchemy; it was a metaphysical and figurative science which had little, if anything, to do with experiment. Al-Jāḥiẓ seems to have had some chemical knowledge, for instance, he knew how to obtain ammonia from animal offals by dry distillation, but it would be absurd to call him a chemist. On the other hand, the great physician al-Rāzī was undoubtedly a genuine chemist: he wrote various chemical treatises, described a number of chemical instruments, attempted to classify mineral substances, and even tried to apply his chemical knowledge to medical purposes. He may be considered a distant ancestor of the iatrochemists of the sixteenth century. He was also a physicist; he used the hydrostatic balance to make investigations on specific gravity. The mathematician al-Nairīzī wrote a treatise on atmospheric phenomena.

The earliest printed book extant is a copy of a Chinese translation of the "Diamond sūtra," published on May 11, 868, for free distribution. The earliest clear reference to block printing in any literature is a Chinese text referring to the year 883.

5 bis. *Muslim Biology*—The Muslims had little interest in natural history; they were certainly not tempted to study it for its own sake, but many of their current views on biological subjects may be found in their literary and historical compilations. The most remarkable example is the "Book of Plants" composed by the historian al-Dīnawarī. The purpose of that book was primarily philological, but it contains much valuable information for the historian of botany. Al-Jāḥiẓ's "Book of Animals" is also a mine of information, though most of it is folk-loric rather than zoological.

6. *French and Scandinavian Travel and Exploration. English and Muslim geography.*—Bernard the Wise visited Egypt and Palestine c. 869 and wrote an account of his journey.

Iceland was discovered (or re-discovered) by various Scandinavian sailors in the sixties. A Norwegian settlement was organized about 874, at Reykjavik.

The greatest geographical writer of Europe was King Alfred, who introduced various interpolations into his Anglo-Saxon translations to impart additional knowledge obtained directly by himself. It is through the king's writings that we know of Ohthere's journeys to Arkhangelsk and to Oslo, and of Wulfstan's exploration of the Baltic.

Ibn Khurdādhbih produced the earliest "Book of Roads and Provinces," indicating the postal stations along a number of roads and the amount of taxation in various localities. Many such books were published from time to time in

Islām. Their purpose was obviously administrative, not scientific, yet they were in fact geographical treatises. The practical needs dominating these books caused them to be very concrete, detailed, and accurate. The historian al-Ya'qūbī wrote a geographical treatise called "The Book of the Countries."

7. *Latin, Byzantine, Muslim (or Arabic), Jewish, and Coptic Medicine*—Bertharius, abbot of Monte Cassino, wrote a medical treatise which is a good specimen of the monastic medicine of those days.

Nicetas compiled a collection of ancient surgical writings from Hippocrates to Paulos Aegineta.

So much medical work was accomplished in Islām that it is expedient to divide the physicians into two groups: those who were primarily practitioners and those who were primarily scholars and who were engaged in translating the Greek medical classics into Syriac and Arabic. Of course, those of the second group were, all of them, foreigners, non-Muslims; but even in the first group, one-half of the physicians were Christians. Thus this activity was Christian rather than Muslim, but we must not forget that by far the greatest of all of them, al-Rāzī, was a Muslim.

To speak of the true physicians first, Sābūr ibn Sahl of Jundīshāpūr wrote an antidotary which was very popular until the middle of the twelfth century. Yaḥyā ibn Sarāfyūn (Serapion the Elder) wrote two medical encyclopaedias in Syriac. These works had a great influence upon mediaeval medicine in the West. Yaḥyā gave minute instructions relative to blood-letting. These two were Christians.

The Persian al-Rāzī was not simply the greatest clinician of Islām and of the whole Middle Ages; he was also, as we have seen, a chemist and physicist. It would be difficult to choose between him and his contemporary al-Battānī: both were very great scientists who would have been conspicuous in any age. I decided to call this period "The Time of al-Rāzī" because the physician is known to a larger public than the astronomer, and also because his influence can be traced more directly throughout many centuries of human effort, East and West. I have already remarked that al-Rāzī might be considered one of the forerunners of the iatrochemists of the Renaissance. He wrote an immense medical encyclopaedia called Al-ḥāwī ("Continens") and a monograph on measles and smallpox which is the masterpiece of Muslim medicine. Ya'qūb ibn akhī Ḥizām was the author of a treatise on horsemanship, which contains some rudiments of veterinary art, the earliest work of its kind in Arabic.

The greatest of the translators was Ḥunain ibn Isḥāq (Joannitius). He collected Greek medical manuscripts, translated many of them, supervised the activities of other scholars, and revised their translations. His rôle with regard to medical literature was very similar to that of Thābit ibn Qurra with regard to the mathematical and astronomical texts. The school of Nestorian translators headed by Ḥunain must have been quite considerable, for between them they managed to translate the greatest part of the Hippocratic and Galenic writings into Syriac and into Arabic. Ḥunain wrote also original works, notably a treatise on ophthalmology and an introduction to Galen's Ars parva which was immensely popular during the Middle Ages. It will suffice to name the other translators of medical writings: Ḥunain's son Isḥāq, Ḥubaish ibn al-Ḥasan, 'Isā ibn Yaḥyā, Stephen son of Basil, Mūsā ibn Khālid, Thābit ibn Qurra, Yūsuf al-Khūrī. Ḥunain was a very great man, but he was more of a scholar than of a scientist proper and his activity, which had already begun in the middle of the previous period, ended in the middle of this one; in other words, al-Rāzī and al-Battānī were one generation ahead of him. The time of Ḥunain, extending from 826 to 877, falls just between that of al-Khwārizmī and that of al-Rāzī.

The earliest medical work in Hebrew appeared at about this time; it is really a sort of popular encyclopaedia dealing not simply with medical subjects but with physiology, embryology, astronomy, etc. It is ascribed to one Asaph Judaeus, otherwise unknown, and was probably derived from Syriac or Arabic sources.

A Coptic papyrus containing a hotchpotch of medical recipes is probably a production of the same time; it is derived from Egyptian, Greek, and Arabic sources, and its interest is purely archaeological.

8. *Latin, English, Byzantine, Syrian, Muslim, and Japanese Historiography*—Anastasius the Librarian translated various Byzantine chronicles into Latin and thus built a much needed bridge between two worlds, the Latin and the Greek, which by this time had already drifted apart considerably. He was the only distinguished Latin[b] historian of the time.

King Alfred performed a task of even greater importance when he ordered the completion and edition of the English chronicles and translated a number of historical works from Latin into English. However, the pregnancy of Alfred's activity would not be appreciated for a considerable time, because Latin remained the language of the learned until the seventeenth century.

The only Byzantine historian of that time was Photios, and he was not a genuine one; a great contrast with the activity of the previous period.

Moses bar Kēphā wrote an ecclesiastical history in Syriac.

The main historical works of this period were written in Arabic: Al-Dīnawarī wrote a general history which is of special value because it gives us the Persian point of view. Ibn Qutaiba also composed a universal history and other historical works. We owe to Ibn 'Abd al-Ḥakam the earliest Muslim account of Egypt. The universal history of al-Ya'qūbī gives us the Shī'ite interpretation of Islām. Finally, two important works were published by al-Balādhurī. With the exception of Ibn 'Abd al-Ḥakam, who was an Egyptian, all these historians, be it noted, were of Persian origin; all wrote in Arabic.

The last three national histories of Japan, composed upon the model of the Chinese dynastic annals, were published respectively in 869, 879, and 901.

9. *Byzantine and Japanese Law*—A new revision of Byzantine law was ordered by Basil the Macedonian (867 to 886) and completed during the rule of his son Leon the Philosopher (886 to 911). The enormous corpus of law thus obtained, the so-called Basilica, remained the official code of the empire until its fall in 1453.

The Japanese continued their codification of law and usage in the Chinese manner. The last two of the "Three Great Codes" were promulgated in 868 and 907.

10. *Latin, English, Byzantine, Slavonic, Syriac, and Arabic Philology*—The main Latin grammarian was Remi of Auxerre, and his work had no special importance.

On the contrary, the value of King Alfred's contributions can hardly be overestimated. A true pioneer, he helped to create a new language and to make of it, not simply a means of voicing trivial needs, but a noble instrument to express with precision the highest thoughts. No king ever did more for the education of his people than Alfred the Great.

Photios compiled a Greek lexicon and was much interested in philological discussions of various kinds. Arethas was a humanist and a distinguished repre-

---

[b] By Latin I mean, writing in Latin. One writing in French I would call a French historian.

sentative of the new Byzantine renaissance. Some of the most precious Greek manuscripts now extant were copied for him.

St. Cyril invented the Glagolitic alphabet, of which the Cyrillic alphabet, now used in Russia, was probably a later development. He translated the Septuagint into Slavonic. He may be called the father of Slavonic literature.

The greatest philologist of the age was Ḥunain ibn Isḥāq. He composed the earliest Syriac lexicon and a Syriac grammar, dealing partly with syntax. But his fame rests chiefly upon his scientific translations from the Greek into Syriac and Arabic. His methods of translation marked a great step forward. Ḥunain tried to obtain the best manuscripts of Greek medical texts, collated them, examined the existing Syriac and Arabic versions, and finally completed his own translations. He has left a catalogue raisonné of the Syriac and Arabic versions of Galen's works available in his day; the critical notes in that catalogue prove his high standards of scholarship. I have already remarked that the purpose of al-Dīnawarī's "Book of Plants" was primarily philological; the names interested him far more than the things. Ibn Qutaiba was the earliest representative of the grammatical school of Bagdad. His concern was style, rhetoric, rather than grammar proper. A great number of Arabic writings were subsequently devoted to literary criticism and rhetoric, but we can not deal with them, for they belong to the history of art rather than to the history of science.

11. *Final Remarks*—We noticed in the previous chapter that Chinese progress was temporarily stopped in the first half of this century. The same remark must be made about Japanese progress in the second half of the century. Was this a consequence of the Chinese stagnation? or was it simply that the magnificent endeavor begun during the Nara period had spent its force? Such an effort as the Japanese had made during that golden century was so great that the strain could not be sustained indefinitely. Hindu activity was also at a standstill. Was this due to the eclipse of Buddhism and to Jaina progress? At any rate, during this period India and the Far East have momentarily disappeared from the scene.

If we pass from the Far East to the Far West we find better conditions there. The two greatest men in the West were respectively Irish and English, Erigena and King Alfred. France produced Bernard the Wise and Remi of Auxerre; Italy, Bertharius and Anastasius. Scandinavian sailors, equal in boldness to the early Phoenicians, began their exploration of the Baltic and the Northern seas.

Proceeding eastward, we witnessed the beginning of Slavonic culture due to the devotion of St. Cyril and St. Methodios; in the Byzantine Empire, a humanistic revival, represented by Photios, Arethas, and Nicetas; in Iran, a remarkable Zoroastrian activity; in Tibet, a new surge of Buddhist learning.

The sum of these activities was certainly far from being contemptible. If nothing else had happened in the world, the study of this period would already have arrested our curiosity and sympathy. Yet all that of which I have spoken was relatively unimportant as compared with the effort which was accomplished at the same time in Islām.

St. Cyril, Erigena, and King Alfred were undoubtedly great men; yet, in spite of their presence in Europe, we may still maintain that the main advance of civilization in those days was due to Muslim initiative. It is true, much of that immense effort was made not by Muslims, but by Christians or by belated Pagans (Ḥarrānians or Sabians). Two of the main scientific leaders, Thābit ibn Qurra and al-Battānī, were of Ḥarrānian origin. The Christians were very numerous; I have already laid sufficient stress upon the activity of Christian translators to make it unnecessary to recall their names, and it will suffice to mention the two foremost Christian scientists of those days, Yaḥyā ibn Sarāfyūn and Ḥunain ibn Isḥāq. It can not be said any longer that most of the work was done by non-Muslims; contributions of the True Believers and those of the kāfirs were about equally important; but it can be easily proved that most of the Muslim work was done by men of Persian origin. To begin with, the four greatest Muslim scientists of the age were Persians, to wit, Ibn Khurdādhbih, al-Rāzī, al-Ya'qūbī, and al-Nairīzī. Al-Māhānī, al-Dīnawarī, Abū Bakr, Ibn Qutaiba, and al-Balādhurī were also men of Persian race. The Ismā'īlī movement took birth in Persia, but the other form of Muslim mysticism, Ṣūfīsm, seems to have originated in Egypt; it is thus probable that Ṣūfīsm was at least partly inspired by the other mystic movements, Christian and Pagan, of which Egypt had been the theater. In all, three Egyptians will be dealt with in this chapter, Dhū-l-nūn, Ibn 'Abd al-Ḥakam, and Aḥmad ibn Yūsuf. Finally, two men of Lower Mesopotamia must still be mentioned: al-Jāḥiẓ and Ḥāmid ibn 'Alī. This was certainly a splendid efflorescence. Bagdad had become the intellectual center of the world, even as Alexandria had been many centuries before. Unfortunately, the golden days of Bagdad were very brief; the disintegration of the caliphate would soon end the supremacy of its capital and involve a corresponding disintegration of intellectual endeavors.

II. RELIGIOUS BACKGROUND

CYRIL AND METHODIOS

Two brothers born in Thessalonica, Cyril in 827, Methodios c. 825. Both have been canonized by the Roman and Greek churches. Cyril's original name was Constantine. They both flourished at Constantinople and, from 864 on, among the Slavs of Moravia. Cyril had previously (860) converted the Khazars[c] of Crimea and of the lower Dnieper; he died at Constantinople in 869. Methodios continued their evangelism in Pannonia; he died in 885. Christian apostles of the Khazars and of the Slavs of Moravia and Pannonia. The Cyrillic alphabet was long ascribed to St. Cyril (after whom it was named). It is probably more correct to say that he invented the Glagolitic alphabet (or Glagolitsa), of which the Cyrillic alphabet (or Kirillitsa) is a later development. At any rate, Cyril it is who first gave an alphabet to the Slavs.

The oldest document in Cyrillic script is dated 998. The Cyrillic alphabet is now used in Russia, Serbia, and Bulgaria. It was once used to write a non-Slavonic language, Rumanian. The oldest Slavonic documents are written in the Glagolitic alphabet; it has now almost entirely fallen into disuse, except perhaps in a few Catholic communities of Dalmatia. "The copy of the Gospels upon which the kings of France formerly took their oath in the Cathedral of Reims was in the Slavonic language, written partly in the Cyrillic and partly in the Glagolitic characters." (C. H. Robinson, op. cit., 300.)

Cyril's greatest work was his translation of the Septuagint into Slavonic. Most of it perished in the thirteenth century. The scriptures now used in the Orthodox Church are different, being based not simply upon the Septuagint, but also upon the Hebrew text and upon the Latin Vulgate.

---

[c] I shall give more information on the Khazars in my note on Ḥasdai ibn Shaprut (second half of tenth century).

Criticism—Franz von Miklosich: Vita Sancti Methodii russico-slovenice et latine (Vindobonae, 1870). Cardinal Domenico Bartolini: Memorie dei santi Cirilli e Metodio (Roma, 1881). Adolphe d'Avril: St. Cyril et St. Méthode, première lutte des Allemands contre les Slaves, avec un essai sur les destinées du glagol (Paris, 1885). L. K. Goetz: Geschichte der Slavenapostel Konstantinus und Methodius (280 p., Gotha, 1897). Fr. Snopek: Konstantinus-Cyrillus und Methodius (Operum academiae Velehradensis, 2, 471 p., Kremsier, 1911). Milan Rešetar: Zur Übersetzungstätigkeit Methods (Archiv f. slav. Philol., vol. 34, 234–239, Berlin, 1912). Josef Vasj: Bis zu welchem Masse bestätigen die kroatisch-glagolitischen Breviere die Annahme einer vollständigen Übersetzung der Hl. Schrift durch Methodius (*ibidem*, vol. 35, 12–44, 1913). C. H. Robinson: Conversion of Europe (292–297, 1917). Franz Přikryl: Denkmale der heiligen Konstantin und Method in Europe (Wien, 1920).

ZOROASTRIANISM

The oldest Pahlawī text on religion—outside of Pahlawī translations[d] of Avesta texts—is the Dīnkart, or Acts of the Religion, of which only Books III to IX, containing about 169,000 words, are extant. This compilation was begun by Ātūr-farnbag, who defended Zoroastrianism in a disputation held in the presence of al-Ma'mūn (caliph from 813 to 833) and was completed by Ātūrpāt c. 881. It contains a vast amount of information on Zoroastrian customs, traditions, history, and literature. Book VIII (19,000 words) is a summary of the 21 treatises (nasks) which apparently formed the whole Zoroastrian literature in Sassanian times. These treatises were divided into three classes (each containing seven treatises) devoted respectively to religious, wordly, and intermediate knowledge. The summary is particularly full with regard to the worldly or legal treatises. Book IX (28,000 words) contains a detailed account of three of the religious treatises.

Text—Text, transliteration, Gudsharātī and English translation by Dastūr Peshotan (Vols. I to VI, Bombay, 1874–1891). Casartelli: Un traité pehlevi sur la médecine, Muséon (vol. 5, 1886. French transl. of §159 of Book III).

Books VIII and IX have been Englished by Edward William West: Contents of the Nasks in Sacred Books of the East (vol. 37, Oxford, 1892).

Criticism—E. W. West: Pahlavi literature, in W. Geiger and E. Kuhn's Grundriss der iranischen Philologie (vol. 2, 91–98, 1896–1904).

Among other Pahlawī texts of the same time, I must still quote the Shikand-gūmānīg vījār (Doubt-dispelling explanation)—a work of c. 16,700 words—because, according to West "it is the nearest approach to a philosophical treatise that remains extant in Pahlawī literature." It upholds Zoroastrianism against atheists, materialists, Jews, Christians, Muslims, and Manichaeans. It was written by Martān-farukh, probably in the second half of the ninth century, before the completion of the Dīnkart. The original Pahlawī text is lost, but we have a Pāzand-Sanskrit version made by Nēryōsang about the end of the twelfth century.

Text—Pāzand-Sanskrit texts edited by Hoṣhang and West (Bombay, 1887). English translation by West, in Sacred Books of the East (vol. 24, 115–251, Oxford, 1885).

Criticism—West, in Geiger and Kuhn's Grundriss (vol. 2, 106).

---

[d] Forming a total of about 141,000 words.

Muslim Theology

DĀ'ŪD AL-ẒĀHIRĪ

David the Literalist. Abū Sulaimān Dā'ūd ibn 'Alī ibn Khalaf al-Iṣfahānī. Born at Kūfa c. 815; flourished at Bagdad; died in 883–84. Muslim jurist. Formerly a Shāfi'īte, he founded an independent school of law, the madhhab al-ẓāhir. This law was based on the surface, the literal sense (ẓāhir), of the Qur'ān, on the ḥadīth, and on nothing else. It did not take any roots in the East, but had some success in the Maghrib and especially in Spain; it has now entirely vanished.

I. Goldziher: Die Ẓahiriten, ihr Lehrsystem und ihre Geschichte (Leipzig, 1884). C. Brockelmann: Arabische Litteratur (vol. 1, 183, 1898). D. B. Macdonald: Development of Muslim Theology (1903).

MUSLIM

Abū-l-Ḥusain Muslim ibn al-Ḥajjāj al-Qushairī al-Nīsābūrī. Born in 817–18 or 822–23; died in 875; buried in Naṣrābādh, suburb of Nīsābūr. Muslim traditionalist. He wrote a collection of traditions, called al-Ṣaḥīḥ, arranged according to the chapters of al-fiqh. It is more theoretical than Bukhārī's work and enjoys less reverence.

There are still four other such collections, all of the ninth century, which are authoritative, though less so than the two Ṣaḥīḥ. The six collections are canonical in the whole Sunnite world.

Text—I do not know any critical edition or translation of Muslim's Ṣaḥīḥ.

Criticism—Ignácz Goldziher: Muhammedanische Studien (vol. 2, 1–274, 1890). C. Brockelmann: Arabische Litteratur (vol. 1, 160–163, 1898).

DHŪ-L-NŪN

Abū-l-Fayḍ Thawbān ibn Ibrāhīm al-Ikhmīmī, al-Miṣrī, nicknamed Dhū-l-Nūn.[a] He originated from Nubia or from Ikhmīm in Upper Egypt; he died in 859–60. Muslim mystic and alchemist. An alchemical and magical treatise called Mujarrabāt is ascribed to him. In the Fihrist he is classified with the alchemists and Ibn al-Qifṭī brackets him with Jābir ibn Ḥaiyān. It is difficult, of course, to say where alchemy begins and where it ends: many Ṣūfīs were more or less alchemists in the same sense as many Chinese Taoists.

At any rate, Dhū-l-Nūn was chiefly famous as a mystic. He is considered by the Ṣūfīs as the originator of their doctrines—it would be more exact to say, of their mental attitude. Ṣūfīsm is the form which mysticism has taken in Islām. It is derived from Christianity, Neo-Platonism, Gnosticism, and Buddhism, all of these foreign elements being adjusted as well as possible in a Muslim frame. Mystic doctrines, everywhere, are essentially syncretic. The word ṣūfī is derived from ṣūf, wool, an allusion to their simple woollen clothing.

C. Brockelmann: Arabische Litteratur (vol. 1, 198, 1898). R. A. Nicholson: Literary History of the Arabs (386–390, 1907). E. G. Browne: Literary History of Persia (vol. 1, 416–444, 1908).

---

[a] Meaning "He of the Fish." (The same nickname is given in the Qur'ān to Jonah!)

Ismā'īlī Propaganda

About the year 864 the Ismā'īlīya,[f] a small sect of the Shī'a, distinguished from the others by its recognition of Muḥammad ibn Ismā'īl as the seventh, last, and perfect Imām and by its fondness for allegorical interpretations (ta'wīl), received a tremendous impetus from 'Abdallāh ibn Maymūn al-Qaddāḥ. This 'Abdallāh, son of Maymūn the oculist, born at Ahwāz in Khūzistān, of Persian race, died in 874–75. He flourished in various places, finally at Salamiyya (near Emessa), which became the center of his propaganda (see M. Th. Houtsma, in Encyl. of Islam, vol. 1, 26, 1908). Under his inspiration the sect became a secret organization fated to wield enormous material and spiritual power. Theirs was a mystical doctrine laying much stress on the correspondence between the microcosm and macrocosm, and the esoteric properties of the numbers seven and (to a less degree) twelve. This doctrine was spread far and wide, with uncanny adroitness, by enthusiastic missionaries (du'āt).[g]

One of the greatest du'āt during the last quarter of the century was Ḥamdān Qarmaṭ ibn al-Ash'ath who flourished near Kūfa.[h] He became the founder of a subsect called after him the Qarmaṭians, whose predatory activities culminated in the sack of Mecca and the stealing of the Black Stone in 930.

A grandson of 'Abdallāh ibn Maymūn and his third successor as head of the Ismā'īlīya, Sa'īd ibn al-Ḥusain,[i] was recognized as Imām (Mahdī) by the Berbers of the tribe of Ketāma in 909–10 and became the founder of the Fāṭimid[j] Empire, the new city of Mahdīya (near Tunis) being his capital. In 969, the Fāṭimids conquered Egypt, which remained in their power until 1171. Thus in less than two centuries the Ismā'īlī du'āt had built up an empire.

See E. G. Browne: Literary History of Persia (vol. 1, 391–415, 1908). Cl. Huart: Encycl. of Islam (vol. 2, 549–552, 1921. With bibliography and an account of the distribution of the Ismā'īlīya to-day). Louis Massignon: Esquisse d'une bibliographie qarmaṭe (Oriental Studies presented to E. G. Browne, 329–338, 1922; Isis, VI, 145).

See my notes on the Brethren of Purity (second half of tenth century) and on the Assassins (second half of the eleventh century).

RAL-PA-CHAN

Tibetan king who ruled in the latter half of the ninth century and completed the organization of Buddhist civilization in his country. Song-tsen Gam-po (q. v., first half of seventh century), Ti-song De-tsen (q. v., second half of the eighth century), and Ral-pa-chan are the three greatest figures of Tibetan history. The Tibetans call them "The Three Religious Kings, Men of Power." It is probable that a large part of the Kanjur and of the Tanjur (q. v., first half of the seventh century) were completed during this period, for we know that many Hindu teachers came then to Tibet to translate religious books. The introduction

---

[f] Also called "Sect of the Seven," Sab'īya; sect of the esoterics, Bāṭinīya, etc.

[g] Plural of dā'ī. The methods of the du'āt suggest comparison with those of the Jesuit propagandists in Christendom. They made converts not simply among Muslims but among Jews, Zoroastrians, and Christians.

[h] See Cl. Huart, in Enc. of Islam (vol. 2, 246, 1915).

[i] Sa'īd ibn al-Ḥūsain ibn 'Abdallāh ibn Maymūn al-Qaddāḥ was born in 873–74 at Salamiyya. In 909–10, he took the name Abū Muḥammad 'Ubaydallāh.

[j] Thus called because Sa'īd ibn al-Ḥusain claimed (apparently without right) to be a descendant of Fāṭima, the Prophet's daughter.

of standard weights and measures from India is also ascribed to Ral-pa-chan. The king was murdered c. 897 by his brother Lang-dar-ma, the so-called Julian of Lāmaism.

Lang-dar-ma succeeded Ral-pa-chan, persecuted the Lāmas, burned their books, etc., but was himself assassinated in the third year of his reign.

L. A. Waddell: Buddhism of Tibet (33–35, 1895. Giving a list of Hindu translators and of their Tibetan associates). Sir Charles Bell: Tibet (27–29, 1924).

III. PHILOSOPHICAL BACKGROUND. GREEK, LATIN, ENGLISH, SYRIAC, AND ARABIC WRITINGS

PHOTIOS

Φώτιος. Born c. 820, died 891? Byzantine scholar of great erudition. Patriarch of Constantinople. His most important book is the "Bibliotheca or Myriobiblon," finished before 857, containing 280 chapters, each of which is a "review" with long extracts of a separate volume (codex). Some of these chapters deal with physicians, physicists, lexicographers, though most of them are devoted to theologians and historians. A Greek lexicon was completed later, either by himself or under his direction.

Text and Translations—Complete works, in Migne's Patrologia graeca (vols. 101–105).

Myriobiblon sive Bibliotheca librorum quos Photius legit et recensuit. Graece edidit David Hoeschelius et notis illustravit, latine reddidit et scholiis auxit Andreas Schottus (Geneva, 1591; Rothomagi, 1653). Latest edition by Imm. Bekker (2 vols., 545 p., Berlin, 1824–25). English translation, by J. H. Freese (6 vols., London, 1920 ff.; the last volume will be devoted to an account of Photios's life and works).

The Lexicon (Λέξεων συναγωγή) was edited by G. Hermann (Leipzig, 1808); by Richard Porson (2 vols., 835 p., London, 1822); finally by S. A. Naber (2 vols., Leyde, 1864–65).

Criticism—Cardinal Joseph Hergenröther: Photius (3 vols., Regensburg, 1867–1869). K. Krumbacher: Byzantinische Litteratur (2. Aufl., 73–79, 515–524, 972, etc., 1897). Edgar Martini: Textgeschichte der Bibliotheke (1. Die Handschriften, Ausgaben und Übertragungen., 135 p., Sächs Ges. d. Wiss., philol. Kl., vol. 28, 6, Leipzig, 1911). Sandys: History of Classical Scholarship (vol. 1, 3d ed., p. 397 sq., 1921).

ERIGENA

Or Eriugena. John Scotus (Scottus) (improperly translated John the Scot). Of Irish origin. Born c. 800, died c. 877. Head of the court school (scola palatina) of Charles the Bald, in France, from c. 843. One of the most original philosophers of the Middle Ages. He attached far more importance to reason versus authority than the scholastics. He had a good knowledge of Greek, so much so that he was able to translate into Latin the works of the Pseudo-Dionysios and of Maximos Confessor. Yet he knew Plato only through Chalcidius's partial translation of the Timaeos. He was deeply influenced by St. Augustine. Under the influence of Chalcidius and Martianus Capella he extended the system of Heraclides to Mars and Jupiter (that is, he said that Jupiter, Mars, Venus, and Mercury circle incessantly around the sun), but this statement is accidental, for the rest of his astronomical knowledge is not at all on the same level. His main work, composed in 867, is the "De divisione naturae," the leading idea of which is the unity of nature, proceeding from God and ultimately resolved into Him.

Text and Translations—Complete works, edited by H. J. Floss, in Migne's Patrologia latina (vol. 122, Paris, 1853). De divisione naturae, edited by Thomas Gale (Oxford, 1681); then by C. B. Schlüter (640 p., Münster, 1838). German translation, Über die Eintheilung der Natur by Ludwig Noack (Berlin, 2 vols., 1870–1874. The study quoted below makes a third volume, 1876).

Criticism—Saint René Taillandier: Scot Erigène et la philosophie scolastique (Paris, 1843). Francis Monnier: De Gothescalci et Joannis Scotis controversia (Paris, 1853. On Gottschalk, see also Hrabanus). Theod. Christlieb: Leben und Lehre des John Scotus (Gotha, 1860). Karl Heinrich Meusel: Doctrinam Joannis Scoti quae continetur libris de divisione naturae cum christiana comparavit (32 p., Bautzen, 1869). Hugo Rähse: Joh. Scotus Stellung zur mittelalterlichen Scholastik und Mystik (Diss., 47 p., Rostock, 1874). L. Noack: Leben und Schriften des Joh. Scotus; die Wissenschaft und Bildung seiner Zeit (Leipzig, 1876). Theodor Wotschke: Fichte und Erigena (Diss., 72 p., Halle a. S., 1896). Alice Gardner: Studies in John the Scot (London, 1900). A. Schmitt: Zwei noch unbenützte Hdsch. des Erigena (Progr., 62 p., Bamberg, 1900. MSS. of the divisio naturae). George John Blewett: The Study of Nature and the Vision of God (Toronto, 1907). M. Manitius: Lateinische Literatur des Mittelalters (vol. 1, 323–339, 1911; vol. 2, 802–804). E. K. Rand: Autographa des Ioh. Scotus aus Ludwig Traube's Nachlass (Bayer. Akad. d. Wiss., philos. Classe, p. 1–12, 1912. Cfr. also by same, The Supposed Autograph of John the Scot. University of California publ. in Classical Philology, vol. 5, 135–141, Berkeley, 1920). Joh. Draeseke: Zu Erigena (Archiv für Gesch. d. Philosophie, vol. 27, 428–448, Berlin, 1914; Isis, II, 438). P. Duhem: Etudes sur Léonard de Vinci (vol. 2, 424–428, 1909. Erigena as a source of Cusanus); Système du monde (vol. 3, 44–62, 1915. Le système d'Héraclide au Moyen Age; vol. 5, 38–75, 1917. Scot Erigène et Avicébron). Paul Lehmann: Zur Kenntnis und Geschichte einiger Joh. Scottus zugeschiebener Werke (Hermes, vol. 52, 112–124, Berlin, 1917; Isis, IV, 134). Henry Bett: Erigena (Cambridge, 1925).

REMI D'AUXERRE

Remigius Antissiodorensis. Flourished in the second half of the ninth century, died 908. French[k] educator. Pupil of Hrabanus Maurus. Taught in St. Germain d'Auxerre, in Reims, and finally in Paris, the last school being the germ of the University of Paris. He wrote commentaries on the Bible, Donat, and Martianus Capella.

Text—Commento di Remigio d'Auxerre all' Aritmetica di Marziano Capella (Vaticana, "Regina Suecorum nº 1970"), with a long introduction by E. Narducci (Boncompagni's Bullettino, vol. 15, 505–580, Roma, 1882).

Criticism—E. K. Rand: Johannes Scottus (Quellen und Unters. zur latein. Philologie des Mittelalters, I, 2, München, 1906; Part II: Der Kommentar des Remigius zu den Opuscula sacra des Boethius). Karl Schutte: Das Verhältnis von Notkers Nuptiae Philologiae et Mercurii zum Kommentar des Remigius (119 p., Münster i. W., 1911).

ALFRED THE GREAT

Ælfred, born at Wantage, Berkshire, in 849; died in 901, buried at Winchester. King of the West Saxons. He defended Wessex, successfully, against the Scandinavian invasions and thus prepared the freedom and union of England. He promoted education and learning. He caused the English Chronicles to be edited and completed. He translated some of the works of St. Augustine, Orosius,

[k] I feel justified in calling him French because he flourished after the Treaty of Verdun, 843, and even after the final dismemberment of the Frankish states after 888.

Bede, Boetius, etc., into Anglo-Saxon. These were very free translations. For example, in his Orosius, some chapters are omitted, others are shortened, and there are many original interpolations of considerable interest. The most important of these deal with geographical subjects and are based upon reports obtained by the king himself.[l] Alfred may be called the greatest (Christian) geographer of his age. He gathered around him some of the best scholars of his time, for example, Erigena. His translations have also an immense literary importance; through them he did not simply teach his people, but he ennobled their language and encouraged them to use it. His greatest literary activity occurred between 886 and 893.

Texts and Translations—Whole works (Jubilee edition), with preliminary essays illustrative of the history, arts, and manners of the ninth century, edited by John Allen Giles (2 vols., London, 1858). A description of Europe and the voyages of Ohthere and Wulfstan. Anglo-Saxon text, with English translation and notes by Joseph Bosworth (London, 1855). G. F. Browne: King Alfred's Books (422 p., London, 1920. Description of Alfred's translations, with selected fragments in English). Many separate editions exist; I have quoted a few of them under the names of the translated authors.

Biographical and General Studies—Asser's (d. 909?) Life of Alfred, together with the annals of St. Neots erroneously ascribed to Asser, edited with notes by Will. Henry Stevenson (517 p., Oxford, 1904). Other edition of Asser's life by L. C. Lane (King's classics) (222 p., London, 1908). Article by E. A. Freeman, in Dictionary of National Biography (vol. 1, 153–162, 1885). Alfred Bowker: Alfred; Chapters on his Life and Times by Various Authors (272 p., London, 1899). Edward Conybeare: Alfred in the Chroniclers (246 p., London, 1900). J. C. Wall: Alfred; his Abbeys of Hyde, Athelney, and Shaftesbury (176 p., London, 1900). Of the many millenary publications which appeared in 1901, I shall quote only: Sir Walter Besant: The Story of King Alfred (187 p., New York, 1901). George F. Bosworth: Alfred, his Life and Times (London, 1901). Warwick H. Draper: Alfred, a Sketch and Seven Studies (158 p., London, 1901). Frederic Harrison: The Writings of King Alfred (New York, 1901). And last, but not least, Charles Plummer: Life and Times of Alfred the Great (244 p., Oxford, 1902).

Special Studies—Milton Haight Turk: The Legal Code of Aelfred (edited with notes, 60 p., Halle, 1890). Heinrich Geidel: Alfred als Geograph (Münch. geograph. Studien, 15, 105 p., 1904). Max Manitius: Lateinische Literatur des Mittelalters (vol. 2, 646–656, 1923. Asser and Alfred). E. D. Laborde: Alfred's System of Geographical Description in his Version of Orosius (Geographical Journal, vol. 62, 133–138, 1923; Isis, VI, 145).

MOSES BAR KĒPHĀ

Born at Balad c. 813; assumed the monastic habit at the neighboring convent of Mār Sergios on the Ṭūrā Ṣahyā;[m] ordained bishop c. 863 under the name of Severos; died in 903; buried at the convent of Mār Sergios. Syriac Jacobite commentator and theologian. Among his many works we may quote commentaries on the whole Bible, a treatise on the Hexaëmeron, a commentary on the dialectics of Aristotle, an ecclesiastical history.

Text—Fragment of the Hexaëmeron translated by François Nau in his Bardesane l'astrologue (Le livre des lois des pays, Paris, 1899. With a circular map).

See my note on George, Bishop of the Arabs, second half of seventh century.

---

[l] See my notes on Ohthere and Wulfstan.

[m] Dry Mountain.

Criticism—Wm. Wright: Syriac Literature (1894). R. Duval: Littérature syriaque (1907). Anton Baumstark: Geschichte der Syrischen Literatur (281, 1922).

Muslim Philosophy

AL-JĀḤIẒ

Abū 'Uthmān 'Amr ibn Baḥr al-Jāḥiẓ, i. e., the goggle-eyed. Flourished in Baṣra and died there in 868–69, being more than ninety Muslim years old. One of the Mu'tazilite leaders in Baṣra, the founder of a sect named after him (al-Jāḥiẓīya). Man of letters, with a genuine interest in the natural and anthropological sciences. His most important work is the Book of Animals (Kitāb al-ḥayawān), a very discursive compilation, the purpose of which is theological and folkloric rather than scientific, but which is nevertheless of great interest to the student of Arabic science and culture. Though partly based on Greek knowledge (chiefly Aristotle), it is intensely Arabic, which explains its great influence upon Arabic literature. Al-Jāḥiẓ knew how to obtain ammonia (and salmiac) from animal offals by dry distillation. His work contains the germs of many later theories (evolution, adaptation, animal psychology).

Texts and Translations—The Kitāb al-ḥayawān was published in Cairo 1323–24 H. A collection of 11 treatises entitled Majmū'at rasā'il, also appeared in Cairo (1324 H). Le Livre des Avares, Texte arabe, publié d'après le manuscrit unique de Constantinople par G. van Vloten (Leyde, 1900).

Criticism—Wüstenfeld: Geschichte der arabischen Aerzte (25–26, 1840). L. Leclerc: Histoire de la médecine arabe (Vol. I, 315, 1876). G. van Vloten: Les Hachwia et Nabita (Actes du XIe congrès international des Orientalistes (3e section, 99–125, Paris, 1897. Contains the text of a theological treatise of al-Jāḥiẓ). C. Brockelmann: Arabische Litteratur (vol. 1, 152–153, 1898). E. Wiedemann: Zur Physik bei den Arabern (Jahrb. für Photographie, 20, 77–81, 1906); Darwinistisches bei Jāḥiẓ. (Beiträge, XLVI, 130–131, 1915). Article in Encycl. of Islam, I, 1000, 1912, unsigned, G. van Vloten?). G. van Vloten: Ein arabischer Naturphilosoph im 9. Jahrhundert (47 p., Stuttgart, 1918. The most comprehensive study available; see Isis, IV, 400). Carra de Vaux: Les penseurs de l'Islam (Vol. 1, 293–310, 1921; vol. 2, 352–353, 1921. Geological questions). Hartwig Hirschfeld: A Volume of Essays by al-Jāḥiẓ. Oriental Studies Presented to E. G. Browne (200–209, 1922).

AL-SARAKHSĪ

Abū-l-'Abbās Aḥmad ibn Muḥammad ibn al-Ṭaiyib al-Sarakhsī Tilmīdh al-Kindī. The last three words mean disciple of al-Kindī; he was indeed al-Kindī's greatest disciple. Tutor and later adviser to al-Mu'taḍid, caliph from 892 to 902; executed in 899–900. Muslim philosopher. He wrote a large number of works on many subjects, but none is apparently extant.

F. Wüstenfeld: Arabische Aerzte (33, 1840). L. Leclerc: Médecine arabe (vol. 1, 294–296, 1876. Includes a list of the writings ascribed to al-Sarakhsī). C. Brockelmann: Arabische Litteratur (vol. 1, 210, 1898).

IV. ARABIC AND LATIN MATHEMATICS AND ASTRONOMY

Arabic Mathematics and Astronomy

AL-MĀHĀNĪ

Abū 'Abdallāh Muḥammad ibn 'Īsā al-Māhānī, that is, from Māhān, Kirmān, Persia. Flourished c. 860, died c. 874 to 884. Mathematician, astronomer.

A series of observations of lunar and solar eclipses and planetary conjunctions, made by him from 853 to 866, was used by Ibn Yūnus. He wrote commentaries on Euclid and Archimedes, and improved Isḥāq ibn Ḥunain's translation of Menelaos's spherics. He tried vainly to solve an Archimedean problem: to divide a sphere by means of a plane into two segments being in a given ratio. That problem led to a cubic equation, $x^3 + c^2b = cx^2$, which Muslim writers called al-Māhānī's equation.

H. Suter: Die Mathematiker und Astronomen der Araber (26, 1900. His failure to solve the Archimedian problem is quoted by 'Umar al-Khayyāmī). See Fr. Woepcke: L'algèbre d'Omar Alkhayyāmī (2, 96 sq., Paris, 1851).

HILĀL AL-ḤIMṢĪ

Hilāl ibn abī Hilāl al-Ḥimṣī. From Emessa in Syria, died c. 883. Translated the first four books of Apollonios into Arabic for Aḥmad ibn Mūsā ibn Shākir.[n]

H. Suter: Die Mathematiker und Astronomen der Araber (p. 27, 1900).

AḤMAD IBN YŪSUF

Abū Ja'far Aḥmad ibn Yūsuf ibn Ibrāhīm ibn al-Dāya al Miṣrī, i. e., the Egyptian. Flourished in Egypt in the second half and died about the end of the third century H., c. 912. Mathematician. Secretary of the Ṭūlūnids, who ruled in Egypt from 868 to 905. He wrote a book on similar arcs (De similibus arcubus), a commentary on Ptolemy's Centiloquium, and a book on proportions ("De proportione et proportionalitate"). The latter book is important because it influenced mediaeval thought through Leonardo da Pisa and Jordanus Nemorarius (theorem of Menelaos about the triangle cut by a transversal; al-qaṭṭā', sector; hence figura cata, regula catta).

Texts and Translations—The Liber Hameti de proportione et proportionalitate and the Liber de arcubus similibus were translated by Gherardo Cremonese. The translation of the commentary on the Centiloquium was possibly made by Plato Tiburtinus; it was ascribed by the translator to 'Alī ibn Riḍwān. First printed Venice, 1493. ("Incipit liber centum verborum ptholemei cum commento haly.") Aḥmad, or else his father Yūsuf ibn Ibrāhīm ibn al-Dāya, may be the author of the History of the Astronomers, ascribed to one Ibn al-Dāya.

Criticism—M. Cantor: Ahmed und sein Buch über die Proportionen (Bibliotheca Mathematica, 7–9, 1888). M. Steinschneider: Iusuf ben Ibrahim und Ahmed ben Iusuf (*ibidem*, 49–52, 111–117). M. Curtze: Über den "liber de similibus arcubus" (*ibidem*, 15, 1889). Suter: Die Mathematiker und Astronomen der Araber (42–43, 1900); Nachträge (163, 1902). C. Brockelmann: Arabische Litteratur (1, 149, 222, 1898). H. Bürger und K. Kohl: Zur Geschichte des Transversalsatzes usw. (Abhdl. zur Gesch. d. Naturwiss., 7, 47–49, 80, 1924; Isis, VIII, 799).

Brockelmann, Bürger, and Kohl, following Ibn Khallikān, seem to confuse this Aḥmad ibn Yūsuf with another one who wrote a biography of Aḥmad ibn Ṭūlūn and died in 945–46? This matter requires elucidation.

AL-NAIRĪZĪ

Latin name: Anaritius. Abū-l-'Abbās al-Faḍl ibn Ḥātim al-Nairīzī (i. e., from Nairīz, near Shīrāz). Flourished under al-Mu'taḍid, caliph from 892 to

---

[n] See my note on the Banū Mūsā (first half of the ninth century). For other translations of Apollonios, see Thābit ibn Qurra and also Abū-l-Fatḥ al-Iṣfahānī (second half of tenth century).

902, died c. 922. Astronomer, mathematician. He compiled astronomical tables and wrote for al-Mu'taḍid a book on atmospheric phenomena. He wrote commentaries on Ptolemy and Euclid. The latter were translated by Gherardo da Cremona. Al-Nairīzī used the so-called umbra (versa), the equivalent of the tangent, as a genuine trigonometric line (but he was anticipated in this by Ḥabash, q. v., first half of ninth century). He wrote a treatise on the spherical astrolabe, which is very elaborate and seems to be the best Arabic work on the subject. It is divided into four books: (1) Historical and critical introduction; (2) description of the spherical astrolabe; its superiority over plane astrolabes and all other astronomical instruments; (3 and 4) applications.

Texts and Translations—Codex Leidensis 399, 1. Euclidis elementa ex interpretatione al-Hadschdschadschii cum commentariis al-Nazirii. Arabice et latine ediderunt R. O. Besthorn et J. L. Heiberg (Copenhagen, 1893 sq. See my note on al-Ḥajjāj in preceding chapter). Anaritii in decem libros priores Elementorum Euclidis commentarii ex interpretatione Gherardi Cremonensis in codice Cracoviensi 569 servata edidit M. Curtze (420 p., Leipzig, 1899. Supplement to Heiberg and Menge's edition of Euclid, 1883–1916). C. Schoy: Abhandlung von al-Nairīzī über die Richtung der Qibla übersetzt und erläutert (Sitzungsber. der bayer. Akad. der Wiss., math. Kl., 55–68, 1922. Together with a table compiled by Ibn al-Shāṭir—1304–1375—giving the longitude, latitude, and inḥirāf of the qibla for about a hundred places; Isis, V, 209).

Criticism—H. Suter: Die Mathematiker und Astronomen der Araber (45, 1900); Nachträge (164, 1902). P. Mansion: Sur le commentaire d'Anaritius relatif auz éléments d'Euclide (Annales de la société scientifique, vol. 24, 47–49, Bruxelles, 1900). H. Suter: Zur Frage des von Nairizi zitierten Mathematikers Diachasimus (Bibliotheca Mathematica, vol. 7, 396, 1907). Hugo Seemann und Th. Mittelberger: Das Kugelförmige Astrolab (Abhdl. zur Gesch. d. Naturw., 8, 32–40, 1915. Analysis of the treatise on the astrolabe; Isis, VIII, 743).

THĀBIT IBN QURRA

Abū-l-Ḥasan Thābit ibn Qurra ibn Marwān al-Ḥarrānī, that is, from Harrān, Mesopotamia, born 826–27 (or 835–36), flourished in Bagdad, died in 901. Ḥarrānian[o] physician, mathematician, astronomer. One of the greatest translators from Greek and Syriac into Arabic; the founder of a school of translators, of which many of his own family were members. Apollonios (Books 5 to 7), Archimedes, Euclid, Theodosios, Ptolemy (geography), Galen, Eutocios were translated by him or under his direction, or translations made by others (e. g., Isḥāq ibn Ḥunain) were revised by him. He published solar observations, explaining his methods. To the eight Ptolemaic spheres he added a ninth one (primum mobile) to account for the imaginary trepidation of the equinoxes (he is chiefly responsible for the introduction of this erroneous theory). His mensurations of parabolas and paraboloids are very remarkable. He improved the theory of amicable numbers (if $p = 3.2^n - 1$; $q = 3.2^{n-1} - 1$; $r = 9.2^{2n-1} - 1$; and if p, q, and r are prime together, $2^n pq$ and $2^n r$ are amicable numbers). Many mathematical, astronom-

[o] I say Ḥarrānian, not Sabian. See Daniil A. Khvolson. Die Ssabier und Ssabismus (2 vols., St. Petersburg, 1856), or more simply R. A. Nicholson's article on Sabians in 11th ed. of Encyc. Brit., or E. G. Browne. Literary History of Persia (vol. 1, 301–304, 1908). The people of Ḥarrān (Ἑλληνόπολις), though they spoke Syriac, were opposed to Christianity; they were deeply attached to Greek culture, especially to the Neo-Platonic philosophy. However, Thābit's sympathies were with the Arabs and he was expelled from his own sect, thus he was a Ḥarrānian without being a Sabian (see Isis, VIII, 345).

ical, also anatomical and medical, writings are ascribed to him (most of them in Arabic, some in Syriac).

Texts and Translations—Eilhard Wiedemann: Die Schrift über den Qarasṭūn (Bibliotheca Mathematica, vol. 12, 21–39, 1912. German translation of a text, Latin versions of which were among the most popular mediaeval writings on mechanics). H. Suter: Über die Ausmessung der Parabel von Thābit (Sitzungsber. d. physik. mediz. Sozietät, vol. 48, 65–86, Erlangen, 1918; Isis, IV, 400); Die Abhandlungen Thābits und Abū Sahl al-Kūhīs über die Ausmessung der Paraboloide (*ibidem*, 186–227; Isis, IV, 400; these two texts are very important; they give one a very high opinion of Thābit's mathematical talent). F. Buchner: Die Schrift über den Qarasṭûn (Sitzungsber. der phys. med. Sozietät., vol. 52, 141–188, Erlangen, 1921. Important; Isis V, 494). E. Wiedemann und J. Frank: Über die Konstruktion der Schattenlinien auf horizontalen Sonnenuhren von Thābit ben Qurra (Det Kgl. Danske videnskabernes selskab, math. medd., IV, 9, 24 p., 1922; Isis, V, 209). Axel A. Björnbo: Thābits Werk über den Transversalensatz. Erlangen 1924. (Text of the Latin translation by Gherardo Cremonese, with German version and notes by H. Suter; Isis, VIII, 737). C. Schoy: Graeco-arabische Studien (Isis, VIII, 35–40, 1926; translation of an Archimedian treatise on the regular heptagon).

Criticism—Fihrist (272, and comment. by index). F. Wüstenfeld: Geschichte der arabischen Aerzte (34–36, 1840. Followed by notices on other members of the same family). Fr. Woepcke: Notice sur une théorie ajoutée par Thābit à l'arithmétique spéculative des Grecs (Journal Asiatique, Vol. 20, 420–429, 1852). L. Leclerc: Histoire de la médecine arabe (vol. 1, 168–172, 1876). H. Suter: Die Mathematiker und Astronomen der Araber (34–38, 1900; Nachträge, 162–163, 1902). P. Duhem: Les origines de la statique (vol. 1, 79–92, 1905. On the liber charastonis). Dreyer: Planetary Systems (276, 1906. Excellent account of the trepidation of the equinoxes). E. Wiedemann: Über die Hebelgesetze bei den Muslimen (Archiv f. Gesch. d. Naturw., vol. 1, 211–213, 1909). C. Pruefer und M. Meyerhof: Die angebliche Augenheilkunde des Thābit (Centralbl. f. Augenheilkunde, vol. 35, 1911. This book on the eye and vision is a later production; see Mit. zur Gesch. d. Medizin, vol. 10, 491). Duhem: Système du monde (vol. 2, 117–119, 238–246, 1914). Lynn Thorndike: Some Mediaeval Conceptions of Magic (The Monist, vol. 25, 107–140 (p. 133), 1915). L. E. Dickson: History of the Theory of Numbers (vol. 1, p. 5, 36, Washington, 1919). E. Wiedemann: Über Thābit, sein Leben und Wirken (Sitzungsberichte der physik. mediz. Soz., vol. 52, 189–219, Erlangen, 1922; Isis, V, 495).

YŪSUF AL-KHŪRĪ

Joseph the Priest. Also called Yūsuf al-Qass (same meaning) or al-Sāhir (the vigilant). He was still living under the caliphate of al-Muqtafī (902 to 908). Physician and mathematician. Translator from Syriac into Arabic. He translated Archimedes's lost work on the triangles and Galen's "De simplicium temperamentis et facultatibus." That first translation was revised by Sinān ibn Thābit ibn Qurra (q. v., first half of tenth century), the second by Ḥunain ibn Isḥāq.

H. Suter: Die Mathematiker der Araber (52, 224, 1900). Max Meyerhof: New Light on Ḥunain ibn Isḥāq (Isis, VIII, 704, 1926).

ISḤĀQ IBN ḤUNAIN

Abu Ya'qūb Isḥāq ibn Ḥunain ibn Isḥāq al-'Ibādī. Died in Bagdad 910–11. Son of Ḥunain ibn Isḥāq and the most important of the translators who worked under him. Physician, mathematician. Translations of Aristotle, Euclid, Ptolemy (the "Almagest"), Menelaos, Archimedes, Autolycos, Hypsicles, and of the pseudo-Aristotelian "De plantis" are ascribed to him. Some of those translations were improved or completed by Thābit ibn Qurra. Medical writings are also ascribed to him; e. g., his father credits him with the translation of two Galenic works into Syriac and of ten into Arabic and remarks that Isḥāq sometimes collated the Arabic translation and the Greek text.

Text and Translations—Aristotelis categoriae cum versione arabica Isaaci Honeini et variis lectionibus textus graeci e versione arab. ductis a. J. Th. Zenker (Leipzig, 1846). The "Liber Euclidis Pythagoraei. Interpretatio Ishak ibn Hunaini. Commentaria Abul-Abbas al-Narizii"—an Arabic manuscript of Leiden (399, 1), edited with a Latin translation by R. O. Besthorn and J. L. Heiberg (Copenhagen, 1893, etc.). It is not, in spite of its title, Isḥāq's translation, but an earlier one by al-Ḥajjāj ibn Yūsuf (q. v., first half of ninth century).

Criticism—Fihrist (pp. 285, 298, and by index). F. Wüstenfeld: Geschichte der arabischen Aerzte (29, 1840). L. Leclerc: Histoire de la médecine arabe (Vol. I, 152–153, 1876). H. Suter: Die Mathematiker und Astronomen der Araber (39, 1900); Encyclopaedia of Islam (vol. 2, 533, 1921). R. P. Bouyges (S. J.): Sur le De plantis d'Aristote-Nicolas à propos d'un manuscrit arabe de Constantinople (Mélanges de l'Université Saint Joseph, vol. 9, 71–89, Beyrouth, 1924; Isis, VIII, 531).

Diffusion of Hindu Numerals

In my note on Muḥammad ibn Ibrāhīm al-Fazārī (second half, eighth century), I suggested that his translation of the Hindu tables included in the Siddhānta was probably the vehicle by means of which the Hindu numerals were introduced into Islām. The tables of al-Khwārizmī and the earliest tables of Ḥabash were based upon al-Fazārī's translation, and probably they diffused the knowledge of the numerals. About 825 appeared the Arabic original of the "Algoritmi de numero Indorum." The earliest Muslim documents containing Hindu numerals are dated 874 and 888; the earliest Muslim zero known is the dot[p] in a manuscript dated 873. The earliest Hindu example of a zero is an inscription of 876 at Gwalior (numbers 50, 270). (Smith and Karpinski: The Hindu-Arabic numerals, 52, 56, 138, 1911; containing references for the dates 873, 874, 876, and 888, above quoted. Notice that the dates 873 and 874 involve a contradiction).

For the diffusion of Hindu numerals outside of Islām, one should bear in mind the intense activity of Muslim traders in the ninth century (see my note on Sulaimān, first half of ninth century). The destruction of Canton in 878 directed Muslim activity into other directions, possibly to some extent westward. Smith and Karpinski (op. cit.) have collected many other examples of relations between East and West in that time.

Ḥāmid ibn 'Alī

Abū-l-Rabī' Ḥāmid ibn 'Alī al-Wāsiṭī. From Wāsiṭ in Lower Mesopotamia. Flourished in the ninth century, probably toward the end. Muslim astronomer. According to Ibn Yūnus, 'Alī ibn 'Īsā and Ḥāmid were the foremost constructors of astrolabes. Ibn Yūnus compares them to Ptolemy and Galen! This proves the importance which Muslims attached to good instruments.

H. Suter: Mathematiker (40, 1900).

---

[p] The Arabic zero has remained a dot to this day.

QUSṬĀ IBN LŪQĀ

Qusṭā ibn Lūqā al-Ba'labakkī, i. e., from Baalbek or Heliopolis, Syria. Flourished in Bagdad, died in Armenia about the end of the third century H., i. e., c. 912. A Christian of Greek origin.[q] Physician, philosopher, astronomer, mathematician. Translations of Diophantos, Theodosios, Autolycos, Hypsicles, Aristarchos, Heron were made or revised by him, or made under his direction. He wrote commentaries on Euclid and a treatise on the spherical astrolabe.

Texts and Translations—The book on the use of the spherical astrolabe was translated into Latin, De sphera solida, by Stephanus Arnaldus, and into Spanish, Libro de la fayçon dell'espera e de sus figuras e de sus huebras di Cozta el Sabio. The latter translation is published in the Libros del saber de astronomia (vol. 1, p. 153–208). There is also a Hebrew translation of the same text.

Baron Carra de Vaux: Les mécaniques ou l'élévateur de Héron d'Alexandrie publiées pour la première fois sur la version arabe de Qostā ibn Lūqā et traduites en français (Journal Asiatique, 9e serie, Vol. I, 386–472; Vol. II, 152–269, 420–514, Paris, 1893). The same text is edited by L. Nix in volume 2 of Heronis Opera omnia (Leipzig, 1900).

Criticism—Fihrist (295 and by index). C. Brockelmann: Geschichte der arabischen Litteratur (Vol. I, 204–205, 512, 1898). H. Suter: Die Mathematiker und die Astronomen der Araber (40–42, 1900); Nachträge (163, 1902). L. Leclerc: Histoire de la médecine arabe (Vol. I, 157–159, 1876). H. Suter: Die Abhandlung Qosṭās und zwei andere Anonyme über die Rechnung mit zwei Fehlern und mit der angenommenen Zahl (Bibliotheca Mathematica, vol. 9, 111–122, 1908). Giuseppe Gabrieli: Nota biobibliografica su Qusṭā (Rendiconti d. Accademia d. Lincei, classe d. sci. mor., vol. 21, 341–382, Roma, 1912. Important). Hugo Seeman und Th. Mittelberger: Das Kugelförmige Astrolab. (Abhdl. zur Geschichte der Naturwiss., 8, 46–49, 1925; Isis, VIII, 743. Qusṭā's treatise on the spherical astrolabe is the earliest of its kind, but its genuineness is not certain).

I quote the following work for the sake of curiosity: William Butler Yeats: A Vision. An Explanation of Life Founded upon the Writings of Giraldus and upon Certain Doctrines Ascribed to Kusta ben Luka (270 p., London, 1925).

JĀBIR IBN SINĀN

Jābir ibn Sinān al-Ḥarrānī is one of the makers of astronomical instruments mentioned in the Fihrist at the end of the mathematical section. Nothing else is said of him, but al-Battānī's full name suggests that this Jābir may have been his father. According to al-Bīrūnī, this Jābir was the first to make a spherical astrolabe.

Fihrist (p. 284); Suter's translation (p. 41). H. Suter: Die Mathematiker (68, 224, 1900). Hugo Seemann und Th. Mittelberger: Das Kugelförmige Astrolab (5, 43, Erlangen, 1925; Isis, VIII, 743).

AL-BATTĀNĪ

In Latin, Albategnius, Albatenius. The origin of that nisba is unknown. Abū 'Abdallāh Muḥammad ibn Jābir ibn Sinān al-Battānī, al-Ḥarrānī, al-Ṣābi', born before 858 in or near Ḥarrān. Flourished at al-Raqqa, on the Euphrates, died in 929 near Sāmarrā. Of Sabian origin, though himself a Muslim. The greatest astronomer of his race and time and one of the greatest of Islām. Various astro-

---

[q] The name Qusṭā is exceedingly rare in Arabic; it is probably a Syriac corruption of the Byzantine name Constans or Constantine.

logical writings, including a commentary on Ptolemy's "Tetrabiblon," are ascribed to him, but his main work is an astronomical treatise with tables ("De scientia stellarum," "De numeris stellarum et motibus"), which was extremely influential until the Renaissance. He made astronomical observations of remarkable range and accuracy from 877 on. His tables contain a catalogue of fixed stars for the years 880–81 (not 911–12). He found that the longitude of the sun's apogee had increased by 16° 47′ since Ptolemy; that implied the discovery of the motion of the solar apsides and of a slow variation in the equation of time. He determined many astronomical coefficients with great accuracy: Precession, 54.5″ a year; inclination of the ecliptic, 23° 35′.[r] He proved the possibility of annular eclipses of the sun. He did not believe in the trepidation of the equinoxes. (Copernicus believed in it!)

The third chapter of his astronomy is devoted to trigonometry. He used sines regularly with a clear consciousness of their superiority over the Greek chords. He completed the introduction of the functions umbra extensa and umbra versa (whence our cotangents and tangents) and gave a table of cotangents by degrees. He knew the relation between the sides and angles of a spherical triangle which we express by the formula[s] $\cos a = \cos b \cos c + \sin b \sin c \cos A$.

Text and Translations—Al-Battānī's astronomical work was translated into Latin in the twelfth century by Robert of Chester (lost) and by Plato of Tivoli. A translation from the Arabic into Spanish was made by order of Alphonso X a century later. Plato's translation was published in Nürnberg (1537), together with al-Farghānī's elements. Albategnius de motu stellarum ex observationibus tum propriis tum Ptolemaei, omnia cum demonstrationibus geometricis et additionibus Ioannis de Regiomonte. (Nürnberg, 1537).

Nallino has published a monumental edition of the Arabic text, from an Escorial manuscript, with a Latin translation: al-Battānī sive Albatenii Opus Astronomicum. Arabice editum, Latine versum, adnotationibus instructum a C. A. Nallino (3 vols., Milano, 1899–1907. Publ. d. R. Osservatorio di Brera).

Criticism—H. Suter: Die Mathematiker und Astronomen der Araber (45–47, 1900); Nachträge (164, 1902). C. A. Nallino, in Encycl. of Islam (I, 680, 1911). Duhem: Système du Monde (II, 230–233, 1914).

ABŪ BAKR

In Latin: Albubather. Abū Bakr al-Ḥasan ibn al-Khaṣīb. Of Persian origin. Flourished probably in the third quarter of the ninth century. Astrologer who wrote in Persian and Arabic and would hardly deserve to be quoted but for the importance given to him in the Middle Ages. The work he is best known by ("De nativitatibus") was translated into Latin by one canonicus Salio in Padua 1218; it was also translated into Hebrew.

Texts and Translations—The De nativitatibus was first published in Venice (1492; 1501) I have seen a later edition (Nürnberg, 1540), entitled: Liber genethliacus sive de nativitatibus.

Criticism—Fihrist (p. 276 and Commentary, p. 131). H. Suter: Die Mathematiker und Astronomen der Araber (32, 1900); Nachträge (162, 1902); Encycl. of Islam, II, 274, 1916.

For Ibn Qutaiba, see my note in Section VIII, below.

---

[r] Newcomb gives the value 23° 34′ 54″ for the year 900.

[s] Of course there are no equations, algebraic or trigonometric, in his work.

Latin Astronomy

See my note on Erigena, in Section III, above.

V. MUSLIM ALCHEMY AND PHYSICS; CHINESE TECHNOLOGY

Muslim Alchemy

See my notes on Dhū-l-Nūn in Section II; on al-Jāḥiẓ, in Section III; on al-Rāzī, in Section VII.

Muslim Physics

See my note on al-Rāzī, in Section VII and on al-Nairīzī, in Section IV.

Chinese Technology; the First Printed Book

The earliest printed book extant is a copy of a Chinese translation of the Diamond Sūtra, printed on May 11, 868, by the care and probably at the expense of Wang[2] Chieh[4] (12493, 1521), for free distribution. It consists of six sheets of text, each 2½ feet long by nearly a foot wide, and one shorter sheet with woodcut, all neatly pasted together to form one continuous roll, 16 feet long. It is thus not by any means a small volume and it shows an advanced technique which implies a long evolution; it is distinctly superior to the early European block prints.[t]

It was discovered by Sir Aurel Stein in 1907 in the "Caves of the Thousand Buddhas," Ch'ien[1] fo[2*] tung[4] (1725, 3589, 12266), at Tung-huang in Kansu (eastern Turkestan), and is now preserved in the British Museum.

The Cave of Tun-huang contained about 15,000 or more books, all written on paper; a large part was selected in 1907 by Sir Aurel Stein to be brought to London and an equally large part was selected the following year by Paul Pelliot to be brought to Paris. There is only one ninth-century document which is dated, the Diamond sūtra of 868; the dates of other documents range from 947 to 983. Tun-huang was an outpost of Chinese culture on the great trade route to the west. Its international importance is shown by the fact that the literature discovered in that famous cave is not simply Chinese; it includes books written in the following languages: Tibetan, Sanskrit, Sogdian, Eastern Iranian, Uighur (Turkish), and even Hebrew.

The Diamond sūtra, Prajñāpāramitā; in Chinese Chin[1]-kang[1] ching[1] (2032, 5895, 2122) was translated into Chinese by Kumārajīva (q. v., first half of fifth century) and again by Hsüan Tsang (q. v., first half of seventh century). The edition of 868 is a copy of Kumārajīva's translation, while, by a strange coincidence, the oldest printed book from Japan (of certain date) is a portion of Hsüan Tsang's translation (1157). The popularity of this sūtra is further attested by the fact that the finest printed book found at Turfan, the Manichean Uighur center, is a Sanskrit edition of it in Lantsa script (c. thirteenth century) and that a third Chinese version of it was found by P. K. Kozlov at Kara-Khoto, Mongolia, in an edition printed in Shensi, dated May 15, 1016, this being the second book in age among those clearly dated. The Kara-Khoto find also contains a Diamond sūtra printed in 1189 by order of the Tangut empress. (There is an English translation of the Diamond sūtra by William Gemmell, London, 1912).

---

[t] See my notes on technology in the second half of the sixth century, on Ming Huang (first half of the eighth century) and Shōtoku-tennō (second half of eighth century)

The earliest clear reference to block printing in Chinese literature is an account of printed books seen by the official Liu[2] Pin (7251, ?)[u] in the province of Szechuen in 883. This tallies well with the date of the earliest Diamond sūtra; it is probable that the latter was printed in a more central part of China. The important point to remember is that this early Chinese printing was almost exclusively Buddhist and Taoist; it was meant for popular consumption and seems to have been despised by the literati, even as western typography was at first despised by the Italian humanists. As late as 932, the art of printing was apparently still confined to two localities, of which Szechuen was one. But then the invention suddenly received such amplification that the man responsible for this became known to posterity as the inventor.[v]

Thomas Francis Carter: Invention of Printing in China (1925. Main documents quoted; Isis, VIII, 365).

VI. FRENCH AND SCANDINAVIAN TRAVEL AND EXPLORATION; ENGLISH AND MUSLIM GEOGRAPHY

BERNARD THE WISE

Bernardus monachus francus. Originated from Brittany or Champagne. Flourished c. 866 to 870. French monk who visited Egypt and Palestine c. 869. He gave a very brief but very interesting account of his journey (nobilissima bibliotheca founded at Jerusalem by Charlemagne for the pilgrims; churches, monasteries; relations between Christians and Muslims).

Text—First edition by Mabillon in 1672, reprinted in Migne's Patrology (vol. 121, 569–574). Francisque Michel: Voyage de Bernard et de ses compagnons (Mémoires de la société de géographie, vol. 4, 781–815, Paris, 1839). Titus Tobler: Descriptiones Terrae Sanctae (392–402, 1874). T. Tobler and A. Molinier: Itinera Hierosolymitana (vol. 1, 307–320, 1880).

English translation by Thomas Wright: Early Travels in Palestine (22–31, London, 1848). Also by J. H. Bernard: The Itinerary of Bernard. How the City of Jerusalem is Situated (Palestine Pilgrims' Text Soc., 23, 14 p., London, 1893).

Criticism—C. Raymond Beazley: Dawn of Modern Geography (vol. 1, 166–74, etc., 1897).

Discovery of Iceland

The discovery of Iceland by Irish monks in 795, reported by Dicuil (q. v., first half of ninth century), did not bear any lasting fruits. The island was probably re-discovered by Vikings in the second half of the ninth century, c. 860 to 870. Icelandic traditions are uncertain on this point. The discovery is ascribed to Naddodd the Viking and also (with greater probability) to a Dane of Swedish kin named Gardar Svavarsson. The island was called Gardarsholm (Snowland). Whatever Naddodd did, Gardar seems to have been the first man to circumnavigate Iceland and to become more closely acquainted with it. A third voyage is supposed to have been made during the same period by a Viking named Floki Vilgerdarson, who came to Iceland from Rogaland via the Shetland and Faroe Islands. These accounts are legendary but plausible, for it is highly probable that Iceland was discovered by various sailors before the beginning of

---

[u] The second word is not found in Giles's Dictionary; the Chinese character is given by Carter.

[v] See my note on Fêng Tao (first half of tenth century).

its permanent settlement by Norwegians. This settlement is supposed to have begun c. 874, when Ingolf Arnarson established himself at Reykjavik.

Fridtjof Nansen: In Northern Mists (vol. 1, 255–257, 263, 1911).

For Alfred the Great, see my note in Section III, above.

OHTHERE

Also: Othere, Othar, Ottar. Lived in northern Norway, possibly in the Lofoten Islands, and later, c. 878 or c. 886, entered the service of Alfred the Great. Scandinavian (Norwegian) explorer who undertook two journeys: one along the coast of Norway northward, in the course of which he passed the North Cape (in lat. c. 71°) and discovered the Polar (or Barents) Sea, the White Sea, and the mouth of the Dwina (present Arkhangelsk).[w] The second journey, less important, took him southwards along the same coast to the fjord of Oslo and thence to Heidaby, or Sleswick, "where the Angles dwelt before they came to this land (Britain)." Accounts of social life in northern Norway, of whale and walrus hunting, of the Finns (or Lapps).

Text—Our unique source of information on Ohthere is Alfred's Anglo-Saxon version of Orosius's Universal History, Alfred's account of these journeys being perhaps his most important contributions to geography.

See Joseph Bosworth: Description of Europe and the Voyages of Ohthere and Wulfstan, written in Anglo-Saxon (1855).

Criticism—Karl Weinhold: Die Polargegenden Europas nach den Vorstellungen des deutschen Mittelalters (Akad. der Wiss., Wien, Sitzungsber., Philos. Kl., vol. 68, 783–808, 1871). Article by C. R. Beazley: Dictionary of National Biography (vol. 42, 69, 1895). Fridtjof Nansen: In Northern Mists (1911).

WULFSTAN

Or Ulfsten. Flourished at the same time as Ohthere. Scandinavian (Danish) explorer. He made a seven days' journey in the Baltic, from Heidaby to Truso on the Elbing (Frissche Haff, in the Bay of Danzig). He gives some information on Esthonia. The account of Wulfstan's journey is preserved in King Alfred's translation of Orosius. Thus was the Baltic added to the map of the world.

For bibliography see my notes on Alfred and Ohthere.

IBN KHURDĀDHBIH

Abū-l-Qāsim 'Ubaidallāh ibn 'Abdallāh Ibn Khurdādhbih (or Khurdādbih). Born about the beginning of the third century H., c. 825. Flourished in al-Jibāl (Media), later in Sāmarrā, 'Irāq, died c. 912. Geographer of Persian descent. Director of posts. His main work is the "Book of Roads and Provinces" (Kitāb al-masālik wal-mamālik), composed c. 846 in Sāmarrā; a revision was completed

[w] His reaching the Dwina has been doubted by Gustav Storm: Om opdagelsen av "Nordkap" og veien til "det Hvide Hav." (Christiania, 1893–94). According to Storm, Ohthere did not go beyond the Kandalashka Fjord. At any rate, no known navigator had sailed in such high latitudes since the time of Pytheas (q. v., second half of fourth century B. C.) who had apparently attained the Arctic Circle; the much higher latitude reached by Ohthere was not reached again, by a known sailor, until 1553 (Sir Hugh Willoughby and Richard Chancellor). The discovery of the White Sea is often ascribed to Chancellor.

in or after 885. It is an important source for the historical topography of the caliphate; it also contains abridged narratives of journeys in far-off countries.

Texts and Translations—First edition with French translation and notes by C. Barbier de Meynard: Le livre des routes et des provinces (Journal Asiatique, vol. 5, 1–127, 227–295, 446–532, 1865). A better text has been published by M. J. de Goeje, with French translation and notes: Bibliotheca geographorum arabicorum, 6 (Leyde, 1889).

Criticism—C. Defrémery: Remarques sur l'ouvrage géographique d'Ibn Khordadbeh et principalement sur le chapitre qui concerne l'empire byzantin (Journal Asiatique, vol. 7, 239–277, 1866). G. Le Strange: The Lands of the Eastern Caliphate (Cambridge, 1905). C. van Arendonck: Encycl. of Islam (Vol. II, 398, 1918).

AL-YA'QŪBĪ

Aḥmad ibn abī Ya'qūb ibn Ja'far ibn Wahb ibn Wāḍiḥ[1] al-'Abbāsī. Flourished until 873–74 in Armenia and Khurāsān; still living in 891. Shī'ite historian and geographer. Author (in 891–92) of the "Book of the Countries" (Kitāb al-buldān), full of topographical and economical detail, and of a universal history down to 872. The history is divided into two parts: the first part deals with Pre-islamic times from the creation; the second, which is shorter, with the history of Islām. It is a conscientious work and of special interest, because of its Shī'ite bias.

Texts and Translations—The Kitāb al-buldān has been edited by A. W. Th. Juynboll (Leiden, 1861). The part dealing with the Maghrib has been published separately, with Latin commentary and index, by M. J. de Goeje (Bibl. geogr. arabic., Leiden, 1892).

The History has been edited by M. Th. Houtsma (2 vols., Leiden, 1883).

Criticism—M. J. du Goeje: Über die Geschichte der 'Abbāsiden von al-Jakūbī (Travaux de la 3e session du congrès des orientalistes, vol. 2, 153–166, 1879). M. Klamroth: Der Auszug aus der Evangelien bei Ja'qūbī (Gymn. Festschrift, Hamburg, 1885); Über die Auszüge aus griechischen Schriftstellern bei al-Jaqubi. Mathematiker und Astronomen. (Z. d. morgenl. Ges., vol. 42, 1–44, Leipzig, 1888). Brockelmann: Arab. Litt. (Vol. I, 226, 1898). E. Wiedemann: Angaben by al-Ja'qūbī (Beiträge v, 438–441, Erlangen, 1905). G. Le Strange: Baghdād under the Abbasid Caliphate (1900); The Lands of the Eastern Caliphate (1905).

VII. LATIN, BYZANTINE, MUSLIM (OR ARABIC), JEWISH, AND COPTIC MEDICINE

BERTHARIUS

Bertario, abbot of Monte Cassino from 857 to his death in 884. Author of medical treatises for monastic use, "De innumeris remediorum utilitatibus" and "De innumeris morbis."

M. Neuburger: Geschichte der Medizin (vol. 2, 255, 1911).

Additional information on early monastic medicine will be found in Henry E. Sigerist: Studien und Texte zur frühmittelalterlichen Rezeptliteratur (228 p., Leipzig, 1923; Isis, VI, 429–430); Die prognostica Democriti (Archiv für Geschichte der Medizin, vol. 13, 157–159, 1921). Julius Jörimann: Frühmittelalterliche Rezeptarien (185 p., 2 pl., Zürich, 1925; Isis, VIII, 536).

[1] His great-grandfather Wāḍiḥ was the famous Shī'ite freedman of al-Manṣūr. He is sometimes called Ibn Wāḍiḥ.

NICETAS

Nicetas the Physician (Νικήτας). Flourished probably at about the end of the ninth century.[y] Byzantine medical editor. He compiled a collection of the surgical treatises of Hippocrates, Apollonios of Citium, Soranos, Rufus, Galen, Oribasios, Palladios and Paulos Aegineta. (Florence, Codex Laurentianus LXXIV, 7).

Text—Graecorum chirurgici libri, Sorani unus de fracturarum signis, Oribasii duo de fractis et luxatis, e collectione Nicetae ab antiquissimo et optimo codice Florentino descripti, conversi et editi ab Antonio Cocchio (Florence, 1754). Hermann Schöne: Apollonius von Kitium. Illustrierter Kommentar zu der hippokrateischen Schrift περὶ ἄρθρων (Leipzig, 1896). Henri Omont (ed.): Collection de chirurgiens grecs avec dessins attribués au Primatice. Reproduction réduite des 200 dessins du MS. latin 6866 de la Bibliothèque Nationale (Paris, 1908).
Criticism—See Schöne's edition (1896) quoted above.

Muslim (or Arabic) Medicine

SĀBŪR IBN SAHL

Flourished at Jundīshāpūr. Died Dec. 3, 869. Christian physician. He wrote an antidotary (Aqrābādhīn), divided into 22 books, which was possibly the earliest of its kind to influence Muslim medicine, and other medical works. This antidotary enjoyed much popularity until it was superseded by Ibn al-Tilmīdh's new one (q. v., first half of twelfth century).

F. Wüstenfeld: Arabische Aerzte (25, 1840). L. Leclerc: Médecine arabe (vol. 1, 112, 1876). C. Brockelmann: Arabische Litteratur (vol. 1, 232, 1898).

YAḤYĀ IBN SARĀFYŪN

Serapion the Elder.[z] Yaḥyā ibn Sarāfyūn. Flourished in Damascus in the second half of the ninth century. Christian physician who wrote in Syriac two medical compilations (Kunnāsh, pandects), one in 12 books, the other in 7 books. The latter was translated into Arabic by various writers and into Latin by Gherardo da Cremona (Practica sive breviarium). It was very popular during the Middle Ages. Its last book deals with antidotes. Ibn Sarāfyūn attached great importance to venesection and gave subtle prescriptions concerning the choice of the veins to be opened.

Texts and Translations—The Practica is also called Therapeutice methodus, Breviarium, Aggregator, Pandectae. Many early Latin editions: Venice, 1479; Ferrara, 1488; Venice, 1497; Basel, 1499, Venice, 1503, etc.
Criticism—Fihrist (296; 303, 1. 3; and comm. 296, note 1). Wüstenfeld: Ge-

---

[y] We know nothing about him and the dating of his life is based upon the dating of the Laurentianus LXXIV, 7, which seems an original manuscript. Some placed this manuscript in the eleventh or even twelfth century, but the latest student of this palaeographical problem, H. Schöne (op. cit.), concludes that the manuscript dates probably from the ninth century and is certainly not of a later date than the middle of the tenth century. For the illustrations of the manuscript see my note on Apollonios of Citium (first half of first century B. C.).

[z] He was called by an editor of the Renaissance (Albanus Torinus, 1543), Janus Damascenus. Hence he is often mistaken for his contemporary Mesüe. He is sometimes mistaken also for Serapion the Younger, whom I have placed tentatively in the first half of the twelfth century, and for Joannes Damascenus (first half of eighth century).

schichte der arabischen Aerzte (49, 1840). L. Leclerc: Médecine arabe (vol. 1, 113–117, 1876). Brockelmann: Ar. Litt. (vol. 1, p. 233, 1898). E. Gurlt: Geschichte der Chirurgie (vol. 1, 612–613, 1898). Rubens Duval: La littérature syriaque (3e éd., 273, 1907).

AL-RĀZĪ

In Latin: Rhazes. Abū Bakr Muḥammad ibn Zakarīyā al-Rāzī. Born in Ray, near Teheran, Persia, about the middle of the ninth century. Flourished in Ray and in Bagdad. Died 923–24. Physician, physicist, alchemist. The greatest clinician of Islām and of the Middle Ages. Galenic in theory, he combined with his immense learning true Hippocratic wisdom. His chemical knowledge was applied by him to medicine; he might be considered an ancestor of the iatrochemists. Of his many writings, the most important are the "Kitāb al-ḥāwī" (Continens), an enormous encyclopaedia of medicine containing many extracts from Greek and Hindu authors and also observations of his own; the "Kitāb al-Manṣūrī" (Liber Almansoris), a smaller compilation in ten books based largely on Greek science, and finally his famous monograph on smallpox and measles "Kitāb al-jadarī wal-ḥaṣba" (De variolis et morbiliis; De peste; De pestilentia), the oldest description of variola and the masterpiece of Muslim medicine. Many contributions to gynaecology, obstetrics, and ophthalmic surgery can be traced back to him.

He made investigations on specific gravity by means of the hydrostatic balance, which he called al-mīzān al-tabī'ī. Various chemical treatises are ascribed to him, and one of them (Arcandorum liber, apocryphal?) contains a list of 25 pieces of chemical apparatus. He also made an attempt to classify chemical substances.

Texts and Translations—Continens. The al-ḥāwī has not been published, and there is not even a single complete manuscript in existence (see Browne, op. cit., 48). A Latin translation, Liber dictus Elhavi, appeared in Brescia (1486), followed by various Venetian editions.

The Liber ad Almansorem, in ten books, was first published in Milano (1481) and was frequently republished. The ninth book, Nonus Almansoris (De curatione aegritudinum qui accidunt a capite usque ad pedes), was especially popular and was often published apart. Jean de Tournemire (q. v., second half of fourteenth century): Clarificatorium super nono Almansoris cum texto Rhasis (Lyon, 1490). Text and French translation of the first book by P. de Koning: Trois traités d'anatomie arabe (844 p., Leyde, 1903). German translation of the Ophthalmology by W. Brunner: Die Augenheilkunde des Rhases (Diss., Berlin, 1900).

There are also separate manuscripts of the second book dealing with temperaments and physiognomy, a subject which took enormous importance in mediaeval times—even as oneirology it became gradually involved with astrology.

Rhazae de pestilentia. First Latin edition, translation by G. Valla (Venice, 1498). Greek translation edited by Jacques Goupyl (Paris, 1548. Together with the works of Alexander of Tralles). John Channing: De variolis et morbiliis, arabice et latine cum aliis nonnulis ejusdem argumenti (290 p., London, 1766). English translation by Greenhill (Sydenham Society, London, 1847). French translations by Jacques Paulet (Paris, 1763) and by Leclerc and Lenoir (Paris, 1866). German translation by Karl Opitz: Klassiker der Medizin (Leipzig, 1911).

Traité sur le calcul dans les reins et dans la vessie, Arabic edition of a monograph of Rhazes by P. de Koning, with French translation, followed by relevant texts extracted from the Fākhir (= the Splendid, Liber pretiosus de morbis particularibus membrorum a vertice ad pedes), another compendium of Rhazes hitherto unpublished.

Steinschneider has published from a Hebrew manuscript the German translation of other texts, notably a book on quackery: Über die Umstände welche die Menschen von den achtbaren Aerzten abwenden (Virchow's Archiv, vols. 36 and 37).

P. Guigues: La guérison en une heure par Razès (Texte et traduction avec notes, Beyrouth, 1904).

Correctif des aliments (Texte arabe, Le Caire, 1305 H.).

The Opera parva. Many editions (e. g., Venice, 1500), include the following: antidotarium, divisiones, introductio in medicinam, aphorismi, de praeservatione ab aegritudine lapidis,[a] de aegritudinibus puerorum, de sectionibus, cauteriis et ventosis, de facultatibus partium animalium.

E. Wiedemann: Zur Geschichte der Alchemie (Sitzungsber. der physik. mediz. Sozietät, vol. 52, 126–128, 1922). German translation of a fragment setting forth Muslim views on the origin and righteousness of alchemy; it is largely devoted to Rhazes's Kitāb al-asrār and is possibly a work of Rhazes (Isis, V, 495).

Criticism.—Fihrist (299–302, 358, books on alchemy, and by index). Miguel Casiri: Bibliotheca arabico-hispanica escurialensis (2 vols., Madrid, 1760). Wüstenfeld: Geschichte der Arabischen Aerzte (Göttingen, 40–49, 1840). L. Leclerc: Histoire de la médecine arabe (vol. 1, 337–354, 1876. See also *ibidem*, 259–278, on Rhazes's sources, Greek, Arabic, Persian). M. Berthelot: La chimie au moyen âge (Paris, 1893. The Latin alchemic writings ascribed to Rhazes are apocryphal). E. Gurlt: Geschichte der Chirurgie (vol. 1, 601–611, 1898). C. Brockelmann: Arabische Litteratur (vol. 1, 233–235, 1898). Suter: Die Mathematiker und Astronomen der Araber (47, 226, 1900). Ed. Pergens: Les conceptions ophtalmologiques personelles de Rhazes dans le Hawi (Annales d'oculistique, vol. 127, 1902). John Ferguson: Bibliotheca chemica (vol. 2, 262–263, Glasgow, 1906). Neuburger: Geschichte der Medizin (Vol. II, 168–175 and passim, 1911). George S. A. Ranking: The Life and Works of Rhazes (International Congress of Medicine, 237–268, London, 1913, historical section. Based upon Oriental documents, chiefly, of course Ibn abī Uṣaibi'a and including a catalogue of Rhazes's writings). T. de Boer: De medicina mentis von den arts Rāzī (Meded. der Akad. van Wetenschappen, Afd. letterkunde, vol. 53, 1–17, Amsterdam, 1920. Apropros of Rhazes's philosophy). Ed. G. Browne: Arabian Medicine (44–53, etc., Cambridge, 1921. Including interesting unpublished fragments). Herbert Otto Illgen: Die abendländischen Rhazes-Kommentatoren des XIV. bis XVII. Jahrhunderts (Diss., Auszug, 8 p., Leipzig, 1921). Carra de Vaux: Penseurs de l'Islam (vol. 2, 268, 276, 390, 1921). Gotthold Steinführer: Razestexte im Dresdener lateinischen Galen (Diss., 12 p., Leipzig, 1921; Isis, V, 209). E. Wickersheimer: A Note on the Liber de medicinis expertis (Annals of Medical History, vol. 4, 323–327, 1922. Sometimes ascribed to Rhazes; Isis, V, 537, VI, 204). Julius Ruska: Al-Rāzī als Bahnbrecher einer neuer Chemie (Deutsche Literaturzeitung, 118–124, 1923); Al-Bīrūnī als Quelle für das Leben und die Schriften al-Rāzī's (Isis, V, 26–50, 1924. Includes a catalogue of Rhazes's writings, 184 in number, Isis, VI, 145). E. Wiedemann: Zur Geschichte des Heuschnupfens (Archiv für Ohrenheilkunde, Bd. III, reprint of half a page undated; apropos of two lost writings of Rhazes dealing with hay fever, see Isis, V, 37, Nos. 38, 39). Julius Ruska: Über den gegenwartigen Stand der Rāzī-Forschung (Archivio di storia della scienza, vol. 5, 335–347, 1924; Isis VIII, 536).

YA'QŪB IBN AKHĪ ḤIZĀM

Abū Yūsuf Ya'qūb ibn akhī Ḥizām. Flourished in Bagdad during the caliphate of al-Mu'taḍid, 892 to 902. Stablemaster of the caliph; he wrote a treatise on horsemanship (Kitāb al-furūsīya), containing some rudiments of the veterinary art, the first Arabic work of the kind.

C. Brockelmann: Geschichte der arabischen Litteratur (vol. 1, 243, 1898).

---

[a] Published by P. de Koning, see above.

ḤUNAIN IBN ISḤĀQ

In Latin, Joannitius. Abū Zaid Ḥunain ibn Isḥāq al-'Ibādī.[b] Born in Ḥīra, 809–10. Flourished at Jundīshāpūr, then in Bagdad, where he died in October 877. Famous Nestorian physician; one of the greatest scholars and of the noblest men of his time. Pupil of Ibn Māsawaih. Employed by the Banū Mūsā to collect Greek manuscripts and translate them into Arabic, he became the foremost translator of medical works. These translations were made partly with the assistance of other scholars.[c]

It is reported that the 'Abbāsid caliph al-Mutawakkil created (or endowed) a school where translations were made under Ḥunain's supervision. It is not too much to say that the translations made by Ḥunain and his disciples marked a considerable progress in the history of scholarship. He took infinite pains to obtain good manuscripts of the Greek medical texts; he collated them, examined the existing Syriac and Arabic versions, and translated them as accurately and as well as possible. His methods remind one of modern methods. To appreciate more fully the value of his efforts, one must realize that the Syriac versions[d] were very unsatisfactory and the Arabic versions already available were hardly better: Ḥunain carefully compared these versions with the Greek text to prepare his new Arabic translations. His activity was prodigious; it began as early as c. 826 and lasted until the end of his days. It is typical of his scientific honesty that he very severely criticized the translations made by himself early in life. As his experience increased, his scientific ideal became more exacting. He translated a great many of Galen's works,[e] also various writings of Hippocrates, Plato, Aristotle, Dioscorides, and Ptolemy's Quadripartitum. The importance of this activity can be measured in another way by stating that the translations prepared by Ḥunain and his school were the foundation of that Muslim canon of knowledge which dominated medical thought almost to modern times.

Various medical and astronomical writings are ascribed to him (e. g., on the tides, on meteors, on the rainbow). His most important work is his introduction to Galen's "Ars parva" ("Isagoge Johannitii ad Tegni Galeni") which was immensely popular during the Middle Ages and played the same part in the teaching of medicine as Porphyry's "Isagoge" in that of logic.[f] Galenic classification extended and elaborated.

Ḥunain wrote a Syriac grammar called "The Book of (diacritical) Points" (Kĕthābhā dhĕ-nuqzĕ), dealing partly with syntax; a treatise on synonyms; and the earliest Syriac lexicon,[g] entitled "Explanation of Greek Words in Syriac."

---

[b] The nisba is derived from 'Ibād, the name of a Christian tribe of Arabs, established near Ḥīra.

[c] Ḥunain would translate from Greek into Syriac; one of his pupils, Ḥubaish for example, would translate the Syriac into Arabic, and Ḥunain would then revise the final text (Fihrist, 289, 1, 15, f., and comm.).

[d] By Sergios of Resaina (q. v., first half of sixth century), by Ayyūb al-Ruhāwī (q. v., first half of ninth century), and others.

[e] According to his own catalogue, mentioned below, he completed 95 Syriac versions (five of them twice) and 39 Arabic versions of various books of Galen.

[f] It is a part of the "Articella," a collection of medical writings made in Salernitan times (possibly by Constantine the African) and including also Hippocrates's "Aphorisms," and "Prognostic," Galen's "Ars parva," and the treatises of Theophilos Protospatharios (q. v., first half of seventh century) on the pulse and on urine.

[g] This lexicon, together with other lexicons of the end of the ninth century, was absorbed into Bar Bahlūl's work (q. v., second half of tenth century).

Text and Translations—Articella sive Thesaurus operum medicorum antiquorum (Venice, 1483, 1487 1491, 1493, etc.). Isagoge Johannitii ad Tegni Galeni (Venice, 1483, 1487; Leipzig, 1497; Strassburg, 1534). Galen: De anatomicis administrationibus Libri XV; Books IX to XV, exist only in Arabic. They have been edited with a German translation by Max Simon: Sieben Bücher Anatomie des Galen (2 vols., Leipzig, 1906. With an excellent Arabic glossary of technical terms). It seems now established that this particular translation was made by Ḥunain's nephew, Ḥubaish. M. Meyerhof und C. Prüfer: Die Augenanatomie des Ḥunain, nach einem illustrierten arabischen MS. hrg. (Archiv für Geschichte der Medizin, vol. 4, 163–190, 1 pl., 1910). Pseudo Galeni in Hippocratis de septimanis commentarium ab Ḥunaino q. f. arabice versum ex codice monacensi primum edidit et germanice vertit Gotthelf Bergsträsser (Corpus medicorum graecorum, XI, 2, 1, 227 p., Leipzig, 1914). Bergsträsser shows that that treatise was not written by Hippocrates, nor commented upon by Galen, nor translated by Ḥunain! L. Cheikho: Un traité inédit de Honein (Orientalische Studien Theodor Nöldeke gewidmet, 1. Bd., 283–291, Giessen, 1906. Arabic text with French translation, on how religious truth can be recognized).

G. Bergsträsser: Ḥunain über die syrischen und arabischen Galen-Übersetzungen (Abhdl. für die Kunde d. Morgenl., 116 p., Leipzig, 1925). Edition and German translation of an extremely important text, a risāla written by Ḥunain in 856 and represented by a single manuscript (Aya Sofia Mosque Library No. 3631). It is a list of all the Galenic works known to Ḥunain, 129 in number, together with mention and criticism of the Syriac and Arabic translations. A very full analysis and commentary was given by Max Meyerhof in Isis, VIII, 685–724, 1926. Both text and analysis reached me too late to be fully used for this Introduction. Any student of the Syriac and Arabic transmission of Greek medicine must refer to them and eventually correct my own notes on the subject. An earlier knowledge of this text would probably have induced me to deal more fully with some of the translators or to speak of a few more of them.

A recently found treatise on ophthalmology is being translated by Max Meyerhof (1926).

Criticism—Fihrist (294 f. and by index). Ferdinand Wüstenfeld: Geschichte der arabischen Aerzte und Naturforscher. Göttingen (26–29, 1840). L. Leclerc: Histoire de la médecine arabe (vol. 1, 139–152, 1786. Leclerc explains the unusual length of this note by saying: "Honein est la plus grande figure du IXe siècle. On peut même dire qu'il est une des plus belles intelligences et une des plus beaux caractères que l'on rencontre dans l'histoire"). H. Suter: Die Mathematiker und Astronomen der Araber (21–23, 1900). J. Hirschberg: Über das älteste arabische Lehrbuch der Augenheilkunde (Sitzungsber. d. preuss. Ak. d. Wiss., Berlin, 1903, 1080–1094. Capital. The original text of Ḥunain's book—the earliest Arabic treatise on ophthalmology—is lost, but there are two mediaeval versions of it—the so-called "Galeni de oculis liber a Demetrio translatus" and the "Liber de oculis Constantini Africani." Hirschberg has compared both Latin texts with Ibn abī Uṣaibi'a's analysis of the lost Arabic text).[h] C. Prüfer und M. Meyerhof: Die aristotelische Lehre vom Licht bei Ḥunain ibn Isḥāq (Der Islam, vol. 2, 117–128, 1911. Including the German translation of a text of Ḥunain); Die Lehre von Sehen bei Ḥunain (Archiv f. Gesch. d. Medizin, vol. 6, 21–33, 1912. Including also a translation of the relevant text). Gotthelf Bergsträsser: Ḥunain ibn Isḥāq und seine Schule. Sprach- und literaturgeschichtliche Untersuchungen zu den arabischen Hippokrates- und Galenübersetzungen (Leiden, 1913. Important). E. G. Browne: Arabian Medicine (24–27, Cambridge, 1921). E. Wickersheimer: A Note on the Liber de medicinis expertis Attributed to Galen (Annals Medical History, vol. 4, 323–327, 1922; Isis, V, 537; VI, 204). Giuseppe Gabrieli: Ḥunayn

[h] This Arabic text has since been recovered. See Meyerhof's edition announced above.

ibn Isḥāq (Isis, VI, 282–292, 1924. Biography and bibliography based on Oriental sources). G. Furlani: Bruchstücke einer syrischen Paraphrase der Elemente des Eukleides (Z. für Semitistik, vol. 3, 27–52, 1924; Isis, VIII, 536). Max Meyerhof: New Light on Ḥunain and his Period (Isis, VIII, 685–724, 1926. Important study essentially based upon the text edited by Bergsträsser in 1925, above mentioned).

For Isḥāq ibn Ḥunain, Ḥunain's son, Thābit ibn Qurra, Yūsuf al-Khūrī, see my notes in Section IV, above.

ḤUBAISH IBN AL-ḤASAN

Nicknamed al-A'sam, because of a lame hand. Son of the sister of Ḥunain ibn Isḥāq. Flourished most probably like the latter at Bagdad in the second half of the ninth century. Pupil of Ḥunain and his partner in the translation of Greek works into Syriac and Arabic. Physician. He seems to have devoted most of his energy to the translation of Galen; Ḥunain credits him with the translation of 3 Galenic works into Syriac and of 35 into Arabic. Many translations were made by him directly from Greek into Arabic. He completed a medical treatise ("Quaestiones medicae") of Ḥunain. His fame has been somewhat eclipsed by that of his uncle; as a matter of fact, many translations made by him were ascribed to Ḥunain.

L. Leclerc: Médecine arabe (vol. 1, 154–157, 1876). Max Meyerhof: New Light on Ḥunain (Isis, VIII, 708, 1926).

'ĪSĀ IBN YAḤYĀ

'Īsā ibn Yaḥyā ibn Ibrāhīm. One of the immediate disciples of Ḥunain. He translated various Galenic works, one into Syriac and twenty-four into Arabic. His Arabic versions were based mostly upon Ḥunain's Syriac versions. He also did a part of the translation of Oribasios. Some medical writings are ascribed to him.

Max Meyerhof: New Light on Ḥunain (Isis, VIII, 709, 1926).

STEPHANOS, SON OF BASILIOS

Iṣṭifan ibn Bāsīl. One of the main pupils and collaborators of Ḥunain ibn Isḥāq. Ḥunain ascribed to him the translation into Arabic of nine Galenic works. Stephanos was the first to translate Dioscorides into Arabic, his task being corrected and completed by Ḥunain and later by Ibn Juljul (q. v., second half of tenth century). The first Arabic version of Oribasios (q. v., second half of fourth century) is also ascribed to him.

Max Meyerhof: New Light on Ḥunain (Isis, VIII, 705, 1926).

MŪSĀ IBN KHĀLID

Dates of birth and death unknown, but mentioned as a member of Ḥunain's translation school. He translated several of the "sixteen books"[i] of Galen, from Ḥunain's Syriac version into Arabic.

Max Meyerhof: New Light on Ḥunain (Isis, VIII, 710, 1926).

---

[i] For which see my note on John the Grammarian, first half of seventh century.

ASAPH JUDAEUS

Asaph ha-Yehudi.[i] Flourished in the ninth or tenth century? Unknown author of a treatise on medicine, probably the oldest of its kind in Hebrew. It deals with the Persian months, physiology, embryology, the four periods of human life, pathology, hygiene, medicinal plants, medical calendar, antidotes, urinology, aphorisms, and the Hippocratic oath. Possibly translated from a Syriac (or an Arabic?) original.

Richard Gottheil: Jewish Encyclopedia (vol. 2, p. 162, 1902. With bibliography). Ludwig Venetianer: Asaf Judaeus, der älteste medizinische Schriftsteller in hebräischer Sprache (Progr., 140 p., Budapest, 1915–1916. Venetianer places him in the seventh century; see Deutsche Literaturzeitung, p. 30, 838, 1917).

Coptic Medicine

A medical Coptic papyrus was discovered at Meshaïkh in 1892 by U. Bouriant. It dates probably from the ninth or tenth century, and the text itself can hardly be much older. It is obviously posterior to the Muslim conquest and thus it offers a very curious combination of Egyptian, Arabic, and Greek influences, the last named being predominant. It is not a theoretical treatise, but a collection of 237 recipes arranged without any order. It is important because of the rarity of medical Coptic texts.

Elaborate edition by Emile Chassinat: Un papyrus médical copte (Mémoires de l'Institut français d'archéologie du Caire, vol. 32, 412 p., 20 pl. facsimile, folio. Cairo, 1921. With French translation, commentary, and indexes; Isis, VI, 145; VII, 184).

VIII. LATIN, ENGLISH, BYZANTINE, SYRIAN, MUSLIM, AND JAPANESE HISTORIOGRAPHY

ANASTASIUS

Anastasius the Librarian. Nephew or son of Arsenius, Bishop of Orta. Consecrated cardinal priest of St. Marcellus in 847, excommunicated in 850; anti-pope against Benedict III; later librarian of the Vatican; died in 897. Italian translator from Greek into Latin. He attended the eighth Council, in Constantinople, 869–70,[k] and later translated its acts into Latin. His translation of Byzantine chronicles (Historia tripertita) was very popular and constituted an important link between Constantinople and Rome. Landolfus, compiling his "Historia miscella," c. 1,000, included in it the "Historia tripertita" almost verbatim. Anastasius's further activity as translator was restricted to hagiographic writings.

Text—For editions of the Historia tripertita, see my note on Theophanes Confessor (first half of ninth century). For editions of other works, see Manitius.
Criticism—M. Manitius: Lateinische Literatur des Mittelalters (vol. 1, 678–689, 1911; vol. 2, 814). Ernst Perels: Papst Nikolaus I und Anastasius Bibliothecarius (Berlin, 1920).

For English, Byzantine, and Syriac Historiography see my notes on Alfred the Great, Photios, and Moses bar Kēphā in Section III.

---

[i] Also called Asaph ben Berechiah; Asaph Qaṭan (the little); Asaph ha-Rofé (the physician); Asaph he-Ḥakam (the wise man); Asaph ben Berechiah ha-Yarḥoni (the astronomer).
[k] That is, the council which deposed Photios.

Muslim Historiography

AL-DĪNAWARĪ

Abū Ḥanīfa Aḥmad ibn Dā'ūd al-Dīnawarī. Born probably between 815 and 825 at Dīnawar, in 'Irāq 'Ajamī. Flourished in Iṣpahān and Dīnawar, died in 895. Persian historian, lexicographer, botanist, astronomer, writing in Arabic. He made astronomical observations in Iṣpahān in 849–50. Astronomical and mathematical writings are ascribed to him. His main works are the "Book of Long Stories" (Kitāb al-akhbār al-ṭiwāl) (a general history from the Persian point of view) and chiefly his "Book of Plants" (Kitāb al-nabāt). The aim of the latter was primarily philological, but it is of very great importance for the historian of botany. The introduction to this book, dealing with botanic and agricultural generalities, seems to have been particularly remarkable.

Texts and Translations—The Book of Long Stories has been published by W. Guirgass (Leiden, 1888); preface, index, etc., published by I. Kratchkovsky (Leiden, 1912). The Book of Plants is lost, but many extracts from it (including from 300 to 400 descriptions of plants) are quoted by later writers, chiefly by Ibn Sīda and Ibn al-Baiṭār. A scientific edition of these fragments, with English translation, is highly desirable.

Criticism—Ernst Meyer: Geschichte der Botanik (vol. 3, 163–167, 1856). L. Leclerc: Histoire de la médecine arabe (vol. 1, 298–300, 1876. Abou Hanifa Eddinoury). C. Brockelmann: Arabische Litteratur (vol. 1, 123, 1898). H. Suter: Die Mathematiker und Astronomen der Araber (31, 1900); Nachträge (162, 1902). Bruno Silberberg: Das Pflanzenbuch des Abū Ḥanīfa. Ein Beitrag zur Geschichte der Botanik bei den Arabern (Zeitschrift für Assyriologie, vol. 24, 225–265, 1910; vol. 25, 39–88, 1911. Important. Silberberg has apparently collected all the fragments of the Kitāb al-nabāt, together with many other relevant texts, and he gives us an analysis of the work; various samples of Abū Ḥanīfa's manner and a good deal of information on early Muslim botany; the first part of this study was also published as a Breslau Diss.). C. Brockelmann, in Encycl. of Islam (I, 977, 1912).

IBN QUTAIBA

Abū Muḥammad 'Abdallāh ibn Muslim ibn Qutaiba al-Dīnawarī. Born at Bagdad in 828–29 of Iranian stock; flourished at Dīnawar, then at Bagdad, where he died c. 889. Muslim philologist, historian, and writer. The first representative of the grammatical school of Bagdad.[l] His most important work is the "Choice Histories" ('Uyūn al-akhbār). His other works may be considered as supplements to it. The "Treatise of History" or "Book of General Knowledge" (Kitāb al-ma'ārif) deals with universal history from the creation.[m] I must quote also the "Book of Poetry and Poets" (Kitāb al-shi'r wa-l-shu'arā') and the "Accomplishments (or training) of the Secretary" (Kitāb adab al-kātib) dealing with orthography, style, the choice of words, etc. He wrote two treatises on astrology.

Text—The 'Uyūn al-akhbār was edited by C. Brockelmann (Leiden, 1898). The Kitāb al-ma'ārif, by F. Wüstenfeld (Göttingen, 1850. Insufficient). The Kitāb al-shi'r, by M. J. De Goeje (Leiden, 1904. German translation of the preface

---

[l] Which succeeded to the schools of Baṣra and Kūfa.

[m] The beginning of it contains literal translations from the Bible. For an analysis of the whole see E. G. Browne: Literary History of Persia (vol. 1, 387, 1908).

by Th. Nöldeke in his Beiträge, 1–51, Hannover, 1864). The Adab al-kātib, by Max Grünert (Leiden, 1900). Also W. O. Sproull. An Extract of Ibn Kutaiba's Adab al-kātib, or the Writer's Guide, with Translation and Notes (Diss., 42 p., Leipzig, 1877).

Criticism—F. Wüstenfeld: Die Geschichtschreiber der Araber (24, Göttingen, 1881). C. Brockelmann: Arabische Litteratur (vol. 1, 120–123, 1898). H. Suter: Die Mathematiker und Astronomen der Araber (31, 1900). Eilhard Wiedemann: Naturwissenschaftliches aus Ibn Qutaiba (Beiträge 43, 101–120, Sitzungsber., Erlangen, vol. 47, 1915. German extracts from the 'Uyūn al-akhbār, dealing with natural history; interesting from the folk-loric point of view).

IBN 'ABD AL-ḤAKAM

Abū-l-Qāsim 'Abd al-Raḥmān ibn 'Abdallāh ibn 'Abd al-Ḥakam. Born in Egypt of an Egyptian family,[n] died at Fusṭāṭ in 870/1. Egyptian historian. His history of the conquest of Egypt, North Africa, and Spain, called Futūḥ Miṣr wal-Maghrib, is the earliest Muslim account of Egypt. It is a critical work based on the best traditions; it was extensively used by later historians.

Text—First complete edition of the Futūḥ Miṣr by Charles C. Torrey (Yale Oriental series, 434 p., New Haven, 1922; Isis, V, 494).

Partial editions: Traditions anciennes relatives à l'établissement des Musulmans dans l'Afrique septentrionale in Ibn Khaldoun. Histoire des Berbères (De Slane) (vol. 1). Ibn Abdolhakami libellus de historia Aegypti antiqua edited by Jos. Karle (Göttingen, 1856). Ibn Abd el-Hakem's History of the Conquest of Spain, edited by John Harris Jones (Göttingen, 1858. Arabic and English).

Criticism—Ibn Khallikān (De Slane) (vol. 2, 14, 598, 1843). F. Wüstenfeld: Geschichtschreiber der Araber (21, Göttingen, 1881). C. Brockelmann: Arabische Litteratur (vol. 1, 148; vol. 2, 692, 1898).

For al-Ya'qūbī, see Section VI, above.

AL-BALĀDHURĪ

Abū-l-'Abbās Aḥmad ibn Yaḥyā Jābir al-Balādhurī.[o] Of Persian birth but very Arabicized. Flourished at the court of the caliphs al-Mutawakkil, al-Musta'īn, and al-Mu'tazz; he died in 892–93. Muslim historian, one of the greatest historians of his time. He wrote two great works (the second being left incomplete, however): (1) the "Conquest of the Lands" (Futūḥ al-buldān), a history of the conquests of Muḥammad and of the early caliphs, based on traditions collected by the author in many countries. It is valuable for the study of Muslim civilization; (2) The "Genealogies of the Nobles" (Ansāb al-ashrāf), that is, the genealogies of the Prophet and his kinsmen. Translations from Persian into Arabic are ascribed to him.

Text—M. J. De Goeje edited the Futūḥ under the title Liber expugnationis regionum (Leiden, 1870). W. Ahlwardt edited the eleventh book of the Ansāb. Anonyme arabische Chronik, Bd. XI vermuthlich das Buch der Verwandschaft der Adligen (Greifswald, 1883). C. H. Becker and others are preparing a complete edition.

The Origins of the Islamic State. English translation of the Futuḥ al-buldān, with notes, by Philip Khūri Hitti and Francis C. Murgotten (2 vols., New York, 1916–1924; Isis, VII, 535).

---

[n] His father was the leader of the Egyptian Mālikites.

[o] His death was caused, they say, by an excessive dose of a drug, the juice of *Anacardium*, called in Arabic balādhur. Hence the nisba?

Criticism—F. Wüstenfeld: Geschichtschreiber der Araber (p. 25, Göttingen, 1881). Carl Brockelmann: Arabische Litteratur (vol. 1, 141, 1898). C. H. Becker: Encyclopaedia of Islam (vol. 1, 6 911).

Japanese Historiography

The last three of the "Six National Histories" (Riku-kokushi)—Japanese annals modeled upon the Chinese ones—were published within this period, as follows:

The "Shoku-Nihon-kōki," dealing with the period 834 to 850. Twenty volumes edited by Fujiwara Yoshifusa in 869.

The "Montoku-jitsuroku," dealing with the period 851 to 858. Ten volumes edited by Fujiwara Mototsune in 879.

The "Sandai-jitsuroku," dealing with the period 859 to 888. Fifty volumes edited by Fujiwara Tokihira in 901 (strictly speaking, this belongs not to this but to the following period).

E. Papinot: Historical Dictionary (513, 1909).

IX. BYZANTINE AND JAPANESE LAW

Byzantine Law

The legal summary compiled by Leon the Isaurian (q. v., first half of eighth century) was repealed by Basil the Macedonian (emperor of the East from 867 to 886). A new Greek version of the Justinianian law, with corrections and additions, was begun under Basil and completed under his son Leon the Philosopher (emperor from 886 to 911). This was an enormous collection divided into 60 books (into 40 under Basil) and called "The Revision of the Ancient Laws" (Ἡ ἀνακάθαρσις τῶν παλαιῶν νόμων); it became chiefly known, however, under the name of "Basilica" (Τὰ Βασιλικά, i. e., νόμιμα). (It bore also the name of ἡ ἑξηκοντάβιβλος.) Additions (scholia) to this corpus were published from time to time, but the "Basilica" remained the official code of Byzantium until the fall of the empire in 1453. Basil had published in 879 a shorter summary of Justinianian law, called Πρόχειρον, and he had drafted a treatise called Ἐπαναγωγὴ τοῦ νόμου.

Text—First edition of the Basilica by Charles Annibal Fabrot (7 vol., fol., Greek and Latin, Paris, 1647). Modern edition by Wilhelm Ernst Heimbach (6 vols., with Latin translation, Leipzig, 1833–1870. This is a fundamental work. The sixth volume contains materials for the history of Byzantine law from 534 to 867). Supplementary volume published by Ferrini and Mercati in 1897.

Ὁ πρόχειρος νόμος, edited by K. E. Zachariae von Lingenthal (Heidelberg, 1837). Ἐπαναγωγή edited by the same (Leipzig, 1852). The so-called Book of the Prefect, ascribed to Leon the Philosopher, is not certainly genuine; in any case it is a very valuable source for the study of contemporary Byzantine civilization, with special reference to guilds, industries, and labor conditions. It was discovered in a Geneva MS. by Jules Nicole in 1892, and published by him the following year. Λέοντος τοῦ σοφοῦ τὸ ἐπαρχικὸν βιβλίον, Le livre du préfet ou l'édit de l'empereur Léon le Sage sur les corporations de Constantinople. (Mémoires de l'Institut national genevois, t. 18, Geneva, 1893.) French translation by the same (83 p., Geneva, 1894).

Criticism—C. Krumbacher: Byzantinische Litteratur (606, 609, 1897). Albert Vogt: Basile I et la civilisation byzantine à la fin du IXe siècle (Paris, 1908). P. de Francisci: Pour une nouvelle édition des Basiliques (Congrès international d'histoire de Bruxelles, 1923. Showing the insufficiency of Heimbach's edition and the need of a new one). M. Christo Macri: L'organisation de l'économie urbaine dans Byzance sous la dynastie de Macédoine (160 p., Paris, 1925; Isis, VIII, 587).

Japanese Law

In my note on Japanese law in the first half of the eighth century, I have alluded to the so-called Three Great Codes (San-dai-kyaku-shiki):

The "Kōnin-kyaku-shiki" promulgated in 811, second year of the Kōnin era, which contains all the ordinances enacted since the promulgation of the Daihō code (40 vols. for the shiki, plus 10 vols. for the kyaku).

The "Jōgwan-kyaku-shiki," published in 868, tenth year of Jōgwan (20 vols. of shiki and 12 vols. of kyaku).

The "Engi-kyaku-shiki," published in 907[p] seventh year of Engi (50 vols. of shiki and 12 vols. of kyaku).

The comparative study of these codes is of interest in showing the gradual assimilation of Chinese law by the Japanese and also their gradual emancipation from it.

X. LATIN, ENGLISH, BYZANTINE, SLAVONIC, SYRIAC, AND ARABIC PHILOLOGY

For Latin philology, see my note on Remi of Auxerre in Section III.

For English philology, see my note on Alfred the Great, *ibidem*.

Byzantine Philology

ARETHAS

'Αρέθας. Born at Patrae, c. 860; Archbishop of Caesarea in Cappadocia at least since 907; still living in 932. Byzantine humanist. Collector of classical writings and commentator. A Euclid was copied for him in 888, a Plato in 895, a Eusebios in 914, etc. The Euclid is in Oxford, the Plato (discovered in 1801 at Patmos by E. D. Clarke) is in Cambridge (Codex Bodleianus Clarkianus 39); a facsimile reproduction of it was published in 1898.

Criticism—K. Krumbacher: Byzantinische Litteratur (2. Aufl., 524, 1897). Petrus Becker: De Photio et Aretha lexicorum scriptoribus (Diss., 91 p., Bonn, 1909). Sandys: History of Classical Scholarship (vol. 1^3, 403, 1921).

For Photios, see my note in Section III.

For Slavonic philology, see my note on St. Cyril in Section II.

For Syriac philology, see my note on Ḥunain ibn Isḥāq in Section VII.

For Arabic philology, see my notes on Ḥunain ibn Isḥāq in Section VII and on al-Dīnawarī and Ibn Qutaiba in Section VIII.

---

[p] This already brings us into the tenth century.

CHAPTER XXXI

THE TIME OF AL-MAS'ŪDĪ

(First Half of Tenth Century)

I. Survey of Science in First Half of Tenth Century. II. Religious Background. III. Cultural Background in Israel and Islām. IV. Muslim, Byzantine, and Chinese Mathematics and Astronomy. V. Byzantine, Muslim, and Chinese Physics, Alchemy, and Technology. VI. English and Muslim Botany. VII. Muslim and Japanese Geography. VIII. English, Byzantine, and Arabic Medicine. IX. Latin, Arabic, and Chinese Historiography. X. Latin, Barbarian, and Japanese Law; Muslim Sociology. XI. Hebrew and Arabic Philology.

I. SURVEY OF SCIENCE IN FIRST HALF OF TENTH CENTURY

1. The overwhelming superiority of Muslim culture continued to be felt throughout the tenth century. Indeed, it was felt more strongly than ever, not only because the foremost men of science were Muslims, but also because cultural influences are essentially cumulative. By the beginning, or at any rate by the middle of the century, the excellence of Muslim science was already so well established, even in the West, that each new Arabic work benefited to some extent by the prestige pertaining to all. To be sure, other languages, such as Latin, Greek, or Hebrew were also used by scholars, but the works written in those languages contained nothing new, and in the field of science, as in any other, when one ceases to go forward, one already begins to go backward. All the new discoveries and the new thoughts were published in Arabic. Strangely enough, the language of the Qur'ān had thus become the international vehicle of scientific progress.

2. *Religious Background*—The written text of the Hebrew Scriptures and its correct pronunciation were finally established in the first half of the tenth century by Ben Asher of Tiberias. A similar task was carried out at the same time, though with less success, by Ben Naphtali. The printed editions of the Hebrew Bible reproduce essentially Ben Asher's text.

The Benedictine organization was most usefully completed about the year 927 by the so-called Reform of Cluny. The Benedictine monasteries had been hitherto practically independent; this had its advantages, but it also had very serious drawbacks, notably the fact that in case of danger, material or spiritual, each house was abandoned to its own resources. The special terrors caused by the invasions of the Normans helped the process of reorganization and unification. The Abbey of Cluny became very rapidly the most important center of religious life in western Christendom; it is not too much to say that from the middle of the tenth century to the middle of the twelfth, Cluny was the main support of European civilization. The chief artisan of Cluny's greatness was its second abbot, Odo, who ruled the order from 927 to 943.

This was also a period of theological reorganization in Islām. The Persian historian al-Ṭabarī composed an elaborate commentary on the Qur'ān and attempted the creation of a new school of law. However, the greatest theologian of the time was al-Ash'arī, who initiated a very powerful reaction against the liberal tendencies which were bidding fair to disintegrate Islām. Al-Ash'arī was the champion of Sunnite orthodoxy; he may be considered the founder of Muslim scholasticism.

3. *Cultural Background in Israel and Islām*—It is of special importance to know the philosophical ideas of the Jews and Muslims of that time, because they were the leaders of civilization. I did not speak of the Jews in my first paragraph, because they were to a large extent included within the sphere of Muslim influence; all of the Jewish philosophers were steeped in Arabic and many preferred to write in Arabic rather than in Hebrew.

Even as in Islām, there was also a strong liberal movement, Qaraism, in Israel. David ben Merwan was a Qaraite, and so was al-Qirqisānī. The former has been called the father of Jewish philosophy; at any rate, his work was one of the channels through which Mu'tazilite discussions reached Israel. We are interested in the latter, because he insisted upon the importance of applying scientific methods to religious matters.

Orthodox Judaism was represented by two great men: Isḥāq al-Isrā'īlī (Isaac Judaeus) paid considerable attention to philosophical problems, but he was chiefly famous as a physician. On the other hand, Saadia ben Joseph (Saadia Gaon) was primarily a philosopher; his main purpose was to reconcile rationalism with the Jewish faith.

The development of Muslim culture was fostered in Spain by the eighth Umayyad caliph of the West, 'Abd al-Raḥmān III. Under his rule, Cordova became one of the greatest centers of civilization. Of course, scientific activity can not be created at once, but we shall see abundant fruits of that Hispano-Muslim civilization in the following chapters. In the meanwhile, the advance of Muslim science continued to take place almost exclusively in the East.

The foremost philosopher of the time was al-Fārābī, who continued the great task undertaken by al-Kindī almost a century before—the assimilation of Greek philosophy and Greek knowledge, its harmonization with the doctrines of Islām. The great geographer al-Mas'ūdī was also a philosopher and an encyclopaedist—the Muslim Pliny.

The transmission of Greek philosophy was accomplished also, in a humbler way, by Christian translators, notably Mattā ibn Yūnus and Yaḥyā ibn 'Adī.

4. *Muslim, Byzantine, and Chinese Mathematics and Astronomy*—Practically all the writings of this period were in Arabic. Let us consider these Arabic writings first. The mathematical production of this period was less abundant and on the whole less brilliant than that of the previous one, but it was, for the first time, exclusively Muslim, and there were at least two very distinguished mathematicians, Abū Kāmil and Ibrāhīm ibn Sinān. Ibn al-Adamī and Ibn Amājūr compiled astronomical tables; the latter was said to be one of the best Muslim observers; he made a number of observations between 885 and 933, being aided by his son 'Alī and by a slave called Mufliḥ. Abū Kāmil perfected al-Khwārizmī's algebra; he made a special study of the pentagon and the decagon and of the addition and subtraction of radicals; he could determine and construct the two (real) roots of a quadratic equation. Abū 'Uthmān translated Book X of Euclid, together with Pappos's commentary upon it. Al-Balkhī and the physician Sinān ibn Thābit wrote various treatises on mathematical, astronomical, and astrological subjects. Al-Hamdānī compiled astronomical tables for Yemen, and his great work on the archaeology of his country contains much information on the scientific views of the early Arabs. Ibrāhīm ibn Sinān was primarily a geometer;

he wrote commentaries on Apollonios and on the Almagest and his determination of the area of a parabola was one of the greatest achievements of Muslim mathematics. Al-'Imrānī wrote astrological treatises and a commentary on Abū Kāmil's algebra.

Hero the Younger composed a treatise on surveying which was simply a rehash of Alexandrian knowledge.

The Old History of the T'ang dynasty edited by Liu Hsü includes a history of Chinese mathematics and astronomy down to 945.

5. *Byzantine, Muslim, and Chinese Physics, Alchemy, and Technology*—I have already referred to the treatise on surveying compiled by Hero the Younger; a contemporary treatise on poliorcetics is also ascribed to him.

Ibn Waḥshīya, who will be dealt with more fully below, was primarily an alchemist and an occultist. His works do not seem to have any chemical importance, but they may help to understand alchemical symbolism.

Al-Fārābī wrote the most important Arabic treatise on music; he had some knowledge of mensural music and was far ahead of the European theorists of his days (e. g., Regino of Prüm and Odo of Cluny).

Fêng Tao is often called the inventor of printing. That statement is not true, without being entirely untrue, for if Fêng Tao did not invent printing, at any rate it was largely due to his initiative and activity that the invention was fully developed. He ordered the printing of a standard edition of the Classics, together with commentaries; that edition, in 130 volumes, was published in 953. This marked the beginning of the Confucian revival, which blossomed during the Sung dynasty, especially during the second half of the twelfth century.

6. *English and Muslim Botany*—The earliest Anglo-Saxon herb-lore will be found in the "Leech Book of Bald," part of which at least may go back to the time of King Alfred. Another leech book, the so-called "Lacnunga," is probably a contemporaneous production.

The most valuable of the many works ascribed to Ibn Waḥshīya is the so-called "Nabataean agriculture," which is not what it claims to be—a translation of ancient "Babylonian" writings; nevertheless, it contains a number of agricultural and botanical facts.

7. *Muslim and Japanese Geography*—One of the characteristic features of Muslim civilization is the importance attached to geographical surveys of various kinds and the richness of its geographical literature. Thus, for this first half of the tenth century, I have to record the words of not less than eleven geographers, all of them Easterners.

Ibn Serapion wrote a geographical account of the world; his descriptions of some of the great rivers, the Euphrates, the Tigris, and the Nile, are particularly valuable, and he explained the system of canals feeding Bagdad. Ibn Rusta compiled an encyclopaedia of which we know only the geographical part. Ibn al-Faqīh wrote a "Book of the Countries," and al-Jaihānī a road-book; both works are lost, but we have some indirect knowledge of them. Abū Zaid told the story of Ibn Wahb's visit to the Chinese court in 870, which contains information not simply about China, but also about India and other eastern countries. It was the most important work of its kind before that of Marco Polo. In 921 Ibn Faḍlān was sent on a mission to the Volga region; his description was the earliest reliable account of Russia. The Christian renegade Qudāma composed another road-book comparable to those of Ibn Khurdādhbih, al-Ya'qūbī, and Ibn Rusta. Al-Balkhī, the mathematician, compiled a geographical treatise which was essentially a collection of maps. Al-Hamdānī wrote a geography of Arabia. Abū Dulaf traveled in Central Asia and India and wrote an account of his journeys, the greater part of which is unfortunately lost.

The ten men of whom I have spoken were, all of them, distinguished geographers; each contributed something to our knowledge; many would have done credit to any period. Yet their fame was overshadowed by that of an eleventh man, who flourished at about the end of this period, the famous al-Mas'ūdī, one of the greatest travelers and one of the greatest geographers of all times. Al-Mas'ūdī's curiosity was universal and his main work is really an encyclopaedia arranged in geographical order.

The poet Ki Tsurayuki wrote in Japanese an account of his journey from the province of Tosa to Kyōto.

8. *English, Byzantine, and Arabic Medicine*—English (or more exactly Anglo-Saxon) medicine was represented by the leech books already dealt with in the botanical section.

Nonnos wrote various medical treatises, largely based upon earlier Byzantine writings.

The newer medical ideas were, all of them, published in Arabic, but not necessarily by Muslims. The greatest physician of the age was a Jew, Isḥāq al-Isrā'īlī (Isaac Judaeus). We owe him, for instance, the main mediaeval treatise on urine. Eutychios, the Melchite patriarch of Jerusalem, composed a medical treatise. Two of the Muslim mathematicians dealt with above, Abū 'Uthmān and Sinān ibn Thābit, became famous as organizers of hospitals; Sinān took pains to raise the scientific standards of the medical profession; Abū 'Uthmān translated Galenic writings into Arabic.

9. *Latin, Arabic, and Chinese Historiography*—The only important work in Latin was written by the German Benedictine, Regino of Prüm. It is a chronicle of the world from Christ's birth to his own days.

Al-Ṭabarī, by far the greatest historian of the time, composed a universal history from the creation to 915. Al-Mas'ūdī's works are historical as much as geographical; they must be used together with al-Ṭabarī's history. The Christian physician Eutychios wrote also historical books.

The most interesting feature in the Arabic historical literature of that time is the importance attached, partly for political and partly for sentimental reasons, to Arabian genealogy and archaeology; three distinguished men, Ibn Duraid, al-Hamdānī, and Abū-l-Faraj al Iṣfahānī, devoted their main efforts to the study of the antiquities of their race. This is easy to explain, for the Arabs were almost completely submerged by Muslims of other races, especially by Persians. Alien peoples—alien not simply in their blood but in many other respects—had taken possession almost exclusively of that civilization which the Arabs had so powerfully started. Unfortunately, such movement as this was of too deep a nature to be stopped or even influenced by literary efforts. These Arabian historians were fighting gallantly for a lost cause.

The earliest Hispano-Muslim historian, Abū Bakr al-Rāzī appeared at this time; he wrote a description and history of Spain which we know only through a later Spanish adaptation.

Liu Hsü edited in 945 the older official history of the T'ang dynasty.

10. *Latin, Barbarian, and Japanese Law; Muslin sociology*—Regino of Prüm composed a summary of canon law. The earliest code of Welsh law was compiled by order of King Howell Dda.

The commentary on Chinese law begun by Kiyowara Natsuno in the first half of the ninth century was completed by Koremune Naomoto. An additional body of ceremonial law was compiled during the Engi era (901 to 923). It is of great importance for the study of Japanese life.

One of the many works of al-Fārābī deserves special mention here, namely, his "Model City," because it contains a criticism of the sociological conditions of those days and a sketch of better ones.

11. *Hebrew and Arabic Philology*—It will suffice to recall the final edition of the Hebrew Bible, of which I spoke in the religious section; the philological bearings of this were as obvious and as important as the purely religious ones. Nothing will help more to intensify philological consciousness and philological study than the editing of a text, and especially a sacred text. From this point of view, philology becomes an essential part of theology and even of religion; that was indeed the point of view of Hebrew and Muslim theologians. It is not surprising that the earliest Hebrew grammar and Hebrew dictionary appeared in this time. They were composed by Saadia ben Joseph, who may be called the founder of Hebrew philology. However, this new activity did not fully develop, as we shall see, until the second half of this century. Even as Latin philology was essentially modeled upon the Greek, Hebrew philology was not a very original movement, but largely the application of the principles of Arabic grammar to a kindred language.

In the meanwhile, Muslim grammarians continued, with special zeal, their own task, one very congenial to their genius. Thus Ibn Duraid compiled an extensive (but very impractical) dictionary, the "Jamhara." The work of Abū-l-Faraj al-Iṣfahānī has also a considerable philological interest. Ibn Duraid and Abū-l-Faraj were philologists, even as they were historians, for nationalist reasons.

12. *Final Remarks*—In spite of considerable activity in certain fields, especially within the Islamic world, this was on the whole a time of rest and fallow, making a sharp contrast at once with the preceding and the following period. But fertile seeds were sown and potential energy stored in many places. For example, the foundation of Cluny gave hopes of rich crops. Before long an admirable civilization was to flourish in Spain, thanks to the intelligent patronage of the Umayyads of Cordova. Centuries of Masoretic criticism had given precision to Jewish thought, but now Qaraism was waking them and sharpening their wits. To complete this very concise analysis of the travail which was then preparing the future, I must still mention the activity of al-Ash'arī, though this would end, not in advancing scientific research, but on the contrary in blocking it.

The eclipse of Hindu, Chinese, and Japanese activities continued with very few exceptions. These exceptions were unimportant, except one, which was very important indeed; it was due to Chinese initiative that printing became a practical reality, a cultural instrument of the first order. Strangely enough, this was not to be understood in the West until half a millennium later.

The Latin world was represented by Odo of Cluny and Regino of Prüm and the Greek by Nonnos and Hero the Younger. That was very little. Even in the Muslim world, Christian activity was considerably reduced; the only Arabic-writing Christians whom I had to name were Eutychios, Mattā ibn Yūnus, and Yaḥyā ibn 'Adī. It is true, the disappearance of Christians was compensated for by an increasing number of Jews, most of them writing in Arabic: the Qaraites David ben Merwan and al-Qirqisānī and the Orthodox Ben Asher, Ben Naphtali, Saadia ben Joseph, and Isḥāq al Isrā'īlī.

The main task of mankind was accomplished by Muslims. The greatest philosopher, al-Fārābī, was a Muslim; the greatest mathematicians, Abū Kāmil and Ibrāhīm ibn Sinān, were Muslims; the greatest geographer and encyclopaedist, al-Mas'ūdī, was a Muslim; the greatest historian, al-Ṭabarī, was still a Muslim. It is true the greatest physician, Isḥāq al-Isrā'īlī, was not a Muslim but an Arabic-speaking Jew. It is interesting to note that this Isḥāq, born in Egypt, practiced in Tunis.

Many of the Muslims were living in Bagdad or in other towns of 'Irāq, but an increasing number of them represented the other parts of Islām. To begin with, there was a very strong Arabian group—al-Ash'arī, al-Hamdānī, Abū Dulaf, Abū-l-Faraj al-Iṣfahānī, Ibn Duraid, al-Mas'ūdī. The Persian group was not quite as strong, yet considerable—Ibn Rusta, Ibn al-Faqīh, Abū Zaid, al-Ṭabarī. Abū Kāmil was an Egyptian; Abū Bakr al-Rāzī a Spaniard; al-Balkhī and al-Jaihānī came from Khurāsān and Transoxiana; finally, al-Fārābī and Ibn Amājūr were Turks! Thus was Muslim culture, the highest culture of those days, stretching from Central Asia to the western end of the world.

II. RELIGIOUS BACKGROUND

Hebrew Scriptures

The text of the Ṣopherim, established in the second century, was purely consonantal. Vowel points and accents were added to it in the seventh century. In the meanwhile, a large body of textual criticism (Māsōrāh) had accumulated and more was being constantly added to it. By the beginning of the tenth century the necessity of establishing a new standard text, together with its Māsōrāh, became urgent, and this was done in the two main Masoretic schools, Tiberias and Babylon.

The Palestinian (or Occidental) tradition was established by Ben Asher; the Māsōrāh may be considered as closed by him. All the western manuscripts are descendants of his own (which is lost); besides, all printed editions of the Hebrew Bible reproduce the Tiberian system of vocalization. The fundamental printed text is that of Jacob ben Ḥayyim ibn Adonijah in four folio volumes (Venice, 1524–25).

The Babylonian (or Oriental) tradition was established by Ben Naphtali. This is now represented only (and very imperfectly) by a few manuscripts obtained during the last century in Crimea and in the Yemen and by the variants of other Masoretic manuscripts.

Abu Said Aaron ben Moses ben Asher flourished at Tiberias in the first half of the tenth century. He wrote also on grammatical subjects and may be regarded as a link between the Masorites and the Hebrew grammarians (Caspar Levias in Jewish Encycl., vol. 1, 18, 1901).

Ben Naphtali flourished also at Tiberias c. 890 to 940 (*ibidem*, vol. 2, 677, 1902).

Reform of Cluny

A new abbey was founded by William the Pious, Duke of Aquitaine, in 910, at Cluny (near Mâcon, Saône-et-Loire). The first abbot was Berno; the second, from 927 to 943, Odo (q. v.). Odo it was who established the rules of Cluny, though they were not written down until the next century. It was a reform of the Benedictine order, hastened by the terrible invasions of the Normans. The discipline was improved and the solidarity between the houses considerably strengthened.

In fact, the order of Cluny was the first real religious order of Christendom since the time of St. Pachomios:[a] that is, all the members of the order were subordinated to the Abbot of Cluny. By the middle of the twelfth century the order embraced 314 monasteries in all parts of Europe and even in Palestine. This polity was essentially different from the old Benedictine polity; it proved extremely successful and beneficial. From the middle of the tenth to the middle of the twelfth century the abbey of Cluny was the chief center of religious life in Western Europe, the main prop of European civilization. After that it declined rapidly, because of the lack of great abbots, and, in 1528, its fate was sealed when it was given in commendam. The order was suppressed in 1790. The wonderful Romanesque basilica built at Cluny between 1088 and 1118 was stupidly destroyed at the beginning of the nineteenth century.

Martin Marrier: Bibliotheca cluniacensis (Paris, 1614). Ernst Sackur: Die Cluniacenser in ihren kirchlichen und allgemeingeschichtlichen Wirksamkeit bis zur Mitte des XI. Jahrh. (2 Bde., Halle a. S., 1892–1894). Article Cluny, in Encyclopaedia Britannica, 11th ed., by the Right Rev. E. C. Butler, O.S.B. François Louis Bruel: Cluni, album historique et archéologique (Matiscone, 1910). Victor Terret: La sculpture bourguignonne aux XIIe et XIIIe siècles. Ses origines et ses sources d'inspiration, Cluny (195 p., 65 pl., Autun, 1914). Lucy Margaret Smith: The early history of the monastery of Cluny (235 p., London, 1920).

Karl Heussi and Herman Mulert: Atlas zur Kirchengeschichte (Tübingen, 1905, a good map (VI, c), showing the diffusion of the reform of Cluny down to the middle of the eleventh century).

ODO OF CLUNY

St. Odo. Born in the French province of Maine in 879; died in 943. Second Abbot of Cluny from 927 to his death. He was the real organizer of this institution, which became under his impulse a great center of culture. He traveled to Italy and induced the Benedictine monasteries, including St. Benedict's own, Monte Cassino and Subiaco, to accept the Cluny reform. He wrote, c. 926, the Dialogus de musica arte and the Liber occupationum. He may be the author of the Regulae Domini Oddonis super abacum, though this important work dates more probably only from the twelfth century.

Texts and Translations—Scriptores ecclesiastici de musica, edited by the abbot Martin Gerbert. St. Blasien (vol. 1, 252–264, 296–302, 1784). Occupatio primum edidit Ant. Swoboda (200 p., Leipzig, 1900).

Criticism—Cantor: Vorlesungen (1. Bd., 3te. Aufl., 843–844, 899–902, 1907).

Muslim Theology

For al-Ṭabarī, see my note in Section IX below.

AL-ASH'ARĪ

Abū-l-Ḥasan 'Alī ibn Ismā'īl al-Ash'arī. Born at Baṣra in 873–74 of one of the oldest Arab families; flourished at Bagdad; died in 935–36. Arab theologian. At first a Mu'tazilite, he was reconverted to Sunnite orthodoxy in 913 and henceforth his whole activity was devoted to the rationalization and the defense of his faith. He was a Shāfi'īte, which explains the fact that his influence was decidedly greater in Shāfi'īte and Mālikite countries, and that he incurred the enmity of the

---

[a] For whom, see my note on Christian monasticism, first half of fourth century.

Ḥanbalites. His attitude was essentially one of moderation. He may be called the founder of Muslim scholasticism. He reestablished theological unity and orthodoxy, but the triumph of his views marked the end of free thought and research in Islām. E. G. Browne compares the destructiveness of his influence to that of Changīz and Hulāgū! (Literary History of Persia, vol. 1, 286, 1908). This is an exaggeration, but the triumph of orthodoxy is always a defeat for the scientific spirit—essentially heterodox—and al-Ash'arī was undoubtedly the greatest theologian of Islām before al-Ghazzālī.

Ibn Khallikān (De Slane) (vol. 2, 227, 669). W. Spitta: Zur Geschichte al-Ash'arī's (Leipzig, 1876). M. A. F. Mehren: Exposé de la réforme de l'islamisme commencée par al-Ash'arī (IVe Congrès des Orientalistes de St. Pétersbourg, vol. 2, 169–331, 1879). Martin Schreiner: Zur Geschichte des Ash'aritentums (VIIIe Congrès des Orientalistes, vol. 1, 79–117, Leiden, 1891). Carl Brockelmann: Arabische Litteratur (vol. 1, 194, 1898). D. B. Macdonald: Development of Muslim Theology (1903, by index; see p. 293–299, a translation of al-Ash'arī's short creed). R. A. Nicholson: Literary History of the Arabs (377–380, 1907). Carre de Vaux: Penseurs de l'Islam (vol. 4, 151–156, 1923).

III. CULTURAL BACKGROUND IN ISRAEL AND ISLĀM

Qaraites

DAVID BEN MERWAN

David ha-Babli, Abū Sulaimān, al-Muqammaṣ (or Miqmaṣ) al-Raqqī. From Raqqa. Flourished in the ninth and tenth centuries, in Babylonia. Qaraite philosopher, called by some the father of Jewish philosophy. His main work is the Ishrun maqalat[b] ("Twenty chapters"), largely based on Mu'tazilite kalām (no Biblical, only Greek and Arabic authorities are quoted). His classification of science was the Aristotelian one as modified by the Muslims (see my note on the Brethren of Purity, next chapter); in that respect his position was that of Orthodox Judaism (see my note on Isḥāq al-Isrā'īlī in the medical section below).

Article by Isaac Broydé and Richard Gottheil in Jewish Encyclopaedia (vol. 4, 466, 1903). Isaac Husik: Medieval Jewish Philosophy (17–22, 1918). H. A. Wolfson: The Classification of Sciences in Mediaeval Jewish Philosophy (Hebrew Union College Jubilee Volume, 263–315, 1925).

AL-QIRQISĀNĪ

Abū Yūsuf Ya'qūb (or Yūsuf Abū Ya'qūb) al-Qirqisānī. A native of Circassia who flourished in the first half of the tenth century. Qaraite theologian and exegete. He was one of the first Qaraites to believe in scientific study. Faith must be based upon reason. He showed the importance of applying scientific methods to religious matters in his Commentary of the Pentateuch (al-riyāḍ wal-ḥadā'iq; the gardens and orchards; sefer ha-gannīm we-pardēṣīm or sefer ha-niẓẓānīm). His work contains much valuable information on the history of Qaraism.

Isaac Broydé: Article Kirkisani, in the Jewish Encyclopedia (vol. 7, 2½ cols., 1904). Abraham de Harkavy and Kaufmann Kohler: Article Karaites and Kara-

[b] An Arabic manuscript of that work (15 chapters) was discovered only in 1898, by Abraham Harkavy, in the Imperial Library of St. Petersburg.

ism (*ibidem*, 438–447). Hartwig Hirschfeld: Qirqisani Studies (59 p., Jews' College, 1918?).

ORTHODOX JEWS

For Isḥāq al-Isrā'īlī, see my note in the medical section (VIII), below.

SAADIA BEN JOSEPH

Saadia Gaon. Sa'īd al-Fayyūmī. Born 892 in Dīlaẓ, Fayyūm; died 942 in Sura, Babylonia. He was appointed Gaon (head of the academy) of Sura in 928. But he soon came into conflict with the exilarch and was banished. Some of his best work was done in exile. He was reinstated as Gaon of Sura about the end of his life. The first great philosopher in Judaism after Philon.[c] The creator of the Jewish philosophy of religion, which includes, of course, epistemological developments. Equally steeped in Aristotle and in Mu'tazilite kalām, he attempted to reconcile rationalism with the Jewish faith. Champion of the Jewish tradition against the Qaraites. He may be considered also the founder of scientific Hebrew philology. The most important of his writings are: on the Jewish calendar; "Agron" (collection), the first Hebrew dictionary, completed in 913 (the words are translated into Arabic); the first Hebrew grammar; an Arabic translation of most of the Old Testament, with commentary, which has remained the standard translation among the Arabic-speaking Jews even to this day; a commentary on the Sefer yeẓīrah; a treatise on faith and dogmas completed in 934. After his death the intellectual center of Judaism shifted from Babylonia to Spain.

Texts and Translations—A complete edition of Saadia's extant writings was begun in 1892 by Joseph Derenbourg (5 vols., published from 1893 to 1899). Mayer Lambert: Commentaire sur le Séfer yesira ou livre de la création (Hebrew, Arabic, and French text, Bibliothèque de l'école des hautes études, 85, Paris, 1891). D. J. Engelkempfer: Die religionsphilosophische Lehre Saadja Gaons über die Hl. Schrift. Aus dem Kitāb al-amānāt wal-i'tiqādāt, übersetzt und erklärt (Beit. zur Gesch. d. Philos. d. Mittelalters, IV, 4, 82 p., Münster, 1903). This Kitāb is the original Arabic text of the treatise on faith above-mentioned; it was translated into Hebrew by Judah ibn Tibbon (q. v., second half of twelfth century). The Arabic text was edited by S. Landauer (Leyden, 1880). S. Schechter: Saadyana, geniza, fragments and writings by R. Saadija Gaon and others (Hebrew) (Cambridge, 1903).

Criticism—Fihrist (p. 23). De Sacy: Chrestomathie arabe (vol. 1, 351, 356 f.). Jacob Guttmann: Die Religionsphilosophie des Saadia dargestellt und erläutert (Göttingen, 1882). W. Bacher: Die Anfänge der hebräischen Grammatik (Leipzig, 1895). S. Horovitz: Die Psychologie bei den jüdischen Religions-Philosophen des Mittelalters von Saadia bis Maimuni (Breslau, 1898–1912). Moritz Steinschneider: Saadia Gaon's arabische Schriften (25 p., Breslau, 1900); Nachträgliches (3 p., Breslau, 1901). Wilhelm Bacher: Article Saadia, in Jewish Encyclopedia (vol. 10, 579–586, 1905. A very elaborate article with long bibliography; see also his article gaon, *ibidem*, vol. 5, 567–572, 1903. With the collaboration of A. Eckstein). Henry Malter: Saadia Gaon, his Life and Works (446 p., New York, 1921).

---

[c] Philon (first half of first century) wrote in Greek; Saadia largely in Arabic.

Muslim Culture and Philosophy

FOUNDATION OF HISPANO-MUSLIM CIVILIZATION; 'ABD AL-RAḤMĀN III

Ibn Muḥammad ibn 'Abdallāh al-Khalīfa al-Nāṣir. Eighth Umayyad caliph of Cordova from 912 to 961. He founded, in 936, a new city, al-Zahrā', near Cordova, in memory of his favorite wife (Zahrā'), and was a great patron of arts and sciences. Arabic Spain became under him and his successors one of the most civilized and best governed countries of the time. Hrosvitha called Cordova "The Jewel of the World."

C. F. Seybold, in the Encyclopedia of Islam (I, 53, 1908). Reinhard Dozy: Spanish Islam (London, 1913).

AL-FĀRĀBĪ

In Latin, Alpharabius. Abū Naṣr Muḥammad ibn Muḥammad ibn Ṭarkhān ibn Uzlagh al-Fārābī. Born in Wasīj near Fārāb, Turkestan, of a Turkish family. Studied in Bagdad; flourished chiefly in Aleppo; died in Damascus 950–51, aged c. 80. Muslim Neo-platonist and encyclopaedist. His system is a syncretism of Platonism, Aristotelianism, and Ṣūfīsm. As he believed the so-called "Theology of Aristotle" (q. v., second half of fifth century), a late Neo-platonic writing, to be genuine, his conception of Aristotelianism was necessarily wrong. He continued the harmonization of Greek philosophy with Islām begun by al-Kindī, preparing the way for Ibn Sīnā. He wrote a number of commentaries on Aristotle (physics, meteorology, logical treatises, etc.), on Porphyry's "Isagoge," on Ptolemy's Almagest." (He was called "the second teacher," Aristotle being the first.) His own writings deal chiefly with psychology and metaphysics. The most important for us are "The Bezels of Philosophy"[d] (Risāla fuṣūṣ al-ḥikam), a short philosophical introduction; "the Model City" (Risāla fī mabādī ārā' ahl al-madīna al-fāḍila), the organization of an ideal city, of great sociological interest, and above all, treatises on the classification and fundamental principles of science, Kitāb iḥṣā al-'ulūm, "De Scientiis," and "De ortu scientiarum" (lost in Arabic). His classification was essentially the Aristotelian one as transmitted through Philoponos's commentary on the "Isagoge."

Al-Fārābī was conversant with the whole scientific thought of his day. He wrote the most important oriental treatise on the theory of music (Kitāb al-mūsīqī); he had some knowledge of mensural music and recognized the major third (4:5) and the minor third (5:6) as consonances.

Texts and Translations—Alpharabii opera omnia quae latina lingua conscripta reperiri potuerunt, edited by Guil. Camerarius (Paris, 1638).

Friedrich Dieterici: Alfārābī's philosophische Abhandlungen (Die Philosophie der Araber, vols. 14–15, Leiden, 1890–1892. Arabic text and German translation of nine small treatises, including "the bezels of philosophy.")

Friedrich Dieterici: Der Musterstaat (Arabic text, Leiden, 1895); German translation (216 p., Leiden, 1900. With a long introduction on al-Fārābī as founder of Muslim philosophy and on the relations between Greek and Muslim philosophy). Die Staatsleitung von al-Fārābī. Deutsche Bearbeitung mit einer Einleitung über das Wesen der arabischen Philosophie (Aus Dieterici's Nachlasse hrg. von Paul Brönnle, 147 p., Leiden, 1904). Das Buch der Ringsteine Fārābīs mit dem Kommentare des emir Ismā'īl (ibn) el-Ḥoseini el-Fārānī (um 1485) übersetzt und erläutert von M. Horten (Beitr. zur Gesch. d. Philos. des Mittelalters,

[d] This title is explained by Dieterici, Alfārābī's Philosophische Abhandlungen (p. 219).

V, 3, 538 p., Münster, 1906). Alfarabi: Über den Ursprung der Wissenschaften. Eine Einleitungsschrift in die philosophischen Wissenschaften hrg. von Clemens Baeumker (*ibidem,* XIX, 3, 31 p., Münster, 1916. That is, the text of the Liber Alpharabii de ortu scientiarum, as translated c. 1130–1150 by Gundisalvi; Isis, IV, 135).

Criticism—J. G. L. Kosegarten: Alii Ispahensis Liber cantilenarum magnus (Greifswald, 1840–1846). Fried. Dieterici (1821–1903): Die Philosophie der Araber im 9. und 10. Jahrh. aus der Theologie des Aristoteles, den Abhandlungen Alfarabis und den Schriften der Lautern Brüder herausgegeben und übersetzt (16 vols., Leipzig, 1858–1895). Moritz Steinschneider: Alfarabi. Des arabischen Philosophen Leben und Schriften, mit besonderer Rücksicht auf die Geschichte der griechischen Wissenschaft unter den Arabern. Grössentheils nach handschriftlichen Quellen (Mémoires de l'académie des sciences de St. Pétersbourg, 7e série, vol. 13, 278 p., 1869). C. Brockelmann: Arabische Litteratur (vol. 1, 210–213, 1898). M. Worms: Die Lehre von der Anfangslosigkeit der Welt bei den mittelalt. arab. Philosophen des Orients und ihre Bekämpfung durch die arabischen Theologen (Mutakallimūn) (Beitr. zur Gesch. d. Philos. des Mittelalters, III, 4, Münster, 1900). H. Suter: Die Mathematiker und Astronomen der Araber (54–56, 1900); Nachträge (165, 1902). A. Loewenthal: Article in Jewish Encyclopedia (Vol. I, 374, 1901). T. J. De Boer: Geschichte der Philosophie im Islam (98–116, 1901). E. Wiedemann: Über al-Fārābī's Aufzählung der Wissenschaften (Beiträge, XI, Sitzungsber. d. phys. med. Sozietät zu Erlangen, vol. 39, 74–101, 1907. According to Wiedemann, al-Fārābī's classification was based on that of Geminos as preserved by Proclos; Cassiodorus in the meanwhile had developed a different system). Carra de Vaux: Encyclopaedia of Islam (vol. 2, 53–55, 1913). P. M. Bouyges: Sur le De scientiis récemment édité en arabe à Saïda et sur le De divisione philosophiae de Gundissalinus (Mélanges de l'Université St. Joseph, vol. 9, 49–69, Beyrouth, 1924). H. G. Farmer: The Arabian Influence on Musical Theory (Journal R. Asiatic Soc., 61–80, 1925; Isis, VIII, 508).

A study of al-Fārābī from our special point of view is much needed. I was unable to state more specifically his contributions to science, to the philosophy of mathematics, for example, because of the lack of preparatory investigations.

For al-Mas'ūdī, see the geographical section (VII) below.

Christian Philosophers Writing in Arabic

MATTĀ IBN YŪNUS

Abū Bishr Mattā ibn Yūnus (or Yūnān, Ionian?). Of Greek origin; educated at Dair[e] Qunnā, Syria; flourished at Bagdad, where he died c. 940. Christian philosopher and translator from Greek into Syriac and Arabic. Teacher of al-Fārābī. He translated Themistios's commentary (for which see second half of fourth century) on Aristotle's De coelo.[f]

H. Suter: Mathematiker (50, 1900).

YAḤYĀ IBN 'ADĪ

Abū Zakarīyā Yaḥyā ibn 'Adī ibn Ḥamīd. Born at Takrīt in 893, he lived in Bagdad and died there in 974. Jacobite translator from Syriac into Arabic. Pupil of Mattā ibn Yūnus and of al-Fārābī. He revised Mattā's translation of Themistios's commentary on Aristotle's "De coelo" and translated the commentary

---

[e] Dair means monastery.
[f] This translation was revised by Yaḥyā ibn 'Adī, q. v., below.

of Alexander of Aphrodisias[9] (q. v., first half of third century) on Aristotle's meteorology.

Texts—Petits traités apologétiques, texte arabe et traduction francaise par Augustin Périer (135 p., Paris, 1920).
Criticism—H. Suter: Mathematiker (59, 68, 1900). Abbé Augustin Périer: Yaḥyā ben 'Adī (Thèse, Paris, 228 p., Paris, 1920; Isis, VII, 185).

IV. MUSLIM, BYZANTINE, AND CHINESE MATHEMATICS AND ASTRONOMY

Muslim Mathematicians

IBN AL-ADAMĪ

Muḥammad ibn al-Ḥusain ibn Ḥamīd. Flourished at the end of the ninth century or the beginning of the tenth. Muslim astronomer. He compiled astronomical tables which were completed after his death by his pupil al-Qāsim ibn Muḥammad ibn Hishām al-Madānī. They appeared in 920–21 under the title Naẓm al-'iqd ("Arrangement of the Pearl Necklace"), together with a theoretical introduction (lost?).

H. Suter: Mathematiker . . . . (44, 1920).

IBN AMĀJŪR

Abū-l-Qāsim 'Abdallāh Ibn Amājūr (or Mājūr?) al-Turkī. He originated from Farghāna, Turkestān, and flourished c. 885–933. Muslim astronomer. One of the greatest observers among the Muslims. He made many observations between 885 and 933, together with his son Abū-l-Ḥasan 'Alī and an emancipated slave of the latter, named Mufliḥ. Father and son are often called the Banū Amājūr. Some of their observations are recorded by Ibn Yūnus. Together they produced many astronomical tables: the Pure (al-khāliṣ), the Girdled (al-muzannar), the Wonderful (al-badī'), tables of Mars according to Persian chronology, etc.

H. Suter: Mathematiker (49, 211, 1900; 165, 1902).

ABŪ KĀMIL

Abū Kāmil Shujā' ibn Aslam ibn Muḥammad ibn Shujā' al-ḥāsib al-Miṣrī, i. e., the Egyptian calculator. He originated from Egypt and flourished after al-Khwārizmī, who died c. 850, and before al-'Imrānī, who died in 955. We may place him tentatively about the beginning of the tenth century. Mathematician. He perfected al-Khwārizmī's work on algebra. Determination and construction of both roots of quadratic equations. Multiplication and division of algebraic quantities. Addition and subtraction of radicals (corresponding to our formula $\sqrt{a} \pm \sqrt{b} = \sqrt{a + b \pm \sqrt{2ab}}$.) Study of the pentagon and decagon (algebraic treatment). His work was largely used by al-Karkhī and Leonardo da Pisa.

Texts and Translations—Gustavo Sacerdote: Il trattato del pentagone e del decagono per la prima volta pubblicato in italiano (Steinschneider's Festschrift,

---

[9] Another commentary of his, on Aristotle's physics, was translated by a Sabian called Ibn Rauḥ and revised by Yaḥyā ibn 'Adī.

169–194, Leipzig, 1896). H. Suter: Die Abhandlung über das Fünfeck und Zehneck (Bibliotheca Mathematica, vol. 10, 15–42, 1910); Das Buch der Seltenheiten der Rechenkunst. Übersetzt und mit Kommentar versehen (*ibidem*, vol. 11, 100–120, 1911). Other works exist in Latin or Hebrew translations. An English translation of Abū Kāmil's algebra is highly desirable.

Criticism—Suter: Die Mathematiker und Astronomen der Araber (43, 1900; Nachträge, 164, 1902). L. C. Karpinski: The Algebra of Abū Kāmil (Bibliotheca mathematica, vol. 12, 40–41, 1912. Based upon the Paris manuscript 7377 A, from which long extracts are quoted). More popular treatment of same subject under same title in American Mathematical Monthly (vol. 21, 37–48, 1914).

ABŪ 'UTHMĀN

Abū 'Uthmān Sa'īd ibn Ya'qūb al-Dimishqī (Or Dimashqī, i. e., the Damascene). Flourished at Bagdad under al-Muqtadir, Khalīfa from 908 to 932. Muslim physician and mathematician. He translated into Arabic works of Aristotle, Euclid, Galen (on temperaments and on the pulse), and Porphyry. His most important translation was that of Book X of Euclid, together with Pappos's commentary on it which is extant only in Arabic. The supervision of hospitals in Bagdad, Mekka, and Medina was intrusted to him in 915.

Text—Heinrich Suter: Der Kommentar des Pappus zum X. Buche des Euklides (Abhandlungen zur Geschichte der Naturwissenschaften, Heft. 4, 9–78, Erlangen, 1922. German translation; Isis, V, 492). An improved translation in English, with commentary, is being prepared by William Thomson (1926).

Criticism—L. Leclerc: Médecine arabe (vol. 1, 374, 1876. Only a few lines). H. Suter: Die Mathematiker und Astronomen der Araber (49, 211, 1900). Max Meyerhof: New Light on Ḥunain (Isis, VIII, 710, 1926).

AL-BALKHĪ

Abū Zaid Aḥmad ibn Sahl al-Balkhī. Born in Shāmistiyān, province of Balkh, died in 934. Geographer, mathematician. A member of the Imāmīya sect; disciple of al-Kindī. Of the many books ascribed to him in the Fihrist, I quote: the excellency of mathematics; on certitude in astrology. His "Figures of the Climates" (Ṣuwar al-aqālīm) consisted chiefly of geographical maps.

The "Book of the Creation and of History" formerly ascribed to him was really written in 966 by Muṭahhar ibn Ṭāhir al-Maqdisī (q. v., next chapter).

M. J. de Goeje: Die Iṣṭakhrī-Balkhī Frage (Z. d. deutschen morgenl. Ges., vol. 25, 42–58, 1871). Suter: Die Mathematiker und Astronomen der Araber (211, 1900). Clément Huart: Arabic Literature (301, London, 1903); Encyclopedia of Islam (vol. 1, 624, 1911).

For Sinān ibn Thābit, see the medical section (VIII) below.
For al-Hamdānī, see the geographical section (VII) below.

IBRĀHĪM IBN SINĀN

Abū Isḥāq Ibrāhīm ibn Sinān ibn Thābit ibn Qurra. Born in 908–9, died in 946. Grandson of Thābit ibn Qurra (q. v., second half of ninth century); his father Sinān, who embraced Islām and died in 943, was also a distinguished astronomer and mathematician (see medical section below). Muslim mathematician and astronomer. He wrote commentaries on the first book of "Conics" and on the "Almagest," and many papers on geometrical and astronomical subjects (for example, on sundials). His quadrature of the parabola was much simpler than that of Archimedes, in fact the simplest ever made before the invention of the integral calculus.

Texts and Translations—H. Suter: Abhandlung über die Ausmessung der Parabel aus dem Arabischen übersetzt und commentiert (Vierteljahrschrift der Naturforschenden Gesellschaft in Zürich, 63, 214–28, 1918; Isis, IV, 580).
Criticism—H. Suter: Die Mathematiker und Astronomen der Araber (53, 1900).

AL-'IMRĀNĪ

'Alī ibn Aḥmad al-'Imrānī. Born at Mosul in Upper Mesopotamia; he flourished there and died in 955–56. Muslim mathematician and astrologer. He wrote a commentary on Abū Kāmil's algebra and various astrological treatises. One of these, on the choosing of (auspicious) days, was translated by Savasorda at Barcelona in 1133 or 1134 (De electionibus) (q. v., first half of twelfth century).

H. Suter: Mathematiker (56, 1900; 165, 1902).

BYZANTINE MATHEMATICS

HERO THE YOUNGER

Hero of Byzantium ('Ηρώ). Flourished in Constantinople c. 938. Land surveyor, who wrote, c. 938, a treatise on surveying, based upon the work of Heron of Alexandria, especially his "Dioptra." He may be also the author of a treatise on poliorcetics, which dates from the same time.

Texts and Translations—A. J. H. Vincent: Extraits des manuscrits relatifs à la géométrie pratique des Grecs (Notices et extraits des MSS., vol. 19, 157–431, 1858. Contains the text of the περὶ διόπτρας of Heron of Alexandria, and of the γεωδαισία ascribed to Hero of Byzantium, p. 348–407, with French translation). The πολιορκητικά were published by Thévenot in his Mathematici veteres (Paris, 1693. De machinis bellicis). Critical edition by C. Wescher: Poliorcétique des Grecs (195–279, Paris, 1867). Extraits des Poliorcétiques de Héron in Albert de Rochas d'Aiglun (1837–1914). La poliorcétique des Grecs (Bulletin de la société d'émulation du Doubs, 1872). Both texts were long known only through the Latin translation published by Francesco Barozzi (Barocius) (Venezia, 1572).
Criticism—Th. Henri Martin: Recherches sur la vie et les ouvrages d'Héron d'Alexandrie (Mémoires présentés à l'Académie des Inscriptions, Vol. 4, 1854). Vincent: Introduction and Notes (1858). See also Heron of Alexandria (first half of first century B. C.).

For Chinese mathematics see my note on Liu Hsü in the historical section (IX), below.

V. BYZANTINE, MUSLIM, AND CHINESE PHYSICS, ALCHEMY, AND TECHNOLOGY

For Byzantine physics and technology, see my note on Hero the Younger, above.
For Muslim alchemy, see my note on Ibn Waḥshīya, in the botanical section (VI), below.
For Muslim physics (music), see my note on al-Fārābī in Section III above.

Chinese Technology

FÊNG TAO

Fêng^{2} Tao^{4} (3586, 10780), or Fêng^{2} Ying^{2} Wang^{2} (3586, 13329, 12493). Born at Ying^{2}-chou^{1} (13329, 2444), Chihli, in 881; prime minister under four of the "Five Dynasties" and under seven emperors! Died in 954. Fêng Tao is traditionally considered by the Chinese as the inventor of printing. Of course, he is not the inventor and had nothing to do with the invention, not even with its technical improvement.[h] But he deserves to be honored, for he did perhaps more than any other man to launch the invention and to develop its full cultural value. Until his time but little printing had been done, and this almost exclusively in Buddhist monasteries.

Fêng Tao, wishing to fix forever the correct text of the Classics, ordered in 932 the preparation and printing of a standard edition under the supervision of the National Academy. Between 836 and 841 the Classics had been cut in stone at Si-an-fu (some of these stones still exist), but without commentary. Fêng Tao's edition, based upon the same manuscript sources, included both text and commentary; it filled 130 volumes and was presented to the emperor in 953.

While this monumental edition was being printed at the national capital, Si-an-fu (Ch'ang-an), another was printed under the direction of Wu^{2} Chao^{4}-i^{4} (12765, 474, 5392) at I-chou (Ch'eng-tu), the capital of the Empire of Shu (Szechuen), but we have only meager records of that rival edition. Buddhist printing was going on too, and about that time it reached Korea. The earliest Korean book is dated 950; it is a sūtra, not translated from the Sanskrit, but originally written in Chinese.

The printing of the Classics marks the beginning of a Confucian, and more generally of a cultural, renaissance which culminated in the twelfth century. It inaugurated the enormous and magnificent activity in printing which is one of the glories of the Sung dynasty. As example of that activity it will suffice to mention the printing of the dynastic histories in many hundred volumes (994 to 1063), the printing of the whole Buddhist canon (Tripiṭaka) c. 972 (1,521 works, most of them translated from the Sanskrit, in 5,000 volumes, 130,000 pages!), the printing of the Taoist canon c. 1016.

H. A. Giles: Chinese Biographical Dictionary (227, Shanghai, 1898). Thomas Francis Carter: Invention of Printing in China (47–54, New York, 1925; Isis, VIII, 366).

VI. ENGLISH AND MUSLIM BOTANY

Anglo-Saxon Botany and Medicine

Books on herbs were studied in England as early as the eighth century, and it is probable that by that time the Anglo-Saxons had already accumulated the greatest part of their herb-lore. The earliest Saxon manuscript, however, wherein that lore is explained is the so-called Leech Book of Bald, dating from about the first half of the tenth century, and which was kept for a time at the monastery of Glastonbury. According to J. F. Payne,[i] the herb-lore contained in that

[h] See my notes on Chinese technology in the second half of the sixth century; Ming Huang (first half of eighth century); Shōtoku-tennō (second half of eighth century); Chinese technology in the second half of the ninth century.

[i] Lecture before the Royal College of Physicians in 1903.

book is more comprehensive than the Salernitan knowledge, though the texts representing the latter are of a later date.[j] The Book of Bald is probably the oldest existing leech-book written in the vernacular. The leech Bald, under whose direction it was compiled from earlier sources, written or oral, was probably in touch with King Alfred. Indeed one of the chapters contains prescriptions sent by Helias, Patriarch of Jerusalem, to the King.

The "Lacnunga" (Recipes) is a much smaller Anglo-Saxon manuscript of the same kind and time. It is still a moot question whether this Anglo-Saxon plant-lore is entirely original or could not be traced back indirectly to Greek sources.

Text—Rev. Oswald Cockayne: Leechdoms, Wortcunning, and Starcraft in early England (Rolls Series, 3 vols., London, 1864–1866; vol. 2, 1865, is entirely devoted to the Book of Bald, with a glossary and an English translation; the text and translation of Lacnunga are in vol. 3, p. 1–80, 1866).

Criticism—J. F. Payne: English Medicine in the Anglo-Saxon Times (Oxford, 1904). Eleanour Sinclair Rohde: Old English Herbals (London, 1922, chapter 1; Isis, V, 457; VI, 213).

Muslim Agriculture

IBN WAḤSHĪYA

Abū Bakr Aḥmad (or Muḥammad) ibn 'Alī Ibn al-Waḥshīya al-Kaldānī or al-Nabaṭī. Born in 'Irāq of a Nabataean family,[k] flourished about the end of the third century H., i. e., before 912. Alchemist. Author of alchemical and occult writings (quoted in the Fihrist). He wrote c. 904 the so-called "Nabataean agriculture" (Kitāb al-falāḥa al-nabaṭīya), an alleged translation from ancient Babylonian sources, the purpose of which was to extol the Babylonian-Aramean-Syrian civilization (or more simply the "old" civilization before the hegira) against that of the conquering Arabs. It contains valuable information on agriculture and superstitions.

This forgery became famous because the great Russian orientalist Khvolson was entirely deceived by it. Of course, Ibn Waḥshīya was as unable to read the cuneiform texts as the Egyptian Arabs the hieroglyphic.

Text—Ahmad ibn Abubekr bin Wahshih. Ancient alphabets and hieroglyphic characters explained, with an account of the Egyptian priests, their classes, initiation, and sacrifices. Arabic text with translation by Joseph Hammer [-Purgstall] (214 p., London, 1806). This is the translation of another apocryphal work, the Kitāb shauq al-mustahām fī ma'rifat rumūz al-aqlām.

Criticism—Fihrist (311–312, 358). See unsigned article in Encyclopedia of Islam (II, p. 427). Ernst Meyer: Geschichte der Botanik (vol. 3, 43–88, 1856. Important). Daniil Abramovich Khvolson: Über die Überreste der altbabylonischen Literatur in arabischen Übersetzungen (Memoirs of the Russian Imperial Acad., vol. 8, 1859). L. Leclerc: Histoire de la médecine arabe (vol. 1, 307–315, 1876). Brockelmann: Geschichte der arabischen Literatur (vol. 1, 242–243, 1898). L. C. Karpinski: Hindu Numerals Among the Arabs (Bibliotheca Mathematica,

[j] The Anglo-Saxons knew and used at least 500 plants.

[k] The Nabataeans were the descendants of the old population of Chaldaea and Babylon; their national language was Aramaic. The term Nabataean was often used, however, in a conventional and indefinite way, as modern occultists use the terms Chaldaean, Coptic, or Hindu.

vol. 13, 97–98, 1913). Lippmann quotes him twice in his Alchemie (p. 352, 415, 1919). E. Wiedemann: Zur nabataeischen Landwirtschaft (Z. für Semitistik, vol. 1, 201–202, 1922).

VII. MUSLIM AND JAPANESE GEOGRAPHY

IBN SERAPION

Ibn Sarāfyūn (?). Not to be mistaken for the physician Yaḥyā ibn Sarāfyūn dealt with in the preceding chapter. Flourished in Mesopotamia at the beginning of the tenth century. Muslim geographer. Author of a book of geography containing a description of the various seas, islands, lakes, mountains, and rivers of the world. His descriptions of the Euphrates and Tigris and of the Nile are particularly interesting. His account of the canals of Bagdad[1] is our main basis for the reconstruction of the mediaeval plan of that city. This reconstruction was splendidly done by Guy Le Strange (1900) who used many other authorities, chiefly Ya'qūbī. Ibn Serapion's account of the network of the water system and Ya'qūbī's description of the highroads radiating from Bagdad complete one another very well.

Text—Guy Le Strange: Description of Mesopotamia and Baghdad, written about the year 900 A. D. by Ibn Serapion. The Arabic text edited from a manuscript in the British Museum with translation and notes (Journal Roy. Asiatic Soc., 1–76, 255–315, 1895).
Criticism—Guy Le Strange: Baghdad during the Abbasid Caliphate (Oxford, 1900; reprinted, 1924).

IBN RUSTA

Abū 'Alī Aḥmad ibn 'Umar Ibn Rusta. Flourished at Iṣfahān, c. 903. Persian geographer. He compiled c. 903 an encyclopaedia called "The Very Precious Things," or "The Precious Bags of Traveling Provisions" (al-a'lāq al-nafīsa), of which the geographical portion is extant. It contains an introduction dealing with the celestial and terrestrial spheres, then proceeds to describe the countries.

Text and Translation—Kitāb al-a'lāq an-nafīsa auctore Ibn Rosteh. . . . . Edidit M. J. De Goeje (Biblioth. geograph. arabic., VII, Leiden, 1892). Extracts have been published by Khvolson with Russian translation.
Criticism—C. van Arendonck: Encyclopedia of Islam (vol. 2, 410, 1918).

IBN AL-FAQĪH

Abū Bakr Aḥmad ibn Muḥammad ibn Isḥāq Ibn al-Faqīh al-Hamadhānī. Born in Hamadhān, Persia. Flourished c. 903. Persian geographer. He completed, c. 903, a "Book of the Countries" (Kitāb al-buldān), often quoted by al-Muqaddasī and Yāqūt. This book is lost, but we have a compendium of it, possibly the work of 'Alī ibn Ja'far ibn Aḥmad al-Shaizarī, c. 1022.

Text—Compendium libri Kitāb al-boldān auctore Ibn al-Faqīh al-Hamadhānī, edited by M. J. De Goeje (Bibliotheca geographorum arabicorum, 5, Leiden, 1885).
Criticism—C. Brockelmann: Arabische Litteratur (vol. 1, 227, 1898).

AL-JAIHĀNĪ

Minister at the Sāmānid court in Transoxiana, flourished c. 893 to 907. Persian topographer. Author of an extensive road-book which is lost, but which was

[1] Posterior to 901; anterior to 945.

possibly used by al-Idrīsī (second half of the twelfth century). He it is who caused Abū Dulaf to go to India.

C. Brockelmann: Arabische Litteratur (vol. 1, 228, 1898. Brockelmann says that al-Jaihānī's work was an elaboration of the Kitāb al-kharāj of Qudāma; then Qudāma's work must be earlier than I have said or al-Jaihānī's later?).

ABŪ ZAID

Abū Zaid al-Ḥasan al-Sīrāfī, i. e., from Sīrāf on the Persian Gulf; contemporary of al-Mas'ūdī. Arabic geographer, who edited, c. 920, the accounts of Muslim travelers in order to complete Sulaimān's relation (see first half of ninth century). He refers particularly to one Ibn Wahb, who visited the Chinese court in 870, and to a merchant from Khurāsān. This compilation was probably entitled "Information about China and India" (Akhbār al-Ṣīn wal-Hind); it is the most important work of its kind before that of Marco Polo. It contains information on China, India, Khurāsān, the southern coast of Arabia, the Zanzibar coast, and describes the sack of Khānfū (Hangchow)[m] in 878.

Texts and Translations—See Sulaimān the Merchant (first half of ninth century), Abū Zaid's work having always been published together with Sulaimān's.

Criticism—The best accounts will be found in Reinaud's Géographie d'Aboulféda (vol. 1, 1848), in his Mémoire of 1849, and in Beazley (1897). See also E. H. F. Meyer: Geschichte der Botanik (vol. 3, 373–378, 1856).

IBN FAḌLĀN

Aḥmad ibn Faḍlān ibn 'Abbās ibn Rāshid ibn Ḥammād. Muslim traveler. Sent by the Caliph al-Muqtadir, in 921, to the King of the Bulgarians, residing along the Volga. His description is the earliest reliable account of Russia. It was almost completely included in Yāqūt's geographical dictionary.

Text and Translation—Christian Martin Frähn: Ibn-Fozlan's und anderer Araber Berichte über die Russen älterer Zeit (Text und Übersetzung, mit Anmerkungen und Beilagen. 360 p., St. Petersburg, 1823).

Criticism—C. Raymond Beazley: Dawn of Modern Geography (Vol. I, 434–438, 1897). Carl Brockelmann: Gesch. d. arabischen Litteratur (Vol. I, 227, 1898).

QUDĀMA

Abū-l-Faraj Qudāma ibn Ja'far al-Kātib al-Baghdādī,[n] died in 948–49. Christian revenue accountant who embraced Islām under the caliphate of al-Muqtafī (902 to 908). He wrote (seemingly after 928) a book on the land-tax (Kitāb al-kharāj), containing an account of the organization of the postal service and much geographical information. The latter is essentially of the kind given in Ibn Khurdādhbih's road-book.

We have, in all, four such Muslim road-books which complement each other. See my notes on Ibn Khurdādhbih and al-Ya'qūbī (second half of ninth century), Ibn Rusta, and Qudāma. Another by al-Jaihānī is lost.

---

[m] Or Canton? (Pelliot. T'oung Pao, vol. 21, 410, 1922). It was the center of Muslim and other foreign trade in China at that time.

[n] Meaning "the secretary of Bagdad." The dates given by me are derived from M. J. de Goeje, but according to Brockelmann (Gesch. der arab. Lit., vol. 1, 228), Qudāma died in 922–23 (?).

Text and Translations—Excerpta e Kitāb al-kharādj, edited and translated into French, with notes and glossary, by M. J. de Goeje at the end of his edition of Ibn Khurdādhbih in Bibliotheca Geographorum Arabicorum (vol. 6, Leyde, 1889).
Criticism—G. Le Strange: The Lands of the Eastern Caliphate (12, Cambridge, 1905).

For al-Balkhī, see the mathematical section (IV), above.

AL-HAMDĀNĪ

Abū Muḥammad al-Ḥasan ibn Aḥmad ibn Ya'qūb al-Hamdānī ibn al-Ḥā'ik.[o] Born of a Yemenite family; died in prison at Ṣan'ā in 945–46. Arab geographer, archaeologist, astronomer. He wrote a geography of Arabia. (Ṣifāt jazīrat al-'Arab) and a great work on the history and antiquities of Yemen called "The Crown" (al-iklīl). This work contains much information on the scientific ideas of the early Arabs (cosmology, astronomy, natural philosophy). He compiled astronomical tables for Yemen.

Text—The Ṣifāt was edited by D. H. Müller (Leiden, 1884).
Only a part of the Iklīl has been published (and translated) by D. H. Müller in the Sitzungsb. der Wiener Akademie (vols. 94 and 97, 1879–1880).
Criticism—F. Wüstenfeld: Geschichtschreiber (p. 36, 1881). C. Brockelmann: Arabische Litteratur (vol. 1, 229, 1898). H. Suter: Mathematiker (53, 1900). R. A. Nicholson: Literary History of the Arabs (11, 12, 24, 1907).

ABŪ DULAF

Abū Dulaf Mis'ar ibn al-Muhalhal al-Khazrajī al-Yanbū'ī. Born in Yambo, near Mecca; flourished in Bukhārā at the court of the Sāmānid prince Naṣr ibn Aḥmad ibn Ismā'īl, who ruled from 913 to 942. Poet and traveler. C. 942 he returned to southern India across Tibet with the embassy of the Hindu prince Kalatli ibn Shakhbar and came back by way of Kashmīr, Afghanistān, and Sijistān. He wrote a narrative of his journeys called "Marvels of the Countries" ('Ajā'ib al-buldān), extracts from which have been preserved by Yāqūt and Qazwīnī.

Kurt de Schlözer: Abu Dolaf Misaris ben Mohalhal De itinere suo asiatico commentarius (Berlin, 1845). C. Brockelmann: Geschichte der arabischen Literatur (vol. 1, 228, 1898). J. Marquart: Das Itinerar des Mi'sar nach der chinesischen Haupstadt, in Osteuropäische und ostasiatische Steifzüge (74–95, Leipzig, 1903). French translation of the texts in G. Ferrand: Relations de voyages arabes, persans et turcs (vol. 1, 208 f., Paris, 1913). Yule: Cathay and the Way Thither (new edition, vol. 1, 1915. Was the journey to China or to India and is the narrative genuine or not? An abstract from Abū Dulaf's travels is given on p. 244–255).

AL-MAS'ŪDĪ

Abū-l-Ḥasan 'Alī ibn al-Ḥusain ibn 'Alī al-Mas'ūdī. Born in Bagdad about the end of the third century H., i. e., before 912. Spent the last ten years of his life in Syria and Egypt, died in Cairo c. 957. Mu'tazilite Arab. Traveler, geographer, historian. He traveled extensively, though the extent of his travels has probably been exaggerated; e. g., it is very doubtful whether he actually reached

[o] Son of the weaver. This name, Ibn al-Ḥā'ik, is sometimes used to designate him.

China and Madagascar. His main work extant is called "Meadows[p] of gold and mines of precious stones" (Murūj al-dhahab wa-ma'ādin al-jawāhir), a historico-geographical encyclopaedia written c. 947 (revised in 956–57). It is remarkable because of the catholicity of its author, who neglected no source of information, and of his truly scientific curiosity (description of the earthquake of 955, of the waters of the Dead Sea, geological discussions, etc.). We find in it the earliest mention of windmills (in Sijistān).[q] Another work written in the last year of his life is the "Book of Indication and Revision" (Kitāb al-tanbīh wal-ishrāf); it is a summary and revision of his life's work; it gives one an outline of al-Mas'ūdī's philosophy of nature and of his views on evolution ("from mineral to plant, from plant to animal, and from animal to man").[r] Al-Mas'ūdī has been compared to Pliny.

Texts and Translations—Les Prairies d'Or. Texte et traduction par C. Barbier de Meynard et Pavet de Courteille (Paris, Société asiatique, 9 vols., 1861–1877. Vols. 4 to 9 were edited by Barbier alone; vol. 9 contains an elaborate index, also a reprint of Silvestre de Sacy's memoir of 1810, quoted below). The fourth chapter of this work (dealing with India) had been published in Arabic and Latin by Joh. Gildemeister before, De rebus indicis loci et opuscula inedita (Bonn, 1838). An English translation was undertaken by Aloys Sprenger (Vol. I, London, 1841. No more published).

The Kitāb al-tanbīh was edited by M. J. de Goeje in his Bibliotheca geographorum arabicorum (vol. 8, Leyden, 1894). An analysis of it had been published previously by Silvestre de Sacy: Le livre de l'indication et de l'admonition ou l'indicateur et le moniteur. (Notices et extraits des MSS., vol. 8, 132–199, 1810. Reprinted in the Prairies d'Or, vol. 9, 301–376.) French translation by Carra de Vaux: Le livre de l'avertissement et de la revision (582 p., Paris, 1896).

Carra de Vaux: L'abrégé des merveilles traduit de l'arabe d'après les MSS. de la Bibliothèque Nationale (450 p., Société philologique, Paris, 1898). This work might be ascribed to al-Mas'ūdī, but I gather from the editor's cautious summary of the question that it is probably not al-Mas'ūdī's, though it can hardly be of a later date. At any rate, it is an important source for the study of Muslim folk-lore in the tenth century.

Further bibliography in Victor Chauvin: Bibliographie des ouvrages arabes (vol. 7, 91–93, 1903).

Criticism—Ibn Khaldūn speaks very highly of al-Mas'ūdī (see his Prolégomènes, p. 65, 1862, but see also p. 73 f., 223 f.). E. H. F. Meyer: Geschichte der Botanik (vol. 3, 269–278, 1856). E. Renan: Les prairies d'or. Mélanges d'histoire et de voyage (253–275, Paris, 1890. Written c. 1873 apropos of Barbier's translation). Friedrich Dieterici: Der Darwinismus im X. und XIX. Jahrh. (Die Philosophie der Araber, 9, 240 p., Leipzig, 1878). C. Brockelmann: Arabische Litteratur (vol. 1, 143–145, 1898). E. Wiedemann: Über den brief des goldenen Hauses von Aristoteles (Beitr. III, Sitzungsb. d. phys. med. Soc., vol. 37, 388–391, Erlangen, 1905.

---

[p] The translation of Murūj by "meadows" does not seem to fit the sense or the parallelism. It has been suggested that it means "washings," in the mining sense. (D. B. M.)

[q] Prairies d'Or (vol. 2, 80). It would seem that windmills were invented by the Muslims or some other Eastern people. An anecdote relative to the caliph 'Umar (A. D. 644) would suggest that windmills were already known in Arabia in the first half of the seventh century (?) The anecdote is quoted by Muir and Weir: The Caliphate (187, Edinburgh, 1915.) The earliest mention of them in the West is found in a French charter of 1105, molendina ad ventum (Magasin pittoresque, vol. 20, 50, 1852).

[r] This was a commonplace among the more philosophical writers of his time. But does he say that the one stage actually developed into the other next to it? Is it not that we found these phenomena in nature and could arrange them in such a series? (D. B. M.)

From Mas'ūdī's Book of Indication and Revision). C. Field: Tales of the caliphs (1909. Based on al-Mas'ūdī). E. G. Browne: Arabian Medicine (117–118, Cambridge, 1921). Carra de Vaux: Les penseurs de l'Islam (vol. 1, 95–105, Paris, 1921; also vol. 2, 2, 42, 190, 202, 354).

KI TSURAYUKI

Or simply Tsurayuki. Born in 833; died in 946. Japanese poet. Chiefly known as principal editor of a collection of Japanese and Chinese poems, the Kokin-wakashū[a] begun in 905, completed in 922. I quote him (with some diffidence) because of his diary of a journey from the province of Tosa (where he had been governor) to the capital, Kyōto. (This took then a hundred days!) That diary, called Tosa-nikki, was written in 935, in "feminine" fashion, that is, not in Chinese, but in Japanese language and script. Its topographical value is small, but its literary and psychological values are great; it is one of the classics of Japanese literature.

W. G. Aston: An Ancient Japanese Classic, the Tosa Diary (Transactions of the Asiatic society of Japan, vol. 3, part 2, 121–130, 1875. Largely reprinted in his History of Japanese Literature). E. Papinot: Historical Dictionary (273, 300, 1909).

VIII. ENGLISH, BYZANTINE, AND ARABIC MEDICINE

For English (or more exactly Anglo-Saxon) medicine see my note on the earliest leech-books in the botanical section (VI), above.

Byzantine Medicine

NONNOS

Theophanes Nonnos (Θεοφάνης Νόννος). Flourished under Constantinos VII Porphyrogennetos, emperor from 912 to 959. Byzantine physician. Upon Constantinos's order, he compiled a medical compendium in 297 chapters (ἰατρικά or ἰατρικόν) largely based upon Oribasios, Aëtios, Alexandros of Tralles, and Paulos Aegineta. He wrote also a treatise on diet and a dispensatory (Τὰ εὐπόριστα, i. e., φάρμακα, the usual (easy to obtain) remedies). His work is uncritical, but remarkably free from many of the superstitions of his day.

Text—'Επιτομὴ τῆς ἰατρικῆς ἁπάσης τέχνης. Greek and Latin edition (Strasbourg, 1568). New edition, Greek and Latin, Epitome de curatione morborum, by Joh. Steph. Bernard (2 vols., Gotha, 1794–1795).
Criticism—Ernst H. F. Meyer: Geschichte der Botanik (vol. 3, 341–344, 1856). Iwan Bloch in Puschmann: Geschichte der Medizin (vol. 1, 560, 1902).

Arabic Medicine

ISḤĀQ AL-ISRĀ'ĪLĪ

Isaac Judaeus. Isaac Israeli the Elder. (Not to be mistaken for the Spanish astronomer Isaac Israeli the Younger; q. v., first half of fourteenth century.) Isaac ben Solomon. Abū Ya'qūb Isḥāq ibn Sulaimān al-Isrā'īlī. Born in Egypt; flourished in Qairawān, Tunis, where he died, a centenarian, about the middle of the tenth century (c. 932?). Jewish physician and philosopher. One of the

[a] Or Kokinshū (ancient and modern poems). It forms 20 volumes and contains more than 1,100 poems, mostly tanka (31 syllables).

first to direct the attention of the Jews to Greek science and philosophy. Physician to the Fāṭimid caliph 'Ubaid Allāh al-Mahdī (909 to 934), he composed at his request many medical writings in Arabic. Translated into Latin in 1087 by Constantine the African, into Hebrew, and into Spanish, their influence was very great. The main medical writings are: on fevers (Kitāb al-ḥummayāt); the book of simple drugs and nutriments (Kitāb al-adwiya al-mufrada wal-aghdhiya; diaetae universales et particulares); on urine (Kitāb al-baul, by far the most elaborate mediaeval treatise on the subject); on deontology, the "Guide of the Physicians" (lost in Arabic; extant in Hebrew under the title of Manhig (or Mūsar) hā-rōfe'īm). He wrote also a medico-philosophical treatise on the elements (Kitāb al-istiqsāt), and another on definitions. Isaac was the earliest Jewish philosopher (or one of the earliest) to publish a classification of the sciences. This was essentially the Aristotelian one as transmitted and modified by the Muslims.

Texts and Translations—The first text to be printed was the Tractatus de particularibus diaetis (Padua, 1487): the three last of the four sections composing the al-ḥummayāt.

First complete edition, Omnia opera Isaaci (Lyon, 1515).

The Guide of the Physicians has been translated into Italian by Soave: Giornale Veneto delle scienze mediche (1861), and into German by David Kaufmann: Magaz. f. d. Wissenschaft d. Judentums (vol. 11, 97–112, Berlin, 1884).

Joh. Peine: Die Harnschrift des Isaac Judaeus (Diss., 78 p., Berlin, 1919; Isis, IV, 579). A better text than that of the Opera omnia (1515).

Salomon Fried: Das Buch über die Elemente. Ein Beitrag zur jüdischen Religionsphilosophie des Mittelalters von Isaak b. Salomon Israeli, nach dem aus dem Arabischen ins Hebräische übersetzten Texte von Abraham b. Samuel Halevi ibn Chasdai (I. Einleitender Theil., 83 p., Leipzig, 1884; reprinted together with Hebrew text in 1900).

Hartwig Hirschfeld: Das Buch der Definitionen in der hebräischen Übersetzung des Nissim b. Salomon (Festschrift zu Moritz Steinschneider, 233–234, 1896; Hebrew text, 131–141).

Criticism—Wüstenfeld: Geschichte der arabischen Aerzte (51–52, 1840). Leclerc: Histoire de la médecine arabe (vol. 1, 409–412, 1876). Jacob Guttmann: Die philosophischen Lehren des Isaac b. Salomon (Beitr. zur Gesch. d. Phil. des Mittelalters, X, 4, 76 p., Münster, 1911). Max Seligsohn: Article Israeli, in Jewish Encyclopedia (vol. 6, 670, 1914). Isaac Husik: History of Medieval Jewish Philosophy (1–16, 1918). Harry A. Wolfson: The Classification of Sciences in Mediaeval Jewish Philosophy (Hebrew Union College Jubilee Volume, 263–315, 1925).

EUTYCHIOS

Sa'īd ibn al-Biṭrīq. Born at Fusṭāṭ 876; died in Alexandria 939–40. Christian physician and historian. Melchite Patriarch of Alexandria from 933 to his death. Author of a treatise on medicine and of historical and apologetical writings.

Texts and Translations—The medical treatise is apparently lost. His universal history, "Jewels Ranged in Order" (Naẓm al-jawhar), has been translated into Latin by Ed. Pococke (Oxford, 1658–1659). Aubrey Stewart: Extracts from Aristeas, Hecataeus, Origen, and other Early Writers (Palestine Pilgrims' Text Society, 28, p. 35–68, London, 1895. English translation of Eutychii Annales, Book II, 213–289).

Criticism—F. Wüstenfeld: Geschichte der arabischen Aerzte (52, Göttingen, 1840). Leclerc: Médecine arabe (vol. 1, 404, 1876). Heinrich Selzer: Sextus Julius Africanus (vol. 2, 409–410, 1885). Encyclopedia of Islam (vol. 2, 33, 1913).

For Abū 'Uthmān, see my note in the mathematical section (IV), above.

SINĀN IBN THĀBIT

Abū Sa'īd Sinān ibn Thābit ibn Qurra. Son of the famous Thābit ibn Qurra (q. v., second half of ninth century). Flourished at Bagdad and died there in 943. Born a Ḥarrānian, he embraced Islām in middle life. Muslim physician, mathematician, astronomer. Various mathematical and astronomical writings are ascribed to him. He was physician to three successive caliphs, al-Muqtadir, al-Qāhir, and al-Rāḍī; they ruled from 908 to 940. His main title to fame is his brilliant administration of the Bagdad hospitals and his efforts to raise the scientific standards of the medical profession. In the year 931–32 the Bagdad leeches were forbidden to practice unless they had been examined and received a diploma. Sinān, who was in charge of this, examined more than 800 of them!

F. Wüstenfeld: Arabische Ärzte (36, 1840); Geschichtschreiber der Araber (1881). L. Leclerc: Médecine arabe (vol. 1, 365–368, 1876). C. Brockelmann: Arabische Litteratur (vol. 1, 218, 1898). H. Suter: Mathematiker (51, 224, 1900). E. G. Browne: Arabian medicine (27, 40–41, Cambridge, 1921).

IX. LATIN, ARABIC, AND CHINESE HISTORIOGRAPHY

Latin Historiography

REGINO OF PRÜM

Born in Altrip, near Spires; abbot of the Benedictine monastery of Prüm, in the diocese of Treves, soon after its pillage by Norsemen in 892, and after 899 of another sacked monastery in Treves. He died at Treves in 915. German historian. He completed in 908 a chronicle of the world from Christ's birth down to his own days. This is one of the most important writings of its kind in the Latin West. He also wrote a work on music ("De armonica institutione") and a summary of canon law ("De synodalibus causis et disciplinis ecclesiasticis").

Texts—First edition of the chronicle (Mainz, 1521). Edition by Pertz in the Monumenta Germaniae historica (vol. 1, 537–629, 1826). Better edition by F. Kurze (Hanover, 1890). Both editions contain also the Continuatio chronicae Reginonis, down to 967, probably by Adalbert, archbishop of Magdeburg, d. 981. German translation by W. Wattenbach (Leipzig, 1890).

The De armonica institutione and a Tonarius are published incompletely in M. Gerbert, Scriptores ecclesiastici de musica sacra (vol. 1, 230–247, 1784); and completely in Edmond de Coussemaker: Scriptores de musica medii aevi (vol. 2, 1–73).

The book on canon law will be found in Migne's Patrology (vol. 132). Also edition by F. G. A. Wasserschleben (Leipzig, 1840).

Criticism—H. Ermisch: Die Chronik des Regino bis 813 (Göttingen, 1872). Hugo Isenbart: Der Verfasser und die Glaubwürdigkeit der Continuatio Reginonis (Diss., 47 p., Kiel, 1889). P. Schulz: Die Glaubwürdigkeit des Regino (Hamburg, 1894). C. Wawra: De Reginone (Breslau, 1901). M. Manitius: Lateinische Literatur des Mittelalters (vol. 1, 695–701, 1911, vol. 2, 814).

Arabic Historiography

AL-ṬABARĪ

Abū Ja'far Muḥammad ibn Jarīr al-Ṭabarī. Born at Āmul, Ṭabaristān, in 838–39; flourished at Bagdad, where he died in 923. Persian historian and theologian; one of the greatest Muslim historians. At first a Shāfi'ite, he tried to found a school of law of his own. He was recognized as one of the independent doctors (mujtahid, imām), but failed to become, as he had dreamt, one of the great imāms, whose writings are canonic. See my note on Ibn Ḥanbal (first half of ninth century). His main work is a "Universal history" (the first comprehensive history written in Arabic), from the creation to 915 ("Annals of the Apostles and the Kings, Kitāb akhbār[1] al-rusul wal-mulūk"); it is remarkably elaborate and accurate. He wrote a very full commentary on the Qur'ān (Tafsīr al-Qur'ān), which contains the largest collection of exegetical traditions.

Text—Annales regum atque legatorum Dei. Incomplete edition in Arabic and Latin by J. G. L. Kosegarten (Greifswald, 1831–1835). A splendid edition of the Tārīkh was published by M. J. de Goeje and others (Leyden, 1879–1901. 13 vols., plus 2 vols. containing the introduction, indexes, and glossary). Geschichte der Perser und Araber zur Zeit der Sasaniden. Aus der arabischen Chronik des Ṭabarī übersetzt von Th. Nöldeke (Leyden, 1879. With elaborate commentary).

Die Geschichte des Maghrib als Anhang zu Ṭabarī hrg. von M. J. de Goeje (Leyden, 1897. Text of a continuation of Ṭabarī's Annals by 'Arib ibn Sa'd, q. v., second half of tenth century). A Persian summary made in 963–64 by the Sāmānid wazīr Abū 'Alī Muḥammad al-Bal'amī was translated into French by Hermann Zotenberg (4 vols., Paris, 1867–1874. An incomplete French translation by Louis Dubeux had appeared in Paris, 1836).

The Tafsīr was published at Cairo in 1902–03 (31 vols.). An account of it, with extracts, was given by O. Loth in the Z. d. d. morgenl. Ges. (vol. 35, 588–628, 1881).

Criticism—The seventh section of the Sixth Discourse of the Fihrist is devoted to him. Ibn Khallikān (De Slane) (vol. 2, 597–598, 1843). F. Wüstenfeld: Geschichtschreiber der Araber (31, 1881). C. Brockelmann: Das Verhältnis von Ibn al-Athīrs Kāmil fit-tārīkh zu Ṭabarīs Akhbār errusul wal mulūk (58 p., Strassburg, 1890); Arabische Litteratur (vol. 1, 142, 1898). R. A. Nicholson: Literary History of the Arabs (145, 350, 1907). E. G. Browne: Literary History of Persia (1908, by index).

For Ibn Duraid, see Section XI; for Eutychios, Section VIII; for al-Hamdānī and al Mas'ūdī, Section VII.

ABŪ-L-FARAJ AL-IṢFAHĀNĪ

Abū-l-Faraj 'Alī ibn al-Ḥusain ibn Muḥammad ibn Aḥmad al-Qurashī al-Iṣfahānī. Born in 897–98 of a Qurashite family established in Ispahan; he was a descendant of Marwān, the last Umayyad caliph, and some of his many books were dedicated to his illustrious relatives of Spain; he flourished at Bagdad, Aleppo, Ray, etc.; died in 967. Arab poet and historian. His "Book of Songs" (Kitāb al-aghānī) is a treasury of Arabian poetry, music, and archaeology; it embodies the researches of earlier humanists, is by far the most important work of its kind, and is an invaluable source for the study of Arabian antiquity. Ibn Khaldūn calls it "the Register of the Arabs" (Prolégomènes, vol. 3, 331, 1868).

[1] Or tārīkh. After the Hijra it takes the form of annals.

Text—The Aghānī has been published in Bulāq (1868) in 20 volumes; a complementary volume was edited by R. A. Brünnow (Leyden, 1888). Other fragments of the text were given by J. Wellhausen in the Z. d. morgenl. Ges. (vol. 50, 146 f.). Indices were published by I. Guidi (Leyden, 1900). A partial edition with Latin translation was edited by J. G. L. Kosegarten: Liber cantilenarum magnus (Greifswald, 1840–1846).

The Book on Monasteries (Kitāb al-diyārāt), an anecdotic account of a great many Christian monasteries in the Near East, is still unpublished.

Criticism—Ibn Khallikān (De Slane) (vol. 2, 249–252, 1843). F. Wüstenfeld: Geschichtschreiber der Araber (44, 1881). C. Brockelmann: Arabische Litteratur (vol. 1, 146, 1898). R. A. Nicholson: Literary History of the Arabs (31, 347, 1907).

ABŪ BAKR AL-RĀZĪ

Abū Bakr Aḥmad ibn Muḥammad ibn Mūsā al-Rāzī. Flourished in Spain, died in 936–37. Hispano-Muslim historian, the earliest whose work has been transmitted to us. The Spaniards call him "El cronista por excelencia." The Arabic text is lost, but we have a Castilian version, itself derived from a Portuguese translation. It contains valuable material relative to the last Visigothic kings and the Muslim conquest of Spain (711, etc.).

Text—His History is the basis of the Cronica del Moro Rasis.

Criticism—P. de Gayangos: Memoria sobre la autenticidad de la Cronica denominada del Moro Rasis (Mem. de la r. acad. de la historia, vol. 8, Madrid, 1852). F. Wüstenfeld: Geschichtschreiber der Araber (34, 1881). C. Brockelmann: Arabische Litteratur (vol. 1, 150, 1898). Enciclopedia universal ilustrada (vol. 49, 753, 1923).

Chinese Historiography

LIU HSÜ

Liu[2] Hsü[4] (7270, 4758). Born in 897; flourished under the Posterior Chin dynasty (one of the five small dynasties; a Turkish dynasty which lasted only from 936 to 947); died in 946. Chinese historian. He completed in 945 and edited the "older" official history of the T'ang dynasty (618–907) in 214 books. This work, called Chiu[4] T'ang[2] shu[1] (2289, 10767, 10024), forms the sixteenth of Twenty-four histories; it is vastly superior to the "new" T'ang history, for which see my note on Ou-yang Hsiu (second half of eleventh century). Chapters 32 to 36 contain a history of Chinese astronomy and mathematics down to 945.

Text—Chinese edition (Chekiang, 1872. 214 chüan in 40 vols.).

Criticism—Wylie: Chinese Literature (21, 1902). Giles: Biographical Dictionary (504, 1898).

X. LATIN, BARBARIAN, AND JAPANESE LAW. MUSLIM SOCIOLOGY.

For Latin law, see my note on Regino of Prum, in the preceding section.

Barbarian Law

Welsh Laws (Leges Walliae). The earliest code of Welsh laws, for which there is a historical foundation, is the code compiled by order of Howell Dda (i. e., the Good) between 943 and 950 (year of his death). Howell Dda had become king of Gwynedd and all Wales in 915 (?). Three different versions of it exist, originating respectively from North, South, and Northeast Wales; the Latin version is shorter than any of these three and different in other ways. This code was essentially Germanic, with only a few traces of Roman influence.

Text—Aneurin Owen: Ancient Laws and Institutes of Wales (London, 1841). A. W. Wade-Evans: Welsh Medieval Law, being a Text of the Laws of Howel the Good, namely, the British Museum Harleian MS. 4353, with Translation, etc. (500 p., Oxford, 1909). Timothy Lewis: The Laws of Howel Dda (Facsimile reprint of Llanstephan MS. 116 in the National Library of Wales, Aberystwyth, 140 p., London, 1912).

Criticism—Hubert Lewis: The Ancient Laws of Wales (474 p., London, 1889). Timothy Lewis: A Glossary of Mediaeval Welsh Law (325 p., Manchester, 1913). Thomas Peter Ellis: Welsh tribal law and custom in the Middle Ages (2 vols., Oxford, 1926; Isis, IX).

For Muslim sociology, see my note on al-Fārābī in Section III, above.

Japanese Law

KOREMUNE NAOMOTO

Japanese jurist who published, in 920, a supplement to the Ryō no gige, called the Ryō no shūge (in 30 vols.). (See my note on Kiyowara Natsuno, first half of ninth century.)

E. Papinot: Historical Dictionary (520, 1909).

ENGI-SHIKI

This is a collection of regulations concerning ceremonies and customs which was published during the Engi (or Yengi) era (901 to 923). It is written in Chinese and fills 50 volumes. It was edited by Fujiwara Tokihira and after his death (in 909) by his brother Fujiwara Tadahira. Among other things it enumerates 75 norito (rituals or prayers) and gives the text of 27. It is a work of great importance for the study of Shintoism and of the earliest Japanese civilization. There were at that time not less than 3,132 Shintō shrines, among which 737 were maintained at the Emperor's charges.

In 1810, Matsudaira Naritake, daimyō of Matsue (Izumo), published a new edition of the Engi-shiki, to which he added 10 volumes.

Some of the norito have been translated by Sir Ernest Satow in the Transactions of the Asiatic Society of Japan (1879).

W. G. Aston: Japanese Literature (Yokohama, 1899. Containing an English translation of the most beautiful norito). E. Papinot: Historical Dictionary (81, 1909). F. Brinkley: Japanese History (63, 1915).

XI. HEBREW AND ARABIC PHILOLOGY

For Hebrew Philology, see my notes on the Hebrew Scriptures in Section II and on Saadia ben Joseph in Section III.

Arabic Philology

IBN DURAID

Abū Bakr Muḥammad ibn al-Ḥasan ibn Duraid al-Azdī. Born at Baṣra of a Southern Arabian family in 837–38; flourished at Baṣra, 'Umān, and from c. 892 in Persia; in 920–21 he returned to Bagdad, where he died in 933. Arab poet, lexicographer, and genealogist. He wrote his main work, a large Arabic dictionary, in Persia (al-jamhara fī-l-lugha "The Collection on the Language," i. e., the all-embracing lexicon). He also wrote a treatise on the genealogy of the Arab tribes (Kitāb al-ishtiqāq, book of etymologies), partly to counteract anti-Arabian (shu'ūbite) propaganda.

Text—The Ishtiqāq was edited by F. Wüstenfeld (Göttingen, 1854). There are many editions, each with Latin translation, of a famous ode, al-maqṣūra, written by Ibn Duraid during his residence in Persia: A. Haitsma (Franeker, 1773); E. Scheidius (Harduvicae, 1786); N. Boysen (Copenhagen, 1828). Willem Bilderdijk: Treuerzang in neerduitsche dichtmaat overgebracht, in Dichtwerken (vol. 4, 367–380, 1856).
Criticism—C. Brockelmann: Arabische Litteratur (vol. 1, 111–112, 1898).

For Abū-l-Faraj al-Iṣfahānī, see my note in the historical section (IX).

CHAPTER XXXII

THE TIME OF ABŪ-L-WAFĀ'

(Second Half of Tenth Century.)

I. Survey of Science in Second Half of Tenth Century. II. Religious Background. III. Cultural Background—Byzantine, Latin, Muslim, Jewish, and Chinese Philosophers. IV. Muslim, Latin, Chinese, and Japanese Mathematics and Astronomy. V. Latin and Muslim Alchemy and Technology. VI. Byzantine, Muslim, and Chinese Natural History. VII. Muslim, Jewish, Scandinavian, and Chinese Geography. VIII. Muslim, Persian, Jewish, Byzantine, and Japanese Medicine. IX. Latin, Byzantine, Jewish, Muslim, and Chinese Historiography. X. Arabic, Syriac, Jewish, Byzantine, Latin, English, and Sino-Japanese Philology.

I. SURVEY OF SCIENCE IN SECOND HALF OF TENTH CENTURY

1. The period which we have just tried to analyze, and then to reconstruct, was on the whole one of comparative rest. There was no retrogression, but the advance of mankind, which had been so vigorously accelerated during the ninth century by the youthful energy of Islām, was then distinctly slowed up. It is not the first time that we thus witness a momentary quieting down of human activity; on the contrary, we have already had occasion to observe many such periods of fallow, e. g., the first half of the second century B. C., the first half of the first century, the second half of the second century, the second half of the fifth, the second half of the sixth, the second half of the seventh, the first half of the eighth. But in each case the slowing up was followed by a new acceleration

In other words, when we study the creative activity of mankind as a whole, we find that humanity behaves very much as an individual man would do, that periods of unusual achievements are generally followed by depressions, and periods of rest and fallow by new efforts. The intellectual progress of mankind would not be correctly represented by a constantly increasing function, but rather by a sort of sinusoidal curve moving steadily upward. But how do we account for human tiredness, considering that the burden is periodically taken up by new generations? Leaving out of the question political and other external factors which must necessarily influence human energy, we may explain the periodical slowing up in two ways. In the first place, the original flame of enthusiasm, which stimulates intellectual advance, is bound to die out gradually unless new men of genius appear from time to time to keep it alive; of course, there are no means of predicting when and where such men will appear. In the second place, the very progress of knowledge is certain to fill the more conservative minds with a growing anxiety, and finally to determine an orthodox reaction. Indeed, new knowledge does not destroy intellectual errors only, but also vested prejudices and sacred traditions; it often replaces certainty by a painful uncertainty and tends to disturb the social equilibrium. The more timid of the leaders have, then, the feeling that they will soon be walking upon the very edge of abysses and they proceed to brake and to resist the forward movement. I speak of this at some length, because we are witnessing occasionally such reactions ourselves, and we may believe that they are due to the revolutionary character of modern science. But science always was revolutionary and heterodox; it is its very essence to be so; it ceases to be so only when it is asleep. The mental anxieties of some of our contemporaries, who are afraid of knowledge, have been shared in all times by some other men of that kidney. For example, in the first half of the tenth century an intellectual reaction was led, very successfully, by al-Ash'arī. Mankind does not go forward as a united body; on the contrary, each advance has to be paid for by a protracted struggle between those who long for more light and those who are afraid of it. The latter are far more numerous than the former, but less intelligent, and thus bound to be beaten in the end; this accounts at once for the sinusoidal advance and for its upward tendency, or, in other words, for the slowness, but also for the continuity of human progress.

To come back to the second half of the tenth century, we shall see presently that it was a period of renewed activity in almost every field; the partial fallowness of the first half of the century was thus amply rewarded by more abundant crops and mankind was able to make a few more leaps forward.

2. *Religious Background*—The greatest religious event was the conversion of Russia to Christianity, after 988, by command of St. Vladimir, the most terrible of the apostles.

There is little to say about the other countries. It will suffice to mention rapidly the activity of Ibn Bābūya, the most important of the Shī'a theologians, and, in Japan, that of Genshin, a Buddhist theologian whose teachings did not bear full fruit until two centuries later.

3. *Cultural Background; Byzantine, Latin, Muslim, Jewish, and Chinese Philosophers*—The leader of Byzantine thought was the Emperor Constantinos VII Porphyrogennetos, who ordered the compilation of a number of encyclopaedic treatises and was a patron of art and learning.

The most prominent teacher and philosopher in the Latin West was Gerbert, who gave considerable luster to the school of Reims before ascending the papal throne in 999 under the name of Sylvester II. Notger was instrumental in transferring the noble traditions of St. Gall to the Low Countries and, under his guidance, Liège became one of the main cultural centers of Christian Europe. Some of the most original and of the most significant writings of that time were due to a Benedictine nun, the learned Hrosritha of Gandersheim.

A very enlightened patronage of learning was carried out in Spain by the ninth Umayyad caliph, al-Ḥakam II (961 to 976), with the assistance of his Jewish minister, Ḥasdai ibn Shaprut. It was largely because of Ḥasdai's generous activity that the intellectual center of Israel was transferred from the academies of Babylonia to Cordova. Some of the Buwayhid princes who were then ruling over southern Persia and Mesopotamia did their full share also to promote learning and research. The most distinguished of these Buwayhids were 'Aḍud al-dawla (949 to 982) and his son, Sharaf al-dawla (982 to 989).

In spite of the efforts of al-Ḥakam and Ḥasdai, the center of Muslim philosophy remained in the East; in fact, practically all of the philosophical work which was then done by Muslims—and their activity was truly prodigious—was done in 'Irāq, or in Persia, or further east still, in Sijistān. The Hierosolymite Muṭahhar ibn Ṭāhir compiled an encyclopaedia entitled "The Book of Creation and History." Muḥammad ibn Aḥmad al-Khwārizmī wrote "The Keys of the Sciences." Ibn Maskawayh was primarily a historian and a moralist and wrote comprehensive treatises on ethics. A secret association established at Baṣra about 983, the so-called Brethren of Purity (Ikhwān al-ṣafā'), caused the publication of a sort of

Neoplatonic-Muslim encyclopaedia, the importance of which can hardly be overestimated. These writings were eventually introduced into Spain, but we do not know whether that introduction was due to Maslama ibn Aḥmad or to his disciple al-Karmānī. If Maslama was the agent, the transmission must have taken place very soon after the original publication; there is nothing impossible in that[a] though a somewhat slower transmission is more plausible. Soon after the appearance of this Neoplatonic encyclopaedia, Ibn abī Ya'qūb al-Nadīm published the celebrated Fihrist, which is essentially a catalogue raisonné of all the works which were then available in Arabic.

All of these encyclopaedic treatises appeared within the last third of the tenth century. Such abundant activity had never occurred before, not even in the best days of Alexandria. I shall still have to quote some of these writings, but I must say here, once for all, that anyone undertaking to study the history of science and civilization in the second half of the tenth century, from whatever angle, must begin by consulting "The Keys of the Sciences," the letters of the "Brethren of Purity," and the "Fihrist."

The same age witnessed the activity of two Chinese encyclopaedists. Wu Shu compiled the earliest Chinese encyclopaedia, the Shih lei fu, and he was one of the collaborators of the far more considerable encyclopaedia, the T'ai-p'ing yü-lan, edited by Li Fang. The Shih lei fu filled thirty volumes, the T'ai-p'ing filled a thousand and included extracts from 1,690 works, of which the great majority are no longer extant.

4. *Muslim, Latin, Chinese, and Japanese Mathematics and Astronomy*—All of the creative work was done in Islām. Muslim mathematicians were so numerous that, for the sake of clarity, I must divide them into three groups—arithmeticians, algebraists, and geometers; astronomers and trigonometricians; astrologers.

Arithmeticians, algebraists, and geometers: It is well to begin this section with a brief account of the progress of Hindu numerals. By the middle of the tenth century a special form of them, the so-called dust (ghubār) numerals, was already used in Muslim Spain. The Eastern Arabic form was represented in an Egyptian grafitto, dated 960–61. Muṭahhar ibn Ṭāhir wrote a number of 10 figures by their means. The earliest Latin example of these numerals is found in a manuscript written in 976 near Logroño, in the Christian part of Spain.

Abū Ja'far al-Khāzin wrote commentaries on the tenth book of Euclid and on other works and solved al-Māhānī's cubic equation. Al-Ṣāghānī investigated the trisection of the angle. Naẓīf ibn Yumn translated the tenth book of Euclid. The great astronomer Abū-l-Wafā' wrote commentaries on Euclid, Diophantos, and al-Khwārizmī, arithmetical and geometrical treatises, and solved a number of geometrical and algebraical problems. Abū-l-Fatḥ improved the Arabic translation of Apollonios's Conics and commented upon the first five books. Al-Kūhī was especially interested in the Archimedian and Apollonian problems leading up to higher equations and discovered some elegant solutions, which he discussed. Al-Sijzī worked along the same lines; he made a special study of the intersections of conics and found a geometrical means of trisecting angles. Al-Khujandī, better known as an astronomer, proved that the sum of two cubic numbers can not be a cubic number. Maslama ibn Aḥmad composed a commercial arithmetic and studied the amicable numbers. (This would confirm that he was acquainted with the writings of the Brethren of Purity, for these

[a] See my note on al-Ḥakam II, below.

were very much interested in the theory of numbers—a natural consequence of their Neoplatonic tendencies.)

Astronomers and trigonometricians: At the very beginning of this period we meet one of the best Muslim astronomers: 'Abd al-Raḥmān al-Ṣūfī, who compiled an illustrated catalogue of stars, based upon his own observations. Ibn al-A'lam was also a famous observer and published astronomical tables. Al-Ṣāghānī invented and constructed astronomical instruments. The Buwayhid rulers, especially Sharaf al-dawla, were deeply interested in astronomy; Sharaf built a new observatory in Bagdad. The instruments were probably made by al-Ṣāghānī, and the great mathematician, al-Kūhī, was the leader of the astronomers.

The foremost of the astronomers employed by Sharaf was the Persian Abū-l-Wafā'. It is true, he is not quite as important as he was once believed to be; he did *not* discover the variation of the moon, but he continued in a masterly way the elaboration of trigonometry. Taken all in all, the fame of Abū-l-Wafā' is more solidly based upon his mathematical than upon his astronomical contributions, but I placed him here because, in those days, trigonometry was considered a branch of astronomy.

Al-Khujandī made astronomical observations in Ray. Abū Naṣr improved the Arabic text of Menelaos's Spherics and dealt with trigonometrical subjects. Maslama ibn Aḥmad edited and revised al-Khwārizmī's astronomical tables, and wrote a commentary on Ptolemy's Planisphere.

Astrologers: The main astrologers were al-Qabīṣī in Syria and Rabī' ibn Zaid in Spain; the latter was a Christian, Bishop of Cordova under al-Ḥakam II.

The main mathematician in the Latin West was Gerbert (Pope Sylvester II). Gerbert had spent some years in Christian Spain and may have been in touch there with Muslim scientists; at any rate, he was the first Christian to give an account of the ghubār numerals (without the zero). Abbo of Fleury wrote a commentary on Victorius's Calculus. Hrosvitha knew the first four perfect numbers. An astrological treatise of that time ascribed to one "Alchandrus," is of considerable interest, as one of the earliest Latin works obviously derived from Arabic and Hebrew sources. It is a very humble production, but it deserves to be singled out as one of the vanguard of that great mass of Latin writings through which Arabic learning will be gradually diverged into Christian Europe. The Swiss Benedictine Helperic wrote probably at the same time a treatise on the calendar. Josephus Sapiens, who lived in Spain, composed a treatise on multiplication and division which was twice quoted by Gerbert. Toward the end of the century, Hériger of Lobbes wrote treatises on the abacus which reenforced the Gerbertian movement and accelerated arithmetical progress.

Chang Ssŭ-hsün constructed a celestial sphere which was moved by the fall of mercury (?).

Abe Seimei introduced into Japan the Chinese custom of changing the name of the era in the first and fifty-eighth year of each sexagesimal cycle.

5. *Latin and Muslim Alchemy and Technology*—A Latin treatise ascribed to Heraclius, and dealing with the "colors and arts of the Romans," dates probably from the end of the tenth century.

The earliest scientific treatise in modern Persian (hitherto the Muslim Persians had written in Arabic) happens to be one of the most important chemical works written by a Muslim until that time. It is really a treatise on materia medica, but it contains abundant information on the preparation and properties of mineral substances. It is obvious that its author, Abū Manṣūr Muwaffak, was unusually steeped in chemistry. More may be learned about the chemical knowledge of those days, in the Eastern Caliphate, in the encyclopaedic works dealt with in Section III.

As to the Muslim West, the medical treatise of Abū-l-Qāsim contains also various items of chemical interest; it explains the preparation of drugs by sublimation and distillation. Two important alchemic writings have been ascribed to Maslama ibn Aḥmad, but they are possibly a little later.

6. *Byzantine, Muslim, and Chinese, Natural History*—Among the compilations made by command of Constantinos VII Porphyrogennetos, I must mention here an agricultural collection, a veterinary encyclopaedia, and a zoological encyclopaedia. These compilations were rather mediocre, but they are useful witnesses of the general knowledge available in those days.

With regard to Muslim knowledge on the same subjects, the best sources are the treatises on materia medica of Abū Manṣūr Muwaffak and al-Tamīmī and the encyclopaedic works already mentioned, chiefly the writings of the Brethren of Purity. A book on the generation of animals is ascribed to Maslama ibn Aḥmad.

Tsan-ning wrote a treatise on bamboo sprouts.

7. *Muslim, Jewish, Scandinavian, and Chinese Geography*—All of the Muslim geographers of this period were easterners. Al-Iṣṭakhrī revised the geographical treatise of al-Balkhī and added colored maps for each country. Buzurg ibn Shahriyār edited a collection of sailor's tales called "The Marvels of India." Ibn Ḥawqal rewrote and amplified al-Iṣṭakhrī's geography, both the text and the maps. Al-Muqaddasī traveled extensively in Islām, and wrote a valuable account of his journeys.

Ibrāhīm ibn Ya'qūb, a Jewish merchant, visited Germany and the Western Slavonic countries and wrote a brief account of his observations.

Eric the Red, a Norwegian sailor, explored Greenland and began its colonization. In 999, his son Leif attempted to sail directly from Greenland to Norway without stopping, but failed; he renewed the attempt in the year 1000, and failed again, but was driven to Wineland, an unknown part of North America. This was the earliest discovery of the New World on record.

Chi-yeh traveled in India to obtain Buddhist books and relics and wrote an account of his journey. Yao-shih wrote a geographical and statistical description of China, which is the earliest important work of its kind extant.

8. *Muslim, Persian, Jewish, Byzantine, and Japanese Medicine*—The subtitle of this section is a little misleading, for the many adjectives tend to hide the fact that everything of importance was done by the Muslims alone.

Muslim physicians were so numerous that it is necessary to divide them into groups, and the most expedient division is, this time, a regional one. Thus I shall deal successively with the physicians who flourished in the Eastern Caliphate (reserving a separate place for one of them who wrote in Persian), in Egypt, in Spain, and in North Africa.

The first group was the most numerous, as we would expect it. Aḥmad al-Ṭabarī wrote a medical treatise called Hippocratic treatments. 'Alī ibn 'Abbās (Haly Abbas), who flourished a little later, was one of the greatest physicians of Islām. He compiled a medical encyclopaedia, "The Royal Book," which was very valuable but was superseded by Avicenna's Qānūn. It contains a number of original observations. Under the patronage of 'Aḍud-al-dawla, a new hospital was established in Bagdad in 979. Al-Ḥusain ibn Ibrāhīm improved the Arabic text of Dioscorides. Abū Sahl al-Masīḥī, who was, as his name indicates, a Christian, wrote a number of medical treatises. He shares with al-Qumrī the fame of having been one of the teachers of Avicenna, the prince of mediaeval physicians. It is even possible that one of Abū Sahl's treatises gave Avicenna the first idea of composing his Qānūn.

Note that all of these were Persians, but all wrote, as far as we know, in Arabic. Another Persian, Abū Manṣūr Muwaffak, had the idea of compiling a great medical treatise in Persian. That treatise deals with materia medica and contains a general outline of pharmacological theory. Its intrinsic value is great, but it has also a considerable extrinsic importance, because it is the oldest prose work in modern Persian.

Two distinguished physicians of that time flourished in Egypt, al-Tamīmī and al-Baladī. The former is chiefly known because of his medical guide (Murshid), the latter wrote a treatise on the hygiene of pregnancy and infancy.

Medical activity in Muslim Spain was almost on the same level as that which obtained in the Eastern Caliphate; in some respects it was even superior. One of the most distinguished of the Spanish physicians, however, was not a Muslim, but a Jew, the great Ḥasdai ibn Shaprut. He translated Dioscorides into Arabic with the aid of the Greek monk Nicholas. 'Arīb ibn Sa'd wrote a treatise on gynaecology, obstetrics, and pediatrics. Abū-l-Qāsim (Abulcasis) was the greatest Muslim surgeon; he exerted a very deep influence upon the development of European surgery down to the Renaissance. Ibn Juljul wrote a commentary on Dioscorides and added a supplement to it, and he compiled a history of the Hispano-Muslim physicians of his time.

The last Muslim country to be considered, Tunis, nurtured also a great physician, Ibn al-Jazzār (Algizar), author of a medical vade-mecum which obtained considerable success throughout the Middle Ages.

I have already spoken of one Jewish physician, Ḥasdai ibn Shaprut, whose cultural rôle was considerable, for the Spanish renaissance was largely due to his enlightened generosity. Another Jewish physician, Donnolo, who was flourishing at the same time in southern Italy, wrote a medical treatise in Hebrew which has the extraordinary peculiarity of being essentially independent of Arabic learning. This Donnolo, and perhaps many other physicians of his kind who did not write or whose writings are lost, acted like a ferment amidst the mixed population of the South Italian harbors.[b] It is probably to him, or to physicians like him, that we have to look to understand the birth of the school of Salerno, the earliest original school of medicine in Christian Europe.

I have nothing to say of Byzantine medicine, beyond recalling the medical encyclopaedia which Theophanes Nonnos compiled by order of Constantinos VII Porphyrogennetos. The emperor ordered also the compilation of a veterinary encyclopaedia.

Yasuyori Tamba wrote the earliest Japanese treatise on medicine which is still extant in its original form. He may be also the author of a contemporary treatise on materia medica.

9. *Latin, Byzantine, Jewish, Muslim, and Chinese Historiography*—This was a golden age of Latin historiography, not so much with regard to quality, which was not very high, as in respect of quantity. A number of chroniclers were at work in many countries. Flodoard of Reims wrote a history of his diocese down

---

[b] Greek, Italian, Jewish, Muslim, etc.

to 961, and annals of his own time. Liudprand of Cremona composed three historical works, one of which contains a good description of Constantinople and of the Byzantine court; this Liudprand was the most original Hellenist of his age. Widukind of Corvey wrote a history of the Saxon emperors Henry I and Otto I. Hrosvitha wrote also a history of Otto I, in verse. The "Salernitan Chronicle" dealing with the history of the Lombard kingdoms of South Italy was put together by a monk of Salerno, c. 978; it is very valuable, because it throws some light upon the many influences which were then interplaying in that corner of Europe and thus unconsciously elaborating a new civilization. Richer of Reims, one of Gerbert's pupils, told the history of the end of the Carolingian dynasty and of the first Capetian king. Hériger of Lobbes, Notger's favorite disciple, wrote the earliest history of the episcopal principality of Liège.

Many histories were being written also in Greek. To begin with, Constantinos ordered the compilation of a historical encyclopaedia, which was a collection of extracts from the works of former historians. Symeon Metaphrastes, the most illustrious of the Byzantine hagiographers, was probably the author of a continuation of Georgios Monachos's chronicle. Leon Diaconos wrote a history of his time which is one of the main sources for the study of Bulgarian and Russian ethnography.

A responsa addressed c. 980 to the Jewish community of Qairawān by Sherira Gaon is of inestimable value for the study of Jewish history from the Talmudic period down to the tenth century.

The most important Muslim historians of the East were Ḥamza, a fanatical Persian, who wrote Arabic annals essentially derived from Persian sources; the moralist Ibn Maskawayh, also a Persian, who compiled an international history, and the famous author of the Fihrist—we may well call him a historian—Ibn abī Ya'qūb al-Nadīm.

Among the Hispano-Muslims we must mention 'Arīb ibn Sa'd, who compiled a chronicle of Muslim Spain and Africa some time between 961 and 976; Ibn al-Qūṭīya, who wrote a history of Andalusia from 711 to 893; and Ibn Juljul, to whom we owe a history of the contemporary physicians and philosophers in Muslim Spain.

Hsieh Chü-chêng edited the older official history of the Five Dynasties. Tsan-ning compiled a collection of Buddhist biographies down to 988.

9 bis. *Byzantine Law*—The Basilica were finally revised by order of Constantinos. The emperor had a genuine interest in the subject and wrote himself books on Byzantine government and ceremonial. His book on the districts and the administration of the empire is of some interest from the standpoint of historical geography and ethnography.

10. *Arabic, Syriac, Jewish, Byzantine, Latin, English, and Sino-Japanese Philology*—Ḥamza dealt with grammatical subjects and gratified his Shu'ūbite tendencies by etymological studies which proved the superiority of the Persian over the Arabic language. Ismā'īl ibn 'Abbād compiled a large Arabic dictionary. Another dictionary was begun by al-Jauharī, wherein the words were classified in the alphabetic order of their last radical letters. This work was completed by his disciple Ibrāhīm ibn Ṣāliḥ. Ibn Jinnī was especially interested in the philosophical aspect of philology. All of these flourished in the East, and all but the last named were Persians. The only Arabic grammarian in the West was Ibn al-Qūṭīya, who composed the first treatise on the conjugations of verbs. At about the same time the most comprehensive Syriac dictionary of mediaeval times was compiled by Bar Bahlūl.

Thus Muslim and Syriac grammarians were far from being inactive, yet their activity was small as compared with that of the contemporary Jewish grammarians. Indeed, the second half of the tenth century was a golden age of Hebrew grammar. This was partly a consequence of the Qaraite propaganda which had considerably stimulated the intellectual life of Israel. I have already observed that from the Jewish (as from the Muslim) point of view, grammatical study was considered to some extent a religious duty. The critical attitude of the Qaraites obliged the best Jewish theologians—whether orthodox or not—to reinvestigate with greater precision the teachings of their faith; this entailed necessarily a deeper understanding of the Hebrew language. These philological studies were carried out at once by Qaraites and by their opponents. For example, Sahl ben Maẓliaḥ and David ben Abraham were Qaraites; Sahl published a Hebrew grammar and a Hebrew lexicon which were very popular; David ben Abraham compiled also a Hebrew dictionary, which contained a summary of Hebrew grammar and a comparison between the Hebrew and the Arabic languages—all this, be it noted, in Arabic.

Sahl was a Palestinian Jew, and David a Moroccan. The orthodox grammarians were flourishing at Cordova under Ḥasdai's patronage. Menahem ben Saruq compiled the first complete dictionary of the Biblical language; that dictionary contained a number of grammatical remarks; it was written in Hebrew. Dunash ben Labraṭ (who had emigrated from Sura) founded a new Hebrew prosody based upon the Arabic. Finally, Ḥayyuj wrote, in Arabic, a Hebrew grammar, which may be considered the foundation of the scientific study of the subject. This grammar was essentially modeled upon the Arabic grammar, but Ḥayyuj had been able to avail himself of the long discussions of Jewish theologians and to summarize their main results.

The most prominent contemporary philologist in the Byzantine Empire was Suidas, who compiled a large Greek dictionary, which contains a great deal of miscellaneous information and is, in fact, a small encyclopaedia.

In the meanwhile, Latin philology was still in a rather childish stage. Abbo of Fleury dealt with prosody and pronunciation. Aelfric wrote a grammar with extracts translated from Priscian and a manual of Latin conversation. We are more interested, however, in his glossary, which is the earliest Latin-English dictionary extant. Aelfric translated various books into Anglo-Saxon.

The earliest Sino-Japanese dictionary was published within the same period by Minamoto no Shitagau.

11. *Final Remarks*—The very length of my summary makes it unnecessary to emphasize the importance of this period. If a very condensed description of the main achievements took so much space, this is already sufficient proof that the intellectual activity was unusually abundant. The reader will have observed that much of that activity took place on a remarkably high level.[c]

But I would like to show, as I have done for the preceding periods, that this activity was not restricted to a single race or nation, but was truly ecumenical.

To begin with, it is very interesting to observe an intellectual revival in China and Japan. It is still very modest, but we shall see it grow. We had to consider

[c] It is worth while insisting on this because of the views adopted by most scholars, let alone uneducated people, about this period. For example, in his excellent Histoire illustrée de la littérature française, vol. 1, 13, Paris, 1923, Gustave Lanson speaking of the end of the tenth century, remarks: "En France comme ailleurs il semble que l'esprit humain subisse une éclipse." A strange eclipse!

the works of the following Chinese: Wu Shu, Li Fang, Chang Ssŭ-hsün, Tsan-ning, Chi-yeh, Yao-shih, and Hsieh Chü-chêng, and of the following Japanese: Genshin, Abe Seimei, Yasuyori Tamba, and Minamoto no Shitagau.

Moving westward, we could not yet discover any trace of a revived activity in India; we might have witnessed perhaps some humble intellectual efforts among the Manichaean Uighūrs in Central Asia, but to find progressive communities, or at least progressive individuals, we would have to wait until we reached the outposts of Islām in Transoxiana. We would then meet the most progressive of the Muslims, the Persians and those living east of Persia. I have spoken of a large number of these; let me quote the most important first: Muḥammad ibn Aḥmad al-Khwārizmī, al-Kūhī, al-Sijzī, 'Abd al-Raḥman al-Ṣūfī, Abū-l-Wafā', 'Alī ibn 'Abbās—a magnificent array! It is probable that many of the Brethren of Purity were Persians, too. The following were less important, yet many of them would have been very prominent in a less favored age: Ibn Bābūya, 'Aḍud al-dawla and his son Sharaf, Abū Ja'far al-Khāzin, Abū-l-Fatḥ, al-Ṣāghānī, al-Khujandī, al-Iṣṭakhrī, Buzurg ibn Shahriyār, Aḥmad al-Ṭabarī, al-Qumrī, Ḥamza, Ibn Maskawayh, Ismā'īl ibn 'Abbād, and al-Jauharī. Of these, I know that they were Persians or hailed from the east of Persia. But among the many other scholars who illustrated the Eastern Caliphate, some were probably of Persian origin or upbringing. The most important of these easterners was Ibn abī Ya'qūb al-Nadīm, the author of the Fihrist, who lived in Bagdad. We know practically nothing about his origin and circumstances. The following were not Persians (or if they were, we do not know it or are not sure of it): Muṭahhar ibn Ṭāhir, Ibn al-A'lam, Abū Naṣr, al-Qabīṣī, Ibn Ḥawqal, al-Muqaddasī, al-Ḥusain ibn Ibrāhīm, al-Tamīmī, Ibn Jinnī.

Speaking of Persians, I almost forgot to recall one, the most remarkable of them, Abū Manṣūr Muwaffak, the first Muslim Persian who thought of publishing a scientific work in his own native language. That was just as original and as daring, as, for example, King Alfred's idea of writing learned books in English. We take such things too much for granted; we do not realize that to do them required an independence of thought amounting almost to genius. Abū Manṣūr's Persian treatise illustrates his own originality; it illustrates also the growing disintegration of the Eastern Caliphate.

There was not yet much activity in northern Africa: Al-Tamīmī and al-Baladī flourished in Egypt; Ibn al-Jazzār in Tunis.

An important center of Muslim culture had arisen in Spain under Umayyad patronage. Al-Ḥakam II was perhaps the most scholarly ruler of Islām. The magnificent city of Cordova became one of the noblest seats of learning in Europe. It fostered such men as Maslama ibn Aḥmad, 'Arīb ibn Sa'd, Ibn Juljul, Ibn al-Qūṭīya, and above all the great surgeon Abū-l-Qāsim, and an equal number of Jews who will be named presently.

The only prominent scholar writing in Syriac was Bar Bahlūl.

The decline in the activity of Arabic-speaking Christians already noticed in the previous chapter was still increased during this period. I had to deal with only three of them: Naẓīf ibn Yumn and Abū Sahl in the East, and the Bishop Rabī' ibn Zaid in Spain—and none of these was really important.

On the contrary, the Jewish contributions increased considerably, and many of them were no longer contributions to Muslim culture, but independent achievements which were sometimes expressed in their own Hebrew language. We first noticed that enigmatic Ibrāhīm ibn Ya'qūb, who traveled in Germany and in the western Slavonic countries. At almost the same time, Donnolo was flourishing in southern Italy, Sherira Gaon in Babylonia, Sahl ben Maẓliaḥ in Palestine, David ben Abraham (and for a few years, Dunash ben Labraṭ) in Morocco. However, the main center of Jewish thought, which had been hitherto in the East (in Babylonia or Palestine), had now been transferred to Cordova, thanks to the intelligence of a great Jewish statesman, Ḥasdai ben Shaprut, himself a distinguished man of science. There flourished Menahem ben Saruq, Dunash ben Labraṭ, and Ḥayyuj.

There remains to be considered Christian Europe, and here, too, notable advances were made. The main Greek writers were Constantinos VII, Symeon Metaphrastes, Leon Diaconos, and Suidas. Byzantine culture was stimulating the Ottonian renaissance and beginning the conquest of Russia. Conditions were improving rapidly in a number of centers; in fact, one of the most gratifying features of this European awakening is the multiplicity of its centers; there are not yet many flowers, but buds are appearing everywhere. Aelfric is at work in England; Notger and Hériger in what is now Belgium; Flodoard, Gerbert, Richer, Abbo in France; Eric the Red and Leif Ericsson in Scandinavia; Vladimir in Russia; Hrosvitha and Widukind in Germany; Helperic in Switzerland; Josephus Sapiens in Spain; Liudprand and the anonymous ancestors of Salerno in Italy. The activity of all of these men was not on as high a level as that of their Muslim contemporaries, not by any means; but they were trudging in the right direction, they were slowly preparing a new European civilization.

II. RELIGIOUS BACKGROUND

ST. VLADIMIR

Born c. 956, died in 1015. Grand Duke of Kiev, finally ruler of all Russia. Soon after his baptism at Kherson, Crimea, in 988, he married Anna, sister of Basilios II Bulgaroctonos (976 to 1025) and introduced Orthodox Christianity into Russia. His rule marks the beginning of Christian Russia.

It is interesting to recall that another sister of the same basileus, Theophano, had been given in marriage in 972 to the young emperor Otto II (born 955; emperor from 967 (973); died 983). The marriage was celebrated by the pope in Rome, where Theophano had arrived "cum innumeris thesaurorum divitiis." Thus did Byzantine culture expand at about the same time into Russia and into Germany. There was no Christian art in Germany east of the Rhine before the second half of the tenth century. Russian art, a direct continuation of Byzantine art, began just a little later at the end of the century, first in Kiev, soon afterwards in Novgorod, Vladimir, and Moscow. The Ottonian artistic renaissance and the birth of Russian civilization were both determined by the Byzantine revival which occurred under the Macedonian dynasty. This is of special interest to the historian of art, but would also deserve to arrest the attention of the historian of science.

L. K. Goetz: Das Kiever Höhlenkloster als Kulturzentrum des vormongolischen Russlands (Passau, 1904). Gustave Schlumberger: L'épopée Byzantine à la fin du Xe siècle (3 vols., Paris 1896–1905). O. M. Dalton: Byzantine art and archaeology (747 p., 457 ill., Oxford, 1911). Charles Diehl: Manuel d'art byzantin (2d ed., 2 vol., 448 ill., 962 p., Paris, 1926).

IBN BĀBŪYA

Abū Ja'far Muḥammad ibn 'Alī ibn Bābūya (Bābawayh) al-Qummī al-Ṣadūq. From Qum in Jibāl; he moved from Khurāsān to Bagdad in 965–66 and died in 991–92 or ten years later. Shī'ite theologian and jurist. His main work, which is still of high authority in the Shī'ite world, is the so-called "Book of Him who has no Lawyer at Hand" (Kitāb man lā yaḥḍuruhu-l-faqīh). This and another work of his, al-'ilal (possibly a part of the former work), contains much miscellaneous information on natural and historical questions.

C. Brockelmann: Arabische Litteratur (t. 1, 187, 1898).

GENSHIN

His family name was Urabe. He is also called Eshin, or Eshin sōzu (sōzu being a Buddhist title of honor). Born in Yamato in 942; monk at the Tendai monasteries of Hiei-zan and Eshin-in, Yokawa; died in 1017. Japanese Buddhist. Theologian, scholar, artist. He prepared the religious awakening and reform of the twelfth and thirteenth centuries.[d] He wrote (in Chinese, of course) many theological books which attracted attention even in China. His books on Paradise, the Intermediate States, and Hell have been particularly influential. They suggest comparison with the Divina Commedia.

III. CULTURAL BACKGROUND—BYZANTINE, LATIN, MUSLIM, JEWISH, AND CHINESE PHILOSOPHERS

CONSTANTINOS VII PORPHYROGENNETOS

Κωνσταντῖνος ὁ πορφυρογεννήτος, born in 905, died in 959. Byzantine Emperor nominally from 912, really from 945, to his death. Patron of arts, letters, and science. He himself wrote books on Byzantine administration and ceremonial, and caused many compilations to be made on law, history, husbandry, medicine, and zoology. These compilations divided into separate manuals, so to say, mark a real progress upon the Roman encyclopaedic writings (see Varro, Pliny, Apuleius). Under his reign, Constantinople became a great cultural center.

Constantine's Own Writings—De thematibus et de administrando imperio, edited in Greek and Latin by Emm. Bekker (Corpus scriptorum historiae Byzantinae, vol. 10, Bonn, 1840. Interesting from the geographical and ethnographical point of view). An excellent edition of the second book only, dealing with Europe, has been given by L. Fr. Tafel (Tübingen, 1846). De ceremoniis aulae byzantinae (Ἔκθεσις τῆς βασιλείου τάξεως), edited in Greek and Latin by Io. Ia. Reiskius (Corpus script. hist. Byz., vols. 8–9, Bonn, 1829–30).

Compilations Made by His Order—(*A*) The Basilica (Τὰ βασιλικά): A digest of law completed under Leon the Wise (emp. from 886 to 911), but revised under Constantine. It superseded the Justinian Code. Edited by W. Ernst Heimbach (6 vols., Leipzig, 1833–1870), with Latin translation and a history of Byzantine law from 534 to 867. (See my note on Byzantine law in the second half of the ninth century.)

(*B*) Historical encyclopaedia: This is a collection of extracts from former historians, a sort of Byzantine predecessor of the modern American compilation called "the historians' history of the world."[e] Excerpta historica jussu imp.

[d] More particularly the creation of the Jōdo-shū, for which see my note on Buddhism in the second half of the twelfth century.

[e] Indeed, the purpose is the same in both cases. And the point of view, the same crude love of genuineness and simplification.

Constantini Porphyrogenniti confecta, edited by U. Ph. Boissevain, C. de Boor, Th. Büttner-Wobst (4 vols., Berlin, 1903–1910).

(*C*) Agricultural collection (Γεωπονικά, αἱ περὶ γεωργίας ἐκλογαί, in 20 books). This compilation, based upon Anatolius's and Cassianos's geoponica, was made c. 950. It was very poorly made. For editions see Cassianos Bassos (second half of the sixth century).

(*D*) Medical encyclopaedia (Ἰατρικά), edited by Theophanes Nonnos (q. v., first half of the tenth century).

(*E*) Veterinary encyclopaedia (Ἱππιατρικά). The date of this compilation is uncertain; it is based upon those made by Apsyrtos, who flourished under Constantine the Great (first half of the fourth century), Hippocrates (probably of the same time), Hierocles (q. v., second half of the fourth century). Veterinariae medicinae libri duo. First Greek edition (Bale, 1537). Hippocratis veterinaria, Greek text with Latin and Italian translations by Petrus Al. Valentini (Roma, 1814). Emm. Miller: Notice sur le MS. grec no. 2322 de la Bibliothèque impériale contenant le recueil des ἱππιατρικά (Notices et extraits des MSS., t. 21, 2ᵉ partie, 1–161, 1865). See also Eug. Oder's edition of Claudii Hermeri mulo-medicina Chironis (504 p., Leipzig, 1901).

Max. Ihm: Die Hippiatrica (Rheinisches Museum für Philologie, vol. 47, 312–318, 1892).

(*F*) Zoological encyclopaedia (Τῶν Ἀριστοτέλους περὶ ζῴων ἐπιτομή) based upon Aristotle in the epitome of Aristophanes of Byzantium (q. v., first half of second century B. C.), upon Aelianos (q. v., first half of third century), and Timotheos of Gaza (c. 500). Two of the four books are lost. Excerptorum de natura animalium libri duo, edited by S. P. Lampros (Supplementum aristotelicum, I, 1, Berlin, 1885).

A similar compilation was made also under Constantinos IX Monomachos (emperor from 1042 to 1054), edited by C. Fr. Matthaei. Ποικίλα Ἑλληνικά (Moscow, 1811).

Criticism—Alfred Rambaud: L'empire grec au dixième siècle. Constantin Porphyrogénète (567 p., Paris, 1870; p. 51 to 174 is devoted to an analysis of Constantine's literary and scientific activity). K. Krumbacher: Geschichte der byzantinischen Litteratur (2. Aufl., 252–264, München, 1897).

For Gerbert, see my note in the mathematical section (IV), below.

NOTGER OF LIÈGE

German form, Notker von Lüttich. Dean in St. Gall; since 972, bishop of Liège, where he died in 1008. Educator. He was the main instrument in the transplantation of the high culture, which had been fostered in St. Gall,[f] into the Low Countries. Under his leadership, Liège became perhaps the foremost intellectual center of the empire. His disciples were soon spread over all of Europe, many of them at the head of bishoprics which became secondary centers of civilization. No works can be certainly ascribed to him. Some of Hériger's works were formerly attributed to him.

Criticism—Godefroid Kurth, in Biographie nationale de Belgique (t. 15, 902–909, 1899); Notger et la civilisation au Xᵉ siècle (2 vols., Paris, 1905). Henri Pirenne: Histoire de Belgique (t. 1, 3 éd., 157, 1909). M. Manitius: Lateinische Literatur des Mittelalters (vol. 2, 219–228, 1923).

[f] St. Gall in Switzerland, thus named after the Irish hermit, St. Gall (or Cellach, Caillech), apostle of the Suevi and Alemanni, who died c. 645. His hermitage was the nucleus of a Benedictine monastery, which was one of the main cultural centers of Europe from the eighth to the eleventh century. James Midgley Clark: The abbey of St. Gall as a center of literature and art (Cambridge, 1926).

HROSVITHA

There are many variants of this name: ts instead of s; w instead of v; with or without the initial h; also Hrotsuit. Born c. 935; flourished and died in the monastery of Gandersheim (Gande Valley, Duchy of Brunswick) at the end of the century. Benedictine nun (not abbess). Historian, dramatist, poet; one of the most original personalities of her time. The six hagiologic comedies written by her were remarkable anticipations of the miracle plays. They contain valuable information on the education and knowledge of her day, notably on the mathematical knowledge. For example, Hrosvitha mentions the first four perfect numbers, 6, 28, 496, 8128. Her main historical work, the Carmen de gestis Ottonis,[g] was completed c. 968.

Text—The first edition of her works, Nürnberg, 1501, was prepared by Conrad Celtes and illustrated by Albrecht Dürer![h] Hrotsvithae opera, edited by Paul von Winterfeld (576 p., Berlin, 1902, with elaborate indexes and notes). Edition by Karl Strecher (Leipzig, 1906).

English translations of the plays by H. J. W. Tillyard (144 p., London, 1923) and by Christopher St. John, i. e., Christabel Marshall (195 p., London, 1923).

Criticism—Siegmund Günther: Geschichte des mathematischen Unterrichts im deutschen Mittelalter (Berlin, 1887). Article by A. W. Ward, in Encyclopaedia Britannica (11 ed., 2 cols., 1910, with bibliography). Max Manitius: Lateinische Literatur des Mittelalters (vol. 1, 619–632, 1911). Johann Schneiderhan: Roswitha von Gandersheim, die erste deutsche Dichterin (215 p., Paderborn, 1912). Evangeline W. Blashfield: Portraits and Backgrounds (New York, 1917. One of the four biographies is devoted to Hrosvitha). L. E. Dickson: History of the Theory of Numbers (Vol. 1, 5, 1919).

AL-HAKAM II

Ibn 'Abd al-Raḥmān III; called al-Mustanṣir bi-llāh, he who seeks his help in God, died in 976. Ninth Umayyad caliph of Cordova, 961 to 976. Great patron of art, science, and education. Perhaps the most scholarly ruler of Islām. Cordova was the greatest city of that time after Constantinople, and its university was the greatest center of learning of Islām. The study of mathematics, astronomy, and medicine was encouraged. Al-Ḥakam sent agents to every part of the Muslim world to obtain manuscripts or copies of them. His library is said to have contained about 400,000 volumes and its catalogue filled 44 volumes. Many of the volumes were annotated by the caliph's own hand. Works composed in the East were often known to him before eastern scholars were aware of their existence.

R. Dozy: Spanish Islam (1913). M. Schmitz: Encyclopaedia of Islam (vol. 2, 223, 1915).

In his efforts to promote learning, al-Hakam was splendidly seconded by his Jewish minister, Ḥasdai ibn Shaprut, for whom see the medical section (VIII), below.

'AḌUD AL-DAWLA

Fanā Khusraw, Abū Shujā' ibn Rukn al-dawla, born in Iṣfahān 936, died in Bagdad 983. Buwayhid sulṭān ruling in southern Persia and 'Irāq from 949

---

[g] That is, Otto I the Great, Holy Roman Emperor, 936–973.

[h] The authenticity of these wood-cuts has been discussed, however. See Dürer, L'oeuvre du maitre (p. 397, Paris, 1908. with bibliography).

to 982. He entered Bagdad in 975, and soon after was granted the title of King or King of Kings (malik al-mulūk) by the caliph Ṭā'i'; he being the first in Islām to bear this title. He was the greatest Buwayhid prince and one of the most illustrious rulers of his time. Founder of a great hospital in Bagdad, completed in 979. Patron of science and art. (M. Seligsohn: Encyclopaedia of Islam, vol. 1, 143, 1908).

The Buwayhid kings, being Persians and Shī'ites, had no interest in defending Sunnite orthodoxy. Hence the influence of al-Ash'arī was not felt during their rule and a sufficient freedom of thought facilitated the development of philosophic and scientific investigations. This helps to explain the magnificent philosophical effort which was made in 'Irāq during the last third of the century.

SHARAF AL-DAWLA

Sharaf al-dawla Abū-l-Fawāris Shīr Zayd. Buwayhid sulṭān, ruling in southern Persia and 'Irāq from 982 to 989; son of 'Aḍud al-dawla (q. v.). He built an observatory in the garden of his palace in Bagdad, to observe the course of the seven planets. Observations were made there in 988 under the direction of al-Kūhī (q. v.). Among the observers were: al-Ṣāghānī (q. v., he probably constructed the instruments); Abū Isḥāq Ibrāhīm ibn Hilāl; Abū-l-Wafā' (q. v.); Abū-l-Ḥasan Muḥammad al-Sāmirī (?); Abū-l-Ḥasan al-Maghrabī.

Stanley Lane-Poole: The Mohammadan Dynasties (141, London, 1894).

MUṬAHHAR IBN ṬĀHIR

Muṭahhar ibn Ṭāhir al-Maqdisī (or al-Muqaddasī, i. e., the native or inhabitant of the Holy City). From Jerusalem, flourished in Bust, Sijistān, c. 966. Encyclopaedist. Author of the Book of the Creation and of History (Kitāb al-bad' wal-tārīkh), a summary of the knowledge of his day based not simply on Muslim, but also on Iranian and Jewish sources. He quotes as a curiosity a very large number, 4,320,000,000 (representing the duration of the world in years according to the Hindus), in Hindu or Devanāgarī numerals.

Text and Translation—Le livre de la création et de l'histoire d'Abou-Zéid Aḥmed ben Sahl el-Balkhī. Publié et traduit d'après le MS. de Constantinople par Clément Huart (3 vols., Paris, 1899–1903. This book was formerly ascribed to al-Balkhī, q. v. Huart's translation is provided with elaborate notes and indexes; for the Hindu numerals, see vol. 2, 135).

Criticism—Cl. Huart: Le véritable auteur du Libre de la création et de l'histoire (Journal Asiatique (9), vol. 18, 16–21, 1901. Concluding that Mutahhar was the author); Arabic literature (284, 291, London, 1903).

MUHAMMAD IBN AHMAD AL KHWĀRIZMĪ

Abū 'Abdallāh Muḥammad ibn Aḥmad ibn Yūsuf al-Khwārizmī;[i] also called al-Kātib, the scribe. From Khwārizm, flourished c. 976. Persian encyclopaedist. He wrote in 976 in Arabic, "The Keys of the Sciences" (Mafātīḥ al-'ulūm), a book which is not second in importance to the Fihrist and the treatises of the Brethren of Purity, for the study of Muslim science and culture at that time.

---

[i] Not to be mistaken for the mathematician also named Abū 'Abdallāh Muhammad al-Khwārizmī (q. v., first half of the ninth century).

It is a classified vocabulary of technical terms.[i] He divides the sciences into two groups: the Indigenous and the Exotic (Greek, Syriac, Persian, Hindu). The former are jurisprudence, scholastic theology (kalām), grammar, secretarial art (including administrative terminology), prosody and poetry, history. The latter, philosophy (falsafa; this includes a classification of the sciences), logic, medicine, arithmetic, geometry, astronomy, music, mechanics (the science of devices), alchemy.

Text and Translation—The text of this encyclopaedia has been published by G. Van Vloten (Leyden, 1895). An English translation is badly needed.

Criticism—C. Brockelmann: Arabische Litteratur (vol. 1, 244, 1898). Edward G. Browne: Literary History of Persia (vol. 1, 372, 378, 382, 1909). Ernst Seidel: Die Medizin im Kitāb mafātīḥ al-'ulūm (Sitzungsberichte der phys. mediz. Soc. in Erlangen, vol. 47, 79 p., 1914).

A number of E. Wiedemann's Beiträge zur Geschichte der Naturwissenschaften, published in the Sitzungsber. der physik. mediz. Societät in Erlangen, deal with the Mafātīḥ al-'ulūm, to wit: (VI) Mechanik und Technik, vol. 38, 16–55, 1906; (X) Technik, vol. 38, 307–313, 1906; (XIV) Geometrie und Arithmetik (vol. 40, 1–29, 1908); (XVIII) Astronomische Instrumente (vol. 41, 32–35, 1909); (XXII) Gewichte und Masse usw. (vol. 42, 303–310, 1910); (XXIV) Chemie (vol. 43, 72–113, 1911); (XXVII) Geographie (vol. 44, 37–40, 1912); (XLVII) Astronomie (vol. 47, 214–242, 1915); (LXVI) Musik (vol. 54, 7–22, 1925). Together with Seidel's study on medicine, above mentioned, this series of papers constitutes an elaborate analysis of the scientific part of the Mafātīḥ, including the translation of many extracts.

IBN MASKAWAYH

See historical section (IX), below.

THE BRETHREN OF PURITY

This is the literal translation of the Arabic phrase Ikhwān al-ṣafā', but it is a little misleading, for the Arabic does not imply the notion of brotherhood. Yet I retain this name, first because it is supported by a long European tradition (Die lauteren Brüder, Les frères de la pureté); second, because this secret association was in fact and of a necessity a brotherhood. It would perhaps be better to say the Brethren of Sincerity, as the word purity is a little ambiguous. Carra de Vaux has recently (1923) suggested that the words Ikhwān al-ṣafā' were originally meant to translate the Greek term φιλόσοφος; that hypothesis is very plausible.

This was a secret association established at Baṣra about 983. Its aims were religious, philosophical, political; its tendencies mu'tazilite and also Ismā'īlite or Qarmaṭian (see my note on the Ismā'īli propaganda in second half of the ninth century). Their philosophy was an eclectic gnosticism, including Iranian, Christian, Hebraic, Syriac, Hindu, Arabic, and Greek elements. They had some knowledge of Aristotle, but were more familiar with Pythagorean and Platonic doctrines; on the whole, their knowledge of Greek philosophy was inferior to that already exhibited by al-Kindī and al-Fārābī. To reconcile Greek science with the Qur'ān they were naturally driven to give mythical and mystical interpretations of both. They believed in the purifying power of knowledge. They wrote

[i] It will be taken up bodily into any adequate future Arabic lexicon. The "Index rerum" (rather of words explained) extends p. 267–319 of Van Vloten's edition.

a series of 52[k] treatises (Rasā'il ikhwān al-ṣafā') forming a sort of encyclopaedia (14 deal with mathematics and logic; then follow 17 dealing with natural sciences, including psychology; 10 with metaphysics; 11 with mysticism, astrology, and magic).

It includes a classification of science which is essentially the Aristotelian one, as transmitted by Philoponos (q. v., first half of the sixth century) and by al-Fārābī (q. v., first half of the tenth century). This particular modification of the Aristotelian scheme has some historical importance, because it contains most of the characteristic features of the later Jewish classifications.

Number mysticism, magical squares (up to 81 numbers). Perfect and amicable numbers. Numerical classifications: things are classified according to their occurrence by twos, or by threes, etc. Isoperimetrical problems.

Explanation of many natural phenomena—tides, earthquakes, eclipses. Sound produced by the vibrations of air. They asked the question: How is it that simultaneous sounds do not mix in the air? They denied the existence of vacuum.

Astrology permeated their chemical views. They were acquainted with the four Aristotelian qualities, also with the Jābirian theory of the constitution of metals.

This encyclopaedia of Muslim knowledge was a collective work. Five of the collaborators are named: (1) Abū Sulaimān Muḥammad ibn Mushīr al-Bustī, al-Muqaddasī; (2) Abū-l-Hasan 'Alī ibn Hārūn al-Zanjānī; (3) Muḥammad ibn Aḥmad al-Nahrajūrī; (4) al-'Awfī; (5) Zaid ibn Rifā'a.

Texts and Translations—Die Abhandlungen der Ichwān es-Safā in Auswahl zum ersten Mal aus arabischen Handschriften herausgegeben von Fr. Dieterici (Leipzig, 1886, with an introduction of 17 pages in German). A great part has been translated by Dieterici in his collection entitled Die Philosophie der Araber (16 vols., Leipzig, 1858–1891). Garcin de Tassy has given a French translation of the Book of Animals, from a Hindustani text. An English translation is badly needed.

Hindustāni translation by Maulwi 'Alī, revised by Duncan Forbes and Chr. Rieu (London, 1861).

Criticism—G. Flügel: Über Inhalt und Verfasser der arabischen Encyclopädie u. s. w. nebst Andeutungen über die Einrichtungen des Bundes der Verbrüderten (Z. d. d. morg. Ges., Vol. 13, 1–43, 1859). Leclerc: Médecine arabe (vol. 1, 393–398, 1876). Lane-Poole: Studies in a Mosque (2d edition, p. 176–207, London, 1893). C. Brockelmann: Arabische Litteratur (vol. 1, 213–214, 1898). De Boer: History of Philosophy in Islam (81–96, 1903). R. A. Nicholson: Literary History of the Arabs (370–372, 1907. Containing further information on the Ismā'īlite tendencies of the sect). Ignaz Goldziher: Über die Benennung der Ichwān al-ṣafā' (Der Islam, vol. 1, 22–26, 1910). Louis Massignon: Sur la date de composition des Rasā'il (*ibidem*, vol. 4, 324, 1913). Duhem: Système du Monde (vol. 2, 204 sq., 1914. On precession). De Boer: Encyclopaedia of Islam (vol. 2, 459, 1919). Carra de Vaux: Les penseurs de l'Islam (t. 2, 379–382, 1921; t. 4, 102–115, 362, 1923). L. Massignon: Esquisse d'une bibliographie qarmaṭe. Oriental Studies Presented to E. G. Browne (329–338, 1922; Isis, VI, 145). Harry A. Wolfson: The Classification of the Sciences in Mediaeval Jewish Philosophy (Hebrew Union College Jubilee Volume, 263–315, 1925; Isis, VIII, 793).

MASLAMA IBN AḤMAD

See mathematical section (IV), below.

[k] Their number is sometimes quoted as 50 or 51.

IBN ABĪ YA'QŪB AL-NADĪM

Abū-l-Faraj Muḥammad ibn Isḥāq ibn abī Ya'qūb al-Nadīm al-Warrāq al-Baghdādī; the two last names mean, the copyist or stationer from Bagdad. Died in 995. Historian, bibliographer. He completed in 987–88,[1] possibly in Dār al-Rūm, Constantinople, his "Index of the Sciences" or Fihrist al-'ulūm. It is, to use his own words, "the index of the books of all peoples of the Arabs and non-Arabs whereof somewhat exists in the language and script of the Arabs, on all branches of knowledge" . . . . together with biographies and appreciations of the authors. It is divided into ten discourses (maqālāt), which are subdivided into sections (funūn). The subject of the discourses can be roughly defined as follows: (1) Languages, writings, Scriptures, Qur'ān; (2) grammar and philology; (3) history, belles lettres, biography, genealogy; (4) poetry; (5) scholastic theology; (6) jurisprudence and tradition; (7) philosophy and "ancient sciences," in three sections (*a*, materialist philosophy and logic; *b*, mathematics, music, astronomy, mechanics, engineering; *c*, medicine); (8) magic and fables; (9) sects and creeds; (10) alchemy.

Because of the sack of Bagdad in 1258, not one in a thousand of the books quoted in the Fihrist is extant. To realize the importance of this index, the reader need but ask himself what it would mean to the classical scholar to have such a catalogue (with biographical notes!) of the libraries of Alexandria or Pergamum.

Text and Translations—Gustav Flügel edited the Fihrist, posthumously published in Leipzig (1871–72) by Joh. Rödiger and August Müller. Volume 1 contains the text; volume 2, the notes and index. There is no complete translation in any language, and no translation at all in English. The scholar who would undertake a complete and annotated translation would be sure to win the gratitude of the whole Republic of Letters.

There are a few partial translations. Of the seventh discourse (the most important to us), Heinrich Suter: Das Mathematiker-Verzeichnis im Fihrist, vollständig ins Deutsche übersetzt und mit Ammerkungen versehen (Zeitschrift für Mathematik und Physik, vol. 37, 1892, Supplement, 1–87; Nachtrag, *ibidem*, vol. 38, 126–127, 1893. Apropos of Archimedes). It is not necessary to refer to the index of this work, for a later work of Suter, Die Mathematiker und Astronomen der Araber (1900), always gives these references.

Of the ninth discourse, D. Chwolsohn: Die Ssabier und der Ssabismus (vol. 2, 1–52, Arabic and German, 53–365 (notes), St. Petersburg, 1856). Gustav Flügel: Mani, seine Lehre und seine Schriften, aus dem Fihrist, im Text nebst Uebersetzung, Commentar und Index (448 p., Leipzig, 1862).

Of the tenth discourse, M. Berthelot: La chimie au moyen âge (T. 3, L'alchimie arabe, 26–40, Paris, 1893).

Criticism—G. Flügel: Über Muḥammad ibn Isḥāq's Fihrist al-'ulūm (Zeitschrift der deutschen morgenländ. Gesell., vol. 13, 559–650, 1859. A long analysis of the Fihrist). For a briefer analysis see E. G. Browne: Literary History of Persia (vol. 1, 383–387, 1902); or R. A. Nicholson: Literary History of the Arabs (1907; 2d impression, 362–364, 1913). C. Brockelmann: Arabische Litteratur (vol. 1, 147, 1898).

For the history of Muslim culture in the tenth century (that is, roughly, the fourth century of the Hijra) see Adam Mez: Die Renaissance des Islams (498 p., Heidelberg, 1922; Isis, V, 210).

---

[1] There are dates in the Fihrist down to 1009, however. The question is very complicated; see Flügel's Vorwort to his edition (p. XIII f.).

WU SHU

Wu[2] Shu[2]* (12748, 10041). Born in Tan[1]-yang[2] (10618, 12883), Kiangsu, 947, died 1002. Chinese encyclopaedist. His Shih[4] lei[4] fu[4] (9990, 6853, 3748) is the earliest Chinese encyclopaedia.[m] It deals with "celestial and terrestrial phenomena, mineralogy, botany, and natural history, arranged, for want of an alphabet, under categories." It is divided into 30 books and 100 articles. Wu shu was also one of the collaborators of the more extensive encyclopaedia edited by Li Fang (q. v.).

An extension of the Shih lei fu, divided into 27 sections and 191 articles, was published in 1699 by Hua[2] Hsi[1]-min[3] (5005, 4048, 7929), under the title Kuang[3] shih[4] lei[4] fu[4] (6397, 9990, 6853, 3748).

A. Wylie: Notes on Chinese Literature (182, also 194, Shanghai, 1867, new edition, 1902). H. A. Giles: Chinese Biographical Dictionary (888, 1898); Chinese Literature (239, 1901). On this and earlier administrative encyclopaedias, see the introduction to the Alphabetical index to the Ch'in[1] ting[4] ku[3] chin[1] t'u[2] shu[1] chi[2]* ch'êng[2] (2114, 11248, 6188, 2027, 12128, 10024, 906, 762) compiled by Lionel Giles (London, 1911).

LI FANG

Li[3] Fang[2] (6884, 3441). Of Jao[2]-yang[2] (5585, 12883) in Chihli 924, died 995. Chinese statesman and encyclopaedist. Chief editor of the encyclopaedia T'ai[4]-p[1]ing[2] yü[4]-lan[3] (10573, 9310, 13645, 6735),[n] the compilation of which was ordered in 977 by the second Sung emperor, T'ai Tsung. Wu Shu, author of a former and smaller encyclopaedia, was associated in the undertaking. It was completed in 987 (or 983?) and is divided into 55 sections comprising 1,000 books. It is a collection of extracts from 1,690 works, the list of which is given at the beginning. This list is itself very precious, for hardly more than one-fifth of these books are extant. Li Fang compiled also an encyclopaedia of biographical and other information, called the T'ai[4]-p'ing[2] kuang[3]-chi[4] (10573, 9310, 6397, 923), wherein 360 authorities are given (the index fills 280 p.).

Text and Translations—The T'ai-p'ing yü-lan was revised and printed with movable type in 1568–1572. A new revised edition by Yüan[3] Yüan[2] (13750, 13744) in 1,000 books appeared in 1812. The T'ai-p'ing kuang-chi was printed in 981, also in 1566. No translations.

Criticism—A. Wylie: Notes on Chinese Literature (183, Shanghai, 1867, 1902). H. A. Giles: Biographical Dictionary (428, 1898); Chinese Literature (239, 1901). Lionel Giles: Index to the T'u Shu (p. 5, 1911).

IV. MUSLIM, LATIN, CHINESE, AND JAPANESE MATHEMATICS AND ASTRONOMY

Further History of the Hindu Numerals

A special form of numerals developed in Spain, which was called, as early as c. 950, ghubār, meaning dust, or ḥurūf al-ghubār (letters of dust). This term suggests that those numerals were used in conjunction with some kind of sand abacus. We have other evidence proving the use of such abacuses by Muslims.

Woepcke has published a document proving that, in 970, ordinary Arabic

[m] Previous compilations were not sufficiently comprehensive to deserve this title.
[n] It is called yü lan because the emperor passed the whole work under review.

forms of the numerals were used alongside the ghubār. In the Jeremias monastery in Egypt a grafitto in Arabic has the date 349 H. (= 960–61) expressed by means of Hindu numerals.

The oldest definitely dated European document containing such numerals is a Latin manuscript, the Codex Vigilanus, written in the Albelda Cloister, not far from Logrōno, on the Upper Ebro, in (Christian) Spain, in 976.

Smith and Karpinski: Hindu-Arabic Numerals (65, 94, 137–139, 1911).

MUṬAHHAR IBN ṬĀHIR

See philosophical section (III) above.

ABŪ JA'FAR AL-KHĀZIN

Al-Khāzin means the treasurer or the librarian. Born in Khurāsān, died between 961 and 971. Mathematician, astronomer. Author of a commentary on the Tenth Book of Euclid and of other mathematical and astronomical writings. He solved by means of conic sections the cubic equation which had baffled al-Māhānī's efforts, the so-called al-Māhānī equation (q. v., second half of ninth century).

Texts and Translations—Abū Ja'far's extant writings are still unpublished. For the manuscripts, see Suter.

Criticism—Fihrist (p. 266, 282); Suter's translation (p. 17, 39). Franz Woepcke: L'algèbre d'Omar Alkhayyāmī (p. 3, Paris, 1851). Carra de Vaux: Bibliotheca Mathematica (3–4, 1898). Suter: Die Mathematiker und Astronomen der Araber (58, 1900); Nachträge (165, 1902).

NAẒĪF IBN YUMN

Naẓīf ibn Yumn (or Yaman?) al-Qass. Al-Qass means the priest (particularly, the Christian priest). Flourished under the Buwayhid sulṭān 'Aḍud al-dawla; died c. 990. Mathematician and translator from Greek into Arabic. He thus translated the Tenth Book of Euclid.

H. Suter: Mathematiker (68, 1900).

ABŪ-L-FATḤ

Abū-l-Fatḥ Maḥmūd ibn Muḥammad ibn Qāsim ibn Faḍl al Iṣfahānī. From Ispahan, flourished probably c. 982. Persian mathematician. He gave a better Arabic edition of the Conics of Apollonios and commented on the first five books.

The Conics had been translated a century before by Hilāl al-Ḥimṣī (books 1 to 4) and Thābit ibn Qurra (Books 5 to 7) (see second half of ninth century).

Text—The commentary is still unpublished. The translation of Books 5 to 7 of the Conics is of considerable importance, for it is through it that we know those books at all, the Greek original being lost. It was translated into Latin by Abraham Ecchellensis[o] and G. A. Borelli, and this Latin version published in Florence, 1661.

---

[o] Maronite, born in Syria, died in Rome, 1664. Professor of Arabic and Syriac in Rome and Paris.

Criticism—H. Suter: Mathematiker und Astronomen der Araber (98, 1900). Ettore Bortolotti: Quando, come e da chi ci vennero ricuperati i sette libri delle coniche di Apollonio. Periodico di matematiche (vol. 4, 12 p., 1924; Isis, VII, 178).

AL-KŪHĪ

Abū Sahl Wījan (or Waijan) ibn Rustam al-Kūhī. Of Kūh, Ṭabaristān, flourished in Bagdad c. 988. Mathematician, astronomer. Many mathematical and astronomical writings are ascribed to him. He was the leader of the astronomers working in 988 at the observatory built by the Buwayhid Sharaf al-dawla. He devoted his attention to those Archimedian and Apollonian problems leading to equations of a higher degree than the second; he solved some of them and discussed the conditions of solvability. These investigations are among the best of Muslim geometry.

Text and Translation—F. Woepcke: L'algèbre d'Omar Alkhayyāmī (p. 54, 103–114, 118, Paris, 1851); Trois traités arabes sur le compas parfait[p] (Notices et extraits, t. 22 (1), 1–175, 1874. Arabic and French; posthumous publication edited by de Slane).

Criticism—M. Steinschneider: Lettere intorno ad Alcuhi a D. Bald. Boncompagni (Roma, 1863). Suter: Die Mathematiker und Astronomen der Araber (75–76, 1900). Cantor: Vorlesungen (1. Bd., 3. Aufl., 742, 748–750, 759, 787, 1907). Suter: Die Abhandlungen Thābit b. Qurras und Abū Sahl al-Kūhīs über die Ausmessung der Paraboloide (Sitzungsber. d. phys. med. Ges., vol. 48, 186–227, Erlangen, 1918; Isis, IV, 400). C. Schoy: Graeco-arabischen Studien (Isis, VIII, 31, 1926).

AL-SIJZĪ

Abū Sa'īd Aḥmad ibn Muḥammad ibn 'Abd al-Jalīl al-Sijzī (short for al-Sijistānī). Lived from c. 951 to c. 1024. Mathematician who made a special study of the intersections of conic sections and circles. He replaced the old kinematical trisection[q] of an angle by a purely geometric solution (intersection of a circle and an equilateral hyperbola).

Texts and Translations—L. Amélie Sédillot: Notice de plusieurs opuscules mathématiques qui composent le MS. arabe N° 1104, ancien fonds de la bibliothèque du Roi (Notices et extraits des MSS., t. 13, 126–150, surtout 136–145, 1838). Franz Woepcke: L'algèbre d'Omar Alkhayyāmī (117–124, Paris, 1851); Trois traités arabes sur le compas parfait (Notices et extraits, t. 22, (1), 112–115, 1874). C. Schoy: Graeco-arabische Studien (Isis, VIII, 21–35, 1926. Containing translation of a treatise on the construction of the regular heptagon and the trisection of the angle).

Criticism—Suter: Die Mathematiker und Astronomen der Araber (80–81, 224, 1900). Cantor: Vorlesungen (1 Bd., 3 Aufl., 750, 1907). H. Bürger und K. Kohl: Geschichte des Transversalensatzes (49–53, Erlangen, 1924. Translation of a treatise of al-Sijzī's on the subject, Isis, VIII, 799).

'ABD AL-RAḤMĀN AL-ṢŪFĪ

Abū-l-Ḥusain 'Abd al-Raḥmān ibn 'Umar al-Ṣūfī al-Rāzī. Born in Ray 903, died 986. One of the greatest Muslim astronomers. Friend and teacher of the

---

[p] Instrument to draw conics of every kind. See my note on Muḥammad ibn al-Ḥusain ibn Muḥammad (second half of twelfth century).

[q] He calls this the solution by "mobile geometry" ("géométrie mobile" in Woepcke's translation).

Buwayhid sultan 'Aḍud al-dawla. His main work is the "Book of the Fixed Stars" illustrated with figures (Kitāb al-kawākib al-thābita al-muṣawwar), one of the three masterpieces of Muslim observational astronomy (the two others being due to Ibn Yūnus, first half of the eleventh century, and Ulūgh Beg, first half of the fifteenth century).

Texts and Translations—Caussin: Les constellations d'Aboulhossain Abderrahman (MSS. de la Bibliothèque du Roi, Nos. 1110, 1111, 1113; Notices et extraits des MSS., t. 12, 236–276, 1831. Text of the introduction of 'Abd al-Raḥmān's main work with French translation). French translation of the whole work by Schjellerup: Description des étoiles fixes (St. Pétersbourg, 1874).

Criticism—Fihrist (284). Suter: Die Mathematiker und Astronomen der Araber (62, 1900); Nachträge (116, 1902); Encyclopedia of Islam (vol. 1, 57, 1908). A. Hauber: Zur Verbreitung des Astronomen Ṣūfī (Der Islam, vol. 8, 48–54, 1918).

IBN AL-A'LAM

Abū-l-Qāsim 'Alī ibn al-Ḥusain al-'Alawī, al-Sharīf al-Ḥusainī. Flourished at the Buwayhid court under 'Aḍud al-dawla (q. v.); died at Bagdad in 985. Muslim astronomer. The accuracy of his observations was praised; he compiled astronomical tables which obtained much favor during at least two centuries.

H. Suter: Die Mathematiker der Araber (62, 1900).

AL-ṢĀGHĀNĪ

Abū Ḥāmid Aḥmad ibn Muḥammad al-Ṣāghānī al-Aṣṭurlābī, i. e., the astrolabe maker of Ṣāghān, near Merv, flourished in Bagdad, died in 990. Mathematician, astronomer, inventor and maker of instruments. He worked in Sharaf al-dawla's observatory and, perhaps, constructed the instruments which were used there. Trisection of the angle.

Text and Translation—See al-Sijzī's treatise on the trisection of the angle. F. Woepcke: L'algèbre d'Omar Alkhayyāmī (p. 117–125, 119, Paris, 1851).

Criticism—Suter: Die Mathematiker und Astronomen der Araber (p. 65, 1900). Cantor: Vorlesungen (1. Bd., 3. Aufl., 742, 750, 1907).

ABŪ-L-WAFĀ'

Abū-l-Wafā' Muḥammad ibn Muḥammad ibn Yaḥyā ibn Ismā'īl ibn al-'Abbās al-Būzjānī. Born in Būzjān, Qūhistān, in 940, flourished in Bagdad, where he died in 997 or 998. Astronomer and one of the greatest Muslim mathematicians. One of the last Arabic translators and commentators of Greek works. He wrote commentaries on Euclid, Diophantos, and al-Khwārizmī (all lost); astronomical tables (zīj al-wāḍiḥ) of which we have possibly a later adaptation; a practical arithmetic; "the complete book" (Kitāb al-kāmil), probably a simplified version of the Almagest. The book of applied geometry (Kitāb al handasa)[r] is probably, in its present form, the work of a disciple.

His astronomical knowledge was hardly superior to Ptolemy's. He did *not* discover the variation, the third inequality of the moon. He simply spoke of the second part of the evection, the Ptolemaic *πρόσνευσις*, essentially different from the variation discovered by Tycho Brahe.

Solution of geometrical problems with one opening of the compass. Construc-

---

[r] Handasa means engineering, surveying, and, especially, architecture.

tion of a square equivalent to other squares. Regular polyhedra (based on Pappos). Approximative construction of regular heptagon (taking for its side half the side of the equilateral triangle inscribed in the same circle).[s] Constructions of parabola by points. Geometrical solution of $x^4 = a$ and $x^4 + ax^3 = b$.

Abū-l-Wafā' contributed considerably to the development of trigonometry. He was probably the first to show the generality of the sine theorem relative to spherical triangles. He gave a new method of constructing sine tables, the value of sin 30′ being correct to the eighth decimal place. He knew relations equivalent to ours for $\sin(\alpha \pm \beta)$ (though in an awkward form) and to

$$2 \sin^2 \frac{\alpha}{2} = 1 - \cos \alpha \qquad \sin \alpha = 2 \sin \frac{\alpha}{2} \cos \frac{\alpha}{2}$$

He made a special study of the tangent; calculated a table of tangents; introduced the secant and cosecant;[t] knew those simple relations between the six trigonometric lines, which are now often used to define them.

No extensive text has been published, but many short ones are included in the papers quoted below. Fihrist (I, 266, 283, Suter's translation, p. 39). J. B. J. Delambre: Histoire de l'astronomie au Moyen Age (156–170, 1819). L. Am. Sédillot: Découverte de la variation par Aboul Wefā (Journal Asiatique, vol. 16, 420–438, 1835. This started a very long controversy on the subject; it contains the relevant text with French translation). F. Woepcke: Analyse et extrait d'un recueil de constructions géométriques par Aboul Wafā (Journal Asiatique, vol. 5, 218–256, 309–359, 1855. Main source for the geometry). F. Woepcke: Sur une mesure de la circonférence du cercle due aux astronomes arabes et fondée sur un calcul d'Aboul Wafā (Journal Asiatique, vol. 15, 281–320, 1860). L. Am. Sédillot: Sur les emprunts que nous avons faits à la science arabe, et en particulier à la détermination de la troisième inégalité lunaire ou variation (Boncompagni's Bullettino, vol. 8, 63–78, Rome, 1875. Containing also the relevant text in Arabic and French). Carra de Vaux: L'almageste d'Abū-l-Wéfa (Journal asiatique, t. 19, 408–471, 1892. Important). C. Brockelmann: Arabische Litteratur (vol. 1, 223, 1898). A. von Braunmühl: Vorlesungen über Geschichte der Trigonometrie (vol. 1, 54–61, 1900). Suter: Die Mathematiker und Astronomen der Araber (71–72, 224, 1900); Nachträge (166–167, 1902). Dreyer: Planetary Systems (252–256, 1906. Clear and brief statement of the controversy on variation; for more detail see Carra de Vaux's paper quoted above). H. Suter: Encyclopaedia of Islam (vol. 1, 112, 1908); Das Buch der geometrischen Konstruktionen des Abu'l Wefā' (Abhd. zur Geschichte der Naturwiss., Heft 4, 94–109, Erlangen, 1922. German translation of an Arabic manuscript; Woepcke's translation of 1855 quoted above had been made from a Persian manuscript. The Arabic text contains less propositions, but gives demonstrations lacking in the Persian. This Arabic text is probably an elaboration by a pupil, Isis, V, 497). H. Bürger and K. Kohl: Zur Geschichte des Transversalensatzes (75, 81–83, Erlangen, 1924; Isis, VIII, 799).

AL-KHUJANDĪ

Abū Maḥmūd Ḥāmid ibn al-Khiḍr al-Khujandī. Of Khujanda, on the Jaxartes, or Sir Daria, Transoxiana, died c. 1000. Astronomer, mathematician. He made astronomical observations, including a determination of the obliquity of

[s] The methods used in solving these geometrical problems suggest a Hindu origin; yet Abū-l-Wafā' did not use Hindu numerals in his arithmetic.

[t] Suter says that the six lines were already known by Ḥabash al-Ḥāsib? For the early history of Muslim trigonometry see my notes in the previous chapters, especially those on Ḥabash (first half of the ninth century) and on al-Nairīzī (second half of the ninth century).

the ecliptic, in Ray in 994. He proved (imperfectly) that the sum of two cubic numbers can not be a cubic number. He[u] may be the discoverer of the sine theorem relative to spherical triangles.

Text—L. Cheikho: The inclination and latitude of lands, Arabic text (Al-mashriq, vol. 11, 60–69, Beirut, 1908. Containing an elaborate account of his determination of the obliquity of the ecliptic). Oskar Schirmer: Studien zur Astronomie der Araber. (Sitzungsber. der physik. med. Soz. zu Erlangen, vol. 58, 43–46, 63–79, 1926. Containing German translation with notes of the same text. Isis, IX).
Criticism—Suter: Die Mathematiker und Astronomen der Araber (74, 213, 1900). E. Wiedemann: Über den Sextant des al-Chogendī (Archiv für Geschichte der Naturwissenschaften, vol. 2, 148–151, 1909.)

ABŪ NAṢR

Abū Naṣr Manṣūr ibn 'Alī ibn 'Irāq. Teacher of al-Bīrūnī; still active in 1007. Muslim mathematician and astronomer; one of three to whom the discovery of the sine theorem relative to spherical triangles is ascribed.[v] He gave in 1007–8 an improved edition of Menelaos's Spherica. Various other writings on trigonometry and astronomy are ascribed to him.

H. Suter: Die Mathematiker und Astronomen der Araber (81, 225, Leipzig, 1900). See my note on Plato of Tivoli (first half of twelfth century).

MASLAMA IBN AḤMAD

Abū-l-Qāsim Maslama ibn Aḥmad al-Majrīṭī. Of Madrid, flourished in Cordova, died in or before 1007. Astronomer, mathematician, occultist. The earliest Hispano-Muslim scientist of any importance. He edited and corrected the astronomical tables of al-Khwārizmī, replacing the Persian by the Arabic chronology. He wrote a treatise on the astrolabe (translated into Latin by Joan. Hispalensis); a commentary on Ptolemy's Planisphaerium translated by Rudolph of Bruges (q.v., first half of twelfth century); a commercial arithmetic (al-mu'āmalāt); a book on the generation of animals (?). He may have introduced into Spain the writings of the Brethren of Purity, or else this was done later by one of his disciples, al-Karmānī.[w] He spoke of the erotic power of amicable numbers (220, 284). Two alchemic writings, the "Sage's Step" (Rutbat al-ḥakīm) and the "Aim of the Wise" (Ghāyat al-ḥakīm), are ascribed to him. The second is well known in the Latin translation made in 1252 by order of King Alfonso under the title Picatrix; the original Arabic text dates probably from the middle of the eleventh century.

Texts and Translations—Rudolph's translation was printed in Bale, 1536 and Venice, 1558: Sphaerae atque astrorum coelestium ratio, natura et motus; ad totius mundi fabricationis cognitionem fundamenta. The astronomical tables of al-Khwārizmī edited by him were translated into Latin by Adelard of Bath (q. v., first half of the twelfth century).
Criticism—Ibn Khaldūn: Prolégomènes. F. Wüstenfeld: Geschichte der arabischen Aerzte (61, 1840). Leclerc: Médecine arabe (vol. 1, 422, 1876). Dozy et De Goeje: Nouveaux documents pour l'étude de la religion des Harraniens (Actes

---

[u] Or else Abū-l-Wafā', or Abū Naṣr?
[v] The two others being his contemporaries Abū-l-Wafā' and al-Khujandī (q. v.). This sine theorem displaced the so-called theorem of Menelaos (second half of first century).
[w] Arabic sources contradict one another on this point. For al-Karmānī, see first half of the eleventh century.

du 6e Congrès des Orientalistes, Leide, 1883, t. 2, 281–366, 1885). Suter: Die Mathematiker und Astronomen der Araber (76–77, 1900; Nachträge, 167, 1902). D. B. Macdonald: Religious Attitude and Life in Islam (101 f., 1909). Hellmut Ritter: Picatrix (Bibliothek Warburg, Vorträge. 94–124, 1923; Isis, VI, 147). E. J. Holmyard: Arabic Chemistry (Nature, vol. 109, 778–779, 1922; Isis, V, 210); Maslama al-Majrīṭī and the Rutbatu'l-ḥakīm (Isis, VI, 293–305, 1924). The Rutbat al-ḥakīm, herein analyzed, is one of the most important sources for the history of chemistry in Muslim Spain. It is often ascribed to al-Majrīṭī, but this ascription is doubtful, because the Rutbat is said to have been composed after the fitna which broke out in 1009. The author is inclined to place the Rutbat in the middle of the eleventh century. It contains a description of the making of mercuric oxide from mercury, a *quantitative* experiment (Isis, VII, 185).

AL-QABĪṢĪ

Abū-l-Ṣaqr 'Abd al-'Azīz ibn 'Uthmān ibn 'Alī al-Qabīṣī (Alcabitius). Pupil of al-'Imrānī (q. v., first half of the tenth century) in Moṣul; after the latter's death in 955–56 he was patronized by the Ḥamdānid sulṭān Sayf al-dawla, who died in 966–67. Famous Muslim astrologer. His main writings are his introduction to the art of astrology (al-madkhal ilā ṣinā'at (aḥkām) al-nujūm) and a treatise on the conjunctions of planets; both were translated into Latin by Joannes Hispalensis (first half of twelfth century). He, or his patron Sayf al-dawla, wrote a poem on the rainbow.

Texts and Translations—Hispalensis's translation of the first text, Alchabitii Abdilazi liber introductorius ad magisterium judiciorum astrorum interprete Joanne Hispalensi, has often been printed, generally with a commentary by Joannes de Saxonia (Bologna, 1473, commentary alone?; Venice, 1481, 1482, 1485, 1491, 1521).

The second text, Tractatus notabilis Alchabitii de conjunctionibus planetarum in duodecim signis et earum pronosticis in revolutionibus annorum, is appended to the editions of the Liber introductorius or Ysagogicus printed in Venice (1485, 1511, 1521). Oronce Fine (1494–1555) translated it into French: Traité des conjonctions des planètes (Paris, 1557).

Criticism—H. Suter: Die Mathematiker und Astronomen der Araber (60, 1900; Nachtrag, 165, 1902); Encyclopaedia of Islam (vol. 2, 593, 1924).

RABĪ' IBN ZAID

Rabī' ibn Zaid al-Usquf. Meaning the bishop (from the Greek ἐπίσκοπος). He was Bishop of Cordova and Elvira under al-Ḥakam II. Flourished at Cordova c. 961. Spanish Christian writing in Arabic. He composed various astrological treatises and dedicated to Ḥakam II a calendar (Kitāb al-anwā', liber anoë) entitled "The Division of Times and the Good of Bodies."

A similar calendar was compiled by 'Arīb ibn Sa'd (q. v., in the medical section below).

Text—The calendar was translated into Latin probably by Gherardo Cremonese. This translation is included in Libri's Histoire (t. 1, 2. ed., 389–452, 1865).

Criticism—R. Dozy: Die Cordovaner 'Arīb ibn Sa'd der Secretär und Rabī' ibn Zaid der Bischof (Z. d. Deutschen Morgenl. Ges., vol. 20, 595–609, 1866). H. Suter: Mathematiker (69, 212, 1900).

GERBERT

Pope under the name of Sylvester II. Born c. 930 in or near Aurillac, Auvergne, died in Rome 1003. French educator and mathematician. One hundred forty-sixth pope, from 999 to his death (the first French Pope, he succeeded the first

German one). He spent a few years in the county of Barcelona (Christian Spain). From 972 on, he taught at the school of Reims, which he illustrated. Various mathematical writings are ascribed to him and some of his letters deal with scientific questions. He wrote on the abacus and on the astrolabe. He was possibly the first Christian to give a scientific account of the ghubār numerals (i. e., the Spanish-Arabic numerals), but without the zero. The legendary ascription to him of supernatural powers and of various mechanical inventions is a testimony to his learning.

Texts and Translations—The most complete edition of his works is that by A. Olleris (816 p., Clermont, 1867, with notes and a biography). Julien Havet has published an edition of the Letters (Paris, 1889). An excellent edition of all the mathematical texts has been given by Nicolaus Bubnov: Gerberti Opera mathematica. Accedunt aliorum opera ad Gerberti libellos aestimandos intelligendosque necessaria (744 p., Berlin, 1899). H. Omont: Opuscules mathématiques de Gerbert et de Hériger de Lobbes (Notices et extraits, t. 39 (1), 4–15, Paris, 1909, ex MS. Latin 886, Bibl. nat.).

Biography and General Criticism—K. F. Hock: Gerbert und sein Jahrhundert (Wien, 1837. Italian translation revised by the author, Milano, 1846). Bilgen: Gerbert's Bundniss mit dem Teuffel (1843). M. M. Büdinger: Über Gerbert's wissenschaftliche und politische Stellung (Diss., 80 p., Marburg, 1851). P. F. Lausser: Gerbert (Aurillac, 1866). A biography of about 200 pages is prefixed to Olleris's edition (1867). E. M. de Barthelemy: Gerbert (Lagny, 1868). Karl Werner: Gerbert von Aurillac, die Kirche und Wissenschaft seiner Zeit (352 p., Wien, 1878). Karl Schultess: Papst Silvester II, als Lehrer und Staatsmann (Progr., 55 p., Hamburg, 1891). F. Picavet: Gerbert, un pape philosophe d'après l'histoire et d'après la légende (Bibl. de l'école des hautes études, sci. religieuses, 9, 240 p., Paris, 1897. Important). Jules Lair: Lettres de Gerbert, in Etudes critiques sur divers textes du Xe et XIe siècles (Paris, 1899). Duc de La Salle de Rochemaure: Gerbert. Le savant, le faiseur de rois, le pontife (752 p., ill., Paris, 1914. Elaborate biography, but of little importance for the study of Gerbert, Man of Science, Isis, V, 496). Max Manitius: Lateinische Literaturgeschichte des Mittelalters (vol. 2, 729–742, 1923).

Scientific Criticism—Chasles: Explication des traités de l'abacus et particulièrement du traité de Gerbert (Comptes Rendus de l'Académie des sciences, t. 16, 156–173, 1843; also *ibidem*, 1393–1420, and t. 17, 143–154, 1843). G. Friedlein: Gerbert, die Geometrie des Boethius und die indischen Ziffern (60 p., 6 pl., Erlangen, 1861). Julien Havet: L'écriture secrète de Gerbert (Comptes Rendus de l'Académie des inscriptions, t. 15, 23 p., 8 pl., 1887). A. Nagl: Gerbert und die Rechenkunst des X. Jahrhunderts (65 p., Wien, 1888). H. Weissenborn: Gerbert. Beiträge zur Kenntnis der Mathematik des Mittelalters (258 p., Berlin, 1888); Zur Geschichte der Einführung der jetzigen Ziffern in Europa durch Gerbert (130 p., Berlin, 1892). P. Tannery et Clerval: Une correspondance d'écolâtres du XIe siècle (Notices et extraits des MSS., t. 36, 1900. Apropos of the geometria, part of which would be posterior to c. 1025; Isis, VI, 432). G. Eneström: Über einen Brief von Gerbert an Adelbold (Bibliotheca mathematica, t. 4, 402, 1903). B. Carrara: L'opera scientifica di Gerberto novellamente discussa ed illustrata (Mem., Acc. d. Nuovi Lincei, t. 26, 195–228, Roma, 1909). M. Simon: Zur Gerbert-Frage (Arch. d. Math., vol. 18, 244–248, 1911). D. E. Smith and L. C. Karpinski: The Hindu-Arabic Numerals (110–122, Boston, 1911). J. Würschmidt: Geodätische Messinstrumente und Messmethoden bei Gerbert und bei den Araben (Archiv d. Math. u. Physik, vol. 19, 315–320, 1912). Duhem: Système du Monde (t. 3, 163 sq., 1915). Lynn Thorndike: History of Magic (vol. 1, 697–718, 1923. Dealing chiefly with a treatise on the astrolabe in 21 chapters and a preface, placed by Bubnov among Gerbert's doubtful works, and with another anonymous astronomical treatise, Digby, 83).

ABBO

Abbo of Fleury, Abbo Floriacensis. Born in or near Orléans c. 945, murdered at La Réole in 1004. Abbot of Fleury (now St. Benoît sur Loire) from 985. Educated in France and England. He wrote before 987 a commentary on Victorius's Calculus (second half of fifth century): "De numero mensura et pondere super calculum Victorii." He wrote also "Quaestiones grammaticales" dealing with prosody and pronunciation.

Texts and Translations—Extracts from Abbo's commentary have been published by Nic. Bubnov in his Gerberti opera mathematica (Berlin, 1899).
Criticism—M. Prou: Grande Encyclopedie, article Abbon (1886). Cantor: Vorlesungen (1. Bd., 3te Aufl., 845–847, 1907). Otto Funke: Die gelehrten lateinischen Lehn- und Fremdwörter in der altenglischer Literatur von der Mitte des 10. Jahrh. bis um das Jahr 1066, nebst einer einleitenden Abhandlung über die Quaestiones grammaticae (227 p., Halle, 1916. See D L Z, 1916, 1980). Max Manitius: Lateinische Literatur des Mittelalters (vol. 2, 664–672, 1893).

HROSVITHA

See philosophical section (III), above.

"ALCHANDRUS"

Alcandrius, Alhandreus, Alchandrinus. (Corruption of the word Alexander or of an Arabic name.) Unknown author of an astrological treatise entitled, in one manuscript (Addit. 17808), "Mathematica Alhandrei summi astrologi." Similar texts are found in at least two other manuscripts, CLM 560 and BN 17868. This treatise dates back at least to the end of the tenth century. It has but little intrinsic value, but its historical interest is considerable because it is one of the earliest Latin works showing unmistakable traces of Arabic and Hebrew origin. It was presumably written by a Jew or with the collaboration of a Jew.

Text—First edition by Richard Roussat: Arcandam de veritatibus et praedictionibus astrologiae (Paris, 1542). It was translated into French (Lyon, 1526, 1625), and by William Warde into English: "The most excellent, profitable and pleasant book of the famous doctor and expert astrologian Arcandram or Alcandrin to find the fatall destiny, constellation, etc., of every man and child by his birth . . . . " (London, 1578, etc.).
Criticism—M. Steinschneider: Ueber die Mondstationen (Naxatra) und das Buch Arcandam (Zeitschrift der deutschen morgenländischen Ges., vol. 18, 118–201, 1864); Die europäischen Übersetzungen aus dem Arabischen bis Mitte des 17. Jahrhunderts (Sitzungsber. der phil. Kl. der Ak. der Wiss., Wien, vol. 149, 30, 1905). F. Cumont: Astrologica (Revue archéologique, t. 3, 1–22, 1916. Cumont regards the Paris Latin manuscript 17868 as a survival of Carolingian science?; Isis, IV, 621). Lynn Thorndike: History of Magic (vol. 1, 710–718, 1923. Analysis of the manuscript text).

HELPERIC

Flourished in St. Gall? c. 978. Benedictine. He wrote in 978 an elementary treatise on the calendar (De computo). His cosmology was influenced by Macrobius (first half of fifth century).

I am not at all certain as to the date and even as to the identity of this author. The date 978 is derived by Duhem from the single manuscript examined by him (Bibliothèque Nationale, Latin 15118; olim S. Victor, 448). This manuscript was written in 978, to be sure, but it was a regular practice for monks copying such manuscripts to bring them up to date by changing the dates of the calculations. Another manuscript in the Library of Augsburg, 8 S. XI, is dated 1044, and gives 969 as the date of the original. Should this Helperic not be identified with Helperic of Auxerre who flourished about the middle of the ninth century?

M. Manitius: Lateinische Literatur des Mittelalters (vol. 1, 446–449, 1911; vol. 2, 806). Pierre Duhem: Système du monde (vol. 2, 71–76, 1915).

JOSEPHUS SAPIENS

Josephus Sapiens or Hispanus, Joseph the Wise or the Spaniard. Flourished in Spain before 984. He wrote before 984 a treatise on multiplication and division, twice mentioned in Gerbert's correspondence. Unfortunately it is lost, and thus we can not appreciate its importance. How much did Josephus Sapiens contribute to the great arithmetical progress which took place in the second half of the tenth century? It is because of the great significance of this movement and of the mystery surrounding his own personality that we speak of him. Suter has tried to identify him with Abū 'Umar (or 'Amr) Yūsuf ibn Hārūn al-Kindī called al-Ramādī, a poet who flourished in Cordova c. 970 and died in 1012–13, but we have no reason to believe that Josephus Sapiens wrote in Arabic, nor is any mathematical work ascribed to this al-Ramādī.[x]

H. Weissenborn: Über den von Gerbert angeführten Joseph Sapiens oder Joseph Ispanus (Bibliotheca mathematica, 21–23, 1893); M. Curtze (*ibidem*, 13–14, 1894); H. Suter (*ibidem*, 84, 1884). C. Brockelmann: Geschichte der arabischen Litteratur (vol. 1, 270, 1898). Nicolaus Bubnov: Gerberti opera mathematica (p. xcii, 101, 102, Berlin, 1899). H. Suter: Die Mathematiker und Astronomen der Araber (79, 1900; Nachträge, 168, 1902).

HÉRIGER

See my note in the historical section (IX), below.

CHANG SSŬ-HSÜN

Chang[1] Ssŭ[1]-hsün[4] (416, 10271, 4881). Flourished under the Sung, c. 979. Chinese mechanician and astronomer. He constructed a celestial sphere moved by the fall of mercury (?).

L. Wieger: La Chine (223, 409, 1920).

ABE SEIMEI

Flourished under Murakami-tennō, who ruled from 947 to 967; died in 1005. Famous Japanese astronomer. He introduced the Chinese custom of changing the name of the era (nengō)[y] in the first and fifty-eighth years of the sexagesimal cycle.

---

[x] This name does not mean "from Ramāda"; it is derived from the word ramād = ashes; this poet was formerly called Abū Janīsh, father of the ashes, Janīsh being a corruption of the Spanish word ceniza = ashes.

[y] For which see my note on Japanese law in the first half of the seventh century.

I have had no occasion to speak of that sexagesimal cycle, chia[3]*-tzŭ[3] (1167, 12317), because its origin is immemorial. The Chinese themselves ascribe it to the Yellow Emperor (Huang Ti), one of their legendary rulers (2698 to 2598 B. C.); but there is no evidence of it before the Han dynasty. It is a period of 60 years, " a cycle of Cathay," each year having a name of two characters. One of these two characters is taken from the series of the Ten (or Heaven) Stems, tien[1] kan[1] (11208, 5814), that is, the five elements, each counted twice—the other from the series of Twelve (or Earth) Twigs, ti[4] chih[1] (10956, 1873); each of which has an animal name. The second series is found all over Central and Eastern Asia; it is possibly of Egyptian origin (see my note in the first half of the first century).

E. Papinot: Historical Dictionary (article nengō, p. 437; also p. 837, 1909). Herbert A. Giles: Chinese-English Dictionary (2d ed., vol. 1, 28, 1912). F. Brinkley: History of the Japanese People (864, 1915). Encyclopaedia sinica (137, 1917).

V. LATIN AND MUSLIM ALCHEMY AND TECHNOLOGY

"HERACLIUS"

The "Libri Eraclii de coloribus et artibus Romanorum" (three books, the first two in verse) were probably written in Rome about the end of the tenth century (the third book may be younger). It is important for the history of technology and of the arts and crafts.

Heraclius von den Farben und Künsten der Römer. Original text und Übersetzung. Mit Einleitung, Noten und Excursen versehen von Albert Ilg (Quellenschriften für Kunstgeschichte, vol. 4, 214 p., Wien, 1873).
Edmund O. von Lippmann: Chemisches und Technologisches aus kunstgeschichtlichen Quellenschriften. I: Heraclius (Chemiker Zeitung, 1916; reprinted in Lippmann's Beiträge, 140–157, 1923; Isis, III, 354).

Muslim Alchemy

See my notes on Abū-l-Qāsim and Abū Manṣūr Muwaffak in the medical section (VIII), below, on the Brethren of Purity in the philosophical section (III), above, and on Maslama ibn Ahmad in the mathematical section (IV), above.

VI. BYZANTINE, MUSLIM, AND CHINESE NATURAL HISTORY

For Byzantine natural history, see my note on Constantinos VII Porphyrogennetos in the philosophical section (III), above.

For Muslim natural history and biology, see my notes on al-Tamīmī in the medical section (VIII) below; on the Brethren of Purity, in the philosophical section (III), above; on Maslama ibn Aḥmad, in the mathematical section (IV), above.

TSAN-NING

Tsan[4]-ning[2] (11521, 8327). Flourished under the Sung, c. 988. Chinese Buddhist. He compiled the Sung[4] Kao[1]-sêng[1]-ch'uan[2] (10462, 5927, 9617, 2740), a collection of Buddhist biographies down to 988 (see my note on Tao-hsüan, second half of the seventh century). A treatise on bamboo sprouts, Sun[3] p'u[3]

(10439, 9515), is also ascribed to him; it contains five sections: different names, production, use as food, history, varia.

A. Wylie: Chinese Literature (152, 209, (1867), 1902). L. Wieger: La Chine (443, 521, 1920).

VII. MUSLIM, JEWISH, SCANDINAVIAN, AND CHINESE GEOGRAPHY

AL-IṢṬAKHRĪ

Abū Isḥāq Ibrāhīm ibn Muḥammad al-Fārisī al-Iṣṭakhrī. Of Iṣṭakhr, i. e. Persepolis, Persia, flourished c. 950. Persian geographer who revised c. 950 the work of al-Balkhī (q. v., preceding chapter) on the Figures of the Climates. His work (masālik al-mamālik), containing colored maps for each country, was in its turn revised by Ibn Ḥawqal. He mentions windmills in Sijistān.[z]

Text and Translations—Liber climàtum el Isstachri ed. Möller (Gotha, 1839. Facsimile edition which contains only a summary of the work, with map). Viae regnorum. Descriptio ditionis moslemicae auctore Abū Isḥāq al-Fārisī al-Iṣṭakhrī, Edidit M. J. de Goeje (Bibl. geogr. arab., 1, Leiden, 1870).

Criticism—E. H. F. Meyer: Geschichte der Botanik (vol. 3, 278–285, 1856). M. J. de Goeje: Die Iṣṭakhrī-Balkhī Frage (Z. d. deutsch. morg. Ges., vol. 25, 42–58, 1871). Short unsigned note in Encyclopaedia of Islam (vol. 2, 560, 1921).

BUZURG IBN SHAHRIYĀR

Buzurg ibn Shahriyār al-Rāmhurmuzī. From Rāmhurmuz in Khūzistān. Flourished in the fourth century H., 912 to 1009. Persian sailor who edited soon after 953–54 a collection of sailors' tales, the Marvels of India (Kitāb 'ajāyib al-Hind).

Text and Translation—Text edited by P. A. van der Lith (Leiden, 1883–1886), with a French translation by L. Marcel Devic.

Criticism—C. Brockelmann: Arabische Litteratur (1, 523, 1898). Encyclopaedia of Islam (vol. 1, 809, 1912).

IBN ḤAWQAL

Abū-l-Qāsim Muḥammad Ibn Ḥawqal. Flourished c. 943–977. Traveler, geographer. He left Bagdad and began his travels in 943. He met al-Iṣṭakhrī probably c. 952 and at the latter's request revised the maps and text of his geography. He then rewrote it and republished it under his own name, with the title "Book of Roads and Provinces" (Kitāb al-masālik wal-mamālik), not before 977. This treatise contained a map for each country.

Text and Translation—Viae et regna. Descriptio ditionis moslemicae auctore Abū'l-Kāsim ibn Haukal. Edidit M. J. de Goeje (Leiden, 1873, Bibliotheca geographorum arabicorum, 2). Sir William Ouseley: The Oriental Geography of Ebn Haukal, an Arabian Traveler of the Tenth Century (363 p., London, 1800). Scriptorum arabum de rebus indicis loci et opuscula inedita. Rec. et illustr. Joannes Gildemeister (Bonn, 1838. Arabic text with Latin translation of fragments from al-Mas'ūdī, Ibn Ḥawqal, Abū-l-Fidā, Qazwīnī).

Criticism—P. J. Uylenbroek: De Ibn Haukalo geographo (Leiden, 1822). C. van Arendonck: Encyclopaedia of Islam (vol. 2, 383, 1916).

---

[z] al-Mas'ūdī mentions them, too. Though I have dealt with al-Mas'ūdī in the previous chapter, it does not follow that al-Iṣṭakhrī's mention was posterior.

AL-MUQADDASĪ

Abū 'Abdallāh Muḥammad ibn Aḥmad ibn Abū Bakr al-Bannā al-Bashārī al-Muqaddasī (meaning, the Hierosolymite; the form al-Maqdisī, more correct, is less usual), Shams al-dīn, the sun of religion. Born in Jerusalem in 947–48. Muslim geographer. He visited all the countries of Islām with the exception perhaps, of Spain, Sijistān, and Sind, made abundant and careful observations and completed in Fārs, 985–86 (improved edition, 3 years later) a relation of his journeys containing much original information. It is called the "Best of Divisions for Knowledge of the Climates" (Aḥsan al-taqāsīm fī ma'rifat al-aqālīm).

Text and Translations—The text was published in Leide (1877) by M. J. de Goeje in his Bibliotheca geographorum arabicorum, pars tertia. Descriptio imperii moslemici auctore al-Mokaddasi (New edition, 1906).

English translation by G. S. A. Ranking and R. F. Azoo in the Bibliotheca Indica published by the Asiatic Society of Bengal (331 p., in 4 parts, Calcutta, 1897–1910. Is this publication completed? I have seen neither tables nor indexes). Partial translation of the chapter dealing with Syria including Palestine, into German, by J. Gildemeister, in Zeitschrift des deutschen Palestina-Vereins (vol. 7, 1884), and into English, by Guy Le Strange, in the publications of the Palestine Pilgrims' Text Society, No. 4, 132 p., map, London, 1886.

Criticism—Alfred von Kremer: Culturgeschichte des Orients unter den Chalifen, (vol. 2, 429–33, Wien, 1877). Brockelmann: Geschichte der arabischen Litteratur, (vol. 1, 1898, 230).

IBRĀHĪM IBN YA'QŪB

Abraham ben Jacob. Born in northern Africa?; flourished c. 965. Jewish merchant and traveler. In and after 965 he traveled into Germany (visited, at Magdeburg, the court of Otto I the Great, emperor from 936 to 973) and into the Western Slavonic countries. His brief account is a valuable source for the study of Western Slavs and of Jewish commerce and settlements in the tenth century.

Text—The account is included in the Kitāb al-masālik of al-Bakrī (q. v., second half of the eleventh century), that is, in the second part of it discovered by Schefer in 1875 in Constantinople. Rosen and Kunik edited the account, together with a Russian translation and commentary, in the Mémoires de l'Académie des Sciences of St. Petersburg (1878). De Goeje published a Dutch translation, with commentary, in the memoirs of the Amsterdam Academy (Verslagen, afd. letterkunde, vol. 9, 187–216, 1880). Bericht über die Slavenlande in Widukindus Corbeiensis. Sächsische Geschichten (1891).

Criticism—C. Brockelmann: Arabische Litteratur (vol. 1, 523, 1898). F. Westberg: Ibrahim's Reisebericht (Mémoires de l'Académie des Sciences, St. Petersburg, vol. 3, 1898); article in Jewish Encyclopaedia (vol. 6, 554, 1904).

ERIC THE RED

Eirik Raude; born in Norway c. 950; went to Iceland c. 970. Scandinavian (Norwegian) sailor and explorer. Being exiled from Iceland for his evil deeds c. 980, he set out for Greenland[a] and spent three years exploring the country

---

[a] Greenland had been discovered shortly after the settlement of Iceland, say, c. 900, by the Norwegian Gunnbjörn, son of Ulf Kråka. See my note on Geography in the second half of ninth century, and also my note on the Age of the Vikings (first half of ninth century).

"from Hvarf right up to north of Davis Strait,[b] and from the outermost belt of skerries to the head of the long fjords." Soon after he began its colonization, which seems to have proceeded rapidly.

In 999, his son Leif (Leif Ericsson), attempted to go from Greenland to Norway, without following the coast and stopping in Iceland, but sailing due east from the southern point of Greenland. This may be considered the first deliberate ocean voyage in history. He did not succeed in reaching Norway without stopping, for he was driven out of his course to the Hebrides; he finally reached Norway in the autumn of the same year. In 1000 he tried again to sail directly from Norway to Greenland without stop, but was carried accidentally to Wineland, an unknown part of the North American coast. For this early discovery of America and subsequent Icelandic discoveries, see my note on geography in the first half of the eleventh century.

According to another tradition of the fourteenth century, far less certain, Wineland had been discovered as early as 985 by another Scandinavian, Bjarne Herjulfsson.

Fridtjof Nansen: In Northern Mists (1911).

CHI-YEH

Chi[4]-yeh[4]* (966, 12991). Born in Hunan, died after 976 at the age of 84 at the monastery of Niu[2]-hsin[1] (8346, 4562), near the mountain O[2]-mei[2] (8430, 7714), in Ssŭ-ch'uan. Chinese Buddhist who traveled to India to obtain relics and manuscripts. He was one of the three hundred monks (śramaṇā) who left Chieh[1] (1440) (a second-class prefecture in the south of Kansu) in 964; he was back home by 976 and left a short narrative of his journey. This is of special interest as being the latest account of India by a Chinese pilgrim before the devastations caused by Maḥmūd of Ghaznī (1001, etc.).

Text—This text was included by Fan Ch'êng-ta (q. v., second half of the twelfth century) in his "Account of a voyage by water to the country of Wu," Wu[2] ch'uan[2] lu[4]* (12748, 2742, 7386), written by him in 1177. It is published in the encyclopaedia Yüan[2]-chien[4]-lei[4]-han[2] (13713, 1644, 6853, 3809).

French translation by G. Schlegel in the Mémoires du comité sinico-japonais, t. 21, 35–64, 1893. Better translation by Edouard Huber in the Bull. éc. franç. d'Extrême Orient, t. 2, 256–259, 1902.

Criticism—Edouard Chavannes: L'itinéraire de Ki-ye (Bull. éc. franç. d'Extrême Orient, t. 4, 75–81. 1904).

YAO-SHIH

Yao[4]-shih[3] (12957, 9893). Flourished during the Sung dynasty, c. 980. Chinese geographer and topographer. Author of a geographical and statistical survey of the empire called T'ai[4]-p'ing[2] huan[2]-yü[2]-chi[4] (10573, 9310, 5041, 13540, 923) the earliest important work of its kind.

There is an immense geographical (or rather topographical) literature in China called ti[4]-li[3] (10956, 6879). For example, the number of gazetteers published from the Sung (or T'ang) dynasty down to our days is truly enormous. Some of the topographical compilations deal with the whole empire; others, chih[4] (1918) deal with each province, shêng[3] (9887); others still, with each prefecture, fu[3] (3682), department, chou[1] (2444), or district, hsien[4] (4545); some are restricted to individual

[b] Rediscovered some 600 years later, in 1585, by John Davis (hence its name).

towns, even small ones. The Library of Congress owns a very large collection of Chinese gazetteers (Isis, IV, 612; V, 528; VII, 260, 568). The descriptions include generally geographical features, hills and rivers, etc., productions of the soil, antiquities, bridges, defences, tombs, temples, accounts of notable men and women.

A. Wylie: Chinese Literature (144, (1867), 1902). L. Wieger: La Chine (476, 525, 1920).

VIII. MUSLIM, PERSIAN, JEWISH, BYZANTINE, AND JAPANESE MEDICINE

AḤMAD AL-ṬABARĪ

Abū-l-Ḥasan Aḥmad ibn Muḥammad al-Ṭabarī. Of Ṭabaristān; was physician to the Buwayhid Rukn al-dawla, c. 970. Persian physician. Author of a compendium of medicine, called Hippocratic treatments, in ten books. Was it written in Persian or in Arabic? It is extant only in Arabic, Kitāb al-mu'ālaja al-buqrāṭīya.

F. Wüstenfeld: Arabische Aerzte (56, 1840). L. Leclerc: Médecine arabe (vol. 1, 358, 1876). C. Brockelmann: Arabische Litteratur (vol. 1, 237, 1898). Julius Hirschberg: Geschichte der Augenheilkunde (deals with Book 4).

'ALĪ IBN 'ABBĀS

'Alī ibn 'Abbās al-Majūsī, that is, the Magian, which means that he, or his father, was of the Zoroastrian faith. Latin name: Ali Abbas or Haly Abbas. Born in Ahwāz, southwestern Persia; flourished under the Buwayhid 'Aḍud al-dawla; died in 994. One of the three greatest physicians of the Eastern Caliphate. He wrote for 'Aḍud al-dawla a medical encyclopedia called "the Royal Book" (Kitāb al-Malikī, Liber regius, regalis dispositio; also called Kāmil al-ṣanā'a al-ṭibbīya), which is more systematic and concise than Rāzī's Ḥāwī, but more practical than Avicenna's Qānūn, by which it was superseded. The Malikī is divided into 20 discourses, of which the first half deal with the theory and the other with the practice of medicine. The best parts of it are those devoted to dietetics and to materia medica. Rudimentary conception of the capillary system. Interesting clinical observations. Proof of the motions of the womb during parturition (the child does not come out; it is pushed out).

Texts and Translations—Arabic edition in two volumes (Cairo, 1294 H.). Latin translation by Stephen the Philosopher, i. e., Stephen of Antioch (q. v., first half of twelfth century), completed in 1127 (Venice, 1492); the same, annotated by Michael de Capella (Lyon, 1523). An earlier translation had been made by Constantinus Africanus under the title Pantegni; the first part (theoretical) was published in Constantinus's works (Bale, 1539); the ninth book of the second part (surgery) was edited by Julius Pagel (Archiv f. Klin. Chirurgie, 81, Bd. 1, 52 p., 1906).

The Discourses 2 and 3, dealing with anatomy, have been edited and translated into French by P. de Koning: Trois traités d'anatomie arabes (90–431, Paris, 1903). Xenophon Gretschischeff: Die Augenheilkunde des Ali Abbas (Diss., German translation, Berlin, 1900). Discourse 9, chapter 34; des maladies qui se produisent dans les reins, leurs causes et leur symptômes in P. de Koning. Traité sur le calcul dans le rein et la vessie par al-Rāzī (Arabic and French, 124–185, Leyde, 1896). Discourse 8, ch. 8–18, translated by Paul Richter: Über die spezielle Dermatologie des 'Alī ibn al-'Abbās (Archiv fur Dermatologie und Syphilis, vol. 113, 849–864, 1912); Über die allgemeine Dermatologie (*ibidem*, vol. 118, 199–208, 1913). Jules

Wiberg: The Anatomy of the Brain in the Works of Galen and 'Alī 'Abbās (Janus, vol. 19, 17–32, 84–104, 1914; Isis, IV, 401).

Criticism—Wüstenfeld: Geschichte der arabischen Aerzte (59, 1840). E. H. F. Meyer: Geschichte der Botanik (vol. 3, 176–178, 1856). Leclerc: Histoire de la médecine arabe (vol. 1, 381–388, 1876. Containing a translation of the introduction to the Malikī, in which 'Alī ibn 'Abbās judges the works of his predecessors). Gurlt: Geschichte der Chirurgie (vol. 1, 615–618, Berlin, 1898). Paul Richter: Beiträge zur Geschichte der Pocken bei den Arabern (Archiv für Geschichte der Medizin, Bd. 5, 311–331, 1911). E. G. Browne: Arabian Medicine (53–57, 109–110, 123, Cambridge, 1921).

AL-ḤUSAIN IBN IBRĀHĪM

al-Ḥusain ibn Ibrāhīm ibn al-Ḥasan ibn Khūrshīd al-Ṭabarī al-Nātilī. Flourished c. 990–91. Translator from Greek into Arabic. He dedicated, in 990–91, an improved translation of Dioscorides to the Prince Abū 'Alī al-Samjūrī.

C. Brockelmann: Arabische Litteratur (189, 207).

AL-QUMRĪ

Abū Manṣūr al-Ḥasan ibn Nūḥ al-Qumrī. From Qum in Jibāl. Flourished probably at Bagdad, about the end of the tenth century and the beginning of the eleventh. Muslim physician. Teacher of Avicenna. He wrote a treatise on medicine, largely based upon al-Rāzī, called The Book of Life and Death (Kitāb ghinā' wa manā'), divided into three parts (internal diseases, external diseases, fevers).

F. Wüstenfeld: Arabische Aerzte (56, 1840). L. Leclerc: Médecine arabe (vol. 1, 358, 1876). C. Brockelmann: Arabische Litteratur (vol. 1, 239, 1898).

ABŪ SAHL AL-MASĪḤĪ

Abū Sahl 'Īsā ibn Yaḥyā al-Masīḥī al-Jurjānī, i. e., the Christian, from Jurjān, east of the Caspian Sea; died at the age of 40 in 999–1000. Christian physician writing in Arabic. Teacher of Avicenna. He wrote an encyclopaedic treatise on medicine in a hundred chapters (al-kutub al-mi'a fī-l-ṣanā'a al-ṭibbīya), which is one of the earliest Arabic works of its kind and may have been in some respects the model of the Qānūn. He wrote various smaller treatises: on measles, on the plague, on the pulse, demonstration of God's wisdom as evidenced in the creation of man, etc.

F. Wüstenfeld: Arabische Aerzte (59, 1840). L. Leclerc: Médecine arabe (vol. 1, 356–357, 1876). C. Brockelmann: Arabische Litteratur (vol. 1, 238, 1898).

ABŪ MANṢŪR MUWAFFAK

Abū Manṣūr Muwaffaq ibn 'Alī al-Harawī. Flourished in Herāt under the Sāmānid prince Manṣūr I ibn Nūḥ, who ruled from 961 to 976. Persian pharmacologist. He was apparently the first to think of compiling a treatise on materia medica in Persian; he traveled extensively in Persia and India to obtain necessary information. He wrote, between 968 and 977, the "Book of the Foundations of the True Properties of the Remedies" (Kitāb al-abniya 'an ḥaqā'iq al-adwiya), which is the oldest prose work in modern Persian. It syncretizes Greek, Syriac, Arabic, and Hindu elements. It deals with 585 remedies (of which 466 are derived from plants, 75 from minerals, and 44 from animals), classified into four groups according to their action. Outline of a general pharmacological theory.

Abū Manṣūr distinguished between sodium carbonate (natrūn) and potassium carbonate (qlī); he had some knowledge of arsenious oxide, cupric oxide, silicic acid, antimony; he knew the toxicological effects of copper and lead compounds, the depilatory virtue of quicklime, the composition of plaster of Paris and its surgical use.

Texts and Translations—The Vienna manuscript of this book is the oldest known Persian manuscript in Europe, copied by the poet Asadī in 1056. It has been most beautifully edited by F. R. Seligmann: Codex vindobonensis sive medici Abu Mansur Muwaffak ibn Ali Heratensis Liber fundamentorum farmacologiae (Pars 1. Prolegomena et textum continens. Vienna, 1838. Together with Latin translation and notes). The Latin translation had been published by F. R. Seligmann before in Vienna (1831–1833). Die pharmakologischen Grundsätze des Abu Mansur übersetzt und mit Erklärungen versehen von Abdul-Chalig Achundow (Koberts Historische Studien aus dem pharmak. Institut der Universität Dorpat III, 113–414, 450–481, Halle, 1893. German translation and notes by Achundow, R. Kobert, Paul Horn, J. Jolly).

Criticism—Leclerc: Histoire de la médecine arabe (vol. 1, 361, 1876). Abdul Chalig Achundow: Commentar zum Liber fundamentorum (Diss., Dorpat, 1892). Ed. O. v. Lippmann: Chemische Kenntnisse vor tausend Jahren (Z. f. angew. Chemie, 640, 1901. Also Abhdl. und Vorträge, vol. 1, 81–96, 1906). Paul Diergart: Das Scheinzink bei Muwaffaq (Mit. zur Gesch. der Medizin, vol. 2, 147–157, 1903). For a study of the most interesting anatomical diagrams of the Vienna manuscript, see Sudhoff in his Studien zur Geschichte der Medizin (Heft 4, Leipzig, 1908). E. G. Browne: Literary History of Persia (vol. 1, 11, 478, 1909). Adolf Fonahn: Quellenkunde der persischen Medizin (80, 81, 134, 1910). Max Neuburger: Geschichte der Medizin (vol. 2, 227, 1911). B. Laufer: Sino-Iranica (194, 580–585, Chicago, 1919. The Hindu elements in Abū Manṣūr). E. G. Browne: Arabian Medicine (92, Cambridge, 1921).

AL-TAMĪMĪ

Abū 'Abdallāh Muḥammad ibn Aḥmad ibn Sa'īd al-Tamīmī al-Muqaddasī (meaning, the native or inhabitant of the Holy City). Born in Jerusalem; he moved, c. 970, to Egypt and was still living there in 980. Palestinian physician. He made pharmaceutical experiments and wrote various medical works, chiefly on materia medica. His main work is a guide (Murshid) on materia medica, which contains much valuable information on plants, minerals, etc. Kitāb al-murshid ilā jawāhir al-aghdhiya wa quwā-l-mufradāt; guide toward (the understanding of) the substances of food-stuffs and (of) the simple drugs.

F. Wüstenfeld: Arabische Aerzte (57, 1840). E. H. F. Meyer: Geschichte der Botanik (vol. 3, 174–176, 1856). L. Leclerc: Médecine arabe (t. 1, 388–391, 1876). C. Brockelmann: Arabische Litteratur (vol. 1, 237, 1898).

Leclerc deals on pages 549–552 with a most interesting manuscript—Escorial 887, old 882—containing what seem to be the notes taken by a student at the consultations of a physician. His physician is one Muḥammad al-Tamīmī, about whom no definite information is given. Leclerc would place him in Toledo, c. 1069, but his conjecture is not convincing. There is a possibility that these two Tamīmī are the same person. In any case, this work seems to be very valuable and to deserve a thorough investigation. About 50 consultations are reported in it.

AL-BALADĪ

Aḥmad ibn Muhammad ibn Yaḥyā al-Baladī. Flourished in Egypt under the wazīr Ya'qūb ibn Kils, who died in 990–91. Egyptian physician. Author of a treatise on the hygiene of pregnant women and of babies (Kitāb tadbīr al-ḥabālā wal-aṭfāl).

C. Brockelmann: Arabische Litteratur (vol. 1, 237, 1898).

ḤASDAI IBN SHAPRUT

Alias Shabrut, Shafrut, Bashrut, Shprot. Abū Yūsuf Ben Isaac ben Ezra. Born c. 915 at Jaén, Andalusia; flourished at Cordova at the court of 'Abd al-Raḥmān III and al-Ḥakam II; died in 970 or 990 at Cordova. Hispano-Jewish physician, translator of Greek into Arabic, patron of science. Physician to the caliph. He discovered a panacea called al-fārūq (the best).

A manuscript of Dioscorides having been presented in 948–49 to 'Abd al-Raḥmān III by the emperor Constantinos VII, Ḥasdai undertook to translate it with the assistance of the Greek monk Nicholas. This monk had been sent to Cordova by the emperor upon the caliph's request, in 951.

He wrote a Hebrew letter to the King of the Khazars[c] describing Andalusia. He was a great patron of Jewish science and it was partly due to his initiative and activity that the intellectual center of Israel was finally transferred from the academies of Babylonia to Spain.

Text—The letter of Joseph, King of the Khazars, to R. Hasdai was first published by J. Akrish. Kol Mebasser. Constantinople, 1577. It has often been reprinted in editions of Judah ha Levi's Kuzari (q. v., first half of twelfth century). German translation by Zedner. Berlin 1840; also by Paul Cassel in the Magyarische Alterthümer, Berlin, 1848, and in Die Antwort, Berlin, 1876, 45–104. French translation by Carmoly in the Revue orientale, 1841.

Criticism—Article by Rabbi Meyer Kayserling in Jewish Encyclopaedia, vol. 6, 248, 1904. R. Dozy. Spanish Islam. London, 1913.

'ARĪB IBN SA'D

'Arīb ibn Sa'd al-Kātib (the secretary) al-Qurṭubī. Flourished at Cordova at the court of 'Abd al-Raḥmān III and al-Ḥakam II, who died in 976. Hispano-Muslim historian and physician.[d] Originally a Christian. He wrote a chronicle of Muslim Spain and Africa some time between 961 and 976. This chronicle was extensively used by Ibn al-'Idhārī (q. v., second half of thirteenth century). He wrote also a treatise on gynaecology, on the hygiene of pregnant women and infants, and on obstetrics (Khalq al-janīn, Creation of the embryo, in 964–65), and a calendar (Kitāb al-anwā').

Text—R. P. A. Dozy: Histoire de l'Afrique et de l'Espagne par Ibn-Adhārī et fragments de la chronique d'Arīb (2 vols., Leyde, 1848–1851); Le calendrier de Cordoue de l'année 961, texte arabe et ancienne traduction latine (Leyde, 1873).

---

[c] The Khazars (Chozars, Ἀκάτζιροι, Χάζαροι) were a Turkish people whose normal territory was included between the Caucasus, the Volga, and the Don with an outlying province (Little Khazaria) in Crimea; their capital was Itil in the delta of the Volga. They were the Venetians of the Caspian (which the Muslims call the sea of the Khazars, Baḥr al-Khazar) and the Euxine. Their history extends from the end of the second to the eleventh century. Their kings and most of the people accepted Judaism c. 740. In 860 some became Christians; see my note on St. Cyril (second half of the ninth century). See good article (3 coll.) by P. L. Gell and Sir Charles N. E. Eliot in Encyclopaedia Britannica, 1911 ("Khazars").

[d] Assuming, as Dozy does (loc. cit., vol. 1, 41) that the authors of the two works quoted below are one and the same person. The name of the physician is also quoted as Gharīb ibn Sa'īd (a name which differs very little in the Arabic writing from the one I have given).

Criticism—R. Dozy: Die Cordovaner 'Arīb ibn Sa'd der Secretär und Rabī' ibn Zeid der Bischof (Z. d. Deutschen Morgenl. Ges., vol. 20, 595–609, 1866). F. Wüstenfeld: Arabische Aerzte (55, 1840); Geschichtschreiber der Araber (46, 1881). L. Leclerc: Médecine arabe (t. 1, 432–436, 1876). C. Brockelmann: Arabische Litteratur (vol. 1, 236, 1898).

ABŪ-L-QĀSIM

Latin names: Abulcasis, Albucasis, Alsaharavius. Khalaf ibn 'Abbās al-Zahrāwī, from Zahrā', near Cordova, where he flourished and died c. 1013. The greatest Muslim surgeon. Physician to al-Ḥakam II (961 to 976). His great medical encyclopaedia in 30 sections, al-taṣrīf (Vade mecum) contains interesting methods of preparing drugs by sublimation and distillation, but its most important part is the surgical, in three books, largely based upon Paulos Aegineta. Great importance attached to cauterization and styptics. Parts of the surgery are devoted to obstetrics and to the surgical treatment of eyes, ears, and teeth. This work was illustrated with views of the surgical instruments. It was early translated into Latin (by Gherardo Cremonese), Provençal and Hebrew. Muslim prejudices against surgery stifled Abū-l-Qāsim's fame in Islām, but in the Christian world his prestige was soon immense.

Texts and Translations—The Kitāb al-taṣrīf liman 'ajiza 'ani-l-ta'ālīf (Concessio ei data qui componere haud valet)[e] has not been published entirely. The earliest part of it to appear was that dealing with the preparation of drugs; Liber servitoris sive liber XXVIII Bulchasin Benaberacerin, interprete Sim. Januensi et Abraamo Judaeo (Venice, 1471). Then a first edition of the surgery was attached to Guy de Chauliac: Chirurgia parva (Venice, 1497). The medical part was next to appear, Liber theoricae necnon practicae Alsaharavii. Edited by Sig. Grimm (Augsburg, 1519). The part dealing with female diseases was included in the collections de gynaeciis, edited by Caspar Wolf (Bale, 1566) and I. Spach (Strasbourg, 1597).

Other editions of the Surgery: Albucasis methodus medendi cum instrumentis ad omnes fere morbos depictis (Bale, 1541, with woodcuts; other mediaeval surgical texts are appended). Albucasis de chirurgia, Arabic text with Latin translation by John Channing (Oxford, 1778). La chirurgie d'Albulcasis traduite par Lucien Leclerc (Paris, 1861). Some extracts from this translation have been published by P. de Koning in his Traité sur le calcul dans les reins et dans la vessie, etc. (Leyde, 1896).

Ernst Seidel: Medizinisches aus den Heidelberger Papyri Schott-Reinhardt, IV (Islam, vol. 3, 273–291, 1912. Pap. 711, containing a part of al-taṣrīf, of the maqālat taqāsim al-amrāḍ, dealing with the aetiology and pathology of the urinogenital system, translated in the Liber theoricae, pars II, tract. XXI, end of cap. X).

Criticism—Wüstenfeld: Geschichte der arabischen Aerzte (p. 85, 1840). L. Leclerc: Histoire de la médecine arabe (t. 1, 437–457, 1876). E. Gurlt: Geschichte der Chirurgie (t. 1, 620–649, 1898. This is the most elaborate account; pls. 4 and 5 contain reproductions of 102 instruments described by Abulcasis). C. Brockelmann: Arabische Litteratur (vol. 1, 239, 1898). Ernest Cordonnier: Le liber servitoris d'Aboulcasis (Janus, vol. 9, 425–432, 481–487, 1904. Brief analysis apropos of the Spanish translation by Alonso Rodriguez of Tudela, published in Valladolid,

---

[e] This is one interpretation of the Arabic title which is difficult to translate. Says D. B. Macdonald: "I think this means 'the giving of control (as to medical treatment) to him who is not equal to the (big) treatises (on medicine)'. I would suggest for Al-taṣrīf alone 'Vade-mecum'."

1516). Robert Valensi: Un chirurgien arabe, Abulcasis (Thèse, Montpellier, 1908). Ch. Niel: La chirurgie dentaire d'Aboulcasis comparée à celle des Maures du Trarza (Revue de stomatologie, t. 18, 169–181, 222–229, 1911). Karl Sudhoff: Beiträge zur Geschichte der Chirurgie im Mittelalter (vol. 2, 16–84, 1918, 22 plates).

IBN JULJUL

'Abū Dā'ūd Sulaimān ibn Ḥassān ibn Juljul. Physician to the Spanish Umayyad Hishām II, Mu'aiyad billāh, caliph from 976 to 1009. Hispano-Muslim physician. He wrote, at Cordova, in 982, a commentary on Dioscorides, and later a supplement to it, and a history of the physicians and philosophers of his time in Spain (Ta'rīkh al-aṭibbā' wal-falāsifa), often quoted by Ibn abī Uṣaibi'a (q. v., first half of thirteenth century).

The aim of the commentary was to determine the drugs dealt with by Dioscorides; the supplement was a list of drugs not mentioned by Dioscorides. As to the origin of these Dioscoridean studies, see my note on Ḥasdai ibn Shaprut. It would seem that Ibn Juljul and others assisted in the translation of Dioscorides into Arabic

F. Wüstenfeld: Arabische Aerzte (57, 1840). E. H. F. Meyer: Geschichte der Botanik (vol. 3, 171–174, 1856). L. Leclerc: Médecine arabe (t. 1, 430-432, 1876). C. Brockelmann: Arabische Litteratur (t. 1, 237, 1898).

IBN AL-JAZZĀR

In Latin, Algizar, Algazirah. Abū Ja'far Aḥmad ibn Ibrāhīm ibn abī Khālid Ibn al-Jazzār. Flourished in Qairawān, Tunis, died in 1009, being more than 80 years old. Physician. Pupil of Isḥāq al-Isrā'īlī (q. v., first half of the tenth century). Of his many writings, the most important, because of its enormous popularity, was his "Traveller's Provision" (Zād al-musāfir) which was translated into Latin by Constantinus Africanus, into Greek by Synesios,[f] and into Hebrew—the titles of these translations being: Viaticum peregrinantis; Τὰ ἐφόδια τοῦ ἀποδημοῦντος; Ẓedat al-derachim. It contains remarkable descriptions of smallpox and measles. He wrote also on the coryza, on the causes of the plague in Egypt, etc.

Text—First chapter of Synesios's translation, dealing with fevers, edited by St. Bernard (Amsterdam, 1749).

Criticism—Ferdinand Wüstenfeld: Geschichte der arabischen Aerzte (60, 1840). Gustave Dugat: Etudes sur le traité de médecine d'Abou Djāfar, intitulé Zad al Moçafir (Journal asiatique (5), t. 1, 289–353, 1853). Leclerc: Histoire de la médecine arabe, t. 1, 413–416, 1876). C. Krumbacher: Byzantinische Literatur (614, 1897). C. Brockelmann: Arabische Litteratur (vol. 1, 238, 1898). Iwan Bloch, in Puschmann: Geschichte der Medizin (vol. 1, 564, 1902). M. Steinschneider: Europäische Uebersetzungen aus dem Arabischen (11, 78, 1904; 17, 1905).

DONNOLO

The name Donnolo is derived from domnulos, δόμνουλος. His real name was Shabbethai ben Abraham ben Joel. Born in Oria, near Otranto, in 913; captured by Saracens in 925 and taken to Palermo, where he studied Arabic; flourished in Otranto (where he learned more Arabic) and Rossano; died after 982.

---

[f] Synesios's translation was incomplete; it contained only two books. A complete Greek translation is ascribed to one Constantinos Rheginos (Ῥηγῖνος) or Memphites (Μεμφίτης).

One of the earliest Jewish writers on medicine, writing in Hebrew.[g] According to his own statement, he studied all the sciences of the Greeks, Arabs, Babylonians, and Indians. His "Precious Book" (Sefer ha-yaqar) is an antidotarium, containing descriptions of 120 drugs, mostly derived from plants. It is almost entirely of classical origin (very few words of Hebrew and Arabic origin).

Donnolo's personality is of considerable interest because it enables us to realize how the so-called "School of Salerno" came gradually into existence. It is just such men as Donnolo who by their very presence created that focus of medical syncretism and eventually of medical teaching in South Italy.

Text and Translations—M. Steinschneider: Donnolo. Fragment des ältesten medizinischen Werkes in hebräischer Sprache (Berlin, 1867. Hebrew text; this seems to have been reprinted with additions: Donnolo. Pharmacologische Fragmente. . . . . Berlin, 1868). David Castelli: Il commento di Sabbatai Donnolo sul libro della creazione.[h] (Publ. d. R. Istituto di Studi Sup., Firenze, 1880. Hebrew text with notes and introduction).

Criticism—Julius Pagel, in Puschmann: Handbuch der Geschichte der Medizin (t. 1, 636, 1902). Richard Gottheil: Article Donnolo in Jewish Encyclopedia (vol. 4, 639, 1903. These two authors contradict one another on the fundamental subject of Donnolo's education; were his teachers Christians or Muslims?, was he an autodidact?). Charles and Dorothea Singer: Origin of the Medical School of Salerno (in Essays on the History of Medicine dedicated to K. Sudhoff, 18 p., Zürich, 1923; Isis, VII, 535).

CONSTANTINOS VII PORPHYROGENNETOS

See Section III, above. See also my note on Nonnos in the preceding chapter.

YASUYORI TAMBA

Japanese physician who flourished c. 982. He compiled c. 982 the Ishinhō, the oldest Japanese treatise on medicine which is still extant in its original form. It is essentially derived from the Ping-yüan-hou-lun of Ch'ao Yüan-fang (q. v., first half of the seventh century) and other Chinese works. It is divided as follows: (1) generalities; (2) acupuncture; (3) diseases of the pneuma; (4) internal diseases; (5) skin diseases; (6) eye, ear, and teeth diseases; (7) hands and feet; (8) abscesses and tumors; (9) wounds; (10) pediatrics; (11) gynaecology and obstetrics; (12) hygiene; (13) sexual hygiene; (14) dietetics; (15) materia medica.

Fujikawa ascribes another work to Yasuyori, a materia medica entitled Honzō-wamyō, dealing with 81 mineral, 509 vegetal, and 182 animal drugs, used in many different forms. Is this an independent treatise or a part of the Ishinhō? At any rate, if the date given by Fujikawa, Engi era (901 to 923), is correct, the Honzō can not have been compiled by the author of the Ishinhō.

Y. Fujikawa: Geschichte der Medizin in Japan (13, 20, 21, 1911).

---

[g] See my notes on Asaph Judaeus, whom I placed tentatively in the second half of the ninth century and whom Donnolo quotes, and on Ḥasdai ibn Shaprut, above. Some of the early translators into Arabic were Jews and, of course, some of the Alexandrian physicians were also Jews, but they wrote in Greek.

[h] I. e., Sefer Yeẓirah.

IX. LATIN, BYZANTINE, JEWISH, MUSLIM AND CHINESE HISTORIOGRAPHY

FLODOARD OF REIMS

Flodoardus Remensis. Born at Epernay c. 894; died at Reims on March 28, 966. French historian. His main work is a chronicle of the Reims diocese from its foundation to 961 ("Historia Remensis ecclesiae"). It is based upon archival documents and is a source of the very first importance for the history of the ninth and tenth centuries. He wrote also annals of his own times (919 to 966). An earlier part, which is lost, dealt probably with the years 894 to 918.

Texts—First French edition by Nicolas Chesneau (Reims, 1581). Historia Remensis ecclesiae, first Latin edition by Sirmond (1611). P. J. F. Lejeune: Histoire de l'Eglise de Reims (2 vols., Reims, 1854. Latin and French). Best edition by J. Heller and G. Waitz in the Monumenta Germ. hist., Scriptores (vol. 13, 409–599, 1881).

Annales edited by Pertz in the Monumenta Germ. hist., Scriptores (vol. 3, 368–408, 1839). Ph. Lauer: Les annales de Flodoard (Coll. de textes pour servir à l'étude de l'histoire, 375 p., Paris, 1905).

Criticism—Max Manitius: Lateinische Literatur des Mittelalters, vol. 2 (155–166, 1923).

LIUDPRAND

Liudprand[i] of Cremona. Born c. 922, flourished at the Lombard court, then at the court of Emperor Otto I; appointed by the latter Bishop of Cremona, died c. 972. Lombard diplomat, annalist, humanist. Intrusted with many missions to Constantinople (950, 968) and to Rome. The most original Hellenist of his age.[j] He wrote three historical works: (1) "The Antapodosis"[k] in six books, dealing with the period 886 to 952; composed in 958 to 962; (2) the "Historia Ottonis," dealing with the years 960–964; (3) the "Relatio de legatione constantinopolitana," a very graphic description of Constantinople and the Byzantine court in 968.

Text—Liudprand's works are edited in Muratori's collection; also by G. H. Pertz in the Monumenta Germaniae historica. Second edition by Ernest Dümmler in 1877. Also in Migne's Latin Patrology (vol. 136, 787–938, 1844).

Partial German translation in the Geschichtschreiber der deutschen Vorzeit (Berlin, 1853; 2d edition, 1890). English translation of the Relatio by Ernest Henderson in the Select documents of the Middle Ages (Bohn Library, 1896).

Criticism—Josef Becker: Textgeschichte Liudprands (46 p., München, 1908). Sandys: History of Classical Scholarship (vol. 1^3, 510, 1921). M. Manitius: Lateinische Literatur des Mittelalters (vol. 2, 166–175, 1923).

WIDUKIND

Widukind of Corvey (Widukindus Corbeiensis). He entered the monastery of Corvey on the Weser c. 941; died after 973, c. 1004? German (Saxon) Benedictine and historian. He wrote (largely c. 968) a history of the Saxon Emperors

---

[i] Many variants by permutation of *i* and *u*, and replacement of one or two *d* by *t*.

[j] Says Sandys. His writings abound in Greek quotations, of special interest because Liudprand sets down their pronunciation, e. g., *ἄθεοι καὶ ἀσεβεῖς* should be pronounced as if athei ke asevis were Latin words.

[k] So-called because written to revenge himself upon the Lombard King Berengar (*ἀνταπόδοσις*, means a turning back, change of direction).

Henry I and Otto I (Res gestae saxonicae, 919 to 973). The composition was influenced by Sallust.

Text—First edition by Martin Frecht (Basel, 1532). Edition by Georg Waitz in the Monum. Germ. hist.; reprinted in Migne's Latin Patrology (vol. 137). This edition was revised by K. A. Kehr (Hanover, 1904).

German translation by Reinhold Schottin (Berlin, 1852; 1891).

Criticism—Max Herrmann: Die Latinität Widukinds (Diss., Greifswald, 1907). Friedrich Brechmann: Die staatsrechtlichen Anschauungen Widukinds (Diss., Münster, 66 p., 1909). M. Manitius: Lateinische Literatur des Mittelalters (vol. 1, 714–718, 1911; vol. 2, 815). Rudolf Teuffel: Individuelle Persönlichkeitsschilderung in den deutschen Geschichtswerken des 10. und 11. Jahrhunderts (128 p., Leipzig, 1914; Isis, II, 438).

HROSVITHA

See philosophical section (III), above.

CHRONICON SALERNITANUM

The very detailed chronicle bearing that name was written by a monk of the St. Benedict monastery in Salerno, c. 978. It deals with the history of the Lombard Kingdoms of South Italy, beginning generally where the chronicle of Paulus Diaconus (q. v., second half of the eighth century) stopped, that is, about the year 744. The latest events chronicled are those of 974. It is of particular value for the study of Muslim and Greek influences in Southern Italy.

Text—Edition by Pertz in the Monumenta Germaniae, scriptores (vol. 3, 467–571).

Criticism—M. Manitius: Lateinische Literatur des Mittelalters (vol. 2, 197–203, 1923).

RICHER

Richer of Reims; Richer of St. Rémi. Born between 940 and 950; flourished at the monastery of St. Rémi at Reims, and at Chartres; died after 997. French monk and annalist. Pupil of Gerbert at Reims. He had some scientific and medical knowledge. His "Historiae" dealt with the end of the Carolingian dynasty in France, the revolution of 987, and the reign of Hugh Capet (987 to 996); he is partial to the Carolingians.

Text—Edited by G. H. Pertz in the Monumenta Germaniae historica (vol. 3, 561–657, 1839); reprinted in Migne's Patrology (vol. 138, 9–170, 1844).

Latin and French edition by Joseph Guadet (Paris, 1845). German translation by Karl v. d. Osten-Sacken (Berlin, 1854; 1891).

Criticism—Ernest Babelon: Les derniers Carolingiens d'après Richer et d'autres sources (Paris, 1878). Max Neuburger: Geschichte der Medizin (vol. 2, 272, 282, 1911). M. Manitius: Lateinische Literatur des Mittelalters (vol. 2, 214–219, 1923).

HÉRIGER

Hériger of Lobbes.[1] Herigerus Laubiensis, abbot of the monastery of Lobbes in Hainaut from 990 to his death in 1007. The earliest Belgian historian and one of the most learned men of his time. The favorite disciple of Notger of

[1] Lobbes (French) = Laubach (German).

Liège (q. v.). He is known chiefly for his historical work, the earliest history ot the episcopal principality of Liège, but is of special interest to us because of his writings on the abacus. The great arithmetical progress which was accomplished at the beginning of the eleventh century (see, e. g., Bernelinus, first half of eleventh century) may be due in part at least to him and not exclusively to Gerbert.

Texts—The Gesta episcoporum Tungrensium, Trajectensium et Leodiensium was first published in Liège (1612). Best edition by R. Koepfe in the Monumenta Germaniae historica (vol. 7, 1846), with an excellent introduction.

Mathematical Writings—Nicolaus Bubnov: Gerberti opera mathematica (p. 205–225, Berlin, 1899). H. Omont: Opuscules mathématiques de Gerbert et de Hériger de Lobbes (Notices et extraits, t. 39 (1), 4–15, Paris, 1909; ex. MS. Bibl. nat., Latin, 886).

Criticism—Godefroid Kurth: Biographie nationale de Belgique (t. 9, 245–51, 1886-87, with bibliography). Cantor: Vorlesungen (1^3, 869–889, 1907). Oskar Hirzel: Abt Heriger von Lobbes (Beiträge zur Kulturgesch. des Mittelalters und der Renaissance, 8, Leipzig, 1910. Also Tübinger Diss.). M. Manitius: Lateinische Literatur des Mittelalters (vol. 2, 219–228, 1923).

CONSTANTINOS VII PORPHYROGENNETOS

See philosophical section (III), above.

SYMEON METAPHRASTES

Συμεὼν ὁ μεταφράστης, flourished probably in the second half of the tenth century. The greatest Byzantine hagiographer. Probably[m] the author (c. 963–969) of a continuation of Georgios Monachos's chronicle, from 842 to 948.

Text—Editio princeps in Latin by Lippomenus in his Vita sanctorum priscorum patrum (Venice, 1556–1558); in vulgar Greek by Agapios Landos, under the title *Νέος παράδεισος* (Venice, 1641). Complete edition of the original text in Migne's Greek Patrology (114–116).

Criticism—K. Krumbacher: Byzantinische Litteratur (200–202, 1897).

LEON DIACONOS

Λέων Διάκονος. Born c. 950 at Caloe on the Tmolus; flourished in Constantinople; accompanied Basil II Bulgaroctonos in the Bulgarian war, 986; died after 992. Byzantine annalist. He wrote, soon after 992, a History of the period 959–975 (wars against the Muslim pirates in Crete, against the Saracens in Asia, against the Bulgarians and Russians). His work is one of the earliest sources for Bulgarian and Russian ethnography.

Text—Editio princeps of the complete work by C. B. Hase with Latin translation, in the Paris Byzantine collection (vol. 34, 1819. With copious commentary and contemporary texts—Greek, Arabic, Latin); reprinted in the Bonn corpus (t. 5, 662 p., 1828) and in Migne's Greek patrology (t. 117).

Criticism—K. Krumbacher: Byzantinische Litteratur (2. Aufl., 265–269, 1897).

It is hardly necessary to refer to Gustave Schlumberger's monumental publications on Byzantine history at the end of the tenth century: Un empereur byzantin au Xe siècle, Nicéphore Phocas (963 to 969) (783 p., ill., Paris, 1890); L'épopée byzantine à la fin du Xe siècle (3 vols., ill., Paris, 1896–1905).

---

[m] This continuation is ascribed to Symeon the Master and Logothete (*Συμεὼν μάγιστρος καὶ λογοθέτης*), but it is probable that the Metaphrast and the Logothete are but one and the same person. See my note on Georgios Monachos (first half of ninth century).

SHERIRA GAON

Sherira ben Ḥanina; born c. 900; flourished at Pumbedita; died c. 1000, in prison. Jewish theologian and chronicler. Last but one Gaon of the Academy of Pumbedita, from 968 to 998. His fame rests chiefly on one of his responsa, addressed c. 980 to the community of Qairawān, Tunis, a chronicle which is our chief source for the Talmudic, post-Talmudic, and geonic periods. Half of it is written in Aramaic and half in Hebrew (see my note on the geonate, first half of the seventh century). Some of Sherira's responsa were written in Arabic.

Text—This chronicle is included in the Ahimaaz Chronicle (q. v., second half of the eleventh century). Edition by J. Wallerstein, with Latin translation, Sherirae Epistola (Breslau, 1861). Adolf Neubauer: Medieval Jewish Chronicles (Oxford, 1887).

Criticism—Rabbi J. Z. Lauterbach, in Jewish Encyclopaedia (Vol. XI, 284, 1905).

HAMZA

Ḥamza ibn al-Ḥasan al-Iṣfahānī. Of Persian birth. Flourished at Bagdad about 961. Persian historian and lexicographer writing in Arabic. Ardent Shu'ūbite.[n] He completed, in 961, annals based essentially upon Persian sources. He wrote also a work dealing with grammatical subjects and etymology (homonyms); in fact, he was more a grammarian and littérateur than a historian.

Text—Hamzae Ispahanensis Annalium libri X, edited by J. M. P. Gottwaldt (2 vols., Leipzig, 1844–1848).

Criticism—C. Brockelmann: Arabische Litteratur (vol. 1, 145, 1898). Eugen Mittwoch: Die literarische Tätigkeit des Ḥamza (Mitt. des Seminars fur orient. Sprachen, vol. 12, 60 p., 1909); Abergläubische Vorstellungen und Bräuche der alten Araber von Ḥamza (*ibidem*, vol. 16, 14 p., 1913; Mit zur Gesch. der Med., vol. 12, 571); Die älteste Influenza-Epidemie in Persien und Mesopotamien (i. J. 855) (Berlin. klin. Wchschrft., 1913. Was this epidemic disease influenza? Sticker thinks it was not).

IBN MASKAWAYH

Abū 'Alī Aḥmad ibn Muḥammad ibn Ya'qūb ibn Maskawayh. Flourished at the court of the Buwayhid Sulṭāns Mu'izz, Rukn, and 'Aḍud al-dawla; died at a very old age in 1030. Persian historian, physician, and philosopher, writing in Arabic. His main work is the Kitāb tajārib al-umam (Experentiae populorum et studia animorum), a universal history down to the death of 'Aḍud al-dawla in 982–83. He wrote a compilation in six parts, on practical wisdom (Kitāb ādāb al-'Arab wal Furs, Institutiones Arabum et Persarum), borrowed from Persian, Hindu, Arabic, and Greek philosophers, and a treatise on the "Refinement of Manners" (Kitāb tahdhīb al-akhlāq), in 6 or 7 parts, which is the best specimen of Neoplatonic ethics composed by a Muslim.

Text—Pars sexta operis Tadjāribo-l-Omami, auctore Ibn Maskoweih, ed. M. J. de Goeje (Fragmenta hist. Arab., vol. 2, Leyden, 1871). H. F. Amedroz and D. S. Margoliouth: The Eclipse of the 'Abbasid Caliphate. Original chronicles of the Fourth Islamic Century, edited, translated, and elucidated (7 vols., Oxford, 1920–1921. Arabic and English text of Ibn Maskawayh's history, together with the continuation of his work by Abu Shuja' Rudhrawari and Hilal ibn Muhassin. Isis, V, 496).

[n] To the extent that he contrived Persian etymologies of purely Arabic words! See E. G. Browne: Literary History of Persia (vol. 1, 269, 1908).

Criticism—L. Leclerc: Médecine arabe (t. 1, 482, 1876). F. Wüstenfeld: Die Geschichtschreiber der Araber (59, 1881). C. Brockelmann: Arabische Litteratur (vol. 1, 342, 1898). For an analysis of Ibn Maskawayh's Tahdhīb see T. J. De Boer's article on Muslim Ethics in the Encyclopaedia of Religion and Ethics (vol. 5, 507, 1912).

IBN ABĪ YA'QŪB AL-NADĪM

See philosophical section (III), above.

'ARĪB IBN SA'D

See medical section (VIII), above.

IBN AL-QŪṬĪYA

Abū Bakr Muḥammad ibn 'Umar ibn 'Abd al-'Azīz ibn al-Qūṭīya; meaning son of the Gothic woman; one of his ancestors had married a Gothic princess in Damascus and had then emigrated with her to Spain. Born and flourished at Cordova. He died there in 977. Hispano-Muslim historian and grammarian. His "History of Andalusia" (Ta'rīkh al-Andalus) deals with the period extending from the Muslim conquest to 893–94. His work on the conjugations of (Arabic) verbs (Kitāb taṣārīf al-af'āl) was the first treatise ever composed on the subject.

Text—O. Houdas: Histoire de la conquête de l'Andalousie (Recueil de textes de l'école de langues orientales vivantes, t. 1, Paris, 1899. Arabic and French). J. Guido: Il libro dei verbi (Leida, 1894).
Criticism—Ibn Khallikān (De Slane) (vol. 3, 79–83, 1868). F. Wüstenfeld: Geschichtschreiber der Araber (46, 1881). C. Brockelmann: Arabische Litteratur (vol. 1, 150, 1898).

IBN JULJUL

See medical section (VIII), above.

HSIEH CHÜ-CHÊNG

Hsieh[1]* Chü[1]-chêng[4] (4371, 2987, 687). Born in Honan 912, died in 981. Chinese historian. He wrote, in 973–74, the older official history of the Five Dynasties (907–59) called Chiu[4] Wu[3]-tai[4]-shih[3] (2289, 12698, 10547, 9893), in 150 books. This work is the eighteenth of the "Twenty-four Histories."

Text—Chinese edition, Hu-Pê ts'ung-wen (150 chüan in 16 vols., 1872).
Criticism—A. Wylie: Chinese Literature (22, (1867), 1902). H. A. Giles: Biographical Dictionary (289, 1898).

TSAN-NING

See Section VI, above.

X. ARABIC, SYRIAC, JEWISH, BYZANTINE, LATIN, ENGLISH, AND SINO-JAPANESE PHILOLOGY

ḤAMZA

See historical Section IX, above.

ISMĀ'ĪL IBN 'ABBĀD

Abū-l-Qāsim Ismā'īl ibn 'Abbād ibn al-'Abbās al-Ṣāḥib al-Ṭālaqānī. Often called Ṣāḥib (meaning Master) Ismā'īl ibn 'Abbād. Born at Iṣṭakhr or Ṭālaqān in 936 or two years later; educated at Ray and Bagdad; wazīr to the Buwayhids of Persia; died in 995–96. Persian patron of humanism and learning. Lexicographer. His main work is a large Arabic dictionary called the Comprehensive (Kitāb al-muḥīt).

C. Brockelmann: Arabische Litteratur (1, 130, 1898). E. G. Browne: Literary History of Persia (1, 1908).

AL-JAUHARĪ

Abū Naṣr Ismā'īl ibn Ḥammād al-Jauharī. Born at Fārāb, Turkestan; he traveled extensively in the Eastern Caliphate for linguistic purposes and settled finally at Nīsābūr, Khurāsān, where he died in 1002 or a few years later. Persian lexicographer. Author of a great Arabic dictionary arranged in the alphabetic order of the last radical letters, Kitāb al-ṣiḥāḥ fī-l-lugha (Book of the Correct (Words) of Language). The same order was followed by many Arabic lexicographers. Al-Jauharī did not carry the fair copy farther than the word ḍād; the Ṣiḥāḥ was then completed by his disciple Abū Isḥāq Ibrāhīm ibn Ṣāliḥ al-Warrāq (the bookseller).

Text—Būlāq edition (1282). Partial edition (Arabic Latin) by Everardus Scheidius (198 p., Harderwijk, 1774).
Criticism—C. Brockelmann: Arabische Litteratur (vol. 1, 128, 1898).

IBN JINNĪ

Abū-l-Fatḥ 'Uthmān ibn Jinnī al-Mauṣilī. Born in 941–42 at Mosul, the son of a Greek slave (Γενναῖος?). Flourished in Mosul and Bagdad; died at the latter place in 1002. Muslim philologist. The chief merit of his many writings is their philosophical treatment of philology.

Text—Ibn Ginnii de flexione libellus, edited in Arabic and Latin by G. Hoberg (Leipzig, 1885), that is, the Jumal uṣūl al-taṣrīf or Mukhtaṣar al-taṣrīf al-mulūkī.
Criticism—C. Brockelmann: Arabische Litteratur (vol. 1, 125, 1898. It is remarked that a deeper study of Ibn Jinnī is one of the most urgent desiderata for the history of Arabic grammar). Oscar Rescher: Studien über Ibn Ginnī und sein Verhältnis zu den Theorien der Baṣrī und Baghdādī (Diss., Berlin, 56 p., Strassburg, 1909).

IBN AL-QŪṬĪYA

See historical section (IX) above.

BAR BAHLŪL

In Arabic: Abū-l-Ḥasan ibn al-Bahlūl (the buffoon). The forename Īshō' (in Arabic 'Īsā, our Jesus) is sometimes wrongly added. Of Awānā, in the district of Ṭīrhān (plain of Sāmarrā) flourished in the second half of the tenth century. Syriac Nestorian lexicographer. He compiled (in Bagdad?) the most comprehensive Syriac dictionary of mediaeval times. His sources were exactly quoted.

Text—Rubens Duval: Lexicon syriacum, auctore Hassano Bar Bahlule, 3 vols., Paris, 1901 (1888–96).
Criticism—R. Duval: Littérature syriaque (298, 1907).

SAHL BEN MAZLIAH

Sahl ben Maẓliaḥ ha-Kohen al-Mu'allim abū al-Sarī. Born at Jerusalem in 910; he traveled extensively. Qaraite theologian, lexicographer and grammarian. He wrote on the calendar and established principles of exegesis. His Hebrew grammar (Sefer diqduqe) and his Hebrew lexicon (Leshon limmudim) were very popular.

Article by Rabbi S. Ochser in Jewish Encyclopaedia (vol. 10, 636, 1905).

MENAHEM BEN SARUQ

Menahem ben Jacob ibn Saruq. Born at Tortosa, flourished at Cordova under the patronage of Isaac and Ḥasdai ibn Shaprut.[o] Hispano-Jewish philologist. His main work is a dictionary of the Biblical language, called Maḥberet, the first complete dictionary of the kind. It contains grammatical remarks and other philological information and, being written in Hebrew, it remained for a long time the main source of instruction in that line for the Jews who were not conversant with Arabic. It was superseded by the work of his chief pupil Ḥayyuj (q. v.), written in Arabic.

Whether Menahem or Ḥayyuj should be called the founder of scientific Hebrew grammar is partly a matter of definition. It seems to me more correct to give the title to Ḥayyuj; yet the work of Menahem was of fundamental importance.

Text—The Maḥberet was edited by Herschell Filipowski. The first Hebrew and Chaldaic Lexicon to the Old Testament (with a brief translation). (London, 1854.)
Criticism—Wilhelm Bacher, in Jewish Encyclopaedia (vol. 8, 470, 1904).

DAVID BEN ABRAHAM

Abū Sulaimān Dā'ūd al-Fāsī, from Fez;[p] flourished in the second half of the tenth century. Qaraite lexicographer. He wrote in Arabic a Hebrew dictionary called Agron (or, in Arabic, Kitāb jāmi' al-alfāẓ, "Collection of Words"). It contains general rules on Hebrew word-formation, grammatical notes, and comparisons of the Hebrew and Arabic languages (partly inspired by Judah ibn Quraish's Risāla).

Article by W. Bacher, in Jewish Encyclopaedia (vol. 4, 459, 1903).

DUNASH BEN LABRAṬ

Both Dunash and Labraṭ are names of Romance origin. He has also been called Adonim the Levite. Born at Fez in a Bagdad family; flourished at Sura, until 942, then at Fez, and later at Cordova. Jewish philologist and poet. Pupil of Saadia Gaon. He founded a new Hebrew prosody based on the Arabic. He criticized bitterly Menahem's dictionary, soon after its appearance. The quarrel, which thus originated between the disciples of Menahem and those of Dunash, introduced the golden age of Hebrew philology in Spain. He seems to have anticipated some of Ḥayyuj's grammatical reforms.

---

[o] Father and son. See my note on Ḥasdai, above.

[p] Fez was an important center for the study of Hebrew philology. See my notes on Judah ibn Quraish (first half of the ninth century) and Dunash ben Labraṭ and Ḥayyuj, below.

Text—Treatises of Dunash were edited by H. Filipowski: Criticae vocum recensiones (London, 1855); and by R. Schröter: Kritik des Dunash ben Labraṭ (Breslau, 1866).

Criticism—Article by Wilhelm Bacher, in Jewish Encyclopaedia (vol. 5, 11, 1903).

ḤAYYUJ

Judah ben David. In Arabic: Abū Zakarīyā Yaḥyā ibn Dā'ūd. Born at Fez, Morocco, c. 950; flourished at Cordova, where he died at the beginning of the eleventh century. Spanish-Hebrew grammarian. The father of scientific Hebrew grammar. He wrote in Arabic and his Hebrew grammar was based essentially on Arabic grammar. (To this day the technical terms of Hebrew grammar are translations of the corresponding Arabic terms.) He made a special study of verbs and punctuation (that is, the Masoretic punctuation to indicate vowels and word-tones). His main works were soon translated into Hebrew by Moses ibn Giqaṭilla (second half of eleventh century) and later by Abraham ibn Ezra (first half of twelfth century).

Text—Leopold Dukes: Grammatische Werke des R. Jehuda Chajjug aus Fetz (Beiträge zur Geschichte der ältesten Auslegung und Spracherklärung des alten Testaments, 3, 204 p., Stuttgart, 1844. Vol. 3 contains Ibn Ezra's translation). John W. Nutt: Two Treatises on Verbs containing Feeble and Double Letters from Moses Gikatilia's Hebrew translation and the Treatise on Punctuation translated by Aben Ezra (edited in Hebrew with English translation, 306 p., London, 1870). First Arabic edition of the Weak and Geminative Verbs in Hebrew by M. Jastrow, Jr. (London, 1897).

Criticism—Bernard Drachmann: Die Stellung und Bedeutung des Jehuda Hajjug in der Geschichte der hebräischen Grammatik (86 p., Breslau, 1885). Article by Caspar Levias, in Jewish Encyclopaedia (vol. 6, 277, 1904).

SUIDAS

Σουΐδας. Flourished about the middle of the tenth century. Byzantine lexicographer. He compiled, before 976, a Greek dictionary, containing much information on the subjects as well as upon the words representing them. It contains many articles devoted to scientific topics, but is especially valuable for the history of literature. It might be called a philological encyclopaedia. The order of works is not strictly alphabetical, but phonetic according to the principle of *ἀντιστοιχία*. Double consonants are often discarded and vowels or diphthongs phonetically equivalent or similar follow one another. We have, for example, the following series: δ, αι, ε, ζ, ει, η, ι, ... , ο, ω, throughout the work.

Earliest notice of colors obtained when tempering (or drawing the temper of) steel in oil. This is the earliest account of tempering-colors of any kind but, of course, such phenomena must have been observed long before by craftsmen.

Text—Princeps edition by Demetrios Chalcondyles (Milano, 1499). Edition by Thomas Gaisford (3 vols., Oxford, 1834). Magnificent edition by Gottfried Bernhardy (2 vols. in 4, Halle and Braunschweig, 1834–1853. With a Latin translation). Poor edition in 1 vol., 1162 p., by Emṃ. Bekker (Berlin, 1854. Bekker re-established the alphabetical order).

Criticism—K. Krumbacher: Byzantinische Litteratur (562–570, 1897). Joseph Bidez: La tradition manuscrite du lexique de Suidas (Preuss. Ak. der Wiss., Sitzungsber., 850–863, 1912).

ABBO

See mathematical section (IV), above.

AELFRIC

Aelfric[q] grammaticus. Born c. 955; educated at Winchester abbey; abbot of Cerne, Dorsetshire, and Eynsham, near Oxford; still living in 1020. English Benedictine. Grammarian and lexicographer. He wrote a Latin grammar, with extracts translated from Priscian (q. v., first half of the sixth century); a glossary, containing some 3,000 words—the oldest Latin-English dictionary extant—and the Colloquium, a manual of Latin conversation. He wrote homilies and translated various books into Anglo-Saxon.

Text—Grammar and Glossary, edited by William Somner (Oxford, 1659). Edition by Julius Zupitza (Berlin, 1880).

Colloquium edited by B. Thorpe: Analecta Anglo-Saxonica (1834); by Wright and Wülker: Vocabularies (vol. 1, 1884).

Exameron anglice or the old English Hexameron. Edited with a modern English translation and parallel passages from the other works of Aelfric, by S. J. Crawford (85 p., Hamburg, 1921. This is not a translation of Basil's Hexaëmeron).

Criticism—Friedrich Albrecht Reum: De temporibus, ein echtes Werk des Abtes Aelfric (Diss., Leipzig, 48 p., 1887). Caroline Louisa White: Aelfric (Yale studies in English, 2, 218 p., New York, 1898). Hugo Brüll: Die altenglische latein Grammatik des Aelfric (Diss., Berlin, 26 p., 1900). S. Harvey Gem: Aelfric (216 p., Edinburgh, 1912). Sandys: History of Classical Scholarship (vol. 1^3, 512–515, 1921). Max Manitius: Lateinische Literatur des Mittelalters (vol. 2, 675–682, 1923. Aethelwold and Aelfric. Aethelwold (or Ethelwold, Adelwold), 908? to 984, Bishop of Winchester, was Aelfric's teacher; Aelfric wrote his life in 1006, Vita Aęthelwoldi).

MINAMOTO NO SHITAGAU

Born in 911; died in 983. Japanese writer and lexicographer. Author of a Sino-Japanese dictionary, the Wamyōshō, wherein the words are classified according to subjects (heaven, earth, etc.).

W. G. Aston: Japanese Literature (127, 1899). E. Papinot: Dictionary of Japan (374, 1909).

---

[q] Not to be mistaken for various contemporary namesakes, notably the archbishops of Canterbury (d. 1005) and York (d. 1051).

CHAPTER XXXIII

THE TIME OF AL-BĪRŪNĪ

(First Half of Eleventh Century)

I. Survey of Science in First Half of Eleventh Century. II. Philosophical and Theological Background. III. Latin, English, Muslim, and Hindu Mathematics and Astronomy. IV. Latin, English, Syrian, Muslim, and Chinese Physics, Chemistry, and Technology. V. Muslim Natural History. VI. Icelandic Discovery of America; Latin Geography; Muslim Geography, Mineralogy, and Geology. VII. Latin, Byzantine, Muslim (or Arabic), and Chinese Medicine. VIII. Latin, Muslim, Armenian, and Syrian Historiography. IX. German, Hebrew, Syriac, and Chinese Philology.

I. SURVEY OF SCIENCE IN FIRST HALF OF ELEVENTH CENTURY

1. The renewal of activity which characterized the second half of the tenth century, continued with greater intensity during the first half of the eleventh century. We shall see, in the last chapter of this book, that that enormous activity was followed by a very definite slowing up during the second half of the century; but we must not anticipate.

To come back to the period under consideration, it would not be too much to say that it marked the climax of mediaeval thought. The great leaders were so many—Ibn Yūnus, Ibn al-Haitham, al-Bīrūnī, Ibn Sīnā, 'Alī ibn 'Īsā, al-Karkhī, Ibn Gabirol (all Muslims except the last, who was a Jew)—that, for a moment at least, the historian is bewildered. Yet, however distinguished all of those men, and many others who will be named presently, two stand out head and shoulders above the others: al-Bīrūnī and Ibn Sīnā (Avicenna). It was chiefly because of them that this period was one of such excellence and distinction. These two men, who, by the way, knew one another, were extremely different. Al-Bīrūnī represents the more adventurous and critical spirit, Ibn Sīnā the synthetic spirit; al-Bīrūnī was more of a discoverer, and in that respect he came nearer to the modern scientific ideal; Ibn Sīnā was essentially an organizer, an encyclopaedist, a philosopher. Both, even the latter, were primarily men of science, and it would be difficult to choose between them but for the accidental fact that al-Bīrūnī's life covered more fully the present period and thus may be said to represent it more completely. Ibn Sīnā was only 20 at the beginning of the century, and his life was untimely cut short in 1037. Al-Bīrūnī's first important work appeared about the year 1000 and he lived until 1048. Thus his time of activity and the first half of the eleventh century are one identical period, and we are fully justified (more fully so than in almost every other case) in calling it the Time of al-Bīrūnī.

2. *Philosophical and Theological Background*—That conditions were not as flourishing in the Latin West, or for that matter in the whole of Christendom, as they were in Islām, will appear at once, for the only outstanding Christian teacher of that time was Notker Labeo. He was the most famous representative of the school of St. Gall, one of the greatest cultural centers of Christian Europe. He translated a number of philosophical books from Latin into German and thus rendered his people an inestimable service, in spite of the fact that most of the knowledge he was thus transmitting to them was already out of date.

Jewish thought, being directly stimulated by the most progressive writings of those days, those of the Muslim philosophers, was naturally on a much higher level. In fact, Jewish philosophy was essentially identical with Muslim philosophy in its various aspects; that is, the more liberal of the Jews were influenced by the Mu'tazilites, while the more conservative found some of their inspiration and pabulum in the works of the orthodox theologians of Islām. This was very easy, because the educated Jews understood Arabic as well as Hebrew; generally they even preferred to write in Arabic. Thus the Qaraite Joseph ha-Ro'eh composed an Arabic treatise which represents the Jewish liberalism of that time, while Samuel ha-Levi, who was the head of the Jewish community of Granada and chose to write in Hebrew, continued the orthodox Talmudic tradition. The greatest Jewish philosopher of that time, Ibn Gabirol (Avicebron), "the Jewish Plato," was also a Spaniard. His influence upon mediaeval scholasticism was considerable, and it is noteworthy that the Christian schoolmen were even more deeply influenced by him than his own religious brethren. Ibn Gabirol was one of the most important links in the transmission of Greco-Muslim philosophy to Christendom.

The great Persian poet Firdawsī completed in 1010 the national epic of his people, the Shāhnāma. The publication of that long poem was a fundamental event in the history of civilization; we must take it into account if we would understand not only the conditions of those days in Iran, but also future developments which it predicated. It is no more possible to understand Persian thought without knowledge of the Shāhnāma than to understand Greek thought without knowledge of the Iliad, or Italian thought without knowledge of the Divine Comedy.

The main Syrian philosopher was Elias bar Shīnāyā, but I shall deal with him more fully in the historical section.

The philosophical record of this period is thus far a very remarkable one, yet all that I have said might be considered only an introduction to the main philosophical movement, which took place, as it had done for the last two and a half centuries, in Islām. The briefest mention of the earliest treatise on oneirology extant in Arabic (that of Naṣr ibn Ya'qūb) is sufficient; but it is necessary to refer to it if one wishes to have a complete view of Muslim thought. Of course, the Muslims attached considerable importance to astrology, and oneirology was simply one of the branches of the luxuriant astrological tree. Al-Bāqilānī completed the work of al-Ash'arī and continued the elaboration of Muslim scholasticism. Al-Karmānī introduced (or reintroduced) the writings of the Brethren of Purity into Spain. Ibn Ṭāhir, a Shāfi'ite ḥakīm of Khurāsān, wrote the earliest history of the "seventy-three" Muslim sects.

All this is not very important, but we now come to the three greatest philosophers and the most encyclopaedic minds of that time: the Egyptian Ibn al-Haitham (Alhazen) and the two Persians, al-Bīrūnī and Ibn Sīnā; I might still add to them the Spaniard Ibn Ḥazm. Ibn al-Haitham was the less philosophically minded of the four, but he must be named here, if only because he was the best embodiment of the experimental spirit in the Middle Ages. I have already indicated the immense importance of the works of the two Persians. Al-Bīrūnī appeals to the scientific mind because of his relative freedom from prejudice and of his intellectual curiosity and courage. For example, he was the first Muslim to make a deep study of Hindu philosophy and became the most important link between two great provinces of mankind, India and Islām. Ibn Sīnā was not less intelligent, but his mind was not quite as open, because his main concern was not so much to know facts as to systematize them; his curiosity was blunted by his synthetic tendencies. His thought represented the climax of Muslim philosophy, that is, of an Aristotelian tradition deeply modified by Neoplatonism and by theology. We must remember that Ibn Sīnā was not simply a philosopher; he was a creative man of science, whose vision was encyclopaedic. On the contrary, the Spaniard Ibn Ḥazm was exclusively a philosopher, or rather a theologian. He would scarcely deserve a place in the history of science but for the fact that his influence in the West was considerable. He wrote a history of Muslim sects and of other religions which was distinctly superior to Ibn Ṭāhir's and was, in fact, the best work of its kind in the Arabic literature.

Wang Ch'in-jo was the chief editor of a vast encyclopaedia which was completed in 1013.

3. *Latin, English, Muslim, and Hindu Mathematics and Astronomy*—A little stream of mathematical thought may be detected in the Latin writings, a stream which will gradually increase, but which will not become truly significant until the thirteenth century, when a sufficient amount of Arabic water will have flowed into it. For the present the stream hardly did more than keep the Gerbertian tradition alive; Notker wrote a compotus; Bernelinus, a pupil of Gerbert, explained the use of the abacus and paid special attention to the Roman (duodecimal) fractions; Adelbold ventured to deal with the measurement of circles and spheres; Guido of Arezzo also wrote on the abacus. Note that each of these men represented a different country. Notker was a Swiss, Bernelinus a Parisian, Adelbold a Dutchman, Guido an Italian, and to these must be added an Englishman, Byrhtferth, who wrote, some time after 1004, a compotus, in Anglo-Saxon. It is to this that the word "English" in my subtitle referred; this might seem a mystification, but it corresponded to a real, though very humble, fact. Byrhtferth's "Handboc" is a compilation of astronomical and astrological lore. The low level of mathematical and astronomical knowledge in Christendom is further illustrated by the curious correspondence exchanged c. 1025 by two schoolmasters, Ragimbold of Cologne and Radolf of Liège.

Let us pass on to Islām. It is almost like passing from the shade to the open sun and from a sleepy world into one tremendously active. For the sake of convenience, I divide the Muslim mathematicians into three groups: those of the West, those of Egypt, who occupy, so to speak, an intermediate position, and those of the East. This is also a logical division, for though communications between the eastern and western ends of Islām were frequent (there were a number of itinerant scholars to whom the universality of Islām seems to have been a continual provocation to move on from place to place), it is clear that local influences were felt more constantly and to greater advantage.

None of the Spanish mathematicians was very important. Al-Karmānī introduced the mathematical ideas of the Ikhwān al-ṣafā'; Ibn al-Samḥ wrote treatises on commercial arithmetic, on mental calculus, and on geometry. Both he and Ibn al-Ṣaffār explained the use of the astrolabe and compiled astronomical tables according to the Siddhānta method. Ibn abī-l-Rijāl (Abenragel), who flourished in Tunis, was a famous astrologer.

The greatest astronomer and trigonometrician of the time was Ibn Yūnus, who lived in Cairo. Everything considered, he was perhaps the greatest Muslim astronomer, and the Fāṭimid rulers of Egypt gave him magnificent opportunities. Indeed, under the sixth Fāṭimid, al-Ḥākim, a sort of academy of science (Dār al-ḥikma) had been established in Cairo, and, as had been the case for the academy founded by al-Ma'mūn in Bagdad two centuries earlier, an observatory was an essential part of it. Ibn Yūnus made excellent use of these exceptional facilities to measure more accurately a number of astronomical constants and to compile improved tables named after his patron, the Hakemite tables. He contributed his share to the development of trigonometry, discovering new solutions of spherical problems and introducing the first of the prosthapheretical formulas. His colleague in al-Ḥākim's academy, Ibn al-Haitham, better known as a physicist, was also a great astronomer and mathematician. He made a curious attempt to measure the height of the atmosphere on the basis of his knowledge of astronomic refraction and of the length of twilight. He solved al-Māhānī's equation and the so-called Alhazen's problem by means of intersecting conics.

The mathematicians of the East were more numerous, and though they could boast no man comparable in his branch of learning to Ibn Yūnus, their work was generally on a very high level and full of originality. Kūshyār ibn Labbān was especially interested in trigonometry; he made a deeper study of the tangent function and compiled new astronomical tables which were soon translated into Persian. He also wrote on astrology and arithmetic. Ibn al-Ḥusain investigated the classical problems of Greek geometry (for example, the duplication of the cube) and tried to solve them by purely geometrical means. Abū-l-Jūd was also a geometer; he made a special study of the regular heptagon and enneagon and of those problems which can not be solved by means of ruler and compass alone; he tried to classify equations with reference to conic sections; he is one of the mathematicians who prepared the work of Omar Khayyam in the following period. The greatest of them all, al-Karkhī was chiefly an arithmetician and algebraist. He solved a number of Diophantine problems and invented a series of new ones. His works contain many original features, but the most extraordinary of these is the systematic neglect of Hindu numerals. No numerals are used, the names of the numbers being written in full. It is as if al-Karkhī had considered the use of Hindu numerals as vulgar and non-scientific.[a] Al-Nasawī wrote a practical arithmetic in Persian and later translated it into Arabic. He explained the Hindu methods and applied them to difficult numerical problems; in these computations the sexagesimal fractions introduced by astronomical measurements were replaced by decimal fractions. Ibn Ṭāhir wrote also arithmetical books of a practical nature; he showed how to solve the complicated inheritance problems entailed by the Muslim fondness for juridical niceties. To al-Bīrūnī we owe the best mediaeval account of Hindu numerals. He composed an astronomical encyclopaedia and a general treatise on mathematics, astronomy, and astrology. He was deterred neither by formidable computations nor by the most difficult geometrical problems of his time, those called after him Albirunic problems. He introduced a simplified method of stereographic projection. As we would expect, the philosophical aspects of mathematics were more to Ibn Sīnā's taste than the more technical details. Yet he contributed some valuable little hints on practical matters, and I would not be surprised if further study of his writings obliged us to add some more discoveries to his credit. The very praise given to encyclopaedists for their synthetic efforts often leads to unjust neglect of their humbler contributions. We already know that in spite of his encyclopaedic activities, Ibn Sīnā found time to carry on a number of astronomical observations and to improve the observational technique.

---

[a] Such aberration is not unique. Compare Newton's use of cumbrous geometrical methods instead of infinitesimals in the Principia.

I named these Eastern mathematicians, as well as possible, in chronological order. This does not, perhaps, bring out with sufficient clearness the full complexity of their activities. In the first place, observe that I did not mention a single astrologer; the only one named in this section flourished not in the East, but in the orthodox Tunis, where there was much less freedom of thought. In the second place, if we leave out of account the astronomical work, which was determined by practical necessities, we find that there were two distinct streams of mathematical thought: the one more theoretical represented by Ibn al-Ḥusain, Abū-l-Jūd, and al-Karkhī, the other, more practical, represented by al-Nasawī and Ibn Ṭāhir. Al-Bīrūnī and Ibn Sīnā can not be included in that classification, for they were equally interested in the most abstruse and in the most practical questions; they had no contempt for humble means, for there are no small matters for great minds.

The only contemporary Hindu mathematician, Śrīdhara, wrote a mathematical treatise of a very elementary nature, but which contains the clearest Hindu account of arithmetical operations (except division) with the zero. The Hindu method of solving quadratic equations seems to have originated with him.

4. *Latin, English, Syrian, Muslim, and Chinese Physics, Chemistry, and Technology*—The Latin writers dealt primarily with music. Indeed, this was a great age of musical organization in the West, an organization which had very probably been brought about, or at any rate stimulated, by Muslim influence. That influence can be inferred from the fact that the very ideas which we now begin to find in the Latin treatises had been expressed before in Arabic writings, for example, in those of al-Fārābī (q. v., first half of the tenth century), to go no further back. Moreover, music could be more easily transmitted by popular contact than almost any other activity, and practical music would be followed, sooner or later, by theoretical music. Thus did it come to pass that Muslim science penetrated Christendom at least partly upon the wings of music.[b]

It is hardly necessary to recall that according to a tradition going back to the Pythagorean days, music was an integral part of science, and later, that its recognition as one of the four branches of the quadrivium, by Martianus Capella (second half of the fifth century) and Boetius (first half of sixth), dominated the whole development of education almost until modern times. It is thus not only legitimate but necessary to include in our survey a brief account of mediaeval music.

During the period under consideration Adelbold of Utrecht composed a treatise on the subject, but the most prominent, as the most popular, writer was Guido of Arezzo. It is possible that his fame is exaggerated, but it has at any rate a symbolic interest; it underlines the musical progress which had been accomplished in Western Christendom by the middle of the eleventh century either by Guido or by others.

The English astrologer and mechanician Oliver of Malmesbury is said to have attempted to fly off from a tower by means of artificial wings attached to his body. It is difficult to know how much truth there is to that story, but in any case it illustrates the persistence of one of the oldest longings of the human heart.

The great Syrian historian Elias bar Shīnāyā wrote, in Arabic, a treatise on the balance; it deals with coins, weights, and measures, and explains the use of various kinds of scales.

---

[b] Proof of this has been ably sketched by H. G. Farmer in the Journal of the Royal Asiatic Soc. (61–80, 1925; Isis, VIII, 508-511).

A chronological account of contemporary Muslim achievements must be started with Ibn al-Haitham, who flourished in Cairo at the beginning of the century. He was not only the greatest Muslim physicist, but by all means the greatest physicist of mediaeval times. His researches in geometrical and physiological optics were the most significant to occur between ancient times and the sixteenth century. His description of the eye and his explanation of vision were distinct improvements. Muslim scientists had developed a great interest in the determination of specific gravity. Al-Bīrūnī continued that tradition and measured the density of 18 precious stones and metals with remarkable accuracy. He observed that the speed of light is incomparably greater than that of sound. Ibn Sīnā investigated all the fundamental questions of physics which could be formulated in his time. He observed, too, that the speed of light, however great, must be finite. His study of music was especially important and far ahead of the contemporary Latin work, which was dealt with at the beginning of this section. He described the doubling with the octave, the fourth and fifth, and even with the third.

A colleague of Ibn al-Haitham in the Cairo Academy, Māsawaih al-Mārdīnī, explained the preparation of empyreumatic oils. Ibn Sīnā entertained original views on chemistry; he did not share the common belief of Muslim alchemists that the coloring or bronzing of metals affected their substance; he thought that the differences between metals were too deep to permit their transmutation. An important alchemical treatise was composed in 1034 by al-Kāthī.

Typography, that is to say, printing with movable type, was invented during the fifth decade of the eleventh century by Pi Shêng. That earliest type, made of clay, was unsatisfactory, but Pi Shêng experimented also with wooden type. The invention does not seem to have reached a practical stage until three centuries later.

Tou P'ing, who flourished probably at about the same time, wrote a treatise on the distillation of liquors. I quote this fact under correction, for it has not yet been seriously investigated. If it is correct, alcoholic distillation might have been practiced in China before being practiced in Europe.

5. *Muslim Natural History*—The works of al-Bīrūnī contain many valuable observations on natural subjects. For example, he remarked that there are certain regularities in the number of petals of flowers. The Nestorian physician Ibn al-Ṭaiyib translated, into Arabic, the pseudo-Aristotelian treatise on plants, adding to it extracts from other botanical writings.

6. *Icelandic Discovery of America; Latin geography; Muslim Geography, Mineralogy, and Geology*—The greatest geographical event of the time was the accidental discovery in 1000 of some parts of the North Atlantic coast of America by Icelandic sailors. An Icelandic colony was established in "Wineland" in 1003 to 1006, but did not last. This account of Icelandic discovery is probably true, but it is impossible to determine the location of their landing-places. Norse sailors and rovers were extremely active during the first half of the century; their activity is very interesting from the historical point of view, but it added nothing to geographical knowledge.

The French chronicler Aimoin of Fleury began his history of the Franks with a topographical introduction. That introduction would hardly deserve to be mentioned, but for the fact that it is the only witness of geographical curiosity in Western Christendom in those days.

Muslim geographers were so active during the ninth century, and even more so throughout the tenth century, that it is somewhat of a surprise to come across a period of relative rest in that particular field. To be sure, there was al-Bīrūnī, who may be counted one of the greatest geographers of all times, but he was alone. His services to geography were manifold and immense. To begin with, he developed the mathematical side of it, carrying on geodetic measurements and determining with remarkable precision the coördinates of a number of places. He introduced a simplified method of stereographic projection. His description of India is a geographical monument of fundamental importance. He explained the occurrence of natural springs and of artifical wells by the laws of hydrostatics. He remarked that the Indus Valley was probably an ancient sea-basin which had gradually filled up with alluvions.

Ibn Sīnā's treatise on minerals was one of the main sources of geological knowledge in Western Europe until the Renaissance.

7. *Latin, Byzantine, Muslim (or Arabic), and Chinese Medicine*—The most significant feature was the appearance of the school of Salerno, the earliest scientific school of Christian Europe. It is impossible to determine how old the school was in those days, but it does not matter, for its former existence, however long, was very obscure. The activity of the school did not begin to become tangible until the first half of the eleventh century, toward the middle of that century. The first literary fruits were of a very humble kind, very inferior to the contemporary works written in Arabic; they are nevertheless of considerable importance, because they mark the beginnings of a new medical evolution. Salerno was never a fountain-head, but it was the earliest distributing center of medical ideas in Europe and all of the later schools were somewhat indebted to it. Two anonymous treatises, the Curae and the Speculum hominis, may date from this period. The three earliest Salernitan physicians whose writings have come down to us were, probably, Gariopontus the Lombard, who compiled a medical encyclopaedia called Passionarius; Petrocellus, author of a Practica, and Alphanus, Archbishop of Salerno, who translated Nemesios into Latin.

Two Byzantine physicians of uncertain date may have flourished about this time: Damnastes, author of a treatise on the care of pregnancy and infancy, and Stephanos Magnetes, author of a dispensatory.

For real advance, we have to look to the Muslim physicians. There are so many that I must again divide them into three groups, those of Spain, those of Egypt, and those of the East.

Spain: Al-Karmānī has already been mentioned; he was at once a mathematician and a surgeon. Ibn al-Wāfid composed a treatise on simple drugs, which is partly extant in Latin, and a treatise on balneology. To these two Muslims may be added the Jew Ibn Janāḥ, who flourished in Saragossa and wrote there, in Arabic, a book on simple remedies.

Egypt: Not less than four great physicians enjoyed the patronage of the Fāṭimid rulers of Egypt. Māsawaih al-Mārdīnī (Mesuë the Younger) compiled a large dispensatory which was immensely popular in mediaeval Europe. For centuries it remained the standard work on the subject. 'Ammār was perhaps the most original oculist of Islām, but his work was superseded by that of his Eastern contemporary, 'Alī ibn 'Īsā. The surgical part of 'Ammār's ophthalmological treatise is particularly important. The third of these physicians, Ibn al-Haitham (Alhazen) has already been dealt with many times; he must be remembered here because of his studies in physiological optics. 'Alī ibn Riḍwān wrote various commentaries on Greek medicine, of which the best known was one on Galen's Ars parva; he also wrote a treatise on hygiene with special reference to Egypt. It should be noted that Māsawaih was a Monophysite Christian; the others were Muslims.

East: The greatest physician of the time and one of the greatest of all times was Ibn Sīnā (Avicenna). His enormous medical encyclopaedia, the Qānūn (Canon), remained the supreme authority, not simply in Islām but also in Christendom, for some six centuries. It contained a number of original observations, but its hold on the people was chiefly due to its systematic arrangement and its very dogmatism. Ibn Sīnā was not as great a physician as Galen, but he had very much the same intellectual qualities and defects and his ascendancy was largely based upon the same grounds. He had the advantage over Galen of being able to take into account the vast experience of Muslim physicians.

Ibn al-Ṭaiyib wrote commentaries on Greek medicine. Abū Sa'id 'Ubaid Allāh, of the famous Bakhtyashū' family, wrote a treatise on love-sickness and discussed the philosophical terms used by physicians. Ibn Buṭlān compiled the so-called Tables of Health, a medical summary, divided into 15 vertical columns; he was perhaps the originator of that typical form of synopsis. Finally 'Alī ibn 'Īsā (Jesu Haly) was the author of the most famous ophthalmological treatise written in Arabic. It is very remarkable that not less than three of these physicians, that is, more than half of them, were Christians living in Bagdad: Ibn al-Ṭaiyib, Abū Sa'īd 'Ubaid Allāh, and Ibn Buṭlān. This testifies for the faithfulness of the Christian community of Bagdad and for the toleration of the Muslim rulers. It should be added that the other physicians, i. e., the Muslims, were far more important.

In 1027, Wang Wei-tê made two copper figures of the human body to illustrate the art of acupuncture.

8. *Latin, Muslim, Armenian, and Syrian Historiography*—A number of important Latin chronicles date from the eleventh century. It is curious that, with the exception of Thietmar and Adelbold, the foremost annalists of the first half century were Frenchmen, while those of the second half were Germans. Aimoin of Fleury wrote a history of the Franks down to 654 and a biography of his teacher Abbo; Thietmar of Merseburg, an elaborate history of Saxony, which deals also to some extent with Slavonic events; Adelbold of Utrecht, a life of the Emperor Henry II; Adhémar of Chabannes, a chronicle of Aquitania; Dudon of St. Quentin, an account in prose and verse of the first dukes of Normandy; Raoul Glaber, an anecdotic history of the period extending from 900 to 1044.

Two distinguished historians flourished in Cordova: Ibn al-Faraḍī, who wrote a collection of biographies of the learned Muslims of Spain, and Ibn Ḥaiyān who compiled a similar work and an immense history of Spain.

The rest of Islām was represented only by al-Bīrūnī, but the latter's contributions were of the very first order. In his chronology of ancient nations he tried to explain the calendars and eras of various peoples; his account of India contains also abundant historical material.

The Armenian Stephen Asolik Tarôneçi wrote a universal history down to 1003, which is especially valuable for the study of Byzantine, Armenian, and Georgian events.

A Syriac chronicle from 25 to 1018 was composed, together with a parallel Arabic translation, by Elias bar Shīnāyā.

I do not know of any important historical work of this period in Chinese or Japanese. It is true the T'ang History was then being compiled, but it was not completed until the following period.

9. *German, Hebrew, Syriac, and Chinese Philology*—It is hardly necessary to insist upon the philological importance of Notker's translations from Latin into German. These translations are the earliest monuments of scientific or philosophical literature in German. Notker's efforts to promote the use of his vernacular might be compared to those made by King Alfred, more than a century earlier, to encourage the use of English, but Notker was on the whole far less successful.

Ibn Janāḥ of Saragossa, the greatest Hebrew philologist of the Middle Ages, completed the work launched by the Hispano-Jewish grammarians of the second half of the tenth century. He compiled a Hebrew grammar and a Hebrew dictionary; both works being written in Arabic. The Cordovan Talmudist Samuel ha-Levi wrote many works on grammar, notably The Book of Riches.

Elias bar Shīnāyā composed a Syriac grammar and an Arabic-Syriac vocabulary, which was the latest Syriac lexicon of mediaeval times. The Nestorian Catholicos Elias of Ṭīrhān edited a collection of ecclesiastic canons and precedents and wrote a treatise on accents and a Syriac grammar wherein the Arabic methods were introduced for the first time. Thus was a cycle completed, for we have seen that the early development of Arabic grammar had been stimulated in the first half of the eighth century by the example of Syriac grammar. But the Arabs and Persians had more genius for grammar than the Syrians, more energy, too. It is not surprising that after an evolution of more than three centuries the parts were reversed; the Arabic grammarians were now the teachers and the Syriac grammarians the pupils.

In the meanwhile, Chinese lexicography continued to progress. Ch'ên P'êng-nien revised Lu Fa-yen's phonetic dictionary and Ku Yeh-wang's graphic dictionary, his revisions being the basis of every modern edition. Sung Ch'i was the principal editor of a great phonetic dictionary, the Chi yün, containing more than 50,000 characters. One of Sung Ch'i's collaborators, Ting Tu, published a smaller dictionary of the same kind, the Li pu yün lüeh, containing only 10,000 characters. This smaller dictionary was very popular.

10. *Final Remarks*—When one tries to draw up the balance-sheet of the first half of the eleventh century, one is at first impressed by the absence of Japanese contributions. The Hindu and Byzantine shares were hardly more important, for India was represented only by Śrīdhara, a second-rate mathematician, and Byzantium by two physicians; we are not even sure that the latter really flourished during this period. It thus happens that some provinces of humanity are resting while others are unusually active; it is really as if, when it comes to the accomplishment of its essential task, mankind was working in shifts.

The essential task of those days was almost entirely accomplished by Muslims. Just think of these men: Ibn Yūnus, Ibn al-Haitham, al-Karkhī, al-Bīrūnī, Ibn Sīnā, 'Ammār, 'Alī ibn 'Īsā, Ibn Ḥazm. They were the real leaders, and all were Muslims. The greatest writer of the age, and one of the greatest of all ages, one of the chief interpreters of humanity, was a Persian, Firdawsī. The most prominent scientists and philosophers next to these were Jews: Ibn Gabirol and Ibn Janāḥ. This is not surprising, for the Jews were steeped in Arabic and were directly influenced by Muslim culture in every respect, except religion. I may here recall that a few Christians were also participating in the building up of Muslim science. All of these Christians were physicians; three of them were flourishing in Bagdad—Ibn al-Ṭaiyib, Abū Sa'īd 'Ubaid Allāh, and Ibn Buṭlān; one in Egypt, Māsawaih al-Mārdīnī.

The two greatest of the Muslim scientists, al-Bīrūnī and Ibn Sīnā, were Persians. Ibn Ṭāhir, Kūshyār ibn Labbān, Ibn al-Ḥusain (?), Abū-l-Jūd, and al-Nasawī were also Persians. Fāṭimid patronage made of Cairo one of the greatest intellectual centers of the time; Ibn Yūnus, Ibn al-Haitham, 'Ammār, and 'Alī ibn Riḍwān were working there. Bagdad under the Buwayhids was also doing its share; Naṣr ibn Ya'qūb, al-Bāqilānī, Ibn al-Ḥusain (?), al-Karkhī, al-Kāthī, and 'Alī ibn 'Īsā were adding some scientific luster to the city of the 'Abbāsid caliphs. Finally, there was Spain, where the protection of the Umayyads and of smaller Muslim dynasties encouraged scientific and literary pursuits. It should be noted, however, that out of the three greatest men of Muslim Spain, Ibn Janāḥ, Ibn Ḥazm, and Ibn Gabirol, only one (Ibn Ḥazm) was a Muslim; the two others were Jews. Samuel ha-Levi was also a Jew, but all the other Spaniards mentioned by me were Muslims—al-Karmānī, Ibn al-Samḥ, Ibn abī-l-Rijāl, Ibn-al-Saffār, Ibn al-Wāfid, Ibn al-Faraḍī, and Ibn Ḥaiyān.

The Armenians gave us a distinguished annalist, Stephen Asolik Tarôneçi, and the Syrians two grammarians, Elias bar Shīnāyā and Elias of Ṭīrhān.

As compared with the Muslim contributions, those of Western Christendom may seem at first view insignificant. This first impression is misleading, for, humble as they were, those contributions were exceedingly pregnant. We may leave out of account the discovery and first settlement of America by Leif Ericsson and Thorfin Karlsefni, for this was a sort of accident which had no lasting consequences; it did not even hasten the day of the final discovery. But the birth of the medical school of Salerno and the scientific organization of European music were considerable events. These beginnings were humble enough; all beginnings are; but Salerno was the first step in a long evolution which was to culminate in the production of a Pasteur, and the wretched efforts of the earliest Latin writers on mensural music were the first steps in another evolution, also exclusively occidental and Christian, which was finally to lead to the creation of a Beethoven!

The other phases of Western activity were relatively unimportant, but it is interesting to observe that the gradual awakening of Europe was not restricted to one center; it affected a number of them. Notker of St. Gall was a Swiss; Ragimbold of Cologne and Thietmar of Merseburg were Germans; Bernelinus of Paris, Aimoin of Fleury, Adhémar of Chabannes, Dudon of St. Quentin, and Raoul Glaber of Cluny were Frenchmen; Oliver of Malmesbury and Byrhtferth of Ramsey were Englishmen; Adelbold of Utrecht and Radolf of Liège belonged to the Low Countries. Note that there were many centers in each country. In fact, every Clunisian monastery, every cathedral school, was a cultural center, but none had the prestige of the main Muslim centers—Bagdad, Ghazna, Cairo, Cordova. Salerno was soon to obtain more importance, but this was to remain practically the only scientific center of international significance in Christendom, until the erection of the earliest mediaeval universities more than a century later.

I have already drawn attention to the temporary arrest of Japanese development. In great contrast to this, the Sung dynasty was opening a new golden age in China. I had to mention a number of distinguished Chinese scholars—Wang Ch'in-jo, Pi Shêng, Tou P'ing, Wang Wei-tê, Ch'ên P'êng-nien, Sung Ch'i, Ting Tu. The repercussion of the glories of the Sung age were to be felt in Japan a little later and were to initiate there a new period of wonderful activity. The best proof that Japan had not yet reached its maturity is afforded by this narrow dependence upon Chinese stimulation.

If we now consider separate subjects, we may say very briefly that the main achievements of this period were, in mathematics, a remarkable development of geometry, algebra, and arithmetic entirely due to Muslim efforts; in astronomy, Ibn Yūnus' observations; in physics, the optical studies of Ibn al-Haitham, the beginning of mensural music in Christian Europe; in the technical arts, the invention of typography by Pi Shêng; in geography, the discovery of America; in geology, the contributions of al-Bīrūnī and Ibn Sīnā; in medicine, the birth of Salerno, the ophthalmological treatises of 'Ammār and 'Alī ibn 'Īsā, the encyclopaedic effort of Ibn Sīnā; in philology, the completion of Hebrew and Syriac grammar and the immense efforts of the Chinese lexicographers. To these should still be added a number of historical and philosophical works, of which it is more difficult to measure the concrete value, but which added immensely to the intellectual prestige of that great period, the time of al-Bīrūnī.

II. PHILOSOPHICAL AND THEOLOGICAL BACKGROUND

NOTKER LABEO

Labeo means the blobber-lipped. He is also called Notker the German, because of his translations. Not to be mistaken for another Notker of St. Gall, the Stammerer (Balbulus), c. 830 to 912, who wrote the words of the beautiful anthem: "Media vita in morte sumus." This Notker was born c. 950, perhaps in Thurgau, Switzerland. He flourished at the Benedictine monastery of St. Gall, where he died from the plague in 1022. He was the most famous teacher of the school of St. Gall (for which see my note on still another Notker, Notger of Liège, second half of the tenth century). He translated Martianus Capella, Boetius, Aristotle (De categoriis, De interpretatione), etc., from Latin into German. He might be called one of the fathers of German literature. He taught logic and wrote a compotus.

Text—Die Schriften Notkers und seiner Schule hrg. von Paul Piper (3 vols., illus., Freiburg i. Br., 1882–1883).

Criticism—Meyer von Knonau, in Allgemeine Deutsche Biographie (24. Bd., 39–41, 1887). Johann Kelle: Die S. Galler deutschen Schriften und Notker Labeo (76 p., 8 pl., München, Bayer. Ak. der Wiss., 1. Cl., Bd. 8, 1888). Paul Hoffmann: Die Mischprosa Notkers des Deutschen (228 p., Palaestra, 58, Berlin, 1910). August Naaber: Die Quellen von Notkers, Boethius (67 p., Diss., Münster, 1911). Karl Schulte: Das Verhältnis von Notkers Nuptiae Philologiae et Mercurii zum Kommentar des Remigius Antissiodorensis (122 p., Münster i. W., 1911). Hans Naumann: Notkers Boethius, Untersuchungen über Quellen und Stil (125 p., Strassburg, 1913). Lynn Thorndike: History of Magic (vol. 1, 677, 1923. About his compotus). James Midgley Clark: The abbey of St. Gall as a center of literature and art (Cambridge, 1926). Max Manitius: Lateinische Literatur des Mittelalters (vol. 2, 694–699, 1923).

Many philological studies have been devoted to Notker. I can not quote them here.

Jewish Philosophy and Theology

JOSEPH HA-RO'EH

Abū Ya'qūb al-Bāṣir. Joseph ben Abraham ha-Kohen ha-Ro'eh (meaning, the seer; Joseph was blind). Al-Bāṣir is the Arabic equivalent for ha-Ro'eh. Flourished in Babylonia and Persia in the first half of the eleventh century. Qaraite theologian and missionary, who applied the theories of the mutakallims to the dogmas of his sect. His principal work is the Muḥtawī (the Comprehending), which is important for the study of Mu'tazilite kalām; it might almost have been written by a Muslim. It was written in Arabic, but was soon translated into

Hebrew, perhaps by Tobiah ben Moses, under the title "Sefer ha-ne'imot" or "Zikron ha-datot."

Article by Isaac Broydé in Jewish Encyclopaedia (vol. 7, 255, 1904). Isaac Husik: Mediaeval Jewish Philosophy (48–55, 1918).

SAMUEL HA-LEVI

Samuel ha-Nāgīd,[c] Ben Joseph ibn Nagdela. Born at Cordova in 993; flourished since 1013 in Malaga, then in Granada where he died in 1055. Jewish statesman, grammarian, Talmudist, poet, patron of learning. Vizier to the Zayrid king of Granada, Ḥabbūṣ, who ruled from 1019 to 1038.[d] He wrote chiefly in Hebrew, but knew Arabic equally well and was familiar with Latin and Berber. He wrote many works on grammar, one of which, the "Book of Riches," was held in very high esteem. He also wrote Talmudic works, of which the most important is a general introduction called the "Entrance to the Talmud" (Mebo ha-Talmud).

Text—Constantin l'Empereur: Clavis Talmudica, completas formulas, loca dialectica et rhetorica priscorum Judaeorum continens (Leyden, 1633).

Criticism—R. Dozy: Spanish Islam (607–616, London, 1913. Dates incorrect). Isaac Broydé, in Jewish Encyclopaedia (Vol. XI, 24–25, 1905; with bibliography).

IBN GABIROL

In Latin, Avicebron (Avencebrol, Avicebrol, etc.). Solomon ben Judah ibn Gabirol, or, in Arabic, Abū Ayyūb Sulaimān ibn Yaḥyā ibn Jābīrūl. Born in Malaga, c. 1021; died in Valencia, c. 1058. Spanish-Jewish philosopher, "the Jewish Plato." The first teacher of Neoplatonism in the West.[e] His main works are a philosophical dialogue called the "Fons vitae" (Yanbū' al-ḥayāt. Translated into Latin in 1150, it exerted a deep influence upon Duns Scotus and other Franciscans) and "The improvement of moral qualities" (Saragossa, 1045), an ethical treatise independent of religious belief. The influence of the "Fons vitae" was far greater upon Christian scholasticism than upon Jewish philosophy.

A thousand years before, Philon had orientalized Platonic philosophy and prepared the way for its Christianization and its Islamization. Avicebron now re-occidentalized the Greco-Muslim philosophy and restored it to Europe.

Text and Translations—Fons vitae ex arabico in latinum translatus ab Joanne Hispano et Dominico Gundissalino. Primum edidit Clemens Baeumker (Beitr. zur Gesch. der Philosophie des Mittelalters, 1, Münster 1892–1895). Ibn Gebirol: La fuente de la vida. Traducida en el siglo XII por Juan Hispano y Domingo González del arábe al latín y ahora por primera vez al castellano por Federico de Castro y Fernández (2 vols., 458 p., Madrid, 1901–1903).

The Improvement of Moral Qualities, edited, with translation and introduction, by Stephen S. Wise (126 p., New York, 1902).

Selected religious poems, translated into English verse by Israel Zangwill, from a critical edition prepared by Israel Davidson (English and Hebrew on opposite pages, 306 p., Philadelphia, 1923).

---

[c] The Nāgīd was the official head of the Jewish community and its representative before the Muslim government, which usually respected its autonomy. Samuel had been nominated nāgīd of Granada in 1027.

[d] Never perhaps did a Jew obtain so much authority and power in a Muslim state. But Samuel used it well.

[e] About this time the center of Jewish intellectual activity passed from the East to the West. Down to the middle of the eleventh century this center had been in Babylonia.

Criticism—Leopold Dukes: Salomon ben Gabirol und die ethischen Werke desselben, mit einer Uebersicht der meisten ethischen Werke der Araber (136 p., Hanover, 1860). J. Guttmann: Die Philosophie des Salomon ibn Gabirol (276 p., Göttingen, 1889). Rudolf Seyerlen: Die gegenseitigen Beziehungen zwischen abendländischer und morgenländischer Wissenschaft mit besonderer Rücksicht auf Salomon ibn Gabirol (akad. Rede) (41 p., Jena, 1899). David Kaufmann: Studien über Salomon ibn Gabirol (Budapest, 1899). S. Horovitz: Die Psychologie bei den jüdischen Religionsphilosophen des Mittelalters von Saadia bis Maimuni. Heft 2. Gabirol (Jahresbericht des jüdischtheologischen Seminars zu Breslau, 77–146, 1900). Article Ibn Gabirol, in Jewish Encyclopedia, by Stephen S. Wise, Michael Friedländer and Gottheil (12 cols., 1904. Important). Michael Wittmann: Zur Stellung Avencebrol's in Entwicklungsgang der arabischen Philosophie. Ein Beitrag zur Erforschung seiner Quellen (Beitr. zur Gesch. der Philosophie des Mittelalters, V, 1, 77 p., Münster, 1905). P. Duhem: Le système du monde (vol. 5, 1–75, 1917). I. Husik: History of Medieval Jewish Philosophy (58–79, New York, 1918).

FIRDAWSĪ

Abū-l-Qāsim Firdawsī. Born probably in 932 at Ṭūs, Khurāsān, where he died in 1020–21. The greatest poet of Persia. He sang the legendary history of his country down to the Muslim conquest in his great epic, the "Book of Kings" (Shāhnāma), begun c. 975, completed in 1010[f] (c. 60,000 lines). Firdawsī might be called the Dante of Iran, and we must include him in our survey on the same grounds as Dante. His poem is a glorious mirror of his age. It contains interesting information on ethnography, primitive technology, and sundry inventions (chess, automats, silk industry, etc.).

Texts and Translations—The complete text of the Shāhnāma was edited by Turner Macan (4 vols., Calcutta, 1829), and by Jules Mohl, with French translation (6 vols., Paris, 1838–1868). Abbreviated English translation (with or without the Persian text) by James Atkinson (London, 1832). English translation by Arthur George Warner and Edmund Warner (8 vols., London, 1905–1923).

Adaptations by Helen Zimmern (London, 1882. Praised by Vambery), and by Ella C. Sykes (London, 1902).

Abridged German translation by Adolf Fr. von Schack (3. Aufl., 3 vols., Stuttgart, 1877). By E. A. Bayer (Sage I–XIII, Berlin, 1890).

Complete Italian translation by Italo Pizzi (8 vols., Torino, 1886–1889).

Criticism (General)—J. J. Ampère: La Schahnameh. (La science et les lettres en Orient, 279–373, Paris, 1865). E. Renan: Le Schahnameh (1877). (Mélanges d'histoire et de voyages, 135–145, Paris, 1890. Both essays suggested by Mohl's translation; Jules Mohl died in 1876.) E. G. Browne: Literary History of Persia (vols. 1–2, 1908–1906). I. Pizzi: Firdusi (62 p., Profili, Modena, 1911. Short essay by the Italian translator of Firdawsī, with bibliography). A. V. Williams Jackson: From Constantinople to the Home of Omar Khayyam (New York, 1911. Chiefly p. 278–296). Cl. Huart: Encyclopaedia of Islam (vol. 2, 110, 1914). Carra de Vaux: Les penseurs de l'Islam (Vol. I, 173–186, Paris, 1921).

Criticism (Special)—Italo Pizzi: L'invenzione del giuco degli scacchi. Versione dal persiano (46 p., Torino, 1886). E. O. von Lippmann: Zur Geschichte der Narkose (Mitt. zur Gesch. d. Medizin, vol. 10, 379, 1910; Abhdl. u. Vorträge, Vol. II, 288–289, 1913).

SYRIAN PHILOSOPHY

See my note on Elias bar Shīnāyā in the historical section (VIII), below.

---

[f] He may be placed indifferently at the end of the tenth century or the beginning of the eleventh. I choose the latter alternative, because the Shāhnāma was not completed until 1010. The date of completion seems to me the most important.

Muslim Philosophy and Theology

NAṢR IBN YA'QŪB

Abū Sa'īd Naṣr ibn Ya'qūb al-Dīnawarī. Flourished c. 1006. He dedicated, in 1006–7, to the Caliph al-Qādir, a treatise on oneirology, Kitāb al-qādirī fī-l-ta'bīr, in 15 chapters.

I mention this treatise mainly because, according to Carl Brockelmann (Geschichte der arabischen Litteratur, vol. 1, 244, 1898), it is the earliest extant in Arabic. This is very strange, because the subject must have appealed to the Muslim mind, and we would expect many earlier treatises to be extant. According to the belief handed down since Hellenistic times, dreams reveal the influence of the macrocosmos upon the soul when sleep has liberated the latter to some extent from the body. Oneirology was thus brought within the compass of astrology and every philosopher, every astronomer, every physician, that is, every man of science, was bound to make some study of it. Thus it ought to be possible to write a history of Muslim oneirology, even if the treatise of Naṣr ibn Ya'qūb was really the earliest *independent* treatise on the subject. It should be noted that the last chapter of this very treatise includes a list of a hundred famous interpreters of dreams; it would seem desirable to investigate this.

It is worth while recalling here that al-Kindī (q. v., first half of ninth century) wrote a treatise which was translated by Gherardo of Cremona under the title "De somno et uisione" (edited by A. Nagy in 1897). See also my note on Aḥmad ibn Sirin (first half of ninth century).

AL-BĀQILĀNĪ

Abū Bakr Aḥmad ibn 'Alī ibn al-Ṭaiyib al-Bāqilānī.[g] Born at Baṣra; flourished at Bagdad, where he died in 1013. Muslim theologian. The most remarkable disciple[h] of al-Ash'arī, whose work he completed. The introduction into the Kalām of the conceptions of atoms and vacuum is ascribed to him by Ibn Khaldūn. He extended atomism to time and motion, conceiving them as essentially discontinuous. This is exceedingly interesting, in spite of the fact that al-Bāqilānī's aim was primarily theological. He wanted to establish the doctrine of God's sole, universal, continuous creative activity. The Greek atomistic theory may have reached him through the writings of Byzantine theologians

Ibn Khallikān (de Slane) (vol. 2, 671–672). M. A. F. Mehren: IIIe Congrès des orientalistes (vol. 2, 228, St. Pétersbourg, 1876). Martin Schreiner: VIIIe Congrès, Stockholm (vol. 2, 108, 1889). C. Brockelmann: Encyclopaedia of Islam (vol. 1, 603, 1911). G. F. Moore: History of Religions (vol. 2, 429, 1919).

AL-KARMĀNĪ

See mathematical section (III), below.

IBN ṬĀHIR

Abū Manṣūr 'Abd al-Qāhir ibn Ṭāhir ibn Muḥammad al-Baghdādī. Flourished at Nīsābūr; died in 1037–38 at Isfarāyin, in Khurāsān. Muslim writer on the history of Muslim philosophy and theology, and mathematician. He belonged to the Shāfi'īte school. His main work is the book on schisms and sects

---

[g] Bāqila means beans. Bāqilānī would mean beans or vegetable seller.
[h] To be exact, a disciple of a disciple of al-Ash'arī.

(Kitāb al-farq bain al-firaq). He wrote various books on arithmetic, of which the most important is entitled "The Completion" (al-takmīl). He was particularly skillful in the solution of inheritance problems.

Text—The Kitāb al-farq was edited in Arabic (very badly) by Muḥammad Badr (385 p., Cairo, 1910. Elaborate review by Goldziher in Z. d. deut. morgenl. Ges., vol. 65, p. 349–364, 1911). English translation by Kate Chambers Seelye (Part I, 232 p., New York, 1920; Isis, IV, 63).

Criticism—Ibn Khallikān (De Slane) (vol. 2, 149, 1843). C. Brockelmann: Arabische Litteratur (vol. 1, 385, 1898. Only seven lines). H. Suter: Die Mathematiker der Araber (90, 1900). Encyclopaedia of Islam (vol. 1, 570), under Baghdādī.

IBN AL-HAITHAM

See note in physical section (IV), below.

AL-BĪRŪNĪ

Abū Raiḥān Muḥammad ibn Aḥmad al-Bīrūnī (or Bairūnī). Born in Khwārizm (Khiva) in 973; sojourned a considerable time in India; died in 1048, probably at Ghazna in Sijistān (Afghānistān). He was by birth a Persian and a Shī'ite; his religion was tempered with agnostic tendencies, but his national, anti-Arabic feelings remained very strong until the end. Traveler, philosopher, mathematician, astronomer, geographer, encyclopaedist. One of the very greatest scientists of Islām, and, all considered, one of the greatest of all times. His critical spirit, toleration, love of truth, and intellectual courage were almost without parallel in mediaeval times. He claimed that the phrase "Allāh is omniscient" does not justify ignorance.

He wrote, in Arabic, a number of books on geographical, mathematical, and astronomical subjects. His main works were: (1) the "Chronology of ancient nations" or "Vestiges of the past" (Kitāb al-āthār al-bāqiya 'ani-l-qurūn al-khāliya), written in 1000 and dealing chiefly with the calendars and eras of various peoples; (2) an account of India (Ta'rīkh al-Hind) composed in Ghazna c. 1030; (3) an astronomical encyclopaedia, the Mas'ūdīc canon (Al-qānūn al-Mas'ūdī fī-l-hai'a wal-nujūm), so-called because it was dedicated in 1030 to the Ghaznawid sulṭān Mas'ūd;[i] (4) a summary of mathematics, astronomy, and astrology (Al-tafhīm li-awā'il ṣinā'at al-tanjīm). His description of Brahmanical India was based upon a deep study of the country and its people. He had been charmed by Hindu philosophy, especially by the Bhagavadgītā. He translated several works from Sanskrit into Arabic (e. g., two of Varāhamihira's works, q. v., first half of sixth century), and on the other hand, transmitted Muslim knowledge to the Hindus.

He gave a clear account (the best mediaeval account) of Hindu numerals (principle of position). Sum a geometric progression apropos of the chess game; it led to the following number: $16^{16} - 1 = 18{,}446{,}744{,}073{,}709{,}551{,}619$. Trisection of the angle and other problems which can not be solved with ruler and compass alone (Albirunic problems). Simplified stereographic projection, similar to that first published by G. B. Nicolosi di Paternò in 1660 (Isis, V, 498).

---

[i] Son of the terrible Maḥmūd, one of the greatest Muslim rulers. Maḥmūd built an empire stretching from Lahore to Samarqand and Iṣpahān. He established a university in his capital Ghazna, and made of it one of the greatest cultural centers of Asia. There gathered such men as Firdawsī and al-Bīrūnī (Stanley Lane-Poole: Mohammedan Dynasties, 285–290, 1893).

Accurate determination of latitudes. Determination of longitudes. Geodetic measurements. Al-Bīrūnī discussed the question whether the earth rotates around its axis or not, without reaching a definite conclusion.

Investigations on specific gravity. Remarkably accurate determination of the specific density of 18 precious stones and metals. As compared with the speed of sound, that of light is immense. The working of natural springs and "artesian" wells is explained by the hydrostatic principle of communicating vessels.

Description of various monstrosities, including what we call "Siamese" twins. Flowers have 3, 4, 5, 6, or 18 petals, never 7 or 9.

The Indus Valley must be considered as an ancient sea basin filled up with alluvions.

Texts and Translations—The Āthār al-bāqiya has been edited by Eduard Sachau (Leipzig, 1878). English translation by same (London, 1879).

Al-Bīrūnī's India was edited by Sachau (London, 1887). English translation by same, with elaborate introduction and notes (2 vols., London, 1888; reprinted 1910).

Das Buch der Auffindung der Sehnen im Kreise, übersetzt und mit Kommentar versehen von Heinrich Suter (Bibliotheca Mathematica, vol. 11, 11–78, 1910. That is, the Kitāb istikhrāj al-awtār fī-l-dā'ira . . . .).

H. Suter: Über die Projektion der Sternbilder und der Länder (Abhd. zur Gesch. der Naturwiss., Heft 4, 79–93, Erlangen, 1922. Translation of the fī tasṭīḥ al-ṣuwar wa tabṭīḥ al-kuwar; Isis, V, 498).

Julius Ruska: Al-Bīrūnī als Quelle für das Leben und die Schriften al-Rāzī's (Isis, V, 26–50, 1923; Isis, VI, 145).

Carl Schoy: Original studien aus al-Qānūn al-Mas'ūdī (Isis, V, 51–74, 1923; Isis, VI, 147); Die Bestimmung der geographischen Breite der Stadt Ghazna (Ann. der Hydrographie, 41–47, 1925; Isis, VII, 536; VIII, 739); Die trigonometrischen Lehren des al-Bīrūnī (160 S., 54 Abb., Hanover, 1925).

Many shorter texts and extracts are included in the papers by Wiedemann quoted in the following paragraph.

Texts and Commentaries Published by Eilhard Wiedemann—Treatise on the Relations of Metals and Jewels (Sitzungsber. d. phys. med. Soz. in Erlangen, vol. 38, 163–166, 1906); Über das al-Berunische Gefäss zur spezifischen Gewichtsbestimmung (Verhdl. d. deut. physik. Ges., vol. 10, 339–343, 1908); Bestimmung des Erdumfanges (Archiv für Gesch. der Naturw., vol. 1, 66–69, 1908); Über die Dimensionen der Erde nach muslimischen Gelehrten (*ibidem*, vol. 3, 253–255, 1911. Extracts from al-tafhīm); Über den Wert von Edelsteinen bei den Muslimen (Der Islam, vol. 2, 345–358, 1911); Über al-Bērūnī (Mit. zur Gesch. der Medizin, vol. 11, 313–321, 1912. With J. Hell); Geographisches von al-Bērūnī (Beitr. 27, Sitzungsber. Erlangen, vol. 44, 1–26, 1912); Biographie von al-Bērūnī nach Ibn-abī Uṣaibi'a (Beitr. 28, *ibidem*, 117–118); Geographisches aus dem mas'ūdischen Kanon (Beitr. 29, *ibidem*, 119–125, 1912); Ein Instrument dass die Bewegung von Sonne und Mond darstellt (Der Islam, vol. 4, 5–13, 1913); Verbreitung der Bestimmungen des spezifischen Gewichtes nach al-Bērūnī (Beitr. 31, Sitzungsber. Erlangen, vol. 45, 31–34, 1914); Über die Wage des Wechselns von al-Chāzinī und über die Lehre von den Proportionen nach al Bīrūnī (Sitzungsber. d. phys. med. Soz., Erlangen, vol. 48, 1–15, 1918. From al-tafhīm, Isis, IV, 402); Einleitung zu dem Werk über die eingehende Behandlung (istī'āb) aller möglichen Methoden für die Herstellung des Astrolabs (Das Weltall. 20. Jahrg., 24–26, 1919); Über Gesetzmässigkeiten bei Pflanzen (Biolog. Zentralblatt, vol. 40, 113–116, 1920; Isis, IV, 402); Über al-Bīrūnī und seine Schriften (Sitzungsber. d. phys. mediz. Soz., Erlangen, vol. 52, 55–96, 1920. Elaborate general account made with the assistance of H. Suter and O. Rescher); Allgemeine Betrachtungen von al-Bīrūnī in seinem Werk über die Astrolaben (Sitzungsber. der physik. med. Soz., Erlangen, vol. 52, 97–121, 1922. With Joseph Frank: text translated from the work quoted above under 1919. It is of special interest for the history of the astrolabe, Isis, V, 498), Meteorologisches aus der Chronologie von al-Bīrūnī (Meteorologische Z., 199–203, 1922); Entsalzung des Meerwassers bei al-Bīrūnī (Chemiker Z., 46, 230, 1922); Erscheinungen bei der Dämmerung und. bei Sonnenfinsternissen (Archiv für Geschichte der Medizin, vol. 15, 43–52, 1923).

General Criticism—Wüstenfeld: Geschichte der arabischen Aerzte (75–76, 1840); Die Geschichtschreiber der Araber (62–64, 1881). C. Brockelmann: Arabische Litteratur (vol. 1, 475–476, 1898); Encyclopaedia of Islam (vol. 1, 726, 1912. See also *ibidem*, 653, 1911, the article Barāhima, Brahmans, by Carra de Vaux). H. Suter and E. Wiedemann: Über al-Bīrūnī (Erlangen, 1920. Quoted above). Carra de Vaux: Penseurs de l'Islam (vol. 2, 1921, passim).

Mathematics and Astronomy—B. Boncompagni: Intorno all'opera d'Albiruni sull'India (Bull. di bibliografia e di storia delle sci. mat., vol. 2, 153–206, 1869). Ed. Sachau: Algebraisches über das Schach bei Bīrūnī (Z. d. deut. morgenl. Ges., vol. 29, 148–156, 1876). Matteo Fiorini: Le projezioni cartografiche di Albiruni (Bol. d. soc. geografica italiana (3), vol. 4, 287–294, 1891). H. Suter: Mathematiker und Astronomen (98–100, 225, 1900; 170–172, 1902); H. Seeman and Th. Mittelberger: Das Kugelförmige Astrolab (40–44, 1925; Isis, VIII, 743. Contains translation of extracts from the Kitāb al-istī'āb al-wujūh al-mumkin fī ṣan'at al-iṣṭarlāb). Oskar Schirmer: Arabische Bestimmungen der Schiefe der Ekliptik (Sitzungsber. d. phys. med. Soz., vol. 58, 49–59, Erlangen, 1926; Isis, IX.)

Physics and Chemistry—J. J. Clément-Mullet: Pesanteur spécifique de diverses substances minérales, procédé pour l'obtenir d'aprés Albirainy. Extrait de l'Ayin-Akbery (Journal asiatique (5), vol. 11, 379–406, 1858. With a translation of the text, translated from Akbar's Institutions). Ed. O. von Lippmann: Naturwissenschaftliches aus der Chronologie der alten Nationen (Chemiker-Z., 245, 1899; Abhdl. und Vorträge, vol. 1, 97–102, 1906).

Geography—J. T. Reinaud: Géographie d'Aboulféda (vol. 1, p. xcv sq., 1848); Mémoire géographique sur l'Inde antérieurement au XIe siècle (Mém. Acad. des Inscriptions, vol. 18 (2), 1–399, 1849).

Medicine—L. Leclerc: Médecine arabe (vol. 1, 480–482, 1876). H. Beveridge: An Unknown Work of Albiruni (Journal Roy. Asiatic Soc., 333–335, 1902. Apropos of a materia medica entitled Kitāb-i-ṣaidana, the translation into Persian of a treatise of al-Bīrūnī by Abū Bakr ibn 'Alī ibn'Uthmān Asfar al-Kāsānī, before 1229). T. W. Arnold: The Caesarean Section, in an Arab manuscript dated 707 A. H. (Oriental studies presented to E. G. Browne, 6–7, 1922. From a manuscript of the Vestiges of the Past).

Varia—Martin Schreiner: Les Juifs dans al-Beruni. Revue des études juives (vol. 12, 258–266, 1886).

IBN SĪNĀ

Abū 'Alī al-Ḥusain ibn 'Abdallāh ibn Sīnā. Hebrew, Aven Sīnā; Latin, Avicenna. Born in 980 at Afshana, near Bukhārā, died in Hamadhān, 1037. Encyclopaedist, philosopher, physician, mathematician, astronomer. The most famous scientist of Islām and one of the most famous of all races, places, and times; one may say that his thought represents the climax of mediaeval philosophy. He wrote a great many treatises in prose and verse; most of them in Arabic, a few in Persian. His philosophical encyclopaedia (Kitāb al-shifā', sanatio) implies the following classification: theoretical knowledge (subdivided, with regard to increasing abstraction, into physics, mathematics, and metaphysics), practical knowledge (ethics, economy, politics). His philosophy roughly represents the Aristotelian tradition as modified by Neoplatonic influences and Muslim theology. Among his many other philosophical works, I must still quote a treatise on logic, Kitāb al-ishārāt wal-tanbīhāt (the Book of Signs and Admonitions). As Ibn

Sīnā expressed his views on almost any subject very clearly, very forcibly, and generally more than once, his thought is, or at any rate can be, known with great accuracy.

His most important medical works are the Qānūn (Canon) and a treatise on cardiac drugs (hitherto unpublished). The Qānūn fī-l-ṭibb is an immense encyclopaedia of medicine (of about a million words), a codification of the whole of ancient and Muslim knowledge. Being similar in many respects to Galen, Ibn Sīnā elaborated to a degree the Galenic classifications (for example, he distinguished 15 qualities of pain). Because of its formal perfection as well as its intrinsic value, the Qānūn superseded Rāzī's Ḥāwī, 'Alī ibn 'Abbās's Malikī, and even the works of Galen, and remained supreme for six centuries.[i] However, the very success of Ibn Sīnā as an encyclopaedist caused his original observations to be correspondingly depreciated. Yet the Qānūn contains many examples of good observation—distinction of mediastinitis from pleurisy; contagious nature of phthisis; distribution of diseases by water and soil; careful description of skin troubles; of sexual diseases, and perversions; of nervous ailments (including love-sickness); many psychological and pathological facts clearly analyzed if badly explained. The materia medica considers about 760 drugs; pharmacological methods are outlined.

Ibn Sīnā's interest in mathematics was philosophical rather than technical, and such as we would expect in a late Neoplatonist. He explained the casting out of nines and its application to the verification of squares and cubes. Many of his writings were devoted to mathematical and astronomical subjects; he composed a translation of Euclid. He made astronomical observations (probably chiefly toward the end of his life in Hamadhān), and devised a contrivance the purpose of which was similar to that of the vernier, that is, to increase the precision of instrumental readings.

He made a profound study of various physical questions—motion, contact, force, vacuum, infinity, light, heat. He observed that if the perception of light is due to the emission of some sort of particles by the luminous source, the speed of light must be finite. He made investigations on specific gravity.

The musical part of the Shifā' marked much progress upon al-Fārābī's musical treatise (q. v., first half of the tenth century), itself so far ahead of occidental knowledge on the subject. It deals with magadizing (taḍ'īf), doubling with the octave, and organizing (tarkīb), doubling with the fourth and fifth, this being a great step toward the harmonic system; doubling with the third seems to have also been allowed. Considering the series of consonances represented by the series $(n + 1)/n$, Ibn Sīnā observed that when $n = 33$, the intervals begin to sound alike, and that above the value $n = 45$ the ear is unable to distinguish them (note that the value $n = 32$ corresponds to a quarter of a tone).

He did not believe in the possibility of chemical transmutation, because in his opinion the differences of the metals were not superficial, but much deeper; coloring or bronzing the metals does not affect their essence. It should be noted that these views were radically opposed to those which were then generally accepted.

Together with Aristotle's Meteorologica (Isis, VI, 138) and the pseudo-Aristotelian Liber de elementis (for which see my note on Aristotle's apocryphal

[i] It is still supreme in Islām. The Muslims still call Ibn Sīnā the prince of all learning, al-Shaikh al-Ra'īs.

writings), Ibn Sīnā's treatise on minerals was the main source of the geological ideas of the Christian encyclopaedists of the thirteenth century.

Ibn Sīnā wrote an autobiography which was completed by his favorite disciple al-Juzajānī.

His triumph was too complete; it discouraged original investigations and sterilized intellectual life. Like Aristotle and Vergil, Avicenna was considered by the people of later times as a magician.

Texts and Translations—Qānūn. The Qānūn was translated into Latin by Gherardo Cremonese and many partial editions of this translation were printed before 1500; Milano, 1473; Padua, 1476, 1497; Venice, 1483, etc. Hebrew translation, Naples, 1491–92.

Many editions have been and are still published in the East: Teheran, Constantinople, Beirut, Būlāq. The Būlāq edition of 1877 is particularly good. The first Arabic edition of the Qānūn in the West appeared in Rome, 1593. Latin translations of the whole Qānūn by Gherardo of Cremona (Venice, 1544, 1582, 1595; Louvain, 1658, etc.).

I have used the edition of Venice, 1582. It contains: Liber Canonis, De medicinis cordialibus (translated by Villanova), Cantica (translated by Armengaud son of Blaise, of Montpellier), De removendis nocumentis (translated by Andrea Alpago of Belluno), De syrupo acetoso (translated by same), and a long Arabic-Latin glossary compiled by the same Andrea Bellunese, an Italian physician of the fifteenth and sixteenth centuries who traveled in the Near East and practiced at Damascus. The same volume contains many notes by Andrea Alpago and by Benedictus Rinius of Venice and a Latin translation by Niccolò Massa, Venetian (d. 1569), of Avicenna's Arabic biography by his disciple Sorsanus (al-Juzajānī?).

Partial editions and translations: Avicennae De morbis mentis interprete Petro Vaterio (Vattier) (Paris, 1659). Kurt Sprengel: Von den Primitivnerven (Beitr. zur Gesch. der Medizin, 105–150, Halle, 1796. Arabic and German). Jos. v. Sontheimer: Die zusammengesetzten Heilmittel der Araber nach dem 5. Buch des Canons übersetzt (Freiburg, 1844). P. de Koning: Traité sur le calcul dans les reins et dans la vessie (Leyde, 1896); Trois traités d'anatomie arabe (Leyde, 1903. Ibn Sīnā's anatomy in French translation, p. 432–781). The following theses of the University of Berlin contain partial translations of the Qānūn into German: J. Cueva (1899); Paul Uspensky (1900); Elias Michailowsky (1900); Th. Bernikow (1900). De urinis, in Ideler: Physici et medici (vol. 2, 286–302, 1841). J. Hirschberg und J. Lippert: Die Augenheilkunde des Ibn Sīnā, übersetzt und erklärt (194 p., Leipzig, 1902).

Collection of metaphysical treatises (2 vols., folio, Venice, 1508; again, 1550).

J. Forget: Le livre des théorêmes et des avertissements (Leiden, 1892. That is, the Ishārāt).

De anima (liber sextus naturalium; part of the Shifā'), Pavia 1490(?) Compendium de anima. Venice, 1526, again 1546 (translated from the Arabic by Andrea Alpago, with notes derived from Arabic commentaries). Compendium on the Soul, Englished by Edward Abbott Van Dyck (Verona, 1906). Carra de Vaux: La Kaçīdah d'Avicenne sur l'âme (Journal asiatique (9), vol. 14, 157–173. Paris, 1899).

M. Horten: Das Buch der Genesung der Seele. Eine philosophische Encyklopädie Avicennas. Die Metaphysik enthaltend Metaphysik, Theologie, Kosmologie, und Ethik übersetzt und erläutert (809 p., Halle a. S., 1907–1909. That is, a part of the Kitāb al-shifā'). A summary of this encyclopaedia, also by Avicenna, called Kitāb al-najāt, liberatio, was printed in Arabic in Rome 1593, together with the Qānūn.

Two arithmetical extracts from the Shifā', on the casting out of nines, were edited and translated by F. Woepcke (Journal Asiatique, vol. 1, 502–504, 1863).

General Criticism—C. Brockelmann: Geschichte der arabischen Litteratur (vol. 1, 452–458, 1898. With list of 99 works). Carra de Vaux: Avicenne (310 p., Paris, 1900. The most elaborate study of Avicenna; clearly and beautifully written; but it does not deal with the medical side). A. Loewenthal: Jewish Encyclopedia (1902). Carra de Vaux: Encyclopaedia of Religion and Ethics (vol. 2, 272–276, 1910). T. J. de Boer: Encyclopaedia of Islam (vol. 2, 419–420, 1918). Guiseppe Gabrieli: Avicenna. Archivio di storia della scienza (vol. 4, 258–270, 1923). Carra de Vaux: Les penseurs de l'Islam (vol. 2, vol. 4, 1921–1923).

Philosophy—S. Landauer: Die Psychologie des Ibn Sīnā (Z. der deut. morgenl. Ges., vol. 29, 335–418, 1875). A. F. van Mehren has published many studies on Ibn Sīnā's philosophy in the Museon of Louvain (vols. 1 to 8, 1882–1889); I quote only one (vol. 3, 383–403, 1884, etc.), Vues d'Avicenne sur l'astrologie et le destin. Otto Alberts: Der Dichter des in uigurisch-türkischem Dialect geschriebenen Kudatku bilik (1069–70), ein Schüler des Avicenna (Archiv für Geschichte der Philosophie, vol. 14, 319–336, 1901). Martin Winter: Über Avicenna's Opus egregium de anima, Liber sextus naturalium (Diss., Erlangen, 53 p., München, 1903. An appendix deals with sense perception, especially optical perception). Avicenna the Poet, in E. G. Browne: Literary History of Persia (vol. 2, 106–111, 1906). Constantin Sauter: Avicennas Bearbeitung der aristotelischen Metaphysik (Diss., München, 52 p., Freiburg i. B., 1912).

Mathematics and Astronomy—P. Tannery: Sur l'invention de la preuve par neuf (Bull. des sciences mathématiques, vol. 6, 142–144, 1882; Mémoires, vol. 1, 185–188). H. Suter: Mathematiker und Astronomen (86–90, 225, 1900; 169, 1902). E. Wiedemann: Auszüge aus Ibn Sīnā's Teile der philosophischen Wissenschaften (Beiträge 5, Sitzungsber. der Erlangen Soz., vol. 37, 425–429, 1905). Karl Lokotsch: Avicenna als Mathematiker, besonders die planimetrischen Bücher seiner Euklidübersetzung (Diss., Bonn, 27 p., Erfurt, 1912). E. Wiedemann: Über ein von Avicenna hergestelltes Beobachtungsinstrument (Z. für Instrumentenkunde, 45, 269–275, 1925; Isis, VIII, 739).

Physics, Chemistry—E. Wiedemann: Über die Entstehung der Farben nach Naṣīr al-dīn al-Ṭūsī (Jahrbuch der Photographie und Reproduktionstechnik, 86–89, Halle, 1908); Ibn Sīnā's Anschauung vom Sehvorgang (Archiv für Gesch. der Naturw., vol. 4, 239–241, 1912); Avicenna's Lehre vom Regenbogen nach seinem Werke al-Schifā' (Meteorol. Z., Heft 11, 533–544, 1913). E. J. Holmyard: Chemistry to the Time of Dalton (22, 1925). H. G. Farmer: The Arabian Influence on Musical Theory (Journal Roy. Asiatic Soc., 61–80, 1925; Isis, VIII, 508–511).

Natural History—E. H. F. Meyer: Geschichte der Botanik (vol. 3, 184–203, 1856). J. Wood Brown: Enquiry into the Life and Legend of Michael Scott (Edinburgh, 1897. Apropos of the Abbrevatio Avicennae or Avicenna de animalibus, translated by Scott into Latin). P. Duhem: Le traité des minéraux attribué à Avicenne (Etudes sur Léonard de Vinci, vol. 2, 302–309, 1909). E. J. Holmyard: Arabic Text of Avicenna's Mineralia (Nature, vol. 117, 305, 1926. This text printed in Manget's Bibliotheca Chemica Curiosa, vol. 1, 636, and elsewhere, is a translation of certain sections of the Shifā').

Medicine—Wüstenfeld: Arabische Aerzte (64–75, 1840). Leclerc: Médecine arabe (vol. 1, 466–477, 1876). E. Gurlt: Geschichte der Chirurgie (vol. 1, 650–659, 1898). Anton Bumm: P. Vattiers Übersetzung (Paris, 1659) des Abschnitts über Geisteskrankheiten in Avicenna's Canon (Münchener mediz. Wchschft., 632–634, 1898). K. Sudhoff: Planta noctis (Archiv für Geschichte der Medizin, vol. 3, 352, 1909. Name of a skin disease in the Latin Qānūn, the result of a misreading in the Arabic, nabāt for banāt; what is meant is filiae noctis, to designate fugitive efflorescences). Willy Eckleben: Die abendländischen Avicenna-Kommentare (Diss., 23 p., Leipzig, 1921; Isis, IV, 401). O. C. Gruner: The Interpretation of Avicenna (Annals of Medical History, vol. 3, 354–360, 1921. Apropos of the small treatise, De viribus cordis, included in the Canon of 1595; possibly a later interpolation). E. G. Browne: Arabian Medicine (1921). Dinguizli: Etude expérimentale et clinique du djélenjoubine d'Avicenne dans le traitement de la tuberculose pulmonaire (Bull. Acad. de médec., 326–330, Paris, 1923; Isis, VIII, 537).

IBN ḤAZM

Abū Muḥammad 'Alī ibn Aḥmad ibn Ḥazm. Born in 994 in a suburb of Cordova; flourished at Cordova; died on his estate near Niebla in 1064. Hispano-Muslim statesman (at one time wazīr), theologian, and historian. The greatest scholar and one of the most original thinkers of Muslim Spain. At first a Shāfi'ite, he later became an ardent Ẓāhirite and applied the extreme literalism of the latter school to dogmatic theology. His main work is the "Book of Religions and Sects" (Kitāb al-milal wal-niḥal), wherein he discusses Judaism, Christianity, Zoroastrianism, Islām, and the four principal Muslim sects. In spite of its strong Ẓāhirite bias, this book is the fairest and most accurate (Muslim) account of Muslim sects.

Text—The Book of Religions was published at Cairo in 1889. It was partly Englished by Friedländer in the Journal of the Amer. Or. Soc., vols. 28–29, 1907 (Isis, IV, 63).

An erotic work, Kitāb ṭauq al-ḥamāma fī-l-ulfa wal-ullāf (meaning The Dove's Neck-band, on Love and Lovers) was edited by D. K. Petrof (206 p., Leide, 1914. Very interesting review by I. Goldziher, in Z. der deutschen morgenl. Ges., vol. 69, 192–207, 1915).

Los caracteres y la conducta. Tratado de moral práctica por Abenhazam de Córdoba. Traducción española por Miguel Asín Palacios (212 p., Madrid, 1916).

Criticism—Ibn Khallikān (De Slane) (vol. 2, 267–272, 1843). F. Wüstenfeld: Geschichtschreiber der Araber (66, 1881). I. Goldziher: Die Ẓāhiriten (Leipzig, 1884). C. Brockelmann: Arabische Litteratur (vol. 1, 400, 1898). D. B. Macdonald: Development of Muslim Theology (1903); Aspects of Islam (chapter 7, 1911). E. Wiedemann: Über eine optische Vorrichtung (Archiv für Geschichte der Naturwiss., vol. 2, 154, 1909. Apropos of Ibn Ḥazm's comparison of the world with a khayāl al-ẓill, what we call "Chinese shadows");[k] Zwei naturwissenschaftliche Stellen aus dem Werk über die Liebe,—über das Sehen und den Magneten (Beitr. 42, Sitzungsber., vol. 47, 93–100, Erlangen, 1915). C. van Arendonck in Encyclopaedia of Islam (vol. 2, 384–386, 1916–1918). A. R. Nykl: Ibn Ḥazm's Treatise on Ethics (American Journal Semitic Lang., vol. 40, 30–36, 1923. That is, the treatise translated by M. Asín; Isis, VII, 186).

WANG CH'IN-JO

Wang[2] Ch'in[1]-jo[4*] (12493, 2114, 5644). Flourished under Chên[1] Tsung[1] (589, 11976). Died in 1024. Chinese scholar. Chief editor of the great administrative encyclopaedia Ts'ê[4*]-fu[3] yüan[2]-kuei[1] (11699, 3682, 13744, 6421), the compilation of which had been ordered in 1005 by the third Sung emperor, Chên Tsung (who ruled from 997 to 1022). The work was completed in 1013 in 1,000 books. It is divided into 31 sections.

Text—Reprinted in 1642.

Criticism—A. Wylie: Chinese Literature (183, (1867), 1902). L. Wieger: La Chine (459, 527, 1920).

---

[k] That comparison became a commonplace in Islām. We find it a little later in 'Umar Khayyām, who speaks of a magic lantern using the Greek word fānūs (φανός), and in the poems of the Egyptian Ṣūfī 'Umar Ibn al-Fāriḍ (1181 to 1235).

III. LATIN, ENGLISH, MUSLIM, AND HINDU MATHEMATICS AND ASTRONOMY

Works Written in Latin and English

NOTKER LABEO

See my note in Section II, above.

BYRHTFERTH

Or Bridferth. Flourished under Æthelred II, King of England from 978 to 1016. Pupil of Abbo of Fleury. Monk of Ramsey in Huntingdonshire. He wrote a commentary on Bede, and, not before 1004, a Handboc or Compotus which is a compilation of astronomical and astrological lore.

Text—The Computus Latinorum ac Graecorum Hebraeorumque et Aegyptiorum necnon et Anglorum is contained in the Bodleian manuscript, Ashmole 328. It is written in Latin and Anglo-Saxon. I understand that Professor G. Hempl, of Stanford University, is preparing an edition of it (see Singer, below).
Criticism—Dictionary of National Biography (vol. 8, 126, 1886) by Henry Bradley. Charles and Dorothea Singer: Byrhtferth's Diagram of the Physiological Fours (St. John College manuscript 17, Oxford). Bodleian Quarterly Record (Vol. II, 47–51, 1 pl., 1917. Wherein further bibliography will be found); An unrecognized Anglo-Saxon medical text. Annals of Medical History (vol. 3, 136–149, 1921. Symbolic representation of the doctrine of macrocosm and microcosm; Isis, V, 498). Max Manitius: Lateinische Literatur des Mittelalters, vol. 2, 699–706, 1923).

BERNELINUS

Flourished at the beginning of the eleventh century. Mathematician. Pupil of Gerbert. He wrote, in Paris, a summary of Gerbert's lessons on the abacus, which is the earliest complete treatise on the subject. It is divided into four parts, of which the first deals with the description of the instrument and multiplication, the second and third with various methods of division, and the fourth with the Roman (duodecimal) fractions.

Text—The Liber abaci was published in A. Olleris's edition of Gerbert's works (357–400, Paris, 1867).
Criticism—André Berthelot: Sur une collection d'écrits mathématiques du moyen âge d'après deux manuscrits du Vatican (Mélanges de l'Ecole française de Rome, vol. 5, 181–222, 1885). Nicolaus Bubnov: Gerberti opera mathematica (Berlin, 1899, by index).

ADELBOLD

Adelbold of Utrecht (or Albaldus, Adelbaldus, Athalbaldius, Adelberón, Adalbold). Born c. 970, educated at Liège and Lobbes; died on Nov. 27, 1026. Nineteenth Bishop of Utrecht since 1010. Correspondent of Pope Sylvester II (Gerbert), to whom he dedicated a paper on the measurement of circle and sphere. If V and d represent the volume and diameter of a sphere, $10/21\ d^3 < V < 11/21\ d^3$. He wrote also on music. He wrote a commentary on a passage of Boetius's Consolation (3, 9) and (c. 1024 to 1026) a Life of the Emperor Henry II (not completed; it stops with the year 1004).

Text—Bernard Pez: Thesaurus anecdotorum novissimus (Tomus III, Pars 2, 81–92, Augsburg, 1721. De ratione inveniendi crassitudinem sphaerae). Nic. Bubnov: Gerberti opera mathematica (300–309, Berlin, 1899. Critical edition, with full bibliography of manuscripts).
Criticism—A. J. van der Aa: Biographisch Woordenboek der Nederlanden (vol. 1, 60–63, Haarlem, 1852). P. Tannery: Intermédiaire des mathématiciens

(Vol. XI, 254–257, 1904; Mémoires, vol. 5, 352–353). M. Manitius: Lateinische Literatur des Mittelalters (vol. 2, 743–748, 1923).

GUIDO OF AREZZO

See my note in physical section (IV), below.

RAGIMBOLD OF COLOGNE AND RADOLF OF LIÈGE

P. Tannery and the Abbé Clerval have published "Une correspondance d'écolâtres du XIe siècle" (Notices et extraits des manuscripts, vol. 36, 487–543, 1900; Tannery's Mémoires, vol. 5, 229–303, see Isis, VI, 432) which is of great value in appreciating the mathematical level of that time. The correspondence took place c. 1025, the two correspondents being Ragimbold of Cologne and Radolf of Liège. It deals with arithmetic and geometry. These two educated and intelligent schoolmasters are not bad calculators (they suggest comparison with the Egyptian Ahmes), but their geometry is very poor, probably below the level of pre-Pythagorean Greece. Radolf is probably the first writer to mention an astrolabe in the Latin West.

P. Tannery: La géométrie au XIe siècle (Revue générale internationale, 343–356, Paris, 1897; Mémoires, vol. 5, 79–102; Isis, VI, 432). M. Manitius: Lateinische Literaturgeschichte des Mittelalters (vol. 2, 778–781, 1923).

Muslim Mathematicians of the West

AL-KARMĀNĪ

Abū-l-Ḥakam 'Amr (or 'Umar) ibn 'Abd al-Raḥmān ibn Aḥmad ibn 'Alī al-Karmānī (that is of Carmona). Born in Cordova, died in Saragossa, 1066, being about 90 years old. Spanish-Muslim mathematician and surgeon. Disciple of Maslama ibn Aḥmad (q. v., second half of tenth century). It is he (or else the latter) who introduced the writings of the Brethren of Purity into Spain.

Wüstenfeld: Geschichte der arabischen Aerzte (80, 1840). Leclerc: Médecine arabe (vol. 1, 544, 1876). Suter: Die Mathematiker und Astronomen der Araber (105, 1900).

IBN AL-SAMH

Abū-l-Qāsim Aṣbagh ibn Muḥammad Ibn al-Samḥ. Flourished at Granada; died May 29, 1035, at the age of 56. Hispano-Muslim mathematician and astronomer. He wrote treatises on commercial arithmetic (al-mu'āmalāt), on mental calculus (ḥisāb al-hawā'ī), on the nature of numbers, two on geometry, two on the astrolabe, its use and construction. His main work seems to have been the compilation of astronomical tables, according to the Siddhānta method (for which see my note on Muḥammad ibn Ibrāhīm al-Fazārī second half of eighth century), together with theoretical explanations (c. 1025).

Text—The Libros del Saber contain (vol. 3, 241–271) a treatise entitled De cuemo puede ell ome fazer una lámina a cada planeta segund que lo mostró el sabio Abulcacim Abnaçahm, which was probably extracted from the tables.
Criticism—H. Suter: Mathematiker (85, 1900; 168, 1902).

IBN ABĪ-L-RIJĀL

In Latin, Abenragel (also Albohazen, Alboacen, which was more correct, for Abenragel was his father's name, rather than his own). Abū-l-Ḥasan 'Alī ibn abī-l-Rijāl al-Saibānī al-Kātib al-Maghribī. Born in Cordova or elsewhere in

Spain or in northern Africa, flourished in Tunis some time about 1016 to 1040, died after 1040.[l] Muslim astrologer. His main work is the "distinguished book on horoscopes from the constellations" (al-bāri' fī aḥkām al-nujūm).[m] It was translated by Judah ben Moses from Arabic into Castilian, then from Castilian into Latin by Aegidius de Tebaldis and Petrus de Regio. He wrote a physiognomic treatise on naevi.

Text and Translations—The Latin translation has often been printed. Editio princeps (Venice, 1485), Praeclarissimus liber completus in judiciis astrorum quem edidit Albohazen Haly filius Abenragel.

Criticism—C. Brockelmann: Arabische Literatur (vol. 1, 224, 1898). H. Suter: Die Mathematiker und Astronomen der Araber (100, 1900; Nachträge, 172, 1902); Encyclopaedia of Islam (vol. 2, 356, 1916).

IBN AL-ṢAFFĀR

Abū-l-Qāsim Aḥmad ibn 'Abdallāh ibn 'Umar al-Ghāfiqī, best known under the name Ibn al-Ṣaffār, meaning son of the coppersmith. Flourished at Cordova; toward the end of his life he retired in Denia and died there in 1035. Hispano-Muslim mathematician and astronomer. He wrote a treatise on the astrolabe and compiled tables according to the Siddhānta method.

Text—The treatise on the use of the astrolabe was translated into Latin by Plato of Tivoli and dedicated by him to Joannes Hispalensis; later it was translated into Hebrew by Prophatius. See my note on Jacob ben Machir ibn Tibbon (second half of thirteenth century).

Criticism—H. Suter: Mathematiker (86, 225, 1900; 169, 1902).

MUSLIM MATHEMATICIANS OF EGYPT

IBN YŪNUS

Abū-l-Ḥasan 'Alī ibn abī Sa'īd 'Abd al-Raḥmān ibn Aḥmad ibn Yūnus (or Ibn Yūnis) al-Ṣadafī al-Miṣrī. Died in Cairo, 1009 (not 1008). The date of his birth is unknown, but his father died in 958–59. Perhaps the greatest Muslim astronomer. A well-equipped observatory in Cairo enabled him to prepare improved astronomical tables. Begun c. 990 by order of the Fāṭimid caliph al-'Azīz (975–996), they were completed in 1007 under the latter's son al-Ḥākim (996 to 1020) and are called after him the Hakemite Tables (al-zīj al-kabīr al-Ḥākimī).[n] They contain observations of eclipses and conjunctions, old and new, improved values of astronomical constants (inclination of the ecliptic, 23° 35′; longitude of the sun's apogee, 86° 10′; solar parallax reduced from 3′ to 2′; precession, 51.2″ a year; no allusion to trepidation) and accounts of the geodetic measurements carried on by order of al-Ma'mūn (q. v., first half of ninth century).

His contributions to trigonometry, though less important than those of Abū-l-Wafā', are considerable. He solved many problems of spherical astronomy by means of orthogonal projections. He introduced the first of those prosthapheretical[o] formulæ which were indispensable before the invention of logarithms,

---

[l] Abū-l-Ḥasan al-Maghribī, who worked at al-Kūhī's observatory in 988, may be identical with him, though the dates make it improbable.

[m] al-bāri', literally the surpassing, overcoming (person or thing), the excellent.

[n] The date of these tables is, thus, briefly, 1007. Hence I place Ibn Yūnus at the beginning of the eleventh century.

[o] Derived from πρόσθεσις, addition, and ἀφαίρεσις, subtraction.

namely, the eqivalent of $\cos\alpha\cos\beta = \frac{1}{2}[\cos(\alpha - \beta) + \cos(\alpha + \beta)]$. Approximate value of $\sin 1° = \frac{1}{3}\cdot\frac{8}{9}\sin\left(\frac{9}{8}\right)° + \frac{2}{3}\cdot\frac{16}{15}\sin\left(\frac{15}{16}\right)°$

Ibn Yūnus's observatory was a part of the Hall of Wisdom (dār al-ḥikma, abode of wisdom) founded in Cairo by the Fāṭimids. This institution, which lasted from 1005 to the end of the Fāṭimid régime (1171), might be considered the second Muslim academy of science, the first being that founded by al-Ma'mūn at Bagdad almost two centuries earlier.

Texts and Translations—Caussin: Le livre de la grande table Hakémite (Extraits du MS. de Leyde, Notices et extraits des MSS., vol. 7, Paris, an XII, 16–240). Arabic text with French translation of a large part of the tables, except the chronological section. Caussin also gives the text and translation of the main sources relative to Ibn Yūnus's life and of Maqrīzī's excellent account of the Cairo observatory (q. v., first half of the fifteenth century).

Carl Schoy: Das 20. Kapitel des Tafeln des Ibn Jūnis. Über die Berechnung des Azimuts aus der Höhe und der Höhe aus dem Azimut (Annalen der Hydrographie und maritimen Meteorologie, 97–111, 1920); Über eine arabische Methode, die geographische Breite aus der Höhe der Sonne im 1. Vertikal zu bestimmen (*ibidem*, 124–133, April, 1921; Isis, IV, 401); Die Bestimmung der geographischen Breite eines Ortes durch Beobachtung der Meridianhöhe der Sonne oder mittels der Kenntnis zweier anderen Sonnenhöhen und den zugehörigen Azimuten (*ibidem*, 3–20, 1922. Translation of chapters 12, 21, and of a part of chapter 11 of the Hakemite tables); Beiträge zur arabischen Trigometrie (Isis, V, 364–399, 1923. Translation of the tenth chapter of the tables, dealing with the calculation of sines; Isis, VI, 201); The Geography of the Moslems (Geographical Review, vol. 14, 257–269, 1924. Text explaining how to determine longitude by observation of lunar eclipses; Isis, VII, 186).

Criticism—Delambre, Histoire de l'astronomie au Moyen Age (76–156, Paris, 1819. Based not simply on Caussin's edition, but also on other texts translated by Sédillot and unpublished). C. Brockelmann: Arabische Litteratur (vol. 1, 224, 1898). Braunmühl: Geschichte der Trigonometrie (vol. 1, 61–65, 1900). Suter: Die Mathematiker und Astronomen der Araber (77–78, 1900; Nachträge, 167, 1902). Dreyer: Planetary Systems (1906). Suter: Encyclopaedia of Islam (vol. 2, 428, 1918).

IBN AL-HAITHAM

See my note in the physical section (IV), below.

Muslim Mathematicians of the East

KŪSHYĀR IBN LABBĀN

Abū-l-Ḥasan Kūshyār ibn Labbān ibn Bāshahrī al Jīlī (i. e., from Jīlān, south of the Caspian Sea). Flourished c. 971 to 1029; his main work was probably done about the beginning of the eleventh century. Persian mathematician and astronomer, writing in Arabic. He seems to have taken an important part in the elaboration of trigonometry. For example, he continued the investigations of Abū-l-Wafā' on the tangent, and devoted much space to this in his tables. His main work was the compilation of astronomical tables, al-zīj al-jāmi' wa-l-bāligh (the comprehensive and mature tables), which were translated into Persian before the end of the century. He wrote also an astrological introduction and an arithmetical treatise (extant in Hebrew).

Texts—Extracts from the tables are published by Ideler in his Hdb. der mathematischen und technischen Chronologie (vol. 2, 547, 624), together with a German translation.
Criticism—C. Brockelmann: Arabische Litteratur (vol. 1, 222, 1898). H. Suter: Mathematiker und Astronomen der Araber (83, 225, 1900; 168, 1902). C. Schoy: Beitraege zur arabischen Trigonometrie (Isis, V, 395. On the sine tables).

IBN AL-ḤUSAIN

Abū Ja'far Muḥammad ibn al Ḥusain. Flourished not long after al-Khujandī (q. v., second half of tenth century). Mathematician. He wrote a memoir on rational right-angled triangles and another on the determination of two mean proportionals between two lines by a geometrical method (*vs.* kinematic method), i. e., by the use of what the Muslims called "fixed geometry," al-handasa al-thābit. Solution of the equation $x^2 \pm a = y^2$.

Texts—For a French translation of the first memoir, see Woepcke in the Atti dell Acc. pontif. d. nuovi Lincei (vol. 14, 1861). Abbreviated French translation of the second text by Carra de Vaux: Une solution du problème des deux moyennes proportionnelles entre deux droites données (Bibliotheca Mathematica, p. 3–4, 1898).
Criticism—Suter: Die Mathematiker und Astronomen der Araber (80, 1900; Nachträge, 168, 1902). Cantor: Vorlesungen (vol. 1, 3d ed., 752–755, 1907).

ABŪ-L-JŪD

Abū-l-Jūd Muḥammad ibn al-Lîth, contemporary of al-Bīrūnī. Mathematician. Solution of Albirunic problems by means of intersecting conics. Regular heptagon and enneagon. Classification of equations and their reduction to conic sections.

Text—Carl Schoy: Drei planimetrische Aufgaben des arabischen Mathematikers Abū-l-Jûd (Isis, VII, 5–8, 3 figs., 1925. Extracts in German from a manuscript of the Khedivial library in Cairo).
Criticism—F. Woepcke: L'algébre d'Omar Khayyam (Paris, 1851. Omar Khayyam's algebra contains problems solved by Abū-l-Jūd, see p. 114, 125). Suter: Die Mathematiker und Astronomen der Araber (97, 1900).

AL-KARKHĪ

Abū Bakr Muḥammad ibn al-Ḥasan (or Ḥusain) al-ḥāsib (the calculator) al-Karkhī, meaning, of Karkh, a suburb of Bagdad. Flourished in Bagdad during the vizierate of Abū Ghālib Muḥammad ibn Khalaf Fakhr al-mulk (glory of the realm), who died in 1016; he died himself c. 1019 to 1029. One of the greatest Muslim mathematicians. His book on arithmetic (the sufficient on calculation, al-kāfī fī-l-ḥisāb) is based chiefly on Greek and Hellenistic knowledge. No numerals of any kind are used, the names of the numbers being written in full. Casting out of the nines and elevens.

$$\text{If } r < (2a + 1), \sqrt{(a^2 + r)} \backsim a + r/(2a + 1).$$

His algebra (called al-fakhrī in honor of the vizier[p] is largely based on Diophantos. Complete solutions of quadratic equations (with proofs; two roots considered if positive and not null). Reduction of equations of the type

[p] It should be noted, however, that al-Karkhī himself was nicknamed Fakhr al-dīn (glory of religion).

$ax^{2p} + bx^p = c$ to quadratic equations. Addition and subtraction of radicals: $\sqrt{8} + \sqrt{18} = \sqrt{50}$; $\sqrt[3]{54} - \sqrt[3]{2} = \sqrt[3]{16}$. Summation of series:

$$\Sigma_1^n i^2 = (\Sigma_1^n i)\ (2n + 1)/3$$
$$\Sigma_1^n i^3 = (\Sigma_1^n i)^2 \text{ (with geometric proof)}$$

Solution of Diophantine equations (including 25 problems not found in Diophantos). Al-Kharkī's neglect of Hindu mathematics was such that it must have been systematic.

Text—Franz Woepcke: Extrait du Fakhrī, précédé d'un mémoire sur l'algèbre indéterminée chez les Arabes (160 p., Paris, 1853). The al-kāfī fī-l-ḥisāb has been translated into German by Ad. Hochheim (published in three parts, Halle, 1878–1880).

Criticism—H. Suter: Die Mathematiker und Astronomen der Araber (84, 1900). M. Cantor: Vorlesungen (vol. 1³, 762–774, 1907). H. Suter: Encyclopaedia of Islam (vol. 2, 764, 1925. Very little).

AL-NASAWĪ

Abū-l-Ḥasan 'Alī ibn Aḥmad al-Nasawī. From Nasā, Khurāsān. Flourished under the Buwayhid sulṭān Majd al-dawla, who died in 1029–30, and under his successor. Persian mathematician. He wrote a practical arithmetic in Persian, before 1030, and later under Majd al-dawla's successor an Arabic translation of it, entitled the "Satisfying (or Convincing) on Hindu Calculation" (al-muqni' fī-l-ḥisāb al-hindī). He also wrote on Archimedes's lemnata and Menelaos's theorem (Kitāb al-ishbā', satiation). His arithmetic explains the division of fractions and the extraction of square and cubic roots (square root of 57,342; cubic root of 3,652,296) almost in the modern manner. It is remarkable that al-Nasawī replaces sexagesimal by decimal fractions, e. g.,

$$\sqrt{17°} = 1/100\ \sqrt{170.000°} = (1/100)\ 412° = 4°\ 7'\ 12''$$

Text and Translations—An analysis of the text of al-muqni', with short extracts has been given by F. Woepcke in the last part of his Mémoire sur la propagation des chiffres indiens (Journal asiatique (6) vol. 1, 489–500, 1863, un traité de calcul indien). German translation of the introduction to the Ishbā' by Eilhard Wiedemann, in appendix to Oskar Schirmer: Studien zur Astronomie der Araber (80–85, Erlangen, 1926; see also 46–48; Isis, IX).

Criticism—Suter: Die Mathematiker und Astronomen der Araber (96, 1900); Über das Rechenbuch des 'Alī ben Aḥmed el-Nasawī (Bibliotheca Mathematica, vol. 7, 113–119, 1906). H. Bürger and K. Kohl: Geschichte des Transversalensatzes (53–55, Erlangen, 1924; Isis, VIII, 799).

For the mathematical contributions of Ibn Ṭāhir, al-Bīrūnī and Ibn Sīnā, see my notes in Section II, above.

HINDU MATHEMATICS

ŚRĪDHARA

Srīdharācārya, i. e., Śrīdhara the Learned. Born probably in 991. Hindu mathematician. He composed, c. 1020, a "compendium of calculation" (gaṇitasāra; also called triśatikā because it consisted originally of 300 couplets) dealing with weights and measures, elementary arithmetic, and most elementary measurements (partly incorrect). No single proof is given. Of the 65 couplets extant, n° 8 deals with zero

$$a \pm 0 = a \qquad 0 \times a = 0 \qquad a \times 0 = 0$$

this being the clearest account of the use of zero in Sanskrit literature (notice that division by zero is not considered). His work on quadratic equations is lost, but according to Bhāskara's own testimony (q. v., twelfth century), the rule for solving quadratic equations, which he proceeds to explain, was first given by Śrīdhara.

Text and Translation—The Sanskrit text was edited by Sudhākara Dvevedī in 1899. An English translation by N. Rāmānujācārya, with a commentary by G. R. Kaye, appeared in Bibliotheca Mathematica (vol. 13, 203–217, 1913; Isis, I, 516).

Criticism—M. Winternitz: Indische Literatur (vol. 3, 473, 574, 1922). D. E. Smith: History of Mathematics (vol. 1, 274, 280, 1923. Facsimile of a page of the Triśatikā on p. 275).

IV. LATIN, ENGLISH, SYRIAN, MUSLIM, AND CHINESE PHYSICS, CHEMISTRY, AND TECHNOLOGY

ADELBOLD OF UTRECHT

See my note in the mathematical section (III), above.

GUIDO OF AREZZO

Wido Aretinus. Born c. 990, died in Fonte Avellana, 1050. Great reformer of musical teaching. As he was the most popular mediaeval writer on the subject, every progress of the musical science in the eleventh century was naturally ascribed to him. For example, the use of the lines of the staff and of the intervals between them. Guido did not invent this use, but he improved it. He it is, too, who designated the notes of the scale by the first syllables of six lines of a hymn to St. John the Baptist: ut, re, mi, fa, sol, la, a designation still used by Latin peoples (save that ut is called do and that si, the seventh note of our scale, was not added until about two centuries later).

His most important work is the "Micrologus de disciplina artis musicae," a complete theory of music composed c. 1030. He wrote, c. 1028, a treatise on the abacus.

Text—The musical writings have been edited by Martin Gerbert in his Scriptores ecclesiastici de musica sacra potissimum (Tomus II, p. 1–61, 1774. Facsimile reprint, Graz, Styria, 1905). Edition of the Micrologus, with German translation and notes by Mich. Hermesdorff (125 p., Trier, 1876).

Criticism—Michele Falchi: Studi su Guido Monaco (112 p., Firenze, 1882. Apropos of the inauguration of a monument to Guido in Arezzo, Tuscany, 1882). Ph. Berthelot, in Grande Encyclopédie (2 1–2 cols., c. 1894). J. Combarieu: Histoire de la musique (vol. 1, Paris, 1913). M. Manitius: Lateinische Literatur des Mittelalters (vol. 2, 748–756, 1923).

OLIVER OF MALMESBURY

Alias Eilmer, Elmer, Aethelmaer. Flourished at the monastery of Malmesbury; he was an old man in 1066. English astrologer and mechanician. He is said by William of Malmesbury (q. v., first half of twelfth century) to have fitted wings to his hands and feet and to have attempted to fly off from a tower with the help of the wind; he fell and broke his legs. He attributed his failure to the lack of a tail. He observed the great comet of April 24, 1066, and predicted then the destruction of his country (the Norman conquest).[q]

[q] The battle of Hastings (or Senlac) occurred on October 14, 1066.

William Hunt, in Dictionary of National Biography (vol. 42, 140, 1895). J. E. Hodgson: History of Aeronautics in Great Britain (55, 1924; Isis, VII, 521).

ELIAS BAR SHĪNĀYĀ

See my note in the historical section (VIII), below.

IBN AL-HAITHAM

Latin name: Alhazen. Abū 'Alī al-Ḥasan ibn al-Ḥasan (or al-Ḥusain) ibn al-Haitham. Born c. 965 in Baṣra, flourished in Egypt under al-Ḥākim (996 to 1020) died in Cairo in 1039 or soon after. The greatest Muslim physicist and one of the greatest students of optics of all times. He was also an astronomer, a mathematician, a physician, and he wrote commentaries on Aristotle and Galen.

The Latin translation of his main work, the Optics (Kitāb al-manāẓir), exerted a great influence upon Western science (R. Bacon; Kepler). It showed a great progress in experimental method. Research in catoptrics: spherical and parabolic mirrors, spherical aberration; in dioptrics: the ratio between the angle of incidence and refraction does not remain constant; magnifying power of a lens. Study of atmospheric refraction. The twilight only ceases or begins when the sun is 19° below the horizon; attempt to measure the height of the atmosphere on that basis. Better description of the eye, and better understanding of vision, though Ibn al-Haitham considered the lens as the sensitive part; the rays originate in the object seen, not in the eye. Attempt to explain binocular vision. Correct explanation of the apparent increase in size of the sun and the moon when near the horizon. Earliest use of the camera obscura.

The catoptrics contain the following problem, known as Alhazen's problem: from two points in the plane of a circle to draw lines meeting at a point of the circumference and making equal angles with the normal at that point. It leads to an equation of the fourth degree. Alhazen solved it by the aid of an hyperbola intersecting a circle. He also solved the so-called al-Māhānī's (cubic) equation (q. v., second half of ninth century) in a similar (Archimedian) manner.

Texts and Translations—The first writing of Alhazen to be published was not his Optics, but a smaller one on twilight, translated by Gherardo Cremonese "De crepusculis et nubium ascensionibus." It appeared in Lisbon, 1542, together with Pedro Nuñez's De crepusculis. It was republished, together with Alhazen's and Vitello's optics, by Fried. Risner (Bale, 1572). Opticae thesaurus. Alhazeni Arabis libri septem nunc primum editi, etc. (288 p.).

L. Am. Sédillot: Du traité des connues géométriques de Hassan ben Haitham (Journal asiatique, vol. 13, 435–458, 1834. Extracts in French; geometrical loci, porisms). J. Baarmann: Abhandlung über das Licht von Ibn al-Haitham (Zeitschrift der deutschen morgenländischen Ges., vol. 36, 195–237, 1882. German and Arabic). H. Suter: Die Kreisquadratur des Ibn el-Haitham (Z. f. Mathematik und Physik, historische Abt., Bd. 44, 33–47, 1899. Arabic and German. Unimportant); Die Abhandlung über die Ausmessung des Paraboloides von Ibn al Haitham (Bibliotheca Mathematica, vol. 12, 289–332, 1912. Translation with commentary).

Carl Schoy: Abhandlung über eine Methode die Polhöhe mit grösster Genauigkeit zu bestimmen (De Zee, 586–601, 1920; Isis, IV, 401); Abhandlung über die Bestimmung der Richtung der Qibla (Z. d. deutschen morgenländischen Gesellschaft, Bd. 75, 242–253, 1921; Isis, IV, 401); Abhandlung über die Natur der Spuren (Flecken) die man auf der Oberfläche des Mondes sieht (Hannover, 1925; Isis, VIII, 538).

General Criticism. Biography—Wüstenfeld: Geschichte der arabischen Aerzte

(76–77, 1840). Leclerc: Médecine arabe (vol. 1, 512–525, 1876). Suter: Die Mathematiker und Astronomen der Araber (91–95, 1900; Nachträge, 169, 1902). M. J. de Goeje: Notice biographique (Archives de la société des sciences de Haarlem, vol. 6, 668–670, 1901). Suter: Encyclopaedia of Islam (vol. 2, 382, 1916). Carra de Vaux: Penseurs de l'Islam (vol. 2, 243–250, 1921).

Scientific Criticism, Chiefly Astronomical and Physical—A large commentary on Ibn al-Haitham's Optics was written by Kamāl al-dīn Abū-l-Ḥasan al-Fārisī (q. v., first half of fourteenth century). Enrico Narducci: Intorno ad una traduzione italiana fatta nel secolo XIV del trattato d'ottica d'Alhazen e ad altri lavori di questo scienziato (Bullett. di bibliografia et di storia d. sci. matemat., vol. 4, 1–48, 1871). Maurice Steinschneider: Sur un ouvrage astronomique inédit d'Ibn Haitham (*ibidem*, vol. 14, 721–740; also vol. 16, 505–513, 1883). L. Schnaase: Die Optik Alhazens (20 p., Stargard, 1890). Dreyer: Planetary Systems (270, 1906. Apropos of Alhazen's attempt to explain the manner in which the epicycles remain parallel to the ecliptic). Hans Bauer: Die Psychologie Alhazens auf Grund von Alhazens Optik (Beitr. zur Gesch. d. Philos. des Mittelalters, X, 5, 81 p., Münster, 1911). E. Gerland: Geschichte der Physik (161–170, 1913). P. Duhem: Système du Monde (vol. 2, 119–124, 1914. Le résumé d'astronomie d'Ibn al Haitham). Singer's Studies in the History and Method of Science (vol. II, 391–392, 1921. List of manuscripts in England; for a short account of Alhazen's optics it is better to refer to Gerland).

Mathematics—F. Woepcke: L'algèbre d'Omar Alkhayyāmī (73–77, 1851. Containing a list of Alhazen's writings). Marcus Baker: Alhazen's Problem. Its Bibliography and an Extension of It (American Journal Mathematics, vol. 4, 327–331, 1881). P. Bode: Die Alhazen'sche Spiegel-Aufgabe in ihrer historischen Entwicklung nebst einer analytischen Lösung des verallgemeinerten Problems (50 p., Frankfurt, 1893). C. Schoy: Behandlung einiger geometrischen Fragepunkte durch muslimische Mathematiker (Isis, VIII, 254–260, 1926; containing interesting problems solved by Ibn al-Haitham; Isis, IX).

Eilhard Wiedemann's Studies—It is expedient to quote separately these many studies which contain fragmentary or abbreviated translations of a number of texts, together with critical notes. They deal with mathematical, astronomical, physical and chemical subjects. (Sitz. Erlangen, means Sitzungsberichte der physikalisch-medizinischen Societät in Erlangen; Beit., means Beiträge zur Geschichte der Naturwissenschaften, a series of papers published by Wiedemann in the Erlangen Berichte.)

Sull' ottica degli Arabi (Bull. di bibliografia e di storia d. sci. mat., vol. 14, 219–225, 1881). Über das Licht der Sterne (Wchschr. f. Astron., Meteor. und Geogr., 1890). Notiz über ein von Alhazen gelöstes arithmetisches Problem (Sitz. Erlangen, vol. 24, 83, 1892). Eine Beobachtung aus der physiologischen Optik (Beit. 2, Sitz. Erlangen, vol. 36, 333–334, 1904). Über die Lage der Milchstrasse (3 p., Sirius, 1906). Ibn al Haitham (Festscrift für J. Rosenthal, 147–177, Leipzig, 1906). Über die Beschaffenheit der Schatten (Beit. 13, Sitz. Erlangen, vol. 39, 226–248, 1907). Kleine Arbeiten von Ibn al Haitham (Beit. 17, Sitz. Erlangen, vol. 41, 1–25, 1909). With J. L. Heiberg: Ibn al-Haithams Schrift über parabolische Hohlspiegel (Bibliotheca mathematica, vol. 10, 201–237, 1907. German and Latin). Schrift über die sphärischen Hohlspiegel (*ibidem*, 293–307. German only). Zu Ibn al-Haithams Optik (Archiv für Geschichte der Naturwiss., vol. 3, 1–53, 1910). Eine Zeichnung des Auges bei dem Bearbeiter der Optik von Ibn al Haitham, Kamāl al-dīn (Centralblatt für Augenheilkunde, vol. 34, 204, 1910). Über die Brechung des Lichts in Kugeln (Beit. 19, Sitz. Erlangen, vol. 42, 15–58, 1910). Erste Erwähnung der Dunkelkammer (Jahrbuch für Photographie, vol. 24, 12–13, 1910). With J. L. Heiberg: Eine arabische Schrift über die Parabol und parabolische Hohlspiegel (Bibliotheca mathematica, vol. 11, 193–208, 1911. Partial translation of a Latin text of

Arabic origin but unknown authorship; I quote it here for the sake of comparison; this text is translated from manuscript 206 of Verona and from the first edition, together with Ptolemy's Quadripartitum, Louvain, 1548). Über das Leben von Ibn al-Haitham und al-Kindī (Jahrbuch für Photographie, vol. 25, 6–11, 1911). Theorie des Regenbogens (Beit. 38, Sitz. Erlangen, vol. 46, 39–56, 1914). Über die Camera Obscura (Beit. 39, Sitz. Erlangen, vol. 46, 155–169, 1914). Ibn al Haitham und seine Bedeutung für die Alchemie (Deutsche Literaturzeitung, 1923, 113–118).

For Māsawaih al-Mārdīnī, see the medical section (VII), below.
For al-Bīrūnī and Ibn Sīnā, see the philosophical section (II), above.

AL-KĀTHĪ

Abū-l-Ḥakīm Muḥammad ibn 'Abd al-Malik al-Ṣāliḥī al-Khwārizmī al-Kāthī. Flourished in Bagdad c. 1034. Muslim chemist, who wrote, in 1034, a treatise on alchemy entitled "Essence of the Art and Aid to the Workers" ('Ain al-ṣan'a wa 'awn-al-ṣana'ā), strikingly similar in some respects to the "Summa perfectionis magisterii" of the Latin Geber (for which see my note on Jābir, second half of eighth century).

H. E. Stapleton and R. F. Azo: Alchemical Equipment in the Eleventh Century (Memoirs of Asiatic Society of Bengal, vol. 1, 47–70, 1 pl., Calcutta, 1905. Containing Arabic text, an analysis of it, and an introduction; very important).

PI SHÊNG

Pi[4*] Shêng[1] (8994, 9880). Flourished under Jên[2] Tsung[1] (5627, 11976), Sung emperor from 1022 to 1063. Chinese alchemist and inventor. During the period 1041 to 1049 he invented typography—the printing with movable type (yin[4] (13282), literally, seal). He used type made of clay and experimented also with wooden type. There is an authentic and clear description of this by a contemporary writer, Shên Kua (q. v., next chapter). Pi Shêng's invention was improved at a later time by an unknown person, who made type of tin, perforated and held in place by a wire, and again in 1314 by Wang Chêng (q. v., first half of fourteenth century).

H. A. Giles: Chinese Biographical Dictionary (626, 1898). G. Vacca: Note cinesi, 4 e 5 (Rivista degli studi orientali, t. 6, 138–142. Chinese texts with translations and notes). T. F. Carter: Invention of Printing in China (159–161, 1925; Isis, VIII, 371).

TOU P'ING

Tou[4] P'ing[2] (11435, 9314). Flourished in the first half of the eleventh century (?). Chinese chemist. Author of a treatise on spirituous liquors called Chiu[3] P'u[3] (2260, 9515). "It consists chiefly of brief notices regarding different kinds of liquor and celebrated distillers."

I know this work only through Wylie's brief notice of it, here reproduced, in Chinese Literature (150 (1867), 1902). In view of the fact that distillation was apparently unknown in Europe before the twelfth century (see my note on alcoholic distillation in the second half of the twelfth century), it would be interesting to investigate Chinese records on the subject. See also my note on the Mappae clavicula (second half of eighth century) and on Chu I-chung (first half of twelfth century).

V. MUSLIM NATURAL HISTORY

See my notes on al-Bīrūnī, in the philosophical section (II), above, and on Ibn al-Ṭaiyib, in the medical section (VII), below.

VI. ICELANDIC DISCOVERY OF AMERICA; LATIN GEOGRAPHY; MUSLIM GEOGRAPHY, MINERALOGY, AND GEOLOGY

The Icelandic[r] Discovery of America

Leif the Fortunate (Leif Ericsson) made a landing on the northeastern coast of America, by accident, in 1000. This is the first discovery of America of which we have a record. Another voyage was undertaken by Thorfin Karlsefni, from Greenland, a few years later (1003 to 1006). An Icelandic colony was established by him in "Wineland"; they seem to have touched Newfoundland and Southern Labrador, to have followed part of the St. Lawrence Valley, and possibly to have coasted Nova Scotia and New England. The colonial experiment failed.

The Scandinavians were never more active than in the first half of the eleventh century. While those of Iceland discovered the New World, other Norsemen invaded various parts of England, of Russia, of Southern Italy, and of Western Europe.

Texts and Translations—The sources are in the first place Adam of Bremen (q. v., next chapter), c. 1075, and in the second place two Icelandic accounts, Eric the Red's saga (c. 1200) and the Grænlendingapáttr, the first of these being the more reliable. Both have been published by C. C. Rafn in Antiquitates Americanae (Copenhagen, 1837) and by the Kongelige Nordiske Oldskriftselskab in Groenlands Historiske Mindesmaerker (vol. 3, Copenhagen, 1845). Arthur M. Reeves: Finding Wineland the Good (London, 1890. Texts with English translation and notes). See also Gathorne-Hardy (1921) below.

Criticism—Gustav Storm: Studier over Vinlandsrejserne (Copenhagen, 1888). Joseph Fischer: Die Entdeckung der Normannen in America (Freiburg i. Br. 1902. English translation by Basil H. Soulsby, 154 p., London, 1903); Die Kartographische Darstellung der Entdeckungen der Normannen in America (Vortrag, Intern. Amerikanisten-Kongress, Stuttgart, 1904, 1906). Fridtjof Nansen: Nord i Taakeheimen (Kristiania, 1911; also in English, In Northern Mists, 2 vols., London, 1911. Claiming that the Icelandic discovery of America is a myth). Nansen's theory has been successfully controverted by subsequent writers. I see no reason to doubt those early voyages, though it will probably remain forever impossible to determine the itineraries of the Icelanders with any accuracy.

Halldór Hermannson: The Northmen in America (Islandica, vol. 2, 1909). William H. Babcock: Early Norse Visits to North America (216 p., Washington, 1913). Gustav Neckel: Die erste Entdeckung Amerikas (Voigtländers Quellenbücher, 43, Leipzig, 1913. Popular but good). William Hovgaard: The Voyages of the Norsemen to America (325 p., New York, 1914). H. P. Steensby: The Norsemen's Route from Greenland to Vineland (110 p., Copenhagen, 1918; Isis, IV, 48). G. M. Gathorne-Hardy: The Norse Discoverers of America. The Wineland sagas translated and discussed (304 p., Oxford, 1921. Excellent; the texts of the sagas are not translated separately, but pieced together so as to present a more continuous account; Isis, IV, 505–508). J. Bunford Samuel: The Icelander, Thorfinn Karlsefni, who visited the Western Hemisphere in 1007 (Philadelphia, 1922). Louis H. Roddis: The Norsemen in the New World (70 p., Minneapolis, 1923). A. Langlois: La découverte de l'Amérique par les Normands (167 p., 3 pl., Paris, 1924; Isis, VII, 536)

---

[r] It is more precise to say Icelandic than Norse, for those who took part in these voyages were all natives of Iceland, except Eric the Red.

AIMOIN OF FLEURY

See my note in historical section (VIII), below.

MUSLIM GEOGRAPHY, GEOLOGY, AND MINERALOGY

See my notes on al-Bīrūnī and Ibn Sīnā in the philosophical section (II), above.

VII. LATIN, BYZANTINE, MUSLIM (OR ARABIC), AND CHINESE MEDICINE

THE SCHOOL OF SALERNO

I have already alluded to this school in my note on Donnolo (second half of tenth century). As distinguished from the many cathedral schools whose purpose was to teach the liberal arts and to educate clerks, Salerno was a scientific or professional school, the first of its kind in Christian Europe. It is impossible to determine exactly its beginning; in all probability it had no definite beginning, but grew and imperceptibly became a famous medical center. It is typical that the earliest official document concerning it is a charter granted in 1231 by the Emperor Frederick II, but by that time the heyday of Salerno was already over and the creation of the first universities had put an end to its monopoly.

Salernum, situated in the Bay of Paestum (just south of the Bay of Naples) was already a health resort in ancient times. On the other hand, the traditions of Greek medicine had never been entirely interrupted in South Italy and Sicily; definite traces of it are found as late as the seventh and eighth centuries. A medical corporation already existed in Salerno in the ninth century. We may be sure that these early Salernitan physicians had some acquaintance with Greek medicine. The presence of Donnolo in the second half of the tenth century suggests the probability of Jewish influences. Politically, Salerno was for many centuries a part of the Lombard Duchy of Benevento; it was often attacked or pillaged by Saracens; in 1077 it was conquered by the Normans. Thus intellectual and political conditions combined to make of Salerno an excellent clearing-house of medical ideas. Barbarian, Latin, Greek, Jewish, and Muslim influences were naturally and gradually syncretized and produced the first medical school of Europe. At the beginning, Muslim influences were accidental and limited, but later they were considerably increased by the activity of Constantine the African (q. v., next chapter). The first literary fruits of the school did not appear before the first half of the eleventh century; the importance of the school grew rapidly during the second half of that century and even more so during the twelfth century. The first Crusade (1096 to 1099) gave it a considerable impulse.

Texts—Salvatore de Renzi: Collectio salernitana ossia documenti inediti e trattati di medicina appartenenti alla scuola medica salernitana, raccolti ed illustrati da G. E. T. Henschel, C. Daremberg, E. S. de Renzi. Premessa la storia della scuola (5 vols., Napoli, 1852–1859). P. Giacosa: Magistri salernitani nondum editi. Catalogo ragionato della esposizione di storia della medicina aperta in Torino nel 1898 (760 p., album of 40 pl., Torino, 1901). Karl Sudhoff: Beiträge zur Geschichte der Chirurgie im Mittelalter. Graphische und textliche Untersuchungen in mittelalterlichen Handschriften (2 vols., Leipzig, 1914–1918; Isis, IV, 186). For the separate texts (including a few anonymous ones like the famous Regimen sanitatis) see the medical sections of the chapters devoted to the eleventh, twelfth, thirteenth, and fourteenth centuries.

Criticism—Salvatore de Renzi: Storia documentata della scuola medica di Salerno (2da edizione, 802 p., Napoli, 1857. The first edition formed the first volume of Renzi's Collectio salernitana). Georges Bécavin: L'école de Salerne et les médecins salernitains (Paris, 1888). Modestino del Gaizo: La scuola medica di Salerno studiata nella storia e nelle leggende (Napoli, 1896). Friedrich Hartmann: Die Literatur von Früh- und Hochsalerno und der Inhalt des Breslauer Codex Salernitanus (Diss., 76 p., Leipzig, 1919. Excellent summary). Charles and Dorothea Singer: The Origin of the Medical School of Salerno (Essays presented to K. Sudhoff, 18 p., Zürich, 1923; Isis, VII, 535).

Two anonymous texts of the school of Salerno date probably from the first half or the middle of the eleventh century,

(*a*) Curae or Tractatus de curis. A treatise similar to the Passionarius compiled by Gariopontus (q. v., below).

Text—Giacosa: Magistri salernitani (177–277, 1901. To be compared also with the shorter text published *ibidem*, 169–174).

Criticism—Neuburger (Geschichte, vol. 2, 295, 1911). Hartmann (Op. cit., 42).

(*b*) The Speculum hominis. A didactic poem of which 1011 verses remain and dating from the middle of the eleventh century. It is pre-Constantinian and largely based upon Isidore of Seville. It is Italian, but not necessarily Salernitan.

Text—Renzi's Collectio salernitana (vol. 5, 173–198, 1859).

Criticism—Neuburger (op. cit., 286).

GARIOPONTUS

Probably a Longobard. Flourished in Salerno; died c. 1050. Salernitan physician. Author (or editor) of a medical encyclopaedia, called Passionarius, a collection of extracts from late Greek, Byzantine, and Roman writers. His treatise on fevers (De febribus) was possibly a part of the Passionarius. The latter enjoyed much popularity.

Texts—Galeni Pergameni [sic!] Passionarius (Lyon, 1526. Possibly an earlier edition, Lyon, 1516?).

Garioponti vetusti admodum medici ad totius corporis aegritudines remediorum πράξεων libri quinque (Basel, 1531, again 1536).

The De febribus was published in the edition of the Passionarius of 1531. Also in the Collectio de febribus (Venice, 1576).

Criticism—E. H. F. Meyer (Geschichte der Botanik, vol. 3, 484–500, 1856). Geyl: Zwei lateinische Handschriften aus dem XI. Jahrh., respective von Gariopontus und Constantinus Afer. (Janus, vol. 14, 161–166, 1909). Neuburger: Geschichte der Medizin (vol. 2, 284–285, 1911). Hartmann: Die Literatur von Früh- und Hochsalerno (4–6, 1919). E. Wickersheimer: A note on the liber de medicinis expertis attributed to Galen (Annals of Medical History, vol. 4, 323–327, 1922. That text is sometimes ascribed to Gariopontus; Isis, V, 537; VI, 204).

PETROCELLUS

Or Petricellus.[a] Probably a contemporary of Gariopontus? Salernitan physician. Author of a Practica (c. 1035?), at least of the first book, based, like Gariopontus's works, upon late Greek and Latin sources. Arabic drugs are mentioned.

Texts and Translations—Practica Petrocelli Salernitani, in S. de Renzi's Collectio salernitana (vol. 4, 185–286, 1856. Text of Paris manuscript, fonds St. Germain 1146, followed by fragments of Books II and III, 287–291). An Anglo-Saxon version of the Practica, made some time between 1035 and 1200, was published by Oswald Cockayne, in Leechdoms, Wortcunning, and Starcraft of early England

[a] See my note on Petronius, second half of twelfth century.

(vol. 3, 82–145, London, 1866. With English translation; this text, from manuscript Harl. 6258 of the British Museum, is badly copied). Better edition by Max Löweneck: Peri didaxeon. Eine Sammlung von Rezepten in englischer Sprache aus dem 11.–12. Jahrh. (Erlangen Beiträge zur Englischen Philologie, 12, 65 p., Erlangen, 1896. Containing the Anglo-Saxon περὶ διδάξεων and the Practica Petrocelli printed on opposite pages).

Criticism—E. Gurlt: Geschichte der Chirurgie (vol. 1, 697–700, 1898). Neuburger: Geschichte der Medizin (vol. 2, 284–285, 1911). Hartmann: Die Literatur von Früh- und Hochsalerno (6, 1919). Karl Bloedner: Petronus, sein klinisches Schriftwerk und der Autor der Übergangszeit Petricellus (Diss., 58 p., Leipzig, 1925; Isis, VIII, 539. Claims that Petrocellus's Practica is a much earlier work than was said above; that it belongs to the early mediaeval period of South Italian medicine which formed the transition between ancient and Salernitan medicine).

ALPHANUS

Flourished in Monte Cassino and in Salerno about the middle of the eleventh century. Archbishop of Salerno. (There were two archbishops of Salerno called Alphanus and it is difficult to say which was the medical writer.) Author of a Latin translation of Nemesios's book (q. v., second half of fourth century) on the nature of man under the title "Prennon fisicon, i. e., stipes naturalium." He wrote a very brief treatise entitled "De quattuor humoribus ex quibus constat humanum corpus."

Text—The translation has been edited by C. Burkhard (166 p., Leipzig, 1917). The De quattuor humoribus is included in S. de Renzi, Collectio salernitana (vol. 2, 411–412, 1853).

Criticism—Hartmann: Die Literatur von Früh- und Hochsalerno (7–9, 1919). Max Manitius (Geschichte der lateinischen Literatur, vol. 2, 618–637, 1923. Alphanus I. von Salerno).

Byzantine Physicians

DAMNASTES

Δαμναστής. Flourished possibly in the eleventh century, or before. Author of a short treatise, in four chapters, on the care of pregnant women and of unborn or newborn children (περὶ κυουσῶν καὶ βρεφῶν θεραπείας).

Iwan Bloch, in Puschmann's Geschichte der Medizin (vol. 1, 564, 1902).

STEPHANOS MAGNETES

Στεφάνος ὁ Μαγνήτης. Flourished probably in the eleventh century. Byzantine medical writer. Author of a dispensatory arranged in alphabetical order of diseases. This work is wrongly ascribed in the Greek manuscript (Vienna) to Stephanos of Athens (q. v., first half of seventh century) and to Dioscorides!

Text—No Greek edition. Latin princeps edition by Caspar Wolf. Alphabetum empiricum de remediis expertis (Zürich, 1581.).

Criticism—Ernst H. F. Meyer: Geschichte der Botanik (vol. 3, 365–379, 1856. Includes a list of plants and a few other drugs).

Arabic-Writing Physicians of the West

AL-KARMĀNĪ

See my note in mathematical section (III), above.

IBN AL-WĀFID

Latin name: Abenguefit. Abū-l-Mutarrif 'Abd al-Raḥmān ibn Muḥammad ibn 'Abd al-Karīm ibn Yaḥyā ibn al-Wāfid al-Lakhmī. From Toledo, where he flourished; born 997, died c. 1074. Hispano-Muslim physician, pharmacologist. His main work, on simple drugs (Kitāb al-adwiya al-mufrada), based on Galen and Dioscorides and also on personal investigations, is partly extant in a Latin translation (De medicamentis simplicibus). He preferred to use dietetic measures, and, if drugs were needed, to use the simplest ones. He advised a method of investigating the action of drugs. He wrote also on balneotherapy.

Text and Translations—The De medicamentis simplicibus has been printed frequently, together with the Latin translation of the works of Māsawaih al-Mārdīnī (Venice, 1549 sq.) or of Ibn Jazla's Taqwīm (Dispositio corporum de constitutione hominis, Strasbourg, 1532). The De balneis sermo is included in the De Balneis quae extant apud Gr., Lat. et Arab. (Venice, 1553).

Criticism—F. Wüstenfeld: Geschichte der arabischen Aerzte (82, 1840). E. H. F. Meyer: Geschichte der Botanik (vol. 3, 205–208, 1856). Leclerc: Histoire de la médecine arabe (vol. 1, 545–547, 1876). C. Brockelmann: Arabische Litteratur (vol. 1, 485, 1898. Two Arabic manuscripts mentioned).

IBN JANĀḤ

See my note in the philological section (IX), below.

Arabic-Writing Physicians of Egypt

MĀSAWAIH AL-MĀRDĪNĪ

Mesuë the Younger. Māsawaih al-Mārdīnī, from Mārdīn in Upper Mesopotamia. Flourished in Bagdad, later at the court of the Fāṭimid caliph al-Ḥākim in Egypt, where he died in 1015 at the age of ninety.[t] Physician. Jacobite Christian.[u] He wrote books on purgatives and emetics (De medicinis laxativis; De consolatione medicinarum et correctione operationum earundem) and on the remedies relative to each disease (De egritudinibus), but his main work is a complete pharmacopoeia in 12 parts called the Antidotarium sive Grabadin medicamentorum compositorum, based on Muslim knowledge.[v] The last-named work was immensely popular. It remained for centuries the standard text-book of pharmacy in the West, and Mesuë was called "pharmacopoeorum evangelista." Distillation of empyreumatic oils.

There is still a third Mesuë (q. v., first half of thirteenth century), author of a treatise on surgery.

Text and Translations—De medicinis universalibus et particularibus (Venice, 1471). There are many other fifteenth and sixteenth century editions of the complete and of separate works. A very elaborate edition of the complete works and of many other mediaeval writings appeared in Venice in 1549 and was often reprinted (see J. L. Choulant's Handbuch der Bücherkunde, 2d ed., 1841, 354–358). Liber de consolatione medicinarum, simplicium, solutivarum (Milano,

[t] That is, if we may depend upon Leo the African's late testimony (first half of sixteenth century). But as no Arabic text of his work is extant, it has been suggested that Mesuë was simply a Western writer living in the eleventh or twelfth century, who had assumed that name to increase his popularity (?). See my note on Ibn Māsawaih (Mesuë the Elder) in first half of the ninth century.

[u] Same restriction as in note *t*.

[v] The latest author quoted in it is Ibn al-Jazzār, who died in 1009 (see second half of tenth century).

1473, etc., many later ed.). Italian translation: Delle medicine semplici solutive (Modena, 1475, etc.).

Adolf Fonahn: Einiges über eine arabische Aqrābādhīn- Handschrift in Berlin. (Janus, vol. 14, 347–353, 1909. The differences between this text and the Latin text of the Antidotarium are so great that the former can not be considered a prototype of the latter).

M. A. F. del Pellegrino: Le livre de la cure des maladies des yeux de Jean Mésué, médecin du XIe siècle (Thèse, 84 p., Bordeaux, 1902. Not seen).

Criticism—F. Wüstenfeld: Geschichte der arabischen Aerzte (63, Göttingen, 1840). E. H. F. Meyer: Geschichte der Botanik (vol. 3, 178–183, 1856). Leclerc: Médecine arabe (vol. 1, 504–507, 1876). E. Gurlt: Geschichte der Chirurgie (vol. 1, 618–620, 1898). Neuburger: Geschichte der Medizin (vol. 2, 226–227, 1911).

'AMMĀR

Latin name, Canamusali. Abū-l-Qāsim 'Ammār ibn 'Alī al-Mawṣilī. From Mawṣil (Mosul) in 'Irāq; flourished in Egypt in the reign of al-Ḥākim, who ruled from 996 to 1020. Physician. The most original of Muslim oculists, his work was eclipsed by that of his contemporary 'Alī ibn 'Īsā, which was more comprehensive. His summary on the treatment of the eye (Kitāb al-muntakhab fī 'ilāj al-'ain) contains many clear descriptions of diseases and treatments, arranged in logical order. The surgical part is especially important (e. g., six operations for cataract, notably operation for soft cataract by suction).

Texts and Translations—'Ammār's Muntakhab was very well translated into Hebrew by Nathan ha-Me'ati, who flourished in Rome in the second half of the thirteenth century. A German version has appeared in J. Hirschberg, J. Lippert, and E. Mittwoch: Die arabischen Augenärzte nach den Quellen bearbeitet (vol. 2, Leipzig, 1905).

The "Tractatus de oculis Canamusali" of David Armenicus (Venice, 1497, 1499, 1500) had been ascribed to 'Ammār, but it is a crude forgery. It has been edited by Paul Pansier in his Collectio ophthalmologica veterum auctorum (fasc. IV). Magistri David Armenici compilatio in libros de oculorum curationibus et diversorum philosophorum de Baldach (56 p., Paris, 1904).

Criticism—Leclerc: Histoire de la médecine arabe (vol. 1, 533–538, 1876). J. Hirschberg: Die arabischen Lehrbücher der Augenheilkunde (Abhdl. der preuss. Akad. der Wiss., 117 p., Berlin, 1905). E. Mittwoch: Encyclopaedia of Islam (vol. 1, 332, 1910).

IBN AL-HAITHAM

See my note in physical section (IV), above.

'ALĪ IBN RIḌWĀN

Abū-l-Ḥasan 'Alī ibn Riḍwān[w] ibn 'Alī ibn Ja'far al-Miṣrī. Born in Jīza near Cairo, c. 998. Flourished in Cairo and died there in 1061 or in 1067. Astrologer, physician. Author of many medical writings of which the most popular was his commentary on Galen's Ars parva, which was translated by Gherardo Cremonese. I may still quote his treatise on hygiene with special reference to Egypt (fī daf' muḍār al-abdān bi-arḍ Miṣr). He wrote various other commentaries on Hippocrates and Galen and on Ptolemy's astrological books.

Texts and Translations—Haly Eben Rodan s. Rodoham Aegyptius. Comment. cet. (Venice, 1496). His commentary to the Quadripartitum will be found in the editions of that book (Venice, 1484, 1493).

---

[w] Or Ruḍwān.

Max Meyerhof: Über Klima und Gesundheit im alten Kairo (Sitzungsber. der phys. med. Soz., Erlangen, vol. 54, 197–214, 4 pl., 1923. Translation of chapter 6 of the fī daf' muḍār; Isis, VIII, 537).

Criticism—Wüstenfeld: Geschichte der arabischen Aerzte (80–82, 1840). Leclerc: Histoire de la médecine arabe (vol. 1, 525–530, 1876). C. Brockelmann: Arabische Literatur (vol. 1, 484, 1898). Suter: Die Mathematiker und Astronomen der Araber (103, 1900). Giuseppe Gabrieli: 'Alī ibn Riḍwān (Isis, VI, 500–506, 1924. Biography derived from Arabic sources).

Arabic-Writing Physicians of the East

IBN SĪNĀ

See my note in the philosophical section (II), above.

IBN AL-TAIYIB

Abū-l-Faraj 'Abdallāh Ibn al-Ṭaiyib al 'Irāqī. Latin name: Abulpharagius Abdalla Benattibus. Died in 1043–44. Nestorian physician. Secretary to Elias I, Nestorian catholicos from 1028 to 1049.[x] Physician at the 'Aḍudite hospital in Bagdad. He had many distinguished disciples, notably Ibn Buṭlān. He wrote many commentaries on Greek medicine, and original memoirs on various medical topics, also a translation of the pseudo-Aristotelian De plantis, with additional excerpts from ancient literature.[y]

For the Arabic translation of the Diatessaron ascribed to him see my note on the Syriac versions of the New Testament (second half of second century).

Criticism—G. S. Assemani: Bibliotheca Orientalis (vol. 3, 1 part, 544–548, 1725). Wüstenfeld: Arabische Aerzte (78, 1840). Leclerc: Médecine arabe (vol. 1, 486–488, 1876). Brockelmann: Arabische Litteratur (vol. 1, 482, 1898).

ABŪ SA'ĪD 'UBAID ALLĀH

Abū Sa'īd 'Ubaid Allāh ibn Jibrīl ibn Bakhtyashū'. Flourished in Maiyāfarīqīn, Jazīrah; friend of Ibn Buṭlān; died in 1058. Physician. The last and possibly the greatest representative of the Bakhtyashū', a Syrian family of physicians which emigrated from Jundīshāpūr to Bagdad in 765. His main works are the Reminder[z] of the Homestayer (Tadhkirat al-ḥāḍir), dealing with the philosophical terms used in medicine, and a treatise on lovesickness (Kitāb al-'ishq maraḍan).

I have already dealt with other members of that illustrious family; see my notes on Jirjīs ibn Jibrīl (second half of eighth century) and on Jibrīl ibn Bakhtyashū' (first half of ninth century).

Wüstenfeld: Arabische Aerzte (14–18, 1840). Leclerc: Médecine arabe (t. 1, 370–374, 1876). C. Brockelmann: Encyclopaedia of Islam (t. 1, 601, 1911).

IBN BUṬLĀN

Abū-l-Ḥasan al-Mukhtār ibn al-Ḥasan ibn 'Abdūn ibn Sa'dūn ibn Buṭlān. Latin name: Elluchasem Elimithar. Flourished in Bagdad; died, probably in Antioch, in or soon after 1063. Christian physician. He wrote synoptic tables

---

[x] Not to be mistaken for his contemporary Elias bar Shīnāyā (q. v., below).

[y] Included in Escorial MS. 883. It would seem worth while to make a close study of this botanical compilation. I have dealt with the De plantis in my note on Nicolaos Damascenos (second half of first century B. C.).

[z] Or Promptuary.

(divided into 15 vertical columns) of hygiene, dietetics, domestic medicine, called the Tables of Health (Taqwīm al-ṣiḥḥa, tabula sanitatis). (Taqwīm, literally straightening, rectification, is used for a tabulation of any kind.) He probably originated that form of synopsis, which was developed by Ibn Jazla (q. v., second half of eleventh century). Medical polemic with 'Alī ibn Riḍwān (q. v.).

Texts and Translations—A Latin version of the Taqwīm, Tacuini sanitatis Elluchasem Elimithar medici de Baldath (Strasbourg, 1531). German translation by Mich. Herr: Schachtafeln der Gesundheit (Strassburg, 1533. Very bad, says Leclerc).

Criticism—Wüstenfeld: Geschichte der arabischen Aerzte (78, 1840). E. H. F. Meyer: Geschichte der Botanik (vol. 3, 203–205, 1856). Leclerc: Histoire de la médecine arabe (vol. 1, 489–492, 1876). C. Brockelmann: Arabische Litteratur (vol. 1, 483, 1898). E. Wiedemann: Magnetische Wirkung nach der Anschauung der Araber (Z. für Physik., 141–142, Braunschweig, 1920. Is the attraction of a piece of iron by a magnet a love attraction or not?) E. G. Browne: Arabian medicine (72–73, 1921).

'ALĪ IBN 'ĪSĀ

'Alī ibn 'Īsā[a] or Jesu Haly. Flourished in Bagdad in the first half of the eleventh century. He is said to have been a Christian. (Is this not due to a confusion with Ḥunain's disciple?) The most famous Arabic oculist. His "manual" or "promptuary for oculists" in three books, Tadhkirat (or risāla, epistle) al-kaḥḥālīn, is the oldest Arabic work on ophthalmology of which the original text is completely extant.[b] It is based partly on ancient knowledge, partly on personal experience. It is at once very detailed and very comprehensive. The first book deals with the anatomy and physiology of the eye; the second with the diseases externally visible; the third with hidden diseases, dietetics, and general medicine from the oculistic standpoint; 130 eye diseases are carefully described; 143 drugs characterized.

Texts and Translations—The popularity of 'Alī's risāla is attested by two mediaeval translations into Latin and one into Hebrew. De cognitione infirmitatum oculorum et curatione eorum (Venice, 1497, 1499, 1500). Modern Latin translation of the first part by C. A. Hille (Dresden, 1845). Improved edition of two Latin texts, respectively translated from the Arabic and the Hebrew, by Paul Pansier (Collectio ophthalmologica veterum auctorum, fasc. III, 185–379). Epistola Ihesu filii Haly de cognitione infirmitatum oculorum sive memoriale oculariorum quod compilavit Ali ben Issa (Paris, 1903). German translation by J. Hirschberg and J. Lippert: Erinnerungsbuch für Augenärzte (with notes and bibliography, forming volume 1 of Die arabischen Augenärzte nach den Quellen bearbeitet, 362 p., Leipzig, 1904). Emir Ariff Arslan: Anatomie de l'oeil de Tezkérath el-kahaline ou Mémorandum des oculistes d'Issa ben Ali (Janus, vol. 8, 466–471, 513, 1903. French translation of the anatomical part of the Tadhkirat); Traitement du chalazion, de l'encanthis, de la dacryocystite et de la hernie de l'iris au Xe siècle (*ibidem*, 617–620. Translation of another extract from the same book; these translations originated a discussion between the author and Hirschberg, in Janus, vol. 8, 514, 649; vol. 9, 54–56, and Mit. zur Geschichte der Medizin, vol. 3, 449, 1904).

---

[a] This form seems more correct than 'Īsā ibn 'Alī. It is at any rate less confusing, for there were at least two other 'Īsā ibn 'Alī's: the one, disciple of Ḥunain (q. v., second half of ninth century) mentioned by Wüstenfeld (Gesch. d. arab. Aerzte 1840, 39); the other, al-Asdī (?), who wrote a book on falconry in the eleventh century? Leclerc: Médecine arabe (vol. 1, 503, 1876).

[b] With the possible exception of the treatise of Ḥunain ibn Isḥāq (q. v., second half of ninth century), of which M. Meyerhof is preparing a translation (April, 1926).

Criticism—J. Hirschberg: Die arabischen Lehrbücher der Augenheilkunde (Abhd. der preuss. Ak. der Wiss., 117 p., Berlin, 1905). Moritz Steinschneider: Zur Oculistik des 'Īsā ben 'Alī (9. Jahrh.) und des sogenanten Canamusali (Janus, vol. 11, 399–408, 1906). E. Mittwoch: Encyclopaedia of Islam (vol. I, 288, 1910). Neuburger: Geschichte der Medizin (vol. 2, 219, 1911). Charles Greene Cumston: A Brief Historical Summary of the Treatment of Trachoma, with Special Reference to the Arabian School and the Writing of Ali Ibn el-Aïssa (Annals of Medical History, vol. 3, 244–251, 1921).

Chinese Medicine

WANG WEI-TÊ

Wang[2] Wei[2]-tê[2]* (12493, 12596, 10845). Flourished under the Sung, c. 1027. In 1027, by order of the emperor, he made two copper figures of the human body to illustrate the art of acupuncture (piercing the flesh with needles), 367 places being indicated. He wrote a treatise on the subject, entitled T'ung[2]-jên[2] Chên[1]-chiu[3] ching[1] (12285, 5624, 615, 2275, 2122).

A. Wylie: Chinese Literature (101, (1867) 1902). J. D. Ball: Things Chinese (8, 1904. Ball says that one of these plates is still extant, but he does not say where; however, he gives various references). Encyclopaedia Sinica (7, 1917. Acupuncture). L. Wieger: La Chine (466, 1920).

It is said that prophylactic inoculation of smallpox was practiced in China at least as early as the eleventh century. This method probably originated in India.

Max Neuburger: Geschichte der Medizin (vol. 1, 105, 1906).

VIII. LATIN, MUSLIM, ARMENIAN, AND SYRIAN HISTORIOGRAPHY

Historians Writing in Latin

AIMOIN OF FLEURY

Aimoinus Floriacensis. Born in Périgord c. 960; flourished at the Fleury monastery (Saint-Benoît-sur-Loire); died after 1010. French chronicler. His main work (begun before 1004) is a history of the Franks (Historia Francorum) from their origins (in ancient Troy!) to 654. It is a mere compilation, but it enjoyed much popularity. He wrote a life of his master Abbo (q. v., second half of tenth century), c. 1005, and an account of the miracles wrought by St. Benedict's relics in Fleury from 887 to 1003. The history of the Franks is preceded by a topographical introduction (Situs Germaniae vel Galliae) in eight chapters, which contains very little original information. Various continuations of it were successively compiled, the latest between 1169 and 1174.

Text—Aimoni Historia Francorum edited by Jacques du Breul (Paris, 1603. Including the continuations). Aimoin's additions to the texts reproduced by him are edited in the Historiens des Gaules et de la France (vols. 3, 11, 12).

The life of Abbo was edited by Mabillon in his Acta Sanctorum ordinis S. Benedicti (century VI, 1, 37–58). Parts of it are included in the Historiens de France (vol. 10).

The best edition of the Miracula S. Benedicti is that of E. de Certain (Paris, 1858. Société de l'histoire de France).

Criticism—Article by E. D. Grand, in Grande Encyclopédie (vol. 1, p. 979). M. Manitius: Lateinische Literatur des Mittelalters (vol. 2, 239–246, 1923).

THIETMAR OF MERSEBURG

Thietmarus (Ditmarus) episcopus Merseburgensis. Son of the Count Siegfried von Walbeck. Born July 25, 975; educated at Quedlinburg and Magdeburg; from 1009 on, Bishop of Merseburg; died in 1018. German historian. He began in 1012, and completed in 1018, the compilation of an elaborate history of Saxony. His work is the best source for the study of contemporary events in Eastern Germany; it contains also some information on the Slav countries. Thietmar apparently had some knowledge of Slavonic.

Text—Facsimile copy of the autograph manuscript (Dresden, Cod. R. 147) with introduction by L. Schmidt: Die Dresdner Handschrift der Chronik des Bischofs Thietmar von Merseburg (Dresden, 1909). This manuscript is not entirely complete, but the text can be completed by means of other manuscripts.

Chronici Ditmari libri VII nunc primum in lucem editi, by Reinerus Reineccius (Francfort, 1580). Best edition by Friedrich Kurze: Thietmari Chronicon (Hanover, 1889). German translation by J. C. M. Laurent (Berlin, 1848); new edition by J. Strebitzki (Leipzig, 1892; third edition, Leipzig, 1912).

Criticism—M. Manitius: Lateinische Literatur des Mittelalters (vol. 2, 265–268, 1923).

ADELBOLD OF UTRECHT

See my note in mathematical section (III), above.

ADHÉMAR OF CHABANNES

Ademarus Cabannensis; also Engolismensis (of Angoulême). Born in 988 at Chabannes, near Chateauponsac, Haute-Vienne; flourished mainly at Limoges and Angoulême; died at Jerusalem in 1034. French (Limousin) monk and chronicler. His main work is a chronicle of French history with special reference to Aquitania (Chronicon aquitanicum), from mythical ages down to 1028, in three books. The first two books are largely copied from older chronicles, but Book 3, dealing with the period 814 to 1028, is the most important source for the history of Aquitania in the tenth and eleventh centuries. It was continued down to 1174 by Hélie de Ruffec, chaplain to Henry II, King of England from 1154 to 1189.

Text—Complete edition by Jules Chavanon (285 p., Collection de textes pour servir à l'étude de l'histoire, 20, Paris, 1897). Partial editions by G. Waitz in Monum. Germ., Scriptores (4, 106–148, 1841), and by Migne in the Latin Patrology (vol. 141, 9–80, 1853).

Jules Lair: Historia (with facsimile plates) in his Etudes critiques sur divers textes des Xe et XIe siècles (Paris, 1899).

Criticism—E. D. Grand (Grande Encyclopédie, vol. 1, 555). M. Manitius: Lateinische Literatur des Mittelalters (vol. 2, 284–294, 1923).

DUDON OF ST. QUENTIN

Dudo decanus S. Quintini Viromandensis. Born at St. Quentin-en-Vermandois. Flourished at the Norman court in 986 to 994 and later; died not later than 1043. French chronicler of the first dukes of Normandy (911 sq.). His work, in prose and verse, De moribus et actis primorum Normanniae ducum, composed between 1015 and 1030, is the basis of all later writings on the subject.

Text—Princeps edition by André Duchesne in his Historiae Normannorum scriptores antiqui (Paris, 1619); reprinted in Migne's Patrology (vol. 141, 609–758). Modern edition by J. Lair in volume 23 of the Mém. de la soc. des antiquaires de Normandie (1865).

Criticism—Ch. V. Langlois in Grande Encyclopédie (vol. 14, 1198, c. 1892). Henri Prentout: Etude critique sur Dudon de Saint Quentin (522 p., Paris, 1916. Voir Revue critique, vol. 2 of 1916, 353–356). M. Manitius: Lateinische Literaturgeschichte (vol. 2, 257–265, 1923).

RAOUL GLABER

Rudolphus Glaber. Meaning Ralph the Bald (or the Beardless); Raoul le Glabre. Born in Burgundy, flourished in various French monasteries, chiefly at Cluny and St. Germain d'Auxerre; died after 1044. French chronicler. He wrote partly at Cluny, partly at St. Germain d'Auxerre, between 1026 and 1044, a history from 900 to 1044 which is largely anecdotic and full of superstition. It contains a moving account of the famine of 1031.[c]

A very gracious line of Glaber's History (III, 4) has often been quoted. It refers to the awakening which was supposed to have taken place soon after the year 1000, when the dread that the world would end in that fatal year had been dissipated: "Erat enim instar ac si mundus ipse excutiendo semet, rejecta vetustate, passim candidam ecclesiarum vestem indueret." There was no panic in that year and apocalyptic fears do not seem to have been much more prevalent then than at many other times.

Text—Editio princeps by Pithou in his Scriptores (1596). Critical edition by Maurice Prou (Coll. de textes pour servir à l'étude. . . . . 1, 158 p., Paris, 1886). French translation by Guizot in his Coll. des Mémoires (vol. 6, 163–355, 1823).

Criticism—Emile Gebhart: L'état d'âme d'un moine de l'an 1000. Revue des Deux Mondes, Oct. 1891 (reprinted in his Moines et Papes). E. Petit: Glaber. (Revue historique, vol. 48, 1892). Maurice Prou in Grande Encyclopédie (vol. 28, c. 1901). George Lincoln Burr: The year 1000 and the antecedents of the crusades. (American Historical Review, vol. 6, 429–439, 1901). Karl Grund: Die Anschauungen des Glaber (Diss., Greifswald, 104 p., 1910). Max Manitius: Lateinische Literatur des Mittelalters (vol. 2, 1923, 347–53).

Muslim Historians

With the notable exception of al-Bīrūnī, dealt with in Section II, the only Muslim historians whom I have to quote were Cordovans.

IBN AL-FARAḌĪ

Abū-l-Walīd 'Abdallāh ibn Muḥammad ibn Yūsuf ibn Naṣr al-Azdī ibn al-Faraḍī. Born at Cordova in 962–63, made the Pilgrimage in 992–93, qāḍī of Valencia in 1009–10; killed during the sack of Cordova by the Berbers, April 21, 1013. Hispano-Muslim historian. Author of biographies of the learned Muslims of Spain. (Continued by Ibn Bashkuwāl, q. v., first half of twelfth century).

Text—The Ta'rīkh 'ulamā' al-Andalus was edited by F. Codera in the Bibliotheca arabico-hispanica (vols. 7–8, Madrid, 1891–92).

Criticism—F. Wüstenfeld: Geschichtschreiber der Araber (Nr. 165, 1881). C. Brockelmann: Arabische Litteratur (vol. 1, 338, 1898).

IBN ḤAIYĀN

Abū Marwān Ḥaiyān ibn Khalaf ibn Husain ibn Haiyān. Born at Cordova in 987–88; died in 1076. Hispano-Muslim historian. Author of an immense history of Spain in 60 volumes (Kitāb al-matīn, Liber solidus) and of a shorter work,

---

[c] In the eleventh century, forty-three famines occurred in France within 73 years (Franz Funck-Brentano. Le Moyen Age, 73).

in 10 volumes, dealing with the biographies of Hispano-Muslim scholars (Kitāb al-muqtabis fī ta'rīkh al-Andalus).

F. Wüstenfeld: Geschichtschreiber der Araber (71, 1881). C. Brockelmann: Arabische Litteratur (vol. 1, 338, 1898).

Armenian Historiography

STEPHEN ASOLIK

Stephen Asolik Tarōneçi (meaning Stephen the Singer of Tarōn). Flourished under Tēr Sargis, Catholicos from 991 to 1019. Armenian historian. Author of a universal history, in Armenian, down to the year 1003. It is a valuable source for Byzantine, Armenian, and Iberian (Georgian) history in the second half of the tenth century. The part dealing with ancient history is entirely derived from Eusebios.[d]

Text—Editio princeps by Chahnazarian (Paris (undated), c. 1853). Second edition by St. Malchasean (Petersburg, 1885).

Russian translation by Emin (Moscow, 1864). French translation of the first two books (out of three) by Dulaurier, with abundant commentary (Paris, 1883). Deuxième partie, traduite et annotée par Frédéric Macler (244 p., Paris, 1917). German translation by A. Burckhardt (Leipzig, 1898).

Criticism—Heinrich Gelzer: Sextus Julius Africanus (466–475, 1898).

Syrian Historiography

ELIAS BAR SHĪNĀYĀ

Elias Bar Sinaeus episcopus Nisibensis. Born in 975; began his monastic life at Mosul; became Bishop of Bēth Nuhādhrē in 1002 and Metropolitan of Nisībis in 1008; died after 1049. Syrian historian, grammarian, lexicographer, theologian, metrologist. The greatest Syriac author of the eleventh century. He also wrote in Arabic, for example, a Nestorian treatise entitled "The Demonstration of the Truth of the Faith," Kitāb al-burhān 'alā ṣaḥīḥ (or rather fī taṣḥīḥ-l-'īmān). His principal work is a chronicle from 25 to 1018, written in Syriac with parallel Arabic translation[e] and indication of the sources.

He wrote a Syriac grammar which was very popular and an Arabic-Syriac vocabulary, classified by subjects (Kitāb al-tarjumān fī ta'līm lughat al-suryān; The interpreter to teach the Syriac language). This was the latest Syriac lexicon of mediaeval times.

He composed, in Arabic, a treatise on the balance (in 16 chapters). This is an elaborate work dealing with various kinds of scales and their use, coins, weights and measures, and problems relative to them (simple problems of proportion solved by the balance).

Text—Earlier portion of the Chronicle to the Muslim conquest edited by Lamy: Elie de Nisibe, sa chronologie (Bruxelles, 1888; with French translation). Later part edited by Friedrich Baethgen: Fragmente syrischer und arabischer Historiker (Abhdl. für die Kunde des Morgenlandes, vol. 8, Leipzig, 1884; with German translation). L. J. Delaporte: La chronographie d'Elie bar-Shinaya (428 p., Bibl. de l'école des hautes études, Paris, 1910; French translation).

---

[d] Eusebios's Histories had been very early translated into Armenian. A part of his work is known only through the Armenian translation. See my note on Eusebios (first half of fourth century).

[e] After the Muslim conquest of Syria, Arabic had gradually become the vulgar language of the Syrians, Syriac becoming to the same extent a learned language.

Richard J. H. Gottheil: A Treatise on Syriac grammar by Mar Elias of Sobha (176 p., Berlin, 1887; Syriac and English).

Paul de Lagarde: Praetermissorum libri duo (Göttingen, 1879; edition of Elias's vocabulary). Tommaso Obizzini (Thomas a Novara) based his Thesaurus arabico-syro-latinus (Rome, 1636) upon Elias's vocabulary.

M. H. Sauvaire: On a Treatise on Weights and Measures by Eliyā (Journal R. Asiatic Soc., vol. 9, 291–313, 1877; French translation). A complete Gotha manuscript of same treatise was analyzed by E. Wiedemann (Beitr. zur Gesch. der Naturwiss., 6, p. 9, Erlangen, Sitzungsber., vol. 38, 1906).

German translation of the Nestorian treatise by L. Horst (Diss., 155 p., Colmar, 1886).

Criticism—G. S. Assemani: Bibliotheca orientalis Clemento-Vaticana (vol. 3, part 1, 266–274, 1725). Wm. Wright: Syriac Literature (235–239, 1894). Thomas Ibel: Die Wage im Altertum (97–103, Erlangen, 1908). Rubens Duval: Littérature syriaque (1907). B. Vandenhoff: Die in der Chronographie des Syrers Elias bar Shinaja erwähnten Sonnen- und Mondfinsternisse (Z. d. deut. morg. Ges., Bd. 74, 77–94, 1920).

IX. GERMAN, HEBREW, SYRIAC, AND CHINESE PHILOLOGY

For German philology see my note on Notker Labeo, in Section II, above.

Hebrew Philology

IBN JANĀḤ

Abū-l-Walīd Marwān ibn Janāḥ. Also called Rabbi Marinus. His Hebrew name was Jonah, meaning the dove; hence, the Arabic Ibn Janāḥ, the winged. Born at Cordova c. 985 to 990, left it c. 1013 and after years of wanderings settled at Saragossa, where his works were written and where he died. Hispano-Jewish grammarian, lexicographer, physician, and theologian.[f] The greatest Hebrew philologist of the Middle Ages. He completed the task undertaken by Ḥayyuj (q. v., second half of tenth century) and placed the study of Hebrew on a firm scientific basis. His main philosophical work is the Kitāb al-tanqīḥ (Book of Minute Research) containing two parts. The first part is a grammar called Kitāb al-luma'; the second part is lexicographic; it is called Kitāb al-uṣūl. Both were translated into Hebrew by Judah ibn Tibbon (q. v., second half of the twelfth century). He wrote a book on simple remedies and their posology (Kitāb al-talkhīṣ.

Text—The Luma' was edited by Joseph Derenbourg and W. Bacher (Paris, 1886). Judah ibn Tibbon's Hebrew translation, called Riqmah, was published by B. Goldberg and Raphael Kircheim (Francfort a. M., 1856). French translation by Rabbi Moïse Metzger: Le livre des parterres fleuris (450 p., Paris, 1889).

The Uṣūl was edited by Neubauer (1875). Judah ibn Tibbon's translation, called Sefer ha-shorashim, was edited by Wilhelm Bacher (638 p., Berlin, 1894–1896).

Opuscules et traités—Texte arabe et traduction française par Joseph et Hartwig Derenbourg (524 p., Paris, 1880).

Criticism—L. Leclerc: Médecine arabe (vol. 1, 1876, 554). Wilhelm Bacher: Aus der Schrifterklärung des Ibn Ganāh (R. Jona) (Leipzig, 1899). Article by W. Bacher, in Jewish Encyclopaedia (vol. 6, 1904, 534–5).

SAMUEL HA-LEVI

See my note in Section II, above.

---

[f] Theology was the purpose, grammar the means. The study of Hebrew philology was a religious duty.

Syriac Philology

ELIAS BAR SHĪNĀYĀ

See my note in Section VIII, above.

ELIĀS OF ṬĪRHĀN

Elias I. Of Karkhā dhĕ-Gheddān; Bishop of Ṭīrhān; he became in 1028 the first Nestorian catholicos; he died in 1049. Syriac theologian and grammarian. He edited collections of ecclesiastical canons, constitutions, and judgments. He wrote a Syriac grammar wherein he introduced the Arabic method,[g] and a treatise on accents.

Text—Freidrich Baethgen: Syrische Grammatik des Mar Elias von Tirhan (116 p., Leipzig, 1880).
Criticism—R. Duval: Littérature syriaque (1907).

Chinese Philology

CH'ÊN P'ÊNG-NIEN

Ch'ên[2] P'êng[2]-nien[2] (658, 8887, 8301). Born in 961, died in 1017. Chinese lexicographer. He revised in 1011 the phonetic dictionary, called Ch'ieh-yün compiled by Lu Fa-yen (q. v., first half of seventh century), and in 1013 the graphic dictionary, called Yü-p'ien, compiled by Ku Yeh-wang (q. v., first half of sixth century). These two revisions are the basis of every modern edition of those dictionaries. His revision of the Ch'ieh-yün was called the "Kuang yün revised under the Sung," Ta[4]-Sung[4] ch'ung[2]-hsiu[1]-kuang[3]-yün[4] (10470, 10462, 2914, 4661, 6397, 13843). It includes about 28,000 characters arranged under 206 rhymes.

H. A. Giles: Biographical Dictionary (96, 1898). Encyclopaedia Sinica (300, 1917, P. Pelliot).

SUNG CH'I

Sung[4] Ch'i[2] (10462, 1089). Canonized as Hui[4] An[1] (5199, 44). Born in 998; flourished in the western provinces and at the Sung court; died in 1061. Chinese historian and lexicographer. He collaborated in the "New History of the T'ang Dynasty," completed in 1060 (the biographical section is said to be entirely his). He completed in 1039, with Ting Tu and others, the compilation of a phonetic dictionary, called Chi[2]*-yün[4] (906, 13843), containing 53,523 characters.

Text—For the history, see my note on Ou-yang Hsiu (next chapter).
Criticism—Giles: Biographical Dictionary (698, 1898). Encyclopaedia Sinica (300, 1917, P. Pelliot).

TING TU

Ting[1] Tu[4] (11253, 12089). Canonized as Wên[2] Chien[3] (12633, 1604). Native of K'ai[1]-fêng[1] fu[3] (5794, 3582, 3682), Honan, in 990, died in 1053. Chinese lexicographer. One of the main collaborators in the great phonetic dictionary, called Chi-yün, and completed in 1039. (See my note on Sung Ch'i, above.) He had completed in the previous year a smaller dictionary of the same kind, the Li[3] pu[4] yün[4] lüeh[4]* (6949, 9484, 13843, 7564) (Concise Rhymes of the Li Department). This contained only 10,000 characters; it was very popular. It was revised in 1252 by Liu[2] Yüan[2] (7270, 13713), who reduced the 206 rhymes to 107.

H. A. Giles: Biographical Dictionary (737, 1898). Encyclopaedia sinica (300, 1917, P. Pelliot).

---

[g] This was done again, and more skilfully, by Barhebraeus (q. v., second half of thirteenth century).

CHAPTER XXXIV

THE TIME OF OMAR KHAYYAM

(Second Half of Eleventh Century)

I. Survey of Science in Second Half of Eleventh Century. II. Philosophical and Theological Background. III. Latin, Byzantine, Muslim, and Chinese Mathematics and Astronomy. IV. Latin, Persian, and Chinese Physics and Technology. V. Latin, Byzantine, Muslim, and Chinese Natural History. VI. Latin and Muslim Geography. VII. Latin, Byzantine, Muslim, and Chinese Medicine. VIII. French, Latin, Byzantine, Jewish, Muslim, Chinese, and Japanese Historiography. IX. Lombard, English, Byzantine, Muslim, Hindu, and Chinese Law and Sociology. X. French, Latin, Greek, Hebrew, Arabic, Persian, Chinese, and Japanese Philology.

I. SURVEY OF SCIENCE IN SECOND HALF OF ELEVENTH CENTURY

1. The second half of the eleventh century was a continuation of the golden age which had begun about the middle of the tenth century; a period of discovery and creation—but that golden age had culminated in the first half of the eleventh century and though intellectual activity was still very intense and of a very high order during the second half, yet there was already a perceptible decline both in the quantity and the quality of the effort. This is not realized at once, because the decline is very small and is hidden by the activity of some very great personalities.

The awakening of Christendom, which we had occasion to observe in the previous chapter, continued during the present period, and for the first time in the course of many centuries, some of the leading personalities were, not Muslims, but Christians, and did not write in Arabic, but in Greek or Latin. However, the main advances were still due to Muslims; but this was almost the end of their intellectual supremacy, and it is for that reason that we end our first volume at this point. The end of the eleventh century was indeed one of the great turning-points in the history of civilization.

The most original creations of this time were made in the field of mathematics, by Muslims, and the most original genius among those to whom we owe these creations was the Persian Omar Khayyam. It is thus very appropriate to call this time the Time of Omar Khayyam, and I do this with the more alacrity, as Omar is already very well known to a large number of readers. It is probable that his name is more familiar to them than that of any other Muslim scientist. It will thus be relatively easy to remember the title, and I trust that this remembrance will reach to some extent the contents of this chapter. The time of Omar Khayyam was the end of the golden age of Muslim science, the end of the Muslim monopoly.

2. *Philosophical and Theological Background*—With regard to the organization of Christendom, we may first recall (without insisting upon it, for it had but little importance from our point of view) the beginning of a new religious order, that of the Augustinian Canons. The appearance of St. Anselm, at about the same time, was an event of far greater importance. Under his rule, the school of Bec, in Normandy, became a famous center of learning. He may be considered one of

the founders of Christian scholasticism. His discussions with Roscelin on the nature of "universals" constitute a landmark in the history of philosophy. They marked the beginning of a controversy to which the Christian schoolmen attached so much importance that it might serve as a "Leitmotiv" in a history of mediaeval thought. Anselm defended the realist and Roscelin the nominalist point of view. The little encyclopaedia called "Imago mundi," long ascribed to St. Anselm, was probably composed by his contemporary Honorius Inclusus.

Byzantine thought is very well reflected in the writings of Psellos, leader of the Neoplatonic revival which occurred in Constantinople. That revival might be compared in some respects to the Platonic Renaissance, which did not begin to blossom in Florence until four centuries later. This will help us to realize the slowness of communications between Eastern and Western Christendom, in great contrast with the speed with which influences were transmitted from one end of Islām to the other.[a] Another great Byzantine writer of the time was Theophylactos, Archbishop of Bulgaria, but as he paid practically no attention to science, it will suffice to mention his name.

Jewish philosophy and theology were represented by three great men, one of them a Qaraite, the two others, orthodox Talmudists. These three men lived in three distant parts of the world. The Qaraite Jeshua ben Judah, a pupil of Joseph ha Ro'eh, flourished probably in Jerusalem; he wrote in Arabic. Alfasi, who lived in Qairawān and died in southern Spain, was the greatest Talmudist of the age. His famous compendium of the legal part of the Talmud, the Halakot, was composed in Hebrew, but some of his responsa were written in Arabic. Finally, the great teacher Rashi flourished in Champagne, where he introduced some of the traditions of German Judaism; he was one of the promoters of rabbinical learning in France; his influence was felt primarily in his native country, but it extended to other parts of Europe and even beyond the pale of Jewry; he wrote exclusively in Hebrew.

A new Muslim sect, that of the Assassins, an off-shoot of the Ismā'īlīya movement, originated in Cairo about 1080. They took possession of the fortress of Alamūt, which remained their main stronghold for a century and a half. Alamūt seems to have been also a center of learning.

The Muslim philosopher who has obtained the largest following in the West, in fact the only one who has become at all popular, is the Persian poet and ṣūfī Omar Khayyam. Like Horace, he belongs to the realm of literature rather than to that of philosophy proper, and I would not speak of him but for his extraordinary mathematical achievements. On the other hand, one of Omar's contemporaries, al-Ghazzālī, was the greatest theologian of Islām. He might be compared to Thomas Aquinas, to whom he was in many ways superior. Al-Ghazzālī was also a Persian and spent part of his life in Omar's native place, Nīshābūr. While Omar Khayyam is the most popular figure of mediaeval times, al-Ghazzālī is probably the noblest.

The only Hindu philosopher of that time was Rāmānuja, who flourished in Southern India. His philosophy was a Vedantic monism, less absolute than that of Śaṅkara.

I must still quote three Chinese philosophers. The first, Shao Yung, who wrote a commentary on the "Book of Changes," need not delay us. The second Chou

---

[a] The transmission of the Epistles of the Brethren of Purity (q. v., second half of tenth century) is a case in point.

Tun-i is, on the contrary, quite important, for he it is who originated the Hsing-li movement, the so-called Neoconfucianism of the Sung dynasty. The third, Shên Kua, was a polygraph rather than a philosopher. His many writings offer considerable archaeological interest; one of them contains the earliest description of printing with movable type and the earliest clear mention of a magnetic needle.

3. *Latin, Byzantine, Muslim, and Chinese Mathematics and Astronomy*—The use of the abacus seems to have become more popular and also more systematic during the eleventh and twelfth centuries. Witness the writings of Bernelinus and Guido of Arezzo, already dealt with, and those of Hermann the Lame and of Gerland. These writings, devoted to the explanation of the abacus, were characterized by the exclusive use of Roman numerals. Hermann the Lame composed also accounts of the astrolabe and of the arithmetical game called rithmomachia. Franco of Liège wrote treatises on the compotus and on the quadrature of the circle. Hirsau built an orrery and wrote an astronomical treatise. Gerland wrote a compotus.

A treatise on the quadrivium was ascribed, probably wrongly, to Psellos, but some of his writings contain valuable information for the history of mathematics. For example, it is due to him that we can date Diophantos's activity.

The decline to which I alluded in my first paragraph is very obvious in this field. For example, the number of Muslim mathematicians is considerably smaller, and though Christian mathematicians seem to become gradually more active, their work is still on too low a level to compensate for the diminution of the Muslim effort. Yet some of the Muslim achievements of that time were exceedingly remarkable. We shall deal successively with Western and Eastern mathematicians.

Important astronomical work was done at Cordova. Ibn Ṣā'id, aided by other Muslim and Jewish astronomers, made a number of observations. These observations were used by al-Zarqālī (Arzachel), for the compilation of new tables, the so-called Toledan tables, which obtained considerable authority in western Europe. Al-Zarqālī invented a new kind of astrolabe and proved the movement of the solar apogee; unfortunately, he confirmed the erroneous theory of the "trepidation" of the equinoxes. His tables were preceded, as usual, by an elaborate trigonometrical introduction. One of the Hūdid kings of Saragossa, Yūsuf al-Mutamin, was a great patron of science and wrote a mathematical treatise which was very much praised.

Passing to the East, we find there only one great mathematician, but a very great one indeed, the beloved poet Omar Khayyam. His activity marks the climax of Muslim efforts in the field of algebra. He conceived a very remarkable classification of equations; for example, he recognized 13 different forms of cubic equations. He tried to solve them all and gave partial geometric solutions of a number of them. He investigated Euclid's postulates and definitions. At the request of the Saljūq sulṭān Jalāl al-dīn he devised in 1074 or soon after a new calendar, which was extraordinarily accurate, probably more so than our own calendar.

The philosopher al-Ghazzālī wrote a treatise on the motion and nature of stars and an astronomical summary; he had some knowledge of magic squares. The Bagdadite Muḥammad ibn 'Abd al-Bāqī wrote a commentary on the tenth book of Euclid.

Even as we witnessed a renewed interest in abacus arithmetic in the Christian

West, there are indications of the awakening of a similar interest in China. Various treatises of the eleventh and twelfth centuries deal with the use of the suan-p'an, which is the Chinese form of abacus. It is impossible to determine whether the suan-p'an derives from the same Roman origin as the European abacus or is an independent invention.

Chou-ts'ung wrote an historical account of the Chinese calendar and devised a new one. Shên Kua, the polygraph already mentioned, dealt with mathematics and astronomy as he did with many other subjects; his works contain the earliest Chinese example of summation of a progression; he prepared the calendar for 1074. Su-sung wrote an astronomical treatise which was illustrated with celestial maps, and he constructed an orrery.

4. *Latin, Persian, and Chinese Physics and Technology*—The development of occidental music under Muslim stimulation, which had begun in the first half of this century, continued unabated during the second half. Hermann the Lame introduced a notation to determine the pitch. Treatises on music were written by Hirsau and by Frutolf. It is noteworthy that these three musicologists were Germans, while the greatest writer on music of the preceding period was an Italian.

Another German monk, Theophilus, wrote a treatise on the arts and crafts, which contains, among other things, the earliest European account of bell-founding.

I have already remarked that Muslim scientists were especially interested in the determination of densities by the hydrostatic method. That tradition was continued by Omar Khayyam. Muslim sailors were probably the first to apply the directive property of a magnetic needle to navigational purposes, and as far as we can know, that anonymous invention was made toward the end of the eleventh century.

The writings of Shên Kua have already been quoted; they are very important for the history of Chinese physics, music, and technology.

5. *Latin, Byzantine, Muslim, and Chinese Natural History*—Marbode, Bishop of Rennes, composed a medical lapidary which enjoyed an immense popularity. That lapidary was of purely pagan inspiration; it combined the scientific tradition derived from Theophrastos and Dioscorides and the magical tradition which had developed in Alexandria; it contained no Christian elements. Another treatise of the same kind and time, and equally popular, was the so-called Macer floridus, a herbal. It was probably composed by Odo of Meung, or by another Frenchman. Both the lapidary and the herbal were written in verse, which helps to explain their popularity.

The Byzantine physician Symeon Seth compiled a botanical dictionary, and his other writings contain various information on natural history.

A treatise on the plants of Andalusia is ascribed to the geographer al-Bakrī. Abū 'Umar ibn Ḥajjāj wrote a treatise on agriculture, thus inaugurating a scientific tradition which did considerable credit to Muslim Spain.

The Chinese were also deeply interested in agriculture and their literature includes a number of valuable treatises dealing with horticulture and various other sides of husbandry. Ts'ai Hsiang composed, in 1059, a treatise on the litchi which is the earliest monograph on any fruit-tree published anywhere. In that same year Fu Kung wrote a treatise on crabs. The great historian Ou-yang Hsiu wrote an elaborate treatise on the peony; the same flower was dealt with also by Wang Kuan, who described 39 varieties of it.

6. *Latin and Muslim Geography*—The most important Latin writing was the history of the diocese of Hamburg compiled by Adam of Bremen; it is our funda-

mental source for the geography of northern Europe and of the Scandinavian colonies; for example, it contains the earliest account of Wineland. Special charts for the use of sailors, the so-called *portolani*, may possibly date back to this period, though the earliest examples extant are of a much later time. Adam's history includes a fragment of the text of a portolano. On the other hand, students of cartography have suggested that the portolani were probably of Byzantine origin. In the absence of sufficient archaeological evidence, this question must necessarily remain very conjectural.

In my previous chapter I remarked that the activity of Muslim geographers, which had been so intense during the ninth and tenth centuries, abated during the present century. For the second half of this century I have to record only two men, one in the West and the other in the East. The Western one, al-Bakrī, is of special importance, because the road-book which he compiled in the traditional manner is the oldest one of its kind due to a Spaniard. He also compiled a dictionary of ancient (i. e., Arabian) geography. The Eastern one is also a very arresting personality. Nāṣir-i-Khusraw was an Ismā'īlī missionary who, starting from Egypt, traveled extensively in the Near East and as far east as Persia. He wrote in Persian an account of his travels, which is equally valuable from the geographical and from the historical point of view.

7. *Latin, Byzantine, Muslim, and Chinese Medicine*—The development of Salernitan medicine was considerably hastened by the efforts of Constantine the African, the first great translator from Arabic into Latin. Thanks to him, the enormous amount of medical experience treasured in Arabic literature began to be available to Latin readers. This stimulated at once the curiosity and the ambition of European physicians. Two other Salernitan physicians of that period deserve special mention: Joannes Afflacius (or John the Saraçen), who completed Constantine's translation of the surgical part of 'Alī ibn 'Abbās's Malikī, and Joannes Platearius the Younger, who wrote a short practica and a treatise on urine. An anatomical treatise, the Anatomia porci, ascribed to one Copho, dates from this same time or from the beginning of the twelfth century. It is one of the earliest texts of its kind in the Christian West; it explains the anatomy of the pig, supposed to be very similar to that of man.

It is hardly necessary to say that the medical efforts of the awakening Europe were not restricted to Salerno. Medical efforts are never interrupted anywhere. As examples of medical interest in France we might refer again to Marbode's lapidary and to Odo's herbal, for the purpose of these works was to a large extent medical.

Psellos wrote various medical treatises in verse and prose and compiled a medical glossary. However, the main monument of Byzantine medicine for that period was the dispensatory published by Symeon Seth. This was another channel through which Muslim knowledge entered Europe. Seth was a translator from Arabic into Greek; his writings contain abundant information on Muslim and indirectly on Hindu medicine. It is interesting to observe the parallel activities of Constantine the African and of Symeon Seth, as if Muslim medicine had premeditated to conquer Europe by an encircling movement.

Ibn Jazla, a Christian renegade living in Bagdad, prepared a medical synopsis in tabular form, thus continuing the tradition of his fellow-citizen and coreligionist Ibn Buṭlān. He wrote also a dispensatory. Sa'īd ibn Hibat Allāh composed a medical summary and a treatise on human physiology and psychology.

To these writings must be added an important ophthalmological treatise written in Persian by Zarrīn Dast.

For Chinese medicine we must refer first of all to the encyclopaedic writings of Shên Kua, and to a treatise of his especially devoted to medicine. P'ang An-shih wrote a treatise on fever, to which his disciple Tung Ping added a dispensatory and a glossary. Ch'ien-i composed a treatise on children's diseases.

8. *French, Latin, Byzantine, Jewish, Muslim, Chinese, and Japanese Historiography*—The most impressive literary monument of this age is the French Chanson de Roland, which we may consider as a historical work, in the same sense as the Iliad and the Odyssey. The historical value lies much less in the distorted historical facts which were the occasion of the poem than in the unconscious description of the manners and customs of the age. We do not read the Chanson de Roland for the sake of Charlemagne and his peers any more than the Iliad for the sake of Helen of Troy. But even as the Iliad is a magnificent mirror of early Greece, the Chanson de Roland is an equally good one of early France.

While the unknown author of the Chanson de Roland was thus helping to lift another vernacular to the dignity of a literary language, a number of German historians were composing valuable annals in Latin. Thus Hermann the Lame wrote a chronicle extending to 1054; Adam of Bremen, a history of the diocese of Hamburg down to 1072 (its great significance has already been pointed out); Lambert of Hersfeld, a history of the papacy and the empire down to 1077; Marianus Scottus, an Irishman established in Germany, a chronological summary from the creation to 1082.

Byzantine historians were equally active. First of all, the philosopher Psellos composed a very valuable history of his own times, and so did the jurist Attaliates; Xiphilinos wrote a summary of Dion Cassios's history, a good part of which has been transmitted to us only in that form; Scylitzes continued Theophanes's chronicle. The preface which Scylitzes added to his work includes a list of previous historians and critical remarks upon them, which proves that Byzantine historiography had already reached by the last quarter of the eleventh century a remarkable degree of consciousness.

The chronicle of Ahimaaz is a fundamental source for the history of early Jewish settlements in Italy. It contains the earliest trace of the story of the "Wandering Jew."

The work of al-Bakrī is of course indispensable for the study of historical geography (the same can be said of any ancient geographical work), but outside of that, it contains much historical and ethnographical information. Another Spaniard, Ibn Ṣā'id, compiled a history of learned men and a summary of universal history. This work is of considerable interest from our special point of view, because it pays special attention to the history of science. These two men were Andalusians, but the latter spent part of his life in Toledo.

Of the contemporary historians who flourished in the Muslim East, I will mention only two, of whom one wrote in Arabic and the other in Persian. The former, Al-Khaṭīb al-Baghdādī wrote an elaborate history of the learned men of Bagdad (Muslims were very fond of that kind of biographical compilations). I have already had occasion to speak of the Persian Nāṣir-i-Khusraw; his work contains an instructive account of life in Egypt under the eighth Fāṭimid, including archaeological and ethnographical information.

Two great Chinese historians lived in this period. Ou-Yang Hsiu, to whom we owe the earliest treatise on Chinese epigraphy, edited the "new" history of the T'ang Dynasty and later the "new" history of the Five Dynasties, these two enormous compilations forming respectively the seventeenth and nineteenth of the Twenty-four Histories. I have already dealt with one of Ou-yang Hsiu's assistants, Sung Ch'i, in the preceding chapter. Ssŭ-ma Kuang undertook a work of a more ambitious scope, writing the annals of China—not of a single dynasty but of many—from c. 400 B. C. to c. 960. His work is very important, not only for intrinsic reasons, but also because it was for a long time the main source of Western knowledge on the subject.

The Eigwa monogatari is a chronicle of Japanese history in the tenth and eleventh centuries, but it deals chiefly with the rule of Fujiwara no Michinaga. The story is told in a very fanciful manner, after the example of the famous Japanese romances of the tenth century.

9. *Lombard, English, Byzantine, Muslim, Hindu, and Chinese Law and Sociology*—The last Lombard code was elaborated toward the end of the eleventh century under the influence of the school of Pavia, where much importance was attached to the study of Roman law.

The so-called Laws of Edward the Confessor are said to have been put together in 1070. The Norman conquerors of England ordered the preparation of a survey of the whole country. That survey, the so-called Domesday Book, was probably completed in 1086. Though its purpose was purely practical, its scientific interest is considerable.

Attaliates wrote a legal compendium which completes our knowledge of the Basilica.

Al-Māwardī, a Shāfi'ite doctor, wrote treatises on the principles of government and on ethics. The Persian Nidhām al-Mulk wrote also a treatise on government. The comparative study of these writings is indispensable for the understanding of the political and the moral thought of the age.

Vijñāneśvara, who flourished in southern India, composed a legal treatise, the Mitāksharā, which obtained and still enjoys considerable authority.

Wang An-shih, prime minister of China from 1068 to 1086, was a great economist; he changed the system of taxation and introduced a number of financial, economical, and educational reforms. He was apparently a man of extraordinary originality—in fact, too much ahead of his time to be truly influential. His reforms were swept away and forgotten after his death.

10. *French, Latin, Greek, Hebrew, Arabic, Persian, Chinese, and Japanese Philology*—Even as the greatest literary event of the previous period had been the publication of the Shāhnāma, by far the most sensational event of this period, was the appearance of the Chanson de Roland. Thus did French literature begin in a masterly way, as the Greek had begun 2,000 years before. It is hardly necessary to insist upon this.

Papias the Lombard composed a Latin dictionary, containing Greek references.

Symeon Seth, of whom I have spoken in the medical section, was primarily a philologist. He composed medical and botanical dictionaries. He was a translator from Arabic into Greek and, indeed, he is best known because of his Greek version of the fables of Kalīla and Dimna.

The Hebrew writings of the great Talmudist Rashi have a special philological interest because of the relatively large number of French words which they contain. Nathan ben Jehiel completed, in 1101, an extensive Hebrew dictionary, the Aruk, which has been used by all subsequent lexicographers. It includes many comparisons, not only with other Semitic languages, but also with Persian, Slavonic, Latin, and Italian. It is one of the greatest monuments of mediaeval learning.

Muslim philology was represented in the West by the great Arabic dictionary of Ibn Sīda and by an anonymous Latin-Arabic glossary. The date of this second work is uncertain, but we can not be far wrong when we place it in the second half of the eleventh century.

The only Arabic philologist of the East was al-Khaṭīb al-Baghdādī, who took special pains to ascertain the orthography of proper names.

A great Persian dictionary was compiled by Asadī. It is worth while noting that that work, which is absolutely fundamental for the study of Persian lexicography, was compiled by a nephew of Firdawsī, he who created the gigantic cornerstone of Persian literature.

The two foremost Chinese personalities of that time did their share in promoting Chinese philology and education. Ssŭ-ma Kuang compiled a dictionary containing a large number of characters classified by radicals. Wang An-shih tried vainly to reform the educational methods of his country; he was too revolutionary to be heeded. If we understand him right, his main contribution to philology—a very great one—was the attempt to put philology in its proper place, the place of a servant, not that of a mistress, of education.

The Eigwa monogatari was the earliest historical work to be written in Japanese. Previous records of Japanese history had been composed in Chinese, the Japanese language being considered too frivolous for such a purpose. This proves that the Japanese language was slowly coming into its own.

11. *Final Remarks*—The essential characteristic of the period is that it marked the beginning of a relative decline in the Muslim contributions, a decline which was partly compensated by the fact that the contributions of other peoples—Christians, Jews, Hindus, Chinese, and Japanese—were taking gradually more importance. We can show that very briefly. The awakening of Latin Christendom is proved by the activity of a number of men, some of whom were very eminent. Italy gave us St. Anselm, who contributed also greatly to the fame of Normandy, both in France and in England. Constantine was an African by birth (born in Carthage), but he flourished in Italy; and so did Joannes Afflacius, Joannes Platearius the Younger, and Papias the Lombard. Honorius Inclusus was probably an Englishman. There were a number of distinguished Frenchmen—Roscelin of Compiègne, Gerland of Besançon, Marbode of Angers, Odo of Meung; to these we might add Franco of Liège. The number of distinguished Germans was even greater—Hermann of Reichenau, Wilhelm of Hirsau, Frutolf of Bamberg, Theophilus, Adam of Bremen, Lambert of Hersfeld—and to these we might add the Irishman Marianus Scottus, who spent his life in Germany.

The increase of activity in Greek Christendom was equally remarkable. It will suffice to recall the names of Psellos, Theophylactos, Symeon Seth, Xiphilinos, Scylitzes, and Attaliates.

In my opinion, the most decisive proof of the awakening of Europe is the sudden appearance of the Chanson de Roland. This is less obviously in our field than the development of European music or medicine, but it is extremely valuable as a symptom of vitality and intellectual independence. The fact that that poem, the greatest monument of (Christian) mediaeval literature, was written, not in Latin, but in a vernacular, is in itself full of significance.

The progress of the Jews was as conspicuous as that of the Christians. We witnessed the activity of Jeshua ben Judah in Jerusalem; of Alfasi, in Tunis (and later in Spain); of Rashi, in France; of Ahimaaz and Nathan ben Jehiel in Italy. At least three of these (Alfasi, Rashi, and Nathan) were very great men.

India's share to intellectual progress, though much smaller than those of Christendom and Israel, showed also distinct increase. South India gave us Rāmānuja and Vijñāneśvara.

The Sung renaissance was now in full swing, though it was not to reach its climax until the following century. The scientists and scholars with whom I have to deal in this chapter form certainly a very fine company—Shao Yung, Chou Tun-i, Shên Kua, Chou-ts'ung, Su-sung, Ts'ai Hsiang, Fu Kung, Wang Kuan, P'ang An-shih, Tung Ping, Ch'ien-i, Ou-yang Hsiu, Ssŭ-ma Kuang, Wang An-shih.

The repercussion of that Chinese revival was now beginning to be felt in Japan, and the fact that the latest national chronicle, the Eigwa Monogatari, was written, not in Chinese, but in Japanese, proves that the Japanese revival was no longer a slavish imitation of that of the Chinese. Japan was awakening for good.

As compared with the imposing lists which precede, the contributions of Islām may seem small, but they were still of a very high quality. In spite of Anselm, Psellos, and Constantine, in spite of the Chanson de Roland, in spite of Alfasi, Rashi, and Nathan, Islām was still at the vanguard of humanity. There was nowhere else in the world, in those days, a philosopher who could at all compare with al-Ghazzālī, neither an astronomer like al-Zarqālī, neither a mathematician like Omar Khayyam. These men were towering far above their contemporaries.

If we proceed to examine more carefully the intellectual condition of Islām, we discover, in the first place, that some of the most important contributions were due to Persians; this was not a novelty, but, what is more startling, they were written in Persian. Al-Ghazzālī was the only Persian who wrote in Arabic; al-Ḥasan ibn al-Ṣabbāḥ, Omar Khayyam, Nāṣir-i-Khusraw, Zarrīn Dast, Nidhām al-Mulk, and Asadī wrote in Persian. Thanks to Firdawsī, Persian had now fully emerged from its subordinate position and would have stood on an equal footing with Arabic if it had been at all possible for a lay language to be comparable to the sacred language of the Qur'ān.

Let me pause a moment to observe that this emancipation of many languages—French, Persian, Hebrew, and Japanese—is in itself a sufficient proof of the awakening and of the increasing consciousness, of the cultural independence of so many nations.

To return to Islām, the city of the caliphs gave us still a number of scientists, but none of great distinction—Muḥammad ibn 'Abd al-Bāqī, Ibn Jazla (of Christian origin), Sa'īd ibn Hibat Allāh, al-Khaṭīb al-Baghdādī, and al-Māwardī. Outside of Persia, the only center of intellectual progress in Islām was Spain, but the heyday of Cordova was already over. Indeed, of the seven scientists and scholars who make us think of the Muslim Spain of those days with gratitude, only one can be connected with Cordova, the geographer al-Bakrī. The greatest of them all, al-Zarqālī[b] flourished in Toledo, and so did the original historian Ibn Ṣā'id. Yūsuf al-Mutamin lived in Saragossa; Abū 'Umar ibn Ḥajjāj in Seville. Of Ibn Sīda, I only know that he was born in Murcia and died in Denia.

If we ask ourselves which were the main achievements of that time, the answer is, a philosophical awakening in the West, a Platonic revival in Constantinople, a Talmudist revival in Europe, the beginning of the Neoconfucian revival in China. All of these, it is true, are less achievements than promises. But the development of astronomy by al-Zarqālī and of algebra by Omar Khayyam were definite

[b] It is true al-Zarqālī was probably born in Cordova.

steps forward. And so was the elaboration of occidental music, the incorporation of Muslim experience into Salernitan medicine by Constantine the African, the ophthalmological treatise of Zarrīn Dast. I leave juridical, sociological, and historical writings out of account, because it is too difficult to measure their concrete value, but I may observe in a general way that this time produced a number of very distinguished historians and a few political thinkers who deserve to be remembered. Finally, this was an age of creation from the point of view of Hebrew and Persian lexicography.

In the midst of all that activity which was felt from the Atlantic shores to distant Japan and from northern Europe to southern India, how did it come to pass that the Muslim endeavor abated? It is difficult to answer such a question, for the reasons are many and complex and some may be hidden. To begin with, the expansive force of Islām was largely spent, the days of exaltation were long gone. Experience had come, it is true; but experience is a poor substitute for genius, and wisdom can never compensate the lack or the loss of intellectual courage. It has been suggested that the decline of Islām was largely due to the growth of orthodoxy and scholasticism. A great orientalist[e] went so far as to say: "The fourth century is the turning-point in the history of the spirit of Islām, and the establishment of the orthodox faith about 500 [i. e., 1106 A. D.] sealed the fate of independent research forever. But for al-Ash'arī and al-Ghazzālī the Arabs might have been a nation of Galileos, Keplers, and Newtons." I do not believe that such a paradoxical statement can be substantiated. It is of course entirely true that the end of the eleventh century was a turning-point in Islām; our readers are already aware of it, and my demonstration of it will be given completely in my second volume, but it is difficult to believe that this stop in intellectual development was due to the crystallization of orthodox tendencies. For one thing, al-Ghazzālī was followed by Averroës. I would rather believe that the orthodox reaction was partly caused by the arrest in intellectual development. Could it not be simply that Islām ceased to develop because it had reached the limit of its growth? The phenomenal growth of Islām was perhaps a case of intellectual precocity rather than one of true intellectual greatness. Al-Ghazzālī was too noble and broad an intellect to be accused of obscurantism, and, at any rate, no man however great could stop the natural growth of a national genius. Instead of blaming external circumstances, it is more rational to believe that it is that genius itself which failed. Its task was accomplished and it would be eventually continued by other peoples.

At any rate, the decline was not yet sufficiently obvious by the end of the eleventh century to be noticed. A decline can never be noticed when it sets in, but only much later. Thus, in those days the Muslims were still conscious of their intellectual supremacy; in fact, they were more conscious of it than they had ever been before. The Christians were beginning to progress, which means that they were more clearly aware of their inferiority; the Muslims were beginning to slow down, and perhaps their growing conceit was one of the causes of their lack of initiative; however, at that juncture their intellectual superiority upon other peoples was immense and undeniable. If there had been some ferocious eugenists among them they might have suggested some means of breeding out all the Christians because of their hopeless inferiority. Mind you, by that time the Muslim supremacy had lasted more than four centuries. Was this not a period of sufficient length to judge a civilization? It would be difficult, indeed, for Americans

[e] Edward Sachau, in his translation of al-Bīrūnī's Chronology (preface, p. x, 1879).

to blame the Arabs if they had reached such a conclusion after only four centuries of experience; and yet that conclusion, however plausible, was all wrong. But that is another story, which I shall try to tell in the second volume of my Introduction.

Yet, at the end of this volume, we see already the dawn of a new age. This may be symbolized in the best fashion by the Chanson de Roland, the song of independence of young Europe. It gratifies our sense of symmetry to realize that this account of intellectual progress which began with the Iliad ends with the French epic, of all mediaeval productions the one which came nearest to the Greek poem. Does it mean that mankind had walked in a circle? Not at all. But it means, what we already know in many other ways, that mankind had come back to a similar turning-point. Thus, when travelers climb a mountain they often rediscover the same vistas, though each time from a higher altitude, and each time with a broader horizon.

The Chanson de Roland is in some ways as primitive as the Iliad; it may even be more primitive. Yet the people who sang it had gone a long way; they had considerable experience and yet they were young; they had already climbed very high and were prepared to climb higher still. But this, I repeat, is another story. . . . .

II. PHILOSOPHICAL AND THEOLOGICAL BACKGROUND

Development of Christian Organization

The Lateran Synod of 1059 exhorted canons, i. e., members of the clergy sharing the revenues of a cathedral, to live in community and to hold all property in common, as prescribed in the Acts of the Apostles, II, 44–45. Some of the canons did not respond to the appeal and remained "secular canons;" others, on the contrary, did respond and adopted the so-called Rule of St. Augustine, an apocryphal compilation of that time, inspired by two extracts from St. Augustine's writings. Thus grew up a new religious order, the Augustinian Canons, also called Austin Canons, Canons Regular, Black Canons (in England). Benedict XII centralized their organization, in 1339, by a system of provincial chapters and visitations. The order exists to-day; also a corresponding order for women (canonesses).

ST. ANSELM

"Doctor magnificus." Born in Aosta, Piedmont, in 1033; he resided in Normandy, at Avranches c. 1059 and later at Bec. In 1063 he became prior of Ste. Marie du Bec (Bec-Hellouin), where his predecessor, Lanfranc, had founded (c. 1045) a school which soon obtained considerable renown. The fame of Bec increased under Anselm's rule; it became one of the greatest seats of learning in the Christian world of that time, a "New Athens." In 1093 he succeeded Lanfranc as Archbishop of Canterbury. He died in 1109.

St. Anselm was one of the first to attempt a new systematization of Christian philosophy on a more logical basis. He developed the so-called ontological argument to prove the existence of God (we do conceive a perfect being; absolute perfection implies existence; hence God exists). In his Proslogium sive fides quaerens intellectum (note the significant title) he claimed that it is necessary to believe in order to understand.[d] This started a controversy with Gaunilon, a monk of Marmoutier, near Tours.

---

[d] Cfr. "Nisi credideritis non intelligetis." Isaiah, VII, 9.

But Anselm's name calls to mind a far more important controversy, one which dominated the whole course of mediaeval philosophy in the West—the quarrel about universals, that is, about general conceptions of species and classes. Do these conceptions correspond to any concrete realities or not? This was not a new problem, but a very ancient one; it had already divided Plato and Aristotle; in fact, it is a problem of all times which is still up-to-date to-day, a phasis of the external conflict between rationalism and empiricism. The early schoolmen found it very clearly formulated in one of their favorite text-books, Boetius's translation of Porphyry's Isagoge. It became one of their dominant preoccupations. In that quarrel, Anselm defended the extreme realist point of view; universals exist before the individual things modeled upon them (universalia ante rem).

St. Anselm has been called the last of the church fathers and the first of the schoolmen; also (by a modern schoolman) "the Gregory VII of science."

Texts and Translations—Opera necon Eadmeri historia, etc., edited by Dom Gabriel Gerberon (Paris, 1675; again 1721). H. Bouchitté: Le rationalisme chrétien à la fin du XIe siècle ou Monologium et proslogium de St. Anselme sur l'essence divine, traduits avec introduction (440 p., Paris, 1842). Same writings and others by Anselm and contemporaries, translated by Sidney Norton Deane (325 p. Chicago, 1903).

Criticism—Alberto Agresti: Dante e S. Anselmo (R. accad. di archeol. di Napoli, 1886, 1887). Comte Domet de Vorges: St. Anselme—Les grands philosophes (340 p., Paris, 1901. The most elaborate study). Joseph Fischer: Die Erkenntnislehre Anselms (Beitr. zur Gesch. d. Phil. des Mittelalters, X, 3, 90 p., Münster, 1911). M. De Wulf: Geschichte der mittelalt. Philosophie (1913, 134–140, with bibliography).

ROSCELIN

Roscelinus de Compendio. Born at Compiègne c. 1050, still living in 1121. French scholastic philosopher. Traditionally considered as the founder of Nominalism (universalia post rem). Universals do not correspond to any objective realities; they are mere words, flatus vocis.

François Picavet: Roscelin, philosophe et théologien d'après la légende et d'après l'histoire (Paris, 1896. Important; enlarged edition, 1911).

HONORIUS INCLUSUS

Honorius Solitarius. Flourished in England (?), c. 1090. Benedictine monk who is probably the author of the treatise called "De imagine mundi," which has been ascribed also to St. Anselm and to Honorius of Autun (q. v., first half of the twelfth century). This cosmographic, geographic, and astronomic compendium was largely based upon Pliny, Isidore, and Bede. It inspired the French poem written c. 1246 by Gauthier of Metz (Image du Monde) which was immensely popular (q. v., first half of the thirteenth century).

Text—Editio princeps, without date or place (Nürnberg, c. 1472). Republished in the first edition of St. Anselm's works (Nürnberg, 1491, Honorius Inclusus being named as the author). Migne: Patrologia latina (in the volume devoted to Honorius of Autun).

Criticism—Ch. V. Langlois: La connaissance de la nature et du monde au Moyen âge. (49–113, Paris, 1911. Full information on the French poem and the works inspired by it.) Duhem: Système du monde (t. 3, 24–34, 1915). J. K. Wright: Geographical lore (103, 124, 1924).

PSELLOS

Michael Psellos the Younger (Μιχαὴλ ὁ Ψελλός). His baptismal name was Constantinos; Michael is a religious name which he assumed later in life. Born in Nicomedia in 1018; flourished in Constantinople; died after 1078. Byzantine polygraph and philosopher. Leader of the Neoplatonic revival which occurred in Constantinople in the second half of the century. That revival may have been partly occasioned by the growth of Muslim intolerance, which reached a height in the East about the middle of the century; the Neoplatonists of Bagdad (descendants of the Ḥarrānians or Sabians) were then obliged to move out.[e] Psellos wrote a history of his time, medical treatises, Aristotelian commentaries, and many other books on various subjects. One of his works, a summary of Aristotelian logic, had an extraordinary fortune; a Latin adaptation of it was prepared by Peter of Spain (q. v., second half of the thirteenth century) and later developed by Occam (q. v., first half of fourteenth century). At his best he reminds one of Voltaire, but more often he makes one think of the Renaissance Platonists. A study of the Byzantine thought and civilization of those days must necessarily be centered upon his works.

A treatise on the quadrivium was ascribed to Psellos by its first editor (Xylander, 1556); it is probably an earlier production (the astronomical part is dated 1008) and is, at any rate, very crude. A letter of Psellos is our sole basis to determine Diophantos's date (q. v., second half of third century).

Texts—The treatise on the four mathematical sciences (Συνοπτικὸν σύνταγμα εἰς τὰς τέσσαρας μαθηματικὰς ἐπιστήμας), a poor Neoplatonic summary ascribed to Psellos, is probably not his, but the work of Gregorios Monachos (Gregorius Solitarius), who wrote c. 1008. The most complete edition of his non-historical works is that published in Migne's Greek patrology (t. 122). The historical works have been edited by Constantine Sathas in his Bibliotheca graeca medii aevi (t. 4 and 5, 1874–1876). Sathas has re-edited the first of these volumes, containing his History (876 to 1077) in London, 1899. Emile Renauld: Chronographie ou Histoire d'un siècle de Byzance (976-1077) (Greek text and French translation, Paris, 1926).

I can but quote a few of the separate editions of his minor works (for more complete list see Krumbacher, op. cit., 436–445). J. Fr. Boissonade's Anecdota Graeca contain the following texts: Vol. 1, 1829, a medical poem, πόνημα ἰατρικόν, 175–132 (also published by J. L. Ideler: Physici et medici graeci minores, vol. 1, 1841, 203–43); medical glossary, λεξικὸν ἰατρικόν, 233–241; περὶ γεωργικῶν, 242–247. Ideler (loc. cit., vol. 2, 1842, 193) contains another medical text, on the bath, περὶ λούτρου. Gottfried Seebode has edited his Short Solutions of Physical questions, ἐπιλύσεις σύντομοι φυσικῶν ζητημάτων (Wiesbaden, 1857). For his miscellany entitled διδασκαλία παντοδαπή, the only complete text is Migne's. See also Tannery, below. Emile Renauld: Une traduction française du περὶ ἐνεργείας διαμόνων (Revue des études grecques, t. 33, 56–95, Paris, 1920. Reprint of Pierre Moreau's translation, Paris, 1573; Isis, V, 212).

E. Jeanselme has translated some fragments from Psellos's annals, of medical interest (see Isis, VII, 186).

Criticism—E. H. F. Meyer: Geschichte der Botanik (vol. 3, 350–356, 1856). Carl Prantl: Michael Psellus und Petrus Hispanus (22 p., Leipzig, 1867. Apropos of Psellos's synopsis of Aristotle's logic, which some had considered a late trans-

[e] See Walter Scott: Hermetica (Vol. I, 97–111, 1924; Isis, VIII, 343). Of course, all Muslim philosophers, were, to some extent, Neo-Platonists, but their philosophy was syncretized with theology.

lation of Petrus's Summula). Alfred Rambaud: Psellos (Revue historique, Avril 1877. Reprinted in his Etudes sur l'histoire byzantine, 111–171, Paris, 1912). P. Tannery: Psellus sur la grande année; sur les nombres; sur Diophante (Mémoires scientifiques, t. 4, 261–282, 1920. Three memoirs first published in 1892, containing the relevant texts; Isis, IV, 342). Karl Krumbacher: Geschichte der byzantinischen Litteratur (2te Aufl. München, 1897). Ch. Diehl: Figures Byzantines (Paris, 1906, contains, p. 291–316, a charming portrait of Psellos's mother, Theodote (Θεοδότη), derived from the biography written by Psellos himself). Paul Würthle: Die Monodie des Psellos auf den Einsturz der Hagia Sophia (Rhetorische Studien, 6, 107 p., Paderborn, 1917. Containing, p. 13–16, a short text formerly ascribed to Procopios, μονῳδία εἰς τὴν ἁγίαν Σοφίαν πεσοῦσαν ὑπὸ σεισμοῦ. If it were Procopios's work it would refer to the earthquake of 558; it refers to that of 986). Ch. Zervos: Un philosophe néoplatonicien du XIe siècle. Psellos. Sa vie, son oeuvre, ses luttes philosophiques, son influence (Thèse, 269 p., Paris, 1919. A very elaborate study with full bibliography). Emile Renauld: Lexique choisi de Psellos (187 p., Paris, 1920; Isis, IV, 580).

THEOPHYLACTOS

Theophylactos Bulgaros or Achridensis (Θεοφύλακτος). Born in Euboea; flourished in Constantinople, and, after 1078, in Achrida, Bulgaria; died after 1107. Archbishop of Bulgaria from 1078 on. Byzantine theologian and writer, second only to Psellos for the extent of his knowledge and the perfection of his style.

As Theophylactos does not interest us directly, I refer the reader for further information (editions, etc.) to Karl Krumbacher: Geschichte der byzantinischen Litteratur (2te Aufl., München, 1897, chiefly on p. 133, 463).

K. Sudhoff: Ein Krankenbericht des Theophylact (Mit. zur Gesch. d. Med., vol. 15, 473, 1916; Isis, III, 323). Joseph Kohler: Der medizinische Inhalt der Briefe des Theophylact von Bulgarien (Diss., 27 p., Leipzig, 1918).

JESHUA BEN JUDAH

In Arabic, Abū-l-Faraj Furkan ibn Asad. Flourished probably at Jerusalem probably in the second half of the eleventh century. Qaraite commentator on the Bible and philosopher of very high reputation among his brethren. They called him the teacher, al-mu'allim. He translated the Pentateuch into Arabic; his Biblical and philosophical studies were also written in Arabic, but soon translated into Hebrew. His point of view was essentially the same as that of his teacher Joseph ha-Ro'eh (q. v., first half of the eleventh century).

Article by Isaac Broydé, in Jewish Encyclopaedia (vol. 7, 157, 1904). Isaac Husik: Mediaeval Jewish Philosophy (55–58, 1918).

ALFASI

Isaac ben Jacob Alfasi. Also called ha-Kohen and Rif from the initials of his name R. Isaac Fasi. (The name Rif is given also to the Halakot.) Born in 1013 near Fez; flourished at Qairawān; in 1088 he fled to Spain, and died at Lucena in 1103. The greatest Talmudist of his age. He wrote a compendium, called Halakot, of the legal part of the Talmud, which superseded every previous one. It was based primarily on the Babylonian Talmud, but subsidiarily on the Palestinian one. Some of his responsa dealing (in Arabic) with legal matters, have also been preserved. The importance of the Halakot can be measured by the number of commentaries which were devoted to it.

Text—The Halakot was edited in Cracow, 1597; then in Basel, 1602. Later editions contain some of the commentaries; for example, the edition in three volumes, folio (Sulzbach, 1762–1766).

Criticism—Article in Jewish Encyclopaedia (vol. 1, 375–377, 1901) by Michael Friedländer.

RASHI

The name Rashi is derived from the initials of his real name, Rabbi Solomon ben Isaac. Born at Troyes, Champagne, in 1040, studied at Worms on the Rhine, returned to Troyes c. 1064, and died there in 1105. Franco-Jewish commentator on the Bible and the Talmud, whose influence upon Jewish thought has been immense. He and his family were the main promoters of rabbinical learning in France. His influence, however, was not restricted to France,[f] for it soon extended to Germany, to Spain and even to the East; nor was it restricted to his brethren; it soon affected the Christian world. He prepared a final recension of the Talmud and wrote commentaries on it and on the Bible, which are valuable because of their clearness, accuracy, learning, and popularity. These commentaries have been the object of a great many supercommentaries. They contain about 2,000 French words written in Hebrew characters (la'azim).

Text—The earliest dated Hebrew printed book was Rashi's Commentary on the Pentateuch (Reggio, Feb. 5, 1475). A new edition, together with the text (the earliest commentary thus printed) appeared at Bologna in 1482. Editio princeps of his commentary on the whole Old Testament, Miqra'ot Gedolot (Venice, 1525). Latin translation by J. F. Breithaupt (Gotha, 1710–1714). German translation of the commentary on the Pentateuch by L. Dukes (Prague, 1838).

Editio princeps of the whole Talmud, with Rashi's commentary (Venice, 1520–1522).

Criticism—Zunz: Rashi (Z. für die Wissenschaft des Judenthums, 227–384, 1823). Arsène Darmesteter: Reliques scientifiques (vol. 1, Paris, 1890). Max Leopold Margolis: Commentarius Isaacidis quatenus ad textum Talmudis investigandum adhiberi possit tractatu 'Erubhin ostenditur (Thesis, Columbia, 67 p., New York, 1891). Article in Jewish Encyclopaedia (vol. 10, 324–328, 1905) by Rabbi Morris Liber and Max Seligsohn. Maurice Liber: Rashi (Englished by Adele Szold, 278 p., Philadelphia, 1906).

The Assassins

The sect of the Assassins was an important offshoot of the Ismā'īlīya (q. v., second half of the ninth century). Their name is the result of a play upon words. It is true that some members of that sect (the Fidā'īs) resorted frequently to political assassinations. However, the name is derived from the Arabic, ḥashīshīyūn, meaning consumers of ḥashīsh (an intoxicating preparation of hemp). The Assassins were also called Mulāḥida, meaning heretics, and their sect, the "New Propaganda."

This new sect was founded or consolidated by al-Ḥasan ibn al-Ṣabbāḥ, a native of Ray, who was residing in Cairo c. 1078 to 1080, and wrote many theological treatises in Persian. He gained possession of the strong fortress of Alamūt (about 6 leagues north of Qazwīn in Jibāl) in 1090–91 and thus secured the existence and the prosperity of the sect. He died in 1124. Other fortresses were conquered and occupied by them in Persia and Syria (1126, etc.). The disorders

---

[f] The main rabbinical schools of France were Troyes, Ramerupt, Dampierre, Paris, and Sens.

caused by the Crusades enabled them to increase their power considerably.[g] It was brought to an end by the Mongols under Hūlāgū in 1256. Remnants of the sect are still extant, however, scattered through the Muslim East; they recognize as their head the Āghā Khān, a lineal descendant of the last grand master of Alamūt.

It should be noted that Alamūt was a seat of learning where some amount of scientific research was carried on and a large library had been gathered. The greater part of it was destroyed by the Mongols, however.

E. G. Browne: Literary History of Persia (vols. 1 and 2, 1900–1906, passim) Encyclopaedia of Islām (vol. 1, 491–492, 1911; vol. 2, 276, 1916).

OMAR KHAYYAM

See mathematical section (III) below.

AL-GHAZZĀLĪ

Latin: Algazel. Abū Ḥāmid Muḥammad ibn Muḥammad al-Ṭūsī al-Shāfi'ī al-Ghazzālī.[h] Born at Ṭūs, Khurāsān, in 1058; flourished in Nīshābūr and Bagdad, traveled as far as Alexandria, and finally returned to Ṭūs, where he died in 1111. The greatest theologian of Islām and one of its noblest and most original thinkers. He may be compared to Aquinas, but "his personal contribution to theology was more considerable than that of the Christian theologian."[i] His personality is vastly more important for the historian of religion than for the historian of science, yet the latter must consider it if he would understand the development of Muslim philosophy. Besides, al-Ghazzālī has exerted a very great influence upon Jewish and Christian scholasticism. (Part of his work was translated into Latin before 1150 by Dominicus Gundissalinus.) He managed to reconcile in a remarkable way his ṣūfī and pragmatic tendencies with strict orthodoxy (cfr. Pascal).

He wrote a treatise on the motion and nature of stars and a summary of astronomy (the second of these works is lost; it is possible that it was only another edition of the first). He had some knowledge of magic squares.

Texts and Translations—Iḥyā 'ulūm al-dīn. Revivifying of the Sciences of the Faith (2 vols., Cairo, 1306 H., 1312 H., etc. Many other oriental editions, commentaries, abridgments). D. B. Macdonald: Emotional Religion in Islām as affected by Music and Singing. Being a translation of a book of the Iḥyā with analysis, annotation, and appendices (Journal R. Asiatic Society, 195–252, 705–748, 1901; 1–28, 1902). Hans Bauer: Islamische Ethik (3 parts, 104, 130, 222 p., Halle a. S., 1916, 1917, 1922. German translation with notes of books 37, 12, and 14 of the Iḥyā).

Kitāb al-durra al-fākhira fī kashf 'ulūm al-ākhira. An eschatological treatise. La perle précieuse, edited by L. Gautier (Genève, 1878). Die kostbare Perle im Wissen der Jenseits, aus dem Arabischen übersetzt von Mohammed Brugsch (116 p., Hanover, 1924).

Kīmiyā al sa'āda (originally written in Persian by al-Ghazzālī, to give in brief the main substance of the Iḥyā). The alchemy of happiness, translated from a

---

[g] The "Old Man of the Mountain" (Shaikh al-Jabal), with whom students of the Crusades are so familiar, was not the grand master of the order, but simply the chief of the Syrian Assassins.

[h] The spelling with two z's is generally preferred in the East. See D. B. Macdonald: The Name al-Ghazzālī (Journal Royal Asiatic Soc., 18–22, 1902). What purports to be his tombstone has since been found and has apparently the two z's.

[i] G. F. Moore: History of Religions (vol. 2, 457, 1919).

Turkish version by H. A. Homes (Albany, N. Y., 1893). Other English translation by Claud Field, from the Hindustani (Wisdom of the East, 115 p., London, 1909).

Mishkāt al-anwār. The Niche for Lights, a ṣūfīstic refutation of Greek philosophy (Englished by W. H. T. Gairdner, 106 p., London, 1924).

Kitāb tahāfut al-falāsifa. The Internal Contradictions (or Vanity) of Philosophy. Known in the West via a Hebrew translation, it influenced Lully (q. v., second half of thirteenth century). T. de Boer: Die Widersprüche der Philosophie nach al-Ghazzālī und ihr Ausgleich durch Ibn Roshd (Strassburg, 1894).

Kitāb al-munqidh min al-ḍalāl. The Liberation from Error. Al-Ghazzālī's philosophical confession, comparable to that of St. Augustine. French translation by August Schmölders: Essai sur les écoles philosophiques chez les Arabes (Paris, 1842). Englished by Claud Field (Wisdom of the East, 60 p., London, 1909).

More editions are quoted by D. B. Macdonald in the Encyclopaedia of Islām, and by C. Brockelmann in his Arabische Litteratur (69 items).

Biography and General Criticism—D. B. Macdonald: The Life of al-Ghazzālī, with Especial Reference to his Religious Experiences and Opinions (Journal American Oriental Society, vol. 20 (1), 71–132, 1899. Important). C. Brockelmann: Arabische Litteratur (vol. 1, 419–426, 1898). Miguel Asín Palacios: Algazel. Dogmática, moral, ascética (912 p., Zaragoza, 1901). Carra de Vaux: Ghazali (330 p., Paris, 1902). I. Broyde: Jewish Encyclopaedia (vol. 5, 649–650, 1903). T. J. de Boer: History of Philosophy in Islam (154–168, 1903). D. B. Macdonald: Development of Muslim Theology (215–42, 1903); Religious Attitude and Life in Islam (220–302, 1909); article in Encyclopaedia of Islam (vol. 2, 146–149, 1914). Aly Bey Bahgat: Notiz über zwei Bronzen des arabischen Museums. (Bull. de l'Institut égyptien, t. 7, 57–63, 1907. Apropos of personal relics of al-Ghazzālī). Henrich Frick: Ghazālī's Selbstbiographie, ein Vergleich mit Augustins Konfessionen (88 p., Leipzig, 1919; Isis, IV, 508; al-Ghazzālī's autobiography is unique in Arabic for the keenness and fullness of its self-revelation). W. R. W. Gardner: Al-Ghazali (112 p., Madras, 1919). Samuel M. Zwemer: A Moslem Seeker after God; Showing Islam at its Best in the Life and Teaching of al-Ghazali (302 p., New York, 1920). J. Obermann: Der philosophische und religiöse Subjektivismus Ghazalis (360 p., Wien, 1921; Jour. Roy. Asiatic Soc., 296, 1923). Maurice Bouyges: Notes sur les philosophes arabes connus des latins au Moyen âge (Mélanges de l'Université St. Joseph, vol. 7, 397–406, 1921); Algazeliana (*ibidem*, vol. 8, 479–520, 1922. Review of ten recent publications, many of which are quoted above).

Special Criticism—H. Suter: Mathematiker (112, 1900). P. Duhem: Système du monde (t. 4, 496–511, 1916). Miguel Asín Palacios: Los precedentes musulmanes del pari de Pascal (Boletin de la Biblioteca Menendez y Pelayo, 65 p., Santander, 1920; Isis, VII, 185).

RĀMĀNUJA

Born probably in 1016–17, flourished at Srīraṅgam, near Trichinopoly; died after 1091, possibly in the twelfth century. Hindu philosopher. He wrote commentaries on the Brahmasūtra and the Bhagavadgītā and also independent Vedantic treatises. His Vedantism was partly a reaction against the extreme advaita (monism) of Śaṅkara (q. v., first half of the ninth century). It is called qualified monism (viśishṭa advaita).

Text—Translation of the Śrībhāshya (commentary on the Brahmasūtra) by G. Thibaut (Sacred Books of the East, vol. 48, 1904). Translation of the Bhagavadgītā, with Rāmānuja's commentary, by A. Govindāchārya Svāmī (Madras, 1898). Erich von Voss: Das angeblich von Rāmānuja verfasste Vedāntatattvasāra (Diss., 74 p., Leipzig, 1906. Sanskrit and German).

Criticism—C. R. Śrīnivāsa Aiyangar: The Life and Teachings of Śrī Rāmānujāchārya (325 p., Madras, 1908). V. A. Sukhtankar: The Teachings of Vedānta according to Rāmānuja (Diss., Bonn, 85 p., Wien, 1908). Article by A. B. Keith in Dictionary of Religion and Ethics (vol. 10, 572–574, 1919). M. Winternitz: Indische Litteratur (vol. 3, 439, 1920).

SHAO YUNG

Shao^{4} Yung^{1} (9777, 13468). Born in Fan^{4}-yang^{2} (3426, 12883), Chihli, 1011; died in 1077. Chinese scholar. Commentator of the Book of Changes. A part of this commentary entitled Huang^{2}-chi^{2*} ching^{1}-shih^{4} shu^{1} (5106, 859, 2122, 9969, 10024) has often been printed separately under the title: On the study of phenomena, Kuan^{1}-wu^{4*} (6363, 12777).

Giles: Chinese Biographical Dictionary (641, 1898).

CHOU TUN-I

Chou^{1} Tun^{1}-i^{2} (2450, 12203, 5421) or Chou^{1} Tzŭ^{3} (2450, 12317). Canonized as Yüan^{2} Ts'ung^{2} (13744, 12028). Born in 1017; died in 1073. Founder of the Confucian revival of the Sung dynasty, the so-called Hsing^{4}-li^{3} (4600,6879).[i] He wrote commentaries on the Book of Changes: I^{4}-ching^{1} (5497, 2122), the "diagram of the ultimate principle", T'ai^{4} chi^{2} t'u^{2} (10573, 859, 12128), wherein he transcends the dualism of the ancient Chinese cosmology, and the "great treatise" T'ung^{1} shu^{1} (12294, 10024).

The leaders of the Sung school of Confucianism form an imposing group of five men, The Five Philosophers, wu^{3} tzŭ^{3} (12698, 12317). Chou Tun-i was the first. He was followed by the two brothers Ch'êng, Ch'êng^{2} Hao^{4} (757, 3894) or Ch'êng Tzŭ (Lo-yang, Honan, 1032 to 1085), and Ch'êng^{2} I^{2} (757, 5421) (Lo-yang, Honan, 1033 to 1107) and their uncle Chang^{1} Tsai^{4} (416, 11485) (Ta-liang, Honan, 1020 to 1076). The fifth and last was the great Chu Hsi (q. v., second half of the twelfth century). This Neo-Confucianism was extremely different from the original doctrine; it was based on metaphysical ideas absolutely foreign to Confucius's mind. It was really a syncretism including many Taoist and Buddhist elements. For a few extracts see L. Wieger: Histoire des croyances en Chine (leçon 71, 1922).

Translations—The first work has been translated into German by Gabelentz, the latter by Grube.

Criticism—Giles: Chinese Biographical Dictionary (164, 1898). Ars Asiatica (vol. 1, 25). Encyclopaedia sinica (111, 435, 1917). D. T. Suzuki: History of Early Chinese Philosophy (London, 1914).

SHÊN KUA

Shên^{3} Kua^{4*} (9849, 6288) or Ch'ên^{2} Huo^{2*} (649, 6288). Born in Ch'ien^{2}-t'ang^{2} (1736, 10767), Chehkiang, in 1030, died in Shensi in 1093. Chinese author, mathematician, astronomer, instrument maker, at one time president of the Han-lin College. He wrote a medical work called Su^{1}-shên^{3} liang^{2}-fang^{1} (10320, 9849, 7017, 3435), but he is chiefly known by a collection of essays called Mêng^{4}-ch'i^{1} pi^{3*}-t'an^{2} (7779, 1009, 8979, 10656) or "Essays from the Torrent of Dreams," in 26 books. It is divided into 17 sections dealing with archaeology and various arts and sciences, but mainly mathematics and music. It contains elementary measurements of areas and volumes, the earliest Chinese example of summation

---

[i] This is difficult to translate. Hsing is human nature; li, reason or logos.

of a progression, the earliest clear mention in any literature of a magnetic needle, the earliest description of printing with movable type.[k] He prepared a new calendar in 1074.

Texts—Mêng-ch'i pi-t'an (editions of 1631, 1696).

Criticism—A. Wylie: Chinese Literature (163, 1902). H. A. Giles: Biographical Dictionary (644, 1898). Y. Mikami: The Development of Mathematics in China and Japan (61–63, 1912). G. Vacca: Caduta di un areolito (Note Cinesi, 2, Rivista degli studi orientali, t. 6, 133–135. Brief extract from the Mêng-ch'i with translation, recording the fall of a meteorite in 1064; other extracts from the Mêng ch'i form the substance of the other Note cinesi, except the first). L. Wieger: La Chine (292, 511, 1920). T. F. Carter: Invention of Printing in China (1925; Isis, VIII, 371. Contains a translation of the text relative to printing).

III. LATIN, BYZANTINE, MUSLIM, AND CHINESE MATHEMATICS AND ASTRONOMY

Abacus Arithmetic

As far as we can judge from contemporary writings, abacuses began to be more systematically used during the eleventh and twelfth centuries. See my notes on Bernelinus and Guido of Arezzo in the previous chapter, and on Hermann the Lame and Gerland in this one. Of course, the abacus could be used and was actually used long before treatises were devoted to it. The tradition of that use can be traced back to classical antiquity and even to Egyptian and Babylonian(?) times. The name of the instrument is probably derived from the Greek ἄβαξ, meaning plate, tablet, abacus. The best summary of the history of the abacus will be found in D. E. Smith, "History of Mathematics" (vol. 2, 156–196, 1925), with abundant references.

The "abacists" used exclusively Roman numerals in their explanations; of course, the shortcomings of these numerals were hardly felt as long as they were not used for the actual computations but simply to put down the final results.

We shall see in my second volume that the use of Hindu numerals began to increase perceptibly in Christian Europe during the twelfth century. (For their earlier history, see note in the second half of the tenth century.) The writers explaining their use were called "algorists." Some of these writers, for example, Adelard of Bath and Radolf of Laon (q. v., first half of the twelfth century), used numerals of both kinds.

For the use of the abacus in England in the eleventh century, see also C. H. Haskins, The Abacus and the King's Curia (English Historical Review, 101–106, 1912).

By a strange coincidence, it would seem that the Chinese became also more interested in abacus arithmetic at about this time. According to Yang Hui (q. v., second half of the thirteenth century) arithmetical treatises called P'an[2]-chu[1] chi[2]* (8620, 2549, 906), Tsou[3]-p'an[2] chi[2]* (11791, 8620, 906), etc., date from the eleventh and twelfth centuries. The titles of these books suggest that they dealt with suan[4]-p'an[2] (10378, 8620) arithmetic (suan-p'an is the Chinese abacus; the Japanese call it soroban; see my note on Hsü Yüeh in second half of the second century). Hsü[3] Kuei[4]-lin[2] (4761, 6435, 7157), who flourished c. 1830, concluded that the suan p'an was used in China at about that time. It is probable that its

[k] For the magnetic needle, see physical section below and for the movable type see my note on Pi Shêng (first half of the eleventh century).

use was even considerably earlier, yet it did not become very common before the fourteenth century. The Chinese suan-p'an may have the same ancestry as the European abacus, but it is impossible to prove that, nor is it necessary to postulate it: The invention of such simple instrument may be caused independently in many places by the same logical necessity.

Y. Mikami: Development of Mathematics in China (111, 1912).

HERMANN THE LAME

Hermann of Reichenau. Hermannus Contractus (paralysis had contracted his body). Born on July 18, 1013; flourished in Reichenau; died on August 24, 1054. Abbot of the Benedictine monastery of Reichenau. He wrote a clear and concise treatise on the abacus (no mention of other numerals than the Roman), an account of the arithmetical game called rithmomachia;[1] two works on the use of the astrolabe (indirectly based on Muslim knowledge), De mensura astrolabii; de utilitatibus astrolabii (before 1048); a chronicle down to 1054; opuscula musica. Hermann introduced a curious notation to determine pitch; this was derived in all probability from Arabic models, for a pitch notation was already known to al-Kindī (q. v., first half of ninth century).

Texts—Aemil. Ussermann: Chronicon Hermanni Contracti ex inedito hucusque codice Augiensi, unacum eius vita et continuatione a Bertholdo eius discipulo scripta (2 vols., Typis San-Blasianis, 1790). German translation upon the text of the Monum. Germ. by K. Nobbe (Berlin, 1851. Geschichtsschreiber der deutschen Vorzeit, 11); 2d edition by W. Wattenbach (77 p., Leipzig, 1893; *ibidem*, 42).

Regule Herimanni qualiter multiplicationes fiant in abbaco. One of many "scritti inediti relativi al calcolo dell' abaco," edited by P. Treutlein (Boncompagni's Bullettino, vol. 10, 643–647, Roma, 1877).

Hermanni Contracti opuscula musica in Martin Gerbert: Scriptores ecclesiastici de musica (vol. 2, 124–153, 1784).

Criticism—R. Peiper: Fortolfi Rythmimachia (Z. für Mathematik, vol. 25, hist. Abt., 167–227, 1880. Notes, p. 198 to end). E. Wappler: Bemerkungen zur Rhythmomachie (Z. für Math., vol. 37, hist. Abt., 1–17, 1892). D. E. Smith and Clara C. Eaton: Rithmomachia, the Great Medieval Number Game (Teachers' College Record, vol. 13, 29–38, 1912). Duhem: Système du Monde (vol. 3, 165, 1915). Lynn Thorndike: History of Magic (vol. 1, 701, 1923. On the De mensura astrolabii ascribed to Hermann). D. E. Smith: History of Mathematics (vol. 1, 198–200, 1923. On rithmomachia). M. Manitius: Lateinische Literatur des Mittelalters (vol. 2, 756–77, 1923. See also on p. 786–787, a note on Meinzo of Constance, who came to Reichenau in 1048 and discussed mathematical questions with Hermann, for example, on the measurement of the circle).

FRANCO OF LIÈGE

Flourished at Liège, where he was leading the cathedral school of St. Lambert in 1047 and where he died in or after 1083. He wrote treatises on the compotus; on the sphere (commented upon by Thomas Aquinas); on the quadrature of the circle (c. 1054?; between 1036 and 1056). The latter contains a history of the subject. Franco was well acquainted with duodecimal fractions, but his geometry was very poor. Value of π, $(9/5)^2 = 3, 24$.

It would seem that Franco of Cologne, who wrote various treatises on music

[1] For another contemporary treatise on that game see my note on Frutolf in the following section.

and was the earliest mensural theorist in the Christian West, lived only about the end of the twelfth century; these two Franco have been confused, e. g., by Stecher. Note that Franco of Liège had also some connection with Cologne, for his treatise on the quadrature was dedicated to Hermann II, Archbishop of Cologne from 1036 to 1056. The matter needs further investigation.

Apropos of the ascription to Franco of the invention of the turquet, see my note on Nāṣir al-dīn al-Ṭūsī (second half of thirteenth century).

Text—Winterberg: Der Traktat Franco's von Lüttich de quadratura circuli (Abhdl. zur Gesch. d. Mathematik, 4. Heft, 135–190, Leipzig, 1882. Together with another shorter treatise on same subject by same author, 183–190).

Criticism—J. Stecher: Biographie nationale de la Belgique (vol. 7, 267–268, c. 1881). P. Tannery et Clerval: Une correspondance d'écolâtres du XIe siècle. (Notices et extraits des Manuscripts, vol. 36, 1900; Mémoires, vol. 5, 229–303; Isis, VI, 432). Cantor: Vorlesungen (vol. 1^3, 876–878, 1907). M. Manitius: Lateinische Litteraturgeschichte des Mittelalters (vol. 2, 781–786, 1923).

WILHELM OF HIRŚAU

See my note in the physical section (IV), below.

GERLAND

Flourished in Besançon c. 1081 to 1084. (Not to be mistaken for another Gerland, canon of Besançon, who appears in documents of 1132–1148.) Abacist. He wrote a treatise on the abacus and a compotus (directions to compute the date of Easter and other movable feasts).

Text—P. Treutlein: Intorno ad alcuni scritti inediti relativi al calcolo dell' abaco. Trattato di Gerlando "De abaco" (Bull. di bibliografia d. sci. mat., vol. 10, 589–607, 1877).

Criticism—B. Boncompagni: Intorno al Tractatus de abaco di Gerlando (Bull. di bibliografia d. sci. mat., vol. 10, 648–656, 1877). C. H. Haskins: Studies in Mediaeval Science (85 and by index, 1924).

Byzantine Mathematics and Astronomy

See my note on Psellos in Section II, above.

Muslim Mathematics and Astronomy

IBN ṢĀ'ID

See historical section (VIII), below.

AL-ZARQĀLĪ

In Latin: Arzachel. Abū Isḥāq Ibrāḥīm ibn Yaḥyā al-Naqqāsh, the engraver. Better known as Ibn al-Zarqāla or al-Zarqālī. From Cordova, lived from c. 1029 to c. 1087. Astronomer. The best observer of his time (observations dated 1061, 1080). He invented an improved astrolabe called ṣafīḥa[m] (saphaea Arzachelis); his description of it was translated into Latin, Hebrew, and many vernaculars. He was the first to prove explicitly the motion of the solar apogee with reference to the stars; according to his measurements it amounted to 12.04″ per year (the real value being 11.8″). On the other hand, comparing his observation of the obliquity of the ecliptic with previous ones, he concluded

[m] The idea in ṣafīḥa is flatness; it is a flat sheet or slab of anything, wood, stone, metal, etc. (D. B. M.)

that it oscillated between 23° 33′ and 23° 53′, thus reënforcing the erroneous belief in the "trepidation" of the equinoxes. He edited the so-called Toledan Tables, planetary tables based upon the observations made by him and probably other Muslim and Jewish astronomers in Toledo (notably Ibn Ṣā'id). These tables were translated into Latin by Gherardo Cremonese and enjoyed much popularity.[n] The trigonometrical introduction (Canones sive regulae tabularum astronomiae) was al-Zarqālī's own work; it explains the construction of the trigonometrical tables.

Texts and Translations—The Toledan Tables, or even their Introduction, are still unpublished. Sapheae recentis res doctrinae patris Abrysakh Azarchelis summi astronomi a Joanne Schonero, etc. (Nürnberg, 1534). Spanish edition in volume 3 of the Libros del Saber (for which see Alfonso X, second half of thirteenth century). There are also early Hebrew and Italian translations.

Criticism—Steinschneider: Etudes sur Zarkali (Bull. di bibliografia e di storia delle sci mat., vol. 14, 171–182, 1881; vol. 16, 493–513, 1883; vol. 17, 765–794, 1884; vol. 18, 343–360, 1885; vol. 20, 1–36, 575–604, 1887. Chiefly devoted to the manuscripts and bibliography); Über eine lateinische Bearbeitung von Zarkali's saphaea (Bibliotheca mathematica, 11–2, 1890). C. Brockelmann: Geschichte der arabischen Litteratur (vol. 1, 472, 1898). A. Wittstein: Über die Wasseruhr und das Astrolabium des Arzachel (Z. f. Math., vol. 39, hist. Abt., 41–55, 81–94, 1894. See Suter, op. cit., 216, 1900). A. von Braunmühl: Geschichte der Trigonometrie (vol. 1, 1900). H. Suter: Die Mathematiker und Astronomen der Araber (109–111, 1900; Nachträge, 173, 1902). Dreyer: Planetary Systems (1906). Duhem: Système du monde (vol. 2, 246–259, 1914). R. T. Gunther: Early Science in Oxford (vol. 2, 200, 1923. Apropos of the saphaea).

YŪSUF AL-MUTAMIN

Of the tribe of the Banū Hūd; king of Saragossa from 1081 to 1085. His father, Aḥmad al-Muqtadir billāh, king from 1046 to 1081, was also a student and a patron of students. Hispano-Muslim mathematician and patron of science. He wrote a mathematical treatise, Istikmāl (Bringing to perfection), of which it was said[o] that it should be studied together with Euclid, the Almagest, and the "middle books."[p]

No copy of Yūsuf's treatise is known; it is strange that a work believed to be so important and written by a king should be lost.

Stanley Lane-Poole: Mohammedan Dynasties (26, 1893). H. Suter: Mathematiker (108, 1900).

OMAR KHAYYAM

Abū-l-Fatḥ 'Umar ibn Ibrāhīm al-Khayyāmī—the tentmaker—Ghiyāth al-dīn. Born in or near Nīshābūr c. 1038 to 1048, died there in 1123–24. Persian mathematician, astronomer, and poet. One of the greatest mathematicians of mediaeval times. His Algebra contains geometric and algebraic solutions of equations of the second degree; an admirable classification of equations, including the cubic; a systematic attempt to solve them all, and partial geometric solutions of most of them (he did not consider negative roots and his failure to use both branches or halves of a conic caused him to miss sometimes one of the positive

[n] Steinschneider has enumerated not less than 48 manuscripts, Arabic or Latin.
[o] By Joseph ben Judah ibn 'Aqnin, q. v., second half of twelfth century.
[p] About which see my note on Nāṣir al-dīn al-Ṭūsī (second half of thirteenth century).

roots). His classification of equations is very different from our own; it is based on the complexity of the equations (the number of different terms which they include). Of course the higher the degree of an equation the more different terms, or combinations of terms, it can contain. Thus Omar recognizes 13 different forms of cubic equation. (The modern classification based primarily upon the degree dates only from the end of the sixteenth and the beginning of the seventeenth century.) Binomial development when the exponent is a positive integer. Study of the postulates and generalities of Euclid.

In 1074–75 the Saljūq sulṭān Malikshāh, Jalāl al-dīn, called him to the new observatory of Ray (or Nīshābūr, or Isfahān?) to reform the old Persian calendar: (30×12) d. $+ 5$ d. $= 365$ d. The latter had been temporarily replaced by the Muslim calendar after the conquest. Omar's calendar was called al-ta'rīkh al-Jalālī;[a] its era was the 10th Ramaḍān 471 = 16 March 1079. There are many interpretations of Omar's reform and to each corresponds a certain degree of accuracy, but at any rate, Omar's calendar was very accurate, probably more so than the Gregorian calendar. The correct interpretation is probably one of the three following, the second being the most probable of them. I quote for each, the authority, then the gist of the change, and finally the resulting error:

According to al-Shīrāzī (d. 1311), 17 intercalary days in 70 years; error, 1 day in about 1,540 years.

According to Ulūgh Beg (d. 1449), 15 intercalary days in 62 years; error, 1 day in about 3,770 years.

Modern interpretation, 8 intercalary days in 33 years; error, 1 day in about 5,000 years.

(The Gregorian calendar leads to an error of 1 day in 3,330 years).

Methods for the determination of specific gravity.

It is impossible not to mention the Rubā'īyāt (quatrains) of Omar Khayyam, which have become, especially since 1859 (when Edward Fitzgerald published the first instalment of his English paraphrase), one of the most popular classics of the world literature. Omar Khayyam was probably not a ṣūfī, but rather an agnostic. Comparisons of his thought with that of Lucretius and that of Voltaire are suggestive but inadequate.

Texts and Translations—Franz Woepcke: L'algèbre d'Omar Alkhayyāmī publiée, traduite et accompagnée d'extraits de manuscrits inédits (Paris, 1851).

A. Christensen: Un traité de métaphysique d'Omar (Le monde oriental, vol. 1, 1–16, 1908).

Texts and Translations of the Rubā'īyāt—Fitzgerald's first edition (London, 1859), contained only 75 quatrains (a facsimile reprint of it was published later by Quaritch, London). The French translation by J. B. Nicolas appeared in Paris, 1867, and was soon followed by Fitzgerald's second edition in 1868; 3d ed., 1872; 4th, 1879; 5th, 1889. In 1882, Edw. Henry Whinfield edited a new translation of 253 quatrains, and in 1885, of 500, together with the Persian text (385 p.; 2d ed. corrected, London, 1901). This translation is less poetical but more scholarly than Fitzgerald's. Of the many other translations, I shall quote only: Justin Huntly McCarthy's (466 q., 1888); John Payne's, published by the Villon Society (278 p., London, 1898); Eben Francis Thompson's, with an introduction by N. H. Dole (Worcester, Mass., privately printed, 878 quatrains, 1906); John Pollen's, with a foreword by the Āghā Khān (158 quatrains "faithfully and literally translated," London, c. 1916).

---

[a] In Persian, ta'rīkh-i-Jalālī or ta'rīkh-i-Malikī, both names being derived from the sulṭān's.

Variorum editions: Robert Arnot: The Sufistic Quatrains of 'Omar, in luding the translations of Ed. Fitzgerald (101 q.), E. H. Whinfield (500 q.), and J. B. Nicolas (464 q.) (417 p., New York, 1903). Nathan Haskell Dole: Reprints in full of Fitzgerald's 1st, 2d, and 5th editions, with minor variants of the 3d and 4th (160 p., Boston, 1899). N. H. Dole: Multi-variorum edition. English, French, German, Italian, and Danish translations comparatively arranged in accordance with the text of Fitzgerald's version, with further selections, notes, biographies and other material (2 vols., Boston, 1896; 2d ed., revised and enlarged, 1898. This is a real encyclopaedia of the subject).

Such literature lends itself admirably to interpolations, and many of the Rubā'iyāt are probably apocryphal; one of them is ascribed to Avicenna (No. 303 of Whinfield's edition).

The cult of Omar Khayyam has grown to such proportions both in Europe and America that the philosopher must take it into account. It is not a mere fad. That cult is probably more genuine than that of Homer or Dante.

General Criticism—J. K. M. Shirazi: Life of Omar al-Khayyāmī (118 p., Edinburgh, 1905 (?). Written from the Persian point of view, based upon unquoted manuscripts sources; the author claims that Omar was of Arab, not of Persian, descent). E. G. Browne: Literary History of Persia (vol. 2, 246 sq., and by index, 1906). A. V. Williams Jackson: From Constantinople to the Home of Omar Khayyam (New York, 1911. Chiefly p. 229–260, illustr.). G. Jacob und E. Wiedemann: Zu Omer-i-Chajjam (Der Islam, vol. 3, 42–62, 1912. Biographical information derived from various Oriental sources; translation of Omar's introduction to his treatise on the postulates, muṣādarat, of Euclid). Otto Rothfeld: 'Umar and His Age (92 p., Bombay, 1922).

Scientific Criticism—H. Suter: Die Mathematiker und Astronomen (112, 225, 1900). F. K. Ginzel: Handbuch der mathematischen und technischen Chronologie (vol. 1, 300–305, 1906). E. Wiedemann: Über Bestimmung der spezifischen Gewichte (Beitr. 8, Sitzungsber., Erlangen, vol. 38, 170–173, 1906. See also the paper of 1912, quoted above). H. Suter: Article Djalālī in Encyclopedia of Islam (vol. 1, 1006–7, 1912). W. E. Story: Omar as a Mathematician (17 p., Boston, 1918).

AL-GHAZZĀLĪ

See my note in the philosophical section (II), above.

MUḤAMMAD IBN 'ABD AL-BĀQĪ

Abū Bakr (?) Muḥammad ibn 'Abd al-Bāqī al-Baghdādī. Flourished c. 1100. Possibly the author of a commentary on the tenth book of Euclid, which was very popular because of its numerical applications. It is entitled "Liber judei[r] super decimum Euclidis" in the translation by Gherardo Cremonese.

Text and Translation—Whoever the author be, this interesting commentary is most probably a work of the eleventh century (or the beginning of the twelfth century). It has been edited twice: by B. Boncompagni, entitled "De numeris et lineis" (66 p., in 4to, without place or date, 1863?), and by M. Curtze in the Supplement to Heiberg's edition of Euclid (252–386, Leipzig, 1899).

Criticism—H. Suter: Über einige noch nicht sicher gestellte Autorennamen in den Übersetzungen des Gerhard von Cremona (Bibliotheca Mathematica, vol. 4, 19–27, 24–25, 1903); Über den Kommentar des Muḥammed ben 'Abdelbāqī

[r] Suter suggests that judei = judicis. One Abū Bakr Muḥammad ibn 'Abd al-Bāqī al-Bazzāz was qāḍī al-māristān (judge of the hospital) in Bagdad, c. 1123. If this personality is identical with the one we are now considering, the commentary on Euclid X would more probably belong to the beginning of the twelfth century.

zum zehnten Buche des Euklides (*ibidem*, vol. 7, 234–251, 1907); Zu dem Buche "De superficierum divisionibus" des Muḥammed Bagdadinis (*ibidem*, vol. 6, 321–322, 1905).

Chinese Mathematics

CHOU-TS'UNG

Chou^{1}-ts'ung^{1} (2450, 12026). Flourished under the Sung, c. 1065. Chinese astronomer. The elaboration of a new calendar, Ming^{2}-t'ien^{1}-li^{4*} (7946, 11208, 6924), was completed under his direction in 1065. The Ming-t'ien-li contains an historical account of the Chinese calendar.

Text—The text of the Ming-t'ien-li will be found in Chapter 74 of the Sung Annals, Sung^{4} shih^{3} (10462, 9893), for which see my note on T'o^{1*}-t'o^{1*} (11375, 11375), first half of fourteenth century.

Criticism—L. Wieger: La Chine (223, 427, 511, 1920).

SHÊN KUA

See my note in the philosophical section (II), above.

SU-SUNG

Su^{1}-sung^{4} (10320, 10448). Flourished under the Sung, c. 1092. Chinese astronomer. He wrote in 1092 a treatise on astronomy, with celestial maps, Hsing^{1}-i^{2}-hsiang^{4} fa^{2*}-yao^{4} (4574, 5455, 4287, 3366, 12889). He constructed an orrery, set to motion by water power.

A. Wylie: Chinese Literature (107, (1867) 1902). L. Wieger: La Chine (390, 520, 1920).

IV. LATIN, PERSIAN, AND CHINESE PHYSICS AND TECHNOLOGY

Latin Physics and Technology

HERMANN THE LAME

See my note in the mathematical section (III), above.

HIRSAU

Wilhelm von Hirsau. Born in Bavaria, educated in Regensburg; abbot of Hirsau since 1069; died at Hirsau on July 5, 1091. German monk. Educator, astronomer, theorist of music. He built an orrery which attracted much attention. His main works are the Astronomica and the Musica. He introduced the reform of Cluny into Germany; the abbey of Hirsau was, during his tenure, the first German abbey to have direct relations with Cluny. He was one of the main champions of Pope Gregory VII (1073 to 1085) in Germany.

Text—Astronomica. The introduction was published by B. Pez: Thesaurus anecdotorum novissimus (vol. 6, 259–264, 1729); also in Migne's Patrology (vol. 150, 1639–1642).

Musica, edited by M. Gerbert: Scriptores ecclesiastici de musica sacra potissimum (vol. 2, 154–182, 1784); also in Migne's Patrology (vol. 150, 1147 to 1178).

Constitutiones Hirsaugienses (adaptation of the Clunisian rule), edited by M. Herrgott: Vetus disciplina monastica (371–570, Paris, 1726); also in Migne's Patrology (vol. 150, 927–1146).

The Philosophicarum et astronomicarum institutionum[a] Guilhelmi olim Hirsaugiensis abbatis libri III (Basel, 1531) is now generally identified with the Philosophia prima (or minor) of Guillaume de Conches (q. v., first half of twelfth century).

[a] Hirsau's philosophical fame was largely based upon that apocryphal work.

Criticism—M. Witten: Der selige Wilhelm, ein Lebensbild aus dem Investiturstreit (66 p., Bonn, 1890). Lauchert in Allgemeine Deutsche Biographie (vol. 43, 221–224, 1898). E. Zinner: Das mittelalterliche Lehrgerät für Sternkunde zu Regensburg und seine Beziehungen zu Wilhelm von Hirsau (Z. für Instrumentenkunde, 43, 278–282, 1923).

FRUTOLF

Alias Furtolf, Fortolf. Flourished at the Michelsberg abbey in Bamberg, died in 1103. German Benedictine and theorist of music. He completed the theory of Gregorian music begun by Guido. He wrote the Breviarium de musica and the Tonarius.

He is probably identical with the author of the Rythmimachia, a German monk who lived toward the close of the eleventh century and wrote on music. This work is one of the earliest devoted to the subject (see my note on Hermann the Lame, above). It was edited by R. Peiper: Fortolfi Rythmimachia (Abhdl. zur Gesch. der Mathematik, H. 3, 167–227, 1880).

Frutolfi Breviarium de musica et Tonarius. Edited by Cölestin Vivell (O. S. B.) (Wien. Akad. d. Wiss., phil. Kl., Sitzungsber., vol. 188, 188 p., 1919; Isis, V, 212).

THEOPHILUS

Unknown monk and craftsman who flourished about the end of the eleventh and the beginning of the twelfth century, probably in Germany. His latest editor, Albert Ilg, would identify him with Rogkerus or Rugerus, monk and goldsmith in the Benedictine monastery of Helmershausen on the Diemel. Author of an encyclopaedia of the arts and crafts, "Diversarum artium schedula," which is of considerable value for the historian of technology. It is derived primarily from Greco-Egyptian sources. Traces of Byzantine and Muslim influences reveal the process of its transmission. It contains among other things the earliest European account of bell-founding.

Text and Translation—Comte Charles de l'Escalopier: Théophile prêtre et moine. Essai sur divers Arts (386 p., Paris, 1843. Latin text with French translation and with an introduction by J. Marie Guichard). Robert Hendrie: An Essay upon Various Arts, in three books by Theophilus called also Rugerus, forming an encyclopaedia of Christian art of the eleventh century (498 p., London, 1847). Albert Ilg: Theophilus Presbyter. Schedula diversarium artium. Revidierter Text, Übersetzung, und Appendix. (Quellenschriften für Kunstgeschichte, vol. 7, 424 p., Wien, 1874).

The Lumen animae (Liber moralitatum elegantissimus, magnarum rerum naturalium, Lumen animae dictus, etc.) first published in 1470 (?), then in Augsburg, 1477, etc., contains many extracts from Theophilus. These have been collected (with German translation) at the end of Ilg's edition, Fragmenta breviarii diversarum artium Theophili, ex editionibus "Luminis animae" collecta (p. 360–371).

Criticism—F. M. Feldhaus: Die Technik (1168, 1387, 1914); Medizinisches aus dem Theophilus (Mit. zur Gesch. d. Med. u. Naturw., vol. 16, 436, 1917); Über die Kennzeichen an Glocken der ältesten Periode (Geschichtsblätter für Technik, vol. 3, 100–104, 1916; Isis, III, 322, wherein read bell twice instead of clock!). E. O. von Lippmann: Chemisches und Technologisches aus kunstgeschichtlichen Quellenschriften, 2. Theophilus Presbyter (Chemiker Z., 1917, 1 sq.; also Beiträge, 158–174, 1923; Isis, V, 497).

Muslim Physics

See my note on Omar Khayyam in the mathematical section (III), above.

Chinese Physics and Technology—Early History of the Compass

The early history of the compass is very obscure. It would seem that the Chinese have known the fundamental property of a magnetic needle for a considerable time, but have applied it chiefly if not exclusively to geomantic purposes (fêng shui, for which see my note on Kuo P'o, first half of fourth century).

The Chinese tradition relative to the compass is represented by the following facts:

In 1027 a "south-pointing chariot," described as a mechanical contrivance, was submitted to the Sung emperor Jên Tsung. As I have recalled above in my note on Shên Kua, that writer, who died in 1093, spoke of the magnetic needle and of its geomantic use, this being the first clear mention in any literature. The earliest mention of the use of a magnetic needle for navigation occurs a little after 1100, but refers to the period 1086 to 1099. Chu^1 $Yü^{4*}$ (2544, 13635) tells us that during that period it was used by foreign (i. e., very probably Muslim) sailors between Canton and Sumatra. In 1107 a "south-pointing chariot," presented to the Sung emperor Hui Tsung, is still described as a mechanical contrivance with cogged wheels, etc. In 1115 the magnetic needle is carefully described in the $Pên^3$-$ts'ao^3$-yen^3-i^4 (8846, 11634, 13130, 5454), but that description contains no reference to its use for navigation.

Putting these facts together—all of which are derived from Chinese sources—we might conclude that the Chinese were the first to perceive the directive property of the magnetic needle, but that they failed to apply it to any rational purpose. The first practical use of the magnetic needle is credited by the Chinese themselves to foreigners, who were, in all probability, Muslims.

For the transmission of that knowledge to Christian Europe see my note on Alexander Neckam (second half of twelfth century).

Jules Klaproth: Lettre à M. le Baron A. de Humboldt sur l'invention de la boussole (Paris, 1834). F. Hirth: History of Ancient China (135, 1908). Albert Schück: Der Kompass (1911–18; Isis, IV, 438). T. F. Carter: Invention of Printing in China (93, 1925).

See my note on Shên Kua in Section II, above.

V. LATIN, BYZANTINE, MUSLIM, AND CHINESE NATURAL HISTORY

MARBODE

Marbodus Redonensis. Born in Angers in 1035; died there in 1123. Bishop of Rennes from 1096 on. At some time between 1067 and 1096 (or 1101) he, composed the Liber lapidum, a medical lapidary in 743 hexameters, which, judging by the number of manuscripts and of translations into various vernaculars, was immensely popular. Indeed it was translated into French (12 versions in verse and prose), Provençal, Italian, Irish, Danish, Hebrew, and Spanish. It deals with the medical and magical properties of 60 precious stones.

There were three types of mediaeval lapidary: the scientific type derived from Theophrastos and Dioscorides; the astrological (or magical) derived from Alexandrian writings; and the Christian derived from Jewish interpretations of the precious stones of Aaron's breastplate and from Apocalyptic allegories. The third tradition can be traced in Bede and Hrabanus Maurus, but then it disappeared for many centuries. The two other traditions were combined in Pliny, later in Isidore's Etymologies, and finally in Marbode. Thus the famous poem composed by the Bishop of Rennes contained no Christian elements; it was exclusively derived from pagan sources. As most European lapidaries were in their turn derived from Marbode, they remained essentially pagan until the appearance in the thirteenth century of the so-called Lapidaire chétien, which combined for the first time the Christian with the two other traditions. The evolution of the lapidaries is thus in great contrast to that of the bestiaries, which had been permeated with Christian doctrines from a very early time (see my note on the Physiologos, second half of the second century).

To complete this brief account, I may add that the Greek astrological traditions reappeared also in Arabic writings, such as the Pseudo-Aristotelian lapidary and 'Uṭārid's lapidary (q. v., first half of the ninth century). Later this Arabic development rejoined the Latin development through the Alphonsine translations (q. v., second half of thirteenth century).

Texts and Translations—Libellus de lapidibus pretiosis nuper editus (Viennae, Pannoniae, 1511). Edition by Jean Macé (Rennes, 1524). De lapidibus pretiosis enchiridion (Freiburg, 1531; Paris, 1531). De gemmarum lapidumque pretiosorum formis, naturis atque viribus (Cologne, 1539). New edition in Migne's Patrologia latina (vol. 171, col. 1725, 1854). Better edition by J. Beckmann: Marbodi liber lapidum seu de gemmis (192 p., Göttingen, 1799. However, this is not a critical edition; the abundance of manuscripts—more than 140!—seems to have deterred scientific editors).

The Lapidarium of Macrobius translated into English verse, in C. W. King (Antique Gems, p. 391–417, 1860). Léopold Pannier: Les lapidaires français des (XIIe, XIIIe et XIVe siècles, réunis, classés et publiés, accompagnés de préfaces, de tables, et d'un glossaire. Avec une préface de Gaston Paris (Bibliothèque de l'école des hautes études, 52, 354 p., Paris, 1882. Capital).

Paul Studer and Joan Evans: Anglo-Norman lapidaries (424 p., Paris, 1924. Scientific edition, with abundant notes and glossary, of a number of Anglo-Norman lapidaries, in prose and verse, derived from Marbode; Isis, IX).

Criticism—Camille Ferry: De Marbodi espiscopi vita et carminibus (107 p., Nemausi, 1877). Paul Neumann: Über die älteste französische Version des dem Bishof Marbod zugeschriebenen Lapidarius (Diss., Breslau, 1880). Vittorio Finzi: Di un' inedita traduzione in prosa italiana del poema de lapidibus praetiosis (dating from the end of the fourteenth century) (Propugnatore, vol. 3, 40 p., Bologna, 1890). Léon Ernault: Marbode, sa vie et ses oeuvres. Extrait des Mémoires de la Société archéologique d'Ille-et-Vilaine (Rennes, 1890. Important).

ODO OF MEUNG

Odo Magdunensis, Odo of Meung on the Loire. Flourished about the end of the eleventh century. He was probably the author of the Macer Floridus de virtutibus (or De viribus) herbarum, a poem describing in 2,269 hexameters the virtues of 77 herbs and roots. This poem is not based on original observation, yet it is very important, for it is one of the earliest Western documents proving a revival of interest in botany.

The authorship of this treatise has been considerably discussed, and the question is not by any means settled. But it is at any rate highly probable that it was written by a Frenchman about the end of the century. It must be placed late enough to account for the traces of Constantine's influence. The latter was literarily active from c. 1058 to 1087 (see medical section).

Text—The first two editions were not illustrated (Naples, 1477; Milano, 1482). Eight different illustrated editions or variants were printed in France at the close of the fifteenth century. They are all undated and unsigned. Louis Baudet:

Macer Floridus. Des vertus des plantes (Collection Pancoucke, seconde série latine française, 15, p. 109–264, Paris, 1845).

Criticism—Hermann Stadler: Die Quellen des Macer Floridus (Archiv für die Geschichte der Naturwissenschaften, vol. 1, 52–65, 1908). Cyrill Resak: Odo Magdunensis, der Verfasser des Macer Floridus und der deutsche Leipziger Macer Text (Diss., 50 p., Leipzig, 1917. Important; with bibliography; Isis, IV, 580). Arnold C. Klebs: Herbals of the Fifteenth Century (Papers of the Bibliographical Society of America, vol. 11, 1917; vol. 12, 1918). Max Manitius: Geschichte der lateinischen Literatur (II. Teil, 539–547, München, 1923).

SETH

See medical section (VII) below.

AL-BAKRĪ

See geographical section (VI) below.

ABŪ 'UMAR IBN ḤAJJĀJ

Flourished in or near Seville c. 1073–74. Hispano-Muslim writer on agriculture. His treatise called "The Sufficient" (al-maqna') was written in 1073–74 and used by Ibn al-'Awwām (q. v., second half of twelfth century). He was a grammarian rather than a botanist.

Ernst H. F. Meyer: Geschichte der Botanik (vol. 3, 248–258, 1856).

TS'AI HSIANG

Ts'ai[4] Hsiang[1] (11519, 4266). Flourished in the Fuhkien province under the Sung, c. 1011 to 1066. Chinese horticulturist. Author of a treatise on the li[4]-chih[1] (*Litchi sinensis*), one of the most popular fruits of Southern China. The treatise, entitled Li[4]-chih[1]-p'u[3] (6985, 1875, 9515), was written in late summer 1059, and a fair copy of it was made by the author in the spring of the following year; that copy was engraved on wooden blocks from which rubbings could be taken. It is divided into seven chapters—origin of the tree, remarkable specimens, trade, use as food, cultivation, time and methods of conservation, varieties. The Li-chih-p'u is the earliest monograph on any fruit tree ever published anywhere.

Text—There are many rubbings of the original blocks and many reprints of them. The Library of Congress owns at least seven, which Michael J. Hagerty is using (1924) to prepare a critical edition and translation.

Criticism—A. Wylie: Chinese Literature (151, (1867) 1902). L. Wieger: La Chine (442, 1920). W. T. Swingle, in Report of Librarian of Congress (274–275, 1924; Isis, VII, 568).

FU KUNG

Fu[4] Kung[1] (3632, 6583). Flourished in 1059. Chinese zoologist. He wrote in 1059 a treatise on crabs, Hsieh[4]-p'u[3] (4427, 9515), consisting of extracts from ancient literature on the subject and of a summary of the author's knowledge. Different species of crabs are considered.

A. Wylie: Chinese Literature (154, (1867) 1902).

OU-YANG HSIU

See my note in the historical section (VIII), below.

WANG KUAN

Wang[2] Kuan[1] (12493, 6363). Flourished in Yang[2]-chou[1] (12876, 2444) c. 1070. Chinese horticulturist. Author of a treatise on the peony, 39 varieties of which are described, Yang[2]-chou[1] shao[1]-yo[4]-p'u[3] (12876, 2444, 9770, 13352, 9515). It is largely derived from an earlier work by Liu[2]-pin[1] (7270, 9260) wherein 31 varieties were described. Yang-chou was famous for the cultivation of peonies.

A. Wylie: Chinese Literature (151, (1867) 1902).

VI. LATIN AND MUSLIM GEOGRAPHY

ADAM OF BREMEN

Adamus Bremensis. Born in Upper Saxony, probably in Meissen, before 1045. Flourished in Bremen; died c. 1076. The first German geographer. His history of the diocese of Hamburg down to 1072 is the fundamental source for the early history, geography, and ethnography of Northern Europe and of the Scandinavian colonies. It contains the earliest record of Wineland[f] and a very valuable account of North European trade. It was largely based on oral information collected in Bremen and in Seeland (Denmark).

Text and Translations—The Historia Hammaburgensis Ecclesiae is divided into four parts, of which the fourth, entitled De situ Daniae et reliquarum quae trans Daniam sunt regionum, descriptio insularum Aquilonis, is the most important. Ed. princeps of the first three parts (Copenhagen, 1579); of the fourth (Stockholm, 1615).

I. M. Lappenberg: Gesta hammaburgensis ecclesiae pontificum, in the Monumenta Germaniae historica, Scriptores (vol. 7, Hanover, 1846). Improved edition by L. Weiland (Hanover, 1876), in the Scriptores rerum Germanicorum ex Monumentis Germaniae historicis recusi. Third edition by Bernhard Schmeidler (Hanover, 1917). Other reprint in Migne's Patrologia (vol. 146).

German translations by Carsten Miesegaas, Bremen, 1825 (this translation, antedating the edition of a scientific text, is negligible), and by J. C. M. Laurent, Berlin, 1850, reëdited by W. Wattenbach. Leipzig, 1893 (Die Geschichtschreiber der deutschen Vorzeit, vol. 11).

Criticism—Augustin Bernard: De Adamo bremensi geographo (Thesis, 104 p., Paris, 1895). Siegmund Günther: Adam, der erste deutsche Geograph (Sitzungsber. d. böhm. Ges. d. Wiss., Prag, 1894). Sven Lönborg: Adam af Bremen och hans skildring af Nordeuropas länder och volk (190 p., Uppsala, 1897). Beazley: Dawn of Modern Geography (vol. 2, 514–518, 1901). Philipp Wilhelm Kohlmann: Adam. Ein Beitrag zur mittelalterlichen Textkritik und Kosmographie (143 p., Leipzig, 1908). K. Kretschmer: Die italienischen Portolane des Mittelalters (195, 235, Berlin, 1909). Axel Anthon Björnbo: Adam af Bremens Nordensopfattelse (126 p., Copenhagen, 1910. Cartographic). Bernhard Schmeidler: Neue Literatur über Adam (Z. des Vereins für Lübeckische Geschichte, Bd. 16, 111–121); Hamburg, Bremen und Nordost-Europa vom 9. bis 11. Jahrhundert (383 p., Leipzig, 1918. Important). Max Manitius: Lateinische Literatur des Mittelalters (vol. 3, 398–413, 1923).

Cartography

The earliest portolani date possibly from the eleventh century, though the earliest extant is one Pisan (in the Bibliothèque Nationale of Paris), not less than two centuries younger. There is a fragment of the text of a portolano in Adam of Bremen. See Konrad Kretschmer: Die italienischen Portolane des Mittelalters (170, Berlin 1909). C. R. Beazley: Dawn of Modern Geography (vol. 2, 470, 1901; vol. 3, 515–516, 1906. Suggesting, after Nordenskjöld and Fiorini,

---

[f] About 1075. It antedates the Icelandic sagas.

a Byzantine origin—about eleventh century—of the thirteenth century Italian portolani).

St. Sever World Map—The Bibliothèque Nationale in Paris owns a map of the world, which is the most important of those derived from the Beatus map (q. v., second half of the eighth century). It is a splendid document of legendary cartography as opposed to the scientific (or empirical) cartography of the portolani. It measures 46 by 72 cm. It was probably drawn at the Monastery of St. Sever, near the middle of the eleventh century. Published in the Choix de documents géographiques (Bibliothèque Nationale, Paris, 1883); also in Konrad Miller: Mappae mundi (vol. 1, 1895).

AL-BAKRĪ

Abū 'Ubaid 'Abdallāh ibn 'Abd al-'Azīz ibn Muḥammad ibn Ayyūb ibn 'Amr. Born in Saltes or Huelva. Flourished in Cordova, died very old in 1094. Oldest Hispano-Muslim geographer whose works are extant. His main work was the "Book of the Roads and the Provinces" (Kitāb al-masālik wal-mamālik), a geographical compilation (in the form of an itinerary) containing also historical and ethnographical information. He also wrote a dictionary of ancient geography (chiefly of Arabia; Kitāb mu'jam ma 'sta'jama). A book on the principal plants and trees of Andalusia is ascribed to him.[u]

Text and Translations—Al-Bakrī's main work is partly lost. The parts dealing with Northern Africa, Egypt, and to some extent with Spain are extant. The African part has been edited by Baron de Slane (Algiers, 1857; improved edition 1910) and translated by him in 1858 (Description de l'Afrique septentrionale). Fragments dealing with the Russians and Slavs have been edited in Russian by Kunik and Rosen (St. Petersburg, 1878). See my note on Ibrāhīm ibn Ya'qūb, second half of tenth century.

The geographical dictionary has been edited by F. Wüstenfeld (2 vols., Göttingen and Paris, 1876–77).

Criticism—Baron de Slane's Introduction (1857). F. Wüstenfeld: Die Wohnsitze und Wanderungen der arabischen Stämme (Abhdl. d. Ges. d. Wiss. zu Göttingen, vol. 14, 84 p., Göttingen, 1869). L. Leclerc: Médecine arabe (vol. 1, 553, 1876). C. Brockelmann: Arabische litteratur (vol. 1, 476, 1898). Franciszek Piekosiński: Al Bekri o Polakach (Nowsze wydawnictwa akademii umiejetności, wydzialow filolog i histor. filozof., vol. 39, 283–295, Cracow, 1900). A. Cour: Encyclopaedia of Islam (vol. 1, 606, 1911).

NĀṢIR-I-KHUSRAW

Abū Mu'īn al-Dīn al-Qubādhiyānī al-Marwazī, i. e. of Merv and Qubādhiyān (Transoxiana). Born in 1003–4, died in 1088–9. Persian poet and traveler; Ismā'īlī missionary from Egypt (the great Ismā'īlī center) to Persia. He was called the Proof (Ḥujja) of Khurāsān. From 1045 to 1052 he traveled in Syria, Palestine, Egypt, Arabia, and Persia, and he has left a diary of his journeys (the Safar-nāma). It contains a valuable account of life in Egypt under the eighth Fāṭimid caliph, al-Mustanṣir (1035 to 1094), and varied geographic, ethnographic, and archaeological information.

Texts and Translations—Sefer Nameh, Relation du voyage de Nassiri Khosrau publié, traduit et annoté par Charles Schefer (Paris, 1881). Partial translation by Guy Le Strange: Diary of a Journey through Syria and Palestine (Palestine Pilgrims' Text Society, 9, 86 p., London, 1888).

---

[u] Leclerc, after certain copies of Ibn abī Uṣaibi'a.

Criticism—E. G. Browne: Literary History of Persia (vol. 2, 221–246, 1906 (1915), and by index).

VII. LATIN, BYZANTINE, MUSLIM, AND CHINESE MEDICINE

Latin Medicine

CONSTANTINE THE AFRICAN

Constantinus Africanus or Afer.[v] Born in Carthage; after many years of travel in the East he settled down in Monte Cassino c. 1056 to 1060 and died there in 1087. The first great translator from the Arabic into Latin. A great number of medical writings, some of Greek origin, were translated by him (or the translations were ascribed to him). He staid for a while in Salerno and his work acted as a ferment upon the Salernitan school. At any rate, he enabled them to take advantage of Muslim experience as well as of their own Greek traditions.

Texts—Eight of his translations are included in the Opera Isaac (Lyon, 1515). A collected edition of his works appeared in Basel (2 vols., 1536–1539).

Separate editions: Therapeutica sive megatechni. Included in Speculum medicinae Galeni (Lyon, 1517). De humana natura vel de membris principalibus corporis humani, de elephantis, de remediorum ex animalibus materia. Together with Albucasis metodus medendi (Bale, 1541). Breviarium dictum viaticum (by Ibn al-Jazzār). Rhazis opera parva (Lyon, 1510). De febribus, included in the Collectio de febribus (Venice, 1576). De animalibus or de animalium virtutibus (in the Pictorius ζωοτροφεῖον, Basel, 1560). Republished by A. Rivinus (Leipzig, 1654) and by J. Ch. G. Ackermann: Parabilium medicamentorum scriptores antiqui (113–124, Nürnberg, 1788).

J. L. Pagel: Die Chirurgie der Pantechni [by 'Alī ibn 'Abbās] nach einer von den Druckausgaben abweichenden Berliner Hdsch. (Archiv. f. Klin. Chirurgie, 81, Bd. 1, 52 p., 1906).

Criticism—E. H. F. Meyer: Geschichte der Botanik (vol. 3, 471–484, 1856). M. Steinschneider: Virchow's Archiv (vol. 37, 351–410, Berlin, 1866). E. Gurlt: Geschichte der Chirurgie (vol. 1, 670–672, 1898). Neuburger: Geschichte der Medizin (vol. 2, 1911). Charles Singer: A Legend of Salerno. How Constantine Brought the Art of Medicine to the Christians (Johns Hopkins Hospital Bulletin, vol. 28, 64–69, 1917). Friedrich Hartmann: Die Literatur von Früh- und Hochsalerno (9–14, 1919. Containing further bibliography). Karl Nord: Zahnheilkundliches aus den Schriften Konstantins von Afrika (Diss., 31 p., Leipzig, 1922). Adolf Mosolff: Zahnheilkundliche Randbemerkungen zu einem Viaticus-Text (Diss., 24 p., Leipzig, 1924; Isis, VII, 536).

JOANNES AFFLACIUS

Joannes Saracenus (John the Saracen). Born c. 1040; died in or after 1103. Salernitan physician, disciple of Constantine. Author of treatises on urology and on fevers. He completed the translation of the surgical part of 'Alī ibn 'Abbās's Malikī, begun by Constantine.

Constantine had translated into Latin the first half of the Malikī, that is, the Theorica, under the title Pantegni. The surgical part, of which he translated the first half, was the ninth particula of the Practica. Afflacius's translation was made with the collaboration of a Pisan physician, called Rusticus, at the

[v] Leo Ostiensis (Leone Marsicano, 1046 to 1115?), monk at Monte Cassino, called him "magister orientis et occidentis."

time of the great expedition against Majorca in 1114 (Haskins). If that is correct, my dates for Afflacius are incorrect; but it is possible that Rusticus simply revised Afflacius's version or completed it after the latter's death?

Text—The Curae de febribus is edited in Renzi's Collectio salernitana (vol. 2, 737–768, 1853). The Curae de urinis was published in Constantini Opera (208–214, Basel, 1539).

Criticism—Neuburger: Geschichte der Medizin (vol. 2, 289, 1911). Hartmann: Die Literatur von Früh- und Hochsalerno (20, 1919). Haskins: Studies in Mediaeval Science (132, 1924).

JOANNES PLATEARIUS

Joannes Platearius the Younger. Flourished about the end of the eleventh century. Salernitan physician influenced by Constantine. Son of Joannes Platearius the Elder, himself an eminent practitioner, from whom he is not easy to distinguish. He wrote a medical compendium (Practica brevis) which was very popular and a treatise on urology (Regulae urinarum).

Text—Editio princeps of the Practica brevis (Ferrara, 1488; frequently re-edited).

The Regulae urinarum are included in Renzi's Collectio salernitana (vol. 4, 409–412, 1856).

Criticism—Hartmann: Die Literatur von Früh- und Hochsalerno (15–17, 1919).

ANATOMIA PORCI

Anatomical treatise ascribed to one Copho; two physicians of that name flourished in Salerno in the second half of the eleventh century. It is one of the earliest anatomical texts of the Christian West. It is clearly post-Constantinian (it may have been written only in the beginning of the twelfth century); that is, it shows traces of Muslim as well as of Greek influence. It is a text-book for the practical study of anatomy based on the assumption that the pig is of all animals the one whose internal structure is nearest to that of man. It is based largely upon personal though crude observations and may be said to mark the beginning of anatomical research in western Christian Europe.

Texts—Editio princeps (Haganoae, 1532). Many other editions, the latest being that of Schwarz: Die medizinischen Handschriften der Universitätsbibliothek (Würzburg, 1907).

Criticism—F. Redecker: Die Anatomia magistri Nicolai physici und ihr Verhältnis zur Anatomie Cophonis und Richardi (Diss., Leipzig, 1917). Hartmann: Die Literatur von Früh- und Hochsalerno (14–15, 39–40, 1919).

LATIN MEDICINE OUTSIDE OF SALERNO

See my notes on Marbode and Odo of Meung in Section V, above.

Louis Dubreuil-Chambardel has published an important study on medicine in Western France in the eleventh and twelfth centuries: Les médecins dans l'Ouest de la France (308 p., Paris, 1914; Isis, II, 438; III, 279). That study based upon archival documents is very valuable for the study of medical practice, but the physicians specifically quoted did not add anything to medical knowledge. The most important physician dealt with is Raoul Leclerc (alias Raoul Malecouronne), a Norman, who was in Chartres c. 1025, studied in Salerno (c. 1030 to 1040), and flourished near Montreuil, in Normandy, also at Marmoutier (1050 to 1057), and Ouche; he returned to Marmoutier in 1061 and died in 1068. Tetbert (born c. 1020) was another physician of the school of Marmoutier.

None of these physicians left any writings, and their fame, however great, remained local.

P. Pansier: Etude sur un manuscrit médical au XIe siècle (Mémoires de l'académie de Vaucluse, vol. 7, 8 p., Avignon, 1907). F. Beaudouin: Maladie et guérison de dame Mabille (Année médicale de Caen, 4 p., 1913); Un médecin de Saint-Cénery au XIe siècle, Raoul Malecouronne (7 p., *ibidem*, 1912).

Byzantine Medicine

PSELLOS

See my note in Section II, above.

SETH

Symeon Seth (Συμεὼν Σήθ). He is sometimes styled πρωτοβεστιάριος, head of the (imperial) wardrobe, and μαγιστὴρ 'Αντιοχείας, master of the palace built by Antiochos. Flourished under Michael VII Ducas (Parapinaces), emperor from 1071 to 1078; still living in 1080. Byzantine encyclopaedist. Translator from Arabic into Greek. His most important work is a dictionary dealing with the medical properties of foodstuffs (Σύνταγμα κατὰ στοιχεῖον περὶ τροφῶν δυνάμενων), of special interest because it is the first occidental dispensatory containing abundant information of Hindu and Arabic origin. For example, on camphor (kāfūr in Arabic, hence the Greek καφουρά), whose sedative and anaphrodisiac properties are mentioned; on musk (Ar. misk), ambergris (Ar. 'anbar), ḥashīsh (καννα βουρόσπερμα), cloves (καρυόφυλλον), nutmeg (κάρυον ἀρωματικόν), julep (Ar. julāb, ζωλάπιον), and various oriental sirups (Ar. sharāb, cfr. our word sherbet). Most, if not all, of these drugs or spices are here mentioned in Greek for the first time. He wrote also a botanical dictionary (Λεξικὸν κατὰ ἀλφάβητον ἑρμηνεῦον ἀκριβῶς τὰς βοτάνας); a treatise on smell, taste, and touch (Φιλοσοφικὰ καὶ ἰατρικά); another on urine (Σύνοψις περὶ οὔρων), etc.

He is perhaps best known, however, as the Greek translator of the fables of Kalīla and Dimna (for which, see my note on Burzūya, second half of sixth century). Seth's translation was apparently based upon a better Arabic text than the one which has come down to us. There are not less than four versions of the Greek text. The Slavonic versions, of which there are at least three, were based upon a Greek original, different from the four Greek versions extant. This shows the extreme popularity of that collection of tales and gives one an idea of the endless textual difficulties which their study involves.

Text—De alimentorum facultatibus (Greek and Latin) edited by Gregorius Gyraldus (Basel, 1538; new edition 1561). Greek and Latin edition, with commentary, by Martinus Bogdanus (Paris, 1658). Edition by Bernhard Langkavel (Leipzig, 1868).

Φιλοσοφικὰ καὶ ἰατρικά, edited by L. Ideler: Physici et medici graeci minores (vol. 2, 283–285, 1842).

Critical edition of the four Greek versions of Kalīla wa Dimna by Vittorio Puntoni (Publ. d. Società asiatica italiana, vol. 2, Florence, 1889).

A study of the various texts ascribed to Seth is much needed if only to test their genuineness.

Criticism—C. Gottlob Kühn: Moschi antiquitates (Progr., Leipzig, 1833). Ernst H. F. Meyer: Geschichte der Botanik (vol. 3, 356–365, 1856. With list of plants mentioned in the Syntagma only). K. Krumbacher: Byzantinische Litteratur (615, 617, 896, 1897). Iwan Bloch, in Puschmann's Geschichte der Medizin (vol. 1, 563–564, 1902).

Muslim Medicine

IBN JAZLA

Abū 'Alī Yaḥyā ibn 'Īsā Ibn Jazla. Latin forms: Bengesla, Buhahylyha, Byngezla, etc. Flourished in Bagdad, died in 1100. Christian physician, who embraced Islām in 1074. His most important work is a medical synopsis, wherein 44 tables of two pages each contain the description and outline the treatment of 352 diseases (8 in each table); it was probably modeled upon a similar work of Ibn Buṭlān (q. v., first half of eleventh century) and is called "Tables of the Bodies with regard to their Constitutions" (Taqwīm al-abdān fī tadbīr al-insān; dispositio corporum de constitutione hominis). He wrote for al-Muqtadī (caliph from 1075 to 1094) an alphabetical list of simple and compound medicines called "The Pathway of Explanation as to that which Man Uses" (Minhāj al-bayān fī mā yasta'miluhu al-insān; methodica dispositio eorum, quibus homo uti solet).

Texts and Translations—A Latin version of the Taqwīm has been published in Strasbourg, 1532, together with Ibn Buṭlān's Taqwīm: Tacuini aegritudinum cet. Buhahylyla Byngezla auctore. German translation, also with that of Ibn Buṭlān's work, by M. Herr (Strassburg, 1533).

Criticism—Wüstenfeld: Geschichte der arabischen Aerzte (84, 1840). Leclerc: Histoire de la médecine arabe (vol. 1, 493–496, 1876). C. Brockelmann: Arabische Litteratur (Vol. I, 485, 1898). T. H. Weir: Encyclopaedia of Islam (vol. 2, 373, 1916).

SA'ĪD IBN HIBAT ALLĀH

Abū-l-Ḥasan Sa'īd ibn Hibat Allāh ibn al-Ḥasan. Flourished in Bagdad under al-Muqtadī, caliph from 1075 to 1094, died in 1101–2. Physician and philosopher. Author of a synopsis of medicine, Al-mughnī fī tadbīr al-amrāḍ wa ma'rifat al-'ilal wal-a'rāḍ (Sufficiens de cura morborum et cognitione causarum et symptomarum) and of a treatise on physiology and psychology called "Discourse on the Creation of Man," Maqāla fī khalq al-insān (De constitutione hominis), dealing with such subjects as reproduction, gestation, parturition, growth, decay, survival of the soul, etc.

Criticism—Wüstenfeld: Geschichte der arabischen Aerzte (83, 1840). Leclerc: Médecine arabe (vol. 1, 492, 1876). C. Brockelmann: Arabische Litteratur (vol. 1, 485, 1898). E. G. Browne: Arabian Medicine (125, 1921).

ZARRĪN DAST

Abū Rūḥ Muḥammad ibn Manṣūr ibn abī 'Abdallāh ibn Manṣūr al-Jamānī (or al-Jurjānī). Zarrīn Dast means the Golden Hand, a good name for an eye surgeon. Flourished under the Saljūq sulṭān Abū-l-Fatḥ Malikshāh ibn Muḥammad, ruling from 1072–73 to 1092–93. Persian oculist. He completed in 1087–88, a very comprehensive and very remarkable treatise on ophthalmology entitled The Light of the Eyes (Nūr al-'ayūn) (in Persian).

Hirschberg: Geschichte der Augenheilkunde bei den Arabern (57 sq., Leipzig, 1905). Adolf Fonahn: Quellenkunde der persischen Medizin (38–41, 1910. Includes a summary of the treatise, based upon Hirschberg).

Chinese Medicine

SHÊN KUA

See my note in Section II, above.

P'ANG AN-SHIH

P'ang^2 An^1-shih^2 (8692, 44, 9921). Flourished under the Sung, c. 1090. Chinese physician. Author of a treatise on fevers called Shang^1-han^2 tsung^3-ping^4-lun^4 (9742, 3825, 12010, 9300, 7475). Tung^3 Ping^4 (12259, 9298), P'ang's pupil, added to it a glossary and an appendix on the composition of medicines.

A. Wylie: Chinese Literature (98, (1867), 1902). L. Wieger: La Chine (380, 485, 1920).

CH'IEN-I

Ch'ien^2-i^4* (1736, 5341). Flourished at the Sung court, c. 1093. Chinese physician. Author of a treatise on infantile medicine, called Ch'ien^2-shih^4 hsiao^3-êrh^2 yao^4-chêng^4 chên^1-chüeh^2* (1736, 9978, 4294, 3333, 12958, 726, 589, 3225).

Text—The treatise was published by the author's nephew, Yen^2 Hsiao^4-chung^1 (13153, 4334, 2877), in 1119. An elaborate edition, with commentary by Hsiung^2 Tsung^1-li^4* (4700, 11976, 6954), appeared in 1440 under the title Lei^4-chêng^4 chu^4-shih^4* ch'ien^2-shih^4 hsiao^3-êrh^2 fang^1-chüeh^2* (6853, 726, 2537, 9983, 1736, 9978, 4294, 3333, 3435, 3225), in 10 books.

Criticism—A. Wylie: Chinese Literature (104, (1867), 1902).

VIII. FRENCH, LATIN, BYZANTINE, JEWISH, MUSLIM, CHINESE, AND JAPANESE HISTORIOGRAPHY

CHANSON DE ROLAND

The "chansons de geste" which are the earliest monuments, if not of the French language, at least of French literature, appeared in the second half of the eleventh century. The suddenness of their appearance invites comparison with the Homeric poems. It is highly probable that poems were composed and recited much before that time (say from the ninth century on) by itinerant minstrels (jongleurs), but the fact remains that the "chansons de geste" now extant are not anterior to the second half of the eleventh century. We have no right to postulate the existence of earlier epics, simply to account for the relative perfection of the famous "Chanson de Roland," which is at once the most ancient and the most beautiful. After all, its beauty may be due, at least in part, to the freshness of the inspiration and to the very novelty of the undertaking; it has often happened to peoples, as to individuals, that their first efforts were the most successful.

A "cantilena Rollandi" was sung by Taillefer at the battle of Hastings (1066). The earliest manuscript of the Chanson de Roland is an Oxford manuscript (Digby 23) which reproduces a text probably anterior to 1080. On the other hand, the present form of the Chanson may date only from the first quarter of the twelfth century. The only complete French poem which is probably earlier than the Chanson de Roland is the Pèlerinage de Charlemagne à Jérusalem which was composed, c. 1060, in the interest of the abbey and fair of St. Denis.

The "chansons de geste," as the title indicates, had at least some historical purpose. The amount of true history which they contain is of course very small—just a little nucleus of truth around which crystallizes, by and by, a large mass of legend. The same may be said of the Homeric poems. It is equally foolish to exaggerate the truthfulness of epic poems, and to deny it altogether. In the case of the "Chanson de Roland," the nucleus of truth was the defeat suffered by the rear-guard of Charlemagne's army in Val Carlos near Roncesvalles (Spanish Navarre), on August 15, 778. The historical fact is twice confirmed by Einhard

(q. v., first half of ninth century). As Charlemagne was returning from Pamplona to France across the Pyrenees, his small rear-guard was attacked and destroyed in one of the passes, not by "Saracens," but by Basque mountaineers. This event must have made a great stir in the locality. Now, Roncesvalles was a necessary stopping-place on the road to Santiago de Compostela, one of the main pilgrimage roads of the Middle Ages. Thus the best conditions combined to allow the crystallization of the legend and its rapid diffusion. There is good reason to believe that the Chanson, as we have it, was composed in or near the Mont St. Michel in Brittany. Its greatest historical value does not lie in the above-mentioned nucleus, however, but in the fact that it gives us unconsciously an excellent picture of the feudal and Christian France of the eleventh century; it illustrates admirably the finest trait of the gentlemen of those days, their intense loyalty to their liege and to God. It contains also some older elements; thus, the trial of the traitor Ganelon is a good account of Frankish criminal procedure.

It is no exaggeration to say that the Chanson de Roland is the noblest monument of early European literature. Its appearance at this time, which marks the beginning of a new (European) civilization, is as significant as the appearance of Homer at the threshold of historical Greece.

Texts—Editions by Francisque Michel (Paris, 1837); by Léon Gautier (Tours, 1872; very often reprinted); by Edmund Stengel (Heilbronn, 1878); by Wendelin Foerster (Heilbronn, 1883); by Joseph Bédier (Paris, 1922); by T. Atkinson Jenkins (Boston, 1924).

Translation in modern French by L. Gautier (1872); L. Petit de Julleville (1878). In English prose by Isabel Butler (177 p., Boston, 1904); in English verse by Arthur S. Way (158 p., Cambridge, 1913); etc.

Criticism—Henri Monin: Dissertation sur le roman de Roncevaux (Paris, 1832. Real discovery of the Chanson). Gaston Paris: Histoire poétique de Charlemagne (Paris, 1865). Léon Gautier: Les épopées françaises (2e ed., 4 vols., Paris, 1878–1894). Pio Rajna: Le origini dell' epopea francesca (Florence, 1884); Le fonti dell' Orlando furioso (2d ed., Florence, 1900). Gaston Paris: La littérature française au moyen âge (Paris, 1890). Joseph Bédier: Les légendes épiques. Recherches sur la formation des chansons de geste (Paris, 1908–1914; 2d ed., 4 vols., 1914–1921). Prosper Boissonade: Du nouveau sur la chanson de Roland (526 p., Paris, 1923; Isis, VII, 187).

The great influence of the pilgrimage roads upon artistic development was studied with considerable care and ingenuity by A. Kingsley Porter: Romanesque Sculpture of the Pilgrim Roads (1 vol. of text, 9 vols. of plates, Boston, 1923; Isis, VII, 536). Even if one can not accept every one of the author's conclusions on particular points, it must be admitted that he has proved his main contention, the importance of the pilgrimage roads for the transmission of artistic ideas in the eleventh and twelfth centuries. That the epic poems and scientific ideas traveled to a large extent along these same roads is highly plausible. Additional evidence will be found in Emile Mâle: L'art religieux du XIIe siècle en France (464 p., Paris, 1922; Isis, VI, 52–56). Georgiana Goddard King: The way of St. James (3 vols., New York, 1920).

Latin Historiography

HERMANN THE LAME

See note in mathematical section (III), above.

ADAM OF BREMEN

See note in geographical section (VI), above.

LAMBERT OF HERSFELD

Also called Lambert of Aschaffenburg, the place where he was ordained priest. Flourished at the abbey of Hersfeld on the Weser, from 1058; died after 1077. German Benedictine and annalist. Pilgrim to the Holy Land. His main work is the Annales from the creation to 1077; the part dealing with the years 1040 to 1077 being very important. It is a history of the papacy and the empire, friendly to the former. His style was influenced by Sallust and Livy.

Text—Editio princeps, 1525. Edition by L. F. Hesse, in Mon. Germ. hist., reprinted in Migne's Patrology (vol. 146, 1027–1248).

German translation by L. F. Hesse (Berlin, 1855; 2d ed. 1883).

Opera omnia, edited by Oswald Holder-Egger (Hanover, 1894).

Criticism—Julius Dieffenbacher: Lambert als Historiograph (Diss., 127 p., Heidelberg, 1890). A. Eigenbrodt: Lampert und die neuere Quellenforschung (Cassel, 1896).

MARIANUS SCOTTUS

Original Irish name: Moelbrigte, meaning Bridget's servant. Born in 1028 in Ireland; after 1056, he flourished in Cologne, Fulda, and Mainz; he died at Mainz in 1082–83. Irish-German monk; annalist and chronologist. His Chronicon is a chronological summary of the history of the world from the creation to 1082; it obtained much success.

Marianus carried on deep studies of chronology and reached the conclusion that Dionysius Exiguus (q. v., first half of sixth century) had made a mistake of 22 years in the date of the Incarnation. He thus proposed to add 22 years to every date and did so in his Chronicon, but no chronologist followed his example. Modern criticism has proved that Marianus's contention was correct, but that he exaggerated Dionysius's mistake. (See my note on the Birth of Christianity, first half of first century).

Text—First edition by Oporinus (Basel, 1559). New edition by Georg Waitz, in the Mon. Germ. hist. (1826). Reprinted in Migne's Patrology (vol. 147, 601–802, 1844).

Criticism—Bartholomew MacCarthy: The Codex palatino-vaticanus n°. 830 (Royal Irish Ac., Todd Lecture Series, vol. 3, 452 p., Dublin, 1892. Insisting on the passages of the Chronicle which are of Irish interest; it contains also extracts from the Leabhar breac, the Books of Leinster and Ballymote, and the Annals of Tigernach). Max Manitius: Lateinische Literatur des Mittelalters (vol. 2, 388–394, 1923).

BYZANTINE HISTORIOGRAPHY

PSELLOS

See my note in Section II, above.

ATTALIATES

See my note in Section IX, below.

XIPHILINOS

Joannes Xiphilinos (Ἰωάννης ὁ Ξιφιλῖνος). From Trebizond. Flourished at Constantinople in the second half of the eleventh century. Byzantine monk and historian. Upon request of the emperor Michael Parapinaces (1071 to 1078), he prepared an epitome of Dion Cassios's history. We owe to him what knowledge we have of Books 61 to 80, and a better knowledge of Books 36 to 60.

Text—See the editions of Dion Cassios (first half of third century).
Criticism—K. Krumbacher: Byzantinische Litteratur (369, 1897).

SCYLITZES

Joannes Scylitzes (Ἰωάννης ὁ Σκυλίτζης). Flourished in Constantinople in the second half of the eleventh century; died not long after 1081. Byzantine annalist. He wrote a continuation of Theophanes's chronicle (q. v., first half of ninth century), dealing with the period 811 to 1079. The preface to his chronicle contains a bibliography of Byzantine historiography with critical remarks.

Text—Complete but bad edition in Latin by J. B. Gabius (Venice, 1570). For the Greek text see the editions of Georgios Cedrenos (Γεώργιος ὁ Κεδρηνός), an annalist who flourished about the end of the century and compiled a world-chronicle from Adam to 1057. The part dealing with the period 811 to 1057 is literally transcribed from Scylitzes! Greek and Latin edition of Cedrenos by G. Xylander (Bale, 1566); by Im. Bekker in the Bonn Byzantine corpus (2 vols., 1838–39), reproduced in Migne's Greek patrology (vol. 121–122). (These editions, except the first, contain also Scylitzes's text for the final period, 1057–1079).

Criticism—K. Krumbacher: Byzantinische Litteratur (365–369, 1897), reproducing a part of the original text of the preface, unique in Byzantine, and perhaps in mediaeval, literature.

JEWISH HISTORIOGRAPHY

AHIMAAZ

Ahimaaz ben Paltiel. Born at Capua in 1017; died at Oria c. 1060. Italo-Jewish chronicler. He wrote, c. 1055, a family history in rhymed Hebrew prose generally called "The Chronicle of Ahimaaz." Its real title is "Book of Genealogies" (Sefer yuḥasin). It is important because of its unique information on early Jewish settlements in Italy (850 to 1054). It records many Jewish manners and superstitions of that time. One has found in it the earliest trace of the story of the "Wandering Jew."

Text—Edited by Adolf Neubauer in his Mediaeval Jewish Chronicles (vol. 2, 1895). English translation, with introduction and notes, by Marcus Salzman (140 p., New York, 1924).

Criticism—Article by Richard Gottheil in Jewish Encyclopaedia (vol. 1, 290–291, 1901).

MUSLIM HISTORIOGRAPHY

AL-BAKRĪ

See my note in the geographical section (VI), above.

IBN ṢĀ'ID

Abū-l-Qāsim Ṣā'id ibn Aḥmad ibn 'Abd al-Raḥmān ibn Muḥammad ibn Ṣā'id al-Qurṭubī al-Andalusī. Also called Qāḍī Ṣā'id. Born of a Cordovan family at Almeria in 1029–30; flourished in Toledo; died on June 16, 1070. Hispano-Muslim historian and astronomer. He wrote in 1067–68 a summary of universal history (Kitāb al-ta'rīf bi ṭabaqāt al-umam; Instructio de classibus gentium); he wrote also a history of learned men, both Muslims and barbarians (this may be a part of the previous work), and a treatise on astronomy. He was a great observer; the observations made by him and other Muslim and Jewish astronomers working with him were of great value to al-Zarqālī for the compilation of his new tables.

In his historical work, the Ṭabaqāt al-umam, Ibn Ṣā'id paid special attention to the history of science. According to him, eight races or nations have contributed most to the progress of science: Hindus, Persians, Chaldaeans, Greeks, Latins (including Oriental Christians), Egyptians, Muslims, and Hebrews. His accounts of the Greeks and Muslims are far more elaborate than those of other peoples. Much use was made of Ibn Ṣā'id's work by Ibn al-Qifṭī and Ibn abī Uṣaibi'a in the first half, and by Barhebraeus, in the second half of the thirteenth century.

Text—Critical edition of the Ṭabaqāt al-umam by Louis Cheikho (S. J.) with notes and tables (Beyrouth, 1912). Father Cheikho had published a less complete edition of the same text in the Mashriq (1911). An English version is very desirable.

Criticism—F. Wüstenfeld: Geschichtschreiber der Araber (No. 206, 1881). C. Brockelmann: Arabische Litteratur (vol. 1, 343, 1898). H. Suter: Mathematiker (106, 1900).

AL-KHAṬĪB AL-BAGHDĀDĪ

Abū Bakr Aḥmad ibn 'Alī ibn Thābit al-Khaṭīb al-Baghdādī, meaning, the preacher of Bagdad. Born c. 1002 in Darzījān, on the Tigris below Bagdad; traveled extensively, and then settled in Bagdad, where he died on September 5, 1071. Muslim traditionalist and historian. He wrote a history of the learned men of Bagdad in 14 volumes (Ta'rīkh Baghdād), a treatise on the criticism of traditions (The adequate book, Kitāb al-kifāya fī ma'rifat uṣūl 'ilm al-riwāya); another on the orthography of proper names (Mu'tanif takmilat al-mu'talif wal-mukhtalif); etc.

Text—G. Le Strange: A Greek Embassy to Bagdad in 917 (Journal Roy. Asiatic Soc., 35–45, 1897) (ex Ta'rīkh).

Criticism—C. Brockelmann: Arabische Litteratur (vol. 1, 329, 1898).

NĀṢIR-I-KHUSRAW

See note in geographical section (VI), above.

CHINESE HISTORIOGRAPHY

OU-YANG HSIU

Ou[1]-yang[2] Hsiu[1] (8492, 12883, 4661). Canonized as Wên[2] Chung[1] (12633, 2877). His tablet was placed in the Confucian temple in 1530. Born in Lu[2]-ling[2] (7402, 7235), Kiangsi, in 1007; died 1072. Chinese historian and statesman. Author of the earliest work on ancient inscriptions, Chi[2]*-ku[3]-lu[4]* (906, 6188, 7386) and of an elaborate treatise on the peony. He edited, c. 1060, the new history of the T'ang dynasty, Hsin[1] T'ang[2] shu[1] (4574, 10767, 10024), in 255 books, with the aid of Sung Ch'i (q. v., first half of eleventh century).[w] Later, taking for models the Ch'un[1] Ch'iu[1] (2854, 2302) and the Shih[3]-chi[4] (9893, 923), he wrote alone the new history of the Five Dynasties, Hsin[1] wu[3]-tai[4]-shih[3] (4574, 12698, 10547, 9893) in 74 books.[x] These two great works form respectively the seventeenth and nineteenth of the Twenty-Four Histories.

Text—Chinese edition of the Hsin T'ang shu (Chekiang, 1873; 255 chüan in 40 vols.); of the Hsin wu-tai-shih. (Hu Pê ts'ung-wên, 1872; 74 chüan in 8 vols.).

Criticism—Wylie: Chinese Literature (21–22, 1902). Giles: Chinese Biographical Dictionary (606, 1898); Chinese Literature (212–216, 1901).

---

[w] The biographical section is ascribed entirely to Sung Ch'i. For the Old T'ang history, see Liu Hsü (first half of tenth century).

[x] For the old history of those dynasties, see Hsieh Chü-chêng (second half of tenth century).

SSŬ-MA KUANG

Ssŭ[1]-ma[3] Kuang[1] (10250, 7576, 6389). His tablet was placed in the Confucian temple in 1267. Native of Hsia[2]* (4221) in Honan in 1019; he died at K'ai[1]-fêng[1] fu[3] (5794, 3582, 3682) in 1086. Chinese historian and lexicographer. His annals of China from c. 400 B. C. to c. 960 were submitted to the emperor in 1066 and completed in 1084. They form the substance of what is still the most complete single work on Chinese history. They were originally called Universal Mirror to help Government, Tzŭ[1] chih[4] t'ung[1] chien[4] (12342, 1845, 12294, 1644). They were remodeled under Chu Hsi's direction (q. v., second half of twelfth century) and are generally known under the name which was then given to them, T'ung[1] chien[4] kang[1] mu[4]* (12294, 1644, 5900, 8080). This reconstruction was not completed until 1223, many years after Chu Hsi's death.

Among other works, he compiled a dictionary called Lei[4] p'ien[1] (6853, 9220) containing over 31,000 characters arranged under 544 radicals.

Text—Father de Mailla's Histoire générale de la Chine (13 vols., 4to, Paris, 1777 to 1785) is essentially a translation (very imperfect) of the T'ung chien kang mu. For a description of it and titles of other works based on it, see Cordier: Bibliotheca Sinica (2e ed., vol. 1, 583–587, 1904). Father Wieger's Textes Historiques (2d ed., 1922–23; Isis, VII, 569) are largely derived from Ssŭ-ma Kuang.
Criticism—H. A. Giles: Chinese Biographical Dictionary (669–671, 1898). Friedrich Hirth: Ancient History of China (264, 1908).

JAPANESE HISTORIOGRAPHY

The Eigwa monogatari, meaning Tale of Glory (or magnificence, splendor), is a chronicle of Japanese history (in 41 books) covering a period of about two centuries, ending in 1092. It deals chiefly with the munificent rule of Fujiwara no Michinaga (966 to 1027)[y] and his two sons. This work is ascribed to Akazome Emon, a female attendant to Michinaga's wife. She could not have written the last part of it; her own part may have ended about the year 1027. As the title suggests, this chronicle was deeply influenced by the two great romances of the first half of the tenth century, the Taketori monogatari and the Ise monogatari. The Eigwa monogatari was the earliest Japanese chronicle written in Japanese, a fact of great significance.

W. G. Aston: History of Japanese Literature (122–125, 1899). Michel Revon: Anthologie de la littérature japonaise (225–228, 1910).

IX. LOMBARD, ENGLISH, BYZANTINE, MUSLIM, HINDU, AND CHINESE LAW AND SOCIOLOGY

BARBARIAN LAW

The last Lombard codes (also the last barbarian codes) date from the eleventh century. The earliest Lombard code (for which, see first half of seventh century) was already very remarkable because of its systematic method of presentation and its terminology derived from Roman law. Under the influence of the law school of Pavia, where the tradition of Roman law was revived, two new codes were elaborated, the Liber legis Langobardorum (or Liber Papiensis) at the begin-

[y] Nicknamed Midō Kwampaku; also Hōjōji no Kwampaku, because he had built with extraordinary splendor the monastery Hōjō-ji; Kwampaku being the name of his dignity, the highest at the Japanese court. Midō was the name of Michinaga's residence, (the richest in Kyōto next to the imperial palace).

ning, and the Lombarda at the end of the century. There are two versions of the Lombarda, called respectively Casinensis and Vulgata.

The school of Pavia, famous from at least the beginning of the eleventh century, was essentially concerned with Lombard law, but it became gradually more interested in Roman law because of its universality (see H. Rashdall: Universities of Europe in the Middle Ages, vol. 1, 106, 1895). See my note on the study of law in the twelfth century.

Text—Edited by F. Bluhme and A. Boretius in the Mon. Germ. hist.

Laws of Edward the Confessor

Edward, King of the English, died in 1066. The laws named after him are said to have been compiled after his death from declarations made on oath by 12 men of each shire in 1070.

Felix Liebermann: Über die Leges Edwardi Confessoris (14 p., Halle a. S., 1896).

Domesday

The conquest of England by William the Conqueror in 1066 and the confiscation of landed estates which followed naturally caused chaotic conditions, which it was urgent to remove as promptly as possible to insure the health of the body politic. It was decided at the Christmas assembly of 1085 to make a survey of the whole country. This survey was completed the following year; it is possible though not certain that the Domesday Book was also completely written in the same year (1086).

Though the aim of the survey was not scientific, but politic and fiscal, it is hardly necessary to insist upon its great scientific importance.

The original manuscript of Domesday forms two volumes. It was at first preserved at Winchester, the early Norman capital, hence its name Liber de Wintonia; it is now in the Public Record Office, London.

Text—Domesday-Book seu Liber censualis, published by order of George III (2 vols., London, 1783). A volume of indexes appeared in 1811 and a fourth volume containing supplementary documents in 1816. Photo-zincographed edition (35 pt., in 33 vols., Southampton, 1861–1864). There are many separate editions relative to individual counties.

Criticism—Robert Kelham: Domesday Book (illustrated, 407 p., London, 1788). Sir Henry Ellis: General Introduction to Domesday Book (2 vols., London, 1833). P. Edward Dove (editor): Domesday Studies, being the papers read at the meeting of the Domesday Commemoration, 1886 (2 vols., London, 1888–1891). F. W. Maitland: Domesday Book and Beyond (542 p., Cambridge, 1897). Adolphus Ballard: The Domesday Inquest (29 p., London, 1906).

Byzantine Law

ATTALIATES

Michael Attaliates (Μιχαὴλ ὁ Ἀτταλειάτης), meaning probably that he originated from Attalia in Pamphylia; flourished in Constantinople from about the middle of the century; died probably not long after 1080. Byzantine jurist and annalist. He wrote (1) in 1072, a legal compendium (Πόνημα νομικὸν ἤτο, σύνοψις πραγματική) which completes our knowledge of the Basilica (second half of the tenth century); (2) in 1077, rules for the hospice and convent founded by him[z] (Διάταξις ἐπὶ τῷ

[z] On such foundations, see Krumbacher (314–319).

παρ' αὐτοῦ συστάντι πτωχοτροφείῳ καὶ τῷ μοναστηρίῳ), with a list of books!; (3) in 1079 or 1080, annals for the period 1034 to 1079.

Text—The legal compendium was first edited by Marquard Freher (Frankfurt, 1596).

The rules were edited K. Sathas in his Μεσαιωνικὴ βιβλιοθήκη (vol. 1, 1–69, 1872). Again by Fr. Miklosich and J. Müller in their Acta et diplomata graeca medii aevi (vol. 5, 293–327, 1887).

The annals, discovered by Brunet de Presle, were edited by Em. Bekker in the Bonn corpus (1853).

Criticism—Waldemar Nissen: Die Diataxis des Michael Attaleiates. Ein Beitrag zur Geschichte des Klosterwesens im byzantinischen Reiche (Diss., Jena, 1894). K. Krumbacher: Byzantinische Litteratur (269–271, 1897).

Muslim Politics

AL-MĀWARDĪ

Abū-l-Ḥasan 'Alī ibn Muḥammad ibn Ḥabīb al-Māwardī. Flourished at Baṣra and Bagdad; died, aged 86, in 1058. Muslim student of politics. He belonged to the Shāfi'ite school. His main work is a "Book on the Principles of Government," Kitāb al-aḥkām al-sulṭānīya, one of the most important of its kind. He wrote also a treatise on ethics, Kitāb ādāb al-dunyā wa-l-dīn, which is still popular in Turkish and Egyptian schools. His works, published by the care of one of his own disciples, were not issued until after his death.

Text—Constitutiones politicae, edited by R. Enger (Bonn, 1853). Traité de droit public musulman traduit et annoté par le comte Léon Ostrogog (vol. 1; vol. 2, part 1, Paris, 1901–1906. Incomplete). Complete translation with careful notes by E. Fagnan: Les statuts gouvernementaux ou Règles de droit public et administratif (600 p., Alger, 1915).

Criticism—R. Enger: De vita et scriptis Māwerdīs (Bonn, 1851). C. Brockelmann: Arabische Litteratur (vol. 1, 386, 1898). Carra de Vaux: Penseurs de l'Islam (vol. 1, 273–277, 1921; vol. 3, 349–360, 1923).

NIDHĀM AL-MULK

Abū 'Alī al-Ḥasan ibn 'Alī ibn Isḥāq. Born in 1018 in Nūqān, one of the twin towns constituting Ṭūs; flourished at the Saljūq court; assassinated in 1092. Persian statesman and student of politics. He wrote in 1092 for the Saljūq sulṭān, Malikshāh,[a] a Treatise on the Art of Government, Siyāsat-nāma, which is probably the most important contribution of that age on the subject. It is written in Persian and is divided into 50 chapters. It contains valuable information not only on government and administration, but also on other topics—heresies, for example.

Text—Siasset Nameh: Texte persan édité par Charles Schefer (216 p., Public. de l'école des langues orientales vivantes, Paris, 1891); French translation and historical notes by the same (*ibidem*, 1893); supplement with biographical information on the author derived from Persian and Arabic works (1897).

Criticism—Review of Schefer's edition by Th. Nöldeke, in Z. der Deutschen Morg. Ges. (vol. 46, 761–768, 1892). E. G. Browne: Literary History of Persia, chiefly chapter 4 of vol. 2, 1906.

---

[a] This Malikshāh has already been mentioned at least twice. See my notes above, on Omar Khayyam and Zarrīn Dast.

Hindu Law

VIJÑĀNEŚVARA

Flourished in Southern India, probably about the end of the eleventh century. Hindu jurist. Author of the Mitāksharā, the most famous commentary on the Yājñavalkya-Smṛiti; i. e., the Dharmaśāstra of Yājñavalkya (c. 350?). The Mitāksharā is still a supreme authority on inheritance questions all over India, except Bengal proper. It has itself been the subject of a number of commentaries.

Text—The Yājñavalkya was edited and translated by A. F. Stenzler (Berlin, 1849). Third edition, together with the Mitākshara (Bombay, 1892). The section of the Mitākshara dealing with the law on inheritance was Englished b H. T. Colebrooke: Two Treatises on the Hindu Law of Inheritance (p. 241–377, Calcutta, 1810); also in the edition of Madras (1864).

Criticism—M. Winternitz: Indische Litteratur (vol. 3, 499, 1922).

Chinese Sociology

WANG AN-SHIH

Wang² An¹-shih²* (12493, 44, 9964). The Japanese call him Oanseki. Born in Lin²-ch'uan¹ (7165, 2728), Kiangsi, in 1021; died in 1086. Chinese economist; radical and fearless reformer. A man of clear insight, who was far ahead of his time, he has been compared to Roger Bacon. Prime minister from 1068 to 1086. He directed great engineering works to prevent floods. He attempted to reform the examination system, requiring an acquaintance with facts rather than with words. "Accordingly[b] even the pupils at village schools threw away their textbooks of rhetoric and began to study primers of history, geography, and political economy." He changed the system of taxation and tried to renovate the financial system. Paper money had been issued in China at least since the beginning of the ninth century; by the middle of the tenth large quantities were in circulation. In Wang's time it was already very difficult to keep the paper currency at par; a few years after his death (c. 1094 to 1107) a rapid inflation began.

Text—Th› Library of Congress has a copy of Wang's collected prose writings, published in 1560, bound in 22 volumes.

Criticism—Giles: Chinese Biographical Dictionary (804–807, 1898); Chinese Literature (220–222, 1901). John C. Ferguson: Wang An-Shih (Journal China Branch, Royal Asiatic Society, vol. 35, 65–75, 1904). E. F. Fenollosa: Epochs of Chinese and Japanese Art (vol. 2, 21, 1911). Couling: Encyclopaedia sinica (591, 1917). For a brief but accurate account of Chinese paper money see T. F. Carter: Invention of Printing in China (70–81, 1925; Isis, VIII, 367).

X. FRENCH, LATIN, GREEK, HEBREW, ARABIC, PERSIAN, CHINESE, AND JAPANESE PHILOLOGY

For French philology see my notes on the Chanson de Roland in the historical section (VIII), and on Rashi in the philosophical section (II), above.

Latin Philology

PAPIAS

Papias the Lombard. Flourished c. 1053 to 1063. Latin lexicographer. He compiled in 1053 to 1063 a Latin dictionary in which he gives the quantity, gender,

[b] Says an unnamed Chinese writer quoted by Giles, op. cit., p. 221.

and inflections of Latin words and quotes Greek words. He defines legal and other technical terms.

Text—Vocabularium. Ed. princeps, Milano, 1476; Venice, 1485, 1491, 1496.
Criticism—Sandys: History of Classical Scholarship (vol. 1³, 521, 594, 666). Max Manitius: Lateinische Literatur des Mittelalters (vol. 2, 717–724, 1893).

Greek Philology

See my note on Seth in the medical section (VII), above.

Hebrew Philology

NATHAN BEN JELIEL

Born at Rome not later than 1035; traveled in Sicily, France, and Italy until c. 1070, when he settled in Rome; he died in 1106. His father, Rabbi Jehiel ben Abraham, had died in 1070. Nathan's two brothers were also very learned, and the three were called "geonim of the house of R. Jehiel." Italo-Jewish lexicographer. He completed, at the beginning of 1101, the Aruk, a monumental Talmudic dictionary upon which all later Hebrew dictionaries have been based. It is one of the greatest mediaeval monuments of learning; the only important work due to the Italian Jewry of that critical age, when Jewish culture was being gradually transferred from East to West. Nathan gave proof in it of much philological genius and of an immense erudition. Many readings are quoted and frequent comparisons made with Aramaic, Arabic, Persian, Latin, Slavonic, and Italian. It contains also a great deal of geographic and ethnographic information and is a mirror of the contemporary Italo-Jewish life.

Text—The earliest printed edition appeared at Rome (?), c. 1477. The best early edition is that of Daniel Bemberg (Venice, 1531). An excellent edition was prepared by Alexander Kohut: Aruch completum sive Lexicon vocabula et res, quae in libris targumicis, talmudicis et midraschicis continentur, explicans (8 vols., Viennae, 1878–1892); Index ad citata quae in Aruch occurrunt; necnon ad collocationem rerum, quae graviores in Talmud continentur. Cum collectione vocabulorum italicorum (Viennae, 1892); Supplement containing sources of Rabbi Nathan's Aruch. Additional foreign words (especially from the Midrash Haggadol). Corrections and explanations to the eight volumes (New York, 1892). Both supplements also by A. Kohut.
Criticism—Article by H. G. Enelow in Jewish Encyclopaedia (vol. 9, 180–183, 1905).
See also my note on Rashi in the philosophical section (II) above.

Arabic Philology

IBN SĪDA

Abū-l-Ḥasan 'Alī ibn Ismā'īl al-Mursī Ibn Sīda. Born blind in Murcia, south-eastern Spain, 1007–8; died at Denia, *ibidem*, in 1065–66. Hispano-Muslim lexicographer. Author of a great Arabic dictionary (Al-Kitāb al-mulakhkhaṣ fī-l-lugha; kitāb al-muḥkam wal-muḥīṭ al-a'ẓam).

C. Brockelmann: Arabische Litteratur (vol. 1, 308, 1898).

Earliest Latin Arabic Glossary

The earliest Latin Arabic glossary is contained in a manuscript which was written in central or western Spain (i. e., Castile or Portugal) at an unknown date. The

Latin writing is of the Wisigothic type, and the Arabic of the Maugrabin type. It is written partly on parchment and partly on paper, two leaves of parchment being each time followed by five leaves of paper (there are in all 42 leaves of parchment and 103 of paper). Paper was not introduced into Spain before the middle of the tenth century; it was not manufactured there before the middle of the twelfth. The vocabulary is very full.

Christianus Fredericus Seybold: Glossarium latino-arabicum. Ex unico quae exstat codice Leidensi undecimo saeculo in Hispania conscripto (594 p., Berlin, 1900. With interesting introduction and notes).

At least two other Latin-Arabic dictionaries were compiled in Spain during the Middle Ages.

The second in point of time was the Vocabulista in Arabico discovered in 1859 by Cl. Michaele Amari in the Riccardiana, Florence, and published in 1871 by Celestino Schiaparelli. This second vocabulary was composed in Catalonia, c. 1275, probably by the Dominican Raimundus Martinus.

The third, and by far the largest, was compiled in Granada by Pedro de Alcala, and printed in Granada, 1505, together with an Arabic grammar (this being the first Arabic grammar and dictionary to be printed). I shall come back to this in my chapter dealing with the second half of the fifteenth century.

AL-KHAṬĪB AL-BAGHDĀDĪ

See my note in historical section (VIII), above.

Persian Philology

ASADĪ

Asadī of Ṭūs; 'Alī ibn Aḥmad; nephew of Firdawsī. Flourished about 1056 to 1060. Persian poet and lexicographer. He composed c. 1060 a Persian lexicon (Lughat-i-Furs) which is very important for the study of the oldest (modern) Persian language and literature.

It is this same Asadī who transcribed, in 1056, the materia medica of Abū Manṣūr Muwaffaq (q. v., second half of tenth century), and this copy of his is the oldest Persian manuscript extant.

Text—Asadī's lexicon was edited from the unique Vatican manuscript by Paul Horn (Göttingen, 1897).

Criticism—E. A. Browne: Literary History of Persia (vol. 1, 1908; vol. 2, 273, 1906).

Chinese Philology

See my notes on Ssŭ-ma Kuang in the historical section (VIII), and on Wang An-shih in the legal section (IX).

Japanese Philology

See my note on the Eigwa Monagatari in the historical section (VIII), above.

BRIEF INDEX

This index is called brief because all references to modern (i. e., nineteenth and twentieth century) scholars have been omitted. This limitation has reduced its size considerably without affecting its usefulness, for the following reasons: The more important authors, such as Tannery, Cantor, Duhem, Steinschneider (to name but a few of the dead), have been quoted so often that their names would have been followed by endless series of numbers which would have left the reader helpless. Moreover, if one wants to find the title of a paper of, say, Tannery on Ecphantos, it will suffice to look up Ecphantos in the index. On the other hand, all the older editors and critics have been indexed, and thus my book may be profitably consulted for the study not only of its own subject-matter but of pre-nineteenth century scholarship.

I must mention another limitation which has enabled me to keep this index within a relatively small size. Generally speaking, the broader topics have been omitted because the reader may be trusted to find his bearings with regard to them by means of the table of contents. For example, does he want to know what my book contains on Chinese mathematics, Byzantine medicine, or Muslim geography, the table of contents will tell him rapidly which sections need be consulted and which may be passed by. Indeed, it would be easy to extract from my book a number of smaller books dealing exclusively with Chinese mathematics, or Byzantine medicine, or any other subject which may have engrossed the reader's attention.

Greek and Latin works have not been indexed under their own titles, except when they were of unknown or doubtful paternity, or in a few cases where they were more popularly known than their authors or had an exceptionally great importance. An obvious example of the last group is the Timaeos. Students of mediaeval Platonism ought to consult such catchwords as "Timaeos" and "Macrocosmos," as well as "Plato" and "Neoplatonism." On the whole, but few Greek and Latin works have been indexed.[a] On the contrary, my index of Oriental titles and terms (chiefly Arabic, Sanskrit, and Chinese) is very full. It is hardly necessary to justify this difference of treatment. Classical scholars have already at their disposal a number of excellent tools which make the finding of literary or archaeological information a relatively easy matter. Oriental scholars are not yet so well equipped. I thought it unnecessary to duplicate the service rendered by many excellent classical treatises; it was better to concentrate my energy upon the urgent needs of Oriental scholarship. I trust that my book will be found particularly useful in this respect.

With regard to scientific topics, it should be remembered that my index is not and can not be exhaustive. For one thing, when I spoke of men of science who dealt with many subjects (e. g., a medical encyclopaedist would deal with every medical subject known in his day), I could but mention a few of these by way of

[a] As the Greek works which required separate indexing are generally best known under their Latin names (e. g., De mundo), it is under that name that they have been classified.

illustration. These few are of course the only ones to be indexed. Thus, the reader consulting such catchwords as "pulse," or "tides," or "womb," or "equation," can not expect to be able to reconstruct from my book a complete history of any of these subjects, but it is hoped that he will find sufficient material and references to be fairly well launched on his own exploration.

Ancient and mediaeval authors were generally known under many names. Some, but not all, of these names have been indexed; in general, each author has been indexed under two or three names. To avoid a superfluity of cross-references, which are a little irritating, the main page is generally quoted after each name, though all the secondary references are listed only once, under the name which I have selected as the most important or convenient. Thus, anyone having found the main information which he needed about a certain author, is invited to consult the index under that author's cardinal name, that is, if he wishes to obtain the additional information which my book probably contains in various other places. Rulers and popes have been indexed only when I have given some specific information about them; they have not been indexed when mentioned only for chronological purposes. A similar remark applies to place-names.

The cardinal names of men of science and scholars to whom a special section is devoted are followed by an indication of their time, then by the number of the page upon which that section is located, finally by the numbers relative to secondary references. For example:

Archimedes (III–2, B. C.), 169–172; 166, 167, etc., means that Archimedes flourished in the second half of the third century B. C., that a special section is devoted to him and will be found on pages 169–172, and that additional information may be found on pages 166, 167, etc.

Such words as liber, sefer, kitāb, risāla have generally been disregarded, the classification being based upon the next significant term. The following words have also been neglected in the classification: in Arabic, al and ibn (except when the latter occurs at the beginning of a name); in Persian, i and ibn (with same restriction); in Hebrew, ha and ben (idem); in Japanese, no. Chinese words have been classified character by character; that is, the first monosyllable determines the fundamental subdivision; the second, the second subdivision, etc. The Umlaut has been classified as if it stood for an e, and the same has been done by extension for every vowel bearing two dots, except in the case of Chinese words, where the dotted vowels follow the undotted ones. Thus the Chu's are classified together, being immediately followed by the Chü's.

I may still add that readers desiring information on the works of modern historians of science may remedy to some extent the voluntary deficiency of my own index by referring to the indices published in the Mitteilungen zur Geschichte der Medizin or in Isis (Vols. I, III, VI, IX).

This index has been compiled under my direction by Dorothy Waterman (Radcliffe, 1928).

GEORGE SARTON.

CAMBRIDGE, MASS.
January 11, 1927.

INDEX

Aachen, 528.
Aaron of Alexandria (vii-1), 479; 462, 463.
Aaron ben Moses ben Asher, 624.
Aaron's breastplate, 764.
Abacists, 756.
Abacus, 299, 473, 560, 663, 670, 686, 714, 720, 740, 756, 757, 758.
Abba Arika (iii-1), 317; 314.
Al-'Abbas ibn Sa'īd al-Jauharī (ix-1), 562; 545.
'Abbāsid court, 524.
Abbo of Fleury (x-2), 671; 653, 655, 732.
'Abd al-'Azīz ibn 'Uthmān al-Qabīṣī, 669.
'Abd al-Laṭīf, 466.
'Abd al-Malik ibn Hishām, 579.
'Abd al-Masīḥ Nā'ima of Emessa, 406.
'Abd al-Qāhir ibn Ṭāhir al-Baghdādī, 706.
'Abd al-Raḥmān III, Umayyad of Cordova (x-1), 628; 620, 680.
'Abd al-Raḥmān ibn 'Abdallāh, 616.
'Abd al-Raḥmān ibn Muḥammad ibn al-Wāfid, 728.
'Abd al-Raḥmān al-Ṣūfī (x-2), 665; 649, 654.
'Abdallāh ibn 'Abd al-'Azīz, 768.
'Abdallāh ibn Amājūr al Turkī, 630.
'Abdallāh ibn Maymūn al-Qaddāḥ, 584, 593.
'Abdallah ibn Muḥammad ibn al-Faraḍī, 734.
'Abdallāh ibn Muslim ibn Qutaiba, 615.
'Abdallāh ibn Sahn ibn Naubakht, 531.
'Abdallāh ibn al-Ṭaiyib al 'Irāqī, 730.
Abe Manao, 575.
Abe Nai-shinnō, 529.
Abe Seimei (x-2), 672; 649, 654.
Abenguefit, 728.
Abenragel, 715.
Aberration spherical. See Spherical aberration.
Abhidhamma, 167.
Abhidharma, 468.
Abhidharmakośa, 350, 492.
Abhidharmakośavyākhyā, 350.
Ablativus, 217.
al-Abniya 'an ḥaqā'iq al-adwiya, 678.
Abortion, 383.
Abraham ben Jacob, 675.
Abraham the Jew, 681.
Abraham ben Samuel Halevi, 640.
Abū 'Alī al-Khaiyāṭ (ix-1), 569; 546.
Abū-l-Aswad al-Du'alī (vii-2), 501; 490.
Abū Bakr (ix-2), 603; 585, 590.
Abū Bakr ibn 'Alī ibn 'Uthmān, 709.
Abū Bakr al-Rāzī (x-1), 643; 622, 624.
Abū Dulaf (x-1), 637; 622, 624, 636.
Abū-l-Faraj al-Iṣfahānī (x-1), 642; 541, 622, 623, 624.
Abū-l-Fatḥ (x-2), 664; 648, 654.
Abū Ḥanīfa (viii-1), 507; 503, 524, 525, 615.
Abū-l-Ḥasan 'Alī, 630.
Abū-l-Ḥasan ibn al-Bahlūl, 689.
Abū-l-Ḥasan al-Maghrabī, 659, 716.
Abū-l-Ḥusain 'Abd al-Raḥmān, 665.
Abū Ja'far ibn Ḥabash, 565.
Abū Ja'far al-Khāzin (x-2), 664; 648, 654.
Abū Janīsh, 672.
Abū-l-Jūd (xi-1), 718; 696, 697, 702.
Abū Kāmil (x-1), 630; 620, 621, 624.
Abū Manṣūr Muwaffak (x-2), 678; 649, 650, 651, 654, 783.
Abū Ma'shar (ix-1), 568; 546, 550, 558, 560.
Abū Muḥammad ibn Mūsā, 561.
Abū Muḥammad 'Ubaydallāh, 593.
Abū Naṣr Manṣūr (x-2), 668; 254, 649, 654.
Abū-l-Qāsim (x-2), 681; 650, 651, 654.
Abū Raiḥān Muḥammad ibn Aḥmad al-Bīrūnī, 707.
Abū Sahl al-Masīḥī (x-2), 678; 651, 654.
Abū Sa'īd al-Ḍarīr (ix-1), 562; 545, 550.
Abū Sa'īd Shādsān, 569.
Abū Sa'īd 'Ubaidallāh (xi-1), 730; 700, 701.
Abū Shuja' Rudhrawari, 687.
Abū 'Ubaida (viii-2), 541; 523, 524.
Abū 'Umar ibn Ḥajjāj (xi-2), 766; 741, 746.
Abū 'Uthmān (x-1), 631; 620, 622.
Abū-l-Wafā' (x-2), 666-667; 562, 648, 649, 654.
Abū-l-Wafā' al-Mubashshir, 130.
Abū Ya'qūb al-Bāṣir, 703.
Abū Yūsuf (viii-2), 525; 520, 524.
Abū Yūsuf Ben Isaac ben Ezra, 680.
Abū Yūsuf Ya'qūb al-Qirqisānī, 626.
Abū Zaid (x-1), 636; 571, 621, 624.
Abulcasis, 651, 681.
Abulpharagius Abdalla Benattibus, 730.
Academy (iv-1, b. c.), 113-116; 111, 414, 439.
Accentuation, 189.
Accursius, 375.
Acetic acid, 532.
Achilles Tatios (iii-1), 322; 315.
Achillini, Alessandro, 557.
Ackermann, J. Ch. G., 375, 769.
Acoustics, 73. See Sound.
Acoustics, architectural, 223.
Acron of Agrigentum (v, b. c.), 102; 83.
Acupuncture, 342, 499, 683, 732.
Ādāb al-'Arab wal Furs, 687.

Ādāb al-dunyā wa-l-dīn, 780.
Adab al-kātib, 615.
Adalbert of Magdeburg, 641.
Adam, Nestorian missionary, 527.
Adam of Bremen (xi-2), 767; 724, 741, 743, 745.
Adamantios Sophista (iv-1), 356; 324, 345, 346.
Adaptation, 128, 597. See Evolution.
Adelard of Bath, 534, 563, 668, 756.
Adelbold of Utrecht (xi-1), 714; 670, 695, 697, 700, 702.
Adelwold, 692.
Ademarus Engolismensis, 733.
Adhémar of Chabannes (xi-1), 733; 700, 702.
Adlington, William, 296.
Adonim the Levite, 690.
Adrastos of Aphrodisias (ii-1), 271; 267, 352.
'Aḍud al-Dawla, Buwayhid, (x-2), 658; 647, 650, 654, 677.
Adulitic inscriptions, 431.
Advaita, 754.
al-Adwiya al-mufrada, 728.
al-Adwiya al-mufrada wal-aghdhiya, 640.
Aegidius de Tebaldis, 716.
Aegimios of Elis, 215.
Aelfred. See Alfred the Great.
Aelfric of Canterbury, 692.
Aelfric grammaticus (x-2), 692; 296, 511, 653, 655.
Aelfric of York, 692.
Aelian (iii-1), 326; 315, 316, 657.
Aelian, tactician, 213.
Aelianos, Claudios. See Aelian.
Aelios Dionysios. See Dionysios.
Aelius Paetus, Sextus (ii-1, b. c.), 189; 179.
Aeneas Tacticos (iv-1, b. c.), 119; 112, 213.
Aeolipile, 208.
Aesculapius, 417, 434.
Aethelmaer. See Malmesbury, Oliver of.
Aethelwold, 692.
Aether. See Quintessence.
Aethicus, cosmography of (vii-2), 495.
Aethicus Ister (or Istriacus), 489, 495.
Aethiopia, 185, 431.
Aethiopic version, 381.
Aëtios of Amida (vi-1), 434; 308, 309, 417, 419, 639.
Afflacius, Joannes (xi-2), 769; 742, 745.
Aflāṭūn, 114.
Africa, circumnavigation, 78.
Africanus, papyrus, 340.
Agatharchides of Cnidos (ii-1, b. c.), 185; 178, 179.
Agatharchos of Samos (v, b. c.), 95; 82.
Agathemeros, 285.
Agathinos, Claudios (i-2), 260; 244.
Agathodaemon, alchemist, 238.
Agathodaemon of Alexandria, 268, 276.
Ages, World, 57.
Āghā Khān, 753, 760.
al-Aghānī, 642.
Agniveśa, 284.
Agobard, St. (ix-1), 555; 544, 549.
Agricola, 263.
Agricultural law, 517.
Agriculture, 158, 186, 197, 198, 256, 323, 355, 370, 452, 528. See Geoponica.
Agrimensores, 397.
Agrippa, Marcus Vipsanius (i-2, b. c.), 223; 219.
Agrippa, map of, 323.
Agron, 627, 690.
Ahimaaz ben Paltiel (xi-2), 776; 743, 745.
al-Aḥkām, 531.
al-Aḥkām al-sulṭānīya, 780.
Aḥmad, astrologer, 558.
Aḥmad ibn 'Abdallāh al-Ghāfiqī, 716.
Aḥmad ibn 'Abdallāh al-Marwazī, 565.
Aḥmad ibn abī Sa'īd al-Harawī, 254.
Aḥmad ibn abī Ya'qūb, 607.
Aḥmad ibn 'Alī al-Baghdādī, 777.
Aḥmad ibn 'Alī al-Bāqilānī, 706.
Aḥmad ibn 'Alī ibn al-Waḥshīya, 634.
Aḥmad ibn Dā'ūd al-Dīnawarī, 615.
Aḥmad ibn Faḍlān, 636.
Aḥmad ibn Ibrāhīm ibn abī Khālid, 682.
Aḥmad ibn Muḥammad al-Baladī, 679.
Aḥmad ibn Muḥammad al-Farghānī, 567.
Aḥmad ibn Muḥammad al-Hamadhānī, 635.
Aḥmad ibn Muḥammad ibn Ḥanbal, 551.
Aḥmad ibn Muḥammad ibn Maskawayh, 687.
Aḥmad ibn Muḥammad al-Rāzī, 643.
Aḥmad ibn Muḥammad al-Ṣāghānī, 666.
Aḥmad ibn Muḥammad al-Sijzī, 665.
Aḥmad ibn Muḥammad ibn al-Ṭaiyib, 597.
Aḥmad al-Muqtadir, 759.
Aḥmad ibn Mūsā, 561, 598.
Aḥmad al-Nahāwandī (ix-1), 565; 545.
Aḥmad ibn Sahl al-Balkhī, 631.
Aḥmad ibn Sirin (ix-1), 558; 544, 568, 706.
Aḥmad al-Ṭabarī (x-2), 677; 650, 654.
Aḥmad ibn Ṭūlūn, 598.
Aḥmad ibn 'Umar Ibn Rusta, 635.
Aḥmad ibn Yaḥyā Jābir al-Balādhurī, 616.
Aḥmad ibn Yūsuf al Miṣrī (ix-2), 598; 585, 590.
Ahmes, 715.
Aḥsan al-taqāsīm fī ma'rifat al-aqālīm, 675.
Aimoin of Fleury (xi-1), 732; 698, 700, 702.
al-'Ain, 542.
'Ain al-ṣan'a wa'awn-al-ṣana'ā, 723.
Air, cause of disease, 99.
Air, corporeality, 87.
Air, principle, 73.
Air, various kinds, 102.
Air. See Pneumatic.
Aiyām al-'arab, 541.
'Ajā'ib al-buldān, 637.
'Ajāyib al-Hind, 674.
Aji Kishi. See Ajiki.

Ajiki, 68, 441.
Ājīvikas, 70.
Akazome Emon, 778.
Akhbār al-rusul wal-mulūk, 642.
Akhbār al-Ṣīn wal-Hind, 636.
al-Akhbār al-ṭiwāl, 615.
Akhmīm, cotton, 535.
Akhmīm, papyrus, 354, 444, 449.
Akhunaten. See Amenhotep.
Alain de Lille, 404.
Alamanni, code of the, 484, 505, 517.
Alamūt, 752, 753.
Alanus ab Insulis, 404.
al-A'lāq al-nafīsa, 635.
Alaric II, 438.
Alaric's Breviary, 417, 438.
Albaldus, 714.
Albategnius, 585, 602.
Albatenius, 602.
Albert the Great, 404, 405.
Albertus, Ioannes, 398.
Albigensian heresy, 333.
Albinus, 528.
Albirunic problems, 707, 718.
Albohazen, 715.
Albubather, 585, 603.
Albucasis, 681.
Albumasar, 568.
Alcabitius, 669.
Alcala, Pedro de, 783.
Alcandrius, 671.
Alchandrus (x-2), 671; 649.
Alchemy, 6, 19, 339, 389, 472, 508, 514, 559, 592, 610, 723 (and passim in the chemical sections; see also Transmutation).
Alchemy, Chinese, 335.
Alchemy, Hellenistic, 238.
Alchemy, Muslim, 335.
Alchemy, Taoist, 193.
Alchvine, 528.
Alcmaeon of Crotona (vi, b. c.), 77; 66.
Alcohol, 534, 723. See Distillation.
Alcuin (viii-2), 528; 506, 521, 527, 549, 555.
Aldhelm, St. (vii-2), 492; 488, 490.
Alexander of Alexandria, 319.
Alexander of Aphrodisias (iii-1), 318-319; 314, 316, 324, 630.
Alexander the Great (iv-2, b. c.), 127; 124, 241, 284.
Alexander, pseudo, 324.
Alexander, romance of, 127.
Alexander of Tralles (vi-2), 453; 427, 434, 443, 444, 639.
Alexandria, 127, 149.
Alexandria, destruction of library of, 466.
Alexandria, Museum. See Museum.
Alexandrian text of the New Testament, 349.
Alf laila wa-laila, 527, 571.
Alfadhol, liber, 531.
Alfalfa, 197.
Alfanus. See Alphanus.
Alfasi, Isaac (xi-2), 751; 402, 739, 745, 746.
Alfonso X, el Sabio, 603, 668, 759.
Alfraganus, 567.
Alfred the Great, King (ix-2), 595; 395, 425, 446, 511, 583, 584, 586, 588, 589, 606, 634, 654, 701.
Alfred of Sareshel, 227.
Alfredus Anglicus, 227.
Algazel, 753.
Algazirah, 682.
Algebra, word, 563.
Algizar, 651, 682.
Algorism, 563.
Algorists, 756.
Alhandreus, 671.
Alhazen, 721.
Alhazen's problem, 721.
'Alī, Abū-l-Ḥasan, 620, 630.
'Alī ibn 'Abbās al-Majūsī (x-2), 677; 303, 650, 654, 710, 769.
'Alī ibn abī-l-Rijāl al-Maghribī, 715.
'Alī ibn abī Sa'īd ibn Yūnus, 716.
'Alī ibn abī Ṭālib, 501, 508.
'Alī ibn Aḥmad ibn Ḥazm, 713.
'Alī ibn Aḥmad al-'Imrānī, 632.
'Alī ibn Aḥmad al-Nasawī, 719.
'Alī ibn Hārūn al-Zanjānī, 661.
'Alī ibn al-Ḥusain al-'Alawī, 666.
'Alī ibn al-Ḥusain al-Iṣfahānī, 642.
'Alī ibn al-Ḥusain al-Mas'ūdī, 637.
'Alī ibn 'Īsā (xi-1), 731; 693, 699, 700, 701, 702, 703.
'Alī ibn 'Īsā al-Asṭurlābī (ix-1), 566; 545, 601.
'Alī ibn Ismā'īl al-Ash'arī, 625.
'Alī ibn Ismā'īl al-Mursī, 782.
'Alī ibn Ja'far al-Shaizarī, 635.
'Alī ibn Muḥammad al-Māwardī, 780.
'Alī ibn Riḍwān al-Miṣrī (xi-1), 729; 598, 699, 702, 731.
'Alī ibn Sahl al-Ṭabarī (ix-1), 574; 546, 547, 549.
'Alīd, 508.
Alimentus, L. Cincius (iii-2, b. c.), 176; 166
Alkindus, 559.
Allatius, Leo, 404.
Alligation, 183.
Alluvia, 228.
Almagest, 273, 274, 367, 429, 561, 562, 565, 601, 628, 631, 666, 759.
Almansoris, liber, 609.
Almeloveen, Theod. Jans van, 340.
Alpago of Belluno, Andrea, 711.
Alphabet. See under name of language; also Brāhmi, Glagolitsa, Kirillitsa.
Alphanus of Salerno (xi-1), 727; 374, 699.
Alpharabius, 628.
Alphonso. See Alfonso.
Alsahavarius, 681.
Altitude, determination of time by an, 565.

al-Amānāt wal-i'tiqādāt, 627.
Amara (or Amarasiṃha) (vi–2), 458; **445.**
Amarakośa, 458.
Amasis, code, 110.
Amber, 55, 264.
Ambergris, 771.
Ambrose, St. (iv–2), 362; 359.
Amenhotep IV, 58.
America, discovery of, 411, 676.
America, Icelandic discovery of, 698, 724.
Amidaism (or Amidism), 364, 553.
Amman, J. C., 392.
'Ammār ibn 'Alī al-Mawṣilī (xi–1), 729; 699, 701, 702, 703.
Ammianus Marcellinus (iv–2), 375; 361.
Ammonia, 597.
Ammonios the lithotomist (i–2, B. C.), 230; 220.
Ammonios Saccas of Alexandria (iii–1), 320; 315.
Ammonios, son of Hermias (vi–1), 421; 335, 415, 418.
Amōghavajra (or Amōgha), 509.
Amos (viii, B. C.), 57–58; 52.
'Amr ibn 'Abd al-Raḥmān al-Karmānī, 715.
'Amr ibn Baḥr al-Jāḥiẓ, 597.
'Amr ibn 'Uthmān ibn Qanbar, 542.
Amyot, Jacques, 252.
An-hsi, 197.
An Tun, 297.
Anacharsis the Scythian (vi, B. C.), 75; 65.
Anaesthesia, 325.
Analects, Confucian. See Lun yü.
Analemma, 208, 277.
Analysis, combinatorial, 139, 425, 475.
Analysis, Diophantine. See Diophantine analysis; Equations, indeterminate.
Analysis, indeterminate. See Equations, indeterminate.
Analysis, mathematical, 113.
Analysis, treasury of, 140.
Analysis, wet. See Chemical analysis.
Anan ben David (viii–2), 524; 520.
Anaritius, 598.
Anastasius the Librarian (ix–2), 614; 578, 588, 589.
d'Anastasy, Johan, **339.**
Anatolios of Alexandria (iii–2), 337; 330, 331, 336, 351.
Anatolius of Beirut, Vindonius (iv–2), 370; 360, 361, 452, 657.
Anatomia porci, 742, 770. See also Pig.
Anatomical diagrams, 538, 679.
Anatomical nomenclature, 282.
Anatomy, comparative, 128.
Anatomy, earliest treatise, 120, 121.
Anatomy, Muslim, 534.
Anatomy, Syrian, 309.
Anaxagoras of Clazomenae (v, B. C.), 86; 81, 82, 83.
Anaxarchos, 136.
Anaximander of Miletos (vi, B. C.), 72; 65.
Anaximenes of Miletos (vi, B. C.), 73; 65.
Anchor, 75.
Ancient Science, 8–14.
Andalusia, 680, 688, 768. See Spain.
Andromachos the Elder (i–2), 261; 244.
Andromachos the Younger (i–2), 261; 244.
Andronicos of Rhodes (i–1, B. C.), 203; 201.
Aneurysms, 280.
Anian, 438.
Anicia Juliana, 259, 431.
Animals, classification of, 333.
Animals, cycle of 12. See Cycle of 12 animals.
Anna, sister of Basilios II, 655.
Annals of the Bamboo Books. See Bamboo books.
Annus confusionis, 216.
Anoë, liber, 669.
Anonymus Byzantinus (vi–1), 430; 416.
Anonymus de rebus bellicis (vi–1), 430; 416.
Anonymus Londinensis, 146, 283.
Ansāb al-ashrāf, 616.
Anselm, St. (xi–2), 748; 738, 745, 746, 749.
Anthemios of Tralles (vi–1), 427; 415, 416, 453.
Anthimus (vi–1), 433; 417.
Anthology, Greek, 408.
Anthony, St. (iv–1), 346–348; 344.
Anti-Lucretius, 205.
Antichthones, 239.
Antidotes, 158, 231.
Antimony, 532, 679.
Antioch, 365, 454.
Antiochean text of the New Testament, 349.
Antiphon (v, B. C.), 93; 82, 352.
Antipodes, 185, 239, 249, 516.
Antistoichia, 691.
Antyllos (ii–1), 280; 268.
Anurādhapura, 167.
Anūshīrwān. See Nūshīrwān the Just.
al-Anwa', 669, 680.
Āpastamba, 74, 75.
Aphrodisiacs, 574.
"Apicius", 340.
Apicius, M. Gabius, 340.
Apiculture, 158, 226.
Apion of Alexandria, 262.
Apocalyptic allegories, 764.
Apocalyptic fears, 734.
Apogee, motion of the solar, 758.
Apogee, sun's, 603, 716.
Apollodoros of Athens (ii–2, B. C.), 198; 192.
Apollodoros (author of the Library), 198.
Apollodoros of Damascus (ii–1), 278; 268.
Apollonios of Citium (i–1, B. C.), 215; 119, 203, 608.
Apollonios Dyscolos of Alexandria (ii–1), 286; 269, 440.

Apollonios of Perga (III-2, B. C.), 173-175; 166, 386, 427, 598, 599, 631, 664, 665.
Apollonios of Tyana, 320.
Apollonios of Tyre, 325.
Apomasar, 558.
Appendix Probi, 265.
Appian (II-2), 311; 290.
Approximate calculations, 273, 561.
Appuleius. See Apuleius, Lucius.
Apsides, motion of solar, 603.
Apsyrtos (IV-1), 356; 345, 375, 657.
Apuleius, Lucius (II-2), 296-297; 253, 289.
Apuleius Platonicus or Barbarus, 296.
Apuleius, pseudo (V-1), 392; 379, 431.
Aqrābādhīn, 608, 729.
Aqueduct, 223, 255.
Aquila of Sinope, 267, 291.
Aquinas, Thomas, 26, 406, 507, 739, 753, 757.
Aquitania, history of, 733.
Arab vs. Persian. See Persian; Shu'ūbite.
Arabia, geography, 637, 768.
Arabian antiquities, 185, 541, 637.
Arabic dictionary, 541, 645, 660, 689, 782.
Arabic grammar, 490, 501, 524, 541, 542, 688, 689, 701, 783.
Arabic-Latin dictionary, 782.
Arabic language, 463, 485.
Arabic names, 43.
Arabic prosody, 541.
Arabic-Syriac dictionary, 735.
Arabic translations, 611; earliest, 495.
Arabic transliteration, 46.
Aramaic, 181, 634, 687.
Aratos of Soli (III-1, B. C.), 157; 150, 206, 207, 322, 367, 371.
Arcandam, 671.
Arcandorum liber, 609.
Arcerianus, Codex, 379, 397.
Arcerius, Joannes (of Groningen), 397.
Archagathos the Peloponnesian (III-2, B. C.), 175; 166.
Archelaos, alchemist, 514.
Archelaos of Athens (V, B. C.), 87; 81, 82.
Archigenes of Apamea (II-1), 280; 268, 307, 434.
Archimedean problem, 169, 182, 598.
Archimedes (III-2, B. C.), 169-172; 166, 167, 206, 397, 427, 546, 554, 598, 599, 600, 601, 632, 662, 665.
Architecture, 223.
Archytas of Tarentum (IV-1, B. C.), 116-117; 111, 112.
Arctic circle, 144, 606.
Are, Hieda no, 516.
Area Celsi, 240.
Areometer, 338.
Aretaeos of Cappadocia (II-2), 307; 289.
Arethas (IX-2), 618; 588, 589.
Arezzo, Guido of (XI-1), 720; 695, 697, 740, 756.
Arianism, 344, 347, 363.
'Arīb ibn Sa'd al-Qurṭubī (X-2), 680; 642, 651, 652, 654, 669.
Arios (IV-1), 348-349. See Arianism.
Aristaeos (IV-2, B. C.), 140-141; 125.
Aristarchos of Samos (III-1, B. C.), 156-157; 150, 602.
Aristarchos of Samothrace (II-1, B. C.), 189; 179, 183.
Aristeas of Jerusalem, 151.
Aristides, 507.
Aristophanes of Byzantium (II-1, B. C.), 189; 179, 657.
Aristotle (IV-2, B. C.), 127-136; 12, 124, 125, 126, 203, 271, 319, 334, 335, 366, 367, 386, 402, 405, 407, 421, 422, 424, 425, 435, 448, 452, 493, 501, 556, 559, 596, 597, 601, 611, 627, 628, 629, 630, 631, 703, 721, 750.
Aristotle's Constitution of Athens, 62.
Aristotle, Lapidary of, 547, 572.
Aristotle, pseudo, 324.
Aristotle, Theology of. See Theology of Aristotle.
Aristoxenos, physician, 303.
Aristoxenos of Tarentum (IV-2, B. C.), 142; 126, 426.
Aristyllos of Alexandria (III-1, B. C.), 156; 150.
Arithmetic, 245, 253. Commercial, see al-Mu'āmalāt. History of, 140, 143.
Arithmetic in nine sections, 183, 338.
Arkhangelsk, 606.
Arlenius, Arnoldus, 188, 263.
Armengaud son of Blaise, of Montpellier, 711.
Armenia, 122, 395.
Armenian alphabet, 397.
Armenian history, 735.
Armenian literature, 398.
Armenian printing (1513), 397.
Armenian translations, 381, 735.
Armillary sphere, 388, 530.
Arnaldus, Stephanus, 602.
Arnarson Ingolf, 606.
Arrian. See Arrianus Flavius.
Arrian the meteorologist (II-1, B. C.), 184; 178.
Arrianus Flavius (II-1), 284; 267, 268, 269, 270.
Ars parva, 307.
Arsenic, 532, 679.
Arsenious oxide, 679.
Art, history, 4.
Artachaees the Persian (V, B. C.), 95; 82.
Artemidoros of Ephesos (II-2, B. C.), 196; 192.
Artemidoros Daldianos, of Ephesos (II-2), 295; 289, 558.
Arteries, 301.
Arthaśāstra, 147.
Arthritis, 435.
Articella, 478, 611, 612.
Articulations, 281.
Aruk, 782.

Āryabhaṭa (v–2), 409; 387, 400, 401, 428, 475.
Āryabhaṭa, another, 409.
Āryabhaṭīya, 409.
Āryāsaṅga. See Asaṅga.
Āryāshṭaśata, 409.
Ārya-Siddhānta, 409.
Arzachel, 758.
Asadī of Ṭūs (xi–2), 783; 679, 745, 746.
Asaṅga (iv–1), 350; 344.
Asaph ben Berechiah ha-Yarḥoni, 614.
Asaph Judaeus (ix–2), 614; 588, 683.
Asaph ha-Yehudi, 614.
Aṣbagh ibn Muḥammad ibn al-Samḥ, 715.
Asclepiades of Bithynia (i–1, b. c.), 214; 203, 239.
Asclepiodotos (i–1, b. c.), 213; 202.
Asclepiodotos of Alexandria (v–2), 405; 399.
Asclepios, 296.
Asclepios of Tralles (vi–1), 423; 415, 416.
al-Asdī, 731.
Asfar al-Kāsānī, 709.
al-Ash'arī (x–1), 625; 619, 623, 624, 647, 659, 706, 747.
Ashi (v–1), 384; 378, 380.
Ashṭādhyāyī, 123.
Ashṭāṅgahṛidayasaṃhitā, 480.
Ashṭāṅgasaṃgraha, 480.
Ashurbanipal, 60, 62.
Asia, Central. See Tarim.
Asia, geography of, 536.
al-Aṣma'ī (viii–2), 534; 523, 524.
Aśoka, Maurya King (iii–2, b. c.), 167–168; 165.
Asomi Shimotsumichi, 519.
al-Asrār, 610.
Assassins, 593, 739, 752.
Asse minutisque eius portiunculis, de, 271.
Assemani, G. S., 437, 730.
Asser, 596.
Assyrian science, 62. See Babylonian.
Asthma, 308.
Astrolabe, 389, 422, 493, 530, 532, 566, 601, 670, 708, 715, 716, 757, 758; spherical, 599, 602.
Astrological chorography, 367.
Astrology, 6, 18, 19, 193, 298, 322, 354, 368; Chinese, 353; Tantric, 509.
Astronomi Veteres, 157, 212.
Astronomical hypotheses, 423.
Astronomical instruments, 193, 322, 388, 566, 602, 666. See Armillary; Astrolabe; Globe, celestrial; Orrery.
Astronomical systems. See Geocentrical; Geoheliocentrical; Heliocentrical; Planetary hypothesis; Planets, theory.
Astronomical tables, 565. See Zīj.
Astronomy, history of, 140, 143, 494.
Astronomy, Little, 142, 211.
Astronomy, Stoic, 212.
al-Aṣṭurlābī, 'Alī ibn 'Īsā, 566.
Asulanus, Fr., 99, 259.
Aśvaghosha (ii–1), 269; 267, 314, 384, 466.
Athanasian creed, 348.
Athanasios, St., 347, 348, 364.
al-Āthār al-bāqiya, 707.
Athenaeos of Attalia (i–2), 260; 244.
Athenaeos, mechanician (ii–2, b. c.), 196; 191, 224.
Athenaeos of Naucratis (iii–1), 326; 316.
Athens, Constitution of, 62.
Atlantis, 113, 115.
Atmosphere, height, 721.
Atomic theory, 88.
Atomism, 82, 137, 205, 214, 248, 706; extended to time and motion, 706; Jaina, 69.
Ātreya (vi, b. c.), 76–77; 66, 284.
Attaliates, Michael (xi–2), 779; 743, 744, 745.
Attalos III, Philometor (ii–2, b. c.), 198; 192.
Aṭṭhasālinī, 385.
Ātūr-farnbag, 591.
Ātūrpāt (ix–2), 591.
Aufidius, 240.
Augrim, 563.
Augustine, Rule of St., 748.
Augustine, St. (v–1), 383; 160, 333, 365, 374, 378, 379, 380, 382, 395, 559, 594, 595.
Augustine, St., Apostle of Britain (596), 446.
Augustinian Canons, 738, 748.
Augustinus Aurelius. See St. Augustine.
Augustus, emperor, 223.
Auraicept na n-éces, 472.
Aurelius Antoninus, Marcus (ii–2), 297; 180, 289, 290.
Aurelius, physician, 392, 417, 434.
Auria, Joseph, 211.
Auricles of the heart, 120, 301.
Ausonius, Decimus Magnus (iv–2), 369; 360, 361.
Auspices, 295.
Austin Canons, 748.
Autolycos of Pitane (iv–2, b. c.), 141–142; 125, 601, 602.
Automata, 116, 208, 554, 705.
Avataṃsakasūtra, 510.
Aven Sīnā, 709.
Avencebrol, 704.
Avendeut, 404.
Averroës, 747.
Avesta, 61, 591.
Avicebron, 595, 704.
Avicenna. See Ibn Sīnā.
Avienus, Rufus Festus (iv–2), 371; 258, 360.
al-'Awfī, 661.
Ayyūb al-Ruhāwī al-Abrash (ix–1), 574; 547, 549.
al-'Azīz, Fāṭimid caliph, 716.
Azutrio, 370.

Bābīs, 420.
Babylonian astrology, 199.
Babylonian astronomy, 71.
Babylonian science, 52, 57, 62.

Bacchios, 216.
Bachet de Méziriac. See Méziriac, Bachet de.
Bacon, Roger, 557, 559, 721, 781.
Bādarāyaṇa, 561.
al-Bad' wal-tārīkh, 659.
al-Badī', 630.
Baeda Venerabilis. See Bede.
Bagdad, 523, 549, 702.
Bagdad academy, 558.
Bagdad, canals, 635.
Bagdad, foundation, 527, 531.
Bagdad, history, 777.
Bagdad, hospitals, 641, 659.
Bagdad, observatory, 659.
Bagdad, sack, 662.
Bagdad, school, 615.
Baḥr al-Khazar, 680.
Bahrdt, C. F., 317.
Bain-marie, 186.
Bairotsana, 538.
Bakhtyashū', 537.
al-Bakrī of Cordova (xi–2), 768; 675, 741, 742, 743, 746.
al-Balādhurī (ix–2), 616; 588; 590.
al-Baladī (x–2), 679; 651, 654.
Balance, 452, 561, 735.
Balbus (ii–1), 271; 267, 268, 397.
Balbus (contemporary of Caesar), 223.
Bald, Leech Book of, 621, 633.
Baldi, Bernadino, 209.
Balīnūs. See Apollonios.
al-Balkhī (x–1), 631; 620, 621, 624.
Ballymote, Book of, 775.
Balneology, balneotherapy. See Hydrotherapy.
Baltic Sea, 239, 606.
Baluze, Etienne, 555.
Bamboo, 673.
Bamboo Books, Annals of the (iii–1, b. c.), 163–164; 150, 342.
Bamboo Grove, Seven Sages of the, 330, 335.
Bandage, 215, 230.
Banū Amājūr, 630.
Banū Mūsā (ix–1), 560; 545, 546, 549, 611.
al-Bāqilānī (xi–1), 706; 694, 702.
Bar Bahlūl (x–2), 689; 611, 652, 654.
Bar-Daiṣān. See Bardesanes.
Bardesanes (ii–2), 298; 289, 332.
Barhebraeus, 737, 777.
al-Bāri' fī aḥkām al-nujūm, 716.
Barlaam and Ioasaph, 333, 507.
Barley-beer, 467.
Barozzi, Francesco, 403, 632.
Barrington, Daines, 395.
Bartholomaeus de Messina, 136.
Basil the Macedonian, emperor, 588, 617.
Basil the Great, Basil, St. (iv–2), 361; 347, 359.
Basilica, 617, 656, 779.
Basilios II Bulgaroctonos, emperor, 655.
al-Baṣra, 466, 523, 660; school, 502, 518.
Bāṭinīya, 593.
al-Baṭrīq (viii–2), 537; 521, 522, 524.
al-Battānī (ix–2), 602; 564, 585, 586, 587, 589.
Baudhāyana, 74.
al-Baul, 640.
Bavarian Law, 505, 517.
Bayt al-ḥikma, 558.
Bazaar of Heraclides, 382.
Beatus Libaniensis (viii–2), 536; 522.
Beatus maps, 536, 768.
Beausobre, comte de, 119.
Beausobre, Isaac de, 333.
Bec, school, 265, 738, 748.
Beckmann, J., 765.
Bede (viii–1), 510–511; 503, 504, 505, 506, 521, 529, 549, 596, 764.
Bedrotus, J., 326.
Beer-brewing, 339, 467.
Beethoven, 702.
Bekneranef. See Bocchoris.
Bell, Japanese, 509.
Bell-founding, 763.
Bellows, 75.
Bellunese, Andrea, 711.
Bemberg, Daniel, 782.
Ben Asher of Tiberias, 619, 623, 624.
Ben Joseph ibn Nagdela, 704.
Ben Naphtali, 619, 623, 624.
Ben Sira, Book of. See Ecclesiasticus.
Benedetto Crespo, 497.
Benedict XII, pope, 748.
Benedict, St. (vi–1), 419; 347, 414, 418, 446, 732.
Benedictine medicine, 536.
Benedictine rule, 419.
Benedictus Cassinensis. See St. Benedict.
Benedictus Crispus, St., 489, 497.
Bengesla, 772.
Benjamin ben Moses Nahawendi, 550.
Bentley, R., 54.
Beowulf, 425.
Berber language, 704.
Berken, 76.
Bernard, Jo. Steph., 393, 639.
Bernard the Wise (ix–2), 605; 586, 589.
Bernardus monachus francus, 605.
Bernelinus of Paris (xi–1), 714; 695, 702, 740, 756.
Berno, 624.
Berossos the Babylonian (iii–1, b. c.), 162; 150, 262.
Bertario, 607.
Bertharius (ix–2), 607; 587, 589.
Berthold, disciple of Hermann the Lame, 757.
Bestiaries, 765. See Physiologos.
Bhagavadgītā, 561, 707, 754.
Bhāshya, 512.
Bhāskara, 720.
Bhaṭṭotpala, 387, 428.

Bianchi, 540.
Bible, translations, 377, 381. See under the names of languages.
Biblical chronology, 59.
Bibliographic basis, 39.
Bidpai, fables of, 449, 540.
Bigot, Emeric, 432.
Bile, 86.
Binomial development, 760.
al-Bīrūnī (xi-1), 707-709; 333, 351, 387, 428, 530, 564, 610, 693, 694, 696, 697, 698, 699, 700, 701, 703.
Birushana, 510.
Biwa, 519.
Bjarne Herjulfsson, 676.
Bkah-hgyur, 467.
Black Canons, 748.
Blayney, Benjamin, 152.
Block printing. See Printing.
Blood, circulation, 129, 160, 301.
Blood, flux and reflux, 87.
Bloodletting, 159, 608.
Bocchoris the Wise (viii, b. c.), 59; 53.
Bodaeus à Stapel, Joannes, 143.
Bodhicaryāvatāra, 490.
Bodhicittam, 490.
Bodhidharma (vi-1), 420; 414.
Bodhisattva, 68.
Bön, 526.
Boerhaave, Hermann, 308.
Boethius. See Boetius.
Boetius, Anicius Manilius Severinus (vi-1), 424-426; 237, 253, 274, 415, 416, 418, 569, 596, 670, 697, 703, 714, 749.
Bogdanus, Martinus, 771.
Bologna, law school, 438.
Bolos Democritos, 89.
Bombelli, R., 336.
Bone drilling, 281.
Bonnet, Claude, 499.
Bordeaux, 240.
Bordeaux-Jerusalem itinerary, 371.
Borelli, G. A., 174, 664.
Botanical dictionary, 771.
Botany. See Flowers; Petals; Plants; Roots.
Botany, Chinese, 340. See Pên-ts'ao.
Botany, medical, 121.
Boulliau, Ismael, 272.
Bower manuscript, 379, 393.
Brahe, Tycho, 125, 141, 275, 666.
Brahmagupta (vii-1), 474; 409, 461, 463, 570.
Brahmanism, 69, 707.
Brāhmasphuṭasiddhānta, 474-475.
Brahmasūtra, 561, 754.
Brāhmi alphabet, 84, 110, 123.
Brain, 77, 86, 94, 128, 143, 159, 160, 373, 678.
Breithaupt, J. F., 752.
Brethren of Purity (x-2), 660; 584, 593, 647, 648, 650, 668, 715.
Breul, Jacques de, 732.
Breviarium Alarici (vi-1), 438; 412.
Bridferth, 714.
Bridge, 278; of boats, 76.
Bṛihajjātaka, 429.
Bṛihatī, 512.
Bṛihatsaṃhitā, 428.
Bronze, 533.
Bronze casting, 75.
Bruno, Giordano, 204.
Brush, writing, 168, 175.
Bryson of Heraclea (v, b. c.), 93; 82.
Bstan-hgyur, 468.
Bubo, 282.
Buddha (vi, b. c.), 68-69; 65, 332.
Buddha, Christian saint, 507.
Buddhacarita, 270, 447.
Buddhaghosa (v-1), 384; 26, 378, 380.
Buddhism, 69; introduction into China, 246; introduction into Japan (vi-2), 448; introduction into Korea (iv-2), 364.
Buddhist bibliography, 420, 491, 509, 673.
Buddhist Canon. See Tripiṭaka.
Buddhist council, 167, 270.
Buddhist dictionary, 487.
Buddhist encyclopaedia, 491.
Buddhist idealism, 350.
Budé, G., 237.
Buhahylyha, 772.
al-Bukhārī (ix-1), 551; 543, 550, 592.
Bukkyō, 448.
al-Buldān, 607, 635.
Bulgarian ethnography, 686.
Bulgarians, 578.
Bulliadus, see Boulliau, Ismael.
Bunsen-Ō. See Confucius.
Bunshō-hakase, 582.
Buppō, 448.
Buqrāt, 101.
Burgh, Benedict, 557.
Burgundian law, 418, 439.
Burgundio of Pisa, 374, 507.
al-Burhān 'ala ṣaḥīḥ, 735.
Buridan, 416.
Burmann, Peter, 266.
Burning of the books, 165, 168, 176.
Burning-glasses. See Mirrors, Burning.
Burzūya (Burzōe) (vi-2), 449; 435, 443.
Butsudō, 448.
Butter, 467.
Buzurg ibn Shahriyār (x-2), 674; 650, 654.
Byngezla, 772.
Byrhtferth of Ramsey (xi-1), 714; 695, 702.

Cadmos of Miletos (vi, b. c.), 79; 66.
Caelius (iii-2), 340; 331.
Caelius Aegineta, 309.
Caelius Aurelianus (v-1), 392; 283, 379, 434.
Caesar, Gaius Julius (i-1, b. c.), 216-217; 186, 201, 203, 219.
Caesarean section, 77, 709.

Caesarean text of the New Testament, 349.
Caillech, 657.
Cairo, 702, 717.
Cairo academy, 717.
Calculus, integral, 169.
Calendar, Carolingian, 527.
Calendar, Chinese, 195, 222, 278 368, 429, 450, 762.
Calendar, Greek, 79, 173.
Calendar, Gregorian, 760.
Calendar, Hellenistic, 184, 327.
Calendar, Japanese, 473, 476.
Calendar, Jewish, 318, 368, 627.
Calendar, Julian, 216, 217.
Calendar, Muslim, 461, 464, 475, 530.
Calendar, Persian, 614, 760.
Calendar, Roman, 213, 216.
Calendar, Syrian, 493.
Calendar, Tibetan, 469.
Calendar. See Compotus; Cycle; Month; Year.
Caligraphy, 554.
Callinicos of Heliopolis (VII-2), 494; 489.
Callippos of Cyzicos (IV-2, B. C.), 141; 125.
Calpurnius, Siculus, 340.
Calvus, Fabius, 99.
Camera obscura, 721, 722, 723.
Camerarius, Guil., 628.
Camerarius, Joachim, 277.
Camerarius, R. J., 128.
Campano, G., 154, 266.
Camphor, 771.
Cāṇakya. See Kauṭilya.
Canal, Athos, 95.
Canal, Çhinese, 168.
Canal of Corinth, 247.
Canal, Nile, 78, 571.
Canamusali, 729.
Canaries (islands), 232.
Candragupta, 147, 161.
Candrakīrti, 316.
Cange, C. du, 482.
Canons Regular, 748.
Canons, secular, 748.
Canton, 601, 636.
Capella, Martianus Mineus Felix (V-2), 407; 400, 421, 594, 595, 697, 703.
Capella, Michael de, 677.
Capet, Hugh, 685.
Capillaries, 160, 677.
Capitulare de villis, 528.
Capitulari Langobardorum, 485.
Capitularies, 527-528.
Capsula eburnea, 100.
Caraka of Kashmir (II-1), 284; 269.
Carakasaṃhitā, 284.
Cardan's suspension, 195, 534.
Cardano, Girolamo, 247, 559.
Carolingian dynasty, history, 685.
Carolingian renaissance, 520, 529.
Carpos, 277.
Cartography. See Maps.
Casaubon, Isaac, 326.
Casaubon, Meric, 297.
Cassianos Bassos (VI-2), 452; 444, 657.
Cassino, Monte. See Monte Cassino.
Cassiodorus Senator, Flavius Magnus Aurelius (VI-1), 426; 381, 415, 416, 417, 418, 455, 629.
Cassios, 240.
Cassios the Iatrosophist (III-1), 324; 315.
Cassius Dionysius of Utica (I-1, B. C.), 213; 197, 202.
Cassius Felix (V-1), 392; 379.
Castellani of Faenza, Pietro Niccolò de, 407.
Casting out elevens, 718.
Casting out nines, 710, 718.
Castor of Rhodes (I-1, B. C.), 216; 203.
Castorius, 324.
Casts, plaster, 142.
Catalepsy, 373.
Cataract, 77, 240, 280, 729.
Catasterisms, 173.
Catheter, 160.
Catilina, 231.
Cato the Censor (II-1, B. C.), 186; 177, 178, 180, 547.
Cato, Marcus Porcius (Censorius; Major). See Cato the Censor.
Cato, Marcus Porcius (Uticensis). See Cato of Utica.
Cato of Utica, 186.
Causis, liber de (V-2), 404; 135, 399.
Caussin de Perceval, 717.
Cauterization, 681. See Moxibustion.
Caxton, 368.
Cedrenos, Georgios, 776.
Celestial bodies, 128, 222; motion, 494; stability, 423.
Celestial globe. See Globe.
Celestial map. See Stars.
Cellach, 657.
Celsos (II-2), 294; 288, 317, 320.
Celsus, Aurelius Cornelius (I-1), 240-241; 160, 235, 236.
Celsus (fl. under Trajan), 271.
Celtes, Conrad, 658.
Celtic medicine, 391.
Cennfaeladh, 472.
Censorinus (III-1), 322; 315.
Censualis, liber, 779.
Centiloquium, 277.
Centrobaric method, 337.
Ceramics, Japanese, 515.
Cerebrum, 301.
Ceylon, 412, 431, 432, 508, 509.
Ch'a ching, 535.
Chalazion, 731.
Chalcidius (IV-1), 352; 344, 345, 346, 385, 594.
Chalcondyles, Demetrios, 55, 57, 691.

Champollion, J. F., 358.
Ch'an, 199.
Ch'an tsung, 48, 420, 447.
Chancellor, Richard, 606.
Chandālas, 391.
Chang Chan, 139.
Chang Chi. See Chang Chung-ching.
Chang Ch'ien (II–2, B. C.), 197; 192.
Chang Ch'iu-chien (VI–2), 450; 444.
Chang Ch'iu-chien suan-ching, 494.
Chang Chung-ching (II–2), 310; 290.
Chang Hêng (II–1), 278; 196, 268, 269.
Chang I-hsi, 514.
Chang Shou-chieh, 476.
Chang Ssŭ-hsün (X-2), 672; 649, 654.
Chang Sui, 514.
Ch'ang-sun No-yen, 486.
Chang Tsai, 755.
Chang Ts'ang (II–1, B. C.), 183; 178, 211, 339, 449, 494.
Chang-tun-jên, 474.
Chang Wên-ming, 497.
Channing, John, 609, 681.
Chanson de Roland (XI–2), 773–774; 743, 744, 745, 746, 748.
Ch'ao-Ts'o (II–2, B. C.), 196; 192.
Ch'ao Yüan-fang (VII–1), 481; 462, 463, 683.
Charastonis, liber, 600.
Charistion, 171.
Charlemagne (VIII-2), 527-528; 439, 521, 523, 527, 576, 605, 773.
Charlemagne, legends, 528.
Charpentier, Jacques, 407.
Charrier, Jean, 255.
Chartier, René, 282, 305, 393.
Chartres, school, 265.
Chauliac, Guy de, 681.
Ch'ê Fêng-ch'ao, 526.
Cheese, 467.
Chemical analysis, wet, 259.
Chemical instruments, 609.
Chemical classification, 609.
Chemistry, name, 339.
Ch'ên dynasty, history, 483.
Ch'ên-chieh, 474.
Ch'ên Han, 364.
Ch'ên Huo, 755.
Ch'ên I, 477.
Chên-kao, 436.
Chên-kuan chêng-yao, 518.
Chên-luan (VI–2), 450; 299, 444.
Ch'ên P'êng-nien (XI–1), 737; 442, 486, 701, 702.
Ch'ên Shou (III–2), 343; 331.
Ch'ên shu, 483.
Ch'ên Tê-an, 447.
Chen Ti, 446.
Chên Tsung, Sung emperor, 713.
Chên Yen tsung, 508, 553.
Chêng[1], harpsichord, 175.
Chêng[4], positive quantity, 183, 339.
Chêng[4]. See Shih Huang-Ti.
Chêng Fa-hua-ching, 447.
Ch'êng Hao, 755.
Ch'êng I, 755.
Ch'êng Mo (III–2, B. C.), 176; 166.
Ch'êng Shih tsung, 470.
Ch'êng Tzŭ, 755.
Chersiphron of Cnossos (VI, B. C.), 75; 65.
Chesneau, Nicolas, 684.
Chess, 451, 705.
Chester, Robert of, 495, 603.
Ch'i, 369.
Ch'i dynasty, history of the northern, 483.
Ch'i dynasty, history of the southern, 438.
Chi Chung-ching. See Chang Chung-ching.
Chi Han (III–2), 340; 331.
Ch'i-hsin-lun, 270.
Chi K'ang (III–2), 335, 336.
Chi-ku-lu, 777.
Ch'i-ku suan-ching, 474.
Ch'i-min yao-shu, 441.
Chi-sō-ki, 575.
Ch'i-su-nung, 466.
Ch'i tsung lung tsan, 466.
Chi-yeh (X–2), 676; 650, 654.
Chi-yün, 737.
Chia. See Hui Yüan.
Chia-i, 199.
Chia-i-ching, 342.
Chia K'uei (I–2), 254; 244.
Chia Kung-yen, 571.
Chia Ssŭ-hsieh (VI–1), 441; 416, 417, 418.
Chia Tan (VIII–2), 536; 522.
Chia-tzŭ, 673.
Chiang Chi (IV–2), 368; 360.
Chiasma, optic, 282.
Chieh-ch'ieh, 450.
Chieh shêng, 66.
Ch'ieh yün, 486.
Chien-chên, 539.
Ch'ien-chin-fang, 498.
Ch'ien fo tung, 604.
Ch'ien Han-shu, 264.
Ch'ien-i (XI–2), 773; 743, 746.
Ch'ien Lo-chih(V-1), 388; 378.
Ch'ien-shih hsiao-êrh yao-chêng chên-chüeh, 773.
Ch'ien tzŭ wên, 441.
Chih, 494, 676.
Chih Ch'uan. See Ko Hung.
Chih-i (VI–2), 447; 443, 553.
Chih K'ai, 447.
Chih Shêng (VIII–1), 509; 504.
Children's diseases. See Pediatrics.
Chilmeadus, Edm., 455.
Chimes, alchemist, 238.
Chin dynasty, history, 482.
Chin-kang ching, 604.
Chin-kuei yao-fang, 355.

Chin kuei yü han yao lüeh fang lun, 310.
Chin shu, 482.
Ch'in ting ku chin t'u shu chi ch'êng, 663.
Ch'in Yüeh Jên. See Pien Ch'iao.
China, Byzantine account, 481.
China, first Arabic account, 571.
China, first use of the word, 257.
China, first western matter of fact mention, 432.
China, geography, 581, 676. See also Maps, Chinese.
Chinese astronomy, history, 494.
Chinese bibliography, 37, 222, 264, 420, 448, 450, 491, 509.
Chinese chronology, 163, 222, 264, 429.
Chinese classics, see
1. I ching.
2. Shu ching.
3. Shih ching.
4. Li chi.
5. Ch'un ch'iu.
to which may be added the Four Books, for which see
1. Lun yü.
2. Ta hsüeh.
3. Chung yung.
4. Mêng-tzŭ.
Chinese classics, glossary, 458.
Chinese classics, printing, 633.
Chinese dictionary, 110, 286, 343, 413, 441, 458, 459, 486, 737, 778.
Chinese dictionary, Japanese, 692.
Chinese education, 441.
Chinese encyclopaedia. See Encyclopaedia.
Chinese epigraphy, 777.
Chinese history, Dynastic Histories (24), see the following words:
1. Shih-chi.
2. Ch'ien Han-shu.
3. Hou Han-shu.
4. San Kuo chih.
5. Chin-shu.
6. Sung-shu.
7. Nan Ch'i shu.
8. Liang-shu.
9. Ch'ên-shu.
10. Wei shu.
11. Pei ch'i shu.
12. Hou Chou shu.
13. Sui shu.
14. Nan shih.
15. Pei shih.
16. Chiu T'ang shu.
17. Hsin T'ang shu.
18. Chiu Wu-tai-shih.
19. Hsin Wu-tai-shih.
Chinese law, history, 581.
Chinese maps, 341, 536, 573.
Chinese metrology. See Metrology.
Chinese money. See Money.
Chinese names, 43.
Chinese philology, 745.
Chinese phonetics, 463.
Chinese science, 36, 52, 506.
Chinese shadows, 713.
Chinese text-book, 441.
Chinese, transcription, 47.
Chinese writing, 168, 175, 176.
Ching chiao pei, 527.
Ching Ching, 527.
Ching-ling tzŭ, 535.
Ching Po (VII-1), 484; 462, 463.
Ching tien shih wên, 458.
Ching-t'u-tsung, 364.
Chirognomy, 295.
Chiron the Centaur, 375.
Chishō-daishi, 552.
Chitatsu, 492.
Chitsū, 492.
Chiu-chang suan-shu, 183, 338.
Chiu-chiḥ-li, 513, 514.
Chiu Mo Lo. See Kumārajīva.
Chiu P'u, 723.
Chiu-shu, 410.
Chiu T'ang shu, 643.
Chiu Wu-tai-shih, 688.
Chords, 194, 253, 273.
Chos-grags, 473.
Ch'os-non-pa, 468.
Chosroës. See Nūshīrwān the Just.
Ch'ou, 339.
Chou, 676. See Chuang Tzŭ.
Chou dynasty, history of the Northern, 483.
Chou-hou-pei-chi-fang, 355.
Chou Hsing-ssŭ (VI-1), 441; 418.
Chou pi suan ching, 494.
Chou ts'ung (XI-2), 762; 741, 746.
Chou Tun-i (XI-2), 755; 27, 739-740, 746.
Chou Tzŭ, 755.
Chou Yung, 413.
Christian era, 429.
Christian history, 395.
Christian missionaries, 377.
Christianity, 11.
Christianity, birth of (I-1), 236.
Christianization of Europe, 380.
Christmann, Jacob, 567.
Chronicles, Books (III-1, B. C.), 163; 150.
Chronicum Paschale (Alexandrinum, Constantinopolitanum), 482.
Chronicum Salernitanum (X-2), 685.
Chronological basis, 37.
Chronology, 357, 510; ecclesiastical, 327; scientific, 172.
Chrysippos of Cnidos (IV-1, B. C.), 121; 112.
Chrysippos of Soli (III-2, B. C.), 169; 166.
Chu-ching yao-chi, 491.
Chu Fa-lan, 246.
Chu Hsi, 110, 755, 778.
Chu lin ch'i hsien, 335.

Chū-ron, 470.
Ch'u-san-ts'ang chi-chi, 420.
Chu shu chi nien, 163.
Chu-suan, 299.
Chu Yü, 764.
Chü-na-lo T'o, 446.
Chü shê tsung, 492.
Ch'ü-t'an, 463, 475.
Ch'ü-t'an Chuan, 475.
Ch'ü-t'an Hsi-ta (VIII-1), 513; 504, 514.
Ch'ü-t'an Lo, 475.
Chuan, 35.
Chuan. See Hsiao chuan.
Chuang Chou. See Chuang Tzŭ.
Chuang Tzŭ (III-1, B.C.), 153; 149.
Ch'un Ch'iu, 67, 777.
Ch'un Ch'iu shih-li t'u-ti ming, 341.
Chung-t'ien-chu-kuo hsing chi, 496.
Chung-ts'ang-ching, 325.
Chung yung, 91.
Chyliferous vessels, 159, 160.
Cicero, Marcus Tullius (I-1, B.C.), 206-207; 186, 193, 201, 203, 207, 217, 221, 385, 425.
Cincius Alimentus, L., 176.
Cineas, 119.
Cinematical construction of curves, 403.
Cinnabar, 355, 369, 533. See Mercury.
Cipelli, Giov., 325.
Circle, divided into 360 degrees, 182, 193.
Circulation of the blood. See Blood.
Circumcision, 309.
Cissoid, 183.
Cistern, problem of the, 208.
Cithara, 61.
Citralakshaṇa, 469.
City of God, 383.
Clarke, John, 369.
Clarke, S., 54.
Classic of Filial Piety, 321.
Classics. See Chinese Classics.
Classification, numerical, 661. See Number.
Classification. See Science, classification.
Claudius Caecus, Appius (IV-2, B.C.), 143; 126, 127.
Claudius Hermerus, 375.
Cleanthes of Assos (III-1, B.C.), 152; 149.
Cleomedes (I-1, B.C.), 211; 202.
Cleonides, 156.
Cleopatra, alchemist, 238, 339.
Cleopatra, physician, 433.
Cleostratos of Tenedos (VI, B.C.), 73; 65.
Clepsydra. See Clock, water.
Climatology, 280.
Clinch, Gul., 282.
Clinical cycle, 262.
Clinical observations, 677.
Clinical teaching, 262.
Clitarchos, 229.
Clock, alarm, 116.
Clock, water, 87, 159, 184, 403, 527, 759.
Clock. See Sun-dial.
Cloves, 434, 771.
Clovis, King, 439.
Cluny, Odo of. See Odo.
Cluny, Reform of (X-1), 624; 619, 623, 762.
Cnidian sentences, 102.
Cnidos, school, 82, 102, 119.
Coan dresses, 452.
Cocceius Auctus, L. (I-2, B.C.), 223; 219.
Cocchi, Antonio, 216, 283, 608.
Coinage. See Money.
Collatio legum Mosaicarum et Romanorum, 376.
Columbus, C., 273, 411.
Columella, Lucius Junius Moderatus of Gades (I-2), 256; 244.
Columna, Hier., 187.
Coma, 305, 373.
Coma Berenices, 173.
Comarios, 238.
Combefis, F., 578.
Combinatorial analysis. See Analysis.
Comet of 1066, 720.
Comets, 184.
Commandino, F., 157, 170, 174, 208, 277, 337, 354, 403.
Compass. See Magnetic needle.
Compass, perfect, 665.
Compass, one opening of the, 666.
Compositiones ad tingenda, 522, 533.
Compostela, Santiago de, 774.
Compotus, 671, 757, 758. See Calendar.
Compurgation, 439.
Conches, Guillaume de, 762.
Conchoid, 182.
Confucian Classics, 451. See Chinese Classics.
Confucianism, 67.
Confucius (VI, B.C.), 67-68; 65, 66, 252, 755.
Conics, 139, 140, 141, 169, 173, 337, 353, 427, 665, 718.
Conjunction, 388, 598, 716.
Conon of Samos (III-2, B.C.), 173; 166.
Conservation of matter and energy, 88, 277.
Constantine the African (XI-2), 769; 611, 640, 677, 682, 725, 742, 745, 746, 747, 765, 769.
Constantine (Cyril), 590.
Constantinople, 617, 656, 684.
Constantinos VII Porphyrogennetos (X-2), 656; 188, 647, 650, 651, 652, 655, 680.
Constantinos IX Monomachos, 657.
Constantinos Memphites, 682.
Constantinos Rheginos, 682.
Constitutionum, codex or liber, 439.
Consuls, Roman, 430.
Consultatio veteris cujusdam juris consulti, 412; 400.
Contact, 710.
Contagion, 225, 256, 710.
Continens, 609.

Continuity, 85, 88, 128.
Copernicus, 141, 603.
Copho, 742, 770.
Copper, 679.
Coptic, 358.
Coptic medicine, 588, 614.
Coptic versions, 291.
Corcyraeus, N. P., 497.
Cord, spinal, 301.
Corder, Balthazar, 406.
Cordova, 623, 628, 654, 655, 658, 702, 746.
Corinth, 247.
Cornarius, Janus, 99, 259, 295, 356, 434, 452, 479.
Corpus juris, 439.
Coryza, 682.
Cos, school, 82, 96, 102, 119.
Cosecant, 667.
Cosmas Indicopleustes (VI–1), 431; 417.
Cotangent, 603.
Cotta, Fabio, 255.
Cotton, 535; introduction into Japan, 522.
Counterearth, 93.
Covarruvias, Diego y Antonio de, 413.
Crabs, 766.
Cramoisy, S., 365.
Crassus, Julius Paulus, 393.
Crateros the Macedonian (III–1, B. C.), 161; 150.
Crates of Mallos (II–1, B. C.), 185; 178, 179.
Crates, Book of, 495.
Cratevas (I–1, B. C.), 213; 202, 296.
Creation, potential, 383, 559.
Cremona, Gerard of, 254, 274, 404, 531, 559, 560, 561, 564, 567, 598, 599, 600, 608, 681, 706, 711, 721, 729, 759, 761.
Crickdale, Robert of, 250.
Crisis, medical notion, 73.
Crispus (VII–2), 497.
Critias, 114.
Critical days. See Days.
Criticism, textual, 189.
Crusades, 725, 753.
Cryptography, 119.
Ctesias of Cnidos (V, B. C.), 107; 83.
Ctesibios of Alexandria (II–1, B. C.), 184; 178, 180.
Cubatures, 169.
Cube, duplication. See Duplication.
Curae, 699, 726.
Curationum, libri V, 536.
Curetonian version, 292.
Curis, tractatus de, 726.
Curtius Rufus, Quintus (I–1), 241; 236.
Curves of double curvature, 116, 337.
Curves, spiric, 182.
Cusanus, 595.
Cycle of 12 animals (I–1), 238; 235.
Cycle of Cathay, 673.
Cycle, clinical, 262.
Cycle, indiction, 430.
Cycle, Metonic, 94, 141, 409.
Cycle, sexagesimal, 672. See Sexagesimal.
Cycle, 8-year, 73, 117.
Cycle, 19-year, 94, 141.
Cycle, 76-year, 141.
Cycle, 304-year, 194. See Calendar; Year, great.
Cyclus metasyncriticus, recorporativus, resumptivus, 262.
Cyril, St. (IX–2), 590; 583, 589.
Cyrillic alphabet, 590.
Cyrillos of Jerusalem, 388.
Cyrus, emperor, 122.

Dacryocystitis, 731.
Daf' muḍār al-abdān, 729.
Daghal al-'ain, 574.
Dagobert I, 484.
Dā'ī, 593.
Dai-jō, 448.
Daibutsu of Nara, 515, 529.
Daidō-rui-shiu-hō, 575.
Daigaku-bettō, 539.
Daigaku no kami, 582.
Daigaku-ryō, 513.
Daihō-ryōritsu, 506, 518, 581.
Daillé, Jean, 406.
Dainichi-Nyorai, 510.
Daishi, 553.
Dalechamps, Jacques, 326.
Damascenus, Joannes (Janus), 574.
Damascios (VI–1), 421; 415, 416, 418.
Damascus, 465.
Damianos, son or pupil of Heliodoros of Larissa (IV–1), 354; 345.
Damnastes (XI–1), 727; 699.
Damocrates, Servilius (I–2), 261; 244.
Dampierre, 752.
Daniel, Book of (II–1, B. C.), 180; 177.
Dānishwar, 462, 482.
Dante Alighieri, 395, 567, 656, 749.
Dante, Ignazio, 404.
Daphnopates, Theodoros, 577.
Dār al-ḥikma, 695, 717.
al-Ḍarīr, 562.
Darkot, pass of the, 505, 515.
Daruma, 420.
Darwin, 119.
Daśagītikāsūtra, 409.
Dasypodius, Konrad, 210, 211.
Dā'ūd al-Fāsī, 690.
Dā'ūd al-Ẓāhirī (IX–2), 592; 583.
David ben Abraham (X–2), 690; 653, 655.
David Armenicus, 729.
David ben Merwan (X–1), 626; 620, 623.
David of Thessalonica, 335.
David, King, 63.
Davis, John, 676.
Davis Strait, 676.

Days, critical, 73, 96.
Days, lucky and unlucky, 57, 632.
Days, seven, 71, 238, 305.
Days, twelve, 238.
Days, twelve divisions. See Hours.
Dead Sea, 638.
Decagon, 630.
Decimal fractions. See Fractions.
Decimal notations. See Numerals, Hindu.
Decius Paulinus Iunior, 430.
Declination, magnetic, 514.
Defecation, 478.
Degree. See Circle.
Degree measurements, 558, 708, 716.
Dellius, Quintus, 228.
Demetrios of Apamea (II-2, B. C.), 198; 192.
Demetrios of Scepsis (II-1, B. C.), 190; 179.
Democedes of Crotona (VI, B. C.), 78; 66.
Democritos of Abdera (V, B. C.), 88-89; 81, 82.
Democritos. See Bolos Democritos.
Democritos, Pseudo (I-1), 238; 235, 378, 388.
Demosthenes Philalethes (I-2), 260; 244, 245.
Dengyō daishi (IX-1), 552; 447, 544, 552.
Denis, St., 773.
Denis of Thrace. See Dionysios Thrax.
Deontology. See Medical.
Dermatology, 435, 677, 683, 710.
Determinism, 365.
Deuteronomy, 62, 107.
Devanāgarī numerals, 659.
Dewez, F. O., 433.
Dexippos, 393.
Dhammapadaṭṭhakathā, 385.
Dhammasaṅgaṇi, 385.
Dharmakīrti, Ācārya (VII-1), 473; 461, 463.
Dharmalakshaṇa, 350, 491.
Dharmaraksha, 270.
Dharmaśāstra, 781.
Dhāt al-shu'batain, 560.
Dhātupāṭha, 123.
Dhū-l-nūn (IX-2), 592; 583, 586, 590.
Dhyāna, 420.
Diabetes, 97, 307.
Diamond sūtra. See Prajñāpāramitā.
Diaphragm, 55.
Diastole, 282.
Diatessaron, 288; 292, 293, 730.
Dicaearchos of Messina (IV-2, B. C.), 145; 126.
Dictionaries, early. See under name of language.
Dicuil (IX-1), 571; 546.
Didaxeon, peri, 727.
Didymos of Alexandria, grammarian (I-2, B. C.), 233; 220.
Didymos of Alexandria, agriculturist and physician (IV-2), 370; 360, 452.
Differences, method of two, 494.
Digambaras, 69.
Digest, 439.
Digestion, 99.
Dignāga Ācārya (IV-2), 366; 359, 360, 473, 491.
al-Dīnawarī (IX-2), 615; 545, 586, 588, 590.
Dīnkart, 591.
Dinostratos (IV-2, B. C.), 140; 125.
Diocles, mathematician (II-1, B. C.), 183; 177, 178.
Diocles of Carystos (IV-1, B. C.) 121; 112, 126.
Diocletian, 358.
Diocletian era, 430.
Diodoros of Sicily (I-2, B. C.), 231; 220.
Diodoros of Tarsos, 293.
Diogenes of Apollonia (V, B. C.), 96; 82.
Diogenes the Babylonian (II-1, B. C.), 181; 177, 179.
Diogenes Laërtios (III-1), 318; 314.
Dion Cassios Cocceianos (III-1), 327; 316, 775.
Dionysian period, 410.
Dionysios, Aelios (II-1), 286; 269, 313.
Dionysios the Areopagite (V-2), 406; 399, 424, 471.
Dionysios of Halicarnassos (I-2, B. C.), 232; 220.
Dionysios Periegetes (I-2), 258; 244, 371, 440.
Dionysios, Pseudo, 594.
Dionysios of Tell-Maḥrē (IX-1), 579; 437, 548.
Dionysios Thrax (II-2, B. C.), 200; 192, 424.
Dionysius. See Denis.
Dionysius, Cassius. See Cassius Dionysius.
Dionysius Exiguus (VI-1), 429; 236, 416, 775.
Dionysodoros of Amisos (II-1, B. C.), 182; 177.
Dionysodoros of Melos, 182.
Diophanes of Nicaea, 214.
Diophantine analysis, 336, 719. See Equations, indeterminate.
Diophantos of Alexandria (III-2), 336-337; 330, 332, 386, 602, 666, 750.
Diopter, dioptra, 145, 193, 208.
Diorismi, 116.
Dioscorides of Anazarbos, Pedanios (I-2), 258-260; 244, 245, 416, 434, 611, 613, 678, 680, 682, 727, 728, 764.
Dioscorides, pseudo, 430.
Dioscoros, 388.
Diphtheria, 434.
Diqduqe, sefer, 690.
Directrix, 337.
Diseases, distribution, 710.
Dislocation of the hip, 198.
Dissection, 282, 301, 574; human, 119, 159, 160.
Distillation, 339, 534, 681. See Alcohol.
Distillation of empyreumatic oils, 728.
Distillation of sea-water, 319.
Ditmarus Merseburgensis, 733.
Diversarum artium schedula, 763.
al-Diyārāt, 643.
Dizabul, Turkish Khan, 453.
Dizziness, 143.
Dô, 468.
Docks, dry, 196.
Dodecahedron, 93, 181.

Dörpfeld, Wilhelm, 53.
Dogmatic school, 120, 121, 146.
Dogs, breeding, 122.
Domesday Book (XI-2), 779; 744.
Domninos of Larissa (V-2), 408; 400.
Donat (donet), 358.
Donatus, Aelius (IV-1), 358; 286, 345, 346, 440, 595.
Donnolo (X-2), 682; 651, 655, 725.
Dōsen, 504, 510.
Dōshō, 367, 491.
Douai Bible, 363.
Dracon, 62, 79.
Drainage of soil, 355.
Dravidian languages, 512.
Dreams, 6, 89, 129, 237, 295, 301, 389, 558, 609, 706.
Dropsy, 308.
Drug-store, 513.
Drying-up of continents, 135.
Du'āt, 593.
Dualism, Chinese, 353.
Dualism, Greek, 77.
Dualism, Jaina, 69.
Dualism, Manichaean, 332.
Dualism, Zoroastrian, 61.
Dubravius, Bishop Janus, 261.
Duchesne, André, 733.
Dudon of St. Quentin (XI-1), 733; 700, 702.
Duel, judicial, 555.
Dürer, Albrecht, 658.
Du Halde, J. B., 342, 436.
Dulva, 468.
Dunash ben Labraṭ (X-2), 690; 653, 655.
Duns Sçotus, 704.
Duodecimal fractions. See Fractions.
Duodenum, 159.
Duplication of cube, 91, 116, 139, 172, 182, 183, 338, 696.
al-Durra al-fākhira, 753.
Dwina, river, 606.
Dyeing, 532, 533.

Ealwhine, 528.
Ear, 87.
Earth, egg-shaped, 225.
Earth, rotation, 94, 141, 156, 183, 409, 708.
Earth, size, 145, 172, 204, 212, 273, 567.
Earth, sphere, 73, 428, 431, 510.
Earthquakes, 105, 204, 227, 248, 375, 661, 751. See Seismometer; Seismoscope.
Earthquake of 955, 638.
East and West, 28.
East-west direction, 271.
Easter Chronicle (VII-1), 482; 462.
Easter, determination, 337, 409. See Calendar.
Ebers papyrus, 99, 146, 310.
Eccentrics, theory of, 173, 194, 273. See Epicycles.
Ecchellensis, Abraham, 174, 664.
Ecclesiastes (II-1, B. C.), 180; 59, 177.
Ecclesiasticus, Book of (II-1, B. C.), 180; 177.
Eclectic school; 260, 307, 308.
Eclipses, 86, 105, 107, 173, 194, 388, 493, 598, 661, 716, 736.
Eclipses, lunar, 208, 717; 722 B. C., 68; 413 B. C., 107.
Eclipses, solar, 763 B. C. (not 787) 57; 722 B. C., 720 B. C., 68; 689 B. C., 59; 610 B. C., 585 B. C., 72; 431 B. C., 106-107; 424 B. C., 107. See Confucius.
Eclipses, solar, annular, 403, 603.
Ecliptic, 254, 514.
Ecliptic, obliquity, 72, 92, 558, 603, 667-668, 709, 716, 758.
Economic history, 4. See Oeconomica.
Ecphantos of Syracuse (IV-1, B. C.), 118; 112.
Edessa, 437; school, 310, 381.
Edictum Perpetuum, 285.
Edictum Theoderici (VI-1), 438.
Edictus Langobardorum, 462, 484.
Education, ancient, 266.
Edward the Confessor, 744, 779.
Eginhard, 576.
Egnazio, G. B., 325.
Egypt, 161, 466; earliest Muslim account, 616.
Egyptian arithmetic, 337, 354, 403.
Egyptian chemistry, 339.
Egyptian law, 59.
Egyptian mathematics, 449.
Egyptian science, 52.
Eigwa monogatari, 744, 745, 746, 778.
Eilmer. See Malmesbury, Oliver of.
Einhard (IX-1), 576; 548, 549, 773.
Eirik Raude, 675.
Eisai, 552.
Eki, 515.
Ekwan, 460, 463, 470.
Electrotherapy, 241.
Elementis, liber de, 135, 710.
Elements, 640; five, 93, 131, 673; four, 87, 93, 208.
Elements in geometry, 140.
Elephantiasis, 308.
Eleven. See Number 11.
Elfsten. See Wulfstan.
Elias Philosophos, 335.
Elias bar Shīnāyā (XI-1), 735; 694, 697, 700 701, 702.
Elias of Ṭīrhān (XI-1), 737; 701, 702.
Ellipse, 173, 403, 570; gardener's construction, 561.
Ellipsoids, 169.
Elluchasem Elimithar, 730.
Elmer. See Malmesbury, Oliver of.
Elohist narrative, 108.
Embryology, 119, 120, 121, 128, 160, 574, 614. See Fetus; Generation; Womb.
Embryotome, 159.
Emerald Table, 533.

Emetics, 728.
Emon Akazome, 778.
Empedocles of Acragas (v, B. C.), 87; 81, 82, 180.
Empereur, Constantin l', 704.
Empirical school, 186, 215, 299, 308.
Empiricism, 749.
Emplastrum diachylum, 241.
Encanthis, 731.
Enchin, 552.
Encyclopaedia, Chinese. See my notes on Êrh-ya; T'ung tien; Shih lei fu; T'ai-p'ing yü-lan; Ts'ê-fu yüan-kuei; see also article Lei shu in Encyclopaedia Sinica (296, 1917).
Engi-kyaku-shiki, 618.
Engi-shiki (x-1), 644.
Engineering, earliest work, 255.
England, history, 455, 595.
English-Latin dictionary, 692.
English language, 584, 588, 596.
Enneagon, 718.
Ennius, Quintus (II-1, B. C.), 187; 84, 177, 178, 180.
Enryaku-ji, 553.
Epaphroditus, 397.
Ephesus, council, 381, 382.
Ephesus, Michael of. See Michael.
Ephoros of Cyme (IV-2, B. C.), 146; 126.
Ephraim, St., 292.
Epicharmos (v, B. C.), 84-85; 81.
Epictetos (II-1), 270; 267, 269, 284, 422.
Epicuros of Samos (IV-2, B. C.), 137; 9, 125, 252.
Epicycles, theory of, 173, 193, 273, 722.
Epicycles and eccentrics, equivalence of, 403.
Epiglottis, 160, 204.
Epigraphy, Chinese, 777.
Epigraphy, Greek, 136, 185.
Epigraphy, Hindu, 167.
Epilepsy, 98, 216, 308, 373.
Epinomis, 118.
Epiphanios, St. (IV-2), 362; 359.
Episynthetic school, 260.
Equant, 273.
Equation of time, 603.
Equations, biquadratic, 667.
Equations, classification, 718, 759.
Equations, cubic, 140, 169, 336, 474, 598, 665, 667, 759.
Equations, determinate, 208, 336, 475.
Equations, indeterminate, 169, 321, 336, 409, 450, 475, 514. See Diophantine analysis.
Equations, linear, 117, 183.
Equations, al-Māhānī's, 598.
Equations, quadratic, 173, 183, 336, 409, 563, 570, 630, 718, 720.
Equinoxes. See Precession; Trepidation.
Erasistratos of Iulis (III-1, B. C.), 159-160; 150, 215, 282.
Erasmus, 242, 266, 275, 294, 363.
Eratosthenes of Cyrene (III-2, B. C.), 172-173; 56, 166, 212.
Erh. See Lao Tzŭ.
Êrh Ya, 84, 110, 353.
Eric the Red (x-2), 675; 650, 655.
Eric the Red's saga, 724.
Ericsson, Leif, 676, 724.
Erigena, John Scotus (IX-2), 594; 406, 423, 584, 586, 589, 596.
Eriugena. See Erigena.
Erotianos (I-2), 264; 245.
Erwig, King, 500.
Erysipelas, 215.
Esdras. See Ezra.
Eshin, 656.
Essenes, 346.
Establishment of a port, 511.
Esthonia, 606.
Estienne, Charles and Robert, 311.
Estienne, Henri, 299, 313, 394, 479.
Estienne, Robert, 293, 328; Robert and Henri, 187.
Ethelwold, 692.
Etheria of Aquitania, 371.
Ethics, Muslim, 780.
Ethicus. See Aethicus Ister.
Ethiopia. See Aethiopia.
Ethnography, ancient, 98, 105.
Etruscan astrology, 408.
Euclid of Alexandria (III-1, B. C.), 153-156; 149, 337, 367, 402, 405, 423, 559, 561, 562, 598, 599, 601, 602, 618, 631, 664, 666, 759, 761.
Euclid's Elements, Book XIV, 181.
Euclid's Elements, Book XV (VI-1), 427; 415, 421.
Euclid of Megara, 153.
Euctemon, 82, 94.
Eudemos of Alexandria (III-1, B. C.), 160; 150.
Eudemos of Rhodes (IV-2, B. C.), 140; 125, 127, 403.
Eudoxos of Cnidos (IV-1, B. C.), 117; 111, 112.
Eudoxos, Papyrus of (II-1, B. C.), 184; 178.
Eugenio of Palermo, 277.
Euhemeros of Messina (IV-2, B. C.), 136-137; 125, 126.
Eumelos, 356.
Eunapios (v-1), 393; 379, 380.
Eupalinos of Megara (VI, B. C.), 76; 65.
Euphrates, 635.
Euric, King, 412.
Euryphon of Cnidos (v, B. C.), 102; 83.
Eusebios of Caesarea (IV-1), 357; 344, 345, 346, 363, 394, 395, 432, 455, 482, 501, 577, 618, 735.
Eusebios of Nicomedia, 348.
Eustathios of Thessalonica, 258, 433.
Eutychios (x-1), 640; 622, 623.
Eutocios (VI-1), 427; 415; 599.

Evagrios Scholasticos (vi–2), 455; 445.
Evangelion da-mĕḥallĕṭē, 292.
Evangelion da-mĕpharrĕshē, 292.
Evection, 273, 666.
Evil, problem, 332.
Evolute, 173.
Evolution, 72, 73, 87, 98, 128, 366, 383, 559, 597, 638. See Adaptation.
Examination system, Chinese, 781.
Exhaustion, method of, 93, 117.
Exilarch, 524.
Exodus, 107.
Experiment, quantitative, 274, 669.
Experimental method, 24.
Expositio totius mundi et gentium, 372.
Eye, 159, 282, 721, 729. See Nerves, optic; Optics; Vision.
Eye diseases. See Ophthalmology.
Eye-salve, 230, 318.
Ezekiel (vi, b. c.), 70; 65.
Ezra (v, b. c.), 108–109; 83, 150.
Ezra, Book of (iii–1, b. c.), 163.

Fa-ching (vi–2), 448; 443.
Fa-hsien (v–1), 390–391; 377, 378, 380, 414.
Fa-shang, 473.
Fa-yang, 473.
Fa-yuan-chu-lin, 491.
Fabius Pictor, Q. (iii–2, b. c.), 176; 166.
Fabricius, J. A., 299, 308, 353.
Fabrot, Charles Annibal, 617.
Fabrotus, A., 578.
al-Faḍl ibn Ḥātim al-Nairīzī, 598.
al-Faḍl ibn Naubakht (viii–2), 531; 521, 524.
Fākhir, 609.
al-Fakhrī, 718.
al-Falāḥa al-nabaṭīya, 634.
Falconry, 731.
Falsafa, 660.
False position, rule, 183.
Famines, 734.
Fan Ch'êng-ta, 676.
Fan ch'ieh, 343, 413, 442.
Fan-ch'o, 536.
Fan Liang-fêng, 454.
Fan Yeh (v–1), 396; 279, 379.
Fang Ch'iao, 482.
Fang Hsüan-ling (vii–1), 482; 462, 463.
Fang yen, 353.
Fānūs, 713.
al-Fārābī (x–1), 628–629; 404, 405, 406, 620, 621, 623, 624, 660, 697.
Farasṭūn, 561.
al-Farghānī (ix–1), 567; 543, 546, 549, 550.
al-Farq, 535.
al-Farq bain al-firaq, 707.
al-Fārūq, 680.
Fāsī, al. See Alfasi.
Fasti Siculi, 482.
Fathers of the Church, 13, 361.
Fāṭima, 579, 593.
Fāṭimid, 593, 702, 717.
Fauchet, Claude, 456.
Fêng, 199.
Fêng shui, 345, 353.
Fêng Tao (x–1), 633; 621.
Fêng Ying Wang, 633.
Ferdinand III, King of Castile and Leon, 500.
Fergil of Salzburg, St. (viii–1), 516; 505.
Fermat, P. de, 174, 336, 352.
Fertilizer, 55, 355.
Festus, Sex. Pompeius, 234.
Fetus, 383, 434. See Embryology; Generation.
Fever and fevers, 120, 121, 280, 310, 383, 453, 478, 640, 769, 773.
Fevers, four, 120.
Fez, 690.
Ficino, Marsilio, 334, 406.
Fidā'īs, 752.
Figulus, Publius Nigidius (i–1, b. c.), 207; 201.
Figura cata, 598.
Fihrist al-'ulūm, 648, 662.
Filiae noctis, 712.
Fine, Oronce, 669.
Finger-prints, 571.
Finger reckoning, 511.
Finns, 606.
al-Fiqh, 551, 592.
Firdaus al-ḥikma, 574.
Firdawsī (xi–1), 705; 435, 457, 694, 701, 745, 783.
Fire, central, 93.
Fire, principle, 85.
Fire-engine, 208.
Firmicus Maternus, Iulius (iv–1), 354; 345, 346, 428.
Fishes, 308, 369; rain of, 326.
Fistulæ, 230.
Fitna, 669.
Five. See Number 5.
Five Dynasties, history, 688, 777.
Flaccus, Verrius (i–2, b. c.), 234; 220.
Flacius Illyricus, 499.
Flavius Basilius Iunior, 430.
Fleming, Abraham, 326.
Flodoard of Reims (x–2), 684; 651, 655.
Floki Vilgerdarson, 605.
Floods, 781.
Florentinos (iii–1), 323; 315.
Flos naturarum, 533.
Flowers, regularities, 708.
Flowers, shapes, 144.
Flying, 720.
Fo kuo chi, 391.
Fo so-hsing tsan, 270.
Focus, 337.
Foesius, Anutius, 99, 393.
Folard, Chevalier de, 188.

Fons Scientiae, 507.
Fons vitae, 704.
Foramina, 281.
Force, 710.
Forces, four, 159.
Forli, Jacopo da, 240.
Forma celi, de, 546, 569.
Fortolf, 763.
Fortunate Islands, 232.
Forum judicum (VII-2), 500.
Fossa Carolina, 528.
Fossils, 73, 105.
Foucquet, Jean, 263.
Fountain, Heron's, 208.
Fountain of Knowledge, 507.
Four. See Number 4.
Fractions, Chinese, 183, 450.
Fractions, continued, 409.
Fractions, decimal, 719.
Fractions, duodecimal, 714, 757.
Fractions, Egyptian, 403.
Fractions, Hindu, 570.
Fractions, sexagesimal. See Sexagesimal.
Franco of Liège (XI-2), 757; 740, 745.
Franks, history, 456, 499, 732.
Franks, law, 439, 484, 774.
Frecht, Martin, 685.
Frechulph of Lisieux (IX-1), 577; 548.
Freculph. See Frechulph of Lisieux.
Fredegarius Scholasticus (VII-2), 499; 489.
Frederick II, emperor, 725.
Freher, Marquard, 780.
French, language, 746, 773.
French dictionary, 752.
Frictions, medical, 96.
Frisian law, 548, 580.
Frisians, 506.
Frobenius, 529.
Frontinus, Sextus Julius (I-2), 255; 244, 245, 397.
Fronto, 297.
Frustum, 208, 475.
Frutolf of Bamberg (XI-2), 763; 741, 745.
Fu[4] (negative), 183, 339.
Fu[3] (prefecture), 676.
Fu Kung (XI-2), 766; 741, 746.
Fu sang, 411.
Fu Jên-chün (VII-1), 475; 461, 463.
Fūdoki (VIII-1), 515; 505.
Fuhito Fujiwara, 518.
Fujiwara, 500, 518.
Fujiwara Fuhito, 518.
Fujiwara no Michinaga, 778.
Fujiwara Mototsune, 517, 617.
Fujiwara Otsugu, 516, 548, 580.
Fujiwara Tadahira, 644.
Fujiwara Tokihira, 517, 617, 644.
Fujiwara Tsuginawa, 516, 541.
Fujiwara Yoshifusa, 516, 617.
Fukuyoshi Ōmura (IX-1), 575; 547.
Fulda, school, 555.
Funūn, 662.
Furkan ibn Asad, 751.
Furu-kotobumi, 516.
al-Furūsīya, 610.
Fuṣūṣ al-ḥikam, 628.
Futūḥ al-buldān, 616.
Futūḥ Miṣr wal-Maghrib, 616.

Gabius, J. B., 776.
Gagnier, Jean, 465.
Gaius (II-2), 311; 290, 396, 438, 440.
Gale, Thomas, 595.
Galen of Pergamum (II-2), 301-307; 55, 160, 240, 261, 269, 281, 288, 289, 290, 308, 310, 373, 382, 392, 424, 434, 478, 479, 537, 556, 573, 574, 599, 600, 611, 613, 631, 710, 721, 728, 729.
Galen, the Sixteen Books, 302, 480, 613.
Galene, 261.
Galenic writings, Byzantine canon, 480.
Galileo, 18, 28, 167, 416, 422.
Gall, St., 657, 703.
Gaṇapāṭha, 123.
Ganelon, traitor, 774.
Gaṇitapāda, 409.
Gaṇitasāra, 719.
Gaṇitasārasaṃgraha, 570.
Ganjin, 510.
Gannīm we-pardēṣīm, sefer ha-, 626.
Gaon (pl., geonim), 471, 524.
Gardar Svavarsson, 605.
Gariopontus (XI-1), 726; 699.
Garnerius, Joannes, 394.
Garnier, Julien, 362.
Gas, natural, 107.
Gatakar, Thomas, 297.
Gāthās, 57, 61.
Gāthāsaṃgraha, 350.
Gauḍapāda, 351.
Gaunilon of Marmoutier, 748.
Gautama. See Buddha, 475.
Gautama Siddharta, 513.
Gauthier of Metz, 749.
Gaza, Theod., 143, 311.
Gazetteers, Chinese, 677.
Geber, 521, 532, 533, 723.
Gechauff, Thomas, 170.
Gelenius, Sigmund, 430.
Gellius, Aulus (II-2), 311; 290.
Gemārā, 384, 401.
Gembō, 513.
Geminos of Rhodes (I-1, B. C.), 212; 202, 354, 403, 629.
Gemmei-tennō, 515.
Generation, 119, 668. See Embryology; Fetus.
Genesis, 107, 362, 422.
Genethlialogy, 368.

Genito-urinary system and troubles. See Urinogenital.
Genka-reki, 476.
Genko Hori, 325.
Genshin (x-2), 656; 647, 654.
Genshō-tennō, 518.
Geocentrical system, 193.
Geodetic measurements. See Degree measurements.
Geographical basis of history, 147, 188.
Geography, history, 172.
Geography, medical, 98.
Geography, Syriac, 501.
Geography of Ptolemy, 275.
Geoheliocentrical system, 141, 407.
Geology, 597, 638, 711.
Geomancy, 353.
Geometrical reduction, 92.
Geometry, fixed, 718.
Geometry, history, 139, 140, 143.
Geometry, mobile, 665.
Geometry, text-book, 92, 140.
Geoponica, 370, 424. See Agriculture.
George, Bishop of the Arabs (VII-2), 493; 488, 489, 490, 501.
Georgian alphabet, 398.
Georgian history, 735.
Georgian versions, 381, 579.
Georgios Monachos (IX-1), 578; 548, 686.
Georgius Florentinus. See Gregory of Tours.
Georgius Trapezuntius. See Trapezuntius, 274.
Gerard of Cremona. See Cremona.
Gerberon, Gabriel, 749.
Gerbert, Martin, 641, 720, 757, 762.
Gerbert (Sylvester II) (x-2), 669-671; 647, 649, 655, 714.
Gerland of Besançon (XI-2), 758; 569, 740, 745, 756.
Gerland, canon of Besançon, 758.
German grammar, 528.
German-Latin glossary, 555.
Gesner, Conrad, 216, 324, 326, 405.
Gesner, J. M., 323.
Geta, Hosidius, 297.
Gharīb ibn Sa'īd, 680.
Ghāyat al-ḥakīm, 668.
Ghazna, 702, 707.
al-Ghazzālī (XI-2), 753-754; 26, 365, 405, 739, 740, 746, 747.
Gherardo Cremonese. See Cremona.
Ghinā' wa manā', 678.
Ghubār numerals, 648, 649, 663, 670.
Giddiness, 373.
Gikū, 552.
Gildas (VI-2), 455; 445.
Gilding, 533.
Gimbals, 195, 534.
Giqaṭilla, Moses ibn, 691.
Glaber, Raoul (XI-1), 734; 700, 702, 734.
Glagolitic alphabet (or Glagolitsa), 590.
Glanders, 356.
Glass, ancient, 389.
Glass, coloring, 533.
Glass manufacture in China, 378, 389.
Glaucias of Tarentum (?) (I-1, B. C.), 215; 203.
Glaucos of Chios (VI, B. C.), 75; 65.
Globe, celestial, 193, 278, 338, 388, 635, 672.
Globe, terrestrial, 185, 635.
Glossarum, liber, 498.
Gnomon, 72, 312.
Gnosticism, 236, 294, 298.
Go, game, 519.
Goar, Jacques, 577, 578.
Gobharaṇa, 246.
God, existence, 748.
Goki-reki, 476.
Golapāda, 409.
Gold. See Gilding.
Gold, Japanese, 515.
Gold mines, 185.
Gold, writing in, 533.
Golden Ass, 296.
Golden section, 113, 117.
Golius, Jacob, 567.
Goriun Skantcheli, 398.
Gortyn, Laws (V, B. C.), 109; 62, 83.
Gotama. See Buddha.
Gotama Siddha, 513.
Gothic language and version, 344, 349.
Gothofredus, J., 396.
Goths, history, 426, 455.
Goths, religion, 348.
Goths. See Gothic; Visigothic.
Gottschalk, 555, 595.
Goupyl, Jacques, 259, 609.
Gout, 308.
Government, principles, 518, 780.
Gouvernement des princes, 557.
Grabadin, 728.
Graenlendingapáttr, 724.
Grafting, 355.
Grammar, early. See under name of language.
Grammar. See Parts of speech.
Grammatical symbols, 265.
Grammaticus, Leo, 578.
Grapevine, 197.
Gravity, 423; center of, 170, 337; specific, 170, 254, 265, 321, 566, 609, 708, 710, 760.
Great Learning, 91.
Great Wall, 168.
Great year, 92, 157.
Greco-Roman culture, 10.
Greece, description of ancient, 300.
Greece, history, 187.
Greek anthology, 408.
Greek civilization, 10.
Greek dictionary, 189, 264, 286, 312, 313, 398, 436, 594, 691, 771.
Greek fire, 494.

Greek grammar, 88, 138, 169, 179, 181, 185, 189, 200, 286, 312; Aristotelian, 501; Stoic, 181.
Greek literature, 264.
Greek miracle, 8, 9.
Greek prosody, 286, 287.
Greek, transliteration, 48.
Greenland, 675.
Gregorian code, 438.
Gregorian music, 763.
Gregorios Monachos, 750.
Gregorius (III-2), 343; 331, 438.
Gregorius Solitarius, 750.
Gregory I, Pope (St. Gregory, Gregory the Great) (VI-2), 445; 443.
Gregory VII, Pope, 762.
Gregory of Nyssa, 373.
Gregory of Tours (VI-2), 456; 445.
Grimm, Sig., 681.
Gronovius, Abraham, 239.
Grotius, Hugo, 319, 540.
Growth, 128.
Grynaeus, Simon, 154, 274, 356, 372, 403.
Guarino of Verona, 228, 240.
Guidi, Guido, 216.
Guido of Arezzo, see Arezzo.
Guido the Geographer, 496.
Guignes, Joseph de, 411, 572.
Guilds, 617.
Guinter, Joh., 392, 479.
Guldin, Habakkuk (Paul), 337.
Gundisalvi, D., 629, 704, 753.
Gundobad, King, 438, 439.
Gunnbjörn, son of Ulf Kråka, 675.
Guru, 526.
Gymnastics, 96, 146, 320.
Gynaecology, 198, 282. See Womb.
Gynaecology, illustrations, 434.
Gyōgi-Bosatsu (VIII-1), 510; 504, 505, 553.
Gyōgi-yaki, 510.
Gyraldus, Gregorius, 771.

Habakkuk (VII, B. C.), 64; 60.
Ḥabash al-Ḥāsib (IX-1), 565; 545, 550, 667.
Habington, Thomas, 456.
Ḥadīth, 525, 550, 551, 592, 777.
Hadrian of Canterbury, 492.
Haemostatic, 230, 280, 282, 681.
Haggādah, 401.
Haggai (VI, B. C.), 70; 65.
Hai-nei hua-i t'u, 536.
Hai-tao suan-ching, 338.
Hair diseases, 481.
Hair-pencil. See Brush, writing.
Ḥaiyān ibn Khalaf ibn Ḥaiyān, 734.
al-Ḥajjāj ibn Maṭar (IX-1), 562; 273, 545.
al-Ḥajjāj ibn Yūsuf (VIII-1), 518; 506.
al-Ḥajjāj ibn Yūsuf ibn Maṭar, 562.
Ḥājjī Khalīfa, 495.
al-Ḥakam II, Umayyad of Cordova (X-2) 658; 647, 654.
Hakemite tables, 716.
al-Ḥākim, Fāṭimid caliph, 695, 716.
Halākā, 401.
Halakot, 751.
Haller, Albrecht von, 392.
Halley, Edmund, 174, 254, 354.
Haly Abbas, 650, 677.
Hamburg, history of the diocese, 767.
Ḥamdān Qarmaṭ ibn al-Ash'ath, 584, 593.
al-Hamdānī (X-1), 637; 620, 622, 624.
Ḥāmid ibn 'Alī al-Wāsiṭī (IX-2), 601; 585, 590.
Ḥāmid ibn al-Khiḍr al-Khujandī, 667.
Hammurabi, 110.
Ḥamza ibn al-Ḥasan al-Iṣfahānī (X-2), 687; 652, 654.
Han dynasty, earlier or western, 264, 299.
Han dynasty, later or eastern, 396.
Han, minor, 343.
Han chi, 299.
Han I-wen-chih, 222, 264.
Han-lin yüan, 512.
Han-Ryoho, 454.
Ḥanbalite school, 551.
al Handasa, 666.
al-Handasa al-thābit, 718.
Hangchow, 636.
Ḥanīfite school, 508.
Hanmer, Meredith, 394.
Hanno (V, B. C.), 103-104; 83.
Ḥarakāt, 519.
Ḥarakāt al-samāwīya, 567.
Harmonic pencil, 353.
Harmony. See Music.
Harmony of the spheres, 73, 272.
Harmony of the world, 85.
Harpsichord, 175.
Ḥarrānian, 589, 599, 668, 750. See Sabian.
Hārūn. See Aaron of Alexandria.
Hārūn-al-Rashīd (VIII-2), 527; 521, 525.
Harvey, Wm., 129, 282, 301.
al-Ḥasan ibn Aḥmad al-Hamdānī, 637.
al-Ḥasan ibn 'Alī ibn Isḥāq, 780.
al-Ḥasan ibn al-Ḥasan ibn al-Haitham, 721.
al-Ḥasan ibn al-Khaṣīb, 603.
al-Ḥasan ibn Mūsā, 561.
al-Ḥasan ibn Nūḥ al-Qumrī, 678.
al-Ḥasan ibn al-Ṣabbāḥ, 746, 752.
al-Ḥasan ibn Sahl ibn Naubakht, 531.
al-Ḥasan al-Sīrāfī, 636.
Ḥasdai ibn Shaprut (X-2), 680; 647, 651, 653, 655, 682, 683.
Ḥashīsh, 752, 771.
Ḥashīshīyūn, 752.
al-Ḥāwī, 609.
Hay fever, 610.
al-Ḥayawān, 597.
Ḥayyuj (X-2), 691; 653, 655.
Health, public, 96. See Hygiene.
Heart, 94, 96, 120, 128, 159, 160, 180; valves, 120, 160. See Auricles.

Heat, 710.
Hebdomadibus, de, 97.
Hebrew dictionary; first, 627; 690, 736, 747 782.
Hebrew grammar; first, 627; 690, 691, 704, 736.
Hebrew history, 63, 79.
Hebrew language, 746.
Hebrew law, 62, 107.
Hebrew philology, 627.
Hebrew prosody, 690.
Hebrew Scriptures, 619, 624.
Hebrew, transliteration, 49.
Hecataeos of Miletos (VI, B. C.), 78; 66.
Hédelin, François, 54.
Hegetor (II-2, B. C.), 198; 192.
Hegira. See al-Hijra.
Heian-kyō, 509.
Height of mountains, 145.
Heijō-tennō, 547, 575.
Helias, Patriarch of Jerusalem, 634.
Heliocentric system, 156, 183. See Geoheliocentric.
Heliodoros the Surgeon (II-1), 281; 268.
Heliodoros the Alchemist (VIII-1), 514; 505.
Heliodoros, son of Hermias (VI-1), 429; 416.
Heliodoros of Larissa, 354.
Hellebore, 55, 260.
Hellenistic civilization, 10.
Helminthology. See Worms.
Helperic (X-2), 671; 569, 649, 655.
Helperic of Auxerre, 672.
Hemorrhoids, 498.
Hemp, Indian, 77.
Hemsterhuis, Tib., 313.
Henbane, 77.
Hêng, 35.
Hêng ch'ao, 364.
Henry I, emperor, 685.
Henry II, emperor, 714.
Hephaestion of Alexandria (II-1), 287; 269.
Hephaestion of Thebes (IV-2), 368; 360.
Heptagon, 172, 600, 667, 718.
Heraclean version, 291.
Heraclides of Damascus, 382.
Heraclides of Pontos (IV-2, B. C.), 141; 125, 272.
Heraclides of Tarentum (I-1, B. C.), 215; 203, 215-216.
Heraclios, Byzantine emperor, 462.
Heraclitos of Ephesos (V, B. C.), 85; 81.
Heraclius (X-2), 673; 649.
Herbal, 213.
Herbal, Chinese. See Pên ts'ao.
Herbarium, 296, 392.
Herbarum virtutibus, de, 296; or medicaminibus, 392.
Herbis femininis, de, 416, 431.
Herbs, 215, 570.
Heredity, 119, 128.
Hériger of Lobbes (X-2), 685; 649, 652, 655.
Herigerus Laubiensis, 685.
Herjulfsson, Bjarne, 676.
Hermann of Dalmatia, 568, 569.
Hermann the Lame of Reichenau (XI-2), 757; 740, 741, 743, 745, 756.
Hermannus Contractus, 757.
Hermannus Secundus (or Dalmata), 568, 569.
Hermant, Godefroy, 349.
Hermerus, Claudius, 375.
Hermes Trismegistos, 238, 296, 320, 332.
Hermetica, 320.
Hermodoros of Salamis (II-2, B. C.), 196; 191.
Hermogenianus (IV-1), 357; 345, 346, 358, 438.
Hermolaos, 433.
Hernia, 77.
Hero the Younger, of Byzantium (X-1), 632; 621, 623.
Hero. See Heron.
Herodian (III-1), 326; 316.
Herodian, grammarian. See Herodianos Aelios.
Herodianic signs, 312.
Herodianos, Aelios (II-2), 312; 286, 290.
Herodianos, historian. See Herodian.
Herodicos of Selymbria (V, B. C.), 96; 83.
Herodotos of Halicarnassos (V, B. C.), 105-106; 83, 535.
Herodotos of Rome (I-2), 262; 244.
Heron of Alexandria (I-1, B. C.), 208-211; 184, 202, 256, 271, 331, 403, 559, 602, 632.
Heron. See Hero.
Herophilos of Chalcedon (III-1, B. C.), 159; 149, 150.
Herr, Mich., 731, 772.
Herrgott, M., 762.
Hervagius, F., 511.
Hervieu, Father, 342.
Hesiod (VIII, B. C.), 57; 52, 164, 189, 200, 402.
Hesychios (Greek N. T.), 349.
Hesychios of Alexandria (V-1), 398; 379.
Hesychios of Miletus (VI-1), 436; 417, 418.
Hexaëmeron, 362, 363, 493, 501, 596, 692.
Hexapla, 291, 317; Syriac, 291.
Hexateuch (V, B. C.), 107-108; 83.
Heyden-Weldt, Joh. Herold, 358.
Hezekiah (VIII, B. C.), 59; 53.
Hi-oki, 476.
Hībhā. See Ibas.
Hiccup, 370.
Hicetas of Syracuse (V, B. C.), 94; 82.
Hieda no Are, 516.
Hierocles (IV-2), 372; 356, 360, 657.
Hieroglyphics, 358.
Hieronymus. See St. Jerome.
Hieronymus, Presbyter, 495.
al-Hijra, 464.
Hilāl al-Ḥimṣī (IX-2), 598; 585, 664.
Hilal ibn Muhassin, 687.
Hildericus, Edo, 212.
Hill and Water Classic, 353.

Hillel II (IV-2), 368; 318, 360.
Himilco (V, B. C.), 104; 83, 371.
Hīnayāna, 270.
Hincmar, 555.
Hindu. See India.
Hindu mathematics, transmission, 521.
Hindu medicine, transmission, 575.
Hindu numerals. See Numerals, Hindu.
Hindu science, 36.
Hip, 198.
Hipparchos of Nicaea (II-2, B. C.), 193-195; 173, 191, 192, 208, 212, 273, 403.
Hippias of Elis (V, B. C.), 92; 82.
Hippiatrica, 356, 372.
Hippocrates of Chios (V, B. C.), 91-92; 82.
Hippocrates of Cos (V, B. C.), 96-102; 83, 146, 215, 240, 264, 283, 304, 305, 392, 424, 434, 478, 537, 556, 573, 608, 611, 657, 677, 729.
Hippocratic corpus, 97, 121; Byzantine, 480.
Hippocratic dictionary, 215, 264.
Hippocratic treatises, 112, 119.
Hippodamos of Miletos (V, B. C.), 95; 82.
Hippolytos, St. (III-1), 320; 314, 316.
Hippon (V, B. C.), 86; 81.
Hippopede, 117, 403.
Hiragana, 519, 553.
Hiroizumi Monobe (IX-1), 575; 547.
Hironari Imube, 580.
Hirosada Idzumo, 575.
Hiroyo Wake, 539.
Hirsau, Wilhelm of (XI-2), 762; 740, 741.
Ḥisāb al-hawā'ī, 715.
Ḥisāb al-jabr wal-muqābala, 563.
Hishām ibn Muḥammad (VIII-2), 541; 523, 524.
Hispalensis, Joannes. See Joannes Hispalensis.
Historia miscella, 614.
Historia tripertita, 614.
Historiography, 7.
History, theory, 188.
Ḥiyal, 561.
Ho Chêng-t'ien (V-1), 388; 378.
Hoeschel, David, 358, 594.
Hohenwang, Ludwig, 368.
Hōjōji no Kwampaku, 778.
Hokké-kyo, 448.
Hōkō-ji, 452.
Holtzmann, Wilhelm. See Xylander.
Homer (IX, B. C.), 53-56; 13, 52, 164, 189, 198, 200, 233, 537, 774.
Homocentric spheres. See Spheres, homocentric.
Honchi-suijaku, 553.
Honoratus, 347.
Honorius, Julius (Orator), 496.
Honorius of Autun, 749.
Honorius Inclusus (XI-2), 749; 739, 745.
Honorius Solitarius, 749.
Honryū-ji, 529.
Honzō wamyō, 683.
Hopper, Marcus, 404.
Horā, 428.
Horace, 221, 739.
Horapollon of Nilopolis (IV-1), 358; 346.
Hori, Genko. See Genko Hori.
Hornanus, H. J., 393.
Horsley, Sam., 174.
Hōryū-ji, 470.
Hosea (VIII, B. C.), 58; 53.
Hospitals, Byzantine, 779.
Hospitals, Japanese, 539.
Hospitals, Muslim, 631, 641.
Hossō-shū, 488, 491.
Hou Chou shu, 483.
Hou Han shu, 396.
Hours, seven, 238.
Hours, 12 double, 71, 238, 429.
Howell, Dda, King, 622, 643.
Hrabanus Maurus (IX-1), 555; 544, 546, 548, 549, 595, 764.
Hrosvitha of Gandersheim (X-2), 658; 647, 649, 652, 655.
Hrotsuit, 658.
Hsi kuo chi, 496.
Hsi-yu chi, 477, 496.
Hsi-yü chi, 477.
Hsi yü t'u chi, 476.
Hsia-hou Yang (VI-2), 449; 444.
Hsiang ch'i, 451.
Hsiang Hsiu, 335.
Hsiao ching, 321.
Hsiao chuan, 286.
Hsiao Tzŭ-hsien (VI-1), 438; 417.
Hsieh Chü-chêng (X-2), 688; 652, 654.
Hsieh-p'u, 766.
Hsien, 676.
Hsien-yü Wang-jên, 195.
Hsin-hsiu pên-ts'ao, 539.
Hsin-lin, 353.
Hsin T'ang shu, 777.
Hsin wu-tai-shih, 777.
Hsing-ching, 504, 514.
Hsing-i-hsiang fa-yao, 762.
Hsing-li, 27, 755.
Hsing Ping, 110.
Hsiung Tsung-li, 773.
Hsü Ch'a-ching, 535.
Hsü Ch'ieh, 286.
Hsü Ching-tsung, 484.
Hsü Ch'ung, 286.
Hsü Hsüan, 286.
Hsü kao sêng ch'uan, 491.
Hsü Kuei-lin, 756.
Hsü Shên (II-1), 285; 269, 441.
Hsü Yüeh (II-2), 299; 289, 756.
Hsüan Tsang (or Yüan) (VII-1), 477-478; 350, 367, 461, 462, 463, 470, 484, 488, 496, 604.
Hsüan Tsung, T'ang emperor, 508.

Hsüan Ying (VII–1), 487; 463.
Hsün Hsü (III–2), 342; 331.
Hsün K'uang (III–2, B. C.), 168–169; 166.
Hsün Yüeh (II–2), 299; 289, 290.
Hua Hsi-min, 663.
Hua Shou, 103.
Hua T'o (III–1), 325; 315.
Hua-yang chên jen, 436.
Huai Nan Tzŭ (II–2, B. C.), 193; 191, 192.
Huang-chi ching-shih shu, 755.
Huang Fu (III–2), 342; 331.
Huang Ti, emperor, 112, 122.
Huang-Ti Chên-chiu chia-i-ching, 342.
Huang Ti Nei ching su-wên, 122, 539.
Ḥubaish ibn al-Ḥasan (IX–2), 613; 612, 587.
Hui An, 737.
Hui Chiao, 343, 491.
Hui-shên (V–2), 410; 400.
Hui Shêng, 431.
Hui Tsung, Sung emperor, 764.
Hui Yüan (IV–2), 364; 359, 469.
Hūlāgū, 753.
al-Ḥummayāt, 640.
Hummelberger, Gabriel, 231, 340, 375.
Humors, theory of, 96, 120, 160, 214, 727.
Ḥunain ibn Isḥāq al-'Ibādī (IX–2), 611; 382, 424, 479, 537, 556, 560, 573, 574, 583, 587, 588, 589, 590, 600.
Hung lieh chieh, 193.
Hung-ming-chi, 420.
Hung-ta, 476.
Huns, 264.
Huns, writing, 457.
Ḥurūf al-ghubār. See Ghubār numerals.
al-Ḥusain ibn 'Abdallāh ibn Sīnā, 709.
al-Ḥusain ibn Ibrāhīm (X–2), 678; 650, 654.
Husbandry. See Agriculture; Geoponica.
Hutton, James, 227.
Huygens, Chr., 167.
Hyaku-ron, 470.
Hydraulics, 195, 245, 255.
Hydrodynamics, 255.
Hydrometer, 388.
Hydrophobia, 373.
Hydrostatics, 170, 708.
Hydrotherapy, 231, 260, 280, 728, 750.
Hygiene, Greek, 160.
Hygiene, Japanese, 575.
Hyginus, agrimensor (II–1), 271; 256, 267, 268, 397.
Hyginus, C. Julius (I–2, B. C.), 226; 219, 220.
Hylozoism, 113. See Macrocosm.
Hypatia (V–1), 386; 378, 380.
Hyperbola, 173. See Conics.
Hyperboloids, 169.
Hypotenuse, 74.
Hypsicles (II–1, B. C.), 181; 177, 178, 180, 601, 602.
Hysteria, 308.
I (doctrine of changes), 448.
I ch'ieh ching yin i, 487.
I Ching (Book of Changes), 67, 163, 322, 448, 755.
I-ching (VII–2), 497; 480, 488, 489, 490.
I-hsing (VIII–1), 514; 504.
I-li chu-shih, 571.
Iamblichos (IV–1), 351–352; 238, 253, 344, 345, 346, 406.
Iatrochemists, 609.
Ibāḍite school, 490, 492, 508.
Ibas (Hībhā), 382, 400, 407.
Iberian (Georgian) history, 735.
Iberian version, 381.
al-Ibil, 534.
Ibn 'Abd al-Ḥakam (IX–2), 616; 588, 590.
Ibn 'Abdi Rabbihi, 556.
Ibn abī-l-Rijāl (XI–1), 715; 695, 702.
Ibn abī Uṣaibi'a, 777.
Ibn abī Ya'qūb al-Nadīm (X–2), 662; 648, 652, 654.
Ibn al-Adamī (X–1), 630; 620.
Ibn al-A'lam (X–2), 666; 649, 654.
Ibn Amājūr (X–1), 630; 620, 624.
Ibn al-Athīr, 541, 642.
Ibn al-'Awwām, 766.
Ibn Bābūya (X–2), 656; 647, 654.
Ibn al-Baiṭār, 615.
Ibn Bakhtyashū', Jibrīl, 573.
Ibn Bakhtyashū', Jirjīs ibn Jibrīl (VIII–2), 537; 522, 524.
Ibn Bakhtyashū', 'Ubaid Allāh ibn Jibrīl, 730.
Ibn Buṭlān (XI–1), 730; 700, 701, 742, 772.
Ibn Daiṣān. See Bardesanes.
Ibn al-Dāya, 598.
Ibn Duraid (X–1), 644; 622, 623, 624.
Ibn Ezra, Abraham, 691.
Ibn Faḍlān (X–1), 636; 621.
Ibn al-Faqīh (X–1), 635; 621, 624.
Ibn al-Faraḍī (XI–1), 734; 700, 702.
Ibn Gabirol (XI–1), 704; 26, 693, 694, 701, 702.
Ibn al-Ḥā'ik, 637.
Ibn al-Haitham (XI–1), 721–723; 693, 694, 696, 698, 699, 701, 702, 703.
Ibn Ḥaiyān. See Jābir.
Ibn Ḥaiyān (XI–1), 734; 700, 702.
Ibn Ḥanbal (IX–1), 551; 543, 550, 557.
Ibn Ḥawqal (X–2), 674; 650, 654.
Ibn Ḥazm (XI–1), 713; 694, 695, 701, 702.
Ibn Hishām (IX–1), 579; 540, 548, 550.
Ibn al-Ḥusain (XI–1), 718; 696, 697, 702.
Ibn Ibāḍ, 'Abdallāh (VII–2), 492; 488, 490.
Ibn al-'Idhārī, 680.
Ibn Isḥāq, Muḥammad (VIII–2), 540; 523, 524.
Ibn Janāḥ (XI–1), 736; 699, 701, 702.
Ibn Jazla (XI–2), 772; 742, 746.
Ibn al-Jazzār (X–2), 682; 651, 654.
Ibn Jinnī (X–2), 689; 652, 654.
Ibn Juljul (X–2), 682; 613, 651, 652, 654.
Ibn Khallikān, 501.

Ibn Khurdādhbih (IX–2), 606; 586, 590, 636.
Ibn Māsawaih (IX–1), 574; 543, 547, 549.
Ibn Maskawayh (X–2), 687; 647, 652, 654.
Ibn al-Muqaffa' (VIII–2), 540; 482, 522, 523, 524.
Ibn al-Nadīm, 333, 495.
Ibn al-Qifṭī, 777.
Ibn Qutaiba (IX–2), 615; 585, 588, 589, 590.
Ibn al-Qūṭīya (X–2), 688; 652, 654.
Ibn Rauḥ, 630.
Ibn Rusta (X–1), 635; 621, 624, 636.
Ibn Sa'd (IX–1), 579; 548, 550.
Ibn al-Ṣaffār (XI–1), 716; 695, 702.
Ibn Sahdā (IX–1), 573; 547.
Ibn Ṣā'id (XI–2), 776; 740, 743, 746.
Ibn al-Samḥ (XI–1), 715; 695, 702.
Ibn Sarāfyūn. See Ibn Serapion.
Ibn Serapion (X–1), 635; 621.
Ibn Shabin, 559.
Ibn al-Shāṭir, 599.
Ibn Sīda (XI–2), 782; 615, 745, 746.
Ibn Sīnā (XI–1), 709–713; 405, 678, 693, 694, 695, 696, 697, 698, 699, 700, 701, 703, 709, 761.
Ibn Sirin, 559.
Ibn Ṭāhir (XI–1), 706; 694, 695, 696, 697, 702.
Ibn al-Ṭaiyib (XI–1), 730; 292, 698, 700, 701.
Ibn al-Tilmīdh, 608.
Ibn Wāḍiḥ, 607.
Ibn al-Wāfid (XI–1), 728; 699, 702.
Ibn Wahb, 571, 636.
Ibn Waḥshīya (X–1), 634; 621.
Ibn Yūnus (XI–1), 716–717; 598, 601, 666, 693, 695, 696, 701, 702, 703.
Ibn al-Zarqāla, 758.
Ibrāhīm al-Fazārī (VIII–2), 530; 521, 524.
Ibrāhīm ibn Hilāl, 659.
Ibrāhīm ibn Muḥammad al-Iṣṭakhrī, 674.
Ibrāhīm ibn Ṣāliḥ al-Warrāq, 652, 689.
Ibrāhīm ibn Sinān (X–1), 631; 620, 624.
Ibrāhīm ibn Yaḥyā al-Naqqāsh, 758.
Ibrāhīm ibn Ya'qūb (X–2), 675; 650, 654.
Iceland, 571, 576, 586; discovery, 605.
Ichi-dai-kyō-shū, 470.
Ichthyophagi, 185.
Iconography, anatomy. See Surgery, illustrations.
Iconography, botany. See Plants, illustrations.
Iconography, diagrams, 213.
Iconography, gynaecology, 434.
Icosahedron, 116, 181.
Idiologos, 312.
al-Idrīsī, 636.
Idzumo Hirosada, 575.
Ierotheus, alchemist, 514.
Iḥṣā al-'ulūm, 628.
Iḥyā 'ulūm al-dīn, 753.
Ijmā', 525, 550.
Ikaruga-dera, 470.
Ikhnaton. See Amenhotep.
Ikhwān al-ṣafā' (X–2), 660. See Brethren of Purity.
al-Iklīl, 637.
al-'Ilal, 656.
Iliad, 53, 743, 748.
'Ilm al-ṣanā'a, 508.
Imago mundi, 739, 749.
Imām (four), 551, 593, 642.
Imāmīya sect, 508.
Impetigo contagiosa, 481.
Impetus, 423.
al-'Imrānī (X–1), 632; 621, 669.
Imube Hironari (IX–1), 580; 548.
Incarnation, 236, 775.
Incommensurable quantities, 73, 92, 116, 117.
Incunabula, 41.
Indefinite, the, 72.
Indeterminate analysis. See Equations, indeterminate.
India, 107, 161, 674, 676, 707. See Hindu.
Indiction, 430.
Indivisible lines, 139.
Induction, 128.
Indukara, 537.
Inertia, 422.
Infinity, 85, 128, 710.
Inflation, financial, 781.
Influenza, 687.
Ingolf Arnarson, 606.
Inheritance problems, Hindu, 781.
Inheritance problems, Muslim, 707.
Inheritance problems, Roman, 285.
Inḥirāf, 599.
Ink, 369, 441.
Inscriptions. See Epigraphy.
Institutes, 439, 440.
Instruments. See Astronomical; Chemical; Surgical; etc.
Involution of points, 337.
Ioasaph. See Barlaam and Ioasaph.
Ionia, 79.
Ionic dialect, 307.
al-Īqā', 542.
al-'Iqd al-farīd, 556.
Ireland, 380, 419.
Irenaeos, St. (II–2), 294; 288.
Iriarte, 372.
Iris, 731.
Irish law, 397.
Iroha, 554.
Iron, 55.
Irrationality. See Incommensurable.
Irrigation, system, 175.
'Īsā ibn 'Alī al-Asdī (falconry), 731.
'Īsā ibn 'Alī, 731.
'Īsā ibn Yaḥyā ibn Ibrāhīm (IX–2), 613; 587.
'Īsā ibn Yaḥyā al-Masīḥī, 678.
Isaac Israeli the Elder, 639.
Isaac Israeli the Younger, 639.

Isaac ben Jacob Alfasi, 751.
Isaac Juďaeus ben Solomon, 620, 639.
Isaac ibn Shaprut, 690.
Īsāghūjī, 335.
Isagoge, 335.
Isaiah (VIII, B. C.), 58-59; 53.
Ise monogatari, 778.
Isḥāq ibn Ḥunain (IX-2), 600; 227, 254, 562, 585, 587, 598, 599.
Isḥāq al-Isrā'īlī (X-1), 639; 620, 622, 623, 624.
al-Ishārāt wal-tanbīhāt, 709.
al-Ishbā', 719.
Ishinhō, 683.
al-'Ishq maraḍan, 730.
Ishrun maqalat, 626.
al-Ishtiqāq, 645.
Isidore of Charax (I-2, B. C.), 230; 220.
Isidore of Seville (Isidorus Hispalensis, St. Isidore) (VII-1), 471-472; 23, 341, 461, 463, 496, 510, 726, 764.
Isidoros of Miletos, 415, 421, 427.
Isis, 40, 44, 45, 238.
Islām, beginning (VII-1), 464-465; 460.
Islām, defense, 575.
Islām, refutation, 507.
Ismā'īl ibn 'Abbād (X-2), 688; 652, 654.
Ismā'īl ibn Ḥammād al-Jauharī, 689.
Ismā'īl (ibn) al-Ḥusain al-Fārānī, 628.
Ismā'īl ibn Muḥammad, 569.
Ismā'īlīya (Ismā'īlī movement or propaganda) (IX-2), 593; 420, 584, 590, 660, 752, 768.
Isoperimetry, 182, 661.
al-Iṣṭakhrī (X-2), 674; 650, 654.
al-Istī'āb al-wujūh al-mumkin, 709.
Iṣṭifan ibn Bāsīl, 613.
Istiḥsān, 508.
Istikhrāj al-awtār, 708.
Istikmāl, 759.
al-Istiqsāt, 640.
Istiṣlāḥ, 525.
Īśvarakṛishṇa (IV-1), 351; 344, 350, 446.
Italy, geography, 226.
Italy, Jewish settlements in, 776, 782.
Italy, Southern, 685.
Itineraria adnotata, 323.
Itineraria picta, 323.
Itineraries, 360, 371; Chinese, 324, 536; Roman, 323.
Itinerarium provinciarum Antonini Augusti, 315, 323.
Iwazumi, Sakaibe, 502.

Jābir ibn Ḥaiyān (VIII-2), 532-533; 508, 520, 521, 523, 524.
Jābir ibn Sinān al-Ḥarrānī (IX-2), 602; 585.
Jacob Anatoli, 567.
Jacob of Edessa (VII-2), 500; 424, 489, 490, 493, 564.
Jacob ben Ḥayyim ibn Adonijah, 624.
Jacob ben Machir ibn Tibbon, 254, 716.
al-Jadarī wal-ḥaṣba, 609.
Ja'far ibn Muḥammad al-Balkhī, 568.
Ja'far al-Ṣādiq (VIII-1), 508; 503, 505.
al-Jāhiliyya, 464, 486.
al-Jāḥiẓ (IX-2), 597; 586, 590.
Jahvistic narrative, 108.
al-Jaihānī (X-1), 635; 621, 624, 636.
Jaimini, 512.
Jaina canon, 69.
Jaina physics, 69.
Jainism, 69, 351.
Jalāl al-dīn Malikshāh, Saljūq sulṭān, 760, 772, 780.
James, St., 493.
James, St., the way of, 774.
al-Jamhara fī-l-lugha, 645.
al-Jamhara fī-l-nasab, 541.
Jāmi' al-alfāẓ, 690.
al-Jāmi' wa-l-bāligh, al-zīj, 717.
al-Jāmi' al-ṣaḥīḥ, 551.
Janus Damascenus, 507, 608.
Japanese archaeology, 580.
Japanese civilization, 445, 463.
Japanese dictionary, 502; Chinese, 692.
Japanese history, National Histories, 516.
Japanese language, 745, 746.
Japanese medicine, beginning, 393.
Japanese names, 43.
Japanese philology, beginning, 490.
Japanese school, earliest public, 539, 554.
Japanese science, 37.
Japanese, transcription, 49.
Japanese writing, 519.
Jātakas, 77.
al-Jauharī (X-2), 689; 652, 654.
Java, 390.
al-Jawāhir wal-aḥjār, 572.
Jehudah. See Judah ha-Nasi.
Jehudah ben Quraish (IX-1), 581; 548, 549, 690.
Jeliel ben Abraham, 782.
Jên Tsung, Sung emperor, 764.
Jên-wu-chih, 321.
Jeremiah (VII, B. C.), 63-64; 60.
Jeremiah, Lamentations, 63.
Jerome, St. (IV-2), 363; 359, 395, 496.
Jerusalem, 163, 466.
Jerusalem library, 605.
Jeshua ben Judah (XI-2), 751; 739, 745.
Jeshua. See Joshua.
Jesu Haly, 731.
Jesus Christ (I-1), 236; 235, 332.
Jesus, Son of Sirach. See Ecclesiasticus.
Jewish antiquities, 262.
Jewish commerce, 675.
Jewish history, 262.
Jewish life in Italy, 776, 782.
Jibrīl ibn Bakhtyashū' (IX-1), 573; 547, 549.
Jikaku daishi (IX-1), 554; 544.
Jimon-shū, 552.

Jinagupta (vi-2), 447; 443.
Jirjīs ibn Jibrīl ibn Bakhtyashū', 537.
Jitō-tennō, 500.
Jñānagupta. See Jinagupta.
Joannes. See John.
Joannes, alchemist, 238.
Joannes Damascenus. See John of Damascus.
Joannes Hispalensis, 404, 556, 563, 567, 568, 569, 668, 669, 704, 716.
Joannes de Saxonia, 669.
Joannitius, 587, 611.
Job, Book of (v, B. C.), 90–91; 82, 83.
Job of Edessa, the Spotted, 574.
Job Lentiginosus, 574.
Jōdo-shū, 364, 656.
Jōgwan-kyaku-shiki, 618.
John. See Joannes.
John, monk in St. Sabbas monastery, 507.
John of Alexandria, 480.
John of Antioch (vii-1), 482; 462, 463. See Malalas, John.
John of Asia (vi-2), 457; 445.
John of Damascus (viii-1), 507; 406, 503, 504, 506, 608.
John of Ephesus. See John of Asia.
John the Grammarian (vii-1), 480; 462, 463. See Philoponos, Joannes.
John the Saracen, 769.
Jōjitsu-shū, 460, 470.
Jonah, 592. See Ibn Janāḥ.
Jongleurs, 773.
Jordanes (vi-2), 455; 426, 445.
Jornandes. See Jordanes.
Josaphat. See Barlaam and Ioasaph.
Joseph, King of the Khazars, 680.
Joseph ben Abraham ha-Kohen, 703.
Joseph the Priest, 600.
Joseph ha-Ro'eh (xi-1), 703; 694, 751.
Joseph the Wise, 672.
Josephus, Flavius (i-2), 262; 245.
Josephus Hispanus, 672.
Josephus Sapiens (x-2), 672; 649, 655.
Joshua. See Jeshua.
Joshua, Book of, 107.
Joshua, King, 79.
Joshua the Stylite, 417, 437.
Jū-ni-mon-ron, 470.
Juan Chi, 335.
Juan Hsien, 335.
Juba II of Mauretania (i-2, B. C.), 232; 220.
Judah, history, 163.
Judah. See Jehudah.
Judah I. See Judah ha-Nasi.
Judah ben David, 691.
Judah al-Harizi, 556.
Judah ha Levi, 680.
Judah ben Moses, 716.
Judah ha-Nasi (ii-2), 295; 288, 384.
Judah ibn Qarīsh. See Jehudah ben Quraish.
Judah ibn Tibbon, 627, 736.
Judaism, 11.
Judei super decimum Euclidis, liber, 761.
Judges, Book of (vi, B. C.), 79.
Judiciorum, liber (vii-2), 500.
Judō, 67.
Jugurtha, 231.
Jukyō. See Judō.
Julian the Apostate (iv-2), 365-366; 352, 359, 361, 393.
Julian Romance, 366.
Julianos of Laodicea (v-2), 410; 400.
Julianus, Flavius Claudius. See Julian the Apostate.
Julianus, Salvius (ii-1), 285; 269.
Julios Africanos, Sextos (iii-1), 327; 293, 315, 316.
Jumal uṣūl al-taṣrīf, 689.
Jundīshāpūr, 382, 415, 417, 419, 435, 537.
Jupiter, 594.
Jūshichi kempō, 473, 500.
Justin Martyr (ii-2), 293; 288.
Justinian I, the Great (vi-1), 439; 285, 414, 415, 418, 419, 454.
Justinianus, Aug., 353.
Justinianus, Flavius Anicius. See Justinian I, the Great.
Justus of Tiberias, 263.
al-Juzajānī, 711.
Jyā, 387.
Jyotiḥśāstra, 428.

K. For Greek words see C; for Semitic words beginning with qāf (or equivalent letter) see Q.
Kabbala, 406.
al-Kabīr al-Ḥākimī, al-zīj, 716.
al-Kāfī fī-l-ḥisāb, 718.
Kai-t'ien, 195.
K'ai-yüan, 513.
K'ai yüan-lu, 509.
K'ai yüan shih chiao lu, 509.
Kaigen, 515.
Kairitsu, 510.
Kālakriyāpāda, 409.
Kalām, 660.
Kalatli ibn Shakbar, 637.
Kalīla wa Dimna, 449, 540, 771.
Kalpa, 222, 387.
Kamāl al-dīn Abū-l-Ḥasan al-Fārisī, 722.
Kamatari, 500.
al-Kāmil, 666.
Kāmil al-sanā'a al-ṭibbīya, 677.
Kana, 519.
Kana Nihongi, 516.
K'ang-chü, 197.
Kanīsa, 566.
Kanishka, 269.
Kanjin (viii-2), 539; 523.
Kanjur (Kang-gyur), 467–469; 538, 593.

Kankah, 521, 530.
Kanshin, 504, 510.
Kao sêng ch'uan, 343, 491.
Kao Tsung, T'ang emperor, 498.
Kapila, 351.
Kara-Khoto, 604.
Karaṇas, 386.
Kardaja, 530.
al-Karkhī (xi–1), 718; 630, 693, 696, 697, 701, 702.
Karlsefni, Thorfin, 724.
Karma, 69.
al-Karmānī (xi–1), 715; 648, 668, 694, 695, 699, 702.
Kārnāmak (vi–2), 457; 445.
Kāśyapa-Mātaṅga (i–2), 246.
Katakana, 519, 553.
al-Kāthī (xi–1), 723; 698, 702.
Kātib al-Wāqidī, 579.
Kātyāyana, 74.
Kauṭilya (iv–2, b. c.), 147–148; 126, 127.
Kawādh, Sassanian King, 420, 437.
al-Kawākib al-thābita al-muṣawwar, 666.
Kegonkyō, 510.
Kegon-shū, 510.
Kêng Shou-ch'ang (i–1, b. c.), 211; 195, 202, 254.
Kenyon papyrus, 340.
Kepler, 18, 338, 721.
Keskinto inscription (ii–2, b. c.), 195.
Kĕthābhā dhĕ-nuqzĕ, 611.
Kevalādvaita, 561.
Key, 75.
Keys of the Sciences, 648, 659.
al-Khail, 534.
Khalaf ibn 'Abbās al-Zahrāwī, 681.
Khālid ibn 'Abd al-Malik al-Marwarrūdhī, 566.
Khālid ibn Barmak, 531.
Khālid ibn Yazīd (vii–2), 495; 489, 490.
Khalīl ibn Aḥmad (viii–2), 541; 523, 524.
al-Khāliṣ, 630.
Khalq al-insān, 534, 772.
Khalq al-janīn, 680.
al-Kharāj, 525, 636.
Khārijites, 492.
al-Khaṭīb al-Baghdādī (xi–2), 777; 743, 745, 746.
Khayāl al-ẓill, 713. (See Encycl. of Islam, ii, 934, 1926).
Khayyam, Omar (xi–2), 759–761; 738, 739, 740, 741, 746.
Khazars, 590, 680.
Khuastuanift, 333.
Khudhāynāmak, 482, 540.
al-Khujandī (x–2), 667; 648, 649, 654.
al-Khwārizmī (ix–1), 563–564; 543, 545, 546, 549, 550, 588, 630, 666, 668. See Muḥammad ibn Aḥmad al-Khwārizmī.
Ki Tsurayuki (x–1), 639; 622.
Kibi Makibi (Kibi no Mabi) (viii–1), 519; 506, 513.
Kidneys, function of, 301.
Ḳiev, 655.
al-Kifāya fī ma'rifat, 777.
Kimimaro, Kuninaka, 515.
Kīmiyā al-sa'āda, 335, 753.
Kimmei-tennō, 454.
Kin-ki, 310.
al-Kindī (ix–1), 559–560; 406, 407, 543, 544, 545, 546, 547, 549, 550, 568, 660, 706, 757.
Kings, Books of (vi, b. c.), 79.
Kiran-hō, 575.
Kircher, Athanasius, 358.
Kirillitsa, 590.
Kiso-kaidō, 515.
Kisrā. See Nūshīrwān the Just.
Kitāb, try following word of Arabic title.
al-Kitāb, 542.
Kiyogimi, Sugawara, 582.
Kiyowara Natsuno (ix–1), 581; 548, 623.
K'o, 429.
Ko chih ching yüan, 451.
Ko Hung (iv–1), 355; 345.
Kōbō daishi (ix–1), 553–554; 519, 544, 548, 549, 552.
Kōbun-in, 539.
Kogo-shūi, 580.
Kojiki, 474, 516, 517.
Kōken, 529.
Kokin-shū, 639.
Kokin-wakashū, 639.
Koma, kingdom of, 364, 365, 492.
Kōmyō-tennō, 539.
Kon-Bu, 393.
Kongō-bu-ji, 553.
Kōnin-kyaku-shiki, 548, 581, 618.
Korean book, earliest, 633.
Korean drugs, 454.
Korean medicine, 379, 393.
Koreans, 264.
Koremune Naomoto (x–1), 644; 623.
Koreyoshi, Sugawara, 582.
Kośa, 458.
Kōshi. See Confucius.
Kōtoku-tennō, 463, 485.
Kōya-san, 553.
Koyomi, 476.
Kramajyā, 387.
Ku-chin t'u shu chi ch'êng, 103, 325.
Ku Hung Ming, 68.
Ku Yeh-wang (vi–1), 441; 418, 737.
Kua-ti-chih, 476.
Kuan-wu, 755.
Kuang shih lei fu, 663.
Kuang-chai, 475.
Kuang hung ming chi, 491.
Kudara, Kingdom of, 364, 448, 454, 476, 492.
Kudatku bilik, 712.
K'uei-chi (vii–1), 473; 461, 463, 491.

Küster, L., 54.
al-Kūfa, 466, 523.
al-Kūfa, school, 502, 518.
al-Kūhī (x–2), 665; 648, 649, 654.
Kujihongi (or Kujiki), 473, 474.
Kūkai, 553.
Kumārajīva (v–1), 384; 378, 380, 447, 604.
Kumārila (viii–1), 512; 504.
Kumūn, 559.
Kung. See Fa-hsien.
K'ung An-kuo (ii–1, b. c.), 181; 177.
K'ung Chi (v, b. c.), 91; 82, 168.
K'ung Ch'iu. See Confucius.
K'ung Fu, 168, 181.
K'ung Fu Tzŭ. See Confucius.
Kung-sun Ch'iao (vi, b. c.), 80; 66.
Kuninaka Kimimaro, 515.
Kunnāsh, 608.
Kuo P'o (iv–1), 353; 110, 345, 764.
Kusha-shū, 488, 492.
Kūshyār ibn Labbān al Jīlī (xi–1), 717; 696, 702.
Kwammu-tennō, 509, 513, 522, 535.
Kwampaku, 778.
Kwangaku-den, 513.
Kwanroku (vii–1), 476; 461, 462, 463, 481.
Kyaku, 518.
Kyōto, 509, 639.
Kyōto sects, 552, 553.

La Rue, C., and C. V. de, 317.
La'azim, 752.
Lacer, C. Julius, 268, 278.
Lacnunga, 621, 634.
Laetus, Pomponius, 226, 255.
Laghujātaka, 429.
Laghv-Āryabhaṭīya, 409.
Lake-village, prehistoric, 105.
Lalitavistara, 469.
Lamaism, 520, 526.
Lambert of Aschaffenburg, 775.
Lambert of Hersfeld (xi–2), 775; 743, 745.
Lamola, Giovanni, 240.
Lamps, Roman, 256.
Lancilotus, Blasius, 340.
Land masses, four, 184, 185.
Landolfus, 614.
Landos, Agapios, 686.
Lands, sinkings or risings, 227.
Lanfranc of Canterbury, 748.
Lang-dar-ma, 594.
Lantsa script, 604.
Lao Chün. See Lao Tzŭ.
Lao Tan. See Lao Tzŭ.
Lao Tzŭ (vi, b. c.), 66–67; 65.
Lapidaire chrétien, 765.
Lapidary, Arabic, 572.
Lapidary, Christian, 362, 765.
Lapidary, Persian, 572.
Lapidary, Syriac, 572.
Lapidary. See Mineralogy and Stones.
Lapps, 606.
Lascaris, A. J., 188.
Lāṭa, 387.
Lateran Synod, 748.
Lathe, 75.
Latin dictionary, 234, 781; Arabic, 745, 782; English, 692; German, 555.
Latin grammar, 200, 245, 265, 440, 692.
Latin language, 220, 245, 380, 486.
Latin prosody, 492.
Latin versions, 291, 363.
Latini, Brunetto, 341.
Latitude, 194, 273, 708.
Laurium, silver mines, 83, 104.
Lauro, Pietro, 295.
Law, natural, 72, 237.
Laws of various peoples. See below under Leges, Legis, Lex, and under names of those peoples.
Leabhar breac, 775.
Lead carbonate, 532.
Lead compounds, 679.
Lead poisoning, 223.
Leclerc, Raoul, 770.
Lederlin, J. H., 313.
Leech Book of Bald, 633.
Leech books, 622.
Leeches, 158, 215.
Lefebvre de Villebrune, 327.
Lefèvre, Jacques, 154.
Leges Walliae, 643.
Legis Langobardorum, liber, 778. See Lex.
Lei-chêng chu-shih ch'ien-shih hsiao-êrh fang-chüeh, 773.
Lei p'ien, 778.
Leiden (or Leyden) Papyrus, 239, 331, 339, 533.
Leif Ericsson, 650, 655, 676, 702, 724.
Leif the Fortunate, 724.
Leinster, Book of, 775.
Lemniscate, spherical, 117.
Lens, emerald, 247.
Lens, eye, 282. See Eye.
Leo the African, 728.
Leo Ostiensis, 769.
Leon (iv–1, b. c.), 116; 111.
Leon the Armenian, emperor, 558.
Leon Diaconos (x–2), 686; 652, 655.
Leon the Iatrosophist, 554.
Leon the Isaurian, emperor (viii–1), 517; 505, 617.
Leon the Philosopher (or the Wise), emperor, 588, 617, 656.
Leon the Philosopher, iatrosophist, 554.
Leon of Thessalonica (ix–1), 554; 544, 546, 547, 549.
Leonardo Pisano, 155, 171, 598, 630.
Leonardo da Vinci. See Vinci.
Leonides of Alexandria (ii–2), 309; 290.

Leprosy, 280, 308, 356, 391.
Lequeux, C., 412.
Lequien, Michel, 507.
Leshon limmudim, 690.
Lesser Seal. See Seal.
Lethargy, 373.
Letters, capital, 189.
Letters in geometrical figures, 92.
Leucippos of Miletos (v, B. C.), 88; 81.
Leunclavius, 558.
Level, 75, 128, 170.
Leviticus, 107.
Lex Alamannorum, 517.
Lex Angliorum, 581.
Lex Baiuwariorum, 517.
Lex Burgundionum, 439.
Lex Dei quam praecipit Dominus ad Moysen, 376.
Lex Frisionum, 580.
Lex Gundobada (Lex Gombata), 439.
Lex Ripuaria, 462, 484, 581.
Lex Romana Burgundionum, 438.
Lex Romana Wisigothorum, 438.
Lex Salica, 439, 581.
Lex Saxonum, 580.
Lex Wisigothorum renovata (vii-2), 500.
Lex. See Leges, Legis.
Lhasa, 467.
Li^{4}* (calendar), 476.
Li^{3} (a distance), 536.
Li^{4} (script), 176, 181.
Li^{3}. See Lao Tzŭ.
Li^{3}-chi^{1}*, 489, 498.
Li^{3} chi^{4} (Record of Rites), 91.
Li Chi-fu (ix-1), 573; 547.
Li-chih-p'u, 766.
Li Fang (x-2), 663; 648, 654.
Li-hsien, 197.
Li huang, 474.
Li Lung-chi, 512.
Li Ping (iii-2, B. C.), 175; 166.
Li Po-yao (vii-1), 483; 462, 463.
Li pu yün lüeh, 737.
Li Shih-min, 474.
Li Shun-fêng (vii-2), 494; 183, 338, 450, 489, 490.
Li Ssŭ, 166, 176.
Li-t'ai (vii-1), 476; 462, 463.
Li Tê-lin, 483.
Li Yen-shou (vii-1), 484; 462, 463.
Liang dynasty, history, 483.
Liang shu, 483.
Liber, try next word of Latin title.
Libraries, public, 185, 217, 222. See under name of special libraries or towns, e. g., Jerusalem.
Licius. See Lieh Tzŭ.
Liechtenstein, P., 274.
Liége, city, 657.
Liége, principality, 686.
Lieh Tzŭ (iv-2, B. C.), 138-139; 125.
Lieh Yü-k'ou. See Lieh Tzŭ.
Lien-tsung, 364.
Life, probable duration, 328.
Ligamentum teres, 198.
Light. See Optics.
Light, nature, 710.
Light, reflection, 208.
Light, speed, 87, 249, 708, 710.
Lighthouse, 161.
Lime, 383, 679.
Lin Hsi-chung, 153.
Lin I, 342.
Lin-tê, 494.
Ling, 500.
Ling ch'u ching, 310.
Ling-hsien, 278.
Ling-hu Tê-fên (vii-1), 483; 462, 463.
Lipari islands, 204, 227.
Lippomenus, 686.
Lister, Martin, 340.
Litchi, 766.
Lithotomy, 77, 230, 240. See Stone, med.
Litteris colendis, de, 529.
Liu An. See Huai Nan Tzŭ.
Liu Hsang, 222.
Liu Hsiao-sun, 450.
Liu Hsin (i-2, B. C.), 222; 219, 220, 264.
Liu Hsü (x-1), 643; 621, 622.
Liu Hui (iii-2), 338; 331, 494.
Liu Hung (ii-2), 300; 289, 338.
Liu-li, 389.
Liu Ling, 335.
Liu Pin (fl. c. 883), 605.
Liu-Pin (described peonies), 767.
Liu Shao (iii-1), 321; 315.
Liu Yüan, 737.
Liudprand of Cremona (x-2), 684; 652, 655.
Liver, five-lobed, 282.
Livius Titus. See Livy.
Livy (i-2, B. C.), 233; 220, 775.
Lo-gyus, 467.
Lo Hsia Hung (ii-2, B. C.), 195; 191.
Lô-pön, 526.
Lo-yang Ch'ieh lan chi, 431.
Loadstone. See Magnet.
Loci, 140, 173.
Loculus, 172.
Loewenklau, Johann, 394.
Logic, Aristotle, 128, 334.
Logic, Buddhist. See Logic, Chinese, Hindu, Japanese.
Logic, Chinese, 91.
Logic, Hindu, 367, 473, 491.
Logic, Japanese, 491.
Logic, Stoic, 169.
Logistica, 354.
Lombard Kingdoms of South Italy, 685.
Lombard Law, 484, 744, 778.
Lombarda, 779.

Lombards, history, 539.
Lombardus, Petrus, 507.
Longitude, 194, 273, 708, 717. See Meridians.
Loom, 55.
Lorica, 456.
Lotus school, 364.
Lotus sūtra (Lotus of the True Law), 384, 447.
Louis le Débonnaire, emperor, 406.
Lovesickness, 710, 730.
Lu, State of, annals, 67.
Lu Chi (III-1), 322; 315.
Lu Fa-yen (VII-1), 486; 459, 463, 737.
Lu Shên, 451.
Lu-Shih Chou-i Shu, 322.
Lu Tê-ming (VI-2), 458; 445.
Lu T'ing-ts'an, 535.
Lu-yu, 369.
Lu Yü (VIII-2), 535; 522.
Lü, 500.
Lü li chih, 264.
Lü tsung, 469, 491.
Lucian of Antioch (IV-1), 349; 344.
Lucian of Samosata, 309.
Lucilius, 248.
Lucretius Carus, Titus (I-1, B. C.), 205-206; 9, 10, 14, 201, 203, 252, 760.
Ludwig the Pious, emperor, 406.
Lughat-i-Furs, 783.
Luidprand. See Liudprand of Cremona.
Lully, R., 754.
al-Luma', 736.
Lumen animae, 763.
Lun-hêng, 252.
Lun yü, 68.
Lung-du-ston-pa-sum-chu-pa, 467.
Lung tsan, 466.
Lūqā ibn Sarāfyūn. See Lūqā ben Serapion.
Lūqā ben Serapion, 572.
Luxations, 281.
Lycanthropy, 308.
Lyceum (IV-2, B. C.), 127-136; 124.
Lycos the Macedonian, 281.
Lycurgos, 62.
Lydgate, John, 557.
Lysippos, 142.
Lysistratos of Sicyon (IV-2, B. C.), 142; 126.

Ma-fei-san (or ma-yao), 325.
Ma Han, 365.
Ma-ming. See Aśvaghosha.
Ma Tuan-lin, 411.
al-Ma'ārif, 615.
Mabādī ārā' ahl al-madīna al-fāḍila, 628.
Mabillon, 605, 732.
Macé, Jean, 765.
Macelarama, 531.
Macellama, 531.
Macer, Aemilius (I-2, B. C.), 231; 220.
Macer Floridus, 231, 741, 765. See Odo of Meung.
Machiavelli, 233.
Machines, seven simple, 336.
Machines, automatic. See Automata.
Macrobius, Ambrosius Theodosius (V-1), 385; 378, 671.
Macrocosm and microcosm, 113, 137, 593, 706, 714.
Mādabā, map of (VI-1), 432; 417.
Madagascar, 638.
al-Madāin, 466.
al-Madd wal-jazr, 560.
Madhab al-ẓāhir, 592.
Mādhavakara (VIII-2), 537; 505, 522.
Mādhavanidāna, 537.
Mādhyamika school, 316, 350, 470.
al-Madkhal ilā ṣinā'at al-nujūm, 669.
Maelstrom, 539.
Maerlant, Jacob van, 557.
Mafātīḥ al-'ulūm, 659.
Magadizing, 710.
al-Maghāzī, 541.
Magic, 6, 19, 320, 555.
Magic lantern, 713.
Magic squares, 272, 661, 753.
Magnaura, 554.
Magnet, 72, 410, 731; surgical use of, 77.
Magnetes, Stephanos. See Stephanos.
Magnetic force, imponderability, 532.
Magnetic needle, 741, 756, 764.
Mago (II-2, B. C.), 197; 192, 213.
Mahābbāshya, 199.
Mahāmaṅgala, 385.
Mahānāma (V-2), 412; 385, 400, 401.
al-Māhānī (IX-2), 597; 254, 585, 590.
al-Māhānī's equation, 664, 721.
Mahāparinirvāṇasūtra, 447.
Mahāsiddhānta, 409.
Mahāvaṃsa, 412.
Mahāvīra (VI, B. C.), 69-70; 65.
Mahāvīra (IX-1), 570; 546, 549.
Mahāyāna, 267, 270, 316.
Mahāyāna Canon, 466. See Tripiṭaka.
Mahāyāna-sūtrālaṃkāra, 350.
Maḥberet, 690.
Mahdī, 593.
Mahendra, 167.
Maheśvara, 458.
Mahinda. See Mahendra.
Maḥmūd the Ghaznawid, 676, 707.
Maḥmūd ibn Muḥammad al Iṣfahānī, 664.
Mailla, Father de, 778.
Maimbourg, Louis, 349.
Maimonides, 26, 402.
Majmū'at rasā'il, 597.
al-Majrīṭī, Maslama ibn Aḥmad, 668.
Makibi, 519.
Malalas, John (VI-2), 454; 445.
Malchos. See Porphyry.
Malecouronne, Raoul, 770.
Mālik ibn Anas (VIII-2), 525; 520, 524.

al-Malikī, 677.
Mālikite school, 525.
Malikshāh, Jalāl al-dīn, Saljūq sulṭān, 760, 772, 780.
Mallet, P. H., 54.
Malmesbury, Oliver of (xi-1), 720; 697, 702.
Malmesbury, William of, 720.
Ma'mar ibn al-Muthannā, 541.
al-Ma'mūn, 'Abbāsid caliph (ix-1), 557; 544, 545, 546, 591.
Ma'mūnic tables, 565; tested, 566.
Man lā yaḥḍuruhu-l-faqīh, 656.
Man shu, 536.
Manāfi' al-aḥjār, 572.
Manao Abe, 575.
Manasseh, 531.
al-Manāẓir, 721.
Mandrocles of Samos (vi, b. c.), 76; 65.
Manes. See Mānī the Zindīq.
Manethon the Egyptian (iii-1, b. c.), 161-162; 149, 150, 262.
Manganese, 532.
Mangey, Thomas, 237.
Manhig hā-rōfe'īm, 640.
Mānī the Zindīq (iii-2), 332-334; 298, 330, 662.
Māni-kābum, 467.
Manichaean zoology, 333.
Manichaeism, 330, 332, 334, 362, 420, 552, 591, 654.
Manilius, Marcus (i-1), 237; 235, 236.
Mankah, 530.
al-Manṣūr, 'Abbāsid caliph (viii-2), 527; 521.
Manṣūr ibn 'Alī ibn 'Irāq, 668.
al-Manṣūrī, 609.
Mantias, 215.
Mantra, 553.
Mantrasūtras, 466.
Manuel Comnenos, emperor, 452.
Manure, 55, 355.
Manutius, Aldus, 259.
Manyō-gana (or Manyō syllabary), 516, 519.
Map of the world, 172, 223, 280, 558.
Mappae clavicula, 522, 533, 723.
Maps, Chinese. See Chinese maps.
Maps, colored, 674.
Maps, first, 72, 78.
Maps. See Projection.
Maps, Ptolemaic, 274, 275, 276.
Maqāla fī khalq al-insān, 772.
Maqālāt, 662.
al-Maqna', 766.
al-Maqṣūra, 645.
Mar Samuel (iii-1), 318; 314, 315, 316.
Marbode (xi-2), 764; 741, 742, 745.
Marbodus Redonensis, 764.
Marcellinos (ii-2), 309; 290.
Marcellos of Side (ii-2), 308; 289, 290.
Marcellus Empiricus of Bordeaux (v-1), 391; 379.
Marcion of Sinope, 332.
Maria, alchemist, 238.
Marianos, alchemist, 495.
Marianus Scottus (xi-2), 775; 743, 745.
Marinos of Alexandria (ii-1), 281; 268, 269.
Marinos of Sichem (v-2), 405; 399.
Marinos of Tyre (ii-1), 279; 268, 269, 273.
Marinus, Rabbi, 736.
Marmor Parium. See Parian Chronicle.
Mars, 594, 630.
Marseille, 144, 240.
Marsicano, Leone, 769.
Martān-farukh (ix-2), 591; 583.
Martialis, Gargilius (iii-1), 323; 315, 355.
Martianus Capella. See Capella, M. M. F.
Martin, St., of Tours, 347, 376, 380, 456.
Martyrs, era of the, 430.
Marwān ibn Janāḥ, 736.
al-Marwarrūdhī (ix-1), 566; 545, 550.
Masāḥa, 564.
Masālik al-mamālik, 674.
al-Masālik wal-mamālik, 606, 674, 768.
Masananda, 364.
Masarjawai, 479.
Māsawaih al-Mārdīnī (xi-1), 728; 698, 699, 700, 701.
Māshāllāh (viii-2), 531; 521, 524.
Maslama ibn Aḥmad (x-2), 668; 563, 648, 649, 650, 654.
Māsōrāh (massora), 291, 624.
Masoretic punctuation, 691.
Masoretic schools, 291, 624.
Massa, Nicolò, Venetian, 711.
Massektōth, 401.
Masson, Papyre, 555.
Massuet, René, 294.
al-Mas'ūdī (x-1), 637; 279, 495, 558, 620, 622, 624, 674.
Māsūya. See Ibn Māsawaih.
Maṭahhar ibn Ṭāhir, 648.
al-Mathālib, 541.
Māṭhara, 351.
Māṭharavṛitti, 351.
Mathematical analysis, 113.
Mathematics, classification, 212, 421.
Mathesis, 354.
al-Matīn, 734.
Matsudaira Naritake, 644.
Mattā ibn Yūnus (x-1), 629; 620, 623.
Maur, St., 419.
Mauricios, emperor, 481.
Maurolycus, 254.
Maurus, 478.
al-Māwardī (xi-2), 780; 744, 746.
Maximos Confessor (vii-1), 471; 461, 463, 594.
Mazdaism. See Zoroaster, Zoroastrianism.
Mazdak (vi-1), 420; 415.
Mdo, 468.
Meadows of gold, 638.
Mean, doctrine of, 91.

Measles, 454, 609, 678, 682. See Smallpox.
Mebo ha-Talmud, 704.
Mechanics, applied, 195.
Mechanics, theoretical, 116.
Mediaeval science, 14.
Mediastinitis, 710.
Medical deontology, 96, 101, 640.
Medical education, 239, 528.
Medical sects, 187.
Medical tables, 730, 772.
Medicina Plinii, 251, 536.
Medicine, Coptic, 588, 614.
Medicine, Roman, 186.
Medicine, Syrian, 309.
Medicinis expertis, liber de, 307.
al-Medīna, 464.
Medma. See Philip of Opus.
Megasthenes (III–1, B. C.), 161; 150.
Meges of Sidon (I–2, B. C.), 230; 220.
Meinzo of Constance, 757.
Mela, Pomponius (I–1), 239; 235, 236, 341.
Melancholy, 373.
Melanchthon, Philip, 277, 567.
Meletios the Monk (VII–2), 497; 459.
Meno, 114.
Memus, Bapt., 174.
Menaechmos (IV–2, B. C.), 139–140; 125.
Menahem ben Saruq (X–2), 690; 653, 655.
Mencius (IV–2, B. C.), 138; 125, 127, 252.
Mende. See Philip of Opus.
Menecrates, C. Q., of Zeophleta (I–1), 241; 235, 236.
Menelaos of Alexandria (I–2), 253–254; 244, 245, 598, 601, 668.
Menelaos, theorem of, 254.
Mêng-ch'i pi-t'an, 755.
Mêng T'ien (III–2, B. C.), 175; 166, 451.
Mêng Tzŭ. See Mencius.
Menodotos, of Nicomedia (II–2), 308; 290.
Menon (IV–2, B. C.), 146; 126, 127.
Menstruation, 18, 208, 309.
Mensural music. See Music.
Mercer, J., 358.
Mercury, element, 258, 532, 533, 572, 669, 672. See Cinnabar.
Mercury, planet, 141, 272, 275, 386, 408, 572.
Meridian, drawing of the, 271, 563.
Meridian, prime, 273.
Meridians, 273, 280. See Longitude.
Mersenne, Marin, 254.
Meru, mountain, 387.
Merula, Paul, 187.
Mesrop, St. (V–1), 397; 379, 380, 381.
Messahala, 531.
Mesuë Major (the Elder), 574, 608.
Mesuë, third, 728.
Mesuë the Younger, 728.
Metagenes (VI, B. C.), 75; 65.
Metals, constitution, 532, 661, 710.
Metals, geologic formation, 532.
Metals, refinement, 532.
Metaphrastes, Symeon. See Symeon Metaphrastes.
Meteorite, 86, 756.
Meteorology, 98, 128, 574, 611; magical, 555.
Method, inductive, 128.
Methodic school, 215, 230, 282, 324.
Methodios, St. (IX–2), 590; 583, 589.
Meton of Athens (V, B. C.), 94; 82, 141. See Cycle, Metonic.
Metrodora (II–1), 283; 268.
Metrodoros (V–2), 408; 400.
Metrology, Carolingian, 527.
Metrology, Chinese, 168, 321.
Metrology, Hellenistic, 303.
Metrology, Hindu, 594, 719.
Metrology, Latin, 440.
Metrology, Muslim, 533, 660.
Metrology, Syrian, 735, 736.
Metrology, Tibetan, 594.
Metsura Omi, 448.
Metz, 539.
Meun, Jean de, 368.
Meung, Odo of, 765.
Meursius, 353.
Méziriac, Bachet de, 336.
Mi tsung, 508.
al-Mi'a fī-l-ṣanā'a al-ṭibbīya, 678.
Miao Fa Lien-hua ching, 447.
Micah (VIII, B. C.), 58; 53.
Michael II Balbos, emperor, 406.
Michael of Ephesus, 422.
Michel, Mount St. See Mont-Saint-Michel.
Michigan mathematical papyrus No. 621, 354.
Michinaga, Fujiwara no, 778.
Micius. See Mo Ti.
Microcosm. See Macrocosm.
Microorganisms, 225. See Contagion.
Microtechne, 307.
Middle books, 759.
Midō Kwampaku, 778.
Midrāsh, 402.
Miḥna, 551.
al-Mijisṭi, 562.
al-Milal wal-niḥal, 713.
Miletos, 79.
Milk, 308.
Milky Way, 722.
Mīmāṃsā, 5, 512.
Minabuchi Shōan, 463, 485.
Minamoto no Shitagau (X–2), 692; 653, 654.
Mineralogy, 143. See Lapidary; Stones.
Mines. See Laurium.
Minetsugu Sugawara, 575.
Ming Huang, T'ang emperor (VIII–1), 512; 451, 504.
Ming-i-pieh-lu, 436.
Ming-Ti, Han emperor, 243, 246.
Ming-t'ien-li, 762.
Minhāj al-bayān, 772.

Minimum length, 208.
Mining (v, B. C.), 104–105; 90.
Mint, first Japanese, 513.
Minutes, 273.
Minutianus, Alex., 206.
Miqra'ot gedolot, 752.
Miracles, absence of, 237.
Mirrors, burning, 170, 183, 427.
Mirrors, spherical and parabolic, 721.
Mis'ar ibn al-muhalhal, 637.
Mishā, 531.
Mishkāt al-anwār, 754.
Mishnāh (Mishna), 288, 291, 401, 402.
Mitākshararā, 781.
Mithridate, 214.
Mithridates Eupator (I–1, B. C.), 214; 202.
Miura, 552.
al-Mīzān al-tabī'ī, 609.
Miẓwot, sefer ha-, 525.
Mnesitheos of Athens (IV–2, B. C.), 146; 126.
Mo, 369.
Mo Ching, 342.
Mo-ho-chih-kuan, 447.
Mo-ni, 552.
Mo-t'êng. See Kāśyapa-Mātaṅga.
Mo Ti (v, B. C.), 91; 82.
Mo Tzŭ. See Mo Ti.
Modestinus, Herennius (III–1), 329; 316, 396.
Moelbrigte, 775.
Moerbeke, Will. of, 134, 170, 404.
Mogasa, 509.
Moist, principle, 72, 86.
Mokshadeva, 477.
Molendina ad ventum, 638.
Momen, 535.
Mommu-tennō, 518.
Monasticism, Buddhist, 346.
Monasticism, Christian, 344, 346.
Monasticism, Jewish, 346.
Money, Carolingian, 527.
Money, Chinese paper, 781.
Monism, 73, 754; absolute, 561.
Monobe Hiroizumi, 575.
Monogatari, 778.
Monotheism, Egyptian, 58.
Monotheism, Hebrew, 57.
Montaigne, 252.
Montanus, 434.
Monte Cassino, 414, 419.
Montfaucon, Bernard de, 317, 432.
Month, synodic, 194. See Calendar.
Months, names of the, 528.
Months, seven, 238.
Months, twelve, 238.
Montoku-jitsuroku, 517, 617.
Mont-Saint-Michel, 774.
Moon, influence, 121, 424.
Moon, light, 73, 86; during eclipse, 251.
Moon, motion, 273.
Moon, nature, 86, 93.
Moon, spots 721.
Moon, variation. See Variation.
Moralitatum elegantissimus, liber, 763.
Morelli, Fed., 308.
Morienus Romanus, 495.
Mortar, 186; hydraulic, 223.
Moschion (VI–1), 433; 283, 417.
Moscow, 655.
Moselle, river, 369.
Moses, alchemist, 238.
Moses of Chorene (V–1), 395; 378, 380, 381.
Moses ibn Giqaṭilla, 691.
Moses bar Kēphā (IX–2), 596; 493, 584, 588.
Moses's tabernacle, model of the universe, 431.
Mōshi. See Mencius.
Motion, 422, 710.
Mototsune Fujiwara, 517, 617.
Mountains, formation, 136, 227; height, 145.
Moxibustion, 499. See Cauterization.
Mu-hu, 552.
Mu-ku Jō-kō kyō, 530.
Mu t'ien-tzŭ-ch'uan, 342.
al-Mu'alāja al-buqrāṭīya, 677.
al-Mu'āmalāt, 668, 715.
al-Mubashshir, Abū-l-Wafā', 130.
al-Mudkhal ilā 'ilm aḥkam al-nujūm, 568.
Mufliḥ, 620, 630.
al-Mughnī fī tadbīr al-amrāḍ, 772.
Muḥammad ibn 'Abd al-Bāqī al-Baghdādī (XI–2), 761; 740, 746.
Muḥammad ibn 'Abd al-Bāqī al-Bazzāz, 761.
Muḥammad ibn 'Abd al-Malik al-Kāthī, 723.
Muḥammad ibn abī-l-Shukr al-Maghribī, 254.
Muḥammad, Abū-l-Qāsim, the Prophet (ṣl'm), 464, 540, 541, 579.
Muḥammad ibn Aḥmad al-Khwārizmī (X–2), 659; 647, 654.
Muḥammad ibn Aḥmad al-Muqaddasī, 675.
Muḥammad ibn Aḥmad al-Nahrajūrī, 661.
Muḥammad ibn Aḥmad al-Tamīmī al-Muqaddasī, 679.
Muḥammad ibn 'Alī ibn Bābūya, 656.
Muḥammad al-Bal'amī, Abū 'Alī, 642.
Muḥammad ibn al-Ḥasan ibn Duraid, 644.
Muḥammad ibn al-Ḥasan al-Karkhī, 718.
Muḥammad ibn Ḥawqal, 674.
Muḥammad ibn al-Ḥusain, 718.
Muḥammad ibn al-Ḥusain ibn Ḥamīd, 630.
Muḥammad ibn Ibrāhīm al-Fazārī (VIII–2), 530; 521, 524.
Muḥammad ibn Idrīs al-Shāfi'ī, 550.
Muḥammad ibn 'Īsā al-Māhānī, 597.
Muḥammad ibn Isḥāq, 540.
Muḥammad ibn Isḥāq al-Warrāq al-Baghdādī, 662.
Muḥammad ibn Ismā'īl al-Bukhārī, 551.
Muḥammad ibn Ismā'īl, seventh Imām, 593.
Muḥammad ibn Jābir ibn Sinān al-Battānī, 602.

Muḥammad ibn Jarīr al-Ṭabarī, 642.
Muḥammad ibn Khālid, 566.
Muḥammad ibn al-Lith, 718.
Muḥammad ibn Manṣūr al-Jamānī, 772.
Muḥammad ibn Muḥammad al-Ghazzālī, 753.
Muḥammad ibn Muḥammad ibn Yaḥyā al-Būzjānī, 666.
Muḥammad ibn Mūsā al-Khwārizmī, 563.
Muḥammad ibn Mushīr al-Bustī, 661.
Muḥammad ibn Sa'd, 579.
Muḥammad ibn al-Sā'ib, 541.
Muḥammad al-Sāmrī, 659.
Muḥammad al-Tamīmī of Toledo (?), 679.
Muḥammad ibn 'Umar ibn al-Farrukhān (IX-1), 568; 546, 550.
Muḥammad ibn 'Umar ibn al-Qūṭīya, 688.
Muḥammad ibn 'Umar al-Wāqidī, 541.
Muḥammad ibn Zakarīyā al-Rāzī, 609.
al-Muḥīt, 689.
Muḥkam wal-muḥīṭ al-a'ẓam, 782.
Muḥtawī, 703.
Muḥyī al-dīn al-Maghribī, 211, 254.
Mu'jam ma 'sta'jama, 768.
Mujarrabāt, 592.
Mujtahid, 642.
al-Mukhtār ibn al-Ḥasan ibn Buṭlān, 730.
Mukhtaṣar al-taṣrīf al-mulūkī, 689.
Mulāḥida, 752.
al-Mulakhkhaṣ fī-l-lugha, 782.
Mulberry tree, 452.
Mulomedicina Chironis, 375.
Mulomedicina Claudii Hermeri, 657.
Mulomedicina Vegetii, 374.
Mundi caelestis terrestrisque constitutione, de, 546, 569.
Mundo, de, 136, 296, 424.
al-Munqidh min al-ḍalāl, 754.
al-Muntakhab fī 'ilāj al-'ain, 729.
al-Muqaddasī (x-2), 675; 635, 650, 654.
al-Muqammaṣ, 626.
al-Muqni' fī-l-ḥisāb al-hindī, 719.
al-Muqtabis fī ta'rīkh al-Andalus, 735.
Muratori, Ludovico Antonio, 533.
al-Murshid ilā jawāhir al-aghdhiya, 679.
Murūj al-dhahab, 638.
Musa, Antonius (I-2, B. C.), 231; 220.
Mūsā ibn Khālid (IX-2), 613; 587.
Mūsā ibn Shākir, sons of, 543, 544, 550, 560.
Muṣādarat, 761.
Muṣannaf, 551.
Mūsar hā-rōfe'īm, 640.
Muscio. See Moschion.
Museum of Alexandria (III-1, B. C.), 158; 150.
Mushtami, 565.
Music, church, 446.
Music, Greek: Aristotle, 132; Aristoxenos, 142; Pythagoras, 73, 253; Terpander, 61.
Music, Hellenistic, 272, 278.
Music, history, 7.
Music, mediaeval Christian, 446, 641, 697, 702, 703, 714, 720, 757, 762, 763.
Music, mensural, 542, 628, 703.
Music, Muslim, 542, 559, 628, 697.
al-Mūsīqī, 628.
Musk, 771.
Muslim civilization, beginning, 463.
Muslim conquests, early (VII-1), 465.
Muslim era, 461, 464.
Muslim names, 43.
Muslim science, 35.
Muslim sects, 706, 713.
Muslim ibn al-Ḥajjāj al-Qushairī (IX-2), 592.
Musnad, 551.
al-Mustanṣir, Fāṭimid caliph, 768.
Mustio. See Moschion.
Musurus, Marcus, 326, 398.
Muṭahhar ibn Ṭāhir al-Maqdisī (x-2), 659; 631, 647, 654.
Mu'tanif takmilat, 777.
al-Mu'taṣim, 'Abbāsid caliph, 558.
al-Mutawakkil, 'Abbāsid caliph, 611.
Mu'tazilites, 550, 557.
Muwaffaq, Abū Manṣūr, 678.
al-Muwaṭṭa, 525.
al-Muzannar, 630.
Mycenaean civilization, 54.
Myōhō, 581.
Myōhōdō, 513.
Mysteriis, de, 352.
Mysticism, Muslim, 435, 583, 584, 592, 593.

al-Nabāt, 615.
Nabataean agriculture, 621, 634.
Nabataeans, 634.
Naddodd the Viking, 605.
Naevi, 716.
Nāgārjuna of Daihak, 316.
Nāgārjuna of Kōsala (III-1), 316; 314, 315, 350, 384, 470.
al-Nahāwandī, Aḥmad ibn Muḥammad, 565.
Nahawendi, Benjamin (IX-1), 550; 525, 543, 549.
Nahum (VII, B. C.), 64; 60.
Nā'ima of Ḥimṣ, 'Abd al-Masiḥ, 406.
al-Nairīzī (IX-2), 598; 154, 585, 586, 590, 667.
al-Najāt, 711.
Nakasendō, 515.
Nakatomi no Kamako, 500.
Nakshatras, 387.
Nālanda, 497, 526.
Nāmaliṅgānuśāsana, 458.
Names, Chinese, 43.
Names, Japanese, 43.
Names, Muslim, 43.
Names and things, 7, 22.
Nan Ch'i shu, 438.
Nan ching, 83, 102, 310.
Nan fang ts'ao mu chuang, 341.
Nan Hua ching, 153.

Nan-kyō, 310.
Nan Shan tsung, 469.
Nan shih, 484.
Nanking, Buddhist academy of, 350.
Naomoto Koremune, 644.
Nara Daibutsu, 509.
Nara period, 504, 505, 509, 513.
Nara sects, six, 510, 552, 553.
Nara, university, 513.
Narabi-no-oka no Otodo, 581.
Naritake Matsudaira, 644.
al-Nasab al-kabīr, 541.
al-Nasawī (xi-1), 719; 696, 697, 702.
Naṣīr al-dīn al-Ṭūsī, 254, 712, 758.
Naṣīr-i-Khusraw (xi-2), 768; 742, 743, 746.
Nasks, 591.
Naṣr ibn Ya'qūb al-Dīnawarī (xi-1), 709; 694, 702.
Nathan ben Jeliel (xi-2), 782; 744, 745, 746.
Nathan ha-Me'at, 729.
Natrūn, 679.
Natsuno Kiyowara, 581.
Nature, Aristotle, 131.
Naturis rerum, de. See Liber de elementis.
al-Naubakht (viii-2), 531; 521, 524.
Navel, 94.
Navigation law, Rhodian, 517.
al-Nawādir al-ṭibbīya, 574.
Naxatra, 671.
Naẓīf ibn Yumn (x-2), 664; 648, 654.
Naẓm al-'iqd, 630.
Naẓm al-jawhar, 640.
al-Naẓẓām (ix-1), 559; 544, 546.
Nearchos (iv-2, b. c.), 145; 126, 284.
Necho (vi, b. c.), 78; 66.
Neckam, Alexander, 764.
Needham, Peter, 452.
Negative quantities, 183, 339.
Negritos, 103.
Nehardea, Academy, 318.
Nehemiah (v, b. c.), 109; 83, 150.
Nehemiah, Book of (iii-1, b. c.), 163.
Nei-ching Su-wên. See Huang Ti.
ha-Ne'imot, Sefer, 704.
Nemesianus, Marcus Aurelius Olympius (iii-2), 340, 331.
Nemesios of Emesa (iv-2), 373; 361, 727.
Nemorarius, Jordanus, 598.
Nengō, 461, 476, 672.
Neoconfucianism, 27, 755.
Neoplatonism, 11, 13, 320, 334, 393.
Neots, St., 596.
Nepal, 467.
Nero, emperor (i-2), 247; 243, 244.
Nerves, 282.
Nerves, optic, 77, 159. See Vision.
Nĕryōsang, 591.
Nestorian chronicle, 489, 499.
Nestorian monument of 781, 520, 526.
Nestorian translators, 587.
Nestorians, 379, 381, 439, 452, 469, 474, 552, 735.
Nestorios (v-1), 381-382; 380.
Newton, 32, 696.
Nicaea, Council, 344, 346, 348, 359.
Nicander of Colophon (iii-1, b. c.), 158-159; 150.
Nicandros. See Nicander.
Nicanor of Alexandria (ii-1), 287; 269.
Nicene symbol, 348.
Nicephoros Patriarches (ix-1), 578; 548.
Nicephoros Phocas, emperor, 686.
Nicephorus, 157.
Nicetas the Physician (ix-2), 608; 281, 587, 589.
Nicholas V, Pope, 240.
Nicholas, Greek monk, 651, 680.
Nicholas of Damascus, 226. See Nicolaos.
Niclas, Joa. Nic., 370, 452.
Nicolaos Damascenos (i-2, b. c.), 226; 219, 220. See Nicholas.
Nicolosi di Paternò, G. B., 707.
Nicomachos of Gerasa (i-2), 253; 244, 245, 272, 296, 408, 422, 423, 425.
Nicomedes (ii-1, b. c.), 182; 177.
Nidāna, 537.
Nidhām al-Mulk (xi-2), 780; 744, 746.
Nien-hao, 485.
Niger, river, 232.
Nigganṭha Nātaputta, 69.
Nightmare, 373. See Dreams.
Nihāvend, 466.
Nihon-kōki (ix-1), 580; 516.
Nihon shoki, 516.
Nihongi (or Nihonki), 516, 517, 575.
Nikāya, 384, 385.
Nile, 105, 136, 232, 247, 431, 635; annual rising, 86; canal, 78.
Nile, exploration of the Upper (i-2), 258.
Nile, floods, 79.
Nilometer, 567.
Nîmes, 223.
Nimrod the Astronomer, 546, 569.
Nine. See Number 9.
Nine sections, Arithmetic rules in, 183.
Nipsus, Marcus Junius, 256, 397.
Nirukta, 110.
Nirvāṇa, 69.
Nisibis, school, 381.
Nissim ibn Salomon, 640.
ha-Niẓẓānīm, sefer, 626.
Nominalism, 749.
Nonnos, Theophanes (x-1), 639; 622, 623, 651, 657.
Nonus Almansoris, 609.
Noria, 580.
Norito, 644.
Normandy, dukes of, 733.
Normans, invasions of, 624.
Notger of Liége (x-2), 657; 647, 655.

Notker Balbulus, 703.
Notker of St. Gall. See Notker Balbulus; Notker Labeo.
Notker the German, 703.
Notker Labeo (XI-1), 703; 693, 695, 701, 702.
Notker of Lüttich. See Notger of Liége.
Nova, 194.
Novellae constitutiones post codicem, 439.
Novellae Post-Theodosianae, 396.
Novgorod, 655.
Nūbakht, 531.
Number 1. See Monism; Monotheism; Unity.
Number 2. See Dualism.
Number 3. See Trinitarianism; Trinity, and other words beginning with tri.
Number 4. See Elements; Fevers; Forces; Humors; Land masses; Qualities; Stages (in diseases); Tantras; Tones. For the Four Books see Chinese Classics.
Number 5. See Elements; Ages of the world; Solids, regular. For the Five Classics, see Chinese classics.
Number 7, 593. See Days; Hours; Months; Planets; Sages; Seven, treatise on; Years.
Number 9. See Casting out.
Number 10. See Stems.
Number 11. See Casting out.
Number 12, 593. See Cycle of animals; Days; Hours; Months; Tables; Twigs; Years.
Number, geometric, 113, 115.
Number mysticism, 18, 73, 113, 351, 661.
Number, nuptial, 113, 115.
Number of years. See Cycle.
Numbers, amicable, 352, 599, 661, 668.
Numbers, cubic, 668.
Numbers, Old Testament, 107.
Numbers, perfect, 253, 658, 661.
Numbers, polygonal, 139, 181, 253, 336.
Numbers, prime, 172.
Numbers, theory, 73, 408.
Numenios of Apamea (II-2), 298; 289.
Numerals, Arabic. See Ghubār.
Numerals, Greek, 312.
Numerals, Herodianic, 312.
Numerals, Hindu, 321, 493, 513, 530, 559, 563, 585, 601, 634, 659, 663, 667, 670, 707, 719, 756. See Zero.
Numerals, introduction into Europe, 426.
Numerals, Roman, 756.
Numerals, Syriac, 407.
Numerals, Tibetan, 469.
Numerical classifications, 661. See Number.
Numeris et lineis, de, 761.
Numisianos of Corinth, 281.
Nuñez, Pedro, 721.
Nuqaṭ, 519.
Nūr al-'ayūn, 772.
Nūshīrwān the Just, 415, 421, 423, 435, 449.
Nutmeg, 771.
Nutrition, 128.
Nyāya, 88.
Nyāyabindu, 473.
Nyāyasūtra, 87.

Oanseki, 781.
Obizzini, Tommaso, 736.
Obsopaeus, Vinc., 188.
Obstetric chair, 283.
Occam, William of, 750.
Ocean, 136, 204, 271.
Octaëteris, 117.
Octahedron, 116.
Odo of Cluny, St. (X-1), 625; 619, 621, 623, 624.
Odo of Meung (XI-2), 765; 741, 742, 745.
Odors, 143.
Oeconomica, 307.
Oenopides of Chios (V, B. C.), 92; 82.
Ohthere (IX-2), 606; 586.
Oil in weaving, 55.
Old Man of the Mountain, 753.
Oliver of Malmesbury. See Malmesbury.
Olympiads, 162.
Olympias, artist, 283.
Olympiodoros (V-1), 389; 378, 379.
Ōmi ritsu-ryō, 490, 500.
Ōmi ryō, 518, 581.
Ōmura Fukuyoshi, 575.
Onasandros (I-2), 255; 244.
One. See Number 1.
Oneirocriticism, oneirology, oneiromancy. See Dreams.
Ōno Yasumaro, 505, 516.
Ophthalmology, 245, 260, 325, 434, 453, 481, 498, 574, 609, 612, 729, 731. See Eye; Eye-salve.
Opium, 55, 215, 241.
Oporinus, 775.
Optics, 153, 276, 354, 559, 721. See Eye; Light; Vision.
Opus, Philip of (IV-1, B. C.), 118; 111, 112.
Ordeal, trial by, 439, 555.
Organ, hydraulic, 184, 208.
Organizing, music, 710.
Organon, 128.
Oribasios (IV-2), 372; 281, 308, 356, 359, 360, 361, 434, 479, 608, 613, 639.
Origen (III-1), 317; 291, 314, 316, 357, 381.
Orion (V-1), 398; 379.
Oros, 398.
Orosius, Paul (V-1), 395; 379, 380, 496, 595, 596, 606.
Orrery, 170, 278, 514, 762.
Orthographic projection, 274, 716.
Osa, 448.
Osius, 352.
Oslo, 606.
Ostanes, 238.
Othere, 606.

Otsugu Fujiwara, 516, 580.
Otto I, Holy Roman Emperor, 658, 675, 684, 685.
Otto II, Holy Roman Emperor, 655.
Ottonian renaissance, 655.
Ou-yang Hsiu (xi-2), 777; 536, 643, 741, 743, 746.
Outflow of water, speed, 255.
Ovaries, 434.
Oviducts, 282, 434.
Ōyu-Ryōda, 454.

π (by which is meant not the symbol, but simply a measure of the accuracy of circle measurements); Adelbold, 714; Apollonios, 173; Archimedes, 169; Brahmagupta, 475; Chang Hêng, 278; Chang Ts'ang, 183; Franco of Liége, 757; Li Shun-fêng, 494; Tsu Ch'ung-chih, 410; Wang Fan, 338.
Pachomios, St. (iv-1), 347; 344, 625.
Pachymeres, Georgius, 406.
Pactus Alamanorum, 462, 484.
Paddle-wheels, 430.
Padma-sambhava, 520, 526.
Paetus, Lucas, 265.
Paginini of Brescia, Alessandro de, 465.
Pahlawī history, 482.
Pahlawī literature, 435, 591.
Pahlawī medicine, 372, 591.
Pahlawī, translations from, 540.
Pahlawī, translations into, 449, 591. See Persian.
Pai hu t'ung, 264.
Pai ma ssŭ, 246.
Pai shou wên, 441.
Paitāmaha-Siddhānta, 386, 387.
Pakche, 364.
Palaemon, Quintus Remmius, of Vicenza (i-2), 265; 245.
Palaeontology. See Fossils.
Palencia, Al. de, 255.
Pāli, literature, 384.
Pāli, transliteration, 50.
Palladios the Iatrosophist (v-1), 392; 379, 608.
Palladius, Rutilius Taurus Aemilianus (iv-1), 355; 345, 346, 364.
Palmerius, P. et M., 363.
Palmyra, 558.
Pammenes, alchemist, 238.
Pamphila of Epidaurus (i-2), 264; 245.
Pamphilia, daughter of Plateus, 452.
Pamphilos of Alexandria (i-2), 264; 245.
Pamphilos the botanist (i-2), 257; 244.
Pamphilos of Caesarea, martyr, 349, 357.
Pamphilos the druggist, 257.
Pan Chao, 264.
P'an-chu chi, 756.
Pan Ku (i-2), 264; 163, 244, 245.
Pan Piao, 264.
Panaetios of Rhodes (ii-2, b. c.), 193; 191, 192.
Pañcasiddhāntikā, 428.
Pañcatantra, 449.
Pancreas, 159, 160.
Pandects, 439.
P'ang An-shih (xi-2), 773; 743, 746.
Pangenesis, 119.
Pāṇini (iv-1, b. c.), 123; 112, 199, 458.
Pantegni, 677, 769.
Pantheism, 73.
Pao-p'o-tzŭ, 355.
Papañcasūdanī, 385.
Paper, 279, 451, 783.
Papias the Lombard (xi-2), 781; 744, 745.
Papiensis, liber, 778.
Papin, D., 309.
Papinian (iii-1), 328; 316, 396, 438.
Papinianus, Aemilius. See Papinian.
Papirius Sextus (vi, b. c.), 80; 66.
Pappos of Alexandria (iii-2), 337; 155, 274, 331, 332, 395, 403, 631, 667.
Pappos, problem of, 337.
Papyrus. See Africanus; Akhmīm; Ebers; Eudoxos; Kenyon; Leiden; Michigan; Sault; Stockholm.
Parabola, 173, 337, 427, 599, 632, 667. See Conics.
Parabolic mirrors, 722.
Paraboloids, 169, 599.
Parallel postulate, 153, 403.
Parallels (latitude), 273, 280.
Parallel of 36°, 280.
Paralysis, 308.
Paramārtha (vi-2), 446; 270, 350, 351, 443.
Paramārthasaptati, 350.
Parapegma, 173.
Parchment, 180, 783.
Paré, Ambroise, 216.
Parentucelli, Tommaso, 240.
Parian Chronicle (iii-1, b. c.), 162-163; 150.
Paris, 365, 752.
Parmenides of Elea (v, b. c.), 85; 81, 82.
Parthia, 230.
Parts of speech, 189, 200, 501.
Pascal, 180, 753.
Passionarius, 726.
Pasteur, 23, 702.
Pāṭaliputra, 167.
Patañjali (ii-2, b. c.), 199; 192.
Patrick, St., 377, 380.
Patristic literature, 361.
Paul. See Paulos; Paulus.
Paul of Alexandria (iv-2), 367; 360, 361, 387, 429.
Paul the Apostle. See St. Paul.
Paul the Persian (vi-2), 448; 443.
Paul, St. (i-2), 246; 236, 243, 248, 293, 380.
Paula, St., 364.
Paulet, Jacques, 609.
Paulinism, 246.

Pauliśa-Siddhānta, 386, 387.
Paulos. See Paul.
Paulos Aegineta (VII-1), 479; 309, 462, 463, 608, 639, 681.
Paulos of Nicaea, 479.
Paulus Diaconus Casinensis (VIII-2), 539; 234, 522, 523.
Paulus, Julius (III-1), 328; 316, 396, 438.
Pausanias (II-2), 300; 104, 289, 290.
Pausanias Atticista (II-2), 312; 290.
Pauw, J. C. de, 287, 358.
Pavia, school, 778, 779.
Pāzand version, 591.
Pearls, 230.
Pediatrics, 245, 260, 282, 481, 680, 683, 727, 773.
Pedro de Alcala, 783.
Pei Ch'i shu, 483.
P'ei-chü (VII-1), 476; 461, 463.
Pei Hsiu (III-2), 341; 331.
Pei shih, 484.
Pelagianism, 377, 382, 395, 411.
Pelagius (V-1), 382.
Pelagonios, 356.
Pèlerinage de Charlemagne à Jérusalem, 773.
Peloponnesian War, history, 106.
Pelops of Smyrna, 281.
Pên ts'ao, 122, 436, 489, 498, 523, 539.
Pên-ts'ao ching-chu, 436.
Pên-ts'ao-yen-i, 764.
Pên-ts'ao. See Shên-ming.
Pena, Jo., 211.
Penny-in-the-slot machines, 208.
Pentagon, 630.
Pentagon, Pythagorean, 92.
Pentateuch, 60, 62, 107.
Peonios, 389.
Peony, 766.
Pergamum, 180.
Pergamum, library, 185.
Perigenes (I-2, B. C.), 230; 220.
Perigetae, 185.
Periodicity, 18.
Perionius, Joachimus, 406.
Peripatetic astronomy, 222.
Peripateticism, 125. See Lyceum.
Periplus. See Arrian; Hanno; Scylax.
Periplus of the Erythrean Sea (I-2), 257; 244.
Perotti, Nicholas, 188.
Perrault, Ch., 54.
Perseus (II-1, B. C.), 182; 177.
Persia, 107, 466.
Persian vs. Arab, 524, 541. See Shu'ūbite.
Persian dictionary, 747, 783.
Persian grammar, 687.
Persian language, 678, 746. See also Pahlawī.
Persian medicine, 435.
Persian, transliteration, 49.
Perspective, 86, 95.
Pĕshīṭtā, 288, 291, 292, 501.
Petals, number, 708.
Petau, Denis, 322, 362, 366, 388, 578.
Peter of Spain, 750.
Petesis, alchemist, 238.
Petit, Guillaume, 540.
Petricellus, 726.
Petrocellus (XI-1), 726; 699.
Petronius, 726.
Petrus. See Peter.
Petrus de Regio, 716.
Peurbach, Georg, 274.
Peutinger, Konrad, 323.
Pez, Bernard, 714, 762.
Phaenias. See Phanias.
Phanias of Eresos (IV-2, B. C.), 144; 126.
Pharmacological theory, 678.
Philagrios of Thessalonica (IV-2), 373; 360, 361.
Philip of Macedon, King, 147.
Philip of Opus. See Opus.
Philip of Thaon, 569.
Philip of Tripoli, 557.
Philippos, 358.
Philistion of Locroi (IV-1, B. C.), 120-121; 112.
Philolaos (V, B. C.), 93-94; 81, 82.
Philology, history, 7. See under names of various languages.
Philon of Byzantium (II-2, B. C.), 195; 184, 191, 534.
Philon the Jew (I-1), 236; 235, 288, 550, 627, 704.
Philoponos, Joannes (VI-1), 421; 13, 253, 415, 416, 418, 480, 661.
Philostorgios, 373.
Philostratos the Athenian (Flavius) (III-1), 319; 314, 315.
Philotimos (IV-2, B. C.), 146; 126.
Philoxenian Syriac version, 291, 349.
Philumenos (II-2), 308; 289, 290.
Phonetics, 123, 463.
Photios (IX-2), 594; 389, 584, 588, 614.
Phrenitis, 373.
Phrynichos (II-2), 313; 290.
Phthisis, 308, 710, 713.
Phyogsglaṅ. See Dignāga.
Physica et Mystica, 239.
Physical instruments. See Diopter.
Physics, Stoic, 260.
Physiognomonia, 297.
Physiognomy, 6, 135, 136, 271, 356, 609.
Physiological experiments, 301.
Physiologos (II-2), 300; 289, 765.
Physiology, 264, 373, 478, 497, 772.
Pi-mi-chiao, 509.
Pi Shêng (XI-1), 723; 698, 702, 703.
Picatrix, 668.
Pictorius, 769.
Pieh-lu, 436.
Pien Ch'iao (V, B. C.), 102-103; 83.
Pien Han, 364.

Pierio Valeriano (Giovan Pietro Dalle Fosse), 358.
Pig, anatomy, 282, 770.
Pighinucci, 251.
Pigments, 533.
Pignoria, Lorenzo, 358.
Pilgrimage of Etheria, 371.
Pilgrimage roads, 774.
Pilgrims, 470.
Pilpay, fables, 449, 540.
P'ing, 494.
Ping-yüan-hou-lun, 481.
Pipes filling a cistern, 208.
Pisa, Leonardo da. See Leonardo Pisano.
Pitch notation, 559, 757.
Pithou, 734.
Placitus Papyriensis, Sextus (IV-2), 375; 361.
Plague, 204, 375, 678, 682.
Plague of Athens (430 to 425), 106, 107.
Plague of 542, 454.
Planetary hypothesis, 277.
Planets, distances, 403, 567.
Planets, seven, 238.
Planets, theory, 273.
Planisphaerium, 277.
Planta noctis, 712.
Plantis, de, 227, 601, 730.
Plants, classification, 341.
Plants, growth and movement, 225.
Plants, illustrations, 213, 258-259, 431.
Plants, sexuality, 128.
Planudes, Maximos, 358.
Plaster of Paris, 679.
Plastic surgery, 77, 240, 280.
Platearius the Elder, Joannes, 770.
Platearius the Younger, Joannes (XI-2), 770; 742, 745.
Plato (IV-1, B. C.), 113-116; 12, 111, 236, 271, 272, 298, 305, 332, 343, 353, 383, 385, 386, 402, 403, 421, 424, 435, 611, 704, 750. See Timaeos.
Plato of Tivoli (Tiburtinus), 569, 598, 603, 668, 716.
Platonic figures, 113.
Pleurisy, 307, 710.
Plinius Secundus, Gaius. See Pliny the Elder.
Plinius Valerianus, 251.
Pliny the Elder (I-2), 249-251; 243, 245, 265, 341, 389, 431, 452, 510, 511, 764.
Pliny, Medicine of, 361.
Plotinos (III-2), 334; 320, 330, 335, 406.
Plutarch of Chaeronea (I-2), 251-252; 186, 243, 245.
Pneumatic school, 260, 307, 324.
Pneumatic theory, 96, 195. See Air.
Pneumatic tricks, 561.
Pneumonia, 307-308.
Po li, 389.
P'o-lo-mên suan ching, 450.
P'o-lo-mên suan-fa, 450.
P'o-lo-mên t'ien-wen-ching, 450.
P'o-lo-mên yin yang suan ching, 450.
Po-lo-mo T'o, 446.
Pococke, Ed., 640.
Poggio Bracciolini, 232, 265.
Points, diacritical, 519.
Poisons, 158, 198, 214, 308.
Polar Sea, 606. See Arctic circle.
Polemon of Laodicea (II-1), 271; 267, 356.
Polemon Periegetes (II-1, B. C.), 185; 178, 179
Polignac, Melchior de, 205.
Polishing of precious stones, 75, 76.
Political history, 4.
Politics, 129.
Pollio, C. Asinius (I-2, B. C.), 222; 219.
Pollux, Julius (II-2), 313; 290.
Polo, Marco, 381, 535, 636.
Polybios (II-1, B. C.), 188; 119, 177, 178, 180, 227, 394.
Polybos of Cos (IV-1, B. C.), 120; 112.
Polyclitos, 229.
Polyhedra. See Solids, regular.
Polyhistor seu de mirabilibus mundi, 341.
Pompeius, 214.
Pontanus, Jacob, 481.
Poridad de la poridades, 556.
Porphyry (III-2), 334; 278, 330, 331, 351, 406, 407, 421, 422, 424, 628, 749.
Porrée, Gilbert de la, 404, 405.
Portolani, 742, 767.
Posidonios (I-1, B. C.), 204; 201, 202, 203, 207, 212, 213, 271.
Posidonios the physician (IV-2), 373; 360, 361.
Posology, 559.
Postulate, fifth. See Parallel postulate.
Postulates, 153.
Potala, 467.
Potash, 258.
Potassium carbonate, 679.
Potter's wheel, 55, 75, 510.
Prabhākara, 512.
Prajñākaramati, 491.
Prajñāpāramitā, 384, 477, 512, 604.
Prākrit, 69.
Praxagoras of Cos (IV-2, B. C.), 146; 126.
Precession of the equinoxes, 71, 136, 156, 194, 222, 300, 367, 403, 531, 567, 603, 716. See Trepidation.
Prefect, book of the, 617.
Pregnancy, 680, 727; anatomy of, 434.
Prehistory. See Lake-villages; World, ages.
Presses, 208.
Prices of wares, 531.
Priestly document, 108.
Primaticcio, 216.
Primum mobile, 599.
Printed book, earliest, 586, 604.
Printed book, earliest dated Hebrew, 752.
Printed documents, earliest, 529.

Printed silk of Nara, 530.
Printing, 444, 451, 512, 633; Tibetan, 469. See Typography.
Priscianos of Lydia, philosopher (vi–1), 423; 415.
Priscianus of Caesarea, grammarian (vi–1), 440; 286, 418, 555, 692.
Priscianus, Theodorus, physician (iv–2), 374; 258, 265, 361.
Probability, 328.
Problem, geometric, 140.
Problemata, 319, 324.
Problems, puzzle, 529.
Problems of pursuit, 529. See Cistern.
Probos (v–2), 407; 382, 400, 424.
Probus, M. Valerius. See Valerius Probus, M.
Proclos the Successor (v–2), 402–404; 154, 212, 274, 399, 400, 405, 406, 415, 629.
Procopios (vi–2), 454; 445.
Procopios of Gaza, 430.
Progress of knowledge, 248.
Progressions, arithmetic, 181, 409, 450.
Progressions, Chinese, 755, 756.
Progressions, geometric, 570, 707.
Progressions. See Series.
Projection, cartographic, 172, 273, 709. See Maps.
Projection, orthogonal (orthographic), 274, 716.
Projection, stereographic, 193, 274, 277, 707.
Projectivity, 254.
Prophatius, 254, 716.
Proportion, problems of, 735.
Proportionals, two mean, 561, 718.
Proprietatibus elementorum, de. See Liber de elementis.
Prosody. See under name of each language.
Prosper of Aquitania, Tiro (v–2), 411; 399, 400.
Prosthapheretical formulæ, 716.
Protagoras of Abdera (v, B. C.), 88; 83.
Proverbs, Book of (iii–1, B. C.), 163; 150.
Psellos, Michael, the Younger (xi–2), 750; 336, 352, 739, 740, 742, 743, 745, 746.
Psychology, 129. See Dreams; Soul.
Psychology, animal, 597.
Ptolemaeos, Claudios. See Ptolemy.
Ptolemaeos II, Philadelphos, 151, 327.
Ptolemaeos IV, Philopator, 166.
Ptolemy (ii–1), 272–278; 208, 267, 268, 269, 334, 337, 367, 386, 387, 403, 457, 537, 559, 564, 567, 598, 599, 611, 668, 729.
Ptolemy. See Almagest.
Ptolemy's theorem, 194, 273.
P'u, 35.
Pu K'ung (viii–1), 509; 504, 508.
P'u-t'i-ta-mo, 420.
Pulisa. See Pauliśa Siddhānta.
Pulley, 170.
Pulse, 88, 99, 146, 159, 260, 280, 282, 306, 309, 310, 325, 342, 478, 481, 499, 678.
Pulsis et urinis, de, 453.
Pumbedita, academy, 461, 471, 687.
Pump, force, 184.
Punctuation, 189, 287, 691.
Purbach. See Peurbach.
Pure Land school, 364.
Purgatives, 728.
Pūrvamīmāṃsāsūtra, 512.
Pushyamitra (Pushpamitra), King, 199.
Puzzle, earliest, 172.
Pyang-khok las-thig, 538.
Pyrites, 532.
Pyrrhon of Elis (iv–2, B. C.), 136; 125.
Pyrrhos, King, 162.
Pythagoras of Samos (vi, B. C.), 73–75; 65, 298, 334, 351, 426.
Pythagoras, theorem of, 74, 75, 183.
Pythagorean doctrine, 351.
Pytheas of Massilia (iv–2, B. C.). 144–145; 126, 606.

al-Qabīṣī (x–2), 669; 649, 654.
Qāḍī Abū Yūsuf, 525.
Qāḍī Ṣā'id, 776.
al-Qādirī fī-l-ta'bīr, 706.
Qādisīya, 466.
Qairawān, 687.
Qānūn fī-l-ṭibb, 678, 710.
al-Qānūn al-Mas'ūdī, 707.
Qaraism, 471, 520, 524, 550, 620, 626, 653.
Qarasṭūn, 561, 600.
Qarmaṭians, 593, 660.
Qaro, Joseph, 402.
al-Qāsim ibn Muḥammad al-Madānī, 630.
al-Qaṭṭā', 598.
Qazwīnī, 637.
Qenneshrē, 493, 579.
Qibla, 599, 721.
al-Qirqisānī (x–1), 626; 620, 623.
Qiyās, 508, 550.
Qlī, 679.
Qoheleth. See Ecclesiastes.
Quackery, 610.
Quadratrix, 140, 182, 337.
Quadrature, 91, 93, 169, 338, 423, 757.
Quadrilaterals, cyclic, 475.
Quadripartitum, 277.
Quadrivium, 421, 425, 750.
Quaestionum, liber, 511.
Qualities, four, 120, 661, 714.
Quantitative study of nature, 73, 669.
Quantity. See qualifying adjective.
Qudāma al-Baghdādī (x–1), 636; 621.
Quercetanus, And., 529.
Quicklime, 383, 679.
Quinta, 291.
Quintessence, 128, 222.
Quintilian of Calagurris (i–2), 265; 245.

Quintilianus, Marcus Fabius. See Quintilian.
Quintos, anatomist, 281.
al-Qumrī (x-2), 678; 651, 654.
Qur'ān, 5, 460, 461, 463, 464, 465, 485, 551, 557, 592, 642.
Qusṭā ibn Lūqā al-Ba'labakkī (ix-2), 602; 209, 370, 585.

Rab. See Abba Arika.
Rabanus. See Hrabanus Maurus.
Rabban al-Ṭabarī, 565.
Rabbenu, or Rabbi. See Judah ha-Nasi.
Rabī' ibn Zaid al-Usquf (x-2), 669; 649, 654.
Rabies, 340.
Rabina (Rabina II, ibn Huna), 384.
Rader, Matthaeus, 482.
Radicals, addition and subtraction, 630, 719.
Radolf of Laon, 756.
Radolf of Liége (xi-1), 715; 695, 702.
Ragimbold of Cologne (xi-1), 715; 695, 702.
al-Raḥma, 532.
Raimundus Martinus, Dominican, 783.
Rainbow, 375, 611, 669, 712, 723.
Ral-pa-Chan (ix-2), 593; 468, 584.
Rāmānuja (xi-2), 754; 739, 746.
Ramerupt, 752.
al-Rāmhurmuzī, 674.
Ranganātha, 388.
Rasa, 316.
Rasā'il ikhwān al-ṣafā', 661.
Rasaratnākara, 316.
Rasāyana, 316.
Rashi (xi-2), 752; 739, 744, 745, 746.
al-Rashīd, 'Abbāsid caliph, 527.
Rationalism, 749.
Ratios, 253.
Ravenna, anonymous geographer of (vii-2), 496; 324, 489.
Ray-fish, electric, 241.
al-Rāzī (ix-2), 609; 479, 574, 586, 587, 588, 590, 678, 710.
Realism, 749.
Recceswinth, King, 500.
Red Hat sect, 526.
Refraction, 211, 212, 274, 721, 722; atmospheric, 274, 721.
Regimen sanitatis, 725.
Regimine principium, de. See Secreta secretorum.
Regino of Prüm (x-1), 641; 621, 622, 623.
Regius, Petrus de, 716.
Regiomontanus, 237, 274, 567, 603.
Regula catta, 598.
Regula sex quantitatum, 254.
Regulae Domini Oddonis super abacum, 625.
Rei-sui, 310.
Reims, history, 684.
Reims, school, 670.
Reineccius, Reinerus, 733.
Reisch, Greg., 531.
Reitz, G. O., 440.
Reki, 476.
Reki-hakase, 476.
Relativity, 6, 85, 88, 153.
Religion, comparative, 251.
Religion, history, 4, 137.
Remediis salutaribus, de, 297.
Remi d'Auxerre (ix-2), 595; 358, 408, 584, 588, 589, 703.
Remigius Antissiodorensis. See Remi d' Auxerre.
Renaudot, Eusèbe, 571.
Repetitae praelectionis, codex, 439.
Réquier, Jean Baptiste, 358.
Respiration, 87, 301.
Responsa, 751.
Retina, 159.
Revolutionibus lunae, de, 410.
Rgyud, 468; rgyud-bṣi, 538.
Rhabanus. See Hrabanus Maurus.
Rhazes, 609. See al-Rāzī.
Rheumatism, 435.
Rhodian navigation law, 517.
Rhubarb, 453.
Rhuphos. See Rufus of Ephesus.
Richer of Reims (x-2), 685; 652, 655, 685.
Richer of St. Rémi. See Richer of Reims.
Rif, 751.
Rigault, Nicolas, 255, 295, 558.
Rigveda, 61, 110. See Veda.
Riku-kokushi, 516, 580, 617.
Rim-po-ch'e, 526.
Rinius of Venice, Benedictus, 711.
Ripuarian law, 484.
Riqmah, 736.
Risāla (fī), try following word of Arabic title.
Risner, Fried., 721.
Risshū, 510.
Rithmomachia, 757, 763.
Ritsu, 500.
Ritsu-shū, 510.
Ritter, J. D., 396.
Rivinus, A., 769.
Rivius, Walther, 223.
al-Riyāḍ wal-ḥadā'iq, 626.
Rodriguez of Tudela, Alonso, 681.
Roger II of Sicily, 452.
Rogkerus, 763.
Roland. See Chanson de Roland.
Rollandi, cantilena, 773.
Romaka-Siddhānta, 386, 387.
Roman antiquities, 225, 284.
Roman culture, 10.
Roman law, 508, 779.
Rome, description c. 547, 457.
Rome, fire of 64, 247.
Rome, history, 176, 187, 188, 233, 311, 327.
Rongo, 68.

Roots of herbs, 214.
Roots, square, 169.
Roots, square and cube, 183, 208, 719.
Roscelin of Compiègne (xi–2), **749**; 739, **745**.
Roseo, Francesco, **407**.
Rosvitha, 658.
Rothar, King, 484.
Roussat, Richard, **671**.
Rova, Moses, 407.
R, Tags-kyi-P, jug-pa, **467**.
Rubā'īyāt, 760.
Rubbings, 451.
Rudolph of Bruges, **668**.
Rudolphus Glaber, **734**.
Ruelle, Jean, of Soissons, **372**.
Ruffec, Hélie de, 733.
Ruffinus, 357.
Rufus of Ephesus (ii–1), **281**; 268, **269**, **434**, 608.
Rugerus, **763**.
Rugviniśćaya, 537.
Ruhnkenius, David, **343**.
Ruinart, Theod., 456.
Rukhāmāt, 567.
Rumanian language, **590**.
Ruminants, 128.
Russia, Christianization, **655**.
Russia, earliest account of, **636**.
Russia, ethnography, **686**. See Slavonic.
Rusticus of Pisa, **769**.
Rutbat al-ḥakīm, **668**.
Ruth, story of, 108.
Rūzbih, 540.
Ryō, 500.
Ryō no gige, 581, **644**.
Ryō no shūge, **644**.
Ryōbu-Shintō, 510, 553.
Rythmimachia. See Rithmomachia.

Sa-ha-pa, 467.
Saadia Gaon, 627.
Saadia ben Joseph (x–1), 627; 620, 623.
Sab'īya, 593.
Śabarasvāmim, 512.
Sabian, 589, 599, **662**, 750. See Ḥarrānian.
Sabinus, 375.
Sābūr ibn Sahl of Jundīshāpūr (ix–2), 608; 587.
Sacrobosco, 545.
Sacy, Lemaistre de, 412.
Saddharmapuṇḍarīka sūtra, 447.
Safar-nāma, 768.
Ṣafīḥa, 758.
Sages of the Bamboo Grove, Seven, 335.
Sages of Greece, Seven, 72, 75, 79.
al-Ṣāghānī (x–2), 666; 648, 649, 654.
Sagundinus, Nicolaus, 255.
Sahak the Great (St. Sahak), 397–398.
Ṣāḥib Ismā'īl ibn 'Abbād, 688.
al-Ṣaḥīḥ, 551, **592**.
Sahl ibn Bishr (ix–1), 569; 545, 546, 549.
Sahl ben Maẓliaḥ (x–2), 690; 653, 655.
Sahl al-Ṭabarī (ix–1), 565; 545, 549.
Saichō, 552.
Ṣā'id ibn Aḥmad al-Qurṭubī, 776.
Sa'īd ibn al-Biṭrīq, 640.
Sa'īd al-Fayyūmī, **627**.
Sa'īd ibn Hibat Allāh (xi–2), 772; 742, **746**.
Sa'īd ibn al-Ḥusain, 593.
Sa'īd ibn Ya'qūb al-Dimishqī, 631.
Ṣaidana, **709**.
Saiki, 553.
Saimei-tennō, 500.
Sakaibe Iwazumi (vii–2), 502; 490.
Śākhā, 428.
Śākyamuni. See Buddha.
Salernitan Chronicle, 652.
Salerno, school, **683**, 685, **699**, 702, 703, 725, 769.
Salic Law, 418, 439.
Salio, canonicus, 603.
Sallust (i–2, b. c.), 231; 220, 685, 775.
Sallust maps, 231.
Sallustius Crispus, Gaius. See Sallust.
Salmawaih ibn Bunān (ix–1), 573; **547**, **549**.
Salmiac, 597.
Salt, 228.
Saltpeter, 494.
Samaritan, 151.
Saṃbhota, 463, **467**.
Saṃgraha, 480.
Saṃhitā, 428.
Sāṃkhya philosophy, 69, 350, 351.
Sāṃkhyakārikā, 351.
Samos, tunnel, **76**.
Sampitsu, 554.
Saṃsāra, 69.
Samuel, Books of, **60**, **63**.
Samuel, King, 63.
Samuel ha-Levi (xi–1), 704; **694**, **701**.
Samuel ha-Nāgīd, 704.
Samuel Yarḥina'ah. See Mar Samuel.
San-dai-kyaku-shiki, 518, 618.
San han, 364.
San kuo chih, 343.
San-lun tsung, 470.
San-p'u-la, 467.
San-t'ung-li, 222.
San tzŭ ching, 441.
al-Ṣanā'a al-ṭibbīya, 678.
Sanad ibn 'Alī (ix–1), 566; 545, 546, 549.
Sandai jitsu-roku, 517, 617.
Sandlice, 481.
Saṅghamitrā, 167.
Sangi, 339.
Śaṅkara (ix–1), 561; 27, 544, 549, 754.
Sanron-shū, 460, 470.
Sanskrit dictionary, 458; Sanskrit-Tibetan dictionary, 468, 469.
Sanskrit grammar, 110, 123.

Sanskrit influence over Chinese, 343, 413.
Sanskrit, transliteration, 50.
Santalbinus, Jac., 393.
Santiago de Compostela, 774.
Śāntideva (VII-2), 490; 488, 490.
Santorio, S., 160.
Saphaea Arzachelis, 758.
Saracenus, Ianus, 259.
Saragossa, 240, 746.
al-Sarakhsī (IX-2), 597; 584.
Sareshel, Alfred of, 227.
Saros, 94.
Satyasiddhi śāstra, 384, 470.
Satyros, anatomist, 281.
Saul, King, 63.
Saul. See St. Paul.
Sault, papyrus, 265.
Saumaise, Claude de, 341.
Sautrāntika, 384.
Savasorda, 632.
Saxon law, 548, 580.
Saxony, history, 733.
Sayf al-dawla, Ḥamdānid sulṭān, 669.
Scabies, 481.
Scale, names of the notes, 720.
Scales. See Balance.
Scaliger, 370, 376.
Scaliger, Jos. Justus, 357, 578.
Scandinavia, 767.
Scenography, 95.
Sceptical school, 308.
Scepticism, 136, 299.
Scheidius, Everardus, 689.
Scheyb, Franz Chr. v., 324.
Schneider, J. G., 256.
Schola medicorum, 239.
Scholasticism, 16, 21; Buddhist, 26; Chinese, 27; Jewish, 26; Muslim, 26, 620, 626; Vedantic, 27.
Schöner, Johann, 569, 759.
Schools, cathedral, monastic, etc., 725. See under place-names.
Schooten, Franz van, 174.
Schottus, Andreas, 594.
Schweighaeuser, Johann, 326, 327.
Sciatica, 435.
Science, ancient, 8-14.
Science, classification, 128, 137, 422, 626, 640, 660, 661, 709.
Science, history, 127, 777.
Science, international, 493.
Science, organization, 127, 128.
Science, spirit of, 24.
Scola palatina, 594.
Scottus. See Scotus.
Scotus, John, 594.
Screw, 170.
Scribonius Largus (I-1), 241; 235, 236.
Script. See Writing.
Scriverius, 255.
Scylax of Caryanda (V, B. C.), 104; 83, 126.
Scylitzes, Joannes (XI-2), 776; 743, 745.
Sea-Island Arithmetical Classic, 338.
Sea-weeds to fertilize soil, 355.
Seal, Lesser, 168, 176.
Seals, 451; Chinese, 175, 451.
Seasons, 141, 429.
Sēbōkht, Severus (VII-2), 493; 488, 489, 490, 500.
Secant, 667.
Seconds, 273.
Secret Teaching, 508.
Secreta Hippocratis, 100.
Secreta secretorum, 136, 544, 556.
Section, golden. See Golden section.
Sections, conic. See Conics.
Sedarīm, 401.
Seed, 121.
Sefer, try following word of Hebrew title.
Seiche, 136.
Seimei, Abe, 672.
Seimei, King of Kudara, 448.
Seismometer, 278.
Seismoscope, 196. See Earthquakes.
Seiwa-tennō, 575.
Selachians, reproduction, 128.
Selection, natural, 205.
Seleucos the Babylonian (II-1, B. C.), 183; 178.
Semen, 119. See Sperm.
Semitic philology, comparative, 582.
Semmei-reki, 476.
Senchus Mór (V-1), 397; 379.
Seneca, Lucius Annaeus of Cordova (I-2), 247-249; 243, 245.
Sêng Hui, 343.
Sêng-yu (VI-1), 420; 415, 491, 509.
Senjimon, 441.
Sens, 752.
Sense impressions, 77, 87.
Senses, 143.
Septima, 291.
Septuagint (III-1, B. C.), 151; 291, 357, 363, 590.
Serapeium, 158.
Serapion of Alexandria (II-1, B. C.), 186; 178.
Serapion the Elder, 608.
Serapion the Younger, 608.
Serenos (IV-1), 353; 345.
Serenus Antissensis. See Serenos.
Serenus Samonicus, Quintus (III-1), 324; 315.
Sergios of Resaina (VI-1), 423; 310, 370, 415, 417, 501, 562.
Sericulture. See Silkworms.
Series of cubes, sum, 719.
Series of squares, sum, 169, 719.
Series. See Progressions.
Servilius Damocrates. See Damocrates, Servilius.
Servitoris, liber, 681.

Seth, Symeon (xi–2), 771; 741, 742, 744, 745.
Setsuyō-yōketsu, 575.
Seven, treatise on, 97. See Number 7.
Sever world map, St., 768.
Severos, iatrosophist, 307.
Severos. See Moses bar Kēphā.
Severus, Alexander, emperor, 239.
Severus, physician, 307.
Severus Sēbōkht, 449.
Seville, 746.
Sex, 128.
Sexagesimal division, 71, 273, 514.
Sexagesimal fractions, 367, 719. See Cycle, Sexagesimal.
Sexta, 291.
Sextius Niger, 259.
Sextos Empiricos (ii–2), 299; 289, 320.
Sextus Philosophicus Platonicus, 375.
Sextus Placitus Papyriensis, 375.
Sexual diseases, 710.
Sexuality of plants, 128.
al-Sha', 534.
Shabbethai ben Abraham ben Joel, 682.
Shaburqān, 332.
Shadow-play. See Khayāl al-ẓill.
al-Shāfi'ī (ix–1), 550; 543.
Shāfi'īte school, 550.
Shāhnāma, 705, 744.
Shāhpuhrakān, 332.
Shaik al-Jabal, 753.
Shaka, 448.
Shan. See Ch'an.
Shan-hai ching, 353.
Shan Tao (vii–1), 469; 460, 463.
Shan T'ao, 335, 336.
Shang-han-lun, 310.
Shang-han tsung-ping-lun, 773.
Shang Shu. See Confucius.
Shao Yung (xi–2), 755; 739, 746.
Shāpūr II, Sassanian King, 372.
Sharaf al-Dawla, Buwayhid sulṭān (x–2), 659; 647, 649, 654, 665.
Shauq al-mustahām, 634.
Shê hsien-jên, 450.
Shê-mo-t'êng. See Kāśyapa-Mātaṅga.
Shê-na-chüeh-to, 447.
Shên Chien, 299.
Shên Kua (xi–2), 755; 723, 740, 741, 743, 746, 764.
Shên-nung, emperor, 112, 122.
Shên-nung Pên-ts'ao, 122, 436.
Shên Wei-yüan, 103.
Shên Yo (v–2, also vi–1), 413 and 437; 400, 401, 417, 442.
Shêng, 676.
Sherira Gaon (x–2), 687; 471, 652, 655.
Sherira ben Ḥanina, 687.
al-Shifā', 709.
Shih An. See Huang Fu.
Shih ch'ên, 429.
Shih-chi, 68, 199, 777.
Shih-ch'ieh-p'u, 420.
Shih Ching, 67.
Shih Huang-Ti, First Emperor (iii–2, b. c.), 168; 165.
Shih lei fu, 663.
Shih Lu, 168.
Shihonryū-ji, 529.
Shī'ite, 607, 656, 659.
al-Shi'r wa-l-shu'arā', 615.
Shikandgūmānīg vījār, 591.
Shiki, 518.
Shimotsumichi Asomi, 519.
Shingon-shū, 509, 552, 553.
Shintan no Shaka, 448.
Shintō, 504, 510, 516, 553, 644.
Ships, Viking, 576.
Shiragi, kingdom of, 364, 365, 492.
al-Shīrāzī, 760.
Shitagau, Minamoto no, 692.
Shō-jō, 448.
Sho-kan-ron, 310.
Shōan Minabuchi, 463, 485.
Shōdō-shōnin, 529.
Shōjiroku (ix–1), 580; 548.
Shoku-Nihonki, 516.
Shoku-Nihon-kōki, 617.
Shōmu-tennō, 513, 515.
Shōphēṭ, 79.
ha-Shorashim, sefer, 736.
Shorthand, 217.
Shōtoku-taishi (vii–1), 473; 460, 461, 462, 463, 470.
Shōtoku-tennō (viii–2), 529; 451, 512, 521, 522.
Shu (one of the Three Kingdoms), history, 343.
Shū, religion, 470.
Shu, vertical, 35.
Shu Ching, 483. See Confucius.
Shu-mu, 37.
Shu-shu chi-i, 299.
Shujā' ibn Aslam al-Miṣrī, 630.
Shun Yü-i (ii–1, b. c.), 187; 178.
Shuo wên, 441.
Shuo wên chieh tzŭ, 286.
Shu'ūbite, 534, 541, 645, 687. See Persian vs. Arab.
Sībawaihi (viii–2), 542; 523, 524.
Sībuya, 542.
Sichard, J., 392.
Sicily, history, 162.
Sicily, school, 82, 102, 120.
Siddhānta, 378, 386, 409, 428, 521, 530, 601, 715, 716.
Siddhārta. See Buddha.
Siddhiyoga, 538.
Sieve of Eratosthenes, 172.
Ṣifāt jazīrat al-'Arab, 637.
Sigismund, King, 439.
Signerte, Guilelmus, 340.

al-Ṣiḥāḥ fī-l-lugha, 689.
al-Sijzī (x-2), 665; 648, 654.
Śikshāsamuccaya, 490.
Silicon, 679.
Silk instead of bamboo, 168.
Silk trade, 191, 197, 439, 452, 453, 705.
Silkworms, 301, 439, 440, 444, 452, 554.
Siloam inscription, 59.
Siloam tunnel, 53, 59.
Silvia of Aquitania, 371.
Simeon. See Symeon.
Simocattes, Theophylactos (or Simocatta) (VII-1), 481; 462, 463.
Simplicios (VI-1), 422; 270, 415, 416, 418.
Sinaitic peninsula, 431.
Sinān ibn Thābit (x-1), 641; 600, 620, 622.
Sindbad the Sailor, 571.
Sine, 380, 387, 388, 409, 717.
Sine table, 667.
Sine theorem, 667, 668.
Sine, versed, 387, 409.
Siphon, 208.
Sīrāfī, 542.
Sīrat rasūl allāh, 540, 579.
Sirmond, J., 394, 396, 684.
Sirr al-asrār, 556.
Sisebut, King, 471.
Siyar mulūk al-'ajam, 540.
Siyāsat-nāma, 780.
Skin diseases. See Dermatology.
Skull and spine, shapes, 478.
Slavonic. See Russia; Bulgarian.
Slavonic Bible, 349, 590.
Slavonic vs. Byzantine, 517, 578.
Slavonic Christianization, 590.
Slavonic history, 675.
Slavonic languages, 590, 733, 782.
Sleep, 77.
Ślokavārttika, 512.
Smallpox, 262, 479, 509, 609, 682, 732. See Measles.
Smith, John, 511.
So-mon, 310.
Socrates (V, B. C.), 89-90; 82, 122.
Socrates of Constantinople (V-1), 394; 379, 380.
Socrates Scholasticus, 394.
Sodium carbonate, 679.
Soga no Umako, 473.
Soghdian (Sogdian), 279, 333, 604.
Soldering iron, 75.
Solidism, 214.
Solids, regular, 93, 113, 116, 140, 427, 667.
Solinus, Caius Julius (III-2), 341; 331.
Solomon, King, 79.
Solomon, Song of, 59.
Solomon, Wisdom of (I-1, B. C.), 208; 202.
Solomon ibn Gabirol, 704.
Solomon ben Isaac, 752.
Solon (VI, B. C.), 79-80; 66.
Somner, William, 692.
Song-tsen Gam-po (VII-1), 466; 460, 463, 468, 525, 593.
Ṣopherim, 151, 288, 290, 624.
Sophia, St., 427, 439.
Soranos of Ephesus (II-1), 282-283; 268, 269, 392, 433, 434, 608.
Soroban, 756.
Sorsanus, 711.
Sosigenes the Peripatetician, 216, 217, 219, 221, 403.
Sostratos of Cnidos (III-1, B. C.), 161; 150.
Soter, Joh., 226.
Soul, 137, 181, 278, 304, 319, 350.
Sound, 128, 223, 661. See Acoustics.
Sound, speed, 249, 708.
Sozomen of Constantinople (V-1), 394; 379, 380.
Sōzu, 476.
Spach, Israel, 433, 681.
Spain, history, 643, 734. See Andalusia.
Speculum hominis, 699, 726.
Speculum uteri, 280, 283.
Sperm, 77, 119.
Speusippos of Athens (IV-2, B. C.), 139; 94, 111, 125.
Sphaera barbarica, 354.
Sphera celi, 569.
Sphere. See Armillary.
Sphere, celestial and terrestrial. See Globe.
Sphere, volume, 714.
Spheres, homocentric, 117, 128, 142.
Spheres, Ptolemaic, 599.
Spherical aberration, 721.
Spherics, 211, 253.
Sphygmology. See Pulse.
Spinoza, 297.
Spiral (Archimedean), 169.
Spiric curves, 182.
Spleen, 373.
Sporos of Nicaea (III-2), 338; 331.
Square rule, 75.
Śramaṇā, 676.
Śrībhāshya, 754.
Śrīdhara (XI-1), 719; 697, 701.
Śrīkaṇṭhadatta, 538.
Ssŭ-ma Ch'ien (II-2, B. C.), 199; 67, 68, 164, 192.
Ssŭ-ma Kuang (XI-2), 778; 67, 744, 745, 746.
Ssŭ-ma Piao, 396.
Ssŭ-ma Ta, 448.
Ssŭ-ma T'an, 199.
Ssŭ shêng, 413, 442.
Ssŭ shih êrh-chang ching, 246.
Stadiasmus maris magni, 321, 372.
Staff, lines of the, 720.
Stages of diseases, four, 262, 280.
Stars, 156, 157, 182, 211, 226, 277, 278, 722, 762.
Stars, catalogue, 172, 194, 254, 273, 278, 603.
Stars, map, 322, 762.

Stars, new, 194.
Stars. See Milky Way.
Statics, 170.
Statios, 322.
Statistics, 328.
Status laxus, mixtus, strictus, 215.
Steam engines, 208.
Steel, 55, 532, 560.
Stems, ten, 673.
Stephanos. See Stephen.
Stephanos of Alexandria (VII-1), 472; 461, 462, 463.
Stephanos of Athens (VII-1), 478; 462, 463, 472, 727.
Stephanos, son of Basilios (IX-2), 613; 587.
Stephanos of Byzantium (VI-1), 433; 417.
Stephanos Magnetes (XI-1), 727; 699.
Stephanus. See Estienne.
Stephanus Arnaldus, 602.
Stephen. See Stephanos.
Stephen of Antioch, 677.
Stephen Asolik Tarōneçi (XI-1), 735; 700, 702.
Stephen the Philosopher, 677.
Stereographic projection. See Projection, stereographic.
Stevin, S., 167.
Stobaeos, Joannes (V-2), 405; 399.
Stockholm papyrus, 331, 340.
Stoicism, 10, 125, 137, 181, 260, 297.
Stomachion, 172.
Stone, med., 609. See Lithotomy.
Stones, precious, 428, 429, 572. See Lapidary; Mineralogy.
Storms, magical explanation, 555.
Strabo, Walafrid. See Walafrid.
Strabon (I-2, B. C.), 227-229; 56, 104, 220, 389.
Straton of Lampsacos (III-1, B. C.), 152; 125, 149, 195.
Styptic. See Haemostatic.
Su-ching, 498, 539.
Su Kung, 489, 498.
Su-shên liang-fang, 755.
Su-sung, 741, 746, 762.
Su-wên, 310, 539.
Suan-ching, 321.
Suan-p'an, 299, 741, 756.
Sublimation, 681.
Suetonius Tranquillus, Caius (II-1), 284; 269, 576.
Ṣūfīsm, 406, 583, 590, 592.
Sugawara Kiyogimi (IX-1), 582; 548.
Sugawara Koreyoshi (IX-1), 582; 548.
Sugawara Minetsugu, 575.
Sui dynasty, history, 483.
Sui shu, 450, 483, 494.
Suidas (X-2), 691; 277, 653, 655.
Suijaku, 553.
Suiko-tennō, 470, 481.
Sulaimān ibn Ḥassān ibn Juljul, 682.
Sulaimān ibn Jābīrūl, 704.
Sulaimān the Merchant (IX-1), 571; 546-547.
Sulphur, 55, 532, 533.
Sulpicius Severus (IV-2), 376; 361.
Śulvasūtras, 74.
Sumaṅgalavilāsinī, 385.
Summa perfectionis magisterii, 723.
Sun, 204, 716. See Apogee; Apsides.
Sun-chên-jên ch'ien-chin-fang, 498.
Sun Ch'iang, 442.
Sun Hsing-yen, 476.
Sun Mien, 486.
Sun p'u, 673.
Sun Shu-jan. See Sun Yen.
Sun Ssŭ-mo (VII-2), 498; 489, 490.
Sun-Tzŭ (III-1), 321; 315, 449. See Sun Wu.
Sun Wu (V, B. C.), 94-95; 82.
Sun Yen (III-2), 343; 331, 413, 442.
Sundials, 157, 211, 632.
Sung, history of the Liu, 437.
Sung Ch'i (XI-1), 737; 701, 702, 744, 777.
Sung kao sêng ch'uan, 491, 673.
Sung-shu, 437.
Sung Yün (VI-1), 431; 414, 416, 419, 447.
Sunnite schools, four orthodox, 551.
Śūnyatā, 316.
Śūnyavāda, 384.
Superficierum divisionibus, de, 762.
Superstition. See Magic.
Sūra, 464.
Sura, Academy, 318, 384, 461, 471.
Ṣūrat al-arḍ, 563.
Surds. See Incommensurable.
Surgery, 681; Japanese, 575.
Surgery, illustrations, 216.
Surgery, plastic. See Plastic.
Surgical instruments, 681.
Surveying, 255, 256, 397, 632.
Sūrya-Siddhānta, 386, 387, 388, 475.
Sushun-tennō, 452.
Suśruta (VI, B. C.), 76-77; 66, 316, 393.
Sūtra, 167, 468.
Sutta. See Sūtra.
Sutta-nipāta, 385.
Ṣuwar al-aqālīm, 631.
Svavarsson, Gardar, 605.
Śvetāmbaras, 69.
Sweat, 143.
Sycosis, 257.
Syennesis, 96.
Sylburg, Friedrich, 232.
Syllabary, Japanese, 519.
Sylva, G. de, 324.
Sylvester II, Pope. 669.
Symbols, algebraic, 336.
Symeon Januensis, 681.
Symeon the Logothete, 579.
Symeon Metaphrastes (X-2), 686; 579, 652, 655.
Symmachos, 291.
Symmachus, 426.

Symmetry, 18.
Syncellos, Georgios (IX-1), 577; 482, 548.
Synesios of Cyrene (V-1), 388; 378, 380, 386, 404.
Synesios, translator from the Arabic, 682.
Syntax, 286, 611.
Syntemachion, 172.
Syntipas, 571.
Syphilis in Japan, 575.
Syriac anatomy, 309, 424.
Syriac dictionary, 611, 689, 735.
Syriac Geoponica, 424.
Syriac grammar, 490, 501, 611, 701, 735, 737.
Syriac language, 735.
Syriac literature, beginning, 401.
Syriac medicine, 309.
Syriac translations, 291, 349, 382; their value, 424, 435, 611.
Syriac, transliteration, 51.
Syrianos (V-1), 386; 378, 380.
Syro-Roman Law Book (V-2), 412; 400.
Systole, 282.

Ta-ch'in, 324, 552.
Ta-hsia, 197.
Ta hsüeh, 91.
Ta-jih ching, 508.
Ta-mo, 420.
Ta-Sung ch'ung-hsiu-kuang-yün, 737.
Ta-t'ang hsi-yü ch'iu-fa kao-sêng-ch'uan, 497.
Ta T'ang K'ai-yüan chan ching, 513.
Ta-yen li, 514.
Ta-yen shu, 514.
Ta-yüan, 197.
Ta-yüeh-ch'ih, 197.
al-Ṭabaqāt al-kabīr, 579.
Ṭabaqāt al-umam, 776.
al-Ṭabarī (X-1), 642; 619, 622, 624.
Tables, astronomical, 565. See Zīj.
Tables, synchronistic, 216.
Tables, synoptic medical, 730, 772.
Tables, Twelve (V, B. C.), 109–110; 83.
Tabula Peutingeriana, 315, 323, 432.
Tacitus, Cornelius (I-2), 263; 245.
Tadahira Fujiwara, 644.
Tadbīr al-ḥabālā wal-aṭfāl, 680.
Tadhkirat al-ḥāḍir, 730.
Tadhkirat al-kaḥḥālīn, 731.
Taḍ'īf, 710.
Tadmor, 558.
al-Tafhīm li-awā'il, 707.
Tafsīr al-Qur'ān, 642.
Tahāfut al-falāsifa, 754.
Tahdhīb al-akhlāq, 687.
Tai-chên, 183, 449, 494.
T'ai chi t'u, 755.
Tai-chiao suan-ching shih-shu, 183, 450, 474, 494.
T'ai ch'u li, calendar, 195.
T'ai-p'ing huan-yü-chi, 676.
T'ai p'ing kuang-chi, 663.
T'ai p'ing yü-lan, 663.
T'ai Shih Kung. See Ssŭ-ma Ch'ien.
T'ai-ts'ang-kung. See Shun Yü-i.
T'ai-ts'ang-kung-fang, 187.
T'ai Tsu, Sung emperor, 552.
T'ai Tsung, T'ang emperor (VII-1), 474; 460, 461, 462, 463, 477, 482, 484, 518, 663.
Taien-reki, 476.
Taihō, 518.
Taikwa daika, 485.
Taikwa no kaishin, 485.
Taillefer, 773.
Taishi, 473, 529.
Taishin-oshō, 510.
Tajārib al-umam, 687.
Taketori monogatari, 778.
al-Takmīl, 707.
al-Talkhīṣ, 736.
Talmud, 401; 241, 318, 384, 399, 401, 402, 471, 752.
Talmud, Babylonian, 401, 751.
Talmud, Palestinian, 401.
Talmudic dictionary, 782.
Tamba Yasuyori, 683.
al-Tamīmī (X-2), 679; 650, 651, 654.
al-Tanbīh wal-ishrāf, 638.
T'ang dynasty, history, 643, 777.
T'ang dynasty, history of its rise, 484.
T'ang hsin pên ts'ao, 498.
T'ang Pên ts'ao, 498.
Tangent, 563, 565, 599, 603, 667, 717.
Tanjur (Tan-gyur), 467–469; 367, 538, 593.
Tanka, 639.
al-Tanqīḥ, 736.
Tantra, 428, 468.
Tantras, four, 522, 538.
Tantravārttika, 512.
Tantrism, 509, 513, 526.
Tao-chien-lu, 436.
Tao-hsüan (VII-2), 491; 420, 441, 446, 460, 463, 469, 488, 490, 509.
T'ao Hung-ching (VI-1), 436; 417, 498.
Tao-shih (VII-2), 491; 488, 490, 496.
Tao tê ching, 66, 477.
T'ao yin chü, 436.
Taoism, 66.
Taoist alchemy, 355.
Taoist canon, 333, 633.
Taqwīm al-abdān fī tadbīr al-insān, 772.
Taqwīm al-siḥḥa, 731.
Targa, Leonh., 240.
Targūm, 151, 402.
al-Ta'rīf bi ṭabaqāt al-umam, 776.
Tarīkh. See Akhbār.
Ta'rīkh al-Andalus, 688.
Ta'rīkh al-aṭibbā' wal-falāsifa, 682.
Ta'rīkh Baghdād, 777.
Ta'rīkh al-Hind, 707.

al-Ta'rīkh al-Jalālī, 760.
Ta'rīkh-i-Malikī, 760.
Ta'rīkh 'ulamā' al-Andalus, 734.
Tarim region, 476, 484.
al-Tarjumān fī ta'līm lughat al-suryān, 735.
Tarkīb, 710.
Tartaglia, N., 170.
Tartar, 259.
Taṣārīf al-af'āl, 688.
Taṣḥīḥ-l-'imān, 735.
al-Taṣrīf liman 'ajiza 'ani-l-ta'ālīf, 681.
Tasṭīḥ al-ṣuwar, 708.
Tathāgata. See Buddha.
Tatian (II–2), 293; 288, 290, 292.
Tatios, Achilles. See Achilles Tatios.
Taugas, 481.
Ṭauq al-ḥamāma, 713.
Taxation, system of, 781.
Ta'wīl, 593.
Taylor, Thomas, 403.
Tea, 343, 467, 535.
Tei-Yuda, 454.
Telegraph, hydraulic, 119.
Telegraph, military, 368.
Telegraph, optical, 327, 554.
Teleology, 206, 302.
Tempe, Vale of, 227.
Tempering colors, 691.
Temporibus, de, 511.
Ten. See Number 10.
Ten-yaku-ryō, 539.
Tenchi-tennō, 500.
Tendai-shū, 448, 552, 553.
Têng Ch'u Ch'ung, 325.
Tenkyō-reki, 476.
Tennō, 529.
Tennō-ki, 473.
Terpander of Lesbos (VII, B. C.), 61; 60.
Tertullian, 160.
Tetanus, 308.
Tetbert, 770.
Tetrabiblon, 277. See Ptolemy; also Aëtios of Amida.
Thābit ibn Qurra (IX–2), 599; 254, 274, 560, 585, 586, 587, 589, 601, 664.
Thales of Miletos (VI, B. C.), 72; 65.
Thanet, Isle of, 341.
Thaon, Philip of, 569.
Thawbān ibn Ibrāhīm al-Ikhmīmī, 592.
Theaetetos of Athens (IV–1, B. C.), 116; 111.
Theater. See Scenography.
Themison of Laodicaea (I–1, B. C.), 215; 203.
Themistios (IV–2), 366; 360, 361, 629.
Theodore of Canterbury, 492.
Theodoretos of Cyrus (V–1), 394; 379, 380.
Theodoric, King of the Ostrogoths, 438.
Theodoric's Edict, 417.
Theodoros of Cyrene (V, B. C.), 92–93; 82.
Theodoros Lector (Anagnostes), 394.
Theodoros of Samos (VI, B. C.), 75–76; 65.
Theodoros, Shāpūr's physician (IV–2), 372; 360, 435.
Theodorus, grammarian, 440.
Theodosianus, Codex (V–1), 396; 379, 438.
Theodosios II, emperor (V–1), 396; 341.
Theodosios of Bithynia (I–1, B. C.), 211; 202, 599, 602.
Theodosios, see Theodoros, Shāpūr's physician.
Theodosios of Tripolis. See Theodosios of Bithynia.
Theodote, 751.
Theodotion, 291.
Theology of Aristotle (V–2), 406; 135, 399, 628
Theomnestos, 356.
Theon of Alexandria (IV–2), 367; 274, 360, 386
Theon of Smyrna (II–1), 272; 267, 268.
Theophanes Confessor (IX–1), 577; 548, 776.
Theophanes continuatus, 577.
Theophanes of Mytilene, 228.
Theophano, sister of Basilios II, 655.
Theophilos Antecessor, 440.
Theophilos, bishop of Alexandria, 158.
Theophilos of Edessa (VIII–2), 537; 522.
Theophilos Protospatharios (VII–1), 478; 462, 463, 611.
Theophilus (XI–2), 763; 741, 745.
Theophrastos, alchemist, 514.
Theophrastos of Eresos (IV–2, B. C.), 143–144; 125, 126, 127, 158, 203, 271, 423, 572, 764.
Theophylactos Bulgaros (or Achridensis) (XI–2), 751; 739, 745.
Theopompos of Chios (IV–2, B. C.), 147; 126.
Theorem, 140.
Therapeutae, 346.
Theriaca, 261, 306.
Thermoscope, 208.
Thessalos of Tralles (I–2), 262; 244.
Theudios of Magnesia (IV–2, B. C.), 140; 125.
Thévenot, 196, 209, 327, 632.
Thi-sroṅ Detsan, 526.
Thietmar of Merseburg (XI–1), 733; 700, 702.
Thistle, 215.
Thīyūfīl ibn Thūmā, 537.
Thomas a Novara, 736.
Thorfin Karlsefni, 702, 724.
Thousand Buddhas, Caves of the, 604.
Thousand Character Essay, 441.
Thousand and One Nights. See Alf laila.
Thrax. See Dionysios Thrax.
Three. See Number 3.
Three Brothers, 560.
Three Kingdoms, annals of, 343.
Thucydides of Athens (V, B. C.), 106–107; 83, 233.
Thuillier, Dom Vincent, 188.
Thuringian law, 548, 581.
Thymaridas of Paros (IV–1, B. C.), 117; 111, 352.
Ti chih, 673.

Ti-li, 676.
Ti-song De-tsen (VIII-2), 526; 520, 521, 538, 593.
T'iao-chih, 197.
Tibetan alphabet, 467.
Tibetan anatomy, 538.
Tibetan Buddhism, 466.
Tibetan civilization, 36, 463.
Tibetan language, 463, 467, 486.
Tibetan law, 526.
Tibetan medicine, 469, 538.
Tibetan numerals, 469.
Tibetan printing, 469.
Tibetan-Sanskrit dictionary, 468, 469.
Tides, 18, 136, 144, 145, 183, 204, 362, 407, 511, 539, 560, 568, 611, 661.
T'ien Chu, 197.
Tien kan, 673.
T'ien-t'ai tsung, 447, 553.
T'ien-wen-shuo, 450.
Tigernach, Annals of, 775.
Tigris, river, 635.
Tiles, 452.
Timaeos, lexicographer (III-2), 343; 331.
Timaeos of Plato, 204, 271, 352, 405, 556, 594.
Timaeos of Tauromenium (III-1, B. C.), 162-163; 113, 114, 150.
Timocharis of Alexandria (III-1, B. C.), 156; 150.
Timotheos of Gaza, 657.
Tin Islands, 104.
Ting, 494.
Ting Tu (XI-1), 737; 701, 702.
Ting Yu-t'o, 454.
Tiro, Marcus Tullius (I-1, B. C.), 217; 203.
Tironian notes, 218.
Tissa, King, 167.
Tō-dai-ji, 509, 510, 515.
T'o-po, 447.
T'o-t'o, 762.
Tobiah ben Moses, 704.
Tokihira Fujiwara, 517, 617, 644.
Tokurai, 393.
Toland, John, 386.
Toledan (or Toletan) Tables, 759.
Toledo, 746, 759.
Toneri-shinnō, 505, 516.
Tones, four, 413.
Tonsils, removal, 240.
Tōrāh, 402.
Tores, 182.
Torinus, Albanus, 251, 608.
Tosa-nikki, 639.
Tōshō-daiji, 510.
Tou P'ing (XI-1), 723; 698, 702.
Tournemire, Jean de, 609.
Tours, 376, 456.
Town-planning, 95.
Toxicology. See Poisons.
Trachea, 77.
Tracheotomy, 214, 280.
Trachoma, 732.
Tradition, Muslim. See Ḥadīth.
Trajan, emperor, 278, 279.
Transmutation, chemical, 710.
Trapezuntius, Georgius, 274.
Trezibond, George of. See Trapezuntius, 274.
Trepidation of the equinoxes, 367, 599, 603, 716, 759. See Precession.
Triangle, area of, 208.
Triangle, right-angled, 570.
Triangle, spherical, 254.
Trigonometry, Greek, 157, 194, 245, 253, 273.
Trigonometry, Hindu, 387, 428.
Trigonometry, Muslim, 563, 603. See Sine; Tangent; Umbra, etc.
Trikāṇḍa, 458.
Trincavelli, 270, 366.
Trinitarianism, 480.
Trinity, persons of, 348.
Trinity, Precious, 391.
Tripartita (or Jus Aelianum), 189.
Tripiṭaka, 167, 467, 469, 508, 552, 633.
Tripoli, Philip of, 557.
Triśatikā, 719.
Trisection of the angle, 182, 561, 665, 666, 707.
Troyes, 752.
True Word, 295, 553.
True Word school, 508.
Tryphon the Jew, 293.
Ts'ai Hsiang (XI-2), 766; 741, 746.
Ts'ai Lun (II-1), 279; 268.
Tsan-ning (X-2), 673; 491, 650, 652, 654.
Ts'ê-fu yüan-kuei, 713.
Tso Ch'iu Ming, 67.
Tso Chuan, 67.
Tsou-p'an chi, 756.
Tsu Ch'ung-chih (V-2), 410; 400, 494.
Tsuginawa Fujiwara, 516, 541.
Tsung, 470.
Tu-ch'in (I-2, B. C.), 230; 220.
T'u shu, 110.
Tu Yu (IX-1), 581; 547, 548.
Tu-Yü (III-2), 341; 331.
Tuan Ch'êng Chi, 355.
Tuberculosis. See Phthisis.
Tun-huang, 604.
Tun-mi, 467.
T'ung chien kang mu, 778.
T'ung-jên Chên-chiu ching, 732.
T'ung-li, 222.
Tung-lin, 353.
T'ung mi, 467.
T'ung-ming, 436.
Tung Ping, 743, 746, 773.
T'ung shu, 755.
T'ung tien, 581.
Tunnel, Naples, 223.
Tunnel, Samos, 76.

Tunnel, Siloam, 59.
Ṭupṭīkā, 512.
Turkish civilization, 445, 453.
Turkish language, 447.
Turkish. See Uighūr.
Turnèbe, A., 237.
Turquet, 758.
Tuscus, Leo, 558.
Ṭutāta, 512.
Twelve. See Number 12.
Twelve Tables. See Tables, Twelve.
Twigs, Twelve, 673.
Twilight, 721.
Two. See Number 2.
Typography, 723, 756.
Tzinitza, 432.
Tzŭ Ch'an. See Kung-sun Ch'iao.
Tzŭ chih t'ung chien, 778.
Tzŭ Hsia (v, B. C.), 110; 84.
Tz'ŭ yüan, 369.

'Ubaidallāh, Abū Sa'īd, 730.
'Ubaidallāh ibn 'Abdallāh ibn Khurdādhbih, 606.
'Ubaidallāh ibn Jibrīl ibn Bakhtyashū', 730.
'Ubaidallāh al-Mahdī, Fāṭimid caliph, 640.
Udānavarga, 469.
Uighūr (or Uigur), literature, 604, 712.
Uighūr, religion, 333, 654.
Uighūr, translations from, 468.
Uighūr, translations into, 447.
Uji, 500.
Ulcers, 498.
Ulfilas (IV-1), 349; 344, 345, 348.
Ulpian (III-1), 328; 315, 316, 396.
Ulpianus, Domitius. See Ulpian.
al-Ulūf, 568.
Ulūgh Beg, 666, 760.
'Umar, caliph, 464, 638.
'Umar ibn al-Fāriḍ, 713.
'Umar ibn al-Farrukhān (IX-1), 567; 537, 546, 550.
'Umar ibn Ibrāhīm al-Khayyāmī, 759.
'Umar ibn Muḥammad ibn Khālid, 566.
Umayado, 473.
Umbra extensa, 603.
Umbra versa, 565, 599, 603.
Unity of life, 29.
Unity of mankind, 31.
Unity of nature, 30, 594.
Unity of science, 31.
Universals, problem of, 21, 749.
Universe, center, 251.
Universe, infinite, 141. See World.
Unknown quantity, 336.
Upanishads, 561.
Upton, John, 270.
Urabe, 656.
Uranorama. See Orrery.
Urine, urology, 478, 614, 640, 769, 770, 771.
Urinogenital system and troubles, 282, 481, 681.
al-Uṣūl, 736.
al-Uṣūl bi-l-nujūm, 568.
Ussermann, Aemil., 757.
Ut, 720.
'Uṭārid ibn Muḥammad (IX-1), 572; 547, 565.
Uterus. See Womb.
'Uthmān ibn Jinnī al-Mauṣilī, 689.
Utkramājyā, 387.
Utramadjyā. See Utkramājyā.
'Uyūn al-akhbār, 615.

Vacuity, doctrine of, 316.
Vacuum, 88, 195, 422, 661, 706, 710.
Vadianus. See Watt, Joach.
Vāgbhaṭa the Elder (VII-1), 480; 462, 463, 497.
Vāgbhaṭa the Younger, 480.
Vairocana, 508, 510, 538.
Vaiśeshika, 69, 88.
Vājñavalkya, 781.
Vajrasūcī, 270.
Valentinian Law of Citations, 311, 396.
Valentinians, 294.
Valeriano, Pierio. See Pierio.
Valerius Probus, M. (I-2), 265; 245.
Valla, G., 157, 319, 609.
Valois, Henri de, 357, 394, 455.
Valturio, 368.
Varāhamihira (VI-1), 428-429; 387, 409, 416, 419, 707.
Vardhamāna. See Mahāvīra.
Variation (third inequality of the moon), 666, 667.
Variola. See Smallpox.
Varro, Marcus Terentius (I-2, B. C.), 225-226; 217, 219, 220.
Vascular system, 96. See Arteries; Capillaries; Chyliferous; Heart; Veins, etc.
Vāsishṭha-Siddhānta, 386, 387.
Vasolli, Pietro, 358.
Vasubandhu (IV-1), 350; 344, 351, 367, 446.
Vasubandhu Asaṅga. See Asaṅga.
Vattier, P., 711, 712.
Veda, 5, 110, 512. See Rigveda.
Vedāṅgas, 110.
Vedānta, 420, 561, 754.
Vedāntatattvasāra, 754.
Vegetables, 121.
Vegetius, Flavius Renatus (IV-2), 368; 360, 361, 577.
Vegetius, Publius Renatus (IV-2), 374; 361.
Veins, 77.
Venantius Fortunatus, 370.
Venatorius. See Gechauff, Thomas.
Venesection. See Blood-letting.
Venus, planet, 71, 141, 272, 353, 386, 408.
Verbs, Arabic, 688.
Verbs, Hebrew, 691.
Vergèce, Ange, 354.

Vergil, Polydore, 455.
Vergilius, Marcellus, 259.
Vergilius Maro, Publius. See Virgil.
Vernier, 710.
Verona. See Guarino of Verona.
Vesalius, 282.
Vespasian, emperor, 239.
Veterinary art, 215, 225, 256, 323, 356, 372, 374, 538, 610. See Mulomedicina.
Veteris cujusdam jurisconsulti consultatio. See Consultatio.
Vetus Itala, 291, 292.
Viaticum peregrinantis, 682.
Victorius of Aquitania (v–2), 409; 400, 429, 671.
Victorius, P., 206, 322.
Vidius, Vidus, 216.
Vigilanus, Codex, 664.
Vijñānavāda, 491.
Vijñāneśvara (xi–2), 781; 744, 746.
Vikings, age of the, 548, 576.
Vilgerdarson, Floki, 605.
Vimala nirbhasa sūtra, 530.
Vimalakīrti sūtras, 384.
Vinaya, 167, 468, 469.
Vinci, Leonardo da, 167, 171, 209, 282.
Vindicianus (iv–2), 374; 361.
Vindonius Anatolius. See Anatolius of Beirut.
Vinet, Helies, 576.
Virgil (i–2, b. c.), 221; 219, 220.
Virgil in the Middle Ages, 222.
Virgilius of Salzburg. See St. Fergil of Salzburg.
Visigothic law, 400, 412, 438, 489, 500.
Vision, '87, 612, 712, 721, 722. See Eye; Nerves, optic; Optics.
Viśishṭa advaita, 754.
Visuddhimagga, 384, 385.
Vitello. See Witelo.
Vitriol, 259, 533.
Vitruvius Pollio, Marcus (i–2, b. c.), 223–225; 209, 219, 220.
Vitruvius Rufus, agrimensor, 397.
Vives, J. L., 266.
Vivisection, 160.
Vladimir, city, 655.
Vladimir, St. (x–2), 655; 647.
Vocabulista in Arabico, 783.
Volcanoes, 204, 227; Campania, a. d. 63, 248; Vesuvius, a. d. 79, 249.
Volga, river, 636.
Volpi, 325.
Voltaire, 750, 760.
Vortex theory, 86.
Vowel marks, 519.
Vṛiddha-gargasaṃhitā (or Vṛiddha-gārgīya), 428.
Vṛiddha-Vāgbhaṭa, 481.
Vṛinda (viii–2), 537; 522.
Vṛindamādhava, 537–538.
Vulcanius, B., 481.
Vulgate, 363, 486.

Wāḍiḥ, 607.
al-Wāḍiḥ, zīj, 666.
Wai-t'ai-pi-yao, 538.
Wake Hiroyo (viii–2), 539; 523.
Walafrid Strabo (ix–1), 570; 546.
Wall, Great (Chinese), 168.
Wallis, John, 278, 335, 337.
Walrus, 606.
Wamyōshō, 692.
Wan li ch'ang ch'êng, 168.
Wandering Jew, 776.
Wang An-shih (xi–2), 781; 744, 745, 746.
Wang Chêng, 723.
Wang Chieh, 604.
Wang Ch'in-jo (xi–1), 713; 695, 702.
Wang Ch'ung (i–2), 252; 244.
Wang Fan (iii–2), 338; 331.
Wang Hsiao-T'ung (vii–1), 474; 461, 463.
Wang Hsüan-ts'ê (vii–2), 496; 489, 490.
Wang Jung, 335.
Wang Kuan (xi–2), 766; 741, 746.
Wang Liang-tung, 448.
Wang Pao-sun, 448.
Wang Ping (viii–2), 539; 522.
Wang Shu-ho (iii–2), 342; 310, 331.
Wang Tao (viii–2), 538; 522.
Wang Tao-liang, 448.
Wang Wei-tê (xi–1), 732; 700, 702.
Wang Ying-lin, 441.
Wang-yu Ling-t'o, 454.
al-Wāqidī (viii–2), 541; 523.
Warde, William, 671.
Warnefrid, Paul, 539.
Wāsiṭ, city, 518.
Water, erosive power, 228.
Water, principle, 72, 86.
Water clock. See Clock.
Water-mills, 467.
Water-proof varnishing, 532.
Waterford, Geoffrey of, 557.
Watt, Joach. v., 570.
Weariness, 143.
Weaving, oil in, 55.
Week, 71.
Wei (one of the Three Kingdoms), history, 343.
Wei Chao, 343.
Wei Chêng (vii–1), 483; 462, 463, 494.
Wei Chung-tsiang. See Wei Tan.
Wei dynasty, history, 483.
Wei dynasty, history of northern, 458.
Wei lüeh, 315, 324.
Wei Shou (vi–2), 458; 445.
Wei shu, 458.
Wei Tan, 369.
Wei Yao. See Wei Chao.

Weights and measures. See Metrology.
Welsh laws, 643.
Wên Chên, 458.
Wên Chien, 737.
Wên Chung, 777.
Wên-ti, Sui emperor, 451.
Whale, 606.
Wheel, potter's. See Potter's.
Wheels, paddle, 430.
Wheels, water. See Noria; Water mills.
Wheelock, Abraham, 511.
Whiston, William, 263, 395.
Whytehorne, Peter, 255.
Widukind of Corvey (x–2), 684; 652, 655.
Wījan ibn Rustam al-Kūhī, 665.
Wilbrord. See Willibrord, St.
William the Conqueror, 779.
William of Hirsau, 745.
Willibrord, St. (viii–1), 506; 503, 529.
Willoughby, Sir Hugh, 606.
Windmills, 638, 674.
Winds, 143, 356; names of the, 528.
Wineland, 676, 724, 767.
Wintonia, liber de, 779.
Wisdom of Jesus. See Ecclesiasticus.
Wisdom of Sirach. See Ecclesiasticus.
Wisdom of Solomon. See Solomon, Wisdom of.
Witchcraft, 555.
Witelo, 559, 721.
Wither, Geo., 374.
Wolf, Casp., 433, 681, 727.
Wolf, F. A., 53.
Wolf, Joh. Christ., 421.
Woman, earliest medical treatise written by a, 283.
Womb, 121, 128, 280, 282, 283, 434; motions of, 677. See Gynaecology; Menstruation.
World, ages, 57.
World, duration of the, 298.
World, end, 734. See Universe.
Worms, intestinal, 435, 453.
Writing, Greek, 55.
Writing vs. language, 152, 333.
Writing, Manichaean, 333.
Writing, Samaritan, 152.
Writing. See Brush; Lantsa; Li (script); Seal, lesser; and under names of languages or peoples.
Wu (one of the Three Kingdoms), history, 343.
Wu Chao-i, 633.
Wu Ching (viii–1), 518; 505.
Wu-ching suan-shu, 450.
Wu ch'uan lu, 676.
Wu K'ung (viii–2), 526; 520.
Wu Shu (x–2), 663; 648, 654.
Wu T'i, Liang emperor, 436.
Wu-ts'ao suan-ching, 449.
Wu Tsung, T'ang emperor, 552.
Wu tzŭ, 755.
Wu-wei, 66, 153.
al-Wuḥūsh, 534.
Wulfila. See Ulfilas.
Wulfstan (ix–2), 606; 586.

Xenarchos of Seleucia (i–2, b. c.), 222; 219.
Xenocrates of Aphrodisias (i–2), 261; 244.
Xenocrates of Chalcedon (iv–2, b. c.), 139; 111, 125, 127.
Xenophanes of Colophon (vi, b. c.), 73; 65.
Xenophon (iv–1, b. c.), 122–123; 90, 112.
Xiphilinos, Joannes (xi–2), 775; 327, 743, 745.
Xylander (Wilhelm Holtzmann), 297, 336, 750, 776.

Ya Shêng. See Mencius.
Yaḥyā. See Yūḥannā.
Yaḥyā ibn abī Manṣūr (ix–1), 566; 545, 549.
Yaḥyā ibn 'Adī (x–1), 629; 620, 623.
Yaḥyā ibn Baṭrīq (ix–1), 556; 544, 547, 549.
Yaḥyā ibn Dā'ūd, 691.
Yaḥyā ibn Ghālib, 569.
Yaḥyā ibn 'Īsā ibn Jazla, 772.
Yaḥyā al-Naḥwī, 480.
Yaḥyā ibn Sarāfyūn (ix–2), 608; 587, 590.
Yājñavalkya-Smṛiti, 781.
Yakkei-taiso, 539.
Yakoshiso Tamafuru, 476.
Yamato-bumi, 516.
Yanbū' al-ḥayāt, 704.
Yang, positive or male principle, 353.
Yang-chou shao-yo-p'u, 767.
Yang Chu (iv–2, b. c.), 138; 125.
Yang-hsiung, 353.
Yang Hsüan-chih, 431.
Yang Hui, 756.
Yang Tzŭ. See Yang Chu.
Yao Ch'a, 483.
Yao Chien (vii–1), 483; 462, 463.
Yao-shih(x–2), 676; 650, 654.
Yao Ssŭ-lien, 483.
ha-Yaqar, sefer, 683.
Ya'qūb ibn akhī Ḥizām (ix–2), 610; 587.
Ya'qūb ibn Isḥāq al-Kindī, 559.
Ya'qūb ibn Ṭāriq (viii–2), 530; 521, 524.
al-Ya'qūbī (ix–2), 607; 587, 588, 590, 635, 636.
Yāqūt, 635, 636, 637.
Yāska (v, b. c.), 110; 83.
Yaśomitra, 350.
Yasumaro, Ōno, 516.
Yasuyo Yoshimine, 580.
Yasuyori Tamba (x–2), 683; 651, 654.
Yatsu-mimi nō Ōji, 473.
Year 1000, 734.
Year, great, 92, 157.
Year, Julian, 216. See Calendar.
Year, sidereal and tropical, 194.
Year, solar, 157.
Years, cycle of. See Cycle.

Years, seven, 238.
Years, twelve, 238.
Yemen, 637.
Yen Chih-t'ui (VI-2), 459; 445, 486.
Yen Hsiao-chung, 773.
Yen-shih chia-hsün, 459.
Yengi. See Engi-shiki.
Yeraḥ, 318.
Yēshū'. See Joshua the Stylite.
Yeẓīrah, sefer, 627, 683.
Yin,[1] negative or female principle, 353.
Yin,[4] seal, 451, 723.
Yin-hai ching-wei, 498.
Ying Kung, 498.
Yoga, 69.
Yogācāra school, 350, 526.
Yogācārabhūmiśāstra, 350.
Yogaśāstra, 199.
Yōrō-ryōritsu, 506, 518.
Yoshifusa Fujiwara, 516, 617.
Yoshimine Yasuyo (IX-1), 580; 548.
Yü p'ien, 441, 442.
Yüan-chien-lei-han, 676.
Yüan-ho chün hsien chih, 573.
Yüan Ts'ung, 755.
Yüan Yüan, 663.
Yuga, 387.
Yūḥannā. See Yaḥyā.
Yuḥannā ibn Māsawaih, 574.
Yuḥasin, sefer, 776.
Yuishiki, 491.
Yün, 486.
Yung Lo Ta-tien, 183, 321, 339, 494.
Yūsuf Abū Ya'qūb al-Qirqisānī, 626.
Yūsuf ibn Hārūn al-Kindī al-Ramādī, 672.
Yūsuf ibn Ibrāhīm ibn al-Dāya, 598.
Yūsuf al-Khūrī (IX-2), 600; 585, 587.
Yūsuf al-Mutamin, Hūdid king of Saragossa (XI-2), 759; 740, 746.
Yūsuf al-Qass or al-Sāhir, 600.

Zaccharias the Rhetor, 445, 457.
Zaccharias Scholasticos, 457.
Zād al-musāfir, 682.
Ẓāhir, 592.
al-Zahrā', city, 628.
Zaid ibn Rifā'a, 661.
Zaid ibn Thābit (VII-1), 465; 460, 464.
Zaleucos, 62.
Zamberti, Bart., 154.
Zanzibar coast, 636.
Zarathushtra. See Zoroaster.
al-Zarqālī (XI-2), 758; 740, 746, 776.
Zarrīn Dast (XI-2), 772; 742, 746, 747.
Zechariah (VI, B. C.), 70-71; 65.
Zedat al-derachim, 682.
Zemarchos the Cilician (VI-2), 453; 444.
Zen-shū, 420, 552.
Zeno of Citium (IV-2, B. C.), 137-138; 125.
Zeno of Elea (V, B. C.), 85-86; 81, 82.
Zeno, emperor, 381.
Zenodoros (II-1, B. C.), 182; 177.
Zenodotos of Ephesos (III-1, B. C.), 164; 151.
Zephaniah (VII, B. C.), 63; 60.
Zero, 513, 601, 670, 719.
al-Zīj, 563, try following word of Arabic title (e. g., jāmi', kabīr, wāḍiḥ).
Zikron ha-datot, 704.
Zodiac, 73, 493.
Zoega, Jörgen, 358.
Zoku Nihon kōki, 516.
Zoku Nihongi, 516, 523, 541.
Zonaras, Joannes, 327.
Zones, 85.
Zoology. See Animals; Apiculture; Bestiaries; Crabs; Fishes; Leeches; Physiologos; Silkworms; Worms, etc.
Zoology, Manichaean, 333.
Zoology, moral, 300, 326, 358.
Zopyros, 215.
Zoroaster (VII, B. C.), 60-61; 60, 332.
Zoroaster, pseudo, 61.
Zoroastrianism, 60, 552, 591, 713.
Zosimos of Constantinople (V-1), 394; 379, 380.
Zosimos of Panopolis (III-2), 339; 331.